THIRD EDITION

General
Zoology

CLAUDE A. VILLEE
HARVARD UNIVERSITY

WARREN F. WALKER, JR.
OBERLIN COLLEGE

FREDERICK E. SMITH
UNIVERSITY OF MICHIGAN

W. B. Saunders Company
PHILADELPHIA · LONDON · TORONTO

W. B. Saunders Company: West Washington Square
Philadelphia, Pa. 19105

12 Dyott Street
London W.C. 1

1835 Yonge Street
Toronto 7, Ontario

Reprinted November, 1968

General Zoology

PREFACE

The field of zoology, along with all of the biologic sciences, has grown enormously in extent and complexity in the last few decades and promises to grow in the future. To deal with this vast array of knowledge, some college courses in zoology are based upon a thorough examination of certain representative animals. Other courses are centered around discussions of broad biologic principles. Each of these approaches has obvious merits, and we have tried in writing this text to blend the two. Neither method can be carried to extreme, for one cannot hope to teach principles without concrete examples, nor can one teach animal types without the intellectual synthesis provided by an understanding of biologic principles.

The special task of anyone writing a textbook is to select with care the topics to be discussed and to present a clear picture of the subject without giving an overwhelming mass of detail. In preparing this text we have endeavored to summarize the factual and theoretical knowledge that constitutes modern zoologic science. However, an appreciation of any science requires not only a grasp of the product of the science—the facts which have been gained in that field—but also an insight into the processes by which such knowledge is acquired. The methods of science are introduced in Chapter 1, and throughout the text examples of experimental work are presented to illustrate modern methods in zoologic science. This text probably includes some material that the instructor will have neither the time nor the inclination to consider in his course. Each instructor, naturally, emphasizes those topics he considers most important; the text provides the interested student with an opportunity to read about subjects which may be omitted or considered only briefly in the lectures and laboratory exercises. In discussing the many subjects which comprise modern zoology, we have tried to distinguish between fact and theory and to cite some of the problems that remain for future zoologists to solve. The conclusions presented and the inferences drawn represent, to the best of our knowledge and ability, the current interpretation of the relevant observations and experiments.

The introductory chapter describes the subsciences of zoology, scientific method and the sources of scientific information. The general concepts basic to a study of the form and function of both invertebrate and vertebrate animals are presented in Part One. Chapters 2 and 3 introduce the chemical and physical concepts needed for an understanding of the dynamic, molecular aspects of cells and tissues. The chemistry and physics relevant to the discussion are not presented separately but are introduced as needed to provide an understanding of the biologic material.

The nature of enzymes, their role in cellular physiology and the principles of bioenergetics are discussed in Chapter 4. Vertebrate and invertebrate animals have had to solve the same major problems in order to survive, and an examination of their physiologic mechanisms shows that they have much in common. The principles of nutrition, digestion, circulation, respiration, excretion, protection, sensation, locomotion, irritability and integration are discussed in Chapter 5 to provide a general background for the discussions of the animal types that follow. The general aspects of reproduction—gametogenesis, fertilization, and development and its control—are considered in Chapter 6.

Part Two opens with a discussion of the principles to taxonomy and systematics, and in the succeeding chapters each major phylum is presented. Several of the minor phyla are considered as a group in Chapter 18, and others are also described along with the major phylum to which they are related in some way. Each invertebrate phylum is introduced with a detailed study of one (or more) representative species. This species is presented as a living animal (e.g., *Euglena, Gonionemus, Dugesia, Nereis, Busycon, Loligo, Astacus, Daphnia, Periplaneta, Asterias*) illustrating some particular way of life. The relations between the animal's morphology and the problems it has faced in its struggle for survival are pointed out. The presentation of each phylum is concluded with a survey of its classes and major orders.

Two chapters are devoted to the arthropods: one describes the morphology of representative arthropods and discusses their taxonomic and evolutionary relationships; the second is devoted to certain problems of arthropod physiology that are of interest for the contrast they provide to comparable aspects of vertebrate biology. This second chapter includes discussions of hormonal phenomena in arthropods and of social mechanisms in insects. The evolutionary origins of the lower invertebrates and their relationships to the higher animals are described in Chapter 13, which includes a discussion of spiral cleavage and of coelomate evolution. Phylogenetic relationships are discussed repeatedly throughout the chapters on the animal kingdom. The synopses of the groups of animals have been expanded in this edition, and the pertinent synopsis has been placed at the end of each chapter dealing with an animal phylum. These synopses may be more useful here than at the end of the book and should provide the student with a quick summary of the most important characters distinguishing each of the phyla and the subordinate groups within each phylum.

Part Three, which presents a discussion of the vertebrates, opens with a consideration of the frog as a representative vertebrate. This is followed by several chapters on the evolution and interrelationships of the various groups of vertebrates which set the stage for the discussions of the structure and function of vertebrate organ systems. Many parts of the chapters dealing with the vertebrates have been rewritten to reflect recent conclusions, derived in large part from paleontological studies, as to the interrelationships of the various groups. New material has been added to the discussions of the mode of locomotion in each group. The mode of life of a group reflects its pattern of locomotion, and studies of locomotion are of importance in characterizing a given group. Some of the illustrations have been changed and new ones have been added. A number of modifications have been made in the discussions of the organ systems to improve the organization and clarity of the material and to reflect advances in our understanding of vertebrate physiology. Chapter 5, which sets forth the basic principles of physiology, both vertebrate and invertebrate, should be reviewed as each specific organ system is studied. Part Three has been written in such a way that it can be studied before Part Two if the instructor desires.

PREFACE

The fundamentals of genetics and evolution are presented in Part Four. These chapters have been extensively revised to include the latest material in this rapidly unfolding aspect of the biologic sciences. Evolution, one of the chief unifying concepts of zoology, is presented throughout the discussions of both invertebrates and vertebrates, but in Chapters 36 to 38 the principles of evolution and certain of the evidence for evolution are discussed in some detail. The discussion of the theory of natural selection has been rewritten to reflect modern concepts of population genetics and differential reproduction.

The final portion of the book, Part Five, is devoted to a discussion of ecology and to certain of its practical implications, such as conservation. Included here is a new chapter on animal behavior written by Brian Hazlett of the University of Michigan.

The questions at the end of each chapter are designed to aid the student in reviewing the material presented and in testing his comprehension of the principles and facts discussed. Annotated references have been added at the end of each chapter to lead the interested student more deeply into the topics discussed. These references are generally ones that can be read and understood by a student equipped with the normal introductory background of the topic, but a few more technical references are included that will lead the interested student into the vast professional literature.

A glossary has been added to this edition which presents pronunciation, derivation and definition for the important and widely used terms and the concepts of zoology and for the phyla and classes of animals. By studying the derivations, the student should learn to recognize important root words and thereby find it easier to learn and to remember the vocabulary of zoology. The definition of terms not included in the glossary will be found in the text by the use of the index.

The illustrations in this book are in large part new and are either original or have been redrawn especially for this book to provide greater clarity. We are deeply indebted to William Osborn, Ellen Cole, and the art department of the W. B. Saunders Company for the care, artistry and originality with which they converted our rough sketches into finished line drawings. The illustrations of general concepts are diagrammatic and designed to clarify some one point. The illustrations of animal structures are realistic in their proportions and generally include an outline of the organism for orientation. Illustrations of whole animals adhere to the actual proportions of the living animal, but some have been simplified by the omission of unnecessary detail. A conscious attempt has been made to provide uncluttered figures that will be clear without distorting the material described.

We continue to be indebted to those colleagues who took time from busy schedules to read certain chapters of the original manuscript: Drs. William Balamuth, Harvey Fisher, Donald Griffin, Nelson Hairston, Dwain Hagerman and Dixy Lee Ray. We are most grateful to the many users of the book, both students and faculty members, who have sent us suggestions based on their experience with the text. We are grateful to all who have made suggestions for the improvement in this revision, but we must, of course, assume the full responsibility for whatever errors and faults remain.

We are indebted to Vernon G. Applegate, Robert S. Bailey, Russell J. Barrnett, Kurt Benirschke, Austin H. Clark, Allan D. Cruikshank, Earl R. Edmiston, Alfred Eisenstadt, Frank Essapian, Don Fawcett, D. Fraser, Fritz Goro, C. Lynn Haywood, Herbert Lang, Daniel Mazia, Jacques Millot, James W. Moffett, Peter Morrison, Jean Luc Perret, J. D. Pye, Col. N. Rankin, Hugh Spencer, L. W. Walker, and Douglas P. Wilson, who have kindly permitted us to use certain of their photographs.

We also want to express our gratitude to the many institutions who have permitted us to use certain of their copyrighted photographs and drawings: Acoustical Society of America, *Acta Endocrinologica,* Ross Allen's Reptile Institute, American Zoological Society, American Museum of Natural History, the Australian News and Information Bureau, Ernst Benn Limited, Benno Schwabe and Company, *Biological Bulletin,* Blakiston Company, Cambridge University Press, S. W. Camp and Company, Chicago Museum of Natural History, University of Chicago Press, Cranbrook Institute of Science, *Experientia,* General Biological Supply House, Johns Hopkins University Press, J. B. Lippincott Company, Marine Studios, Maternity Center Association, McGraw-Hill Book Company, National Audubon Society, *Natural History, Nature,* New York Zoological Society, Oxford University Press, Philadelphia Zoological Society, Reinhold Publishing Company, San Diego Zoo, *Science, The Scientific American,* The Shedd Aquarium, The Smithsonian Institution, Ward's Natural Science Establishment, The Williams & Wilkins Company, and the United States Army.

Our special thanks are due to members of the staff of the W. B. Saunders Company who have given so liberally of their time and effort in preparing this revised edition. Finally, we want to express our deep appreciation to our secretaries, Marie Cook and Christine Kaminski, who have spent many hours transcribing our rough copy into a form acceptable for publication.

CLAUDE A. VILLEE

WARREN F. WALKER, JR.

FREDERICK E. SMITH

CONTENTS

Part One GENERAL CONCEPTS

Chapter 1

INTRODUCTION 3

  1.1 Zoology and Its Subsciences 3
  1.2 The Scientific Method 4
  1.3 History of Zoology 7
  1.4 Applications of Zoology 12
      Questions 13
      Annotated References 13

Chapter 2

THE PHYSICAL AND CHEMICAL BASIS OF LIFE 14

  2.1 Characteristics of Living Things 14
  2.2 Cellular Organization 16
  2.3 Chemical Composition of Living Matter 18
  2.4 Organic Compounds of Biologic Importance 23
  2.5 Physical Characteristics of Cellular Constituents 27
      Questions.. 29
      Annotated References 29

Chapter 3

CELLS AND TISSUES 30

  3.1 The Cell and Its Contents 30
  3.2 The Nucleus and Its Functions 31
  3.3 Cytoplasmic Organelles 35
  3.4 Mitosis 36
  3.5 Regulation of Mitosis 41
  3.6 The Study of Cellular Activities........................... 41
  3.7 Energy 43
  3.8 Molecular Motion 43

3.9   Diffusion 43
3.10 Exchanges of Material Between Cell and Environment 45
3.11 Tissues.. 47
3.12 Body Plan and Symmetry 53
      Questions.. 54
      Annotated References 55

Chapter 4

CELL METABOLISM 56

4.1   Chemical Reactions 56
4.2   Enzymes 57
4.3   Factors Affecting Enzymatic Activity 60
4.4   Respiration and Cellular Energy 61
4.5   The Dynamic State of Cellular Constituents 69
4.6   Biosynthetic Processes.. 70
4.7   Special Types of Metabolism 71
      Questions.. 72
      Annotated References 72

Chapter 5

PRINCIPLES OF PHYSIOLOGY... 74

5.1   Types of Nutrition.. 74
5.2   Ingestion, Digestion and Absorption 75
5.3   Circulation 78
5.4   Respiration 80
5.5   The Elimination of Wastes Other than Carbon Dioxide 84
5.6   Protection 87
5.7   Motion 88
5.8   The Mechanism of Muscular Contraction 90
5.9   Irritability and Response..................................... 93
5.10 The Nerve Impulse 93
5.11 Transmission at the Synapse 96
5.12 Sense Organs 97
5.13 Coordination and Integration.............................. 99
      Questions.. 101
      Annotated References 101

Chapter 6

REPRODUCTION 102

6.1   Asexual Reproduction 102
6.2   Sexual Reproduction... 104
6.3   Meiosis... 104
6.4   Spermatogenesis 106
6.5   Oögenesis 109
6.6   Reproductive Systems 109
6.7   Fertilization 110
6.8   Embryonic Development 112

6.9   Protection and the Embryo 116
6.10 The Control of Development 118
      Questions.. 122
      Annotated References 122

Part Two   **THE ANIMAL KINGDOM**

Chapter 7

THE PRINCIPLES OF TAXONOMY 125

7.1   The Science of Taxonomy 125
7.2   The Binomial System 125
7.3   Higher Categories 126
7.4   Uses of Taxonomy 126
7.5   Definitions 127
7.6   The History of Taxonomy 128
      Questions.. 130
      Annotated References 130

Chapter 8

THE PHYLUM PROTOZOA 131

8.1   Organelles 132
8.2   Class Flagellata 134
8.3   Class Sarcodina 138
8.4   Class Ciliata 141
8.5   Class Suctoria.. 144
8.6   Class Sporozoa 144
8.7   Reproduction in the Protozoa... 145
8.8   Relationships Among the Protozoa 148
      Synopsis of Protozoa... 148
      Questions.. 149
      Annotated References 149

Chapter 9

THE PHYLUM PORIFERA 150

9.1   General Characteristics 150
9.2   The Classes of Sponges 152
9.3   Reproduction 154
      Synopsis of Sponges 156
      Questions.. 156
      Annotated References 156

Chapter 10

THE PHYLA COELENTERATA AND CTENOPHORA 157

10.1 *Gonionemus:* General Behavior 157
10.2 *Gonionemus:* Feeding and Digestion 159

10.3 *Gonionemus:* Diffusion 161
10.4 *Gonionemus:* Nervous System... 161
10.5 *Gonionemus:* Reproduction 162
10.6 Classes of the Phylum Coelenterata 163
10.7 Class Hydrozoa 164
10.8 Class Scyphozoa 166
10.9 Class Anthozoa... 168
10.10 Fresh-water Coelenterates: *Hydra* 170
10.11 The Phylum Ctenophora 172
10.12 The Regulation of Form.. 173
        Synopsis of the Radiate Phyla 174
        Questions 175
        Annotated References 175

Chapter 11

THE PHYLUM PLATYHELMINTHES 176

11.1 *Dugesia:* Habitat and Appearance 176
11.2 *Dugesia:* Feeding and Digestion 177
11.3 *Dugesia:* Sensation and Movement 178
11.4 *Dugesia:* Water Balance and Excretion................................ 179
11.5 *Dugesia:* Reproduction 180
11.6 *Dugesia:* Regeneration and Polarity 181
11.7 Class Turbellaria.. 182
11.8 Class Trematoda 183
11.9 Class Cestoda 185
        Synopsis of the Flatworms 187
        Questions 187
        Annotated References 187

Chapter 12

THE PHYLA ASCHELMINTHES AND NEMERTEA 188

12.1 Classification of the Aschelminthes 188
12.2 Class Rotifera 189
12.3 *Philodina* 190
12.4 Reproduction in Rotifers 191
12.5 Cell Constancy... 191
12.6 Interspecies Induction 192
12.7 Senescence 192
12.8 Resistance to Desiccation 192
12.9 Class Nematoda 193
12.10 The Vinegar Eel, *Turbatrix aceti*.. 194
12.11 The Pig Roundworm, *Ascaris lumbricoides* 195
12.12 Molting 196
12.13 Parasitism 196
12.14 Class Gastrotricha 196
12.15 Class Kinorhyncha 196
12.16 Class Gordiacea 196
12.17 Class Acanthocephala 197
12.18 Phylum Nemertea 197

Synopsis of Roundworms and Ribbon Worms 199
Questions 199
Annotated References 199

Chapter 13

INTRODUCTION TO THE HIGHER INVERTEBRATES.. 200

13.1 Origin of the Metazoa.. 200
13.2 Origin of a Digestive Tract and Nervous System..................... 201
13.3 The Evolution of Three Germ Layers 201
13.4 The Evolution of the Coelom 202
13.5 Spiral Cleavage and Its Evolutionary Importance 203
13.6 Evolution Within the Eucoelomata 204
Questions 206
Annotated References 206
A Key to the Animal Kingdom 207

Chapter 14

THE PHYLUM MOLLUSCA 208

14.1 General Features of the Mollusks 208
14.2 Class Amphineura 209
14.3 Class Gastropoda: General Features 211
14.4 *Busycon* 211
14.5 Other Gastropods 213
14.6 Class Pelecypoda: General Features 215
14.7 *Venus mercenaria* 215
14.8 Other Pelecypoda 217
14.9 Class Scaphopoda 219
14.10 Class Cephalopoda: General Features 219
14.11 *Loligo* 221
14.12 Other Cephalopods.. 224
Synopsis of Mollusks 225
Questions 226
Annotated References 226

Chapter 15

PHYLUM ANNELIDA 227

15.1 General Features of the Annelid Worms 227
15.2 Classification of the Annelids 228
15.3 *Nereis* and *Lumbricus:* Habitat and Habit 229
15.4 *Nereis* and *Lumbricus:* External Morphology..................... 229
15.5 *Nereis* and *Lumbricus:* Body Wall................................. 231
15.6 *Nereis* and *Lumbricus:* Nervous System 232
15.7 *Nereis* and *Lumbricus:* Digestive System 233
15.8 *Nereis* and *Lumbricus:* Circulatory System....................... 234
15.9 *Nereis* and *Lumbricus:* Excretory System 234
15.10 *Nereis* and *Lumbricus:* Reproduction 235
15.11 Reproductive Periodicity and Palolo Worms 236
15.12 Earthworms and the Soil 237

15.13 Other Annelid Worms 237
15.14 Class Hirudinea 238
15.15 The Relationships of Annelids, Mollusks and Arthropods 238
15.16 The Trochophore Larva.. 241
        Synopsis of Annelids 242
        Questions 243
        Annotated References 243

Chapter 16

PHYLUM ARTHROPODA **244**

16.1   Classification of the Arthropods 244
16.2   Class Crustacea 247
16.3   *Astacus,* A Crayfish... 247
16.4   External Morphology of the Crayfish 247
16.5   Internal Anatomy of the Crayfish.. 251
16.6   *Daphnia,* The Water Flea 253
16.7   Other Crustaceans 254
16.8   The Subphylum Labiata 256
16.9   *Periplaneta americana,* A Cockroach 257
16.10 External Morphology of the Cockroach 258
16.11 Internal Anatomy of the Cockroach 259
16.12 Classification of the Insecta 262
16.13 Metamorphosis 265
16.14 *Apis mellifera,* The Honeybee... 265
16.15 The Subphylum Chelicerata 268
16.16 *Argiope,* An Orb Spider.. 269
16.17 The Phylum Onychophora 270
        Synopsis of Arthropods and Onycophorans 271
        Questions 274
        Annotated References 274

Chapter 17

PHYSIOLOGY OF THE ARTHROPODA **275**

17.1   Molting 275
17.2   Arthropod Hormones 277
17.3   Patterns of Muscular Innervation 281
17.4   The Flight Mechanism in Insects 282
17.5   Vision.. 284
        Questions 288
        Annotated References 288

Chapter 18

MINOR PHYLA.. **289**

18.1   Mesozoa... 289
18.2   Entoprocta.. 290
18.3   Sipunculoids and Echiuroids 290
18.4   The Priapuloids 291
18.5   The Phoronids and Brachiopods.. 291

18.6 The Bryozoa 292
18.7 The Chaetognatha 293
Synopsis of Minor Phyla 294
Questions 294
Annotated References 294

Chapter 19

THE PHYLA HEMICHORDATA AND ECHINODERMATA **295**

19.1 The Phylum Hemichordata 295
19.2 Classification of the Echinoderms 298
19.3 *Asterias forbesi*, A Typical Five-rayed Starfish 299
19.4 Class Asteroidea, The Starfish 303
19.5 Class Crinoidea, The Sea Lilies 303
19.6 Class Holothuroidea, The Sea Cucumbers 304
19.7 Class Echinoidea, The Sea Urchins, Heart Urchins and Sand Dollars 306
19.8 Class Ophiuroidea, The Brittle Stars 307
19.9 Relationships Among Echinoderm Classes 307
19.10 Relationships Among the Hemichordata, Echinodermata, and Chordata 308
Synopsis of Hemichordates and Echinoderms 312
Questions 312
Annotated References 313

Chapter 20

THE CHORDATES... **314**

20.1 Chordate Characteristics 314
20.2 Subphylum Urochordata 315
20.3 Subphylum Cephalochordata 318
20.4 Subphylum Vertebrata 321
20.5 The Origin of Chordates 322
Synopsis of Chordates 324
Questions 324
Annotated References 325

Part Three **VERTEBRATE LIFE AND ORGANIZATION**

Chapter 21

THE FROG—A REPRESENTATIVE VERTEBRATE................................. **329**

21.1 Frogs and Other Amphibians 329
21.2 External Features 330
21.3 Skin and Coloration 331
21.4 Skeleton... 332
21.5 Muscular System.. 336
21.6 Body Cavity and Mesenteries 339
21.7 Digestive System.. 339
21.8 Respiratory System... 341

21.9   Circulatory System 343
21.10 Excretory System.. 346
21.11 Reproductive System 348
21.12 Sense Organs 349
21.13 Nervous System 350
21.14 Endocrine Glands 352
21.15 Life Cycle 353
        Questions 354
        Annotated References 355

Chapter 22

A HISTORY OF VERTEBRATES: FISHES 356

22.1   Methods of Determining the History of Animals.................... 356
22.2   Vertebrate Beginnings 359
22.3   Living Jawless Vertebrates 361
22.4   Jaws and Paired Appendages 363
22.5   Characteristics of Cartilaginous Fishes............... 364
22.6   Evolution of Cartilaginous Fishes 368
22.7   Lungs and Swim Bladders 369
22.8   Evolution of Bony Fishes 370
        Synopsis of Fishes 378
        Questions 381
        Annotated References 381

Chapter 23

A HISTORY OF VERTEBRATES: AMPHIBIANS AND REPTILES 383

23.1   The Transition from Water to Land....................... 383
23.2   Characteristics of Amphibians........................... 384
23.3   Evolution of Amphibians 386
23.4   Amphibian Adaptations.................................... 388
23.5   Characteristics of Reptiles................................ 392
23.6   Evolution and Adaptations of Reptiles 395
        Synopsis of Amphibians and Reptiles 404
        Questions ....,... 406
        Annotated References 406

Chapter 24

A HISTORY OF VERTEBRATES: BIRDS 408

24.1   Principles of Flight... 408
24.2   Structure of Birds.. 412
24.3   The Origin and Evolution of Birds...................... 418
24.4   The Bird Way of Life 421
        Synopsis of Birds.. 425
        Questions 427
        Annotated References 427

Chapter 25

A HISTORY OF VERTEBRATES: MAMMALS 428

25.1 Characteristics of Mammals 428
25.2 Primitive Mammals 433
25.3 Adaptive Radiation of Eutherians 435
       Synopsis of Mammals 445
       Questions 446
       Annotated References 447

Chapter 26

PROTECTION, SUPPORT AND MOVEMENT 448

26.1 The Integument 448
26.2 The Skeleton 451
26.3 Joints 457
26.4 Muscles 457
       Questions 459
       Annotated References 459

Chapter 27

DIGESTION AND RESPIRATION 461

27.1 The Mouth 461
27.2 The Pharynx and Esophagus 463
27.3 The Stomach 464
27.4 The Liver and Pancreas 465
27.5 The Intestine 465
27.6 Digestion of Foods 467
27.7 The Control of Digestive Secretions 468
27.8 Absorption and Utilization of Materials 469
27.9 Respiratory Membranes 473
27.10 The Respiratory System of Fishes 473
27.11 The Respiratory System of Terrestrial Vertebrates 475
27.12 The Mechanics and Control of Breathing 477
       Questions 479
       Annotated References 479

Chapter 28

BLOOD AND CIRCULATION 480

28.1 The Vertebrate Circulatory System 480
28.2 Blood Plasma 481
28.3 Red Blood Cells 482
28.4 Platelets and Blood Clotting 484
28.5 White Blood Cells 484
28.6 Immunity 486
28.7 Blood Groups 487
28.8 The Rh Factor 488
28.9 Patterns of Circulation 488
28.10 The Fetal Circulation 493

28.11 Changes at Birth 494
28.12 Flow of Blood and Lymph.................................... 495
       Questions 501
       Annotated References 501

Chapter 29

THE UROGENITAL SYSTEM—EXCRETION AND REPRODUCTION 503

29.1 Evolution of the Kidneys and Their Ducts 503
29.2 The Nephron and Its Function 505
29.3 The Gonads 511
29.4 Reproductive Passages 513
29.5 Mammalian Reproduction... 515
      Questions 517
      Annotated References 517

Chapter 30

SENSE ORGANS 519

30.1 Receptor Mechanisms 519
30.2 Some Microscopic Receptors 520
30.3 The Eye... 521
30.4 The Lateral Line and The Ear.. 526
      Questions 531
      Annotated References 531

Chapter 31

NERVOUS COORDINATION 532

31.1 Organization of the Nervous System 532
31.2 Peripheral Nervous System 535
31.3 Central Nervous System 540
      Questions 548
      Annotated References 548

Chapter 32

HORMONAL INTEGRATION 550

32.1   Endocrine Glands 550
32.2   Methods of Investigating the Endocrine Glands 551
32.3   The Thyroid Gland.. 553
32.4   The Parathyroid Glands.. 557
32.5   The Islet Cells of the Pancreas 557
32.6   The Adrenal Glands 559
32.7   The Pituitary Gland 562
32.8   The Testes.. 567
32.9   The Ovaries 568
32.10 The Estrous and Menstrual Cycles.................................. 570
32.11 The Hormones of Pregnancy 571
32.12 Other Endocrine Glands 572

32.13 Endocrine Interrelationships 573
32.14 Pheromones 573
       Questions 575
       Annotated References 575

Chapter 33

THE DEVELOPMENT OF MAMMALS **576**

33.1 Early Stages of Mammalian Development 576
33.2 Formation of the Notochord and Neural Tube 579
33.3 The Digestive Tract and Its Derivatives 580
33.4 Differentiation of the Mesoderm 582
33.5 Growth of the Embryo 584
33.6 Twinning 584
       Questions 586
       Annotated References 586

Part Four   **GENETICS AND EVOLUTION**

Chapter 34

PRINCIPLES OF HEREDITY **589**

34.1 History of Genetics.. 589
34.2 Mendel's Discoveries... 589
34.3 Chromosomal Basis of the Laws of Heredity 591
34.4 Genes and Alleles 591
34.5 A Monohybrid Cross 592
34.6 Laws of Probability.. 593
34.7 Test Crosses 593
34.8 Incomplete Dominance... 594
34.9 A Dihybrid Cross... 594
34.10 Deducing Genotypes... 595
34.11 The Genetic Determination of Sex..................................... 597
34.12 Sex-linked Characteristics... 599
34.13 Linkage and Crossing Over 600
34.14 Chromosome Maps.. 603
34.15 The Interactions of Genes... 603
34.16 Polygenic Inheritance 607
34.17 Multiple Alleles 609
34.18 Inbreeding and Outbreeding 611
       Questions 611
       Annotated References 613

Chapter 35

CHEMICAL AND MATHEMATICAL ASPECTS OF GENETICS **614**

35.1 The Chemistry of Chromosomes... 614
35.2 The Role of DNA in Heredity 616
35.3 The Watson-Crick Model of DNA 617
35.4 What is a Gene? 622

35.5 The Genetic Code 624
35.6 The Synthesis of DNA: Replication 626
35.7 Transcription of the Code: The Synthesis of Messenger RNA 627
35.8 Types of RNA: Messenger, Ribosomal and Transfer 628
35.9 The Synthesis of a Specific Polypeptide Chain 628
35.10 Changes in Genes: Mutations 631
35.11 Gene-Enzyme Relations 633
35.12 Genes and Differentiation.. 636
35.13 The Mathematical Basis of Genetics: The Laws of Probability 640
35.14 Population Genetics 641
35.15 Human Cytogenetics 643
       Questions 645
       Annotated References 645

Chapter 36

THE CONCEPT OF EVOLUTION 646

36.1 The Principle of Organic Evolution 646
36.2 Development of Ideas About Evolution 646
36.3 Background for *The Origin of Species* 648
36.4 The Darwin-Wallace Theory of Natural Selection 649
36.5 Populations and Gene Pools... 650
36.6 Differential Reproduction... 651
36.7 Mutations, The Raw Material of Evolution 653
36.8 Balanced Polymorphism 655
36.9 Adaptive Radiation 655
36.10 Speciation 657
36.11 The Origin of Species by Hybridization 658
36.12 Straight-line Evolution 659
36.13 The Origin of Life 660
36.14 Principles of Evolution 663
       Questions 663
       Annotated References 664

Chapter 37

THE EVIDENCE OF EVOLUTION 665

37.1 The Fossil Evidence 665
37.2 The Geologic Time Table.. 666
37.3 The Geologic Eras 667
37.4 The Evidence from Taxonomy.. 673
37.5 The Evidence from Morphology.. 674
37.6 The Evidence from Comparative Physiology and Biochemistry 675
37.7 The Evidence from Embryology.. 676
37.8 The Evidence from Genetics and Cytology 678
37.9 The Evidence from the Geographic Distribution of Organisms 679
37.10 The Biogeographic Realms 680
       Questions 681
       Annotated References 682

Chapter 38

THE EVOLUTION OF MAN... 683

38.1 The Primates 683
38.2 Prosimians.. 683
38.3 Anthropoids 684
38.4 The Modern Great Apes 686
38.5 The Man-Apes 687
38.6 Fossil Ape-Men 688
38.7 Fossil Members of the Genus *Homo* 691
38.8 Modern Man (*Homo sapiens*) 692
38.9 Cultural Evolution 693
       Questions 694
       Annotated References 694

Part Five **ANIMALS AND THEIR ENVIRONMENT**

Chapter 39

ECOLOGY 699

39.1 Ecosystems 699
39.2 Habitat and Ecologic Niche................................. 700
39.3 The Cyclic Use of Matter 701
39.4 The Carbon Cycle 701
39.5 The Nitrogen Cycle 702
39.6 The Water Cycle 702
39.7 Mineral Cycles.. 703
39.8 The Energy Cycle 703
39.9 Factors Limiting the Ranges of Animals 704
39.10 Types of Interactions Between Species 706
39.11 Competition 706
39.12 Beneficial Associations 707
39.13 Negative Interactions....................................... 708
39.14 Intraspecific Relations 709
39.15 Food Chains 709
39.16 Communities and Populations............................. 710
39.17 Populations and Their Characteristics 711
39.18 Population Cycles 714
39.19 Cyclic Phenomena in Biology: Circadian Rhythms 715
39.20 Population Dispersal 717
39.21 Biotic Communities 717
39.22 Community Succession 718
39.23 The Dynamic Balance of Nature 719
       Questions 720
       Annotated References 720

Chapter 40

ADAPTATIONS, BIOMES AND ECOSYSTEMS................................ 721

40.1 Structural Adaptations 721

40.2   Physiologic Adaptations 722
40.3   Color Adaptations 723
40.4   Adaptations of Species to Species 724
40.5   The Distribution of Animals... 724
40.6   Terrestrial Life Zones 725
40.7   The Tundra Biome 725
40.8   The Forest Biomes 728
40.9   The Grassland Biome... 731
40.10 The Chaparral Biome... 732
40.11 The Desert Biome 733
40.12 The Edge of the Sea: Marshes and Estuaries 734
40.13 Marine Life Zones 734
40.14 Fresh-water Life Zones... 738
       Questions 739
       Annotated References 739

Chapter 41

ANIMAL BEHAVIOR.. 740

By Brian A. Hazlett

41.1   Behavior Patterns: Feeding 740
41.2   Behavior Patterns: Orientation 744
41.3   Behavior Patterns: Aggression....................................... 746
41.4   Behavior Patterns: Communication 748
41.5   Behavior Patterns: Mating 750
41.6   Behavior Patterns: Parental Care 752
41.7   Behavior Patterns: Dominance Hierarchies........................ 753
41.8   Social Systems 753
41.9   Factors Affecting Behavior 756
41.10 Types of Responses.. 758
41.11 Physiologic Condition 760
41.12 Rhythmic Phenomena 761
41.13 Learning, Conditioning and Imprinting 762
41.14 Genetic Control of Behavior... 764
41.15 Methods of Studying Behavior....................................... 765
       Questions 767
       Annotated References 767

Chapter 42

PARASITISM.. 769

42.1   The Origin of Parasitism 769
42.2   Ectoparasites 771
42.3   Parasites of the Digestive Tract 774
42.4   Parasites in Body Tissues 776
42.5   Intracellular Parasites 780
42.6   Adaptations to Parasitism 781
42.7   Host Specificity 784
42.8   Social Parasites 785

Questions 785
Annotated References 785

Chapter 43

CONSERVATION 786

43.1 Agriculture 786
43.2 Forestry 787
43.3 Wildlife 788
43.4 Marine Fisheries 790
43.5 Public Health 791
43.6 Human Ecology 791
Questions 792
Annotated References 792

GLOSSARY 793

INDEX 821

PART ONE

GENERAL CONCEPTS

1 _____ INTRODUCTION

1.1
Zoology and Its Subsciences

Zoology is one of the biologic sciences, the one dealing with the many different aspects of animal life. Since a "zoo" is a collection of animals, one could easily guess that "zoology" deals with animals. A visit to a zoo, interesting though it is, can barely begin to suggest the enormous variety of animals that are living today. (There are about one million different kinds of animals!) In addition to the ones living at present, a host of other kinds of animals have lived in past ages but are now extinct.

Modern zoology concerns itself with much more than the simple recognition and classification of the many kinds of animals. It includes the study of the structure, function and embryonic development of each part of an animal's body; of the nutrition, health and behavior of animals; of their heredity and evolution; and of their relations to the physical environment and to the plants and other animals of that region.

Enough facts about animals and their ways are known to fill a whole library of books, and more information appears every year from the intensive researches of zoologists in the field and in the laboratory. No zoologist today can know more than a small fraction of this enormous body of knowledge. Zoology is now much too broad a subject to be treated thoroughly in a single textbook or to be encompassed by a single scientist. Most zoologists are specialists in some limited phase of the subject—in one of the subdivisions of zoology. The sciences of **anatomy, physiology** and **embryology** deal with the structure, function and development, respectively, of an animal. Each of these may be further subdivided according to the kind of animal investigated, e.g., invertebrate physiology, arthropod physiology, insect physiology or comparative physiology. **Parasitology** deals· with those forms of life that live in or on and at the expense of other organisms. **Cytology** is concerned with the structure, composition and function of cells and their parts, and **histology** is the science of the structure, function and composition of tissues. The science of **genetics** investigates the mode of transmission of characteristics from one generation to the next and is closely related to the science of **evolution,** which studies the way in which new species of animals arise and how the present kinds of animals are related by descent to previous animals. The study of the classification of organisms, both animals and plants, is called **taxonomy.** The science of **ecology** is concerned with the relations of a group of organisms to their environment, including both the physical factors and the other forms of life which provide food or shelter for them, compete with them in some way, or prey upon them.

Some zoologists specialize in the study of one group of animals. There are **mammalogists, ornithologists, herpetologists** and **ichthyologists** who study mammals, birds, reptiles and amphibians, and fishes, respectively; **entomologists,** who investigate insects; **protozoologists,** who study the single-celled animals, and so on.

In recent years advances in chemistry and physics have made possible quantitative studies of the molecular structures and events underlying biologic processes. The term **molecular biology** has been applied to analyses of gene structure and function and genic control of the synthesis of enzymes and other proteins, studies of subcellular structures and their roles in regulatory processes within the cell, investigations of the mechanisms underlying cellular differentiation, and analyses of the molecular basis of evolution by comparative studies of the molecular structure of specific proteins—enzymes, hormones, cytochromes, hemoglobins—in different species.

The science of zoology thus includes both a tremendous body of facts and theories about animals and the means for learning more. The ultimate source of each fact is in some carefully controlled observation or experiment made by a zoologist. In earlier times, some scientists kept their discoveries to themselves, but there is now a strong tradition that scientific discoveries are public property and should be freely published. In a scientific publication a man must do more than simply say that he has made some particular discovery; he must give all of the relevant details of the means by which the discovery was made so that others can repeat the observation. It is this criterion of *repeatability* that makes us accept a certain observation or experiment as representing a true fact; observations that cannot be repeated by competent investigators are discarded.

When a scientist has made some new observation, or carried out a series of experiments that add to our knowledge in a field, he writes a report, called a "paper," in which he describes his methods in sufficient detail so that another worker can repeat them, gives the results of his observations, discusses the conclusions to be drawn from them, perhaps formulates a theory to explain them or discusses how they are explained by a previous theory, and finally indicates the place of these new facts in their particular field of science. The knowledge that his discovery will be subjected to the keen scrutiny of his colleagues is a strong stimulus for repeating the observations or experiments carefully before publishing them. He then submits his paper for publication in one of the professional journals in the particular field of his discovery. There are several thousand zoological journals published all over the world. Some of the more important American ones are the *Journal of Experimental Zoology, Journal of Cellular and Comparative Physiology, Biological Bulletin, Physiological Zoology, American Journal of Physiology, Anatomical Record, Ecology* and the

journals devoted to research on a particular group of animals, such as the *Journal of Mammalogy.* The paper is read by one or more of the board of editors of the journal, all of whom are experts in the field. If it is approved, it is published and becomes part of "the literature" of the subject.

At one time, when there were fewer journals, it might have been possible for one man to read them all each month as they appeared, but this is obviously impossible now. Journals such as *Biological Abstracts* assist the hard-pressed zoologist by publishing, classified by fields, short summaries or abstracts of each paper published, giving the facts found, the conclusion reached, and an exact reference to the journal in which the full report appears. A considerable number of journals devoted solely to reviewing the newer developments in particular fields of science have sprung up in the past 35 years; some of these are *Physiological Reviews, Quarterly Review of Biology, Nutrition Reviews, Annual Review of Physiology* and *Vitamins and Hormones.* The new fact or theory thus becomes widely known through publication in the appropriate professional journal and by reference in abstract and review journals and eventually may become a sentence or two in a textbook.

The professional societies of zoologists and the various special branches of zoology have annual meetings at which new discoveries may be reported. Two of the largest annual meetings are those of the American Institute of Biological Sciences and the Federation of American Societies for Experimental Biology. There are, in addition, national and international gatherings, called **symposia,** of specialists in a given field to discuss the newer findings and the present status of the knowledge in that field. For example, the discussions of the Cold Spring Harbor Symposia in Quantitative Biology, held each June at the Long Island Biological Laboratory in Cold Spring Harbor, are published and provide an excellent review of some particular field. A different subject is discussed each year.

1.2
The Scientific Method

The ultimate aim of each science is to reduce the apparent complexity of natural phenomena to simple, fundamental ideas and relations, to discover all the facts, and the relationships among them. The essence of the scientific method is the posing of questions and the search for answers, but they must be "scientific" questions, arising from observations and experiments, and "scientific" answers, ones that are testable by further observation and experiment. The Danish physicist Niels Bohr puts it this way, "the task of science is both to extend the range of our experience and to reduce it to order."

There is, however, no single "scientific method," no regular, infallible sequence of events which will reveal scientific truths. Different scientists go about their work in different ways. George Sarton, in the *Study of the History of Science,* points out that "Even as all kinds of men are needed to build up a community, even so we need all kinds of scientists to develop science in every possible direction. Some are very sharp and narrow-minded, others broad-minded and superficial. Many scientists, like Hannibal, know how to conquer, but not how to use their victories. Others are colonizers rather than explorers. Others are pedagogues. Others want to measure everything more accurately than it was measured before. This may lead them to the making of fundamental discoveries, or they may fail, and be looked upon as insufferable pedants."

The ultimate source of all the facts of science is careful, close observation and experiment, free of bias and done as quantitatively as possible. The observations or experiments may then be analyzed, or simplified into their constituent parts, so that some sort of order can be brought into the observed phenomena. Then the parts can be reassembled and their interactions made clear. On the basis of these observations, the scientist constructs a **hypothesis,** a trial idea about the nature of the observation, or about the connections between a chain of events, or even about cause and effect relationships between different events. It is in this ability to see through a mass of data and construct a reasonable hypothesis to explain their relationships that scientists differ most and that true genius shows itself.

The role of a hypothesis is to penetrate beyond the immediate data and place it into a new, larger context, so that we can interpret the unknown in terms of the known. There is no sharp distinction between the usage of the words "hypothesis" and "theory," but the latter has, in general, the connotation of greater certainty than a hypothesis. A **theory** is a conceptual scheme which tries to explain the observed phenomena and the relationships between them, so as to bring into one structure the observations and hypotheses of several different fields. The theory of evolution, for example, provides a conceptual scheme into which fit a host of observations and hypotheses from paleontology, anatomy, physiology, biochemistry, genetics and other allied sciences.

A good theory correlates many previously separate facts into a logical, easily understood framework. The theory, by arranging the facts properly, suggests new relationships between the individual facts, and suggests further experiments or observations which might be made to test these relationships. It may predict new phenomena that will be observed under certain circumstances and finally may provide the solution for practical problems. A good theory should be simple and should not require a separate proviso to explain each fact; it should be flexible, able to grow and to undergo modifications in the light of new data. A theory is not discarded because of the existence of some isolated fact which contradicts it, but only because some other theory is better able to explain all of the known data.

Once a hypothesis has been established, the rules of formal logic can be applied to deduce certain consequences. In physics, and to a lesser extent in the biologic sciences, the hypotheses and deductions can be stated in mathematical terms, and far-reaching conclusions may be deduced. From these inferences, one can predict the results of other observations and experiments. Each hypothesis is ultimately kept, amended or discarded on the basis of its ability to make valid predictions. A hypothesis must be subject to some sort of experimental test—i.e., it must make a prediction that can be verified in some way—or it is mere speculation. Conversely, unless a prediction follows as the logical outgrowth of some theory it is no more than a guess.

The finding of results contrary to those predicted by the hypothesis causes the investigator, after he has assured himself of the validity of his observation, either to discard the hypothesis or to change it to account for both the original data and the new data. Hypotheses are constantly being refined and elaborated. There are few scientists who would regard any hypothesis, no matter how many times it may have been tested, as a statement of absolute and universal truth. It is rather regarded as the best available approximation to the truth for some finite range of circumstances. For example, the Law of the Conservation of Matter was widely adhered to until the work of Einstein showed that it had to be modified to allow for the possible interconversion of matter and energy.

Ideally, the scientific method consists of making careful observations and arranging these observations so as to bring order into the phenomena. Then one postulates a hypothesis or conceptual scheme which will explain the facts at hand and make predictions about the results of further experiments or observations. Sciences differ widely in the extent to which prediction is possible, and the biologic sciences have been held by some to be not truly "scientific," for they are not completely predictable. However, even physics, which is generally regarded as the most scientific of the sciences, is far from completely predictable.

The history of science shows that, although many scientists have made their discoveries by following the precepts of the ideal scientific method, there have been occasions on which important and far-reaching theories have resulted from making incorrect conclusions from erroneous postulates, or from the misinterpretation of an improperly controlled experiment! There are instances in which, in retrospect, it seems clear that all the evidence for the formulation of the correct theory was known, yet no scientist put the proper two and two together. And there are other instances in which scientists have been able to establish the correct theory despite an abundance of seemingly contradictory evidence.

In most scientific studies one of the ultimate goals is to explain the cause of some phenomenon, but the hard-and-fast proof that a cause and effect relationship exists between two events is really very difficult to obtain. If the circumstances leading to a certain event always have a certain factor in common in a variety of cases, that factor may be the cause of the event. The difficulty, of course, lies in making sure that the factor under consideration is the *only* one common

to all the cases. It would be wrong, for example, to conclude from the observation that drinking Scotch and soda, bourbon and soda, and rye and soda all produce intoxication, that soda is the only factor in common and therefore is the cause of the intoxication. This method of discovering the common factor in a series of cases that may be the cause of the event (known as the **method of agreement**) can seldom be used as a valid proof because of this difficulty of being sure that it is indeed the only common factor. The simple observation that all people suffering from beriberi have diets which are low in thiamine is not proof that a deficiency of this vitamin causes the disease, for there may be many other factors in common.

Experiments based on the **method of difference** provide another way of elucidating cause and effect relations. If two sets of circumstances differ in only one factor, and the one containing the factor leads to an event and the other does not, the factor may be considered the cause of the event. For example, if two groups of rats are fed diets which are identical except that one contains all the vitamins and the second contains all but thiamine, and if the first group grows normally but the second fails to grow and ultimately develops polyneuritis, this would be a strong suggestion (but would not be acceptable as absolute proof) that polyneuritis, or beriberi in rats, is caused by a deficiency of thiamine. By using an inbred strain of rats that are as alike as possible in inherited traits, and by using littermates (brothers and sisters) of this strain, one could make certain that there were no hereditary differences between the controls (the ones getting the complete diet) and the experimentals (the ones getting the thiamine-deficient diet). One might postulate that the thiamine-free diet does not have as attractive a taste as the one with thiamine, and the experimental animals simply eat less food, fail to grow, and develop the deficiency symptoms because they are partially starved. This source of error can be avoided by "pair-feeding," by pairing in some arbitrary way each control and experimental animal, then weighing the food eaten each day by each experimental animal and giving only that much food to the corresponding control member of the pair.

One of the more useful methods of detecting cause and effect relationships is the **method of concomitant variation.** If a variation in the amount of one given factor produces a parallel variation in the effect, the factor may be the cause. Thus, if several groups of rats were given diets with varying amounts of thiamine, and if the amount of protection against beriberi varied directly with the amount of thiamine in the diet, one could be reasonably sure that thiamine deficiency is the cause of beriberi.

It must be emphasized that it is seldom that we can be more than "reasonably sure" that X is the cause of Y. As more experiments and observations lead to the same result, the probability increases that X is the cause of Y. When experiments or observations can be made quantitative, when their results can be counted or measured in some way, the methods of statistical analysis provide a means for calculating the probability that Y follows X simply as a matter of chance. Scientists are usually satisfied that there is some sort of cause and effect relationship between X and Y if they can show that there is less than one chance in a hundred that the observed X-Y relationship could be due to chance alone. A statistical analysis of a set of data can never give a flat yes or no to a question; it can state only that something is very probable or very improbable. It can also tell an investigator approximately how many more times he must repeat the experiment to show with a given probability that Y is caused by X.

The proper design of experiments is a science in itself, and one for which only general rules can be made. In all experiments, the scientist must ever be on his guard against bias in himself, bias in the subject, bias in his instrument and bias in the way the experiment is designed.

Each experiment must include the proper **control group** (indeed some experiments require several kinds of control groups). The control group is one treated exactly like the experimental group in all respects but one, the factor whose effect is being tested. The use of controls in medical experiments raises the difficult question of the moral justification of withholding treatment from a patient who might be benefited by it. If there is sufficient evidence that one treatment is indeed better than another, a physician would hardly be justified in further experimentation. However, the medical literature is full of treatments now known to be useless or even detrimental, which were used for many years, only to be abandoned finally as experience showed that they were ineffective and that the evidence which had originally suggested their use was improperly controlled. There is a time in the development of any new treatment when the medical profession is not only morally justified, but really morally required, to do carefully controlled tests on human beings to be sure that the new treatment is better than the former one.

In medical testing it is not sufficient simply to give a treatment to one group of patients and not to give it to another, for it is widely known that there is a strong psychologic effect in simply giving a treatment of any sort. For example, a group of students in a large western university served as subjects for a test of the hypothesis that daily doses of extra amounts of vitamin C might help to prevent colds. This grew out of the observation that people who drink lots of fruit juices seem to have fewer colds. The group receiving the vitamin C showed a 65 per cent reduction in the number of colds contracted during the winter in which they received treatment as compared to the previous winter when they had no treatment. There were enough students in the group (208) to make this result statistically significant. In the absence of controls, one would have been led to the conclusion that vitamin C does help to prevent colds. A second group of students were given "placebos," pills identical in size, shape, color and taste to the vitamin C pills but without any vitamin C. The students were not told who was getting vitamin C and who was not; they only knew they were getting pills that might help to prevent colds. The group getting the placebos reported that they had a 63 per cent reduction in the number of colds! This controlled experiment thus shows that vitamin C had nothing to do with the decrease in the number of colds and that the reductions reported in both groups were either psychologic effects or simply the result of a lesser amount of cold virus on the campus that year. There have been reports that other substances, called bioflavonoids, present in fruit juices may have some effect in protecting against the common cold. Comparable carefully controlled experiments are needed to substantiate this report.

1.3
History of Zoology

Man's interest in animals is probably somewhat older than the human race, for the ape-men and man-apes that preceded him in evolution undoubtedly learned at an early time which animals were dangerous, which could be hunted for food, clothing or shelter, where these were to be found, and so on. Some of prehistoric man's impressions of the contemporary animals have survived in the cave paintings of France and Spain (Fig. 1.1). Some animals were regarded as good or evil spirits. Later man decorated pottery, tools, cloth and other objects with animal figures.

The early Egyptians had a wealth of knowledge about animals and had domesticated cattle, sheep, pigs, cats, geese and ducks. The Greek philosophers of the fifth and sixth centuries B.C., Anaximander, Xenophanes, Empedocles and others, speculated on the origin of the animals of the earth. One of the earliest classifications of animals is found in a Greek medical book of this time which classifies animals primarily as to whether or not they are edible. Aristotle (384–322 B.C.) was one of the greatest Greek philosophers and wrote on many topics. His *Historia animalium*

contains a great deal of information about the animals of Greece and the nearby regions of Asia Minor. Aristotle's descriptions are quite good and are recognizable as those of particular animals living today. The breadth and depth of his zoologic interests are impressive—he made a careful study of the development of the chick and of the breeding of sharks and bees, and he had notions about the functions of the human organs, some of which, not too surprisingly, were quite wrong. He presented an elaborate theory that animals have gradually evolved, based on a metaphysical belief that nature strives to change from the simple and imperfect to the more complex and perfect. His contributions to logic, such as the development of the system of inductive reasoning from specific observations to a generalization which explains them all, have been of inestimable value to all branches of science.

The Greek physician, Galen (131–201 A.D.), was one of the first to do experiments and dissections of animals to determine structure

Figure 1.1   Paintings by Upper Paleolithic man from the wall of the cavern at Lascaux, Dordogne, France. (Photo by Windels Montignac.) (Villee: Biology, 5th ed.)

Figure 1.2 Galen (131–201 A.D.). The founder of experimental physiology. (Courtesy of J.A.M.A., from the series Medical Greats.)

and functions (Fig. 1.2). The first experimental physiologist, he made some notable discoveries on the functions of the brain and nerves and demonstrated that arteries carry blood and not air. His descriptions of the human body were the unquestioned authority for some 1300 years, even though they contained some remarkable errors, being based on dissections of pigs and monkeys rather than of human bodies. Pliny (23–79 A.D.) and others in succeeding centuries compiled encyclopedias (Pliny's *Natural History* was a 37 volume work) regarding the kinds of animals and where they lived, which are remarkable mixtures of fact and fiction. Some of the ones written in the Middle Ages were called "bestiaries." The zoologic books written in the Middle Ages are, almost without exception, copied from Aristotle, Galen and Pliny; no original observations were made to corroborate or refute the accuracy of these authorities.

The Renaissance in science began slowly with scholars such as Roger Bacon (1214–1294) and Albertus Magnus (1206–1280) who were interested in all branches of natural science and philosophy. The genius Leonardo da Vinci (1452–1519) was an anatomist and physiologist as well as a painter, engineer and inventor. He made many original observations in zoology, some of which came to light only much later, when his notebooks were deciphered.

One of the first to question the authority of Galen's descriptions of human anatomy was the Belgian, Andreas Vesalius (1514–1564), who was professor at the University of Padua in Italy (Fig. 1.3). By actual dissections and detailed, clear drawings of what he saw, Vesalius revealed many of the inaccuracies in Galen's descriptions of the human body. He published his observations and illustrations in *De Humani corporis fabrica* (On the Structure of the Human Body) in 1543. Since Vesalius dared to reject the authority of Galen, he was the object of much adverse criticism and was finally forced to leave his professorial post.

Just as Vesalius had emphasized the importance of relying on original observation rather than on authority in anatomy, so did William Harvey (1578–1657) in physiology (Fig. 1.4). Harvey, an English physician, received his medical training at the University of Padua, where Vesalius had taught. He returned to England and investigated the circulation of the blood. In 1628 he published *Exercitatio anatomica de motu cordis et sanguinis*

Figure 1.3 Andreas Vesalius (1514–1564). In his *De Humani corporis fabrica*, he established the basis for modern anatomy. (From Garrison: History of Medicine. 4th ed. Philadelphia, W. B. Saunders Co., 1929.)

Figure 1.4 William Harvey (1578–1657). He proved the circulation of the blood by the first quantitative physiologic demonstration. (From Garrison: History of Medicine. 4th ed. Philadelphia, W. B. Saunders Co., 1929.)

in animalibus (Anatomical Studies on the Motion of the Heart and Blood in Animals). At that time blood was believed to be generated in the liver from food and to pass just once to the organs of the body where it was used up. The heart was believed to be nonmuscular and to be expanded passively by the inflowing blood. Harvey described, from direct observations on animals, how first the atria (auricles) and then the ventricles fill and empty by muscular contraction. He showed by experiment that when an artery is cut blood spurts from it in rhythm with the beating of the heart, and that when a vein is clamped it becomes full of blood on the side away from the heart and empty on the side toward the heart. He showed that valves in the veins permit blood to flow toward the heart but not in the reverse direction (Fig. 1.5). From these experiments he concluded that blood is carried away from the heart in arteries and back to the heart in veins. Furthermore, by measuring how much blood is delivered by each beat of the heart, and by measuring the number of heartbeats per minute, he could calculate the total flow of blood through the heart per minute or hour. This he found to be so great that it could not be generated anew in the liver but must be recirculated, used over and over again. This was the first quantitative

physiologic argument. He inferred that there must be small vessels connecting arteries and veins to complete the circular path of the blood but, lacking a microscope, he was unable to see them. In later years he made a careful study of the development of the chick, published in 1651 as *Exercitationes de generatione animalium.* In this he postulated that mammals, like the chick, develop from an egg.

The development of the compound microscope by the Janssens in 1590 and by Galileo in 1610 provided the means for attacking many problems in zoology and botany. Robert Hooke (1635–1703), Marcello Malpighi (1628–1694), Antony van Leeuwenhoek (1632–1723) and Jan Swammerdam (1637–1680) were some of the first microscopists. They studied the fine structure of plant and animal tissues. Hooke was the first to describe the presence of "cells" in plant tissue, Leeuwenhoek was the first to describe bacteria, protozoa and sperm, and Malpighi was the first to describe the capillaries connecting arteries with veins. The light microscope has been modified and improved greatly in the past century, and man's ability to see the fine structure of cells has been greatly extended by the invention of the phase microscope and of the electron microscope. The latter, with good resolution at magnifications as great as 80,000 to 100,000 diameters, has revealed a whole new level of complexity in the structure of all kinds of cells.

John Ray (1627–1705) and Linnaeus (Karl von Linné) (1707–1778) brought order into the classification of animals and plants and devised the binomial system (two names, genus and species) for the scientific naming of the kinds of animals and plants. Linnaeus first used this binomial system consistently in the tenth edition of his *Systema naturae* (1758).

Contributions to our understanding of the embryonic development of animals were made by Fabricius, the professor of Anatomy at Padua who taught William Harvey, and by Harvey, Malpighi, and Kaspar Wolff (1759). Wolff proposed the theory of epigenesis, the concept that there is a gradual differentiation of structure during development from a relatively structureless egg. Karl Ernst von Baer (1792–1876) established the theory of germ layers and emphasized the need for comparative studies of development in different animals.

Following William Harvey, physiology was

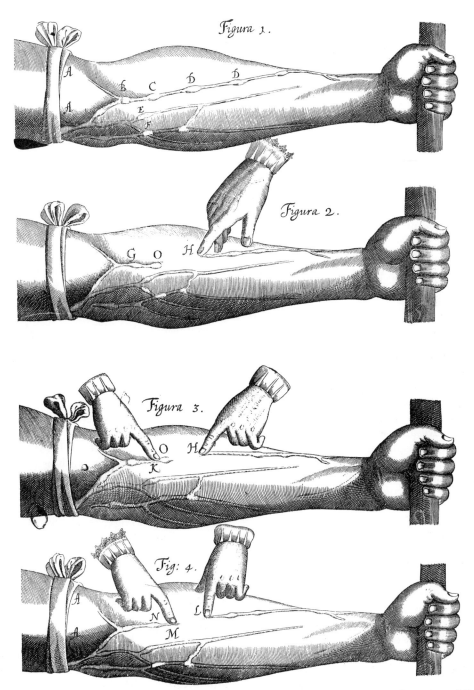

Figure 1.5 Harvey's illustrations to demonstrate the direction of blood flow. *1*, The formation of "knots" at valves. *2*, Stripping a portion of a vessel to show that there is no back flow. *3* and *4*, Demonstration of valvular blocking of blood flow. (From Harvey: Exercitatio Anatomica de Motu Cordis et Sanguinis in Animalibus. Translation by C. D. Leake: Anatomical Studies on the Motion of the Heart and Blood, Springfield, Ill., Charles C Thomas, 1931.)

advanced by René Descartes (1596–1650), who was a philosopher rather than an experimenter. He believed that "animal spirits" are generated in the heart, stored in the brain, and pass through the nerves to the muscles, causing contraction or relaxation, according to their quantity. Charles Bell (1774–1842) and François Magendie (1783–1855) made notable contributions to our understanding of the function of the brain and spinal nerves. Johannes Müller (1801–1858) studied the properties of nerves and capillaries; his textbook of physiology stimulated a great deal of interest and research in the field. Claude Bernard (1813–1878) was one of the great advocates of experimental physiology, and contributed significantly to our understanding of the role of the liver, heart, brain and placenta. Henry Bowditch (1840–1911) discovered the "all-or-none" principle of the contraction of heart muscle and established the first laboratory for teaching physiology in the United States. Ernest Starling (1866–1927) made many contributions to the physiology of circulation and the nature of lymph and with William Bayliss (1866–1924) elucidated the hormonal control of the function of the pancreas.

The Scottish anatomist John Hunter (1728–1793) and the French anatomist Georges Cuvier (1769–1832) were pioneers in the field of comparative anatomy, studying the same structure in different animals. Richard Owen (1804–1892) developed the concepts of homology and analogy. Cuvier was one of the first to study the structure of fossils as well as of living animals and is credited with founding the science of paleontology. Cuvier believed strongly in the unchanging nature of species and carried on bitter debates with Lamarck, who in 1809 proposed a theory of evolution based on the idea of the inheritance of acquired characters.

One of the most important and fruitful concepts in biology is the **cell theory,** which has gradually grown since Robert Hooke first saw, with the newly invented microscope, the dead cell walls in a piece of cork. The French biologist René Dutrochet clearly stated in 1824 that "all organic tissues are actually globular cells of exceeding smallness, which appear to be united only by simple adhesive forces; thus all tissues, all animal organs are actually only a cellular tissue variously modified." Dutrochet recognized that growth is the result of the increase in the volume of individual cells and of the addition of new cells. Two Germans, botanist M. J. Schleiden and zoologist Theodor Schwann, studied many different plant and animal tissues and are generally credited with formulating the cell theory, for they showed that cells are the units of structure in plants and animals, and that organisms are aggregates of cells arranged according to definite laws. The presence of a nucleus within the cell, now recognized as an almost universal feature of cells, was first described by Robert Brown in 1831.

Zoology, along with the other biologic sciences, has expanded at a tremendous rate in the past century, with the establishment of the subsciences of cytology, embryology, genetics, evolution, biochemistry, biophysics, endocrinology and ecology. The discoveries and new techniques of chemistry and physics have made possible new approaches to the biologic sciences that have attracted the attention of many biologists. So many men have contributed to the growth of zoology in this past century that only a few in each field can be mentioned: Mendel, deVries, Morgan and Bridges in genetics, Darwin, Dobzhansky, Wright and Goldschmidt in evolution, and Harrison and Spemann in embryology. Many others will be mentioned as these subjects are discussed in detail in the text.

The establishment and growth of the marine biologic laboratories, such as the ones at Naples (Italy), Woods Hole (Mass.), Pacific Grove (Calif.), Friday Harbor (Wash.) and elsewhere, have played an important role in fostering research in zoologic sciences. There are comparable stations for the study of fresh-water biology, such as the one at Douglas Lake, Michigan.

1.4
Applications of Zoology

Some of the practical uses of a knowledge of zoology will become apparent as the student proceeds through this text. Zoology is basic in many ways to the fields of medicine and public health, agriculture, conservation and to certain of the social sciences. There are esthetic values in the study of zoology, for a knowledge of the structure and functions of the major types of animals will greatly increase the pleasure of a stroll in the woods or an excursion along the seashore. Trips to zoos, aquariums and museums are also rewarding in the glimpses they give of the host of different kinds of animals. Many of these are beautifully colored and shaped, graceful or amusing to watch, but all will mean more to a person equipped with the basic knowledge of zoology which enables him to recognize them and to understand the ways in which they are adapted to survive in their native habitat.

QUESTIONS

1. How would you define "science" and "zoology"? Is zoology a science?
2. Contrast a hypothesis and a law.
3. What is the role of theories in science?
4. How would you catalog the subsciences of zoology?
5. Describe in your own words the mode of operation of the scientific method.
6. Discuss the tests that would be necessary to prove that event A is the cause of event B.
7. How may the method of concomitant variation be used to show cause-and-effect relationships?
8. What is a "placebo"? How are they used in medical experiments?
9. How would you go about proving that "aminodichloro sneezic acid" is a cure for hay fever?
10. What contributions to zoology were made by (a) Aristotle, (b) Galen, (c) Vesalius, (d) William Harvey, (e) Leeuwenhoek, (f) von Baer, (g) Claude Bernard, (h) Georges Cuvier and (i) Richard Owen?

ANNOTATED REFERENCES

Beveridge, W. I. B.: The Art of Scientific Investigation. New York, W. W. Norton & Co., 1957. One of the best over-all surveys of the scientific method.

Cannon, W. B.: The Way of an Investigator. New York, W. W. Norton & Co., 1945. An autobiography with many interesting anecdotes illustrating the application of the scientific method to medical research.

Conant, J. B.: Science and Common Sense. New Haven, Yale University Press, 1951. A general presentation of the methods of science; one of the classics in this field.

Feibleman, J. K.: Testing Hypotheses by Experiment. Perspect. Biol. Med., 4:91, 1960. An excellent, brief discussion of scientific methods.

Gabriel, M. L., and S. Fogel: Great Experiments in Biology. New York, Prentice-Hall, Inc., 1955. By extensive quotations from the original papers, traces the development of some of the basic concepts of zoology.

Guthrie, D.: A History of Medicine. Philadelphia, J. B. Lippincott Co., 1946. Describes the early phases of the development of anatomy and physiology along with other medical sciences.

Sedgwick, W. T., H. V. Tyler, and R. P. Bigelow: A Short History of Science. New York, Macmillan, 1939. A classic survey of the early development of the sciences in general.

Singer, C.: A History of Biology. Revised ed. New York, Abelard-Schumann, 1959. A general history of the biological sciences.

Wilson, E. B.: An Introduction to Scientific Research. New York, McGraw-Hill Book Co., 1952. An excellent discussion in nontechnical terms of the methods of science and some of the factors to be considered in planning and carrying out scientific investigation.

2 THE PHYSICAL AND CHEMICAL BASIS OF LIFE

To define the field of zoology, or animal biology, it might seem a simple task first to differentiate the living from the nonliving and then to separate the living into plants and animals. Yet each of these is quite difficult to do sharply and clearly. Organisms such as cats, clams and cicadas are clearly recognizable as animals, but sponges, for example, were considered to be plants until well into the nineteenth century, and there are single-celled organisms which, even today, are called animals by zoologists and plants by botanists. Even the line between living and nonliving is indistinct, for the viruses, too small to be seen with an ordinary light microscope, can be considered either the simplest living things or very complex, but nonliving, organic chemicals.

Most biologists are agreed that all the varied phenomena of life are ultimately explainable in terms of the same physical and chemical principles which define nonliving systems. The idea that there are no fundamental differences between living and nonliving things is sometimes called the **mechanistic theory of life.** A corollary of this is that when enough is known of the chemistry and physics of vital phenomena it may be possible to synthesize living matter. An opposite view, widely held by biologists until the present century, stated that some unique force, not explainable in terms of physics and chemistry, is associated with and controls life. The view that living and nonliving systems are basically different and obey different laws is called **vitalism.** Many of the phenomena that ap-

peared to be so mysterious when first discovered have subsequently proved to be understandable without invoking a unique life force, and it is reasonable to suppose that future research will show that other aspects of life can also be explained by physical and chemical principles.

2.1
Characteristics of Living Things

All living things have, to a greater or lesser degree, the properties of specific organization, irritability, movement, metabolism, growth, reproduction and adaptation.

Organization. Each kind of living organism is recognized by its characteristic form and appearance; the adult organism usually has a characteristic size. Nonliving things generally have much more variable shapes and sizes. Living things are not homogeneous, but are made of different parts, each with special functions; thus the bodies of animals and plants are characterized by a specific, complex organization. The fundamental structural and functional unit of living things, both animals and plants, is the **cell.** It is the simplest bit of living matter that can exist independently and exhibit all the characteristics of life. A typical cell, such as a liver cell (Fig. 2.1), is polygonal in shape, with a **plasma membrane** separating the living substance from the surroundings. Almost without exception, each cell has a **nucleus,** typically spherical or ovoid in shape,

14

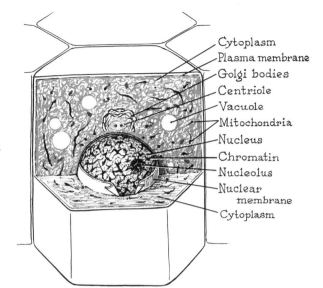

Figure 2.1 Schematic drawing of a generalized animal cell.

which is separated from the rest of the cell by a **nuclear membrane.** The nucleus, as we shall see later, has a major role in controlling and regulating the cell's activities. It contains the hereditary units or **genes.** A cell experimentally deprived of its nucleus usually dies in a short time; even if it survives for several days it is unable to reproduce.

Irritability. Living things are irritable; they respond to stimuli, to physical or chemical changes in their immediate surroundings. Stimuli which are effective in evoking a response in most animals and plants are changes in light (either in its color, intensity or direction), temperature, pressure, sound, and in the chemical composition of the earth, water, or air surrounding the animal. In man and other complex animals, certain cells of the body are highly specialized to respond to certain types of stimuli: the rods and cones in the retina of the eye respond to light, certain cells in the nose and in the taste buds of the tongue respond to chemical stimuli, and special groups of cells in the skin respond to changes in temperature or pressure. In lower animals such specialized cells may be absent, but the whole organism responds to any one of a variety of stimuli. Single-celled animals such as the ameba will respond by moving toward or away from heat or cold, certain chemical substances, or the touch of a microneedle. Indeed, many of the cells of higher animals have a similar generalized sensitivity.

Movement. A third characteristic of living things is their ability to move. The movement of most animals is quite obvious—they wiggle, swim, run or fly. The movement of plants is much slower and less obvious, but is present nonetheless. A few animals—sponges, corals, hydroids, oysters, certain parasites—do not move from place to place, but most of these have microscopic, hairlike projections from the cells, called **cilia** or **flagella,** to move their surroundings past their bodies and thus bring food and other necessities of life to themselves. The movement of an animal body may be the result of muscular contraction, of the beating of cilia or flagella, or of the slow oozing of a mass of cell substance (known as ameboid motion).

Metabolism. All living things carry on a wide variety of chemical reactions, the sum of which we call **metabolism.** There is no way of observing the occurrence of most of these chemical reactions without the aid of special apparatus such as respirometers to measure oxygen utilization and carbon dioxide production and thermometers to measure heat production. Elaborate physical and chemical equipment and substances labeled with radioactive or stable isotopes are used to trace in detail the paths of metabolism and their respective quantitative importance to the animal or plant under investigation. Such studies have shown that all cells are constantly taking in new substances, altering them chemically in a multitude of ways, building new cell components, and transforming the potential energy of some of the molecules taken in into kinetic energy and heat. The large molecules taken in — proteins, fats, carbohydrates and others — are broken down stepwise to yield energy and simpler substances. This constant release and utilization of energy is one of the unique and characteristic attributes of living things. The rate of metabolism is affected by temperature, age, sex, general health and nutrition, by hormones, and by many other factors.

Those metabolic processes in which simpler substances are combined to form more complex substances and which result in the storage of energy and the production of new cellular materials are termed **anabolic.** The opposite processes, in which complex substances are broken down to release energy, are called **catabolic.** Both types of metabolism occur continuously and are intricately interdependent so that they become, in practice, difficult to distinguish. Complex compounds of one sort may be broken down and their parts recombined in new ways to yield new compounds. The interconversions of carbohydrates, fats and proteins that occur continuously in most animal cells are examples of combined anabolic and catabolic processes. Furthermore, the synthesis of most molecules requires energy, so that some catabolic processes must occur to supply the energy to drive the anabolic reactions of these syntheses.

Growth.   Both plants and animals grow; nonliving things do not. The increase in mass may be brought about by an increase in the *size* of the individual cells, or by an increase in the *number* of cells. An increase in cell size may occur by the simple uptake of water, but this is not generally considered to be growth. The term **growth** is restricted to those processes which increase the amount of living substance of the body. This is commonly measured by the amount of nitrogen, of protein or of nucleic acid (see p. 26) present, but objections may be raised to the use of any single one of these parameters. Growth may be uniform in the several parts of an organism, or, perhaps more commonly, growth is differential, greater in some parts than in others, so that the body proportions change as growth occurs.

Growth may occur throughout the life span of an organism or may be restricted to a part of it. One of the truly remarkable aspects of the process is that each organ continues to function while undergoing growth.

Reproduction.   If there is any one characteristic that can be said to be the *sine qua non* of life, it is the ability to reproduce. Since individual animals grow old and die, the survival of the species depends upon the replacing of these individuals by new ones. Although at one time worms were believed to arise from horse hairs in a trough of water, maggots from decaying meat and frogs from the mud of the Nile, we now know that each can come only from previously existing ones. One of the fundamental tenets of biology is that "all life comes only from living things." The process of reproduction may be as simple as the splitting of one individual into two. In most animals, however, it involves the production of specialized eggs and sperm which unite to form the zygote or fertilized egg, from which the new organism develops. In some animals, the liver flukes for example, reproduction involves several quite different forms, each of which gives rise to the next in succession until the cycle is completed and the adult reappears.

Adaptation.   To survive, an animal or plant must be able to adapt to its surroundings. Each particular species can achieve adaptation either by seeking out a suitable environment or by undergoing modifications to make it more fitted to its present surroundings. This ability to adapt is a further characteristic of all living things. Adaptation may involve immediate changes which depend upon the irritability of cells, or it may be the result of a long-term process of mutation and selection. It is obvious that no single kind of organism can adapt to all the conceivable kinds of environment; hence there will be certain areas where it cannot survive. The list of factors which may limit the distribution of a species is almost endless: water, light, temperature, food, predators, competitors, parasites, and so on.

2.2
Cellular Organization

The living substance that makes up each cell was termed **protoplasm** by the Bohemian physiologist Purkinje in 1839. As more has been learned about cell structure and function, it has become clear that the living contents of the cell comprise an incredibly complex system. Although "protoplasm" is still a convenient term for all the organized constituents of the cell, it is not strictly meaningful in a physical or chemical sense. The living substance of most animal cells is hidden by a protective covering of skin, hair or shell, but in the ameba, we can observe the naked living substance and find that it is a viscid, jellylike substance, slimy to the touch, which is colorless or faintly yellow or pink.

When seen under the light microscope, the cell may appear to contain granules or fibrils of denser material, droplets of fatty substances or fluid-filled vacuoles, all suspended in the clear, continuous, semifluid "ground substance." The cell constituents comprise a complex colloidal system (see

p. 28) whose consistency varies from liquid (sol) to a firm jelly (gel). The change from sol to gel is reversible, and the consistency may vary from moment to moment and from one part of the cell to another. Some of the formed bodies within the cell—mitochondria, endoplasmic reticulum and Golgi apparatus —are specialized parts of the living substance; others are nonliving accumulations of fat, protein, carbohydrate or pigments.

Mitochondria. When animal cells are viewed through the electron microscope (Fig. 2.2), the **mitochondria** are seen to be large, round, oval or sausage-shaped structures with a double membrane separating the mitochondrial substance from the surrounding ground substance. The inner

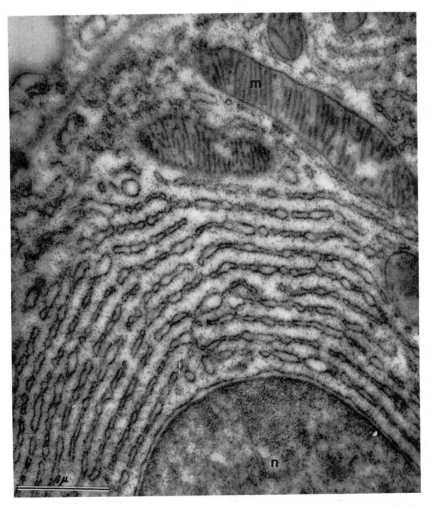

Figure 2.2 An electron micrograph of a section of a cell from the pancreas of a guinea pig. A segment of the nucleus (n) surrounded by its nuclear membrane, some mitochondria (m), which are sausage-shaped structures with double-layered transverse partitions, and the paired, spaghetti-like strands of the endoplasmic reticulum are evident. (Courtesy of G. Palade.)

membrane is thrown into folds which extend deep into the center of the mitochondrion.

Mitochondria from all animals from protozoa to man have the same basic structure. As we shall see in Chapter 4, there is experimental evidence that the mitochondria are complex enzyme machines. The folds within the mitochondria are the sites of many of the enzymes which catalyze reactions by which the cell obtains energy from foodstuff molecules. Purified mitochondria, prepared by homogenizing cells and subjecting the homogenate to high speed centrifugation, are able to metabolize carbohydrates, fatty acids and amino acids to carbon dioxide and water and trap the energy released in a biologically useful form. Mitochondria swell and contract as they carry out these processes.

Ribosomes and Microsomes. In addition to mitochondria, cells contain smaller spherical particles, not visible with the light microscope, which are either free or are attached to the membranous sheets of **endoplasmic reticulum** (Fig. 2.2). These ribonucleoprotein particles, termed **ribosomes,** are the sites of protein synthesis. When cells are cut in thin sections and viewed in the electron microscope, the endoplasmic reticulum appears as long thin strands, like strands of spaghetti.

After mitochondria have been sedimented from homogenized cells by centrifugation, a heterogeneous group of smaller particles, termed **microsomes,** can be sedimented by subsequent centrifugation at higher speeds, at about 100,000 times the force of gravity. Ribosomes can be separated from the rest of the microsomal fraction by appropriate procedures and can carry out protein synthesis in vitro under carefully controlled conditions. The microsomes, like mitochondria, are organized masses of enzymes. The enzymes of the microsomes are concerned with the synthesis of proteins and of certain other complex molecules in the cell.

Golgi Apparatus. Most cells (mature sperm and red blood cells are notable exceptions) contain another type of inclusion, the **Golgi apparatus,** visible in the light microscope when the tissue section has been properly stained. They may appear as granules, threads, rods or canals. Golgi bodies are stained by the dye neutral red; mitochondria take up the dye Janus green.

In the electron microscope the Golgi complex appears as parallel arrays of membranes without granules which may be distended in certain regions to form small vesicles or vacuoles filled with material. Some cytologists believe that the Golgi complex serves as a temporary storage space for substances produced in the granular endoplasmic reticulum and that the Golgi canals are connected to the plasma membrane to provide for the secretion of these products.

Much has been learned in recent years of the role each of these particles plays in the economy of the cell. Cells are homogenized in special glass grinding tubes to break the cell membrane and release the intracellular structures. Then, by subjecting the homogenate to increasing amounts of centrifugal force in an ultracentrifuge, first the nuclei, then the mitochondria, and finally the microsomes can be sedimented separately. When these sedimented particles are examined in the electron microscope, they are found to have the same structure exhibited by comparable structures in the intact cell. The separated particles can then be suspended in suitable incubation media and their metabolism can be studied. Such separated mitochondria and microsomes will carry out many biochemical reactions, and much is now known about the functions of each of these particles. The liquid left after the homogenate has been subjected to high centrifugal force to sediment the microsomes contains many other enzymes which apparently exist in the cell more or less free in the ground substance.

Where, you may ask, is life localized—in the mitochondria? in the microsomes? in the ground substance? The answer, of course, is that life is not a function of any single one of these parts, but of the whole integrated system of many component parts, organized in the proper spatial relationship and interdependent on one another in a great variety of ways.

2.3

Chemical Composition of Living Matter

Chemical analysis of any animal from ameba to man reveals a fundamental similarity in composition. The four **chemical elements,** carbon, oxygen, hydrogen and nitrogen, make up 90 per cent or more of the substance of any animal or plant cell.

Potassium, sulfur, calcium and phosphorus are four other elements usually present to the extent of 1 per cent or more each. Since bone is largely composed of calcium and phosphorus, the amount of these elements is much greater in a bony animal than in a completely soft-bodied one. Smaller amounts of sodium, chlorine, iron, iodine, magnesium, copper, manganese, cobalt, zinc and a few others complete the list. The unique aliveness of living matter does not depend on the presence of some rare or unique element, for these same elements are abundant in the atmosphere, in the sea and in the earth's crust. The phenomenon of life depends, instead, upon the complexity of the interrelationships of these common, abundant elements.

For convenience in writing chemical formulas and reactions, chemists have assigned to each of the elements a symbol, usually the first letter of the name of the element: O, oxygen; H, hydrogen; C, carbon; N, nitrogen. A second letter is added to the sym-bol of those elements with the same initial letter: Ca, calcium; Co, cobalt; Cl, chlorine; Cu, copper; Na, sodium (Latin *natrium*).

Atoms and Ions. The chemical properties of an element are determined primarily by the number and arrangement of **electrons** (negatively charged particles of extremely small mass) revolving in the outermost orbit around the atomic nucleus and to a lesser extent by the number of electrons in the inner orbits. These, in turn, depend upon the number and kind of particles, protons and neutrons, in the nucleus. A proton has a positive electric charge and a mass about 1800 times greater than the mass of an electron. A neutron has no electric charge and its mass is essentially the same as that of a proton.

The number of electrons in the outermost shell varies from zero to eight in different kinds of atoms (Fig. 2.3). If there are zero or eight electrons in the outer shell the element is chemically inert and will not readily combine with other elements. When there

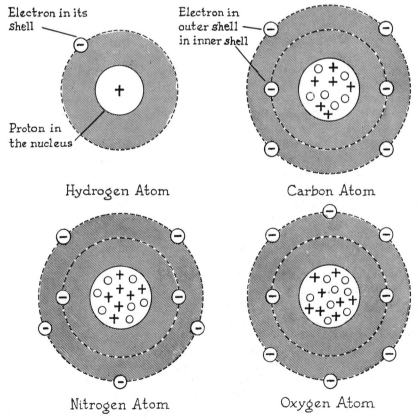

Figure 2.3 Diagrams of the structure of the atoms of the four chief elements of living matter: hydrogen, carbon, nitrogen and oxygen. The symbols used are $\bigcirc$, neutron; +, proton; $\ominus$, electron.

are fewer than eight electrons, the atom tends to lose or gain electrons in an attempt to achieve an outer orbit of eight electrons. Since the number of protons in the nucleus is not changed, this loss or gain of electrons produces an atom with a net positive or negative charge. Such electrically charged atoms are known as **ions.** Atoms with one, two or three electrons in the outer shell tend to lose them to other atoms and become positively charged ions because of the excess protons in the nucleus (e.g., Na^+, sodium ion; Ca^{++}, calcium ion). These are termed **cations** because they migrate to the cathode of an electrolytic cell. Atoms with five, six or seven electrons in the outer shell tend to gain electrons from other atoms and become negatively charged ions or **anions** (e.g., Cl^-, chloride ion). Anions migrate to the anode or positively charged electrode of an electrolytic cell. Because they bear opposite electric charges, anions and cations are attracted to each other. Atoms such as carbon, which have four electrons in the outer orbit, neither lose nor gain electrons, but share them with adjacent atoms.

Physical research has shown that most elements are composed of two or more kinds of atoms, which differ in the number of neutrons in the atomic nucleus. The different kinds of atoms of an element are called **isotopes** (iso = equal, tope = place), because they occupy the same place in the periodic table of the elements. All the isotopes of a given element have the same number of electrons circling the atomic nucleus. The development of the cyclotron and nuclear reactor made possible the artificial production of a host of new isotopes. The availability of these new isotopes, in turn, made possible a new type of biologic research, that of tracing particular elements and compounds through their many devious metabolic pathways, and of measuring the time required for any given substance in the body to be replaced by new molecules of that substance. This tracing is possible because, although the several isotopes of an element have the same chemical properties, they have different physical properties. Some are radioactive and emit rays or particles which can be detected by an instrument such as the Geiger counter. Others are differentiated in a mass spectrometer by the slight difference in the mass of the atomic nucleus which results from the presence there of an extra neutron.

Thus, with radioactive calcium one can study the rate of formation of bone (and the effects of a host of variables such as vitamin D intake or rate of parathyroid activity on this process), or the rate of secretion of shell by a clam or oyster. Or, one can prepare sugar labeled with radioactive carbon (^{11}C or ^{14}C) or heavy carbon (^{13}C), inject it into an experimental animal, and determine the metabolic paths of glucose—its conversion to glycogen, fat and protein—and their respective amounts. Many problems of long standing in zoology and the other biologic sciences have been solved by this method.

The analysis of the human body reveals that it contains about 50 per cent carbon, 20 per cent oxygen, 10 per cent hydrogen, 9 per cent nitrogen, 4 per cent calcium, 2.5 per cent phosphorus (P), 1 per cent potassium (K), 0.8 per cent sulfur (S), 0.4 per cent sodium (Na), and 0.4 per cent chlorine (Cl). Analyses of other animals would yield comparable results. Such analyses are not very informative unless the animal has some unusual element. Tunicates, for example, are unusual in that they contain a large amount of the element vanadium (V).

Chemical Compounds. Most elements are present in living material as **chemical compounds,** substances composed of two or more different kinds of atoms or ions. The smallest particle of a substance having the composition and properties of a larger part of the substance is called a **molecule.** The molecules of a pure compound are always composed of two or more elements combined in a fixed ratio. Water molecules, for example, always contain two atoms of hydrogen and one of oxygen. Chemists state this fact by writing the formula of water as H_2O. A chemical formula represents both the kinds and the relative proportions of the atoms present in a molecule.

A large part of each cell is simply **water.** In an animal such as man, the water content ranges from about 20 per cent in bone to 85 per cent in brain cells. The water content is greater in embryonic and young cells and decreases as aging occurs. About 70 per cent of our total body weight is water; as much as 95 per cent of a jellyfish is water. Water has a number of important functions in living systems. Most of the other chemicals present are dissolved in it; they must be dissolved in water in order to react. Water also dissolves the waste products of metabolism and assists in their removal. Water has a great capacity for absorbing heat with a minimal change in its own temperature; thus, it protects the living material against sudden thermal changes. Since water absorbs a large amount of heat as it changes from a liquid to a gas, the mammalian body can dissipate excess heat by the evaporation of sweat. Water's high heat conductivity makes possible the even distribution of heat throughout the body. Finally, water has an important function as a lubricant. It is present in body fluids wherever one organ rubs against another and in joints where one bone moves on another.

A **mixture** contains two or more kinds of atoms or molecules which may be present in varying proportions. Air is a mixture of oxygen, nitrogen, carbon dioxide and water vapor, plus certain rare gases such as argon. The proportions of these constituents may vary widely. Thus, in contrast to a pure compound, which has a fixed ratio of its constituents and definite chemical and physical properties, a mixture has properties which vary with the relative abundance of its constituents.

Molecules may be composed of one, two or many kinds of atoms. Those of gaseous oxygen or nitrogen are made of two of the same kind of atom—O_2 and N_2. The molecules of table salt, sodium chloride, are composed of one atom of sodium and one of chlorine ($NaCl$). A common sugar, of great physiologic importance, is **glucose,** whose molecules contain six carbon, 12 hydrogen and six oxygen atoms; its formula is written $C_6H_{12}O_6$.

To learn more about the constituents of cells, biochemists have used very sensitive analytical techniques and have taken great pains to preserve the extremely labile substances present in these enormously complicated systems. To prevent the disappearance of certain substances it is necessary to quick-freeze a bit of excised tissue, or even a whole small animal, by dropping it directly into liquid air. Biochemical research has made it abundantly clear that the composition of every cell is constantly changing, that the cell constituents are in a "dynamic state." There is a continuous synthesis of large, energy-rich molecules and continual decomposition of these into smaller, energy-poor ones. Some of the most important compounds are present in cells only in extremely minute amounts at any given time, although the total amount formed and used in a 24 hour period may be quite large. An appreciation of this may be gained from the following consideration: when substances undergo chemical reactions in sequence (and almost all the reactions of importance biologically are sequences or "cycles"), such as $A \rightarrow B \rightarrow C \rightarrow D$, the rate of the whole process is controlled by the rate of the slowest reaction in the chain. For example, if reaction $A \rightarrow B$ is 10 times as fast as $B \rightarrow C$, and if $C \rightarrow D$ is 100 times as fast as $B \rightarrow C$, then the least reactive substance, B, will tend to accumulate and the most reactive one, C, will be present in the smallest amount. For this reason many of the most active and important substances are present in cells in extremely minute amounts. This, coupled with their chemical instability, has made their detection and isolation difficult. There are probably many such intermediate compounds that remain to be discovered.

The compounds present in cells are of two main types: inorganic and organic. The latter include all the compounds (other than carbonates) that contain the element carbon. The element carbon is able to form a much wider variety of compounds than any other element because the outer shell of the carbon atom contains four electrons, which can be shared in a number of different ways with adjacent atoms. At one time it was believed that organic compounds were uniquely different from other chemical substances and that they could be produced only by living matter. This hypothesis was disproved when the German chemist Wöhler succeeded in 1828 in synthesizing urea (one of the waste products found in human urine) from the inorganic compounds ammonium sulfate and potassium cyanate. Since that time thousands of organic compounds have been synthesized, some of which are quite complex molecules of great biologic importance such as vitamins, hormones, antibiotics and drugs.

Inorganic Compounds. The inorganic compounds important in living systems are acids, bases and salts. An **acid** is a compound which releases hydrogen ions (H^+) when dissolved in water.* Acids turn blue litmus paper to red and have a sour taste. Hydro-

---

*Other definitions of acid and base, such as those by Brønsted or Lewis, may be useful in understanding certain more complex reactions. Brønsted defines an acid as a proton donor and a base as a proton acceptor.

chloric (HCl) and sulfuric (H_2SO_4) are examples of inorganic acids; lactic ($C_3H_6O_3$) from sour milk and acetic ($CH_3 \cdot COOH$) from vinegar are two common organic acids. A **base** is a compound which releases hydroxyl ions (OH^-) when dissolved in water. Bases turn red litmus paper blue. Sodium hydroxide (NaOH) and ammonium hydroxide (NH_4OH) are common inorganic bases.

For convenience in stating the degree of acidity or alkalinity of a fluid, the hydrogen ion concentration may be expressed in terms of pH, the negative logarithm of the hydrogen ion concentration. On this scale, a neutral solution has a pH of 7 (its hydrogen ion concentration is 0.0000001 or 10^{-7} molar), alkaline solutions have pH's ranging from 7 to 14 (the pH of 1 M NaOH), and acids have pH's from 7 to 0 (the pH of 1 M HCl). Most animal cells are neither strongly acid nor alkaline but contain a mixture of acidic and basic substances; their pH is about 7.0. Any considerable change in the pH of a cell is inconsistent with life. Since the scale is a logarithmic one, a solution with a pH of 6 has a hydrogen ion concentration 10 times as great as that of one with a pH of 7.

When an acid and a base are mixed, the hydrogen ion of the acid unites with the hydroxyl ion of the base to form a molecule of water (H_2O). The remainder of the acid (anion) combines with the rest of the base (cation) to form a **salt.** For example, hydrochloric acid (HCl) reacts with sodium hydroxide (NaOH) to form water and sodium chloride (NaCl) or common table salt:

$$H^+Cl^- + Na^+OH^- \rightarrow H_2O + Na^+Cl^-$$

A salt may be defined as a compound in which the hydrogen atom of an acid is replaced by some metal.

When a salt, an acid or a base is dissolved in water it separates into its constituent ions. These charged particles can conduct an electric current; hence these substances are known as **electrolytes.** Sugars, alcohols and the many other substances which do not separate into charged particles when dissolved, and therefore do not conduct an electric current, are called **nonelectrolytes.**

The tissues and body fluids of animals contain a variety of mineral salts, of which sodium, potassium, calcium and magnesium are the chief cations (positively charged ions) and chloride, bicarbonate, phosphate and sulfate are the important anions (negatively charged ions). The body fluids of land vertebrates resemble sea water in the kinds of salts present and in their relative proportions, but the total concentration of salts is only about one-fifth as great as in sea water. Most biologists now believe that life originated in the sea. The cells of those early organisms became adapted to function optimally in the presence of this pattern of salts. As larger animals evolved and developed body fluids, this pattern of salts was maintained, even as some of the descendants migrated into fresh water or onto the land, for any marked change in the kinds of salts present would inhibit certain enzymes and place that kind of animal at a marked disadvantage in the competition for survival.

Some animals have evolved kidneys and other excretory organs that selectively retain or secrete certain ions, thus leading to body fluids with somewhat different relative concentrations of salts. The concentration of each ion is determined by the relative rates of its uptake and excretion by the organism.

Although the concentration of salts in cells and in the body fluids is small, this amount is of great importance for normal cell functioning. The concentrations of the respective cations and anions are kept remarkably constant under normal conditions; any marked change results in impaired function and finally in death. A great many of the enzymes which mediate the chemical reactions occurring in the body require one or another of these ions—for example, magnesium, manganese, cobalt, potassium—as cofactors. These enzymes are unable to function in the absence of the ion. Normal nerve function requires a certain concentration of calcium in the body fluids; a decrease in this results in convulsions and death. Normal muscle contraction requires certain amounts of calcium, potassium and sodium. If a frog heart, for example, is removed from the body and placed in a solution of sodium chloride, it soon stops beating and remains in the relaxed state. If placed in a solution of potassium chloride, or in a mixture of sodium and calcium chloride, it ceases beating in the contracted condition. But if it is placed in a solution of the three salts in proper proportion it will continue to beat for hours. Under the proper conditions, the strength of the heartbeat is proportional to the concentration of calcium ions in the fluid bathing the heart; this method is sensitive enough to be used to measure the concentration of calcium ions. In addition to these several specific effects of particular cations, mineral salts serve an important function in maintaining the osmotic relationships between each cell and its environment.

2.4

Organic Compounds of Biologic Importance

The major types of organic substances present in cells are the carbohydrates, proteins, fats, nucleic acids and steroids. Some of these are required for the structural integrity of the cell, others to supply energy for its functioning, and still others are of prime importance in regulating metabolism within the cell. The basic pattern of the types of substances, and even their relative proportions, is remarkably similar for cells from the various parts of the body and for cells from different animals. A bit of human liver and the substance of an ameba each contain about 80 per cent water, 12 per cent protein, 2 per cent nucleic acid, 5 per cent fat, 1 per cent carbohydrate and a fraction of 1 per cent of steroids and other substances. Certain specialized cells, of course, have unique patterns of chemical constituents; the brain, for example, is rich in certain kinds of fats.

Carbohydrates. The simplest of the organic substances are the carbohydrates — the sugars, starches and celluloses — which contain carbon, hydrogen and oxygen in a ratio of 1 C : 2 H : 1 O. Carbohydrates are found in all living cells, usually in relatively small amounts, and are important as readily available sources of energy. Both **glucose** (also known as dextrose) and **fructose** (also called levulose) are simple sugars with the formula $C_6H_{12}O_6$. However, the arrangement of the atoms within the two molecules is different and the two sugars have somewhat different chemical properties and quite different physiologic roles. Such differences in the molecular configurations of substances with the same chemical formula are frequently found in organic chemistry. Chemists indicate the molecular configuration of a substance by a **structural formula** in which the atoms are represented by their symbols — C, H, O, N, etc. — and the chemical bonds or

forces which hold the atoms together are indicated by lines. Hydrogen has one such bond; oxygen, two; nitrogen, three; and carbon, four. The structural formulas of glucose and fructose are compared in Figure 2.4. Note that the lower four carbon atoms have identical groups in the two sugars; only the upper two show differences.

Carbon atoms can unite with each other as well as with many other kinds of atoms and form an almost infinite variety of compounds. Carbon atoms linked together may form long chains (as in fatty acids), branched chains (certain amino acids), rings (purines and pyrimidines) and complex rings (steroids). Molecules are in fact three-dimensional structures, not simple two-dimensional ones as these formulas suggest. There are more complex ways of representing the third dimension of the molecule. Since the properties of the compound depend in part on the exact nature of its three-dimensional structure, its **conformation,** such three-dimensional formulas are helpful in understanding the intimate relations between molecular structure and function.

Glucose is the only simple sugar which occurs in any quantity in the cells and body fluids of both vertebrates and invertebrates. The other carbohydrates eaten by vertebrates are converted to glucose in the liver. Glucose is an indispensable component of mammalian blood and is normally present in a concentration of about 0.1 per cent. No particular harm results from a simple increase in the concentration of glucose in the body fluids, but when the concentration is reduced to 0.04 per cent or less, the brain cells become hyperirritable. They discharge nerve impulses which result in muscular twitches, convulsions, and finally unconsciousness and

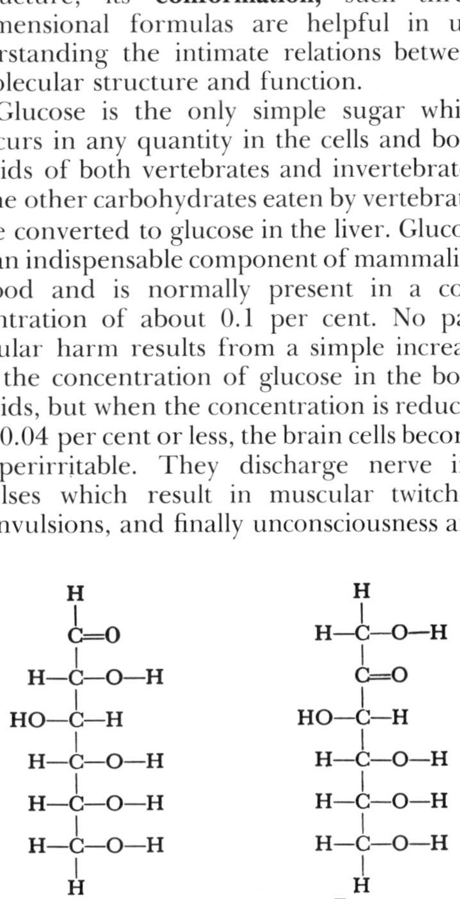

Figure 2.4 Structural formulas of two simple sugars.

death. Brain cells use glucose as their prime metabolic fuel, and a certain minimum concentration of glucose in the blood is required to supply this. A complex physiologic control mechanism, which operates like the "feedback" controls of electronic devices and which involves the liver, pancreas, pituitary and adrenal glands, maintains the proper concentration of glucose in the blood.

The double sugars, with the formula $C_{12}H_{22}O_{11}$, consist of two molecules of simple sugar joined by the removal of a molecule of water. **Sucrose,** or table sugar, is a combination of glucose and fructose. Other common double sugars are **maltose,** composed of two molecules of glucose, and **lactose,** composed of glucose and galactose. Lactose, found in the milk of all mammals, is an important item in the diet of the young of these forms. Fructose, the sweetest of the common sugars, is more than 10 times sweeter than lactose; sucrose is intermediate.

Most animal cells contain some **glycogen** or animal starch, the molecules of which are made of a very large number—thousands— of molecules of glucose joined together by the removal of an H from one and an OH from the next. Glycogen is the form in which animal cells store carbohydrate for use as an energy source in cell metabolism. The glycogen molecules within a living cell are constantly being built up and broken down. Glucose and other simple sugars are not a suitable storage form of carbohydrate for, being soluble, they readily pass out of the cells. The molecules of glycogen, which are much larger and less soluble, cannot pass through the plasma membrane. Glycogen is typically stored intracellularly as microscopic granules, which can be made visible by special stains. Glycogen is readily converted into small molecules such as glucose-phosphate (p. 66) to be metabolized within the cell.

Cellulose, also composed of hundreds of molecules of glucose, is an insoluble carbohydrate which is a major constituent of the tough outer wall of plant cells. The bonds joining the glucose molecules in cellulose are different from those joining the glucoses in glycogen and are not split by the amylases that digest glycogen and starch.

Glucosamine and galactosamine, nitrogen-containing derivatives of the sugars glucose and galactose, are important constituents of supporting substances such as connective tissue fibers, cartilage and chitin, a constituent

of the hard outer shell of insects, spiders and crabs.

Carbohydrates serve as a readily available fuel to supply energy for metabolic processes. Glucose is metabolized to carbon dioxide and water with the release of energy. A few carbohydrates combine with proteins or lipids to serve as structural components of certain cells. **Ribose** and **deoxyribose** are five-carbon sugars that are components of ribonucleic acid (RNA) and deoxyribonucleic acid (DNA).

Fats. The term **fat,** or lipid, refers to a heterogeneous group of compounds which share the property of being soluble in chloroform, ether or benzene, but are only very sparingly soluble in water. True fats are composed of carbon, hydrogen and oxygen, but have much less oxygen than carbon. Each molecule of a true fat contains one molecule of **glycerol,** $C_3H_5(OH)_3$, and three molecules of some **fatty acid,** joined together by the removal of three molecules of water (Fig. 2.5). The fats differ in the kinds of fatty acids present. Oleic acid, $C_{17}H_{33}COOH$, is a common fatty acid, and triolein, the fat containing three molecules of oleic acid, has the formula $C_{57}H_{104}O_6$. Fats have a greasy or oily consistency; some, such as beef tallow or bacon fat, are solid at ordinary temperatures, others such as whale oil or cod liver oil are liquid.

Fats are important both as fuels and as structural constituents of cells, especially cell membranes. They yield more than twice

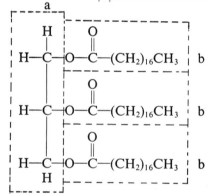

Figure 2.5 Structural formula of tristearin, a fat composed of glycerol (*a*) and three molecules of stearic acid (*b*). In the formula, $(CH_2)_{16}$ represents a chain of sixteen carbon atoms joined in a line, $-\overset{\overset{H}{|}}{\underset{\underset{H}{|}}{C}}-\overset{\overset{H}{|}}{\underset{\underset{H}{|}}{C}}-\ldots$, to each of which are attached two hydrogen atoms. (Villee: Biology, 5th ed.)

as much energy per gram as do carbohydrates and thus are a more economical form for the storage of food reserves. Carbohydrates can be metabolized to release energy very quickly and thus serve as short-term storage forms. Fats provide for a longer-term storage of food reserves. Carbohydrates are readily converted by cells into fats and may be stored in this form. This, of course, is the explanation for the observation that sugars and starches are "fattening." The reverse process may also occur, but to a lesser extent. Experiments with fats labeled with radioactive carbon atoms have shown that these may be converted in the animal body to carbohydrates such as glucose.

The nuclear membrane, the plasma membrane around the cell, and the membrane around the mitochondria all contain fatty substances. The myelin sheath which surrounds nerve fibers (p. 53) is exceptionally rich in lipids. In some animals, such as mammals, there are large deposits of fat just under the skin which serve as fuel reserves and as insulators to decrease the loss of heat from the body. The lipid stores of animals such as sharks and starfish are in the form of oils found in the liver.

Related to the true fats are the phospholipids, waxes and cerebrosides, all of which contain fatty acids. The **phospholipids,** which contain phosphorus and nitrogen in addition to glycerol and fatty acids, are important structural and functional components found especially in mitochondria and microsomes. **Waxes,** such as beeswax and lanolin, contain a fatty acid plus an alcohol other than glycerol. **Cerebrosides,** as their name indicates, are fatty substances found especially in nerve tissue. They contain galactose, long chain fatty acids, and a long chain amino alcohol, sphingosine. The metabolic roles of these special fats are not clear at present.

Steroids. Steroids are complex molecules containing carbon atoms arranged in four interlocking rings, three of which contain six carbon atoms each and the fourth of which contains five. Vitamin D, male and female sex hormones, the adrenal cortical hormones, bile salts and cholesterol are examples of steroids. **Cholesterol** (Fig. 2.6) is an important structural component of nervous tissue and other tissues, and the steroid hormones are of great importance in regulating certain aspects of metabolism.

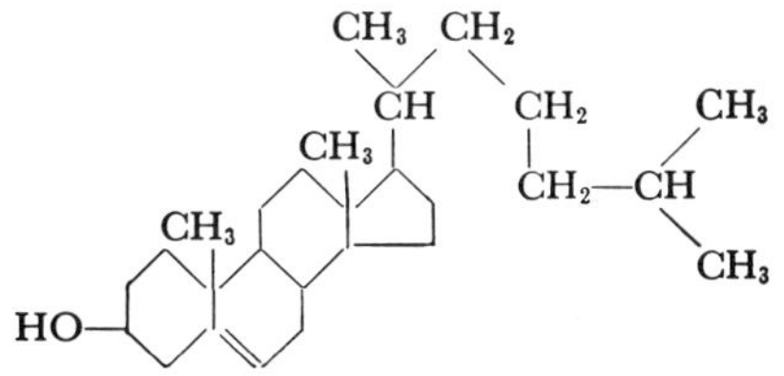

Figure 2.6 Structural formula of a sterol, cholesterol.

Proteins. Proteins differ from carbohydrates and true fats in that they contain nitrogen in addition to carbon, hydrogen and oxygen. Proteins typically contain sulfur and phosphorus also. Proteins are among the largest molecules present in cells and share with nucleic acids the distinction of great complexity and variety. Hemoglobin, the red pigment found in the blood of all vertebrates and many invertebrates, has the formula $C_{3032}H_{4816}O_{872}N_{780}S_8Fe_4$ (Fe is the symbol for iron). Although the hemoglobin molecule is enormous compared to a glucose or triolein molecule, it is only a small- to medium-sized protein. Many, indeed most, of the proteins within a cell are **enzymes,** biological catalysts which control the rates of the many chemical processes of the cell.

Protein molecules are made of simpler components, the **amino acids,** some 30 or more of which are known. Since each protein contains hundreds of amino acids, present in a certain proportion and in a particular order, an almost infinite variety of protein molecules is possible. In recent years, powerful analytical methods have been developed which permit one to determine the arrangement of the amino acids in a given protein molecule. **Insulin,** the hormone secreted by the pancreas and used in the treatment of diabetes, was the first protein whose structure was elucidated. Work culminating in 1957 revealed the sequence of the 124 amino acids that comprise the molecules of the enzyme ribonuclease, secreted by the pancreas.

Each cell contains hundreds of different proteins and each kind of cell contains some proteins which are unique to it. There is evidence that each species of animal and plant has certain proteins which are different from those of all other species. The degree of similarity of the proteins of two species is a measure of their evolutionary relationship. The **theory of species specificity** states that each species has a characteristic pattern of its constituent proteins and that this pattern differs at least slightly from that of related species and more markedly from those of more distantly related species. Because of the interactions of unlike proteins, grafts of tissue removed from one animal will usually not grow when implanted on a host of a different species, but degenerate and are sloughed off by the host. Indeed, even grafts made between members of the same species will usually not grow, but only grafts between genetically identical donors and hosts—identical twins or members of a closely inbred strain.

Amino acids, the unit building blocks of proteins, differ in the number and arrangement of their constituent atoms, but all contain an amino group (NH_2) and a carboxyl group (COOH). The amino group enables the amino acid to act as a base and combine with acids; the carboxyl group enables it to combine with bases. For this reason, amino acids and proteins are important biological "buffers" and resist changes in acidity or alkalinity. Protein molecules are built up by linkages, **peptide bonds,** between the amino group of one amino acid and the carboxyl group of the adjacent one (Fig. 2.7). Pure amino acids have a rather sweet taste. The proteins eaten by an animal are not incorporated directly into its cells but are first digested to the constituent amino acids to enter the cell. Subsequently each cell combines the amino acids into the proteins which are characteristic of that cell. Thus, a man eats beef proteins in a steak, but breaks them down to amino acids in the process of digestion, then rebuilds them as human proteins—human liver proteins, human muscle proteins, and so on.

Proteins and amino acids may serve as energy sources in addition to their structural and enzymatic roles. The amino group is removed by an enzymatic reaction, **deamination,** and then the remaining carbon skeleton enters the same metabolic paths as glucose and fatty acids and eventually is converted to carbon dioxide and water by the Krebs tricarboxylic acid cycle (p. 64) and associated paths. The amino group is excreted as ammonia, urea, uric acid or some other nitrogenous compound, depending on the kind of animal. In prolonged fasting, after the supply of carbohydrates and fats has been exhausted, the cellular proteins may be used as a source of energy.

Animal cells can synthesize some, but not all, of the different kinds of amino acids; different species differ in their synthetic abilities. Man, for example, is apparently unable to synthesize eight of these; they must either be supplied in the food eaten or perhaps synthesized by the bacteria present in the intestine. Plant cells apparently can synthesize all the amino acids. The ones which an animal cannot synthesize, but must obtain in its diet, are called **essential amino acids.** It must be kept in mind that these are no more essential for protein synthesis than any other amino acid, but are simply essential constituents of *the diet,* without which the animal fails to grow and eventually dies.

Nucleic Acids. The biologic importance of the nucleic acids has been fully appreciated only in recent years. These complex molecules, as large as or larger than most proteins, were first discovered in 1870, when Miescher isolated them from the nuclei of pus cells. Nucleic acid molecules contain carbon, hydrogen, oxygen, nitrogen and phosphorus; they gained their name from the fact that they are acidic and were first identified in nuclei. They contain

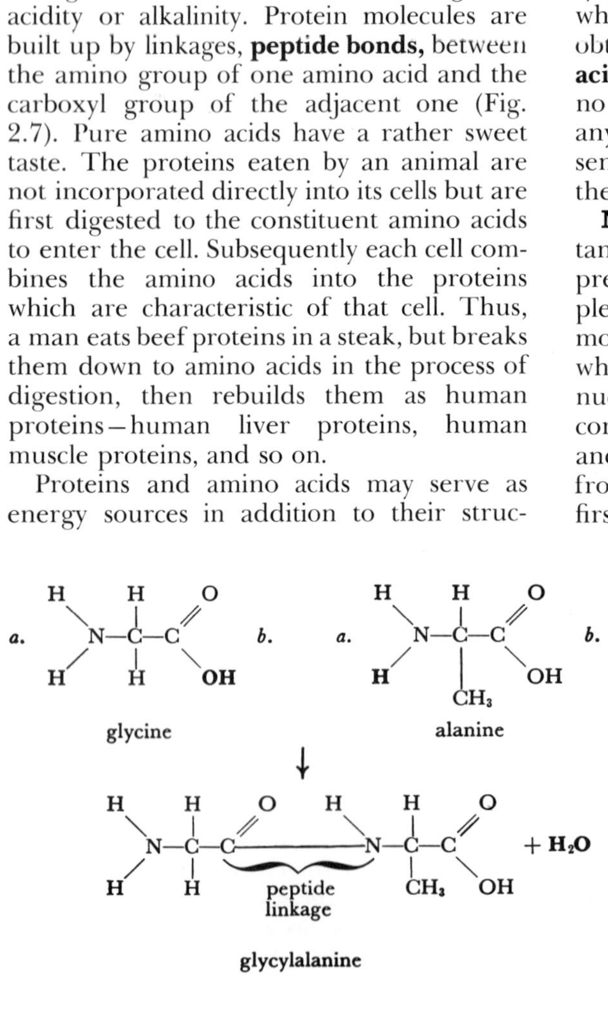

Figure 2.7 Structural formulas of the amino acids glycine and alanine, showing, (*a*) the amino group and, (*b*) the acid (carboxyl) group. These are joined in a peptide linkage to form glycylalanine by the removal of water.

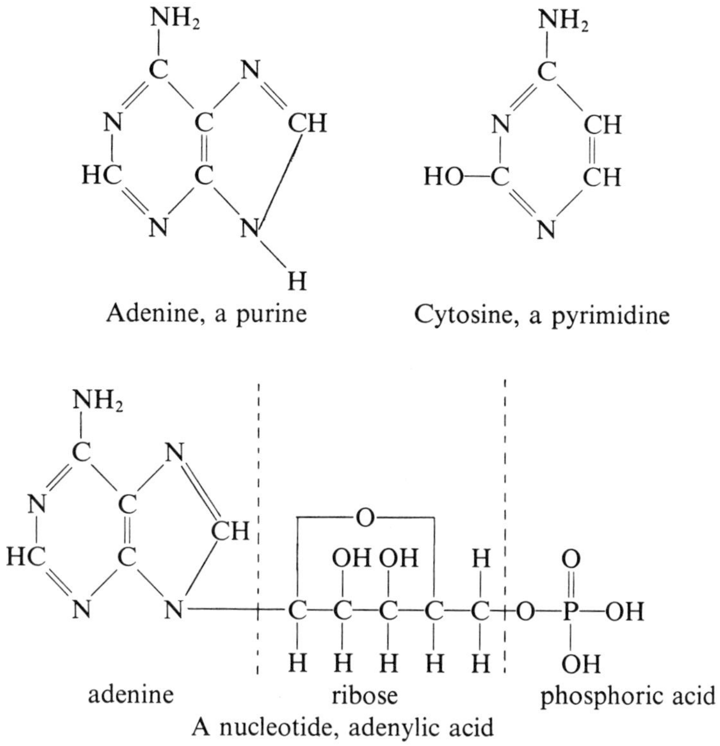

Adenine, a purine   Cytosine, a pyrimidine

adenine   ribose   phosphoric acid

A nucleotide, adenylic acid

Figure 2.8 Structural formulas of a purine, adenine; a pyrimidine, cytosine; and a nucleotide, adenylic acid. (Villee: Biology, 5th ed.)

nitrogenous organic bases (purines and pyrimidines), five-carbon sugars (ribose or deoxyribose) and phosphoric acid (Fig. 2.8). For a long time it was thought that there were but two kinds of nucleic acid—one containing the sugar ribose and called **ribose nucleic acid** or RNA and found in cytoplasm, and one containing deoxyribose and called **deoxyribonucleic acid** or DNA and located in the cell nucleus. Since 1948 experiments have made it clear that there are many different kinds of RNA and DNA. Today RNA and DNA are used as generic terms for classes of substances which differ in their details of structure and metabolic functions. RNA contains the purines **adenine** and **guanine** and the pyrimidines **cytosine** and **uracil,** together with ribose and phosphoric acid. DNA contains adenine, guanine, cytosine and the pyrimidine, thymine, together with deoxyribose and phosphoric acid. The molecules of nucleic acids are made of linear chains of **nucleotides** (units composed of a nitrogenous base, a sugar and phosphoric acid), each of which is attached to the next by ester bonds between the sugar part of one and the phosphoric acid of the next. The specificity of the nucleic acid resides

in the specific order of the four kinds of nucleotides present in the chain. Thus, CCGATTA might represent a segment of a DNA molecule.

It is now clear that DNA is responsible for the specificity and chemical properties of the genes, the units of heredity located in the nucleus. The ribonucleic acids play important roles in the synthesis of protein and perhaps of other large molecules as well and are found, free or linked to proteins, in the ribosomes, nucleus and mitochondria and in the liquid ground substance of the cell.

2.5

Physical Characteristics of Cellular Constituents

The properties of cell constituents depend not only on the kinds and quantities of substances present, but on their physical state as well. A mixture of a substance with water, or other liquid, may result in a true solution, a suspension or a colloidal solution, differentiated by the size of the dispersed particles. In a **true solution,** the ions or molecules of the dissolved substance (called the solute) are of extremely small size, less than 0.0001 micron in diameter. The solute particles are either ions or small molecules dispersed among the molecules of the dissolving liquid (called the **solvent**). A true solution is transparent and has a higher boiling point and a lower freezing point than pure water. Most acids, bases, salts and some nonelectrolytes, such as sugars, form true solutions in water.

The dispersed particles in a **suspension,** in contrast, are much larger (greater than 0.1 micron) and are composed of aggregations of many molecules. They tend to settle out if the suspension is allowed to stand. Muddy water, for example, contains particles of clay in suspension. Suspensions are opaque rather than transparent, and have the same boiling and freezing points as pure water.

A colloidal solution contains particles intermediate in size between those of a true solution and a suspension, particles from 0.001 to 0.1 micron in diameter. A colloidal solution, or colloid, is transparent or translucent, has about the same boiling and freezing points as pure water, and is stable; it does not tend to separate into its constituent parts on standing. The particles of a colloidal solution may have a positive or a negative charge, but usually they all have the same charge and tend to repel each other. The presence of the charge is a factor which tends to keep the particles dispersed. A colloidal solution has the unique property of changing from a liquid state, or **sol,** to a solid or semisolid state or **gel** (Fig. 2.9). A familiar example of the change from sol to gel occurs when a package of gelatin is dissolved in hot water. The particles of gelatin (a protein) are dispersed through the

water and a liquid colloidal solution, a sol, results. As the gelatin cools, the gelatin particles aggregate and become the continuous phase, the water particles become dispersed as small droplets in the gelatin and a semisolid gel results. The gel can be converted back to a sol by reheating. The gelatin-water mixture is a liquid sol when it consists of particles of gelatin dispersed in water and a solid gel when the droplets of water are dispersed in gelatin. The sol-gel change in a substance may be effected by changing the temperature, the pH or the salt concentration or by mechanical agitation (whipping cream, for example). The change is reversible, but if the system is subjected to large changes of temperature, acidity, alkalinity or salt concentration, the colloidal solution is destroyed; the particles aggregate to form larger particles and settle out.

Many of the properties of colloids are a result of the enormous amount of surface area between the dissolved particles and the dissolving medium. For example, a cube 1 cm. on each edge has a total surface area of 6 sq. cm., but an equal volume of material divided into particles 0.01 micron on an edge has a total surface area of 6,000,000 sq. cm. Many chemical reactions occur only at a surface, and for this reason a colloidal system is a much better medium for chemical reactions than any other type of mixture.

Many of the unique properties of the cell's contents follow from the fact that it is a colloidal system composed of protein molecules in water. The protein molecules are too large to form a true solution in water and too small to settle out. The substance of the cell is constantly and rapidly changing from sol to gel and back; one portion of a

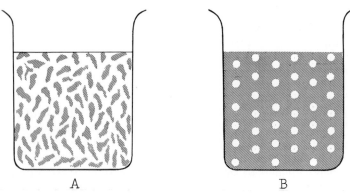

A   B

Figure 2.9 Diagram of a colloidal solution as (*A*) a sol and (*B*) a gel. The sol contains water as the continuous phase in which the colloidal particles (dark rods) are dispersed. In the gel the colloidal particles have coalesced to form a continuous lacy network in which the water droplets (light circles) are dispersed.

cell may be a sol while others are gels. The constant, rapid change from sol to gel is one expression of the "aliveness" of the cell. Any extreme of temperature, acidity or alkalinity, or the presence of certain chemicals will cause an irreversible change to the gel or sol state and the cellular contents are no longer alive. Each cell contains a large amount of water—80 per cent of muscle is water, for example—yet, because the water is part of a colloidal system, bound to the proteins present, muscle itself can become quite solid during contraction. Muscle contraction, like many other biologic phenomena, involves a change from the sol state to the gel. Shortly after death muscle undergoes *rigor mortis,* an irreversible change to the gel state.

QUESTIONS

1. Discuss the characteristics of living things. Are any of these found in nonliving systems? Can you think of any which should be added to the list? Any which do not seem essential?
2. Describe an experiment to test the theory that worms develop from horsehairs in a water trough. What observations do you suppose led to this hypothesis? Can you supply an alternative hypothesis that explains the observation without invoking spontaneous generation?
3. Discuss the ways in which the following animals are adapted to their mode of life: honey bee, salmon, frog, field mouse.
4. What are the distinguishing characteristics of mitochondria, microsomes and Golgi bodies? What are the functions of each?
5. What is the exact meaning of each of the following terms: atom, isotope, ion? Could a single particle of matter be all three simultaneously?
6. In what ways are isotopes used in zoological research?
7. What is the most abundant compound in living matter? What are its functions?
8. Discuss what is meant by the "dynamic state" of the cellular constituents.
9. What distinguishes organic and inorganic compounds?
10. What is meant by the symbol pH?
11. What are the functions in living matter of each of the following: salts, fats, proteins, nucleic acids, steroids?
12. What are the chief properties of colloidal solutions? Describe three examples of colloidal solutions other than the ones discussed in the text.

ANNOTATED REFERENCES

Baker, J. J. W., and G. E. Allen: Matter, Energy and Life. Reading, Mass., Addison-Wesley, 1965. A presentation of thermodynamic principles and their application to studies of living systems.

Grunwald, E., and R. H. Johnsen: Atoms, Molecules and Chemical Change. Englewood Cliffs, N.J., Prentice-Hall, Inc., 1960. An introductory treatment of basic physics and chemistry.

White, E. H.: Chemical Background for the Biological Sciences. Englewood Cliffs, N.J., Prentice-Hall, Inc., 1964. Interesting presentations of the structure of atoms and molecules and the nature of chemical reactions plus a variety of topics related to the subjects of this chapter.

For more detailed discussions of acids, bases, salts and organic compounds and of the physical and chemical principles relating to life processes, consult one of the standard texts of college chemistry such as:

Hutchinson, E.: Chemistry: Elements and Their Reactions. 2nd. ed. Philadelphia, W. B. Saunders Co., 1964.

Sienko, M. J., and R. A. Plane: Chemistry. 2nd ed. New York, McGraw-Hill Book Co., 1961.

Watt, G. W., L. F. Hatch and J. J. Lagowski: Chemistry. New York, W. W. Norton & Co., 1964.

The Scientific American publishes excellent discussions of certain topics related to biology. Several hundred of these have been reprinted as "offprints" by Wm. Freeman Co., San Francisco. They are too numerous to cite individually but comprise a rich source of collateral reading.

CELLS AND TISSUES

The living substance of all animals is organized into units called cells. Each cell contains a nucleus and is surrounded by a plasma membrane. Mammalian red blood cells lose their nucleus in the process of maturation, and a few types of cells such as those of skeletal muscles have several nuclei per cell, but these are rare exceptions to the general rule of one nucleus per cell. In the simplest animals, the **protozoa,** all of the living material is found within a single plasma membrane. These animals may be considered to be unicellular, i.e., single-celled, or acellular, with bodies not divided into cells. Many protozoa have a high degree of specialization of form and function within this single cell (Fig. 3.1), and the single cell may be quite large, larger than certain multicellular, more complex organisms. Thus, it would be wrong to infer that a single-celled animal is necessarily smaller or less complex than a many-celled animal.

3.1

The Cell and Its Contents

The term "cell" was applied by Robert Hooke, some 300 years ago, to the small, box-like cavities he saw when he examined cork and other plant material under the newly-invented compound microscope. The important part of the cell, we now realize, is not the cellulose wall seen by Hooke, but the cell contents. In 1839 the Bohemian physiologist Purkinje introduced the term "protoplasm" for the living material of the cell. As our knowledge of cell structure and function has increased, it has become clear that the living contents of the cell comprise an incredibly complex system of heterogeneous parts. Purkinje's term "protoplasm" has no clear meaning in a chemical or physical sense, but it may be used to refer to all the organized constituents of a cell.

In this same year, 1839, a German botanist, Schleiden, and Schwann, his fellow countryman and a zoologist, formulated the generalization which has since developed into the **cell theory:** The bodies of all plants and animals are composed of cells, the fundamental units of life. The cell is both the structural and functional unit in all organisms, the fundamental unit possessing all the characteristics of living things. A further generalization, first clearly stated by Virchow in 1855, is that new cells can come into existence

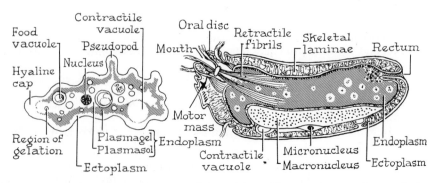

Figure 3.1 Diagrams of an ameba (left) and *Epidinium* (right) to illustrate the range in complexity of the single-celled animals.

only by the division of previously existing cells. The corollary of this, that all cells living today can trace their ancestry back to the earliest living things, was stated by August Weismann about 1880.

The bodies of higher animals are made of many cells, which differ in size, shape and functions. A group of cells which are similar in form and specialized to perform one or more particular functions is called a **tissue.** A tissue may contain nonliving cell products in addition to the cells themselves. A group of tissues may be associated into an **organ,** and organs into **organ systems.** For example, in a vertebrate, the digestive system is composed of a number of organs: esophagus, stomach, intestine, liver, pancreas, and so on. Each organ, such as the stomach, contains several kinds of tissue—epithelium, muscle, connective tissue, nerves—and each tissue is made of many, perhaps millions, of cells.

If a single-celled animal is placed in the proper environment it will survive, grow and eventually divide. For most single-celled animals, a drop of sea water or pond water will provide the environment required. It is more difficult to culture cells removed from a multicellular animal—a man, chick or frog. This was first accomplished in 1907 by Ross Harrison of Yale, who was able to grow cells from a salamander in a drop of nutrient medium containing blood plasma. Since then, many different kinds of cells from animals and plants have been cultured in vitro,* and many important facts about cell physiology have been revealed in this way.

The cells of different organs and different animals present a bewildering variety of sizes, shapes, colors and internal structures, but all have certain features in common. Each cell is surrounded by a plasma membrane and contains a nucleus and a number of kinds of subcellular organelles—mitochondria, granular endoplasmic reticulum, smooth endoplasmic reticulum, centrioles and the Golgi complex.

The **plasma membrane** is an integral functional part of the cell, which controls the entrance and exit of nutrients, secretions and waste products and thus regulates the contents of the cell. The plasma membrane is permeable to certain substances and not to others; in addition, it is capable of doing

work to "pump" substances into and out of the cell. Very few substances are found at the same concentration within the cell and in the surrounding fluid; some concentrations are much higher, others are lower, than in the environment. The activities of the plasma membrane are responsible for maintaining these differences. When it fails to do this, the cell dies.

The chemical and physical nature of the plasma membrane is not completely known but it appears from high resolution electron micrographs to be a three-layer sandwich some 120 Angstrom units thick. The inner and outer layers, each 30 Angstrom units thick, are protein and enclose a middle layer of phospholipid molecules 60 Angstrom units thick. The plasma membranes of animal, plant and bacterial cells and the membranes of a variety of subcellular organelles all appear to have a similar protein-lipid-protein structure, which has been termed the **unit membrane.**

Nearly all plant cells have, in addition to the plasma membrane, a thick cell wall made of cellulose. This nonliving wall, lying outside the plasma membrane, is secreted by the cell substance. It is pierced by fine holes, through which substances may pass, and the cytoplasm of one cell may connect with that of adjacent cells. These tough, firm cell walls provide support to the plant body.

3.2
The Nucleus and Its Functions

The **nucleus** of the cell is usually spherical or ovoid. It may have a fixed position in the center of the cell or at one side, or it may be moved around as the cell moves and changes shape. The nucleus is separated from the cytoplasm by a nuclear membrane which controls the movement of materials into and out of the nucleus (Fig. 3.2). The electron microscope reveals that the nuclear membrane is double-layered and that there are extremely fine channels through the nuclear membrane through which the nuclear contents and cytoplasm are continuous (Fig. 3.3).

The nucleus is an important center of control and is required for growth and for cell division. Some cells, the ameba for example, can survive for many days after the nucleus has been removed by a microsurgical operation. To demonstrate that it is the absence of

---

* In vitro, Latin *in glass*. The cells are removed from the animal body and incubated in glass vessels.

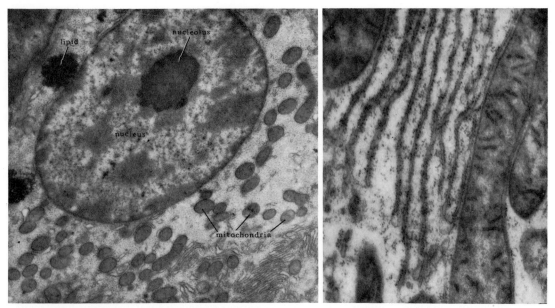

Figure 3.2 *A*, Electron micrograph of the nucleus and surrounding cytoplasm of a frog liver cell. The spaghetti-like strands of the endoplasmic reticulum are visible in the lower right corner. Magnified 16,500 times. *B*, High power electron micrograph of mitochondria and endoplasmic reticulum within a rat liver cell. Granules of ribonucleoprotein (ribosomes) are seen on the strands of endoplasmic reticulum and structures with double membranes are evident within the mitochondria in the upper left corner and on the right. Magnified 65,000 times. (Electron micrographs courtesy of Dr. Don Fawcett.) (Villee: Biology, 5th ed.)

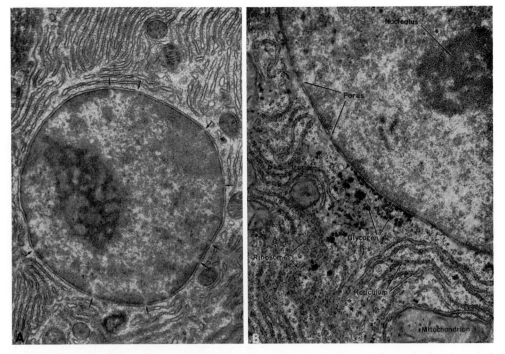

Figure 3.3 Electron micrographs showing pores in the nuclear membrane. The endoplasmic reticulum is evident in both pictures; *B*, shows the ribosomes on the endoplasmic reticulum. *A*, Magnified 20,000 times; *B*, magnified 50,000 times. (Electron micrographs courtesy of Drs. Don W. Fawcett and Keith R. Porter.)

the nucleus, not the operation itself, that causes the ensuing death, one can perform a **sham operation.** A microneedle is inserted into an ameba and moved around inside the cell to simulate the operation of removing the nucleus, but the needle is withdrawn without actually removing the nucleus. An ameba subjected to this sham operation will recover, grow and divide. A controlled experiment such as this, in which two amebas are subjected to the same operative trauma and the one with the nucleus lives whereas the one without the nucleus dies, provides strong evidence of the vital role of the nucleus in regulating the metabolic processes that underlie growth and cell division.

A classic demonstration of the role of the nucleus in the control of cell growth is pro-

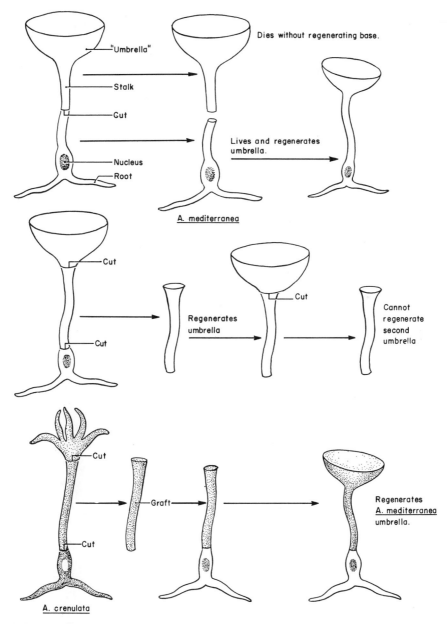

Figure 3.4 Hämmerling's experimental demonstration of the production of an umbrella-regenerating substance by the nucleus of the alga, *Acetabularia.* Lower line, when a stalk from *A. crenulata* is grafted onto the base (white) of an *A. mediterranea* plant, the stalk regenerates an umbrella whose shape is that characteristic of *A. mediterranea* plants. (Villee: Biology, 5th ed.)

vided by the experiments of Hämmerling with the single-celled plant *Acetabularia mediterranea*. This marine alga, which is 4 to 5 cm. long, is mushroom-shaped, with "roots" and a stalk surmounted by a flattened, disc-shaped umbrella. The single nucleus is located near the base of the stalk. Hämmerling cut across the stalk (Fig. 3.4) and found that although the lower part, containing the nucleus, could live and regenerate an umbrella, the upper part would eventually die without regenerating a stalk and roots. In further experiments, Hämmerling first severed the stalk just above the nucleus, then made a second cut just below the umbrella. The section of stalk thus isolated, when replaced in sea water, was able to grow a partial or complete umbrella. This might seem to show that a nucleus is not necessary for regeneration; however, when Hämmerling cut off this second umbrella the stalk was unable to form a new one. From experiments such as these, Hämmerling concluded that the nucleus supplies some substance necessary for umbrella formation. This substance passes up the stalk and instigates umbrella growth. In the experiments described here, some of this substance remained in the stalk after the initial cuts, enough to produce one new umbrella. After that amount

of "umbrella substance" was exhausted by the regeneration of an umbrella, no second regeneration was possible in the absence of a nucleus.

A second species, *Acetabularia crenulata*, has a branched instead of a disc-shaped umbrella. When a piece of *crenulata* stalk (without a nucleus) is grafted onto the base of a *mediterranea* plant (containing a *mediterranea* nucleus) a new umbrella will develop at the top of the stalk. The shape of the umbrella is determined not by the species of the stalk but by the species of the base (Fig. 3.4, lower part). The nucleus, through the action of its genes, provides the specific information that controls the type of umbrella that is regenerated and can override the tendency of the stalk to form an umbrella characteristic of its own species.

When a cell has been killed by fixation with the proper chemicals and then stained with the appropriate dyes, several structures are visible within the nucleus (Fig. 3.5). Within the semifluid ground substance are suspended a fixed number of extended, linear, threadlike bodies called **chromosomes,** composed of DNA and proteins and containing the units of heredity, the **genes.** In a stained section of a nondividing cell the chromosomes

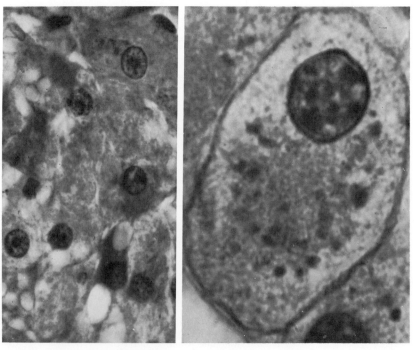

Figure 3.5 Tissue sections of human adrenal gland stained to show cellular details; left, magnified 600 times; right, magnified 1500 times. (Courtesy of Dr. Kurt Benirschke.)

typically appear as an irregular network of dark-staining threads and granules termed **chromatin.**

The nucleus also contains one or more small spherical bodies, **nucleoli,** which are difficult to see in a living cell with an ordinary light microscope but are evident by phase microscopy. The cells of any particular animal have the same number of nucleoli. The nucleolus disappears when a cell is about to divide and reappears after division is complete. If the nucleolus is destroyed by carefully localized ultraviolet or x-irradiation, cell division is inhibited. This does not occur in control experiments in which regions of the nucleus other than the nucleolus are irradiated.

3.3
Cytoplasmic Organelles

One or two small, dark-staining cylindrical bodies, called **centrioles,** are found in the cytoplasm near the nucleus of animal cells. With the electron microscope each centriole is revealed to be a hollow cylinder with a wall in which are embedded nine parallel, longitudinally oriented groups of tubules, with three tubules in each group. The centriole plays a role in cell division in determining the location of the spindle fibers on which the chromosomes move (p. 38). It would appear, however, that centrioles are not essential for cell division, for plant cells are able to divide without them.

Those cells that bear cilia on their exposed surfaces have a structure at the base of each cilium, the **basal body,** that resembles the centriole in the presence of nine parallel tubules. Each cilium contains nine peripherally located longitudinal filaments and two centrally located ones. Like centrioles, basal bodies can duplicate themselves.

The cytoplasm may contain droplets of fat and crystals or granules of protein or glycogen which are simply stored for future use. In addition, it contains the metabolically active cell organelles, **mitochondria, endoplasmic reticulum** and **Golgi bodies.**

Mitochondria range in size from 0.2 to 5 microns and in shape from spheres to rods and threads (Fig. 3.2). Their number may range from just a few to more than 1000 per cell. When living cells are examined, their mitochondria appear to move, change shape and size, fuse with other mitochondria to form longer structures, or cleave to form smaller ones. Each mitochondrion is bounded by a double membrane, an outer smooth membrane and an inner one folded into parallel plates that extend into the central cavity and may fuse with folds from the opposite side. Each of these plates is a unit membrane composed of a middle double layer of phospholipid molecules with a layer of protein molecules on each side. These shelflike inner folds, termed **cristae,** contain the enzymes of the electron transmitter system, of prime importance in converting the potential energy of foodstuffs into biologically useful energy for cellular activities. The mitochondria have been dubbed the "powerhouses" of the cell.

Those cells especially active in the synthesis of proteins are crowded with the membranous labyrinth of the **endoplasmic reticulum;** other cells may have only a scanty supply. In a thin section these appear as a profusion of spaghetti-like tubular strands, but in three dimensions are sheet-like membranes. Some of the endoplasmic reticulum is granular and has bound to it a profusion of **ribosomes,** small nucleoprotein particles on which protein synthesis occurs. The remainder of the endoplasmic reticulum is agranular and consists of smooth sheets believed to play some role in cellular secretion.

Golgi bodies, found in all cells except mature sperm and red blood cells, consist of an irregular network of canals lined with membranes without granules. The Golgi bodies are usually concentrated in the part of the cytoplasm near the centrioles and appear to have a role in the production or storage of secretions. They may have the appearance of granules, rods, threads or canals.

Lysosomes are intracellular organelles about the size of mitochondria but less dense. They are membrane-bounded structures that contain a variety of enzymes capable of hydrolyzing the macromolecular constituents of the cell. In the intact cell these enzymes are segregated within the lysosome, presumably to prevent their digesting the contents of the cell. Rupture of the lysosome membrane releases the enzymes and accounts, at least in part, for the lysis of dead cells and the resorption of cells such as those in the tail of a tadpole during metamorphosis.

The cytoplasm of certain cells, chiefly those of lower animals, contains **vacuoles,** cavities filled with fluid and separated from the rest of the cytoplasm by a vacuolar membrane. Most protozoa, and the endoderm cells of coelenterates and flatworms, have **food vacuoles** in which food is digested. Digestive enzymes are secreted from the cytoplasm into the cavity of the vacuole, the food is digested, and the products of digestion are absorbed through the vacuolar membrane into the cytoplasm. The protozoa living in fresh water have the problem of eliminating the water which enters the cell constantly by osmosis (p. 45). These forms have evolved **contractile vacuoles,** which alternately fill with water from the adjacent cytoplasm and then eject the water to the surrounding environment.

Most animal cells are quite small, too small to be seen with the naked eye. The diameter of the human red blood cell is about 7.5 microns (a micron is 0.001 mm.), but most animal cells have diameters ranging from 10 to 50 microns. There are a few species of giant amebas with cells about 1 mm. in diameter. The largest cells are the yolk-filled eggs of birds and sharks. The egg cell of a large bird such as a turkey or goose may be several centimeters across. Only the yolk of a bird's egg is the true egg cell; the egg white and shell are noncellular material secreted by the bird's oviduct as the egg passes through it.

The limit of the size of a cell is set by the physical fact that, as a sphere gets larger, its surface increases as the square of the radius but its volume increases as the cube of the radius. The metabolic activities of the cell are roughly proportional to cell volume. These activities require nutrients and oxygen, and release carbon dioxide and other wastes which must enter and leave the cell through its surface. The upper limit of cell size is reached when the surface area can no longer provide for the entrance of enough raw materials and the exit of enough waste products for cell metabolism to proceed normally. The limiting size of the cell will depend on its shape and its rate of metabolism. When this limit is reached the cell must either stop growing or divide.

3.4
Mitosis

Because of the limitation on the size of individual cells, growth is accomplished largely by an increase in the *number* of cells. When a single-celled protozoan divides, the resulting two cells are separate individuals, members of a new generation. In multicellular animals, cell division results in an increase in the number of cells per individual, but the process of cell division is fundamentally the same in both. This process of cell division, called **mitosis,** is extremely regular and ensures the qualitatively and quantitatively equal distribution of the hereditary factors between the two resulting daughter cells. Mitotic divisions occur during embryonic development and growth, in the replacement of cells that wear out, such as blood cells, skin, the intestinal lining, and so on, and in the repair of injuries.

When a dividing cell is stained and examined under the microscope, dark-staining bodies, called **chromosomes,** are visible within the nucleus. Each consists of a central thread, the **chromonema,** along which lie the **chromomeres** — small, beadlike, dark-staining swellings. It has been suggested that the chromomeres are, or contain, the genes, for breeding experiments have shown clearly that these hereditary units lie within the chromosome in a linear order. However, the correlation between chromomeres and genes is not regular; some chromomeres contain several genes and some genes have been located between chromomeres. Several theories have been formulated to account for these swellings of the chromosomes, but at present their true significance is not clear.

Each chromosome has, at a fixed point along its length, a small clear circular zone called a **centromere** that controls the movement of the chromosome during cell division. As the chromosome becomes shorter and thicker just before cell division occurs, the centromere region becomes accentuated and appears as a constriction.

One of the very regular characteristics of any kind of animal or plant is the number of chromosomes in each nucleus. Every cell in the body of every human being, for example, has 46 chromosomes. There are many other kinds of animals and plants which happen to have 46 chromosomes per cell as well; so the factor of chief importance in differentiating different kinds of animals is not simply the number of chromosomes per cell but the kind of genes in the chromosomes. The chromosome number for most kinds of animals lies between 10 and 50. One kind of roundworm has only two chromosomes per cell, certain crabs have 200, and one kind of radiolarid, a marine protozoan, has 1600 or so chromosomes in its nucleus.

Chromosomes occur in pairs; the 46 chromosomes of each human cell consist of two of each of 23 different kinds. The chromosomes differ in length and shape and in the presence of identifying knobs or constrictions along their length (Fig. 3.6). In most animals, the morphologic features of the chromosomes are distinct enough so that one can identify the individual pairs.

Cell division must be an extremely exact process to ensure that each daughter cell receives exactly the right number and kind of chromosomes. If we tamper experimentally with the mechanism of cell division, and the resulting cells receive more or less than the proper number of chromosomes, marked abnormalities of growth, and perhaps the death of these cells, will follow. Mitosis may be defined as the regular process of cell division by which each of the two daughter cells receives exactly the same number and the same kind of chromosomes that the parent cell contained. This process involves what appears to be a longitudinal splitting of each chromosome into two halves. There is now abundant evidence that no such splitting can indeed occur; instead, each original chromosome brings about the synthesis of an exact replica of itself immediately beside itself. The new chromosome is made, sometime before the visible mitotic process begins, from raw materials present in the nucleus. When the process is complete, the original and the new chromosomes separate and become incorporated into different daughter cells. The role of the complicated mitotic machinery is to separate the "original" and "replica" chromosomes and deliver them to opposite ends of the dividing cell so they will become incorporated into different daughter cells.

The term mitosis in a strict sense refers to the division of the nucleus into two daughter nuclei and the term **cytokinesis** is applied to the division of the cytoplasm to form two daughter cells, each containing a daughter nucleus. Nuclear division and cytoplasmic division, although almost invariably well synchronized and coordinated, are separate and distinct processes.

Each mitotic division is a continuous process, with each stage merging imperceptibly into the next one. For descriptive purposes biologists have divided it into four stages: **prophase, metaphase, anaphase** and **telophase** (Fig. 3.7). Between mitoses a cell is said to be in the resting stage. It is difficult to visualize from a description or diagram of mitosis, or from examining a fixed and stained slide of cells, just how active a process cell division is. Motion pictures made by phase microscopy reveal that a cell undergoing division bulges and changes shape like a gunny sack filled with a dozen unfriendly cats.

Prophase. The chromatin threads condense and the chromosomes appear as a tangled mass of coiled threads within the

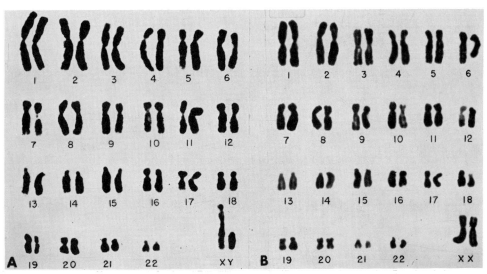

Figure 3.6 Human chromosomes. *A,* Normal male. *B,* Normal female. (Photographs courtesy of Dr. Melvin Grumbach.)

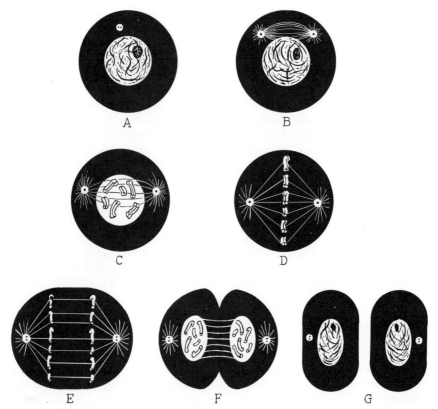

Figure 3.7 Mitosis in a cell of a hypothetical animal with a diploid number of six (haploid number = 3); one pair of chromosomes is short, one pair is long and hooked, and one pair is long and knobbed. *A*, Resting stage. *B*, Early prophase, centriole divided and chromosomes appearing. *C*, Later prophase, centrioles at poles, chromosomes shortened and visibly double. *D*, Metaphase, chromosomes arranged on the equator of the spindle. *E*, Anaphase, chromosomes migrating toward the poles. *F*, Telophase, nuclear membranes formed; chromosomes elongating; cytoplasmic division beginning. *G*, Daughter cells, resting phase.

nucleus. Early in prophase the threads are stretched maximally so that the individual chromomeres are visible. Later in prophase the chromosomes shorten and thicken and the chomomeres lie so close together that individual ones cannot be distinguished. The reduplication of the chromosomes has occurred previously and in many species of animals the double nature of each chromosome is apparent.

Early in prophase the **centriole,** a small granular structure in the cytoplasm, divides and the daughter centrioles migrate to opposite sides of the cell. Between the separating centrioles a spindle forms. The **spindle** is composed of protein threads with properties similar to those of the contractile proteins of muscle fibrils. The protein threads of the spindle are arranged like two cones base to base, broad at the center or equator of the cell and narrowing to a point at either end or pole. With a microneedle attached to a micromanip-

ulator the spindle can be moved as a unit from one part of the cell to another. By appropriate techniques spindles may be isolated from dividing cells (Fig. 3.8). At the end of prophase, the centrioles have divided and gone to the opposite poles of the cell, the spindle has formed between them and the chromosomes have become short and thick.

Metaphase. When the chromosomes are fully contracted and appear as short, dark-staining rods, the nuclear membrane disappears and the chromosomes line up in the equatorial plane of the spindle. The short period during which the chromosomes are in this equatorial plane is known as the metaphase. This is much shorter than the prophase; although times for different cells vary considerably, the prophase lasts from 30 to 60 minutes or more, and the metaphase lasts only two to six minutes.

During the metaphase the centromere of each chromosome divides and the two chro-

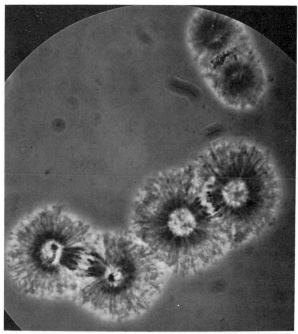

Figure 3.8 Photomicrograph of the mitotic apparatus isolated from dividing cells of a sea urchin embryo. Each mitotic apparatus includes spindle fibers, asters and chromosomes. A metaphase figure appears in the upper right and two anaphase figures below. (Courtesy of Daniel Mazia.) (Villee: Biology, 5th ed.)

matids become completely separate daughter chromosomes. The division of the centromeres occurs simultaneously in all the chromosomes, under the control of some as yet unknown mechanism. The daughter centromeres begin to move apart, marking the beginning of anaphase.

Anaphase. The chromosomes separate (Fig. 3.9), and one of the daughter chromosomes goes to each pole. The period during which the separating chromosomes move from the equatorial plate to the poles is known as the anaphase and lasts some three to 15 minutes. The spindle fibers apparently act as guide rails along which the chromosomes move toward the poles. Without such guide rails the chromosomes would merely be pushed randomly apart and many would fail to be incorporated into the proper daughter nuclei. The mechanism by which the chromosomes are moved apart is not clear. Experiments suggest that some substance between the chromosomes takes up water, swells, and pushes the chromosomes apart. Other experiments indicate that some of the spindle fibers are contractile and can pull the chromosomes toward the poles. The chromosomes moving toward the poles usually assume a V shape with the centromere at the apex pointing toward the pole. It appears that whatever force moves the chromosome to the pole is applied at the centromere.

Telophase. When the chromosomes have reached the poles of the cell, the last phase of mitosis, telophase, begins. Several processes occur simultaneously in this period: a nuclear membrane forms around the group of chromosomes at each pole, the chromosomes elongate, stain less darkly, and return to the resting condition in which only irregular chromatin threads are visible, and the cytoplasm of the cell begins to divide. Division of the cytoplasm is accomplished in animal cells by the formation of a furrow which circles the cell at the equatorial plate and gradually deepens until the two halves of the cell are separated as independent daughter cells. The events of telophase require some 30 to 60 minutes for their completion.

The mitotic process results in the formation of two daughter cells from a single parent cell with each daughter cell having exactly the same number and kind of chromosomes, and of the units of heredity (genes) contained in these chromosomes, as the parent cell. Since all the cells of the body are formed by mitosis from a single fertilized egg, each cell has the same number and kind of chromosomes, and the same number and kind of genes, as every other cell.

The speed and frequency of cell division vary greatly from tissue to tissue and from one animal to another. In the early stages of embryonic development, there may be only

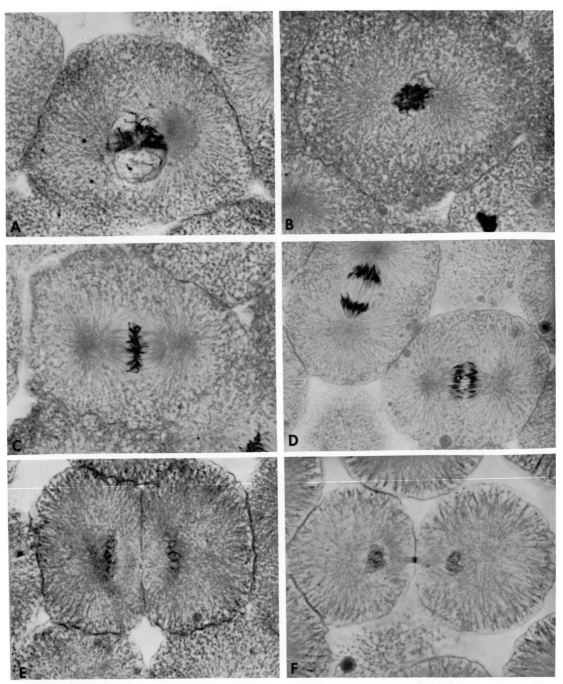

Figure 3.9 Photographs of stages in mitosis in the white fish blastula. *A*, early prophase; *B*, later prophase; *C*, metaphase; *D*, two cells in early and late anaphase respectively; *E*, early telophase; and *F*, late telophase. The dark spot connecting the two cells in *E* is the remainder of the spindle. (Photographs courtesy of Dr. Susumu Ito.)

30 minutes or so between successive cell divisions. In certain adult tissues, notably the nervous system, mitoses are extremely rare. In other adult tissues, such as the red bone marrow, where red blood cells are produced, mitotic divisions must occur frequently to supply the 10,000,000 red blood cells each human being produces every second of the day and night.

3.5
Regulation of Mitosis

The factors which initiate and control cell division are not known exactly. The possible role of the ratio of cell surface to cell volume was discussed previously (p. 36). The ratio of *nuclear* surface to *nuclear* volume may also be important. Since normal cell function requires the transport of substances back and forth through the nuclear membrane, growth will eventually result in a state in which the area of the nuclear membrane is insufficient to meet the demands of the volume of cytoplasm. Cell division, by splitting the volume of cytoplasm into two parts and increasing the area of nuclear membrane, will restore optimal conditions. There is some evidence to suggest that the chromosomes may release a substance or substances which initiate, first, the nuclear events of prophase and metaphase and, secondly, the reactions in the cytoplasm which form a cleavage furrow and bring about the division of the cytoplasm.

Another theory postulates the initiation of mitosis by a "cell division hormone." The mitoses of the cells of an egg undergoing cleavage occur simultaneously, which suggests that a periodically released hormone may control these divisions. The experiments of Haberlandt indicate that dying cells release a substance which stimulates cell division. He cut a potato in half and examined the cut edge for mitoses. He found that if he cleaned the cut edge to remove all cell debris few mitoses occurred. If he did not clean the cut edge, cell divisions were more frequent, and if he put some mashed cells on the cut edge an even greater number of cell divisions resulted. He concluded that cut potato cells release a "wound hormone" which stimulates cell divisions in adjacent cells. Marshak and Walker were able to prepare an extract of the nuclei of rat liver cells and then to separate this into two fractions. One fraction, when injected into other rats, increased, and the other decreased, the rate of cell division in liver cells.

3.6
The Study of Cellular Activities

Despite great differences in size, shape and location in the body, all cells have many metabolic activities in common. Each cell has a host of enzymes which enable it to release energy by converting sugars, fats and proteins to carbon dioxide and water. Each cell synthesizes its own structural proteins and enzymes. Superimposed on this basic pattern of metabolism common to all cells may be other activities peculiar to each type of cell. For example, muscle cells have special proteins, **myosin** and **actin,** which are contractile; particular digestive enzymes are produced by the cells lining the stomach and intestine; and the cells of the pituitary, adrenal and thyroid glands manufacture characteristic hormones.

There are many ways of studying cellular activity and each of these provides useful information about cell morphology and physiology. Living cells suspended in a drop of fluid can be examined under an ordinary microscope or with one equipped with **phase contrast lenses.** In this way one can study the movement of an ameba or a white blood cell, or the beating of the cilia on a paramecium. Cells from a many-celled animal—a frog, chick or man—can be grown by **"tissue culture"** for observation over a long period of time. A complex nutritive medium, made of blood plasma, an extract of embryonic tissues and a mixture of vitamins, is prepared and sterilized. A drop of this is placed in a cavity on a special microslide, the cells to be cultured are added aseptically, and the cavity is sealed with a glass cover slip. After a few days the cells have exhausted one or more of the nutritive materials and must be transferred again to a fresh drop of medium. Cells transferred regularly in this fashion will grow indefinitely—tissue from a chick heart was grown for over 20 years at the Rockefeller Institute in New York. Such experiments revealed that cells in tissue culture do not grow old, for at the end of the 20 year period the cells were as vigorous and grew as fast as the original cells. Cells isolated from a sarcoma (a type of cancer) grow with unusual vigor in tissue culture and grow more rapidly in plasma from a healthy person than in plasma from a person with a sarcoma. This observation suggests that the presence of sarcoma cells in the body stimulates certain healthy cells elsewhere to produce some substance which inhibits to some extent the malignant growth.

Cell morphology may be studied by using a bit of tissue that has been killed quickly with a special "fixative," then sliced with a machine called a microtome, and stained with special dyes. The stained slices, mounted on a glass slide and covered with a glass cover slip, are then ready for examination under the microscope. Since the nucleus, mitochondria and other specialized parts of the cell are chemically different, they will combine with different dyes and be stained characteristic colors (Fig. 3.5). For observation in the electron microscope a bit of tissue is fixed with osmic acid, mounted in acrylic plastic for cutting in extremely thin sections, and then placed on a fine grid to be inserted into the path of the electron beam. Both light microscopy and electron microscopy have revealed many details about cell structure.

Some clue as to the location and functioning of enzymes within cells can be obtained by **histochemical** studies, in which a cell is fixed by methods which do not destroy enzymic activity. Then the proper chemical substrate for the enzyme is provided and, after a specified period of incubation, some substance is added which will form a colored compound with one of the products of the reaction mediated by the enzyme. The regions of the cell which have the greatest enzymic activity will have the largest amount of the colored substance (Fig. 3.10). Methods have been worked out which permit the demonstration and localization of a wide variety of enzymes. Such studies have given an interesting insight into the details of cell function.

Another method of investigating cell function is to measure, by special microchemical analyses, the amounts of chemical used up or produced as a bit of tissue is incubated in a special enclosed glass vessel. In such experiments much has been learned of the roles in cell metabolism of vitamins, hormones and other chemicals by adding these substances one by one and observing the resulting effects.

Every living cell, whether it is an individual unicellular animal or a single component of a multicellular one, must be supplied constantly with nutrients and oxygen. These materials are constantly being metabolized — used up — as the cell goes about its business of releasing energy from the nutrients to provide for its myriad activities. Some of the substances required by the cell are brought to it and taken in by complex active processes which require the expenditure of energy by the cell. Other substances are brought to the cell by the simpler, more easily understood physical process of **diffusion.** To understand this process, so important in many biologic phenomena, we must first consider some of

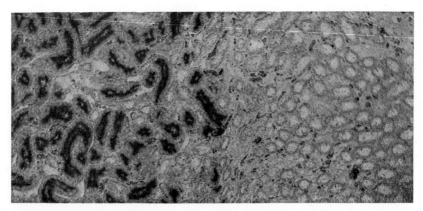

Figure 3.10 Histochemical demonstration of the location of the enzyme alkaline phosphatase within the cells of the rat's kidney. The tissue is carefully fixed and sectioned by methods which do not destroy the enzyme's activity. The tissue section is incubated at the proper pH with a naphthyl phosphate. Some hydrolysis of the naphthyl phosphate occurs wherever the phosphatase enzyme is located. The naphthol released by the action of the enzyme couples with a diazonium salt to form an intensely blue, insoluble azo dye which remains at the site of the enzymatic activity. The photomicrograph thus reveals the sites of phosphatase activity, i.e., the sites at which the azo dye is deposited. The cells of the proximal convoluted tubules (left) have a lot of enzyme; those of the loop of Henle (right) have little or no activity. (Courtesy of R. J. Barrnett.) (Villee: Biology, 5th ed.)

the basic physical concepts of energy and molecular motion.

3.7
Energy

Energy may be defined as the ability to do work, to produce a change in matter. It may take the form of heat, light, electricity, motion or chemical energy. Physicists recognize two kinds of energy: **potential energy,** the capacity to do work owing to the position or state of a body, and **kinetic energy,** the capacity to do work possessed by a body because of its motion. A rock at the top of a hill has potential energy; as it rolls downhill the potential energy is converted to kinetic energy.

Energy derived ultimately from solar energy is stored in the molecules of foodstuffs as the chemical energy of the bonds connecting their constituent atoms. This chemical energy is a kind of potential energy. When these food molecules are taken within a cell, chemical reactions occur which change this potential energy into heat, light, motion or some other kind of kinetic energy. Light is a kind of kinetic energy that may be thought of as the movement of photons or light quanta. All forms of energy are at least partially interconvertible, and living cells constantly transform potential energy into kinetic energy or the reverse (Table 3.1). If the conditions are suitably controlled, the amount of energy entering and leaving any given system can be measured and compared. Such experiments have shown that energy is neither created nor destroyed, but simply transformed from one

form to another. This is an expression of one of the fundamental laws of physics, the Law of the Conservation of Energy. Living things as well as nonliving systems obey this law.

3.8
Molecular Motion

The constituent molecules of all substances are constantly in motion. Despite the fact that wood, stone and steel seem very solid, their component molecules vibrate continuously within a very restricted space. The prime difference between solids, liquids and gases is the freedom of movement of the molecules present. The molecules of a solid are very closely packed and the forces of attraction between the molecules permit them to vibrate but not to move around. In the liquid state the molecules are somewhat farther apart and the intermolecular forces are weaker, so that the molecules can move about with considerable freedom. The molecules in the gaseous state are so far apart that the intermolecular forces are negligible and molecular movement is restricted only by external barriers. Molecular movement in all three states of matter is the result of the inherent heat energy of the molecules, the kinetic energy which is determined by the temperature of the system. By increasing this **molecular kinetic energy,** one can change matter from one state to another. When ice is heated it becomes water, and when water is heated it is converted to water vapor.

If a drop of water is examined under the microscope, the motion of its molecules is not evident. If a drop of India ink (which contains fine carbon particles) is added, the carbon particles move continually in aimless zigzag paths, for they are constantly being bumped by water molecules and the recoil from this bump imparts the motion to the carbon particle. The motion of such small particles is called **brownian movement,** after Robert Brown, an English botanist, who first observed the motion of pollen grains in a drop of water.

Table 3.1 Energy Transformations in Cells

Transformation	Type of Cell
Chemical energy to electrical energy	Nerve, brain
Sound to electrical energy	Inner ear
Light to chemical energy	Chloroplast
Light to electrical energy	Retina of eye
Chemical energy to osmotic energy	Kidney
Chemical energy to mechanical energy	Muscle cell, ciliated epithelium
Chemical energy to radiant energy	Luminescent organ of firefly
Chemical energy to electrical energy	Sense organs of taste and smell

3.9
Diffusion

Molecules in a liquid or gaseous state will diffuse, that is, move in all directions until they are spread evenly throughout the space available. **Diffusion** may be defined as the movement of molecules from a region of high concentration to one of lower concentration brought about by their kinetic energy. The rate of diffusion is a function of the size of the molecule and the temperature. If a bit of sugar is placed in a beaker of water, the sugar will dissolve and the individual sugar molecules will diffuse and come to be distributed evenly thoughout the liquid (Fig. 3.11). Each molecule tends to move in a straight line until it collides with another molecule or the side of the container; then it rebounds and moves in another direction. By this random movement of molecules, the sugar eventually becomes evenly distributed throughout the water in the beaker. This could be demonstrated by tasting drops of liquid taken from different parts of the beaker. If a colored dye is used in place of sugar, the process of diffusion can be observed directly. The molecules of sugar or dye continue to move after they have become evenly distributed throughout the liquid in the container; however, as fast as some molecules move from left to right, others move from right to left, so that an equilibrium is maintained.

Any number of substances will diffuse independently of each other. If a lump of salt is placed in one part of a beaker of water and a lump of sugar in another, the molecules of each will diffuse independently of the other and each drop of water in the beaker will eventually have some salt and some sugar molecules.

The rate of movement of a single molecule is several hundred meters per second, but each molecule can go only a fraction of a millimicron before it bumps into another molecule and rebounds. Thus the progress of a molecule in a straight line is quite slow. Diffusion is quite rapid over short distances but it takes a long time—days and even weeks—for a substance to diffuse a distance measured in centimeters. This fact has important biologic implications, for it places a sharp limit on the number of molecules of oxygen

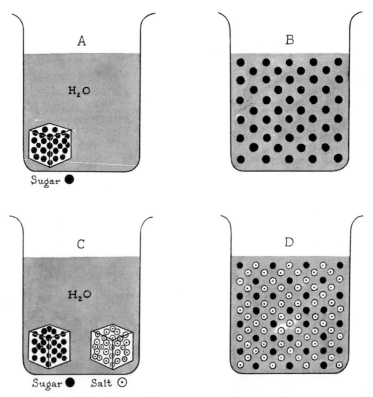

Figure 3.11 Diffusion. When a cube of sugar is placed in water (*A*) it dissolves and its molecules become uniformly distributed throughout the water as a result of the molecular motion of both sugar and water molecules (*B*). When lumps of sugar and salt are placed in water (*C*), each type of molecule diffuses independently of the other and both salt and sugar become uniformly distributed in the water (*D*).

and nutrients that can reach an organism by diffusion alone. Only a very small organism that requires relatively few molecules per second can survive if it remains in one place and allows molecules to come to it by diffusion. A larger organism must have some means of moving to a new region or some means of stirring its environment to bring molecules to it, or it may live in some spot where the environment is constantly moving past it — in a river, for example, or in the intertidal region at the seashore. The larger land plants have solved this problem by developing an extensively branched system of roots which can tap a large area of the surrounding environment for the needed raw materials.

3.10
Exchanges of Material Between Cell and Environment

All nutrients and waste products must pass through the plasma membrane to enter or leave the cell. Cells are almost invariably surrounded by a watery medium — the fresh or salt water in which an organism lives, the tissue sap of a higher plant, or the plasma or extracellular fluid of a higher animal. In general, only dissolved substances can pass through the plasma membrane, but not all dissolved substances penetrate the plasma membrane with equal facility. The membrane behaves as though it had ultramicroscopic pores through which substances pass, and these pores, like the holes in a sieve, determine the maximum size of molecule that can pass. Factors other than simple molecular size, such as the electric charge, if any, of the diffusing particle, the number of water molecules bound to the diffusing particles and its solubility in fatty substances, may also be important in determining whether or not the substance can pass through the plasma membrane.

A membrane is said to be **permeable** if it will permit any substance to pass through, **impermeable** if it will allow no substance to pass, and **differentially permeable** if it will allow some but not all substances to diffuse through. The nuclear and plasma membranes of all cells and the membranes surrounding food and contractile vacuoles are differentially permeable membranes. Permeability is a property of the *membrane,* not of the diffusing substance.

The diffusion of a dissolved substance through a differentially permeable membrane is known as **dialysis.** If a pouch made of collodion, cellophane or parchment is filled with a sugar solution and placed in a beaker of water, the sugar molecules will dialyze through the membrane (if the pores are large enough) and eventually the concentration of sugar molecules in the water outside the pouch will equal that within the pouch. The molecules then continue to diffuse but there is no net change in concentration for the rates in the two directions are equal.

A different type of diffusion is observed if a membrane is prepared with smaller pores, so that it is permeable to the small water molecules but not to the larger sugar molecules. A pouch may be prepared of a membrane with these properties and filled with a sugar solution, and the pouch then fitted with a cork and glass tube and placed in a beaker of water so that the levels of fluid inside and outside of the pouch are the same. The sugar molecules cannot pass through the membrane and so must remain inside the pouch. The water molecules diffuse through the membrane and mix with the sugar solution, so that the level of fluid within the pouch rises. The liquid within the pouch is 5 per cent sugar, and therefore only 95 per cent water; the liquid outside the membrane is 100 per cent water. The water molecules are moving in both directions through the membrane but there is a greater movement from the region of higher concentration (100 per cent, outside the pouch) to the region of lower concentration (95 per cent, within the pouch). This diffusion of water or solvent molecules through a membrane is called **osmosis,** and is illustrated diagrammatically in Figure 3.12.

If an amount of water equal to that originally present in the pouch enters, the solution in the pouch will be diluted to 2.5 per cent sugar and 97.5 per cent water, but the concentration of water outside the pouch will still exceed that inside and osmosis will continue. An equilibrium is reached when the water in the glass tube rises to a height such that the weight of the water in the tube exerts a pressure just equal to the tendency of the water to enter the pouch. Osmosis then occurs with equal speed in both directions through the differentially permeable membrane and there will be no net change in the amount of water in the

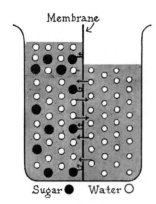

Figure 3.12 Diagram illustrating osmosis. When a solution of sugar in water is separated from pure water by a semipermeable membrane which allows water but not the larger sugar molecules to pass through, there is a net movement of water molecules through the membrane to the sugar solution. The water molecules are diffusing from a region of higher concentration (pure water) to a region of lower concentration (the sugar solution).

pouch. The pressure of the column of water is called the **osmotic pressure** of the sugar solution. The osmotic pressure results from the tendency of the water molecules to pass through the differentially permeable membrane and equalize the concentration of water molecules on its two sides. A more concentrated sugar solution would have a greater osmotic pressure and would "draw" water to a higher level in the tube. A 10 per cent sugar solution would cause water to rise approximately twice as high in the tube as a 5 per cent solution.

It is evident from this discussion that dialysis and osmosis are simply two special forms of diffusion. Diffusion is the general term for the movement of molecules from a region of high concentration to a region of lower concentration, brought about by their kinetic energy. Dialysis is the diffusion of dissolved molecules through a differentially permeable membrane, and osmosis is the diffusion of solvent molecules through a differentially permeable membrane. In biologic systems the solvent molecules are almost universally water.

The salts, sugars and other substances dissolved in the fluid within each cell give the intracellular fluid a certain osmotic pressure. When the cell is placed in a fluid with the same osmotic pressure as that of its intracellular fluid, there is no net entrance or exit of water, and the cell neither swells nor shrinks. Such a fluid is said to be **isotonic** or isosmotic with the intracellular fluid of the cell. Normally, the blood plasma and body fluids are isosmotic with the intracellular fluids of the body cells. If the environmental fluid contains more dissolved substances than the fluid within the cell, water will tend to pass out of the cell and the cell shrinks. Such a fluid is said to be **hypertonic** to the cell. If the environmental fluid has a lower concentration of dissolved substances than the fluid in the cell, water tends to pass into the cell and the cell swells. This fluid is said to be **hypotonic** to the cell. A solution of 0.9 per cent sodium chloride, 0.9 gm. per 100 ml. of water, sometimes loosely called "physiological saline," is isotonic to human cells.

A cell placed in a solution that is not isotonic with it may adjust to the changed environment by undergoing a change in its water content, so that it eventually achieves the same concentration of solutes as in the environment. Many cells have the ability to pump water or certain solute molecules into or out of the cell and in this way can maintain an osmotic pressure that differs from that of the surrounding medium. Amebae, paramecia and other protozoa that live in pond water, which is very hypotonic to their intracellular fluid, have evolved **contractile vacuoles** (see Fig. 3.1) which collect water from the interior of the cell and pump it to the outside. Without such a mechanism the cells would quickly burst from the water entering the cell.

The power of certain cells to accumulate selectively certain kinds of molecules from the environmental fluid is truly phenomenal. Human cells (and those of vertebrates in general) can accumulate amino acids so that the concentration within the cell is two to 50 times that in the extracellular fluid. Cells also have a much higher concentration of potassium and magnesium, and a lower concentration of sodium, than the environmental fluids. Certain primitive chordates, the tunicates (Chap. 19), can accumulate vanadium so that the concentration inside the cell is some 2,000,000 times that in the surrounding sea water, and seaweeds have a comparable ability to accumulate iodine. The transfer of water or of solutes in or out of the cell against a concentration gradient is physical work and requires the expenditure of energy. Some active physiologic process is required to perform these transfers; hence a cell can move molecules against a gradient only as long as it is alive. If a cell is treated with some metabolic poison, such as cyanide, it quickly loses its ability to maintain concentration differences on the two sides of its plasma membrane.

3.11
Tissues

In the evolution of both plants and animals, one of the major trends has been toward the structural and functional specialization of cells. The cells which comprise the body of one of the higher animals are not all alike, but are differentiated and specialized to perform certain functions more efficiently than an unspecialized animal body could. This specialization has also had the effect of making the several parts of the body interdependent, so that an injury to, or the destruction of, cells in one part of the body may result in the death of the whole organism. The advantages of specialization are so great that they more than outweigh the disadvantages. The cells of the body which are similarly specialized are known as a tissue. A **tissue** may be defined as a group or layer of similarly specialized cells which together perform certain special functions. The study of the structure and arrangement of tissues is known as **histology.** Each tissue is composed of cells which have a characteristic shape, size and arrangement; the different types of tissue of the vertebrate body are readily recognized when examined microscopically. Certain tissues are composed of nonliving cell products in addition to the cells; connective tissue contains many fibers in addition to the fibroblasts or connective tissue cells, and bone and cartilage are made largely of proteins and salts secreted by the bone or cartilage cells.

The cells of a multicellular animal such as man may be classified in six major groups, each of which has several subgroups. These are epithelial, connective, muscular, blood, nervous and reproductive tissues.

Epithelial Tissues. Epithelial tissues are composed of cells which form a continuous layer or sheet covering the surface of the body or lining cavities within the body. There is usually a noncellular **basement membrane** underlying the sheet of epithelial cells. The epithelial cells in the skin of vertebrates are usually connected by small cytoplasmic processes or bridges. The epithelia of the body protect the underlying cells from mechanical injury, from harmful chemicals and bacteria, and from desiccation. The epithelial lining of the digestive tract absorbs water and nutrients for use in the body. The lining of the digestive tract and a variety of other epithelia produce and give off a wide spectrum of substances, some of which are used elsewhere in the body and some of which are waste products which must be eliminated. Since the entire body is covered by an epithelium, all of the sensory stimuli must pass through some epithelium to reach the specific receptors for those stimuli. The functions of epithelia are thus protection, absorption, secretion and sensation. The lining of the digestive tract, windpipe, lungs, kidney tubules and urinary bladder, and the outer layer of the skin are some familiar examples of epithelial tissues.

The cells in epithelial tissues may be flat, cuboidal or columnar in shape, they may be arranged in a single layer or in many layers, and they may have fine hairs or cilia on the free surface. On the basis of these structural characteristics epithelia are subdivided into the following groups.

Squamous epithelium is made of thin flattened cells the shape of flagstones or tiles (Fig. 3.13). It is found on the surface of the skin and the lining of the mouth, esophagus and vagina. The endothelium lining the cavity of blood vessels and the mesothelium lining the coelom are squamous epithelia. In the lower animals the skin is usually covered with a single layer of squamous epithelium, but in man and the higher animals the outer layer of the skin consists of stratified squamous epithelium, made of several layers of these flat cells.

The kidney tubules are lined with **cuboidal epithelium,** made of cells that are cube-shaped and look like dice (Fig. 3.13). Many other parts of the body, such as the stomach and intestines, are lined by cells that are taller than they are wide. An epithelium composed of such elongated, pillar-like cells is known as **columnar epithelium** (Fig. 3.13). Columnar epithelium may be simple, consisting of a single layer of cells, or stratified, composed of several layers of cells.

Either cuboidal or columnar epithelial cells may have cilia on their free surface.

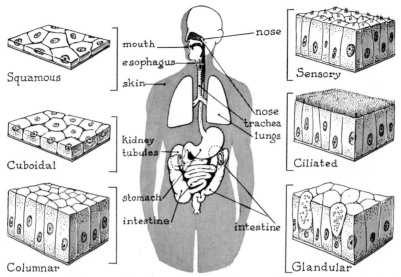

Figure 3.13   Diagram of the types of epithelial tissue and their location in the body.

Ciliated cuboidal epithelium is found in the sperm ducts of earthworms and other animals, and ciliated columnar epithelium lines the ducts of the respiratory system of man and other air-breathing vertebrates. The rhythmic, concerted beating of the cilia moves solid particles in one direction through the ducts. Epithelial cells, usually columnar ones, may be specialized to receive stimuli. The groups of cells in the taste buds of the tongue or the olfactory epithelium in the nose are examples of sensory epithelium. Columnar or cuboidal epithelia may also be specialized for secreting certain products such as milk, wax, saliva, perspiration or mucus. The outer epithelium of most worms secretes a thin, continuous, noncellular protective layer, called the **cuticle,** which covers the entire body. Insects, spiders, crabs and other arthropods secrete a cuticle which may be quite thick and strengthened with deposits of chitin and salts. The hard protective shells of oysters and snails, composed of calcium carbonate, are secreted by epithelial cells in the mantles of these animals.

Connective Tissues.   The connective tissues—bone, cartilage, tendons, ligaments, fibrous connective tissue and adipose tissue—support and bind together the other tissues and organs. Connective tissue cells characteristically secrete a nonliving material called the **matrix,** and the nature and function of each connective tissue is determined primarily by the nature of this intercellular matrix. The actual connective tissue cells may form only a small and inconspicuous part of the tissue. It is the matrix, rather than the connective tissue cells themselves, which does the actual connecting and supporting.

Fibrous connective tissue consists of a thick, interlacing, matted network of fibers in which are distributed the cells that secreted the fibers (Fig. 3.14). There are three types of fibrous connective tissue, widely distributed throughout the body, which bind skin to muscle, muscle to bone, and so on. These include very delicate **reticular fibers;** thick, tough, unbranched, flexible, but relatively inelastic **collagen fibers;** and long, branched **elastic fibers. Adipose tissue** is rich in fat cells, specialized connective tissue cells which store large quantities of fat in a single drop in the cytoplasm. Ligaments and tendons are specialized kinds of fibrous connective tissue. **Tendons** are composed of thick, closely packed bundles of collagen fibers, which form flexible cables that connect a muscle to a bone or to another muscle. A **ligament** is fundamentally similar in constitution to a tendon and connects one bone to another. An especially thick mat of fibrous connective tissue is located in the lower layer of the skin of most vertebrates; when this is chemically treated—"tanned"—it becomes leather. Connective tissue fibers contain a protein called **collagen.** Treating the fibers with hot water converts some of the collagen into the soluble protein gelatin. The amino acid compositions of gelatin and collagen are nearly identical. The collagen units compris-

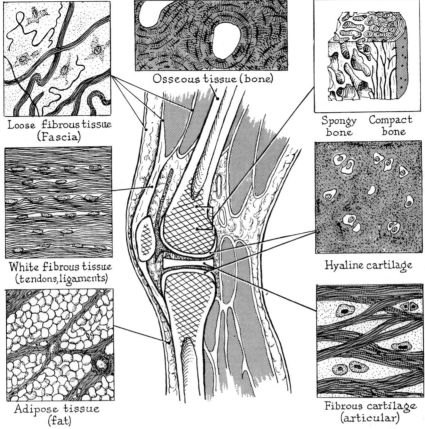

Loose fibrous tissue
(Fascia)

Osseous tissue (bone)

Spongy   Compact
bone   bone

White fibrous tissue
(tendons, ligaments)

Hyaline cartilage

Adipose tissue
(fat)

Fibrous cartilage
(articular)

Figure 3.14 Diagram of the types of connective tissue and their location in the knee joint.

ing the fibers consist of a helix made of three peptide chains joined by hydrogen bonds.

The supporting skeleton of vertebrates is composed of cartilage or bone. In some, for example, the sharks, the skeleton is made entirely of cartilage. **Cartilage** appears as the supporting skeleton in the embryonic stages of all vertebrates, but is largely replaced in the adult by bone in all but sharks and rays. Cartilage can be felt in man as the supporting framework of the pinna of the ear (the external ear flap) or the tip of the nose. It is made of a firm but elastic matrix secreted by cartilage cells which become embedded in the matrix (Fig. 3.14). These cartilage cells are alive; they may secrete collagenous fibers or elastic fibers to strengthen the cartilage.

Bone consists of a dense matrix composed of proteins and calcium salts identical with the mineral hydroxyapatite, $Ca_3(PO_4)_2 \cdot CaCO_3$. About 65 per cent of the bone is made of this mineral. The bone cells (osteoblasts) secrete both the protein

and the calcium salts. The osteoblasts become surrounded and trapped by their own secretion and remain in microscopic cavities (lacunae) in the bone as living osteocytes (Fig. 3.14). The protein is laid down as minute fibers which contribute strength and resiliency and the mineral salts contribute hardness to bone.

At the surface of each bone is a thin fibrous layer called the **periosteum** (peri, around; osteum, bone) to which the muscles are attached by tendons. The periosteum contains cells, some of which differentiate into osteoblasts and secrete protein and salts to bring about growth and repair. Most bones are not solid but have a marrow cavity in the center. The apparently solid matrix of the bone is pierced by many microscopic channels (haversian canals) in which lie blood vessels and nerves to supply the bone cells. The bony matrix is deposited, usually in concentric rings or lamellae, around these haversian canals. Each bone cell is connected to the adjacent bone cells and to the haversian canals by cellular extensions which lie in minute canals (canaliculi) in the matrix. The bone cells obtain oxygen and raw materials and eliminate wastes by way of these canaliculi. The details of the architecture of a bone can be observed by grinding a slice of bone extremely thin and mounting it on a slide for inspection under a microscope. Bone contains not only bone-secreting cells, but also bone-destroying cells. By the action of these two types of cells, the shape of a bone may be altered to resist changing stresses and strains. Bone formation and destruction is regulated by the availability of calcium and phosphate, by the presence of vitamin D, and by the hormones thyrocalcitonin and parathyrin, secreted by the thyroid and parathyroid glands. The marrow cavity of the bone may contain yellow marrow (largely a fat depot) or red marrow, the tissue in which red and certain white blood cells are formed.

Muscular Tissues.   The movements of most animals result from the contraction of elongated, cylindrical or spindle-shaped cells, each of which contains many tiny, longitudinal, parallel, contractile fibers called **myofibrils,** composed of the proteins myosin and actin. Muscle cells perform mechanical work by contracting—by getting shorter and thicker; they are unable to do work by pushing. Three types of muscle tissue are found in vertebrates: skeletal, cardiac and smooth (Fig. 3.15). **Cardiac muscle** is found only in the walls of the heart; **smooth muscle** in the walls of the digestive tract, the urinary and genital tracts, and the walls of arteries and veins; and **skeletal muscle** makes up the muscle masses which are attached to and move the bones of the body. Cardiac and skeletal muscle cells are among the exceptions to the rule that cells have but one nucleus; each of these cells has many nuclei. The nuclei of skeletal muscle cells have an unusual position, at the periphery of the cell, just below the plasma membrane. Skeletal muscle cells are extremely long, two or more centimeters in length; indeed, some investigators believe that the muscle cells extend from one end of the muscle to the other, so that their length is equal to that of the muscle. Muscle fibers range in thickness from 10 to 100 microns; continued, strenuous muscle activity increases the thickness of the fiber. The myofibrils of skeletal and cardiac muscle have alternate dark and light cross bands or **striations.** These striations appear to have some fundamental role in contraction, during which the dark band remains constant but the light band shortens. The contraction of skeletal muscles is generally voluntary, under the control of the will, that of cardiac and smooth muscles is involuntary. Cardiac muscle cells are striated but have centrally located nuclei. Smooth muscle cells are not striated, have

A, SKELETAL MUSCLE FIBERS

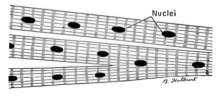

B, SMOOTH MUSCLE FIBERS

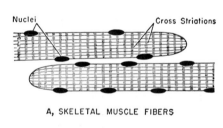

C, CARDIAC MUSCLE FIBERS

Figure 3.15 Types of muscle tissue. (Villee: Biology, 5th ed.)

Table 3.2 Comparison of Vertebrate Muscle Tissues

	Skeletal	*Smooth*	*Cardiac*
Location	Attached to skeleton	Walls of viscera: stomach, intestines, etc.	Wall of heart
Shape of fiber	Elongate, cylindrical, blunt ends	Elongate, spindle-shaped, pointed ends	Elongate, cylindrical; fibers branch and fuse
Number of nuclei per cell	Many	One	Many
Position of nuclei	Peripheral	Central	Central
Cross striations	Present	Absent	Present
Speed of contraction	Most rapid	Slowest	Intermediate
Ability to remain contracted	Least	Greatest	Intermediate
Type of control	Voluntary	Involuntary	Involuntary

pointed ends, and have centrally located nuclei. Smooth muscle contracts slowly but can remain contracted for long periods of time. In some of the invertebrates the voluntary muscles of the body, such as the ones which close the shell of an oyster, are smooth muscles. Striated muscles can contract very rapidly but cannot remain contracted; a striated muscle fiber must relax and rest before it is able to contract again. The muscles of insects, spiders, crabs and other arthropods have cross striations and contract very rapidly. The distinguishing features of the three types of muscle are summarized in Table 3.2.

Vascular Tissues. The **blood,** composed of a liquid part—**plasma**—and of several types of **formed elements**—red cells, white cells and platelets—may be classified as a separate type of tissue or as one kind of connective tissue. The latter classification is based on the fact that blood cells and connective tissue cells originate from similar cells; however, the adult cells are quite different in structure and function. The **red cells** of vertebrates contain the red pigment hemoglobin, which has the property of combining easily and reversibly with oxygen. Oxygen, combined as oxyhemoglobin, is transported to the cells of the body in the red cells. Mammalian red cells are flattened, biconcave discs without a nucleus; those of other vertebrates are more typical cells with an oval shape and a nucleus.

There are five different kinds of **white blood cells**—lymphocytes, monocytes, neutrophils, eosinophils and basophils (Fig. 3.16). These have no hemoglobin but move around and engulf bacteria. They can slip through the walls of blood vessels and enter the tissues of the body to engulf bacteria there. The fluid plasma transports a great variety of substances from one part of the body to another. Some of the substances transported are in solution, others are bound to one or another of the plasma proteins. The plasma of vertebrates is a light yellow color; in certain invertebrates the oxygen-carrying pigment is not localized in cells, but is dissolved in the plasma and colors it

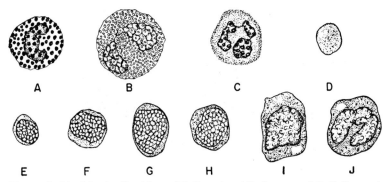

Figure 3.16 Types of white blood cells. *A,* basophil; *B,* eosinophil; *C,* neutrophil; *E–H, a variety of lymphocytes; I* and *J,* monocytes; *D,* a red blood cell drawn to the same scale. (Villee: Biology, 5th ed.)

red or blue. **Platelets** are small fragments broken off from cells in the bone marrow; they play a role in the clotting of blood (Chap. 28).

Nervous Tissues. Cells specialized for the reception of stimuli and the transmission of impulses are called **neurons.** A neuron typically has an enlarged cell body, containing the nucleus, and two or more cytoplasmic processes, the nerve fibers, along which the nerve impulse travels to the next neuron (Fig. 3.17). Nerve fibers vary in width from a few microns to 30 or 40 microns and in length from a millimeter or two to a meter or more. The neurons are connected end to end so that impulses may be transmitted all through the body. Two types of nerve fibers are distinguished: **axons,** which transmit impulses away from the cell body, and **dendrites,** which transmit them to the cell body. The junction between the axon of one neuron and the dendrite of the next neuron in the chain is called a **synapse.** At the

synapse the axon and dendrite do not actually touch; there is a small gap between the two. Transmission of an impulse across the synapse is by a different mechanism from that which passes an impulse along the nerve fiber. An impulse can travel across the synapse only from an axon to a dendrite; thus, the synapse serves as a valve to prevent the backflow of impulses. Neurons show widely diverse patterns in shape of the cell body and in number and length of dendrites and axons.

The cell bodies of neurons commonly occur in groups; there are columns of cell bodies in the spinal cord, sheets of cell bodies over the surface of parts of the brain, nodules of cell bodies ("nuclei") within the brain, and the ganglia of the cranial and spinal nerves. A **ganglion** is a group of nerve cell bodies located outside the central nervous system. A nerve consists of a group of axons and dendrites bound together by connective tissue. Each nerve fiber—axon or dendrite—is surrounded by one or two sheaths, a

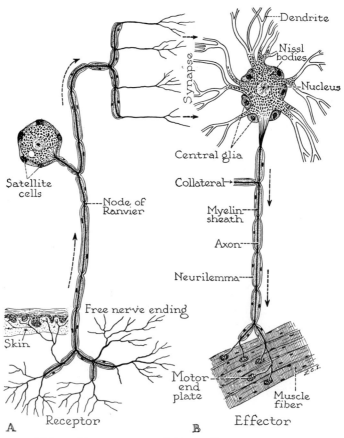

Figure 3.17 Diagrams of (*A*) an afferent neuron and (*B*) an efferent neuron. The arrows indicate the direction of the normal nerve impulse. (King and Showers: Human Anatomy and Physiology, 5th ed.)

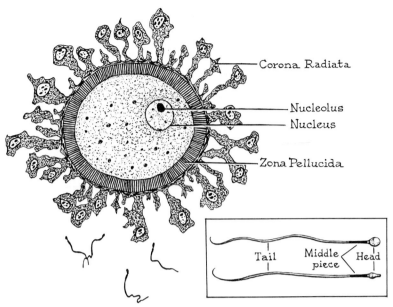

Figure 3.18   Human egg and sperm, magnified 400 times. *Inset,* side and top views of a sperm, magnified about 2000 times. The egg is surrounded by other cells which form the corona radiata.

neurilemma and/or a **myelin sheath.** The neurilemma is a delicate, transparent, tubelike membrane made of cells which envelop the fiber. The myelin sheath is made of noncellular, fatty material which forms a glistening white coat between the fiber and neurilemma. The myelin sheath is interrupted at fairly regular intervals along the nerve by constrictions called the nodes of Ranvier. Nerve fibers are either "medullated" and have a thick myelin sheath, or "non-medullated" and have an extremely thin myelin sheath. Nerve fibers in the brain and spinal cord have a myelin sheath but no neurilemma; those in the autonomic nerves to the viscera, and the nerves of many invertebrates, are nonmyelinated and have a very thin or no myelin sheath but a neurilemma. The nerves to the skin and skeletal muscles of vertebrates have both a myelin sheath and a neurilemma surrounding them.

Nervous tissue contains, in addition to neurons, several different kinds of supporting cells called **neuroglia.** These have many cytoplasmic processes, and the cells and their processes form an extremely dense supporting framework in which the neurons are suspended. The neuroglia are believed to separate and insulate adjacent neurons, so that nerve impulses can pass from one neuron to the next only over the synapse, where the neuroglial barrier is incomplete.

Reproductive Tissues.   The **egg cells** (ova) formed in the ovary of the female and the **sperm cells** produced by the testes of the male constitute the reproductive tissues— cells specially modified for the production of offspring (Fig. 3.18). Egg cells are generally spherical or oval and are nonmotile. A typical egg has a large nucleus, called the germinal vesicle, and a variable amount of yolk in the cytoplasm. Shark and bird eggs have enormous amounts of yolk which provides nourishment for the development of the embryo until it hatches from the shell. Sperm cells are small and modified for motility. A typical sperm has a long **tail,** the beating of which propels the sperm to its meeting and union with the egg. The **head** of the sperm contains the nucleus surrounded by a thin film of cytoplasm. The tail is connected to the head by a short **middle piece.** An **axial filament,** formed by the centriole in the middle piece, extends to the tip of the tail. Most of the cytoplasm is sloughed off as the sperm matures; this decreases the weight of the sperm and perhaps renders it more motile.

3.12
Body Plan and Symmetry

To refer to the regions of an animal body, zoologists use the term **anterior** for the head

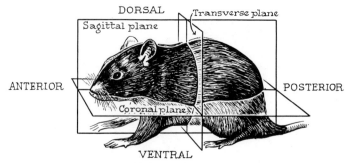

Figure 3.19 Diagram to illustrate transverse, sagittal and frontal planes in a bilaterally symmetrical animal.

end and **posterior** for the tail end; the back side is the **dorsal** side and the belly side is the **ventral** side. The midline of the body is **medial** and the sides are **lateral.** The part of a structure nearer the point of reference is **proximal,** the part farther away is **distal.**

A body is symmetrical if it can be cut into two equivalent halves. A few kinds of protozoa can be cut into two equal halves by any plane through the center; they are said to be **spherically symmetrical.** Coelenterates and echinoderms are **radically symmetrical;** they can be cut into two equal halves by any plane which includes the axis running from top to bottom through the center. In such animals a top and bottom side can be distinguished. Most other animals are **bilaterally symmetrical,** and can be cut into two equivalent halves only by a plane passing from anterior to posterior and from the dorsal to ventral sides in the midline. In such a bilaterally symmetrical animal, three types of planes or cuts can be made to get different views: sagittal, frontal and transverse (Fig. 3.19). A **sagittal section** is one made by cutting in the median vertical plane; thus it includes the anterior-posterior axis and the dorsoventral axis but is at right angles to the right-left axis. A **frontal section** is at right angles to a sagittal section and includes the anterior-posterior axis and the right-left axis, but is perpendicular to the dorsoventral axis. **Transverse sections** are cut at right angles to the anterior-posterior axis and include a dorsoventral and a right-left axis.

QUESTIONS

1. How would you define a cell? What is meant by the cell theory?
2. Contrast the meaning of the term cell in the time of Robert Hooke, in the time of Schleiden and Schwann, and at present.
3. How would you define a tissue? List and give the distinguishing characteristics of the several types of animal tissues.
4. Describe the parts of a typical animal cell and give the functions of each.
5. Describe the methods that may be used to investigate the functioning of an ameba. Of a mammalian liver cell.
6. In a human cell undergoing mitosis, how many chromosomes are present in the metaphase? In the anaphase? In the resting daughter cell?
7. Outline briefly the events which occur in each stage of mitosis. Illustrate your discussion with diagrams of mitosis in the cell of an animal with four pairs of chromosomes.
8. What factors may regulate cell division?
9. What are the assumptions underlying histochemical studies of cell function?
10. Differentiate clearly between diffusion, dialysis and osmosis. Of what biologic importance is the process of diffusion?
11. In what ways do gases, liquids and solids differ?
12. Define the term energy. Differentiate between potential and kinetic energy.
13. What is a differentially permeable membrane? Give some examples of differentially permeable membranes in the human body.
14. How would you measure the osmotic pressure of the contents of a red blood cell?
15. What kinds of tissue make up the human tongue, stomach, liver, heart, eye?

16. Compare the matrix present in bone, cartilage and fibrous connective tissue.
17. How would you describe the position of a rhinoceros' tusks? Of a camel's hump? Of a cobra's hood?

ANNOTATED REFERENCES

Bloom, W., and D. Fawcett: Textbook of Histology. 8th ed. Philadelphia, W. B. Saunders Co., 1962. One of the standard texts of histology with many superb illustrations of the structure of tissues.

DeRobertis, E. D. P., W. W. Nowinski and F. A. Saez: Cell Biology. 4th ed. Philadelphia, W. B. Saunders Co., 1965. Contains a detailed presentation of the structure and properties of a wide variety of cells.

Fawcett, D.: The Cell: Its Organelles and Inclusions. Philadelphia, W. B. Saunders Co., 1966. An excellent discussion of cell structure illustrated by electron micrographs of outstanding quality.

Hall, T. S.: A Source Book in Animal Biology. New York, McGraw-Hill Book Co., 1951. The development of the cell theory is presented in an interesting fashion by means of long quotations from some of the original scientific papers.

Much of the September 1961 issue of the Scientific American was devoted to the cell and its properties. Included are an article by Jean Brachet, The Living Cell, which describes the cell as a highly organized factory for the assembly of specific molecules; an article by Heinz Holter, How Things Get Into Cells; and one by Teru Hayashi, How Cells Move. Many other subjects relating to cell structure and function have been discussed in other issues of Scientific American.

4 _____ CELL METABOLISM

All living cells have complex and efficient systems for transforming one type of energy into another by appropriate chemical reactions. In animal cells the chemical energy of carbohydrates and other organic molecules is transformed by the process of **cellular respiration** into the "biologically useful" energy of energy-rich phosphate compounds. In subsequent energy transformations this biologically useful energy is used by the cells to do work — the mechanical work of muscle contraction, the electrical work of conducting a nerve impulse, the osmotic work of moving molecules against a gradient, or the chemical work of synthesizing molecules for cellular growth. The energy finally passes to the environment as heat, a useless form of energy. Cells have evolved some remarkable energy transducers to carry out these transformations, together with efficient control systems to regulate them and enable the cell to adjust to variations in environmental conditions.

The chemical reactions of cells, which provide for their growth, irritability, movement, maintenance and repair, and their reproduction, are termed **metabolism.** The metabolic activities of animal, plant and bacterial cells are remarkably similar, despite the apparent differences of the organisms themselves. In all cells, sugars and related substances are continually being metabolized, via a large number of intermediate compounds, to water and carbon dioxide with the release of energy which is made available to the cell for further use.

Green plants differ from animals in their ability to photosynthesize, that is, to capture the energy of sunlight and to use it to synthesize complex, energy-rich substances from simple raw materials — water, carbon dioxide, nitrates and phosphates. Animal and bacterial cells have the ability to "fix" carbon diox-

ide, to incorporate it into any one of a number of organic compounds and thus build a new compound with one more carbon atom in the chain. Only green plants and a few bacteria, however, can utilize radiant energy to fix carbon dioxide; animals and the rest of the bacteria must get energy for the reaction from some energy-releasing process such as the metabolism of glucose.

4.1
Chemical Reactions

A chemical reaction is a change involving the molecular structure of one or more substances; matter is changed from one substance, with its characteristic properties, to another, with new properties, and energy is released or absorbed. Hydrochloric acid (HCl), for example, reacts with the base, sodium hydroxide (NaOH) to yield water (H_2O) and the salt, sodium chloride (NaCl); in the process energy is released as heat. The chemical properties of HCl and NaOH are very different from those of NaCl and H_2O. In chemical shorthand a plus sign connects the symbols of the reacting substances, HCl and NaOH, and the products, NaCl and H_2O. An arrow indicates the direction of the reaction:

$$HCl + NaOH \rightarrow NaCl + H_2O + energy \text{ (heat)}$$

Most chemical reactions are reversible and this reversibility is indicated by a double arrow: $\rightleftharpoons$.

Atoms are neither destroyed nor created in the course of a chemical reaction; thus the sum of each kind of atom on one side of the arrow must equal the sum of that kind of atom on the other side. This is an expression of one of the basic laws of physics, the **Law of the Conservation of Matter.** The direction of a reversible reaction is determined by the energy relations of the several chemicals involved, their relative concentrations, and their solubility.

One of the factors determining the rate of a chemical reaction is the **temperature;** the reaction rate approximately doubles with each increase of 10° C. This is true of the chemical reactions occurring in living cells as well as those in a test tube, and is another bit of evidence that the chemical reactions of living things are fundamentally similar to those of nonliving ones.

The formula for the net changes that occur when a cell metabolizes glucose in the presence of oxygen may be written as:

$$C_6H_{12}O_6 + 6\ O_2 \rightleftharpoons 6\ H_2O + 6\ CO_2 + energy$$

A census of the carbon, hydrogen and oxygen atoms will reveal that there are equal numbers of each kind on the two sides of the arrow; thus this reaction is said to be balanced. Energy is released as the glucose molecule is broken down. To reverse the reaction, and thus synthesize glucose, an equivalent amount of energy must be supplied. In photosynthesis the radiant energy of sunlight is absorbed by the green pigment chlorophyll and converted to chemical energy which can be used to synthesize glucose and other compounds.

There are a number of units of energy, including the erg, the joule and the foot-pound, but the one most widely used in the biologic sciences is the **Calorie.** The kilocalorie, or Calorie written with a capital C, is the amount of heat required to raise 1 kilogram of water 1 degree centigrade (strictly, from 14.5° C. to 15.5° C.). Other forms of energy, such as light, electricity or the energy of motion or position, can be converted to heat and measured by the resulting increase in temperature of a known amount of water. Each gram of glucose, when metabolized to carbon dioxide and water, yields 3.74 Calories. An easy figure to remember is that a gram of carbohydrate yields about 4 Calories.

Catalysis. Many of the substances that are rapidly metabolized by living cells are remarkably inert outside the body. A glucose solution, for example, will keep indefinitely in a bottle if it is kept free of bacteria and molds. It must be subjected to high tempera-ture or to the action of strong acids or bases before it will decompose. Living cells cannot utilize conditions as extreme as these, for the cell itself would be destroyed long before the glucose, yet glucose is rapidly decomposed within cytoplasm at ordinary temperatures and pressures and in a solution which is neither acidic nor basic. The reactions within the cell are brought about by special agents known as **enzymes,** which belong to the class of substances known as catalysts. A **catalyst** is an agent which affects the velocity of a chemical reaction without altering its end point and without being used up in the course of the reaction. The list of substances which may serve as a catalyst in one or more reactions is long indeed. Water is an excellent catalyst for many reactions. Pure, dry hydrogen gas and dry chlorine gas do not react when mixed, but if a slight trace of water is present they react with explosive violence to form hydrogen chloride. Metals such as iron, nickel, platinum and palladium, when ground into a fine powder, are widely used as catalysts in industrial processes such as the hydrogenation of cottonseed and other vegetable oils to make margarine or the cracking of petroleum to make gasoline. A minute amount of catalyst will speed up the reaction of vast quantities of reactants, for the molecules of catalyst are not exhausted in the reaction but are used again and again.

4.2
Enzymes

The speed and specificity of the myriad chemical reactions that occur in cells are regulated by the catalysts called enzymes, produced by the cell. Man has used the fermenting of grape juice and the souring of milk, which are enzymic processes, for thousands of years. Pasteur showed about 100 years ago that these processes occur only when specific microorganisms are present, and inferred that the enzymes (he called them "ferments") were active catalysts only when they were a part of the living cell. In his experiments he was unable to separate the active catalysts from the living cell and concluded that enzymes were living things which lost activity when separated from the cell. Liebig, in contrast, believed that enzymes were simply complex organic compounds that did not require a living cell in order to function, but he, too, was unable to remove an enzyme from a cell and have it retain its activity. Pasteur and Liebig had a classic, long-lasting argument over their divergent views. The question was finally settled, after both Liebig and Pasteur had died, when Eduard Büchner in 1897 extracted an enzyme preparation from yeast which, though completely devoid of cells, was able to metabolize glucose. In the succeeding years, hundreds of other enzymes have been extracted from a wide variety of cells and shown to have their activity unimpaired; some have been purified and prepared as pure crystalline substances. We can now define enzymes as organic catalysts which are produced by living cells but which are active independently of the cell. Enzyme-controlled reactions are basic to all the phenomena of life: respiration, digestion, excretion, growth, muscle contraction, nerve conduction, and so on. There is no need to postulate some mysterious vital force, as Pasteur did, to account for these phenomena.

Properties of Enzymes. All the enzymes that have been isolated and crystallized to date have proved to be proteins. They are usually colorless, but may be yellow, green, blue, brown or red. Most enzymes are soluble in water or dilute salt solution, but some, for example, the enzymes located in the mitochondria, are bound together by lipoproteins and are insoluble in water. Enzymes are usually named by adding the suffix "-ase" to the name of the substance acted upon, called the **substrate.** Thus, sucrose is split by the enzyme sucrase and urease is the enzyme which attacks urea.

The catalytic ability of enzymes is truly phenomenal; without them chemical reactions would occur much too slowly to permit life to continue. Each molecule of the enzyme **catalase,** extracted from beef liver, will decompose 5,000,000 molecules of hydrogen peroxide (H_2O_2) per minute at 0° C. Hydrogen peroxide is a poisonous substance produced as a by-product in a number of enzyme reactions. Catalase protects the cell by decomposing the peroxide. The number of molecules of substrate acted upon per minute by a molecule of enzyme is called the **turnover number** of the enzyme. The turnover number of catalase, at 0° C., is 5,000,000. Most enzymes have high turnover numbers, which explains why they can be so remarkably effective even though present in the cell in minute amounts. Hydrogen peroxide can be split by iron atoms alone, but it would take 300 *years* for an iron atom to split the same number of molecules of H_2O_2 that a molecule of catalase, which contains one iron atom, splits in one *second.* This example of the evolution of a catalyst emphasizes one of the prime characteristics of enzymes—they are very efficient catalysts.

Although enzymes in general catalyze specific reactions, they do differ in the number of kinds of substrates they will attack. **Urease** is an example of an enzyme which is absolutely specific. Urease decomposes urea to ammonia and carbon dioxide and will attack no substance other than urea. Most enzymes are not quite so specific, and will attack several closely related substances. **Peroxidase,** for example, will decompose several different peroxides in addition to hydrogen peroxide. A few enzymes are specific only in requiring that the substrate have a certain kind of chemical bond. The **lipase** secreted by the pancreas will split the ester bonds connecting the glycerol and fatty acids of a wide variety of fats.

In theory, enzyme-controlled reactions are reversible; the enzyme does not determine the direction of the reaction but simply accelerates the rate at which the reaction reaches equilibrium. The classic example of this is the action of the enzyme lipase on the splitting of fat, or union of glycerol and fatty acids. If one begins with a fat, the enzyme catalyzes the splitting of this to give some glycerol and fatty acids. If one begins with a mixture of fatty acids and glycerol, the enzyme catalyzes the synthesis of some fat. When either system has operated long enough, the same equilibrium mixture of fat, glycerol and fatty acid is reached:

$$fat \rightleftharpoons glycerol + 3 \ fatty \ acids$$

The equilibrium point is determined by complex thermodynamic principles, which will not be discussed. Since reactions give off energy when going in one direction, it is obvious that an equivalent amount of energy in the proper form must be supplied to make the reaction go in the opposite direction. To drive an energy-requiring reaction, some energy-yielding reaction must occur at about the same time. In most biologic systems, energy-yielding reactions result in the synthesis of "energy-rich" phosphate esters, such as the terminal bonds of **adenosine triphos-**

phate (abbreviated as ATP). The energy of these energy-rich bonds is then available for the conduction of an impulse, the contraction of a muscle, the synthesis of complex molecules, and so on, much as the energy of a storage battery made by a generator is available for light, heat or running a motor. Biochemists use the term "coupled reactions" for two reactions which must occur together so that one can furnish the energy, or one of the reactants, needed by the other.

Enzymes generally work in teams in the cell, with the product of one enzyme-controlled reaction serving as the substrate for the next. We can picture the inside of a cell as a factory with many different assembly lines (and disassembly lines) operating simultaneously. Each of these assembly lines is composed of a number of enzymes, each of which catalyzes the reaction by which one substance is converted into a second. This second substance is passed along to the next enzyme, which converts it into a third, and so on along the line. From germinating barley seeds one can extract two enzymes that convert starch to glucose. The first, amylase, splits starch to maltose and the second, maltase, splits the double sugar maltose to two molecules of the single sugar glucose. Eleven different enzymes, working consecutively, are required to convert glucose to lactic acid. The same series of 11 enzymes is found in human cells, in green leaves and in bacteria.

Some enzymes, such as pepsin and urease, have been found to consist solely of protein. Many others, however, consist of two parts: one is protein (called the **apoenzyme**) and the other (called a **coenzyme**) is some smaller organic molecule, usually containing phosphate. Coenzymes can usually be separated from their enzymes and, when analyzed, have proved to contain some vitamin—thiamine, niacin, riboflavin, etc.—as part of the molecule. This finding has led to the generalization that all vitamins function as parts of coenzymes in the cell. Neither the apoenzyme nor the coenzyme alone has catalytic properties; only when the two are combined is activity evident. Certain enzymes require for activity, in addition to a coenzyme, the presence of one or more ions. Magnesium (Mg^{++}) is required for the activity of several of the enzymes in the chain which converts glucose to lactic acid. **Salivary amylase,** the starch-splitting enzyme of saliva, requires chloride ion as an activator. Most, if not all, of the elements required by plants and animals in very small amounts—the so-called **trace elements,** manganese, copper, cobalt, zinc, iron, and others—serve as enzyme activators.

Enzymes may be present in the cell either dissolved in the liquid phase or bound to, and presumably an integral part of, one of the cell particles. A water extract of ground liver contains all the 11 kinds of enzymes necessary to convert glucose to lactic acid. The respiratory enzymes, which catalyze the metabolism of lactic acid and the carbon chains of fatty acids and amino acids to carbon dioxide and water, are integral parts of the mitochondria.

The Mechanism of Enzyme Catalysis. Many years ago Emil Fischer, the German organic chemist, suggested that the specificity of the relationship of an enzyme to its substrate indicated that the two must fit together like a lock and key (Fig. 4.1). The idea that an enzyme combines with its substrate to form a reactive intermediate enzyme-substrate complex, which subsequently decomposes to release the free enzyme and the reaction products, was formulated mathematically by Leonor Michaelis more than 50 years ago. By brilliant inductive reasoning, he assumed that such a complex does form, and then calculated what the relationships between enzyme concentration, substrate concentration, and the velocity of the reaction should be. Exactly these relationships are observed experimentally, which is strong evidence that Michaelis' assumption, that an enzyme-substrate complex forms as an intermediate, is correct. Direct evidence of the existence of enzyme-substrate complexes was obtained by David Keilin of Cambridge University and Britton Chance of the University of Pennsylvania. Chance isolated a brown-colored peroxidase from horseradish and found that when this was mixed with the substrate, hydrogen peroxide, a green-colored enzyme-substrate complex formed. This, in turn, changed to a second, pale red complex which finally split to give the original brown enzyme and the products of the reaction. By observing the changes of color, Dr. Chance was able to calculate the rates of formation and of dissociation of this complex.

It is clear that when it is part of an enzyme-substrate complex, the substrate is much more reactive than it is when free. It is not clear, however, *why* this should be true. One explanation postulates that the enzyme unites

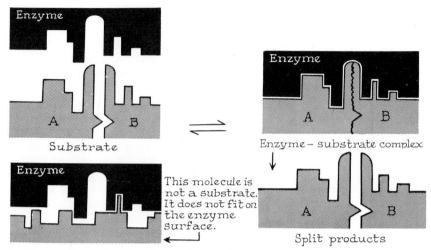

Figure 4.1 Diagram illustrating the concept of a specific enzyme surface which permits the formation of a specific enzyme-substrate complex.

with the substrate at two or more places, and the substrate molecule is held in a position which strains its molecular bonds and renders them more likely to break.

One approach to the study of enzymic action is to investigate the detailed structure of the enzyme molecule itself. It is now possible to determine the kinds of amino acids present in an enzyme molecule, their relative numbers and the sequence of amino acids in the peptide chain or chains comprising the enzyme protein. Ribonuclease, which consists of 124 amino acids in a single chain that is looped on itself like a pretzel, was the first enzyme for which it was possible to give the exact sequence of amino acids for the entire molecule. Such analyses of the structure of the enzyme molecule may provide clues as to the mechanism of enzymic catalysis. It is probable that only a relatively small part of the enzyme molecule (termed the "active site") is involved in combining with the substrate. Studies of the sequence of amino acids in this part of the enzyme should be especially fruitful in throwing light on the mechanism of enzyme action.

4.3
Factors Affecting Enzymic Activity

Temperature. The velocity of most chemical reactions is approximately doubled by each 10 degree increase in temperature, and, over a moderate range of temperature, this is true of enzyme-catalyzed reactions as

well. Enzymes, and proteins in general, are inactivated by high temperatures; the higher the temperature, the more rapidly the enzymic activity is lost. Native protein molecules exist at least in part as **spiral coils,** or helices, and the denaturation process appears to involve the unwinding of the helix. Enzyme inactivation is a reversible process if the temperature is not too high and has not been applied more than a short time. Most organisms are killed by exposure to heat because their cellular enzymes are inactivated. The processes of protein denaturation and enzyme inactivation show a striking parallelism and this is one bit of substantiating evidence that enzymes are proteins. The enzymes of man and other warm-blooded animals operate most efficiently at a temperature of about 37° C.—body temperature—whereas those of plants and cold-blooded animals work optimally at about 25° C. Enzymes are generally not inactivated by freezing; their reactions continue slowly, or perhaps cease altogether at low temperatures, but their catalytic activity reappears when the temperature is again raised to normal.

Acidity. All enzymes are sensitive to changes in the acidity and alkalinity—the pH—of their environment and will be inactivated if subjected to strong acids or bases. Most enzymes exert their greatest catalytic effect only when the pH of their environment is within a certain rather narrow range. On either side of this optimum pH, as the pH is raised or lowered, enzymic activity rapidly decreases. The protein-digesting enzyme of the stomach, pepsin, is remarkable in that it has a pH optimum of 2.0; it will work only in an extremely acid medium. The protein-digesting enzyme secreted by the pancreas, trypsin, in contrast, has a pH optimum of 8.5, well on the alkaline side of neutrality. Most intracellular enzymes have pH optima near neutrality, pH 7.0. This marked influence of pH on the activity of an enzyme is what would be predicted from the fact that enzymes are proteins. The topic is too complex to be discussed in detail, but the number of positive and negative charges associated with a protein molecule, and perhaps the shape of the molecular surface, are determined by the pH. Probably only one particular state of the enzyme molecule, with a particular number of negative and positive charges, is active as a catalyst. From these considerations it is clear that the catalytic ability of a protein molecule would be expected to be strongly influenced by the pH of the environment.

Concentration of Enzyme, Substrate and Cofactors. If the pH and temperature of an enzyme system are kept constant and if an excess of substrate is present, the rate of the reaction is directly proportional to the amount of *enzyme* present. This method is used, indeed, to measure the amount of some particular enzyme present in a tissue extract. If the pH, temperature and enzyme concentration of a reaction system are held constant, the initial reaction rate is proportional to the amount of *substrate* present, up to a limiting value. If the enzyme system requires a coenzyme or specific activator ion, the concentration of this substance may, under certain circumstances, determine the over-all rate of the enzyme system.

Enzyme Inhibitors. Enzymes can be inhibited by a variety of chemicals, some of which inhibit reversibly, others irreversibly. **Cytochrome oxidase,** one of the "respiratory enzymes," is inhibited by cyanide, which forms a complex with the atom of iron present in the enzyme molecule and prevents it from participating in the catalytic process. Cyanide is poisonous to man and other animals because of its action on the cytochrome enzymes. One of the enzymic steps in the conversion of glucose to lactic acid is inhibited by fluoride ion and another by iodoacetate. These substances, and others, have been used as tools by biochemists to investigate the properties and sequences of enzyme systems.

Enzymes themselves may act as poisons if they get into the wrong place. As little as 1 mg. of crystalline trypsin injected intravenously will kill a rat. Certain snake, bee and scorpion venoms contain enzymes that destroy blood cells or other body tissues.

4.4
Respiration and Cellular Energy

All the phenomena of life — growth, movement, irritability, reproduction, and others — require the expenditure of energy by the cell. Living cells are not heat engines; they cannot use heat energy to drive these reactions but must use chemical energy, chiefly in the form of energy-rich phosphate bonds, abbreviated $\sim P$. All living cells obtain biologically useful energy primarily by enzymic reactions in which electrons flow from one energy level to another. For animals, oxygen is the ultimate electron acceptor. Oxygen reacts with the electrons and with hydrogen ions to form a molecule of water. Electrons are transferred to oxygen by a system of enzymes, called the **electron transmitter system,** localized within the mitochondria. Electrons are removed from a molecule of some foodstuff and transferred by the action of a specific enzyme to some primary electron acceptor. Other enzymes transfer the electrons from the primary acceptor through the several components of the electron transmitter system and eventually combine them with oxygen (Fig. 4.2). The chief source of energy-rich phosphate bonds, $\sim P$, in the cell is from the flow of electrons through the acceptors and the electron transmitter system. This flow of electrons has been termed the "electron cascade," and we might picture a series of waterfalls over which electrons flow, each fall driving a water wheel, an enzymic reaction by which the energy of the electron is captured in a biologically useful form, that of the energy-rich phosphate bonds of ATP.

ATP is the "energy currency" of the cell. All the energy-requiring reactions of cellular metabolism utilize ATP to drive the reaction. Energy-rich molecules do not pass freely from one cell to another but are made at the site in which they are to be utilized. The energy-rich bonds of ATP that will drive the

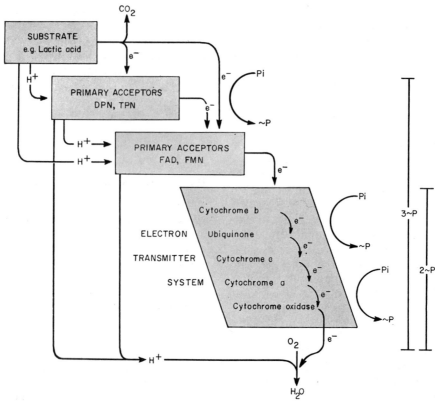

Figure 4.2 Diagram of the reactions of the "electron cascade," the succession of metabolic steps by which electrons are transferred from substrate to oxygen and the energy is trapped in a biologically useful form as energy-rich phosphate bonds. ~P. (Villee: Biology, 5th ed.)

reactions of muscle contraction, for example, are produced in the muscle cells.

Processes in which electrons (e⁻) are removed from an atom or molecule are termed **oxidations;** the reverse process, the addition of electrons to an atom or molecule, is termed **reduction.** An example of oxidation and reduction is the reversible reaction

$$Fe^{++} \rightleftharpoons Fe^{+++} + e^-$$

The reaction toward the right is an oxidation (the removal of an electron) and the reaction toward the left is a reduction (the addition of an electron). Each oxidation reaction, in which an electron is given off, must be accompanied by a reduction, a reaction in which the electron is accepted by another molecule, for electrons do not exist in the free state. The passage of electrons in the electron transmitter system is a series of oxidation and reduction reactions termed **biologic oxidation.** When the energy of this

flow of electrons is captured in the form of ~P, the process is termed **oxidative phosphorylation.** In most biologic systems, two electrons and two protons (that is, two hydrogen atoms) are removed together and the process is known as **dehydrogenation.**

The specific compounds of the electron transmitter system that are alternately oxidized and reduced are known as **cytochromes.** Each cytochrome contains a heme group similar to the one present in hemoglobin. In the center of the heme group is an iron atom which is alternately oxidized and reduced—converted from Fe^{++} to Fe^{+++} and back—as it gives off and takes up an electron.

Another component of the electron transmitter system, **ubiquinone** (also called coenzyme Q), consists of a head, a six-membered carbon ring, which can take up and release electrons, and a long tail composed of 10 repeating units. These repeating units, called isoprenoid groups, each consisting of five carbon atoms, are the basic structural units of molecules of rubber.

Lactic acid, the acid of sour milk, is an important intermediate in metabolism. It undergoes a dehydrogenation to yield pyruvic acid. Its molecule contains the configuration $H-\overset{|}{\underset{|}{C}}-OH$ from which two hydrogens can be removed enzymically by **lactic dehydrogenase** (LDH). In this reaction, and in all dehydrogenations, the electrons removed are transferred to a **primary acceptor,** in this case, diphosphopyridine nucleotide, DPN. The product of the dehydrogenation reaction, pyruvic acid, cannot undergo dehydrogenation directly, for it does not have a structure suitable for attack by a dehydrogenase and must undergo further enzymic action to attain such a molecular configuration. The next reaction of pyruvic acid is a **decarboxylation,** the release of carbon dioxide. Carbon dioxide is derived in biologic systems only from carboxylic groups (COOH) by the process of decarboxylation. The product of the decarboxylation reaction, acetaldehyde, has two carbons instead of three but still is not in a form suitable for dehydrogenation. It must undergo a "make-ready" reaction, a reaction that will result in an $H-\overset{|}{\underset{|}{C}}-OH$ configuration suitable for dehydrogenation. The particular reaction that follows involves a complex organic molecule named **coenzyme A** which is abbreviated CoA—SH. In this abbreviation "—SH" represents the active end of the molecule, a sulfhydryl group composed of sulfur and hydrogen, and "CoA" represents the remainder of this complex molecule. The combination of coenzyme A with acetaldehyde is a substance with an $H-\overset{|}{\underset{|}{C}}-OH$ group that can be dehydrogenated to give acetyl coenzyme A.

Another type of dehydrogenation, which involves a different molecular configuration, is exemplified by the oxidation of succinic acid. The dehydrogenation of molecules having a $-CH_2-CH_2-$ group involves a **flavin** as the hydrogen and electron acceptor. Succinic acid is oxidized to fumaric acid in the course of which two of its hydrogens are transferred to a flavin. The product, fumaric acid, cannot be dehydrogenated directly but undergoes a make-ready reaction in which a molecule of water is added to yield malic acid. Malic acid has a configuration of $H-\overset{|}{\underset{|}{C}}-OH$ which is suitable for dehydrogenation.

In the reactions by which carbohydrates, fats and proteins are oxidized the cell utilizes these three simple types of reactions, dehydrogenation, decarboxylation and make-ready reactions. They may occur in different orders in different chains of reactions. All the dehydrogenation reactions are, by definition, oxidations, reactions in which electrons are removed from a molecule. The electrons cannot exist in the free state for any finite period of time and must be taken up immediately by other compounds, electron acceptors. There are two main types of primary electron acceptors, the pyridine nucleotides—**diphosphopyridine nucleotide** (abbreviated **DPN**) and **triphosphopyridine nucleotide** (abbreviated **TPN**)—and the flavin nucleotides—**flavin adenine dinucleotide (FAD)** and **flavin mononucleotide (FMN).** The pyridine nucleotides, the functional end of which is the vitamin **niacin,** accept two electrons and one hydrogen ion from molecules having the $H-\overset{|}{\underset{|}{C}}-OH$ configuration, such as lactic or malic acid, and become reduced pyridine nucleotides (e.g., DPNH), releasing one proton. The flavin nucleotides, which contain the vitamin **riboflavin,** serve as electron acceptors in reactions involving the $-CH_2-CH_2-$ configuration such as the dehydrogenation of succinic acid. The FAD of succinic dehydrogenase is bound very tightly to the protein part of the enzyme and cannot be removed easily. Such tightly bound cofactors are termed **prosthetic** groups of the enzyme.

The reduced pyridine nucleotides, DPNH or TPNH, cannot react with oxygen. Their electrons must be passed through the intermediate acceptors of the electron transmitter system before they can react with oxygen. The flavin primary acceptors usually pass their electrons to the electron transmitter system but some flavoproteins can react directly with oxygen. An enzyme that can mediate the transfer of electrons directly to oxygen is termed an **oxidase;** one that mediates the removal of electrons from a substrate to a primary or intermediate acceptor is termed a **dehydrogenase.**

The acetyl coenzyme A formed by the oxidation of lactic acid, or formed by the oxidation of fatty acids, undergoes a series of reactions involving dehydrogenation, decarboxylation and make-ready reactions which have been termed the **Krebs citric acid cycle.** Acetyl coenzyme A undergoes a make-ready reaction by combining with oxaloacetic acid, which contains four carbons, to yield citric acid, which contains six carbons (Fig. 4.3). Citric acid has neither an

$$H-\overset{|}{\underset{|}{C}}-OH \quad \text{nor a} \quad -CH_2-CH_2- \text{ group}$$

and cannot undergo dehydrogenation. Two make-ready reactions involving the removal and addition of a molecule of water yield isocitric acid which can undergo dehy-

$$\text{drogenation at its } H-\overset{|}{\underset{|}{C}}-OH \text{ group. The}$$

hydrogen acceptor is a pyridine nucleotide, usually TPN, and the product is oxalosuccinic acid, which undergoes decarboxylation to yield α-ketoglutaric acid. Just as pyruvic acid is converted to the coenzyme A derivative of an acid with one less carbon atom, α-ketoglutaric acid is converted to succinyl coenzyme A by reactions requiring DPN, coenzyme A, thiamine pyrophosphate and lipoic acid as coenzymes. α-Ketoglutaric acid

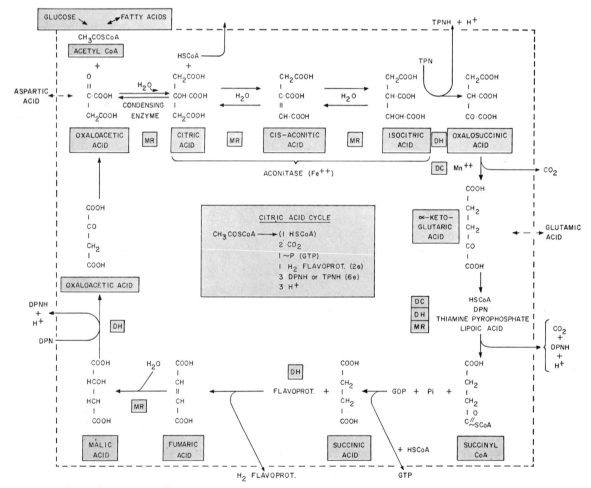

Figure 4.3 Diagram of the cyclic series of reactions, termed the Krebs citric acid cycle, by which the carbon chains of sugars, fatty acids and amino acids are metabolized to yield carbon dioxide. The reactions are designated as DH, dehydrogenations; DC, decarboxylations; and MR, make-ready. The over-all reaction effected by one "turn" of the cycle is summarized in the center. (Villee: Biology, 5th ed.)

is metabolized by a dehydrogenation, a decarboxylation and a make-ready reaction using coenzyme A to yield succinyl coenzyme A.

The bond joining coenzyme A to succinic acid is an energy-rich one, ~S, like the bond joining coenzyme A to acetic acid in acetyl coenzyme A. The energy of the bond of acetyl coenzyme A is utilized in bringing about the addition of the acetyl group to oxaloacetic acid. The energy in the ~S bond in succinyl coenzyme A can be converted to an energy-rich phosphate bond, ~P, in the form of ATP. The reaction of succinyl coenzyme A with inorganic phosphate yields succinyl phosphate and coenzyme A. The phosphate group is then transferred to ADP to form ATP and free succinic acid. This is an example of an energy-rich bond synthesized at the **substrate level** by reactions not involving the electron transmitter system. Only a small fraction of the total energy-rich bonds made in metabolism are formed by reactions such as this. Normal cells metabolizing in a medium containing oxygen synthesize most of their ATP by oxidative phosphorylation in the electron transmitter system.

The further oxidation of succinic acid to fumaric, malic and oxaloacetic acid completes the cycle, for the oxaloacetic acid is then ready to combine with another molecule of acetyl coenzyme A to form a molecule of citric acid. In the course of this cycle, two molecules of CO_2 and eight hydrogen atoms are removed, and one molecule of ~P is synthesized at the substrate level. The Krebs citric acid cycle is the final common pathway by which the carbon chains of carbohydrates, fatty acids and amino acids are metabolized.

The carbon chain of a fatty acid is metabolized by a series of reactions which begins by a reaction with ATP and then with coenzyme A to yield the fatty acetyl coenzyme A (Fig. 4.4). Palmitic acid, which contains 16 carbons, reacts to form palmityl coenzyme A. Palmityl coenzyme A undergoes a dehydrogenation between the second and third carbons of the chain. The hydrogen acceptor for this dehydrogenation is a flavin, for the configuration undergoing dehydrogenation is $—CH_2—CH_2—$. The product of this dehydrogenation undergoes a make-ready reaction, the addition of a molecule of water,

to yield a molecule which has an $H—\overset{|}{\underset{|}{C}}—OH$

configuration. This, in turn, undergoes a dehydrogenation utilizing DPN as the hydrogen acceptor (Fig. 4.4). The resulting molecule can undergo a make-ready reaction with coenzyme A to clip off a two-carbon unit, acetyl coenzyme A, and leave a carbon chain which is two carbons shorter. This molecule is in the activated state—it contains coenzyme A on its carboxyl group—and is ready to be dehydrogenated by the enzyme which uses flavin as a hydrogen acceptor. This repeating series of reactions,

1. The activation reaction: $R \cdot CH_2 \cdot CH_2 \cdot COOH + ATP \longrightarrow R \cdot CH_2 \cdot CH_2 \cdot CO \cdot AMP + PyroPO_4$

$R \cdot CH_2 \cdot CH_2 \cdot CO \cdot AMP + HSCoA \longrightarrow R \cdot CH_2 \cdot CH_2 \cdot COSCoA + AMP$

2. Dehydrogenation: $CH_3(CH_2)_{10}CH_2 \cdot CH_2 \cdot \underline{CH_2 \cdot CH_2} \cdot COSCoA + Flavoprot. \rightleftharpoons CH_3(CH_2)_{10}CH_2 \cdot CH_2 \cdot CH =$

$CHCOSCoA + H_2Flavoprot.$

3. Make-ready: $CH_3(CH_2)_{10}CH_2 \cdot CH_2 \cdot CH = CHCOSCoA + H_2O \rightleftharpoons CH_3(CH_2)_{10}CH_2 \cdot CH_2 \cdot CHOH \cdot CH_2 \cdot COSCoA$

4. Dehydrogenation: $CH_3(CH_2)_{10}CH_2 \cdot CH_2 \cdot CHOH \cdot \underline{CH_2} \cdot COSCoA + DPN \rightleftharpoons CH_3(CH_2)_{10} CH_2 \cdot CH_2 \cdot CO \cdot CH_2 \cdot$

$COSCoA + DPNH + H^+$

5. Make-ready: $CH_3(CH_2)_{10}CH_2 \cdot CH_2 COCH_2 \cdot COSCoA + HSCoA \rightleftharpoons CH_3(CH_2)_{10}\underbrace{CH_2 \cdot CH_2 \cdot COSCoA}_{} +$

$CH_3COSCoA$

Acetyl CoA

To Reaction 2 and Repeat Sequence

Sum: $C_{16}H_{32}O_2 \longrightarrow 8CH_2COSCoA + \underbrace{7H\ Flavoprot. + 7DPNH}_{} + 7H^+$

28e

Figure 4.4 The series of reactions by which fatty acids are oxidized, two carbons at a time, to yield acetyl coenzyme A. (Villee: Biology, 5th ed.)

which includes dehydrogenations and make-ready reactions but not decarboxylations, cleaves a fatty acid chain two carbons at a time (Fig. 4.4). Seven such series of reactions will split palmitic acid to eight molecules of acetyl coenzyme A.

Glucose is also converted ultimately to acetyl coenzyme A. The series of glycolytic reactions begins, as with fatty acids, by one in which glucose is "activated." Glucose reacts with ATP to yield glucose-6-phosphate and ADP, a reaction catalyzed by the enzyme **hexokinase.** After this make-ready reaction, other make-ready reactions establish a configuration which can undergo dehydrogenation (Fig. 4.5). A rearrangement yields fructose-6-phosphate and the transfer of a second phosphate from ATP forms fructose-1,6-diphosphate. Fructose-1,6-diphosphate is split by an enzyme, **aldolase,** into two three-carbon sugars, glyceraldehyde-3-phosphate and dihydroxyacetone phosphate. These two are interconverted by a separate enzyme. Glyceraldehyde-3-phosphate then reacts with a compound containing an —SH group which is part of the enzyme mole-

$$\text{cule to yield an H} \overset{|}{\underset{|}{-\text{C}-}} \text{OH configuration}$$

that can undergo dehydrogenation with DPN as the hydrogen acceptor. The product of the reaction, phosphoglyceric acid bound to the SH group of the enzyme, then reacts with inorganic phosphate to yield 1,3-diphosphoglyceric acid and free enzyme —SH. The phosphate in carbon 1 is an energy-rich group which can react with ADP to form ATP. This, like the energy-rich phosphate of succinyl phosphate, is one made at the substrate level. The resulting 3-phosphoglyceric acid undergoes a make-ready rearrangement to yield 2-phosphoglyceric acid. Then, in an unusual reaction, an energy-rich phosphate is generated by the removal of water by a **dehydration,** rather than by the removal of two hydrogens, a **dehydrogenation.** The product, phosphopyruvic acid, can transfer its phosphate group to ADP to yield ATP and free pyruvic acid. This is the second energy-rich phosphate group generated at the substrate level in the metabolism of glucose to pyruvic acid. Each glucose molecule yields two molecules of glyceraldehyde-3-phosphate and hence a total of four energy-rich phosphates are produced as glucose is

metabolized to pyruvic acid. However, two energy-rich phosphates are utilized in the process, one to convert glucose to glucose-6-phosphate and the second to convert fructose-6-phosphate to fructose-1,6-diphosphate. The net yield in the process is $2 \sim P$ ($4 \sim P$ produced minus $2 \sim P$ used up in the reactions). Pyruvic acid is then metabolized to acetyl coenzyme A by the reactions described previously.

Amino acids are oxidized by reactions in which the amino group is first removed, a process called **deamination,** then the carbon chain is metabolized and eventually enters the Krebs citric acid cycle. The amino acid alanine, for example, yields pyruvic acid when deaminated, glutamic acid yields α-ketoglutaric acid, and aspartic acid yields oxaloacetic acid. These three amino acids can enter the Krebs citric acid cycle directly. Other amino acids may require several reactions in addition to deamination to yield a substance which is a member of the Krebs cycle but ultimately the carbon chains of all the amino acids are metabolized in just this way.

The major reactions by which biologically useful energy is produced occur when the electrons are transferred from the primary acceptors, such as the pyridine nucleotides, through the electron transmitter system. The enzymes of the electron transmitter system are located within the substance of the mitochondrion in the mitochondrial membranes. They are very closely related spatially and it seems likely that the electrons flow through a solid phase rather than between enzymes that are in solution. The components of the electron transmitter system are given (Fig. 4.2) in the order of their oxidation-reduction potentials, which range from -0.32 volt for the pyridine nucleotides to $+0.81$ volt for oxygen. However, it is not known whether a particular electron in passing from pyridine nucleotide to oxygen must go through each and every one of the intermediates or whether it might skip some steps. It probably has to pass through at least three different steps to account for the $3 \sim P$ which are made for each pair of electrons that pass from pyridine nucleotide to oxygen.

Oxidative phosphorylation is measured by the rate at which inorganic phosphate, P_i, is converted to ATP as DPNH or some other substance undergoes oxidation. It is

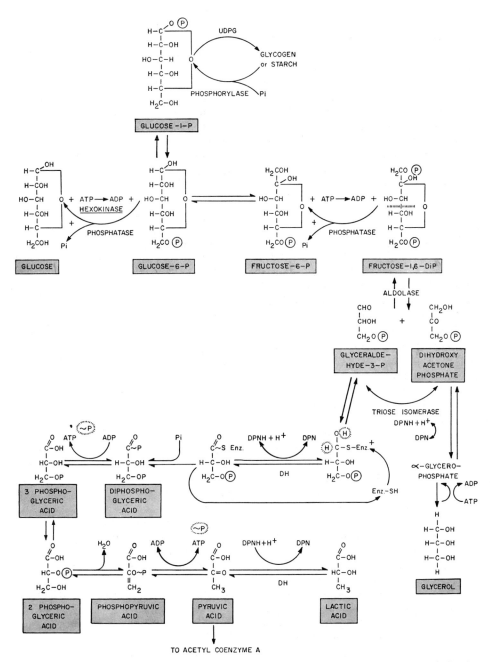

Figure 4.5 Diagram of the series of reactions by which glucose and other sugars are metabolized to pyruvic acid. Note that most of the steps are reversible, indicated by double arrows.

Other steps are essentially irreversible; glucose-6-phosphate is converted to glucose by a separate enzyme, a glucose-6-phosphatase, and not by the hexokinase that catalyzes the conversion of glucose to glucose-6-phosphate. (Villee: Biology, 5th ed.)

possible to prepare mitochondria by homogenizing the cells and separating the subcellular particles by centrifugation. Such mitochondria when removed carefully from the cell will carry out oxidative phosphorylation. It is even possible to disrupt mitochondria by ultrasonic vibration and obtain submitochondrial particles which will carry out oxidative phosphorylation. In these purified systems DPNH will be oxidized and oxygen will be utilized only if ADP is present to accept the energy-rich phosphate produced by the flow of electrons. The flow of electrons is tightly coupled to the phosphorylation process and will not occur unless phosphorylation can occur also. This, in a sense, prevents waste, for electrons will not flow unless energy-rich phosphate can be formed.

The flow of electrons from pyridine nucleotides to oxygen, a total drop of 1.13 volts (from -0.32 to $+0.81$ volt), would yield 52,000 calories per pair of electrons if the process were 100 per cent efficient. This may be calculated from the formula $\Delta G' = -nF\Delta E$, where $\Delta G'$ is the change in free energy, n is the number of electrons involved (2), F is the Faraday (23,040 calories) and ΔE is the difference in the oxidation-reduction potentials of the reactants (1.13 volts). Under experimental conditions most cells will produce at most 3 $\sim$P per pair of electrons as the electrons pass from pyridine nucleotide to oxygen. Each $\sim$P is equivalent to about 7000 calories. Hence, the 3 $\sim$P amount to about 21,000 calories. The efficiency of the electron transmitter system may then be calculated as 21,000/52,000 or about 40 per cent.

The fact that phosphorylation is tightly coupled to oxidation or electron flow provides a system of control which can regulate the rate of energy production and adjust it to the momentary rate of energy utilization. In a resting muscle cell, for example, oxidative phosphorylation will occur until all of the ADP has been converted to ATP. Then, since there are no more acceptors of $\sim$P, phosphorylation must stop. Since oxidation is tightly coupled to phosphorylation the flow of electrons will cease.

When the muscle contracts, the energy required is obtained from the splitting of energy-rich terminal phosphate of ATP to yield ADP and inorganic phosphate plus energy. The ADP formed can then serve as an acceptor of $\sim$P, phosphorylation begins, and the flow of electrons to oxygen occurs. Oxidative phosphorylation continues until all of the ADP has been converted to ATP. Electric generating systems have an analogous control device which adjusts the rate of production of electricity to the rate of utilization of electricity.

Some interesting calculations of the overall energy changes involved in metabolism in the human body have been made by E. G. Ball of Harvard University. Since the conversion of oxygen to water involves the participation of hydrogen atoms and electrons, the total flow of electrons in the human body can be calculated and expressed in amperes. From the oxygen consumption of an average 70 kg. man at rest -264 ml. per minute $-$ and the fact that each oxygen atom requires two hydrogen atoms and two electrons to form a molecule of water, Dr. Ball calculated that 2.86×10^{22} electrons flow from foodstuff, via dehydrogenases and the cytochromes, to oxygen each minute. Since an ampere equals 3.76×10^{20} electrons per minute, this flow of electrons amounts to 76 amperes. This is quite a bit of current, for an ordinary 100 watt light bulb uses just a little less than 1 ampere.

The flow of electrons from substrate to oxygen involves a potential difference of 1.13 volts (from -0.32 to $+0.81$ volt). Since volts $\times$ amperes $=$ watts, $1.13 \times 76 = 85.9$ watts. The body, then, uses energy at about the same rate as a 100 watt light bulb, but differs from it in having a much larger flow of electrons passing through a much smaller voltage change.

Earlier in this chapter we stated that the conversion of glucose to carbon dioxide and water yields about 4 Cal./gm. Let us now dissect the over-all equation

$$C_6H_{12}O_6 + 6\ O_2 \rightarrow 6\ CO_2 + 6H_2O + energy$$

and review where the energy is released (Table 4.1).

In glycolysis (reaction 1, Table 4.1), glucose is activated by the addition of 2 $\sim$P and converted to 2 pyruvate + 2 DPNH + 4 $\sim$P. Then the two pyruvates are metabolized (reaction 2) to 2 CO_2 + 2 acetyl CoA + 2 DPNH. Finally in the citric acid cycle (reaction 3), the two acetyl CoA are metabolized to 4 CO_2 + 6 DPNH + 2 H_2FP + 2 $\sim$P.

These reactions can be added together (re-

Table 4.1

(1)	$C_6H_{12}O_6 + 2 \sim P \longrightarrow$	2 pyruvate + 2 DPNH + 4 $\sim$P
(2)	2 pyruvate $\longrightarrow$	2 CO_2 + 2 acetyl CoA + 2 DPNH
(3)	2 acetyl CoA $\longrightarrow$	4 CO_2 + 6 DPNH + 2 H_2FP + 2 $\sim$P
(4) Sum	$C_6H_{12}O_6 \longrightarrow$	6 CO_2 + 10 DPNH + 2 H_2FP + 4 $\sim$P
(5)	$C_6H_{12}O_6 + 6 O_2 \longrightarrow$	6 CO_2 + 6 H_2O + 30 $\sim$P + 4 $\sim$P + 4 $\sim$P

action 4) by eliminating items that are present on both sides of the arrows. Then, since the oxidation of DPNH in the electron transmitter system yields 3 $\sim$P per mole, the 10 DPNH = 30 $\sim$P. The oxidation of H_2FP yields 2 $\sim$P per mole and 2 H_2FP = 4 $\sim$P. Summing these we see that the complete aerobic metabolism of 1 mole (180 gm.) of glucose yields 38 $\sim$P (reaction 5). Each $\sim$P is equivalent to about 7000 calories and the 38 $\sim$P = 266,000 calories.

When a mole of glucose is burned in a calorimeter some 690,000 calories are released as heat. The metabolism of glucose in an animal cell releases 266,000/690,000 or about 40 per cent of the total energy as biologically useful energy, $\sim$P. The remainder of the energy is dissipated as heat.

4.5

The Dynamic State of Cellular Constituents

The body of an animal or man appears to be unchanging as days and weeks go by and it would seem reasonable to infer that the component cells of the body, and even the component molecules of the cells, are equally unchanging. In the absence of any evidence to the contrary, it was generally held, until about 30 years ago, that the constituent molecules of animal and plant cells were relatively static and that, once formed, they remained intact for a long period of time. A corollary of this concept is that the molecules of food which are not used to increase the mass of protoplasm are rapidly metabolized to provide a source of energy. It followed from this that one could distinguish two kinds of molecules: relatively static ones that made up the cellular "machinery," and ones that were rapidly metabolized and thus correspond to cellular "fuel."

However, in 1938 Rudolf Schoenheimer and his colleagues at Columbia University began a series of experiments in which amino acids, fats, carbohydrates and water, each suitably labeled with some "heavy" or radioactive isotope, were fed to rats. Schoenheimer's experiments, which have been confirmed many times since, showed that the labeled amino acids fed to the rats were rapidly incorporated into body proteins. Similarly, labeled fatty acids were rapidly incorporated into the fat deposits of the body, even though in each case there was no increase in the *total* amount of protein or fat. Such experiments have demonstrated that the fats and proteins of the body cells—and even the substance of the bones—are constantly and rapidly being synthesized and broken down. In the adult the rates of synthesis and degradation are essentially equal so that there is little or no change in the total mass of the animal body. The distinction between "machinery" molecules and "fuel" molecules becomes much less sharp, for some of the machinery molecules are constantly being broken down and used as fuel.

The one exception to the rule of molecular flux is provided by the molecules of DNA that constitute the units of heredity, the genes, within the nucleus of the cell. Experiments with labeled atoms have shown that the molecules of DNA are remarkably stable and are broken down and resynthesized only very slowly, if at all. The amount of DNA per nucleus is constant, and new molecules of DNA are synthesized each time a cell divides. The stability of the DNA molecules may be important in ensuring that hereditary characters are transmitted to succeeding generations with as few chemical errors as possible. In contrast, the molecules of RNA undergo constant synthesis and degradation.

From the rate at which labeled atoms are incorporated it has been calculated that one-half of all the tissue proteins of the human body are broken down and rebuilt every 80 days. The proteins of the liver and blood serum are replaced very rapidly, one-half of them being synthesized every 10 days. The muscle proteins, in contrast, are replaced much more slowly, one-half of the total number of molecules being replaced every 180 days. The celebrated aphorism of Sir Frederick Gowland Hopkins, the late English biochemist, sums up this concept very succinctly: "Life is a dynamic equilibrium in a polyphasic system."

4.6
Biosynthetic Processes

Our discussion thus far has dealt with processes that break down molecules of foodstuffs and conserve their energy in the biologically useful form of $\sim$P. Cells have the ability to carry out an extensive array of biosynthetic processes utilizing the energy and, as raw materials, some of the five-, four-, three-, two- and one-carbon compounds that are intermediates in the metabolism of glucose and other compounds.

This whole subject of intermediary metabolism, by which an enormous variety of compounds is synthesized, is much too complicated and detailed to be discussed here. The enzyme controlling each reaction is genetically determined and the over-all maze of enzyme reactions by which any compound is synthesized includes a variety of self-adjusting control mechanisms to regulate and integrate the reactions. Several basic principles of cellular biosynthesis can be distinguished:

1. Each cell, in general, synthesizes its own proteins, nucleic acids, lipids, polysaccharides and other complex molecules and does not receive them preformed from other cells. Muscle glycogen, for example, is synthesized within the muscle cell and is not derived from liver glycogen.

2. Each step in the biosynthetic process is catalyzed by a separate enzyme.

3. Although certain steps in a biosynthetic sequence will proceed without the use of energy-rich phosphate, the over-all synthesis of these complex molecules requires chemical energy.

4. The synthetic processes utilize as raw materials relatively few substances among which are acetyl coenzyme A, glycine, succinyl coenzyme A, ribose and pyruvate.

5. These synthetic processes are in general not simply the reverse of the processes by which the molecule is degraded but include one or more separate steps which differ from any step in the degradative process. These steps are controlled by different enzymes and this permits separate control mechanisms to govern the synthesis and the degradation of the complex molecule.

6. The biosynthetic process includes not only the formation of the macromolecular components from simple precursors but their assembly into the several kinds of membranes that comprise the outer boundary of the cell and the intracellular organelles. Each cell's constituent molecules are in a dynamic state and are constantly being degraded and synthesized. Thus, even a cell that is not growing, not increasing in mass, uses a considerable portion of its total energy for the chemical work of biosynthesis. A cell that is growing rapidly must allocate a correspondingly larger fraction of its total energy output to biosynthetic processes, especially the biosynthesis of protein. A rapidly growing bacterial cell may use as much as 90 per cent of its total biosynthetic energy for the synthesis of proteins.

Although many of the steps in biosynthetic processes involve the formation of anhydro bonds—e.g., the peptide bonds of protein, the glycosidic bonds of polysaccharides, the ester bonds of lipids and nucleic acid—these bonds are not formed by reactions in which water is removed. The biosynthesis of sucrose in the cane sugar plant, for example, does not proceed via

$$\text{glucose} + \text{fructose} \rightleftharpoons \text{sucrose} + H_2O$$

This reaction would require energy, some 5500 calories per mole, to go to the right if all reactants were present in the concentration of 1 mole per liter. However, the concentration of glucose and fructose in the plant cell is probably less than 0.01 mole per liter, whereas the concentration of water is very high, about 55 moles per liter. Thus, the equilibrium point of the reaction under these conditions would be very far to the left.

Instead, one or more of the reactants is activated by a reaction with ATP in which the terminal phosphate is enzymatically transferred to glucose with the conservation of some of the energy of ATP. The glucose phosphate, with a higher energy content than free glucose, can react with fructose via another enzyme-catalyzed reaction to yield sucrose and inorganic phosphate.

ATP + glucose →
        ADP + glucose-1-phosphate
glucose-1-phosphate + fructose →
        sucrose + phosphate
Sum: ATP + glucose + fructose →
        sucrose + ADP + P_i

This reaction proceeds to the right because there is a net decrease in free energy. The 7000 calories of the ~P bond are used to supply the 5500 calories needed to assemble the glucose and fructose into sucrose; the over-all decrease in free energy is 1500 calories per mole. Since water is not a product of this reaction, the high concentration of water in the cell does not inhibit it. The same principle applies to the synthesis of the peptide bonds of proteins, the ester bonds of lipids and nucleic acids, and the glycosidic bonds of polysaccharides, but in many of these not one but *two* terminal phosphates of ATP are transferred as a unit in the reaction by which one of the molecules is activated. The activated molecule may be X ~PP or X ~AMP, depending on which part of the ATP is transferred to the substrate molecule. In either case the reaction ultimately involves the hydrolysis of 2 ~P with an energy utilization of 14,000 calories per mole.

X + ATP → X ~PP + AMP
X ~PP + Y → XY + PP_i
PP_i + H_2O → P_i + P_i
Sum: X + Y + ATP → XY + AMP + 2P_i

4.7
Special Types of Metabolism

The metabolic paths just described, by which carbohydrates, fats and proteins are metabolized to carbon dioxide and water, with the concomitant release of biologically available energy, are common to almost all cells. Certain cells have, in addition, one or more unique metabolic abilities such as the enzymic shortening of certain kinds of protein molecules (i.e., muscle contraction), the enzymic synthesis of substances with specific biologic activities such as hormones, the production of electricity by specialized organs such as that of the electric eel, or the enzymic production of light by a variety of fish, insects, molds and bacteria.

Bioluminescence. A number of animals, and some molds and bacteria as well, have an enzymic mechanism for the production of light. Luminescent animals are found among the protozoa, sponges, coelenterates, ctenophores, nemerteans, annelids, crustaceans, centipedes, millipedes, beetles, flies, echinoderms, mollusks, hemichordates, tunicates and fishes. From this wide and irregular distribution of the light-emitting ability it is clear that the enzymes for luminescence have appeared independently in a number of different evolutionary lines. It is sometimes difficult to establish that a given organism is itself luminescent; in a number of instances animals once believed to be luminescent have been shown instead to contain luminescent bacteria. When the bacteria are removed the animal is no longer able to emit light. Several different exotic East Indian fish have **light organs** under their eyes in which live luminous bacteria (Fig. 4.6). The light organs contain long cylindrical cells which are well provided with blood vessels to supply an adequate amount of oxygen to the bacteria. The bacteria emit light continuously and the fish have a black membrane, somewhat similar to an eyelid, that can be drawn

Figure 4.6 *Anomalops katoptron,* a luminescent fish from the waters of the Malay Archipelago. The crescent-shaped luminescent organs below the eyes are equipped with reflectors. (After Steche.) (Villee: Biology, 5th ed.)

up over the light organ to turn off the light. How the bacteria come to collect in the fish's light organ, as they must in each newly hatched fish, is a complete mystery.

Some animals have accessory lenses, reflectors and color filters with the light-producing organ, and the whole complex assembly is like a lantern. Certain shrimp have such complicated light-emitting organs.

The production of light is an enzyme-controlled reaction, the details of which differ in different organisms. Bacteria and fungi produce light continuously if oxygen is available. Most luminescent animals, in contrast, give out flashes of light only when their luminescent organs are stimulated. The name **luciferin** has been given to the material which is oxidized to produce light and **luciferase** to the enzyme which catalyzes the reaction. The luciferin and luciferase from one species may be quite different chemically from those in another. The oxidation of luciferin by luciferase can occur only in the presence of oxygen. It is possible to extract luciferin and luciferase from a firefly, mix the two in a test tube with added magnesium and adenosine triphosphate, and demonstrate the emission of light in the test tube. The energy for the reaction is supplied by the ATP, and under certain conditions the amount of light emitted is proportional to the amount of ATP present. This system can be used to measure the amount of ATP in a tissue extract.

The amount of light produced by certain luminescent animals is amazing. Many fireflies produce as much light, in terms of lumens per square centimeter, as do modern fluorescent lamps. Different kinds of animals may emit lights of different colors, red, green, yellow or blue. One of the more spectacular luminescent beasts is the "railroad worm" of Uruguay, the larva of a beetle, which has a row of green lights along each side of its body and a pair of red lights on its head. The light produced by luminescent organisms is entirely in the visible part of the spectrum; no ultraviolet or infrared light is produced. Since very little heat is given off in the process, bioluminescence has been called "cold light."

What advantage an animal derives from the emission of light can only be guessed at. For deep-sea animals, which live in perpetual darkness, light organs might be useful to enable members of a species to recognize one another, to serve as a lure for prey or as a warning for would-be predators. Experiments have shown that the light emitted by fireflies serves as a signal to bring the two sexes together for mating. The light emitted by bacteria and fungi probably serves no useful purpose to the organisms, but is simply a by-product of oxidative metabolism, just as heat is a by-product of metabolism in other plants and animals.

QUESTIONS

1. How would you define the term "metabolism"?
2. What factors affect the rate of a chemical reaction in the test tube? In a living cell?
3. Define the following terms: enzyme, coenzyme, apoenzyme, substrate, turnover number, energy-rich phosphate, coupled reactions.
4. What might be the advantage to a cell of having all the enzymes that act in sequence on a given substance localized in a particular intracellular organelle such as a mitochondrion or microsome?
5. Discuss the several meanings of the term "respiration."
6. Indicate briefly how the carbon chain of an amino acid might become part of (a) a glycogen molecule and (b) a fatty acid molecule in an animal cell.
7. What factors do you suppose have led to the evolution of luminescent organs in animals?
8. Suppose you discovered a new species of bioluminescent worm. How could you prove that it was the worm itself and not some contaminating bacterium that was producing the light?

ANNOTATED REFERENCES

Baldwin, E. B.: Dynamic Aspects of Biochemistry. 4th ed. New York, Cambridge University Press, 1964. A detailed and technical but very well-written and interesting account of cellular metabolism.

Dixon, M., and E. C. Webb: The Enzymes. 2nd ed. New York, Academic Press, 1964. Presents, in considerable depth and detail, the structure and kinetic properties of enzymes together with a classification of enzymes by function.

Harvey, E. N.: Bioluminescence. New York, Academic Press, 1952. A classic presentation of the interesting phenomenon of "living light."

Henderson, L. J.: The Fitness of the Environment. New York, Macmillan, 1913. Advanced the thesis that the environment had to have certain physical and chemical characteristics for life to develop.

Lehninger, A. L.: Bioenergetics. New York, Benjamin, 1965. An excellent discussion of the principles of thermodynamics and their application to biologic systems.

Schoenheimer, R.: The Dynamic State of the Body Constituents. Cambridge, Harvard University Press, 1949. Describes the classic experiments that demonstrated the rapid renewal of the chemical constituents of tissues.

The standard college textbooks of biochemistry may be consulted for more detailed discussions of the topics presented in this chapter. These include:

Conn, E. E., and P. K. Stumpf: Outlines of Biochemistry. New York, John Wiley & Sons, Inc., 1963.

Harrow, B., and A. Mazur: Textbook of Biochemistry. 9th ed. Philadelphia, W. B. Saunders Co., 1966.

Karlson, P.: Introduction to Modern Biochemistry. (Translated by C. H. Derring.) New York, Academic Press, 1965.

5 _____ PRINCIPLES OF PHYSIOLOGY

From the discussion of cell metabolism in the preceding chapter, it should be evident that all animal cells are faced with certain common problems. To have survived, each animal—vertebrate or invertebrate, multicellular or unicellular—must have solved, in one way or another, the problems of getting foodstuffs and oxygen, of eliminating carbon dioxide and wastes, of responding suitably to stimuli from the environment, of moving to new areas and of reproducing its kind. A survey of the animal kingdom will reveal that in the course of evolution an almost bewildering variety of solutions to these problems have arisen. At this point in our discussion, however, we want to emphasize what is common to the physiology and morphology of animals rather than what differences exist. The details of the variety of animal forms will be presented in Chapters 8 to 33.

5.1
Types of Nutrition

Organisms that can synthesize their own foodstuffs are said to be **autotrophic** (self-nourishing). An autotroph needs only water, carbon dioxide, inorganic salts and a source of energy to survive. Green plants are autotrophs which obtain energy from sunlight for the synthesis of organic molecules.

The purple bacteria, like the green plants, are photosynthetic autotrophs and certain other bacteria are chemosynthetic autotrophs, obtaining energy for the synthesis of foodstuffs from the oxidation of certain inorganic substances—ammonia, nitrites or

hydrogen sulfide. No animal is autotrophic; animals obtain their foodstuffs by eating autotrophs or by eating other animals which ate autotrophs. Ultimately, the foodstuff molecules of all animals are synthesized by energy obtained by these autotrophic organisms either from sunlight or from the oxidation of inorganic compounds.

The organisms which cannot synthesize their own food from inorganic substances, and hence must live either by eating autotrophs or decaying matter, are called **heterotrophs.** All animals and fungi (molds), as well as most bacteria, are heterotrophs. Three types of heterotrophic nutrition are found in the animal kingdom; holozoic, saprozoic and parasitic.

In **holozoic nutrition,** the type generally found in animals, food is obtained as particles of some size which must be eaten and digested before it can be absorbed into the cell. Holozoic organisms must find and catch other organisms; this has required the evolution of a variety of sensory, nervous and muscular structures to find and catch food and some sort of digestive system to convert the food into molecules small enough to be absorbed. Animals that feed chiefly upon plants are termed **herbivores,** those that eat other animals are called **carnivores,** and those that eat both plants and animals are known as **omnivores.** The morphology and mode of functioning of the digestive system in different kinds of animals are correlated with the nature of food eaten, peculiarities of the manner of life, and so on. Carnivores, for example, characteristically have strong proteolytic (protein-digesting) enzymes; whereas herbivores have weak proteolytic, but strong carbohydrate-splitting, enzymes.

Although such familiar protozoa as amebae and paramecia do ingest food particles, many protozoa, as well as yeasts, molds and most bacteria, cannot ingest solid food. Instead, the required organic nutrients are absorbed through the cell membrane as dissolved molecules. Plants and animals with this type of heterotrophic nutrition are known as **saprophytic** and **saprozoic,** respectively. Saprophytes can grow only in an environment which contains decomposing animal or plant bodies, or plant or animal by-products which will supply the necessary dissolved organic substances.

A third type of heterotrophic nutrition, **parasitism,** occurs when one organism (the parasite) lives on or within the body of another living organism (the host) and obtains its food from it. Almost every animal is the host for one or more parasites; these obtain their nutrients either by ingesting and digesting solid particles from the host, or by absorbing organic molecules through their cell walls from the surrounding body fluids or tissues of the host. Some parasites cause little or no harm to the host. Others harm the host by destroying cells, by robbing it of nutrients or by producing toxic waste products, thereby producing definite symptoms of disease. Some parasites have lost all traces of a digestive system and get nutrients only by absorbing organic substances through their body wall. Any given parasite is usually restricted to one or a few species of hosts; thus, most of the parasites that infect man will not infect other animals. In the course of evolution, the parasite becomes adapted to the specific conditions of temperature, pH, and the concentration of salts, vitamins and other nutrients found in one particular host and cannot survive elsewhere.

5.2

Ingestion, Digestion and Absorption

The protozoa have no digestive system and most protozoans have no specialized structure for taking in food. Amebae capture food by extruding two cellular evaginations, called **pseudopods,** which surround the prey (Fig. 5.1). The pseudopods meet around the prey and form a **food vacuole** containing the particle to be eaten. Digestive enzymes are secreted into this food vacuole, the food particle is digested, and the molecules of digested food are absorbed through the wall of the vacuole into the cytoplasm, where they are metabolized to release energy or to provide for the maintenance and growth of the animal. Paramecia and other ciliates have a permanent **oral groove** lined by cilia. The beating of the cilia passes food particles to a cell mouth, where they are collected into food vacuoles. The canals of sponges are lined by **collar cells,** which capture and ingest microscopic food particles in food vacuoles. In sponges and protozoa digestion is intracellular, occurring in food vacuoles within the cytoplasm of the cell.

The body of the coelenterate consists of two layers of cells; the inner one is specialized for digestion and absorption. Food—small animals and plants caught by the tentacles—passes through the mouth and enters the central **gastrovascular cavity.** The endoderm cells secrete digestive enzymes into this cavity and some digestion occurs. This is **extracellular digestion,** occurring in a special digestive cavity, and is found in most animals. Some partly digested food particles are taken up by the endoderm cells in food vacuoles in which **intracellular digestion** occurs. There is no separate anal aperture; undigested wastes leave the gastrovascular cavity by the mouth. Digestion in the flatworms, such as planaria, is similar to that in the coelenterates: food enters and wastes leave the branched digestive tract via the same opening and digestion is partly extracellular and partly intracellular. The gastrovascular cavity of the flatworm is greatly branched and the branches extend throughout most of the body, thus facilitating the distribution of digested food.

In most of the rest of the invertebrates, and in all the vertebrates, the digestive tract is a tube with two apertures; food enters by the mouth and any undigested residue leaves by the anus. The digestive tract may be short or long, straight or coiled, and subdivided into specialized organs. These organs, even though they may have similar names in different kinds of animals, may be quite different, and may even have different functions. The digestive system of the earthworm, for example, includes a **mouth,** a muscular **pharynx** which secretes a mucous material to lubricate the food particles, an **esophagus,** a soft-walled **crop** where food is stored, a thick muscular **gizzard** where food is ground

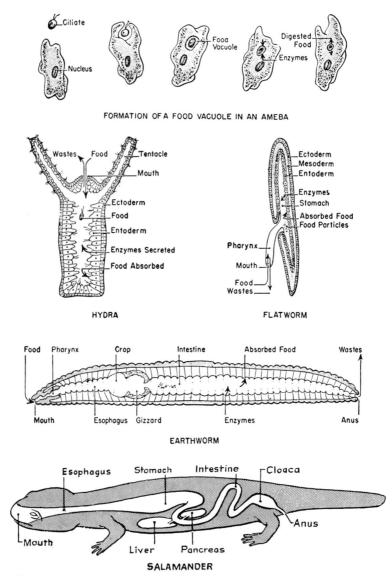

FORMATION OF A FOOD VACUOLE IN AN AMEBA

HYDRA　　　　　　　　　　　　　　FLATWORM

EARTHWORM

SALAMANDER

Figure 5.1　The digestive systems of ameba, hydra, flatworm, earthworm and a vertebrate (salamander). (Partly from Villee: Biology, 5th ed.)

against small stones, and a long straight **intestine** in which extracellular digestion occurs and through the wall of which the food is absorbed. Many invertebrates—worms, squid, crustacea, sea urchins—have hard, toothed mouth-parts for tearing off and chewing bits of food.

The vertebrate digestive system, described in detail in Chapter 27, is similar in basic plan to that of the earthworm, but has undergone further evolution and specialization. There is a separate **small intestine,** where most digestion and absorption occurs, and a follow-ing **large intestine** in which digestion and absorption, especially the absorption of water, are completed. The vertebrate digestive system also includes the **liver** and **pancreas,** connected to the small intestine by ducts. These large digestive glands produce, among other things, certain enzymes and other substances required for digestion.

The Digestive Process.　Digestion, whether in ameba or man, involves the splitting of complex molecules into simpler ones by the addition of water, a process called **hydrolysis.** There are specific hydrolases for the enzymic splitting of proteins, fats and carbohydrates. The digestive enzymes of vertebrates include the protein hydrolases **pepsin,** secreted by the stomach; **trypsin** and **chymotrypsin,** secreted by the pancreas; and several **peptidases,** secreted by the pancreas and intestinal mucosa. **Lipases,** which split fats, are secreted by the pancreas. The carbohydrate-splitting enzymes include **amylases,** secreted by the pancreas and salivary glands, and **maltase, sucrase** and **lactase,** secreted by the intestinal mucosa. Each enzyme has a specific pH optimum, ranging from a very acid one for pepsin to an alkaline one for trypsin. The molecules of protein, fat and polysaccharide originally present in the food are too large to pass through the wall of the digestive tract; the digestive process converts these to amino acids, fatty acids, glycerol and single sugars, which are able to be absorbed through the wall of the digestive tract into the body.

Herbivorous animals typically have a pouch in which the cellulose-rich food is subjected to bacterial digestion, for the animal itself has no enzyme to digest the cellulose walls of the plant cells. In the rabbit and horse this pouch is the **caecum,** located at the junction of the small and large intestine. The products of bacterial digestion are absorbed into the blood stream. The cow and other ruminants have a large, complex **rumen** between the esophagus and stomach in which the plants are digested by bacteria and protozoa which were eaten along with the plants. The bacteria convert cellulose to acetic acid, and a large part of the cow's calories are absorbed as acetic acid directly from the rumen. The bacteria further contribute to the cow's economy by synthesizing vitamins and amino acids from the material ingested.

In those animals in which digestion occurs within food vacuoles, the products of digestion pass across the membrane of the food vacuole and are then available for intracellular metabolic processes. In animals with extracellular digestion, the products are generally taken through the cells lining the digestive tract and on into the circulatory system for distribution to the cells of the body. In mammals, the amino acids and simple sugars are absorbed in part by energy-requiring processes and in part by simple diffusion. The cells lining the intestine comprise a **differentially permeable membrane** which permits the passage of amino acids and simple sugars but prevents the passage of intact proteins and polysaccharides. In many animals, the lining of the intestine is thrown into folds, which increase the area available for absorption. Amino acids and sugars are taken up by the blood stream for transport; in contrast, the products of fat digestion in mammals cross the intestinal mucosa, are reformed into fats, and enter the lymph vessels (p. 492) to be carried to other parts of the body.

A discussion of the eventual fate of the absorbed food would involve all the reactions of cell metabolism, some of which were discussed in Chapter 4. The amino acids serve as raw materials for the synthesis of cell proteins. Amino acids may undergo **deamination** (removal of the amino group) and their carbon chains are then used to synthesize glycogen and other carbohydrates, to synthesize fatty acids, or they are metabolized in the Krebs citric acid cycle to yield energy. The amino group may be excreted as ammonia or may be combined with carbon dioxide, by yet another complex series of enzymic reactions, to form **urea.** This waste product is synthesized largely in the liver, carried in the blood to the kidneys and excreted in the urine.

The sugars absorbed are converted into glycogen for storage primarily in liver and muscle. Glycogen synthesis occurs to a lesser extent in other tissues. Liver glycogen can be converted enzymically into glucose and secreted into the blood stream. One of the prime functions of the vertebrate liver is the maintenance of a constant concentration of glucose in the blood. It does this by absorbing glucose from the blood coming from the intestine just after a meal, when the blood has a high concentration of glucose, and by secreting glucose into the blood stream between meals. The glycogen in muscle and other tissues cannot be converted to glucose (no glucose-6-phosphatase is present) and hence must be utilized locally. Carbohydrates are rapidly converted to fats if more are taken in than can be used directly. These, plus the fats taken in as food, are stored for use between meals.

Nutritional Requirements. In addition to proteins, fats and carbohydrates, animals require water, minerals and vitamins to maintain health and to grow. **Minerals** are constantly lost from the body in urine, feces and sweat, and an equivalent amount must be taken in with the food. Most foods contain adequate supplies of minerals, and mineral deficiencies are comparatively rare. Certain human deficiency diseases may be traced to a lack of iron, copper, iodine, calcium or phosphorus. A disease which was resulting in the death of whole herds of sheep in Australia was finally shown to be due to a deficiency of cobalt. The soil in that region, and hence the grass eaten by the sheep, was very poor in this metal, which is required as a trace element for normal metabolism.

Water is required by every animal. Aquatic animals have no problem about obtaining water; indeed, their problem is to prevent the osmotic inflow of water and the consequent bursting of their cells. Many land animals drink water, but others, certain desert animals for example, obtain all they require from the food eaten, and from the water formed when the food molecules are metabolized.

Vitamins are organic substances required in small amounts in the diet. They differ widely in their chemical structure but are similar in that they cannot be synthesized in adequate amounts by the animal and hence must be present in the diet. There are two major groups of vitamins: those that are soluble in fats or lipid solvents, the **fat soluble vitamins** A, D, E and K, and those that are readily soluble in water, the **water soluble vitamins** C and the B complex. *What is a vitamin for one animal is not necessarily one for another animal.* That is, some species can synthesize certain of these required substances and hence do not need them in their food. It is probable that all plants and animals require these vitamin molecules for similar metabolic functions; organisms differ, however, in their ability to synthesize them. Only man, monkeys and guinea pigs, for example, require vitamin C in the diet; other animals can make it from some other substance. The vitamins whose role in metabolism is known—niacin, thiamine, riboflavin, pyridoxine, pantothenic acid, biotin, folic acid and cobalamin (vitamin B_{12})—have proved to be constituent parts of one or more **coenzyme** molecules. **Vitamin A** is a part of the light-sensitive pigment of the retina of the eye (p. 524). A lack of any one of these vitamins produces a particular deficiency disease with characteristic symptoms, e.g., **scurvy** (lack of vitamin C), **beriberi** (lack of thiamine), **rickets** (lack of vitamin D) and **pellagra** (lack of niacin).

5.3
Circulation

The metabolic processes of all cells require a constant supply of food and oxygen and constant removal of wastes, and all organisms have solved in one way or another the problem of transporting substances from one part of the body to another. In protozoans the transport of substances is effected by the diffusion of the molecules, aided generally by streaming movements of the cytoplasm itself. The flowing of the cytoplasm from rear to front as an ameba moves, and the circular movement of the cytoplasm in protozoa with a fixed shape (such as paramecia) are examples of these (Fig. 5.2). Transport from cell to cell in simple multicellular animals such as sponges, coelenterates and flatworms occurs by diffusion. This is aided in some animals by the stirring of the body fluids brought about by the contraction of the muscles of the body wall. Diffusion, you will recall, is the movement of molecules from a region of high concentration to a region of lower concentration. The rate of diffusion is directly proportional to the difference in concentration in the two regions and inversely proportional to the distance separating them. From this we can see that an adequate supply of food and oxygen can be maintained by diffusion alone only in a small animal; in a larger animal the slower diffusion rate over the greater distance would not suffice. Such animals must develop some system of internal transport—some type of circulatory system. Not only absolute size, but also the shape and the activity of an animal determine the need for a circulatory system.

The **proboscis worms** or Nemertea are the simplest living animals to have a distinct circulatory system; it consists of a dorsal and two lateral blood vessels which extend the whole length of the body and are connected by transverse vessels. The earthworm has a more complex circulatory system: a **dorsal vessel** in which blood flows anteriorly, a **ventral vessel** and a **subneural vessel** in which blood flows posteriorly, and five pairs of pulsating tubes ("hearts") at the anterior end which drive blood from the dorsal to the ventral vessel (Fig. 5.2). In other segments of the body a network of vessels connecting dorsal and ventral vessels ramifies through the body wall and the wall of the intestine. The blood in these vessels does not flow regularly in one

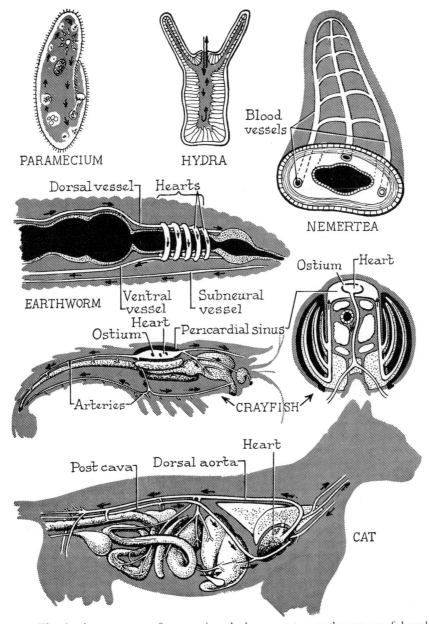

PARAMECIUM   HYDRA

Blood vessels

NEMERTEA

Dorsal vessel   Hearts

EARTHWORM   Ventral vessel   Subneural vessel

Ostium   Heart

Heart   Pericardial sinus
Ostium

Arteries   CRAYFISH

Post cava   Dorsal aorta   Heart

CAT

Figure 5.2   The circulatory systems of paramecium, hydra, nemertea, earthworm, crayfish and cat.

direction but ebbs and flows as the vessels constrict and dilate.

A typical circulatory system includes **blood vessels** and **heart** and the fluid within them — the **blood** — which, in turn, is composed of a fluid — **plasma** — and **blood cells** or corpuscles. Oxygen is carried in most circulatory systems not simply dissolved in the plasma but in combination with a heme protein. The one found in the earthworm and man is **hemoglobin,** a red iron-containing pigment. The hemoglobin of vertebrate blood is located in cells, the red blood cells. In many invertebrates, the hemoglobin or other pigment is dissolved in the plasma, and whatever cells are present are colorless. The respiratory pigment of crab blood is a different heme protein, blue-green **hemocyanin,** which contains copper in place of iron.

The circulatory system of the annelid

worms and the vertebrates is said to be "closed"; i.e., the blood in the course of circulation remains within blood vessels. In contrast, the circulatory system of arthropods and mollusks is "open"; the blood vessels open to the body cavity, called a **hemocoel,** and blood circulates partly within blood vessels and partly through the cavity of the hemocoel in making a complete circuit. In the typical arthropod, the heart and other organs lie free in the hemocoel and are bathed in blood. In the annelid worm and vertebrates, the organs lie in the coelomic cavity and are supplied by blood which reaches them in closed vessels. The arthropod heart is generally a single, elongate, muscular tube lying in the dorsal midline. In each segment of the body there is a pair of openings, supplied with valves to prevent backflow. Blood enters the heart from the pericardial sinus, which is part of the hemocoel, through these openings (ostia) and is moved forward by **peristaltic waves,** waves of contraction preceded by waves of relaxation along the tube. Blood is carried in vessels to the head and to other parts of the body, whence it returns to the heart through the hemocoel.

The hearts of most invertebrates are single muscular tubes which develop only very low pressures—a few millimeters of mercury—as they pump blood. In the vertebrates, with closed circulatory systems, a higher pressure, as high as 100 to 200 mm. Hg, is required to drive the blood through the tremendous number of narrow capillaries. This has led to the evolution of powerful, thick-walled hearts. The chamber of the vertebrate heart called the **ventricle** has quite thick walls. A certain amount of pressure is required to distend the muscular ventricle and cause the blood to flow in and fill it during the relaxation phase (diastole). The low pressure in vertebrate veins is not sufficient to do this. The vertebrate heart has a second chamber, the **atrium,** with walls thin enough to be filled by the low venous pressure yet strong enough to pump blood into the ventricle and distend it. The octopus, whose heart is similarly arranged with two different chambers, has the highest blood pressure, 35 to 45 mm. Hg, of any of the invertebrates.

The vertebrate heart is enclosed in a special cavity, the **pericardial cavity,** separated from the rest of the body by a thin, strong sheet of connective tissue, the **pericardium.** This cavity provides space for the heart to change in volume as it beats.

The circulatory systems of all vertebrates are essentially similar: a closed system composed of heart, aorta, arteries, capillaries and veins arranged in a basically similar plan. **Arteries** carry blood away from the heart to the tissues, **veins** carry blood back to the heart from the tissues, and **capillaries** are minute, thin-walled vessels connecting the arteries to the veins and completing the circuit from heart to heart. Only the capillaries have walls thin enough to permit the exchange of food, gases and wastes between blood and tissues.

The principal evolutionary changes in the vertebrate circulatory system have been associated with the change from gills to lungs as respiratory organs. The changes in the pattern of circulation permit the delivery of oxygen-rich blood to the brain and muscles. The pattern of circulation in many lower vertebrates is such that some mixing of oxygen-rich and oxygen-poor blood occurs. Mammals and birds can be warm blooded because their circulatory systems supply enough oxygen to the tissues to support a metabolic rate high enough to maintain a high body temperature in cold surroundings.

5.4
Respiration

The energy requirements of cells are met by the release of energy, generally by oxidative processes, from foodstuff molecules. The essential feature of these biologic oxidations is the transfer of hydrogen atoms from one molecule, the hydrogen donor, to another, the hydrogen acceptor. There is a series of compounds, each of which accepts hydrogen (or its electron) from the preceding and donates it to the following. The ultimate hydrogen acceptor in animal metabolism is usually oxygen, which is converted to water. We may define **cellular respiration** as the sum of the processes in which oxygen is utilized, carbon dioxide is produced and energy is converted into biologically useful forms such as ATP. For these processes to continue, the supply of oxygen must be renewed constantly and the carbon dioxide produced must be removed.

Animals differ tremendously in their general levels of activity and hence in their requirements for energy and for oxygen. As a corollary of this, animals differ in their susceptibility to oxygen deprivation. A mouse, which uses 2500 cu. mm. of oxygen per gram per hour when resting, and as much as 20,000 cu. mm. per gram per hour when active, rapidly dies of suffocation when deprived of oxygen or when poisoned with carbon monoxide. But an earthworm, which uses 60 cu. mm., or a sea anemone, which uses only 13 cu. mm. of oxygen per gram per hour, has a much lower rate of metabolism and does not readily suffocate. "Life" goes on in these lower animals at a much lower rate, in general, than it does in birds and mammals. There are exceptions to this generalization, and some animals with low rates of oxygen consumption are very sensitive to oxygen deprivation.

The transfer of gases across the cell membrane to the surrounding body fluid—or pond or sea water—is also part of the respiratory process. In the larger and more complex animals, further exchange of gases must occur between the body fluids—blood and interstitial fluid—and the outside environment, an exchange which usually involves some specialized respiratory surface, such as **lungs** or **gills.** The molecules of oxygen or carbon dioxide, whether in man or ameba, move simply by diffusion, from a region of high concentration to a region of lower concentration. The diffusion gradients are maintained, for oxygen is constantly utilized and carbon dioxide is produced within the cell. Physiologists use the terms partial pressure and tension of a gas to describe these diffusion gradients quantitatively.

The **partial pressure** of a gas is simply the pressure due to that one gas in a mixture of gases. It is calculated by multiplying the total pressure of the mixture of gases by the percentage of that gas in the mixture. Air, for example, normally has a pressure of about 760 mm. Hg and is one-fifth oxygen. The partial pressure of oxygen in air is 760×0.20 or 152 mm. Gas molecules dissolved in a liquid have a certain tendency to escape, to leave the liquid and enter the gaseous phase. This escaping tendency can be measured by the pressure of that gas in the gaseous phase in contact with the liquid which is required to prevent any net loss of the gas, i.e., to maintain equilibrium. When a liquid and gas are in contact, an equilibrium is reached when the rate at which molecules pass from the liquid to the gas equals the rate at which they pass from the gas to the liquid. This escaping tendency, known as the **tension** of the gas, is expressed numerically in terms of the partial pressure of the gas with which it would be in equilibrium. Notice that the gas tension is a measure of the tendency of the dissolved gas to diffuse out of the solution, and is not a measure of the *quantity* of gas present. The actual quantity of gas in solution is a property of both the gas and the liquid, and may vary considerably from one liquid to another. Water and blood in equilibrium with air would each have an oxygen tension of 152 mm. Hg, but the water would contain only 0.2 ml. of oxygen per 100 ml., whereas blood (because of the presence of hemoglobin) would contain 20 ml. of oxygen per 100 ml. A solution of pure hemoglobin containing the same amount of hemoglobin as blood (15 gm. per 100 ml.) would also contain 20 ml. of oxygen per 100 ml. and have an oxygen tension of 152 mm. Hg.

The Respiratory Surfaces. The protozoa and the simpler invertebrates—sponges, coelenterates and flatworms—obtain oxygen from and give off carbon dioxide to the surrounding water. The process is termed **direct respiration,** since the body cells exchange oxygen and carbon dioxide directly with the surrounding environment. The cells of the larger, more complex animals cannot exchange gases directly with the environment and some form of **indirect respiration** occurs: the cells exchange gases with the body fluids (**internal respiration**) and the body fluids exchange gases with the external environment via a specialized respiratory surface (**external respiration**) (Fig. 5.3). The respiratory surface for many animals is simply the skin, or perhaps the lining of the mouth. Fishes, many amphibia, mollusks, crustacea and some worms have developed **gills**—fine filaments of tissues containing blood channels and covered with an epithelium. Gases diffuse from the surrounding water through the thin, moist membrane to the blood vessels. The amount of dissolved oxygen in sea water is relatively constant, but the amount in freshwater ponds may fluctuate widely.

Insects and certain other arthropods have openings, called **spiracles,** in each segment of the body through which air passes, via a system of branched air ducts, called **tracheae,** to all of the internal organs. The ducts end in microscopic, fluid-filled tracheoles; oxygen and carbon dioxide pass by diffusion through the walls of the tracheoles to the adjacent tissue cells. The larger insects can pump air through the tracheae by contraction of muscles in the abdominal walls. This is an efficient

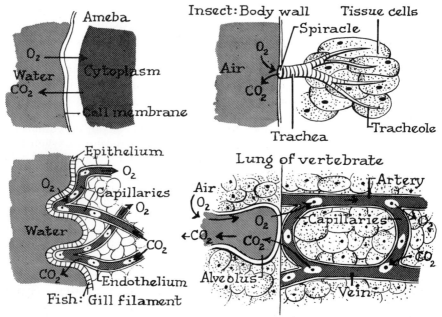

Figure 5.3 Respiration in an ameba, in the tracheal system of an insect, in the gill of a fish, and in the lung of a higher vertebrate.

system for gas exchange in animals of the size of insects, for the oxygen reaches the tissue cells and carbon dioxide is removed by diffusion alone; no energy need be expended, as in the vertebrates, in maintaining a rapid flow of blood to keep the body cells supplied with oxygen.

The higher vertebrates have developed lungs for external respiration. These are hollow spaces, usually greatly subdivided into thousands of small hollow pockets (alveoli), kept moist with water, and richly supplied with blood vessels. The walls of the alveoli are very thin and supplied with a rich bed of capillaries. The network of elastic fibers between the alveoli supports them and makes the lung very pliable. The arrangement of the lung alveoli, as pockets, tends to minimize the loss of water and thus keeps the alveolar surface moist.

However different respiratory surfaces may appear morphologically, they are essentially similar in consisting of a thin, moist membrane richly supplied with blood vessels separating body fluid and external environment. There is no evidence to support the hypothesis that the cells of the lung actively secrete oxygen into the blood stream. It can be calculated that diffusion is rapid enough to supply the oxygen required. Oxygen mole-

cules move from the air to the cells within the body along a steep diffusion gradient, from a region of high concentration to a region of lower concentration. The partial pressure of oxygen in air is about 150 mm. Hg, and that of the air in the lungs is about 105 mm. Hg. The oxygen tension of blood going to the tissues is about 100 mm. Hg and that of blood returning from tissues to lungs is about 40 mm. Hg. The oxygen tension in tissues may vary from 0 to 40 mm. Hg.

Means of Obtaining Oxygen. Air contains about 210 ml. of oxygen per liter. Fresh pond water has dissolved in it about 7 ml., and sea water about 5 ml., of oxygen per liter. An air-breathing animal has an obvious advantage over a water-breathing one with respect to oxygen supply, for the solubility of oxygen in water is low and its rate of diffusion is much less in water than in air. To overcome this handicap, animals breathing water usually have some mechanism to pass a fresh supply of water constantly over the respiratory surface. Air-breathing animals—earthworms for example—obtain enough oxygen by diffusion from the air in their burrows and need not stir up that air. The marine worms which live in burrows or tubes, in contrast, undulate their bodies to provide a current of water through the burrow. An even more dramatic example of this is provided by the shore crab, which can live in air or water. This animal has a set of gills located in a gill chamber between the upper shell and the attachment of the legs. A paddle-shaped part (the scaphognathite) of the second maxilla moves back and forth in the gill chamber to keep a current of water flowing over the gills. If the scaphognathites are paralyzed, the crab will soon die if placed in sea water, but will live indefinitely in air, for the rate of diffusion from air is rapid enough to supply all the oxygen the animal normally needs.

The ability of blood to carry oxygen and carbon dioxide depends to a large extent on the presence of a heme-protein pigment, such as hemoglobin. If blood were water, it could carry only about 0.2 ml. of oxygen and 0.3 ml. of carbon dioxide in each 100 ml. Whole blood, because of the properties of hemoglobin, can carry some 20 ml. of oxygen and 30 to 60 ml. of carbon dioxide per 100 ml. Hemoglobin is found in all of the major groups of animals above the flatworms; certain groups—mollusks and crustacea, for example—have other heme pigments such as hemocyanin. In the respiratory organ, the lung or gill, the heme pigment unites with oxygen. For example, hemoglobin unites with oxygen to form **oxyhemoglobin:**

$$Hb + O_2 \rightleftharpoons HbO_2$$

The reaction is reversible and hemoglobin releases the oxygen when it reaches a region where the oxygen tension is low. The combination of oxygen with hemoglobin and the release of oxygen from oxyhemoglobin are controlled by the amount of oxygen present and by the amount of carbon dioxide present. Carbon dioxide reacts with water to form **carbonic acid,** H_2CO_3, hence an *increase* in the concentration of carbon dioxide results in an *increased* acidity of the blood. The oxygen-carrying capacity of hemoglobin *decreases* as blood becomes more acid; thus, the combination of hemoglobin with oxygen is controlled indirectly by the amount of carbon dioxide present. This results in an extremely efficient transport system: In the capillaries of the tissues, the concentration of carbon dioxide is high and a large amount of oxygen is released from hemoglobin by the combined action of low oxygen tension and high carbon dioxide tension. In the capillaries of the lung or gill, carbon dioxide tension is lower and a large amount of oxygen is taken up by hemoglobin by the combined action of high oxygen tension and low carbon dioxide tension.

Hemoglobin plays an important role in the transport of carbon dioxide and in the maintenance of a constant blood pH; its functions in these and in the transport of oxygen are intimately interrelated. Some carbon dioxide is carried in a loose chemical union with hemoglobin, as **carbamino Hb,** and a small amount is present as carbonic acid, but most of it is transported as bicarbonate ion, HCO_3^-. The CO_2 produced by cells dissolves in the tissue fluid to form H_2CO_3 (the reaction is catalyzed by the enzyme **carbonic anhydrase**), but the carbonic acid is neutralized to bicarbonate by the sodium and potassium ions released when oxyhemoglobin is converted to hemoglobin. The details of these chemical reactions are rather

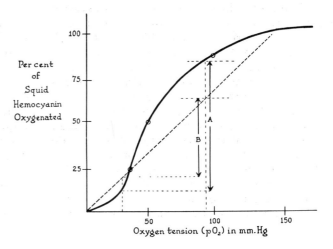

Figure 5.4 The amount of oxygen combined with hemocyanin is related to the oxygen tension (pO_2) by the S-shaped curve (solid line). Because of this, a greater amount of oxygen (*A*) is delivered to the tissue by a given decrease in pO_2 than there would be (*B*), if the properties of hemocyanin were such that there was a linear relationship between the percentage of hemocyanin oxygenated and the oxygen tension (dotted line).

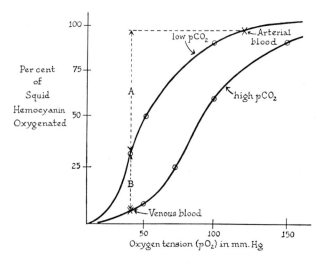

Figure 5.5 The effect of carbon dioxide tension (pCO_2) on the delivery of oxygen to tissues. The dotted line *A* indicates the amount of oxygen delivered as the pO_2 falls from that of arterial blood to that of venous blood. The dotted line *B* indicates the extra amount of oxygen delivered because the pCO_2 increases at the same time.

complex, but in essence they depend on the fact that oxyhemoglobin is a stronger acid than reduced hemoglobin; hence some cations are released when HbO_2 is converted to Hb. In the process of evolution this one molecule has become endowed with all the properties needed for the transport of large amounts of oxygen and carbon dioxide with a change of only a few hundredths of a pH unit in the blood.

The properties of the heme pigments are such that the amount of oxygen taken up by the pigment is not directly proportional to the oxygen tension; a graph of the relationship gives an **S**-shaped curve (Fig. 5.4). The blood is a more effective transporter of oxygen than it would be if the oxygen content were a simple linear function of oxygen tension. The effect of carbon dioxide (really the change in pH brought about by changes in carbon dioxide content) on the combination of oxygen with the pigment is shown in Figure 5.5. The **oxygen dissociation curves** for arterial blood, with low carbon dioxide tension, and for venous blood, with high carbon dioxide tension, illustrate how much more oxygen is delivered to the tissue by a given amount of blood as carbon dioxide is taken up in the tissue capillaries. The properties of the heme proteins of different species are quite different and, in general, are adapted to the amount of carbon dioxide present. This is low in water-breathing animals and high in air-breathing animals. This emphasizes the point that the evolution of air-breathing animals from water-breathing ones involved marked changes not only in

the morphology of the respiratory organs but also in the chemical properties of the heme proteins serving as blood pigment.

5.5
The Elimination of Wastes Other than Carbon Dioxide

In the course of the metabolic processes by which substances are utilized for energy production and cellular growth and maintenance, wastes are produced which must be removed. The constant synthesis and degradation of proteins, nucleic acids and other nitrogen-containing substances results in the formation of ammonia, urea, uric acid and creatinine, nitrogenous wastes which are toxic and would seriously interfere with metabolism if they accumulated. They are removed from the blood and other body fluids of vertebrates by the **kidneys.** The role of the vertebrate kidney, and of the excretory organs of most other animals, is not limited to the elimination of nitrogenous wastes but includes the *regulation* of the volume of body fluids—i.e., the water content of the body—and the *regulation* of the concentration of salts, acids, bases and organic substances in the body fluids. Cells require a constant environment for their continued normal functioning. The kidneys, by excreting certain substances and conserving others, maintain the required constancy of the blood and body fluids. The substances to be excreted are in solution, generally, in the intracellular fluid, and the excretory process may involve simple diffusion or active processes in which energy is expended.

In most protozoa, the removal of wastes is accomplished by diffusion through the cell membrane into the surrounding water where the concentration is lower. Protozoa living in fresh water have the additional problem of ridding the body of the water which constantly enters the cell by osmosis because the concentration of salts is greater in the cell than in the surrounding environment. These forms have evolved a **contractile vacuole,** which fills with fluid from the surrounding cellular contents and then empties to the exterior. Sponges and coelenterates have no specialized excretory organs and their wastes simply diffuse from the intracellular fluid to the external environment.

The simplest animals with specialized excretory organs are the flatworms and nemerteans, which have **flame cells** (Fig. 5.6) equipped with flagella, and a branching system of excretory ducts from the flame cells to the outside. The flame cells lie in the fluid which bathes the cells of the body, and wastes diffuse into the flame cells and thence into the excretory ducts. The beating of the flagella (which suggests a flickering flame when seen under the microscope) presumably moves fluid in the ducts out through the excretory pores and thus aids diffusion. As in the contractile vacuoles of the protozoa, the chief role of the flame cells is probably the regulation of the water content of the animals. Some of the metabolic wastes are removed by diffusion through the lining of the gastrovascular cavity.

Each segment of the body of an earthworm contains a pair of specialized excretory organs known as **nephridia.** A nephridium is a long, coiled tubule, opening at one end to the body cavity in a funnel-shaped structure lined with cilia, and at the other end to the outside of the body via an excretory pore. Around each tubule is a coil of capillaries, which permits the removal of wastes from the blood stream. As fluid passes through the nephridium, moved by the beating of the cilia in the funnel and the contraction of the muscles in the body wall, water and substances such as glucose are reabsorbed by the capillaries and the wastes are concentrated and pass out of the body. The earthworm excretes a very dilute, copious urine, at a rate of about 60 per cent of its total body weight each day.

The crustacean excretory organs are the **green glands,** a pair of large structures located at the base of the antennae and supplied with blood vessels. Each gland consists of three parts: a coelomic sac, a greenish glandular chamber with folded walls, and a canal which leads to a muscular bladder. Wastes pass from the blood to the coelomic sac and glandular chamber; the fluid in them is isotonic with the blood. Urine collects in the bladder and then is voided to the outside through a pore at the base of the second antenna.

The excretory organs of insects, the **malpighian tubules,** are quite different from those of the crustaceans. They lie within the body cavity (hemocoel) and empty into the digestive tract. Wastes diffuse into these tubules and are excreted into the cavity of the digestive tract.

The kidneys, the vertebrate excretory organs, remove wastes from the blood and regulate its content of water, salts and organic substances. The structural and functional unit of the kidney is the **kidney tubule** (Fig. 5.6). This is in close contact with the blood stream, for a tuft of capillaries projects into the funnel-shaped **Bowman's capsule** at the end of the tubule. The tubule may be quite long and looped and in contact with additional capillaries along its length. It eventually opens to the outside of the body via collecting ducts and other intermediate tubes. Substances are filtered into the kidney tubules from the blood capillaries in the Bowman's capsules. Then, some substances are reabsorbed into the blood stream and others are secreted from the blood into the urine as the liquid flows through the tubules and past the additional capillaries there. The kidney must expend energy to move certain of the substances excreted or reabsorbed against a diffusion gradient. The excretory process would be very wasteful and inefficient if the urine leaving the body had the same composition as the fluid in the Bowman's capsule. However, as the urine passes down the kidney tubule, water, sugar, salts and many other substances are reabsorbed, whereas the waste products such as ammonia and urea are not. It is by this **selective reabsorption** of certain substances, and by the addition of others to the urine, that the kid-

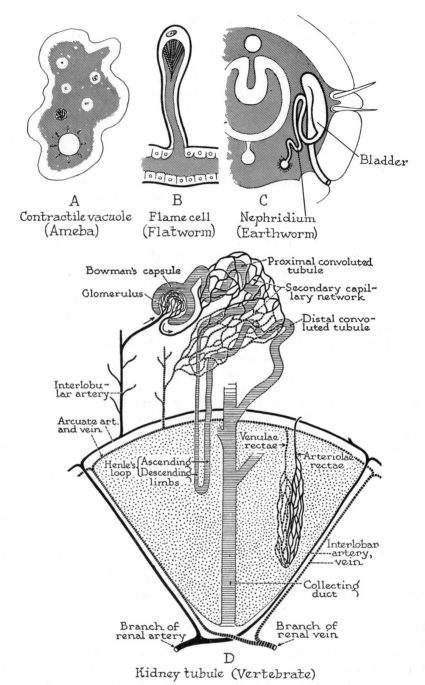

A
Contractile vacuole
(Ameba)

B
Flame cell
(Flatworm)

C
Nephridium
(Earthworm)

Bladder

Bowman's capsule

Glomerulus

Proximal convoluted
tubule

Secondary capil-
lary network

Distal convo-
luted tubule

Interlobu-
lar artery

Arcuate art.
and vein

Venulae
rectae

Henle's
loop

Ascending
Descending
limbs

Arteriolae
rectae

Interlobar
artery,
vein

Collecting
duct

Branch of
renal artery

Branch of
renal vein

D
Kidney tubule (Vertebrate)

Figure 5.6 The excretory systems of (*A*) ameba, (*B*) flatworm, (*C*) earthworm and (*D*) vertebrate.

ney tubules regulate the composition of the blood and body fluids. In the higher animals such as man, the lungs, skin and digestive tract also remove certain wastes from the body.

The most important waste products excreted by animals are the nitrogenous ones which result from the deamination of amino acids and from the breakdown of nucleic

acids. The **ammonia** formed by deamination is toxic but quite soluble and readily diffusible. If plenty of water is available, as it is for fresh-water animals, the ammonia diffuses out as such, either directly through the body surface, or through gills and excretory organs if these are present. Animals living on land cannot afford to excrete the amount of water which would be required to eliminate ammonia. In land animals, ammonia is converted metabolically to some other substance to be excreted. In mammals, the nitrogenous wastes from amino acid metabolism are excreted largely as **urea,** which is a soluble, small molecule that diffuses readily and is less toxic than ammonia. Urea requires a moderate amount of water for its excretion. Reptiles and birds convert their nitrogenous wastes largely to **uric acid** for excretion. This substance is only slightly soluble so that once it has been formed and excreted into the kidney tubules, water may be reabsorbed and the uric acid is excreted as a paste or dry powder. Insects, which are largely terrestrial animals, also excrete uric acid. The uric acid is excreted into the malpighian tubules whence it leaves the body via the digestive tract as a dry paste. Some animals simply accumulate precipitated uric acid in some organ of the body—the "fat body" of the insect is an example. Nitrogenous wastes in this form are removed from the body fluids as effectively as those actually excreted from the body in urine.

Some of the vertebrates living in or on the sea have evolved special means for dealing with salt. The bony fishes, for example, drink salt water and then secrete the salt through their gills. Marine turtles and seagulls can secrete the salt from the sea water they drink by special salt glands located in the head. The ducts from the salt glands empty either into the nasal cavities or onto the surface of the head.

5.6

Protection

The complex physicochemical system that constitutes a cell requires protection against the many adverse effects of the surrounding environment. The ameba is an exception to the general rule that animals have some protective covering. The cellular contents of the ameba are separated from the surrounding environment only by the plasma membrane. Many other protozoa have a tough, flexible, noncellular **pellicle** surrounding the cell and some secrete hard, durable, calcareous or siliceous shells. All the multicellular animals have some protective covering or **skin** over the body. The skin may consist of one or many layers of cells and may be reinforced by scales, hair, feathers, shells or secretions of mucus or cutin. Hair, feathers and certain scales, such as those of reptiles, are composed of insoluble proteins called **keratins** derived from dead cells in the skin. The skin has a number of functions: it protects the underlying cells against mechanical and chemical injuries; it prevents the entrance of disease organisms; it prevents excessive loss of water from land animals and excessive uptake of water by fresh-water animals; and it protects underlying cells against the harmful effects of the ultraviolet rays in sunlight.

The skin is an effective radiator by which the body can eliminate the heat which is constantly produced in cellular metabolism. One of the factors controlling the rate of heat loss in higher vertebrates is the size of the blood vessels in the skin. To conserve heat in a cold environment, the blood vessels are constricted to decrease the rate of blood flow. The reverse occurs in a warm environment and the rate of heat loss can be increased by the evaporation of water, i.e., sweat, from the surface of the skin.

A great many animals have a firm framework or **skeleton** which protects and supports the body and provides for the attachment of muscles. Some animals manage to survive without a skeleton but these are mostly aquatic forms. The slug and earthworm are among the few exceptions to the rule that terrestrial animals require a skeleton. To raise part of the body off the ground, some stiff, hard framework is required to support the soft tissues against the pull of gravity. The appendages of arthropods and vertebrates have a hard, but jointed and bendable, skeletal framework which serves as levers for locomotion. The skeleton also covers and protects such delicate organs as the brain, spinal cord and lungs. The marrow cavities of vertebrate bones contain tissues which produce red blood cells and certain of the white blood cells.

An animal's skeleton may be an **exoskeleton,** located on the outside of the body, or an **endoskeleton,** located within the body. The hard shells of lobsters, crabs and insects and the calcareous shells of oysters and clams are examples of exoskeletons. An exoskeleton provides excellent protection for the body, and muscles can be attached to its inner surface so as to move one part with respect to another. However, the presence of an exoskeleton usually interferes with growth. The arthropods have solved this problem by periodically shedding the shell. To do this the shell is first softened—that is, some of the calcium salts deposited in it are dissolved—

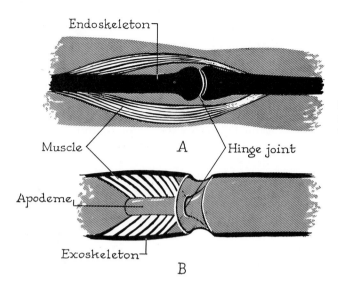

Figure 5.7 A comparison of (*A*) the vertebrate endoskeleton with (*B*), the arthropod exoskeleton, showing the arrangement of the muscles and skeleton at a joint.

the shell is split and the animal crawls out of the old shell. It then undergoes a period of rapid growth before the new shell, which formed under the old one, is hardened by the deposition of calcium salts. During this **molting** process the arthropod lacks protection and is weak and barely able to move. Hard, calcareous exoskeletons are present in most mollusks and arthropods, and in corals, bryozoa and a variety of lesser invertebrates. A clam or oyster secretes additional shell at the margin as it grows; the shell gets both larger and thicker as the animal grows. Many marine worms secrete calcareous tubes in which they live. Though these shells are not directly a part of the animal body, they are, in certain respects, the functional equivalent of an exoskeleton.

The vertebrate skeleton, lying within the soft tissues of the body, provides an excellent framework for their support and does not interfere with their growth. The arrangement of the parts of the skeleton is essentially the same in all the vertebrates. The details of this will be discussed in Chapter 26.

The skeleton of vertebrates is composed of many individual **bones** or **cartilages.** The region where two hard parts meet and move one on the other is known as a **joint.** The fundamental differences in the mechanics of the vertebrate and arthropod joints are illustrated in Figure 5.7. The muscles of the vertebrate surround the bones; each is attached by one end to one bone and by its other end to another bone. Its contraction thus moves one bone with respect to the other.

The muscles of the arthropod lie *within* the skeleton and are attached to its inner surface. The arthropod exoskeleton has certain regions—joints—in which the exoskeleton is thin and flexible so that movements may occur. The muscle may stretch across the joint, so that its contraction will move one part on the next. Or, the muscle may be located entirely within one section of the body or appendage and be attached at one end to a tough **apodeme,** a long, thin, firm part of the exoskeleton extending into that section from the adjoining one.

5.7
Motion

Most if not all cells possess the ability to contract, a process which involves the transformation of chemical energy into mechanical energy. The chemical energy of the energy-rich phosphate bonds synthesized in glycolysis and in biologic oxidation (p. 62) is converted into the mechanical energy of contractile protein molecules such as **actomyosin.** The basic process for the conversion of chemical to mechanical energy appears to be fundamentally similar in all cells, though the nature of the contracting protein molecule may differ somewhat. The mechanical behavior of a contracting muscle and the energy used can be measured and compared with the chemical, electrical and thermal changes coincident with contraction to try to understand the nature of the contractile mechanism.

Ameboid motion is the irregular flowing of the cellular contents seen in amebas, in the amebocytes of sponges, in the white blood cells of vertebrates and in the general process of cytoplasmic motion which occurs during cell division. Careful microscopic study of a moving ameba reveals that not all of the cytoplasm streams simultaneously. There is a solid, nonmoving layer at the surface of the cell which surrounds a core of liquid, flowing cytoplasm. At the rear of the moving ameba, cytoplasmic gel is converted to sol to flow forward. At the front end, the streaming cytoplasm bulges out in a projection known as a **pseudopod** (false foot) and changes from a sol to a gel. The push for the movement of the sol is believed to come from the contraction of the gel comprising the layer near the surface of the cell. The tip of the pseudopod is covered with a thinner gel layer than that elsewhere in the cell and hence is the part to bulge when contraction occurs. By regulating the thickness of the local areas in the cell wall, the ameba can determine where a pseudopod will form and hence in which direction he will move. The animal has no permanent front and rear ends. Ameboid motion is a crawling motion, not a swimming one; the cell must be attached to some physical substrate in order to move.

Another type of motion is seen in the movable, slender, hair-like processes which project from certain cells. These are termed **flagella** if each cell has one or a few long, whiplike processes and **cilia** if each cell has many short processes. Flagella are found on certain protozoa (the flagellates), on the collar cells of sponges and on certain cells lining the gastrovascular cavity of coelenterates. Cells equipped with cilia occur very widely: in certain protozoa (called ciliates), on the body surfaces of ctenophores, flatworms and rotifers, on the tentacles of bryozoa, certain worms and coelenterates, on the gills of clams and oysters, and lining certain ducts in the vertebrate body such as the bronchi and oviducts. The paramecium (see Fig. 8.12) is an example of a ciliate, with some 2500 short cilia covering each single-celled animal. The cilia beat in a coordinated rhythm, not simultaneously but one after another, so that waves of ciliary movement pass along the body surface. The effect of the combined effort of the cilia beating backward is to move the animal forward. The cilia beat somewhat obliquely so that the animal revolves on its long axis and moves in a spiral path. The beating of the cilia is under the control of the animal, and by reversing the ciliary beat it can back up and turn around. The beating of cilia and flagella is believed to result from the contraction of fibrils within these projections, but the details of the process are quite unknown. Cilia beat quite rapidly, up to 40 beats per second. At the high magnifications achieved by the electron microscope the fibrils extending down the long axis of the flagellum or cilium can be seen.

Muscles. Motion in most animals is a function of the contraction of specialized cells, the muscle cells. The contractile material, **actomyosin,** is fundamentally similar in smooth, striated and cardiac muscles of vertebrates and in the muscles of invertebrates as well. Muscles that contract rapidly and briefly, such as the skeletal muscles of mammals, are striated, whereas those that contract slowly and remain contracted for a long time, such as those in the walls of the digestive tract or urinary bladder, are unstriated. This basic physiologic and histologic correlation is evident in the contractile cells of coelenterates, for those of jellyfish, which contract in twitches, have microscopic cross striations and those of sea anemones, which contract very slowly, are unstriated.

The coelenterate contractile cells in the ectoderm are arranged at right angles to those in the endoderm; contraction of one or the other decreases either the length or the diameter of the body. Flatworms typically have muscle fibers oriented in three different planes, but roundworms have only longitudinal fibers in the body wall. A roundworm can bend or straighten its body but cannot twist or extend its length. Segmented marine and earthworms have an outer layer of circular fibers and an inner layer of longitudinal fibers in the body wall. Since the body cavity is filled with fluid which is incompressible, the contraction of the circular muscles stretches the longitudinal muscles and extends the body, making it longer and thinner. The contraction of the longitudinal muscles makes it shorter and thicker.

Mollusks generally have slow, nonstriated muscles, but the scallop, which can swim actively by clapping its two shells together, has two muscles connecting the shells. One of these is nonstriated and contracts slowly, serving to keep the shells closed at rest, and the other is striated and twitches rapidly to power the swimming movements.

The arthropods have complex patterns of separate muscles rather than simple layers of muscles as in the worms. These muscles vary in size and attachment and provide for the movement of the segments of the body and their many-jointed appendages. The arthropod muscles are located within the exoskeleton and attach to its inner surface. A lobster or grasshopper has hundreds of separate muscles.

The muscles of vertebrates are generally attached to bones or cartilages as pairs which tend to pull in opposite directions (Fig. 5.8). Since muscles can pull but cannot push, this antagonistic arrangement allows for movement in both directions. The end of the muscle which remains relatively fixed when a muscle contracts is known as its **origin;** the end which moves is called the **insertion;** and the thick part between the two is called the **belly** of the muscle. Thus, the **biceps,** which bends or flexes the forearm, has its origin on the scapula and on the upper end of the humerus, and its insertion on the radius in the forearm. Its antagonist, the **triceps,** which straightens or extends the forearm, has its origin on the scapula and upper part of the humerus and its insertion on the ulna. The contraction of a muscle is stimulated by a

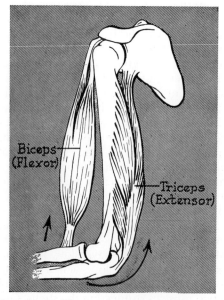

Figure 5.8 The muscles and bones of the forearm, showing the antagonistic arrangement of the biceps and triceps muscles.

nerve impulse reaching it via a motor nerve fiber from the central nervous system. The drug, **curare,** the chief ingredient of the arrow poison used by the South American Indians, blocks the junction between nerve and muscle so that impulses cannot pass and the muscle is paralyzed. A curare-paralyzed muscle can still be caused to contract by direct electric stimulation, a demonstration that muscle is independently irritable.

5.8
The Mechanism of Muscular Contraction

The functional unit of vertebrate muscles, called the **motor unit,** consists of a single motor neuron and the group of muscle cells innervated by its axon, all of which will contract when an impulse travels down the motor neuron. In man, it is estimated that there are some 250,000,000 muscle cells but only some 420,000 motor neurons in spinal nerves. Obviously, some motor neurons must innervate more than one muscle fiber. The degree of fine control of a muscle is inversely proportional to the number of muscle fibers in the motor unit. The muscles of the eyeball, for example, have as few as three to six fibers per motor unit, whereas the leg muscles have perhaps 650 fibers per unit.

If a single motor unit is isolated and stimulated with brief electric shocks of increasing intensity, beginning with shocks too weak to cause contraction, there will be no response until a certain intensity is reached, then the response is maximal. This phenomenon is known as the "all-or-none effect." In contrast, a whole muscle, made of many individual motor units, can respond in a graded fashion depending upon the number of motor units which are contracting at any given time.

A muscle given a single stimulus, a single electric shock, responds with a single quick twitch. The changes which accompany a **single twitch** are shown in Figure 5.9. A twitch consists of (1) a very short **latent period,** the interval between the application of the stimulus and the beginning of the contraction; (2) a **contraction period,** during which the muscle shortens and does work; and (3) a **relaxation period,** longest of the three, during which the muscle returns to its original length. The latent period represents the interval between the conduction of the action

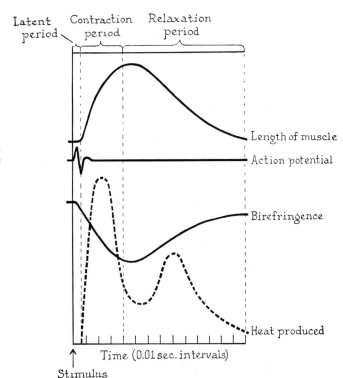

Figure 5.9 Diagram of the changes that occur in a muscle during a single muscle twitch. See text for discussion.

current and the completion of the changes in the structure of the actomyosin which enables it to contract. The first event after the stimulation of a muscle is the initiation and propagation of an electrical response, the muscle **action potential,** followed by the changes in the structure of actomyosin observed as a change in the total birefringence of the muscle, by its shortening, and by the production of heat. Following a twitch there is a **recovery period** during which the muscle is restored to its original condition. If a muscle is stimulated repeatedly at intervals short enough so that succeeding contractions occur before the muscle has fully recovered from the previous one, the muscle becomes fatigued and the twitches become feebler and finally cease. The fatigued muscle will regain its ability to contract if it is allowed to rest.

Muscles do not usually contract in individual twitches but in more sustained contractions evoked by a volley of nerve impulses reaching them in rapid succession. This state of sustained contraction is known as **tetanus;** the individual motor units are stimulated in rotation. Thus individual muscle fibers contract and relax, but do this in rotation so that the muscle as a whole remains partially contracted. The strength of the contraction de-

pends on the fraction of the muscle fibers which contract at any given moment.

All normal skeletal muscles are in a state of sustained partial contraction, called **tonus,** as long as the nerves to the muscle are intact. Tonus, then, is a state of mild tetanus, maintained by a constant flow of nerve impulses to the muscle.

The problem of how a muscle can exert a pull is far from solved, but it is now believed that the molecules of actin and myosin shorten either by some sort of folding of the protein chain or by the sliding together of the component parts. The energy for the contraction is derived from the energy-rich phosphate bonds of adenosine triphosphate and phosphocreatine and these are renewed by the energy derived from the glycolysis of glycogen to lactic acid. This latter process, which can occur without utilizing oxygen, provides energy for the resynthesis of adenosine triphosphate and phosphocreatine.

Capturing food or evading enemies may call for prolonged bursts of muscular activity. Although both the rate of breathing and the rate of the heartbeat may increase markedly during prolonged exertion, these changes could not supply the muscles with enough oxygen to enable them to contract repeatedly if the contraction process itself required oxygen. That muscle contraction, and part of the recovery process, occur without the utilization of oxygen is clearly important for survival. During violent exercise glycogen is converted to lactic acid faster than the lactic acid can be oxidized. Lactic acid accumulates and the muscle is said to have incurred an "oxygen debt," which is repaid after the period of exertion by continued rapid breathing. This supplies enough extra oxygen to oxidize part of the accumulated lactic acid. Some of the energy released by the oxidation of the lactic acid in the Krebs cycle and the electron transmitter system (Fig. 4.2) is used to resynthesize glycogen from the remainder of the lactic acid and to restore the energy-rich compounds, ATP and phospho-

creatine, to their normal condition. A muscle that has contracted many times has depleted its stores of energy-rich phosphates and glycogen and has accumulated a lot of lactic acid; it is unable to contract again and is said to be **fatigued.** A fatigued muscle will contract if stimulated directly and the nerve to the muscle can conduct impulses. The point of fatigue is the junction between nerve and muscle where the nerve impulse instigates muscle contraction.

Electron micrographs reveal that each muscle fiber is made of two kinds of longitudinal filaments, thicker primary filaments of myosin and thinner secondary filaments of actin. The alternating light and dark bands evident in the light microscope (see Fig. 3.15) consist of dense A bands and light I bands

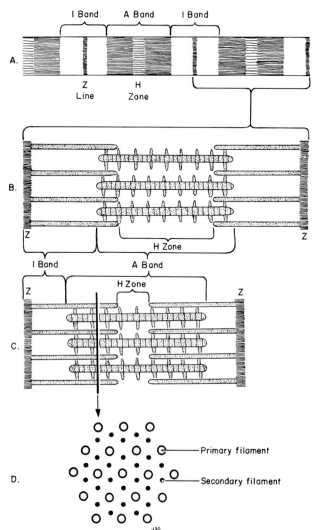

Figure 5.10 Diagrams illustrating the sliding filament hypothesis of the mechanism of muscle contraction. *A,* Diagram of part of a single myofibril showing the pattern of light (I) and dark (A) bands. *B,* Longitudinal view of the arrangement of thick and thin filaments within a myofibril in the relaxed state. *C,* Longitudinal view of the arrangement of thick and thin filaments in a contracted myofibril, showing that the I band decreases in thickness. Note that the two types of filaments appear to slide past one another during contraction. *D,* Transverse view through *C* at arrow, showing each thick primary filament surrounded by six thinner secondary filaments. (Adapted from H. E. Huxley.)

(Fig. 5.10). Each unit consists of an A band and half of each adjacent I band; it is separated from the next unit by a thin dense **Z** line through the middle of the I band. The central portion of the A band is the somewhat less dense H zone. The thick primary filaments occur only in the A band. The thinner secondary filaments are located in the I band but extend into the A band for some distance and interdigitate with the primary filaments. The secondary filaments appear to be smooth but the primary filaments appear to have minute spines every 60 to 70 Å along their length which project toward the adjacent secondary filament (Fig. 5.10*B*).

During contraction the length of the A band remains constant but the I band shortens and the length of the H zone within the A band decreases. Huxley and others have proposed that during contraction the filaments maintain their same length but the primary and secondary filaments slide past each other. During contraction the thin secondary filaments of actin are believed to extend farther into the A band, decreasing its central H zone and narrowing the I bands as the ends of the primary myosin filaments approach the Z band (Fig. 5.10*C*). The physicochemical mechanism by which this sliding may occur is not yet clear; perhaps the spiny bridges are broken and then re-formed farther along the filament. The energy of the ~P may be utilized in forming new bridges, new cross-linkages, between the primary and secondary filaments.

It was noted in Figure 5.9 that an action potential was associated with muscle contraction. In general, muscles are arranged with their fibers in parallel, so that the voltage difference in a large muscle is no greater than that of a single fiber. In the **electric organ** of the electric eel, however, the electric plates are modified muscle cells (motor end plates) arranged in series. Although each plate has a potential difference of about 0.1 volt, the discharge of the entire organ, made of several thousand plates, amounts to several hundred volts.

5.9

Irritability and Response

The muscles just described, together with cilia, glands, nematocysts and so on, are **effectors**—they do things. To ensure that these effectors do the right things at the right time, animals are equipped with **receptors**—a variety of sense organs—and with nervous and endocrine systems to coordinate the activity of the effectors.

Irritability or excitability is a fundamental property of all kinds of cells. Waves of excitation are conducted, although very slowly, by eggs and by plant cells. Many of the ciliates have a network of **neurofibrils** which connect the bases of the cilia together with special fibrils to the gullet and other special structures of the body. It would appear that this net conducts impulses which coordinate the beating of the cilia and the functioning of the special organelles, for coordination is lost when the net is cut by a microneedle. There are no nerve cells in sponges, but waves of excitation can be conducted from cell to cell at about 1 cm. per minute. There are spindle-shaped contractile cells around the openings of the pores. These have been termed "independent effectors" because they respond to touch by contracting and thus combine sensory and motor functions.

The simplest special coordinating system is the **nerve net** found in coelenterates. The coelenterate nerve fibers are found all over the body in a diffuse network; a few sea anemones and medusae have rudimentary nerve trunks composed of aggregations of nerve fibers. Conduction in the nerve net progresses in all directions; the fibers are not actually fused together, but impulses pass from one fiber to an adjacent one in either direction.

5.10

The Nerve Impulse

Galvani, in the eighteenth century, first showed that a muscle contracts when an electric shock is applied to the nerve leading to it. DuBois-Reymond in the nineteenth century showed that when a stimulus is applied to a sense organ electrical disturbances can be detected in the efferent nerves. With the development of improved instruments for detecting these weak currents, the electrical disturbances in nerve fibers were shown to have a potential of about 0.05 volt, to last for a very short time, about 0.0005 second, and to travel along the nerve at speeds as great as 100 yards per second.

The transmission of a nerve impulse is not

simply an electrical phenomenon, like the passage of a current in a wire. It is a physico-chemical process, which uses oxygen and produces carbon dioxide and heat. The transmission of a nerve impulse obeys the "all-or-none law": The conduction of the impulse is independent of the nature or strength of the stimulus starting it, provided that the stimulus is strong enough to start any impulse. The energy for the conduction of the impulse comes from the nerve, not from the stimulus, so that, although the speed of the conducted impulse is independent of the strength of the stimulus, it is affected by the state of the nerve fiber. Drugs or low temperature can retard or prevent the transmission of an impulse. The impulses transmitted by all types of neurons are believed to be essentially alike. That one impulse results in a sensation of light, another in a sensation of pain, and a third in the contraction of a muscle is a function of the way the nerve fibers are connected and not of any special property of the impulses.

Our present knowledge of the nature of the nerve impulse has been derived in large part from experiments using the large axons found in squid, crayfish and certain worms. The giant axon of the squid is large enough, nearly 1 mm. in diameter, so that investigators can introduce microelectrodes and micropipettes into the substance of the nerve fiber and measure the electrical potential across the nerve membrane. According to the present membrane theory of nerve conduction, the electrical events in the nerve fiber are governed by the differential permeability of the plasma membrane of the neuron to sodium and potassium ions, and these permeabilities, in turn, are regulated by the electric field across the surface. The interaction of these two factors, differential permeability and electric field, leads to the requirement for a certain critical threshold of change for excitation to occur. Excitation is a regenerative release of electrical energy from the nerve membrane and the propagation of this change along the fiber is a brief, all-or-none electrical impulse called the **action potential.**

To understand what happens when a nerve impulse passes along the fiber, we must first have a clear picture of the state of the resting nerve fiber. The nerve fiber is, in essence, a long cylindrical tube whose surface membrane separates two solutions of different chemical composition, though they have the same total number of ions. In the external medium sodium and chloride ions predominate, whereas within the cell potassium and various organic anions predominate. The concentration of sodium in the external medium is some 10 times greater than that within the cell and the concentration of potassium in the internal medium is some 30 times greater than that in the surrounding medium.

These concentrations of Na^+ and K^+ are kept relatively constant but there is a steady flux of ions in and out of the cell. The cell membrane of the nerve fiber, like other cell membranes, actively transports certain ions from the internal medium to the exterior and other ions in the reverse direction. As a result of this differential distribution of ions on the two sides of the membrane, there is a potential difference from 0.06 to 0.09 volt across the membrane, with the interior being negatively charged with respect to the outside (Fig. 5.11).

These differences in electrical potential

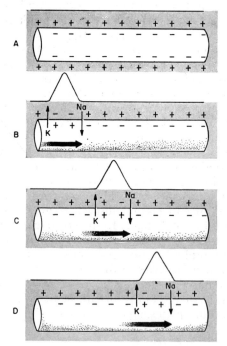

Figure 5.11 Diagram illustrating the membrane theory of nerve transmission. *A*, Resting nerve, showing the polarization of the membrane with positive charges on the outside and negative charges on the inside. *B–D*, Successive stages in the conduction of a nerve impulse, showing the wave of depolarization of the membrane and the accompanying action potential propagated along the nerve. (Villee: Biology, 5th ed.)

and ionic concentrations are maintained in the resting (i.e., nonconducting) nerve by the active transport of sodium ions from the internal medium to the interstitial fluid that surrounds the nerve fiber, a process which has been termed the **sodium pump.** The extrusion of sodium ions from the cell is an energy-requiring reaction, the energy for which is derived from metabolic processes within the nerve. When the nerve fiber is poisoned with a substance such as cyanide, the sodium pump is turned off.

The extrusion of sodium ions is accompanied by the entrance of potassium ions and, although the details of the process are unknown, it appears that there is an exchange of cations at the cell surface, with a potassium ion entering for each sodium ion extruded. The cell membrane has a relatively low ionic permeability so that, even when the sodium pump is turned off (by a metabolic poison, for example), it takes many hours before the concentration gradients of sodium and potassium across the membrane disappear. The cell membrane is differentially permeable to the two ions; it is much more permeable to potassium than to sodium. In the normal resting state of the nerve fiber, there is an excess of positively charged ions on the outside of the membrane (Fig. 5.11).

Electrical studies of the cable properties of the nerve fiber have shown that the axon could hardly serve as a passive transmission line because its cable losses are enormous. When a weak signal is applied to the fiber, one too small to excite the usual relay mechanism of the fiber, it fades out within a few millimeters of its origin. The nerve impulse could not be propagated over the long distances in the nerve unless there were some process to boost the signal. This is the function of the excitatory process, which regenerates and reamplifies the signal all along the the nerve fiber. The cable properties of the nerve fiber are important in allowing a change in electrical potential to spread along the nerve fiber for a short distance (even though it is rapidly attenuated) and thus stimulate the excitatory process in the adjacent portion of the nerve.

The excitation of a nerve, the generation of a nerve impulse, involves a momentary change in the permeability of the nerve membrane which permits sodium ions to enter. The entrance of the sodium ion leads to a depolarization of the nerve membrane; it

becomes positively charged on the inside and negatively charged on the outside. Although the permeability of the membrane to sodium ions is very low at the usual resting potential, the permeability to sodium increases as the membrane potential decreases. This permits a leakage of sodium ions down the concentration gradient into the interior of the cell. This further decreases the membrane potential and further increases the permeability to sodium. This process becomes progressive (it is "self-reinforcing") and results in the upward spike of the action potential wave (Fig. 5.11). When the interior of the fiber becomes positively charged with respect to the exterior, the further net influx of sodium ions is prevented. The potential difference across the membrane may momentarily reach 0.04 volt, with the inside of the fiber now positively charged with respect to the outside. This is followed by a period of increased permeability to potassium, and potassium ions pass along their concentration gradient from inside the cell to outside.

The return of the membrane potential to its original state of negative inside and positive outside is not brought about by a reversal of the movement of the ions—there is no expulsion of the amount of sodium ions that entered during the ascending phase of the action potential—but by the leakage outward of an equivalent quantity of potassium ions. Both sodium and potassium ions are moving down their respective concentration gradients during the passage of an impulse. The actual quantities of ions involved, however, are so small that there is no detectable change in the concentration of either ion in the fiber during one impulse. The giant axon of the squid could conduct several hundred thousand impulses, even if its sodium pump were turned off, before its store of accumulated ions would be exhausted.

The propagation of each impulse is followed by a period of inexcitability, the **absolute refractory period,** during which the fiber cannot transmit a second impulse. Because of the changes in permeability that accompany the depolarization of the nerve membrane, the fiber cannot respond to a second stimulus. Excitability returns when the normal permeability relations have been restored.

The nerve impulse is thus a wave of "depolarization" that passes along the nerve fiber. The change in membrane potential in one region makes the adjacent region more permeable and, in this way, the wave of depolarization is transmitted along the fiber. The entire cycle of depolarization and repolarization requires only a few thousandths of a second.

Experiments by the English physiologist Adrian, published in 1926, provided the explanation as to how the nervous system transmits differences in intensity. By applying graded stimuli to an isolated sense organ and amplifying and measuring the impulses in its nerve, Adrian showed that variations in the intensity of a stimulus lead to variations in the *frequency* with which impulses are transmitted: the stronger the stimulus, the more impulses per second. This principle is true for both vertebrate and invertebrate sensory nerves. In contrast, a single impulse in a vertebrate motor nerve elicits a single twitch of all the muscle fibers in the motor unit. The differences in the strength of contraction of the muscle as a whole are due to variations in the total number of motor units actively contracting at any given moment. In the motor nerves of invertebrates, however, the frequency of the impulses does affect the strength of contraction of the muscle innervated. A single nerve impulse will, in general, not stimulate the muscle to contract. At least two successive impulses are required, and the strength of contraction is inversely proportional to the interval between the two. In many arthropods all the muscle fibers in a given muscle are innervated by branches of a single nerve fiber (axon). A single impulse in the axon will not produce contraction but repeated impulses will; the tension in the muscle increases with the frequency of the stimulation. It would appear that, although the arrival of a single impulse at the nerve-muscle junction is unable to bring about muscle contraction, it does affect the junction in such a way as to make it possible for a second impulse to do this if it arrives soon enough after the first. This phenomenon is known as **facilitation.**

The speed of propagation of the nerve impulse varies considerably from one nerve to another, and even more from one animal to another. Conduction is, in general, more rapid in those neurons with greater diameters. A number of animals—squid, lobsters and earthworms—have special **giant axons** which conduct impulses many times faster than the adjacent small fibers. Conduction is more rapid in those nerves surrounded by a thick myelin sheath. The speed of conduction is greater in those nerves in which the myelin sheath is interrupted periodically by nodes of Ranvier.

5.11
Transmission at the Synapse

Where the tip of the axon of one nerve comes close to the tip of the dendrite of the adjoining nerve is a region called the **synapse.** Transmission of impulses across the synapse from one neuron to the next is slower than transmission along a nerve fiber. Synaptic transmission may be either electrical or chemical. Electrical transmission implies that, despite the apparent morphologic separation of the two neurons, an effective local circuit connection exists and permits enough current to pass from one to the other to stimulate an impulse in the second. Chemical transmission is basically different from the process by which an impulse is transmitted along a nerve fiber. It assumes that the physical interruption of the nerve fiber at the synapse prevents cable transmission across the junction and that this is replaced by a chemical mediator. It involves the release of a specific chemical from the tip of the axon (an example of **neurosecretion**) and the attaching of this chemical mediator to specific molecular sites in the dendrite (an example of **chemoreception**) which produces a change in the properties of the membrane of the dendrite and leads to the initiation of a new nerve impulse.

When a nerve impulse reaches the tip of certain vertebrate nerves it stimulates the secretion of acetylcholine. This diffuses across the synaptic junction and attaches to a special chemoreceptor on the surface of the dendrite of the adjacent neuron. The combination of the chemical with the chemoreceptor leads to a depolarization of the membrane and sets up a new action potential which passes along that neuron. Tissues contain a powerful **cholinesterase,** an enzyme which specifically splits acetylcholine to its constituents, which are inactive, and thus the continued stimulation of the adjacent neuron is prevented.

The mechanism of synaptic transmission in other types of nerves is the subject of controversy. There is evidence that acetylcholine plays some role, perhaps the major one, in synaptic conduction in the central nervous system of vertebrates and certain invertebrates. Sympathin, a chemical similar to or identical with the hormone epinephrine, is the chemical mediator across certain synapses in the sympathetic nervous system. Synaptic transmission is greatly affected by the concentration of cations such as potassium and calcium, and these ions may play some direct role in transmission.

Much evidence has accumulated to show that chemical transmission at the synapse is a general phenomenon, and some investigators have argued that all synaptic transmission is chemical. However, the experiments of Furshpan and Potter in 1957 showed that transmission across the giant synapse in an abdominal ganglion of the nerve cord of the crayfish is by electrical means. The membranes at this special synapse are able to act as a rectifier and allow current to pass easily in one direction, from the axon of a connector neuron to the dendrite of a motor neuron.

Synapses are important functionally because they are points at which the flow of impulses through the nervous system is regulated. Not every impulse reaching a synapse is transmitted to the next neuron. The synapses, by regulating the route of nerve impulses through the nervous system, determine the response of the organism to a specific stimulus.

The important details of the arrangement of the neurons to form the central nervous systems of the higher invertebrates and of the vertebrates will be discussed in later chapters. The invertebrate nervous system consists of one or more pairs of **ganglia**—collections of nerve cell bodies—at the anterior end of the body and one or more nerve cords extending posteriorly. The invertebrate nerve cord is solid and is typically located on the ventral side of the body; the vertebrate nerve cord is single, hollow, and located on the dorsal side of the body.

5.12

Sense Organs

Physiologic experiments show that nerve fibers can be stimulated directly by a variety of treatments—by electric shocks, by the application of chemicals or by mechanical cutting or crushing. In the intact organism, of course, sensory nerve fibers are activated by the **sense organs** to which they are connected. Sense organs, like nerve fibers, respond to a variety of treatments, but each is specialized so that it is extremely sensitive to one particular kind of stimulus. The negligible amount of vinegar which can be tasted, or the least amount of vanillin which can be smelled, has no effect when applied directly to a nerve.

Sense organs may be classified according to the type of stimulus to which they are sensitive. We can distinguish (1) **chemoreceptors**—smell and taste; (2) **mechanoreceptors**—touch, pressure, hearing and balance; (3) **photoreceptors**—sight; (4) **thermoreceptors**—hot and cold; and (5) undifferentiated nerve endings which serve the pain sense. Sense organs may also be classified by the location of the stimulus: thus **exteroceptors** supply information about the surface of the body (touch, pressure, taste, heat, cold); **proprioceptors** supply information about the position of the body (stretch receptors in muscles and joints, equilibrium organs which sense orientation in the field of gravity); **distance receptors** report on objects away from the body (sight, smell and hearing), and **interoceptors** provide sensations of pain, fullness, and so on, from internal organs.

When a sense organ is stimulated continuously it may either give off a continuous stream of nerve impulses or it may quickly cease responding to the stimulus. The proprioceptors of the body are generally of the first type, nonadaptive, whereas the exteroceptors are generally **adaptive,** and soon become nonresponsive to a continuing stimulus. The advantage of sense organ adaptation is clear: it prevents a continual train of nerve impulses impinging on the brain from all the body's sense organs, yet does not interfere with the body's responding to changes in the pattern of stimuli which are likely to be important for survival.

The actual excitation of the sensitive cells of the sense organ is either via mechanical stress, via chemical stimulation by contact of the molecules of some substance from the environment, or via some chemical process induced in the sense cell by the stimulus. An example of the latter is the chemical reaction induced by light falling on the sensitive cells of the retina of the eye.

The functioning of a sense organ in animals other than man can be deduced from its morphology and nerve connections. It can be investigated by connecting the efferent nerve to an amplifier and oscilloscope, applying stimuli to the sense organ, and measuring the resulting nerve impulses. It can also be investigated at the behavioral level, by training the animal to associate one situation with a given stimulus and a second situation with a different stimulus, and then observing its ability to distinguish between the first and second stimuli as they are gradually changed to resemble each other.

Chemoreceptors. Our own senses of taste and smell can be distinguished, for the taste buds are organs in the lining of the mouth which respond to substances in watery solution, whereas the olfactory epithelium is in the lining of the nose and responds to substances which enter as gases. In most lower animals, the distinction between taste and smell is blurred, for chemoreceptors are found over much of the surface of the head and part of the body in fish, and insects have chemoreceptors in their feet. Chemoreceptors are sensitive to remarkably small amounts of certain chemicals. Most people can detect ionone, synthetic violet odor, at a concentration of one part in 30 billion parts of air. Certain male insects can detect the odor given off by the female of the species over a distance of 3 km. Several thousand different odors can be recognized by man, but there is no clear correlation between the chemical composition of a substance and its smell.

Chemoreceptors are probably the most primitive of the distance receptors, and many kinds of animals depend solely upon them for finding food, avoiding predators and meeting mates.

Mechanoreceptors. The skin of man and other mammals contains several kinds of sense organs. By making a survey of a small area of skin, point by point, and testing for regions sensitive to touch, pressure, temperature and pain, it has been found that receptors for each of these sensations are located in different spots. Then, by comparing the distribution of the types of sense organs and the types of sensations, it has been possible to identify the sense organ for each stimulus. In lower animals the sensory organs are less differentiated and the identification of a particular nerve ending with a given sensitivity is usually impossible.

The sense cells at the base of the bristles of insects are clearly mechanoreceptors, and indeed it has been possible to record impulses in the efferent nerves when the bristle is moved.

The mammalian ear is a remarkably complex organ which contains the senses of **hearing** and **equilibrium.** It can detect the direction of the force of gravity or of linear acceleration, because it contains **otoliths,** masses of calcium carbonate, attached to slender processes of cells in such a way that the weight of the otolith will pull or push on these processes. Motion of the head about any of its axes is detected by the motion of the fluid in the semicircular canals, which moves clumps of hair-like processes attached to sense cells in the walls of the canals.

Organs of balance, called otocysts or **statocysts,** are found in most phyla of animals, even in coelenterates. These are usually hollow spheres of sense cells, in the middle of which is a statolith, a particle of sand or calcium carbonate, pressed by gravity against certain sense cells. As the animal's body changes position, the statolith is pressed against different sense cells and the animal is then stimulated to regain its orientation with respect to gravity.

The detection and analysis of sound waves involves the conversion of the sound waves to mechanical vibrations of the ear drum and middle ear bones, and then to waves of motion in the liquid filling the cochlea of the inner ear. The cochlea contains many sense cells with fibers of differing lengths which respond to sounds of different frequencies. The ear is basically a mechanoreceptor responding to the mechanical displacement of sense cells, or their fibers or hairs, produced by sound waves or by changes in position.

Many arthropods, especially insects, have sense organs which respond to sound waves; these organs consist of a fine membrane stretched in such a way that it is free to respond to the vibrations of sound waves. The nerve from the sound-sensitive organ of the locust has been tapped, and recordings of the nerve impulses from it show that it can respond to sound waves between 500 and 10,000 cycles per second. The human ear responds to frequencies between 20 and 20,000 c.p.s., dogs are sensitive to sounds as high as 40,000 c.p.s., and the sensitivity of the bat ear extends to high-pitched 80,000 c.p.s. noises.

Certain insects have balance organs which have evolved from the second pair of wings.

These club-shaped structures, called **halteres,** beat up and down as the wings do and serve as "gyroscopes." When the direction of the beat is changed, sense organs in the base of the haltere are stimulated and give off nerve impulses. This has been shown by recording the nerve impulses passing though the nerves from the halteres.

Photoreceptors. Almost all animals are sensitive to light and respond to variations in light intensity. Even protozoa which have no special light-sensitive organ show a generalized ability to respond to light. Many higher animals—usually the burrowing ones—have no recognizable "eyes" but have a general sensitivity to light over all or a large part of the body. Clams, for example, respond to sudden changes in light intensity by drawing in their siphon, and earthworms withdraw into their burrows when the light intensity is increased.

Most animals, even coelenterates, have some sort of specialized structure for the perception of light. A simple invertebrate eye usually consists of a cup-shaped layer of pigment cells which screen the light-sensitive cells from light coming from all directions but one. Light-sensitive cells are embedded between these pigment cells.

The cephalopods—the octopus, squid, and relatives—alone among the invertebrates have well-developed **camera eyes** which are superficially similar to vertebrate eyes, with retina, lens, iris, cornea and a mechanism for focusing for near and far vision. Although it is difficult to determine how well an octopus can see, we can infer from the structure of the eye that it should be the functional equivalent of the vertebrate eye.

The eyes of arthropods—insects and crabs—are **mosaic eyes,** composed of many, perhaps thousands, of visual units called **ommatidia.** Each ommatidium has a clear outer cornea, under which is a lens which focuses the light on the end of the light-sensitive element made of eight or so retinal cells. These are believed to respond as a unit. Each ommatidium is separated from the adjacent ones by rings of pigment cells, so that it is a tube with light-sensitive elements at the base which can be reached only by light parallel to the axis of the tube. A mosaic eye presumably forms a very poor image composed of a series of rather large dots like a poor newspaper photograph. But a mosaic eye is particularly sensitive to the motion of objects in its surroundings, for any movement would change the amount of light falling on one or more of the ommatidia.

Thermoreceptors. Temperature-sensitive cells are found in a wide variety of animals, from the lowest to the highest. Ciliates such as paramecia will avoid warm or cold water and will collect in a region where the temperature is moderate. Some insects have thermoreceptors, either in the antennae or all over the body. Insects that suck blood from warm-blooded animals are attracted to their prey by the temperature gradients nearby. This has been shown experimentally, for blood-sucking bugs are much less able to find their prey after their antennae have been removed. Fish apparently have fairly sensitive thermoreceptors, for a change of only 0.5° C. will change the behavior of sharks and bony fish.

As far as we know, all nerve impulses are qualitatively similar. The impulse set up by the ringing of a bell is exactly like the impulse initiated by the pressure of a pin against the skin, or the impulse in the optic nerve which results from light falling on the retina. The qualitative differentiation of stimuli must depend upon the pattern of connections between sense organ and brain. The ability to distinguish red from green, hot from cold, or red from cold is due to the fact that particular sense organs and their individual sensitive cells are connected to particular parts of the brain.

5.13
Coordination and Integration

The activities of the several parts of a many-celled organism must be coordinated if that organism is to survive, and the greater the degree of complexity, the greater the specialization of the parts, the greater is the need for precise integration of their separate functions. Coordination of activity is achieved by two major systems, nervous and endocrine. The nerves and sense organs provide for rapid and precise adaptation to environmental factors. The **endocrine system,** the glands of internal secretion which secrete substances into the blood stream (or its equivalent in lower animals), provides for less rapid but longer lasting adaptations, such as general body growth, differentiation, development of sex organs and mating behavior, responses to stress, control of tissue metabolism and regulation of pigmentation. The reflexes and other nervous mechanisms by which coordination and integration are achieved will be discussed in Chapter 31.

The substances secreted by endocrine glands, called **hormones,** cannot be defined as belonging to any particular class of chemicals; some are proteins, some are amino acids and some are steroids. Hormones may be defined as substances secreted by cells in one part of the body which are carried by the blood stream to some other part where they affect cell activities in a definite and characteristic fashion. Acetylcholine and sympathin fit this definition of a hormone and are sometimes referred to as **neurohormones** to emphasize this. Whether a hormone will affect a specific tissue, and the nature of the effect produced, is a function of the tissue; each tissue will respond only to certain hormones. Hormones produced in one animal will usually affect the cells of other animals in related species, orders and even, in some cases, classes. The endocrine glands of the vertebrates will be discussed in Chapter 32.

The processes under endocrine control in invertebrates include molting, pupation and metamorphosis in arthropods, pigmentation in mollusks and arthropods, and growth and differentiation of secondary sex characteristics in annelids and arthropods. The development of insects, by a series of molts and metamorphoses, is controlled by two hormones, ecdysone and juvenile hormone. Ecdysone is secreted by the **prothoracic glands** which, in turn, are under the control of a prothoracicotropic hormone secreted by the intercerebral gland in the brain. It induces molting accompanied by metamorphosis. Juvenile hormone is secreted by the corpora allata, paired glands in the posterior head region; it permits molting but inhibits metamorphosis. Transplantation of corpora allata into developing insects prevents metamorphosis for several successive molts so that giant adults eventually result.

The leaves of yew trees and certain weeds have been found to produce substances with ecdysone-like activity. It has been postulated that the capacity to secrete these substances has evolved as a protection to the plants against moths; moth larvae eating the leaves and ingesting these substances undergo premature molting and die.

The molting of crabs and other crustaceans is a complex process involving many biochemical processes which must occur in proper sequence. This is under the control of at least two hormones, one secreted by the sinus glands in the eyestalk and the other secreted by the paired Y organs located beneath the external adductor muscles of the mandibles. The sinus glands are the expanded tips of neurosecretory cells whose nuclei constitute the X organ located on the surface of the brain. The hormones are actually produced in the X organ and released in the sinus gland (p. 277). The removal of the eyestalk results in premature molting and in more frequent successive molts. If sinus glands from other crabs are transplanted to crabs without eyestalks, molting is delayed. Thus, the hormone of the X organ inhibits and delays molting. The hormone of the Y organ triggers the first stage of molting and removal of the Y organ prevents further molting.

The development of secondary sex characteristics in members of many invertebrate phyla is under hormonal control. When the gonads are removed surgically, or destroyed by parasites, the sex characteristics either fail to form or regress if present initially. There is some evidence that the sinus gland of crustaceans and the corpora allata glands of insects secrete hormones which regulate the activity of the ovaries and thus are analogous to the gonadotropic hormones secreted by the vertebrate pituitary gland (p. 566).

Certain aspects of cellular metabolism in some invertebrates appear to be regulated by hormones, but there is no clear evidence as yet of any effect of a vertebrate hormone on cellular metabolism in any invertebrate. The sinus gland of crabs secretes a hormone which decreases basal metabolic rate; an increase in oxygen consumption follows removal of the sinus gland and a return to the normal rate follows injection of extracts of the glands. The sinus gland hormone produces an increase in the concentration of blood sugar when injected into crabs, providing another interesting parallel between the secretions of the sinus gland and those of the vertebrate pituitary.

Hormones play a role in determining **pigmentation** in the octopus, squid, crabs, insects, fish, amphibia and reptiles. In most animals, color changes are produced by streaming movements of the pigment-laden cytoplasm of the color cells (**chromatophores**). The chromatophores of the cephalopod have smooth muscle fibers attached in such a way that their contraction spreads out the pigment-containing cytoplasm. Crustaceans can be separated into two major groups, those that darken and those that lighten in color when the eyestalk is removed. Injection of eyestalk extracts has diametrically opposite effects in the two types, because of basic differences in the responses of the chromatophores. More recent experiments have shown that there are at least three different chromatophore-regulating hormones in crustaceans.

A number of endocrine organs are closely associated with the nervous system and undoubtedly evolved from such tissue; others evolved independently of the nervous system. It would seem useless to try to argue which is the more "primitive" coordinating system— nervous or endocrine. Both had their earliest traces in very primitive, single-celled animals and each type evolved independently of the other to its present state.

QUESTIONS

1. Distinguish the types of animal nutrition. Give an example of each.
2. Discuss the similarities and differences of the process of digestion in ameba, planaria, earthworm and man.
3. What is the function of the rumen, the gizzard, the pancreas, the atrium and the hemocoel?
4. How would you define a vitamin? What difficulty is involved in formulating this definition?
5. Compare the circulatory systems of a proboscis worm, an earthworm and a caterpillar.
6. Define "partial pressure" and "tension" of a gas.
7. Contrast direct and indirect respiration. What are the characteristics of an effective respiratory surface?
8. Discuss briefly the role of hemoglobin in the transport of oxygen and carbon dioxide.
9. Compare the excretion of nitrogenous wastes in ameba, earthworm, insect and man.
10. Discuss the advantages and disadvantages of exoskeletons and endoskeletons.
11. What functions may be served by the skin of an animal?
12. Compare the processes of ameboid, ciliary and muscular motion.
13. What is the explanation of the "all-or-none" response of a motor unit to stimulation?
14. Describe the sequence of events in a single muscle twitch.
15. What is meant by tetanus, tonus and oxygen debt?
16. Compare the transmission of an impulse along a nerve fiber and across a synapse.
17. Compare the physiologic properties of the two major coordinating systems of vertebrates. To what extent are these present in invertebrates?

ANNOTATED REFERENCES

Baldwin, E. B.: An Introduction to Comparative Biochemistry. 4th ed. New York, Cambridge University Press, 1964. A fascinating presentation of principles and facts relative to the various physiologic and biochemical adaptations evolved by animals to enable them to survive.

Florey, E.: General and Comparative Animal Physiology. Philadelphia, W. B. Saunders Co., 1966. An excellent treatise of the functional aspects of a wide range of vertebrates and invertebrates.

Prosser, C. L., and F. A. Brown: Comparative Animal Physiology. 2nd ed. Philadelphia, W. B. Saunders Co., 1961. Contains a wealth of information about the physiologic adaptations of vertebrates and invertebrates.

Schmidt-Nielsen, K.: Animal Physiology. 2nd ed. Englewood Cliffs, N.J., Prentice-Hall, Inc., 1964. A brief treatment in paperback form that covers the essentials of physiologic processes in animals.

Popular, relatively nontechnical accounts of many of the subjects discussed in this chapter are among the Scientific American articles published as offprints by the Wm. Freeman Co., San Francisco.

6 _____ REPRODUCTION

The processes needed for the day-to-day survival of the organism—nutrition, respiration, excretion, coordination, and the rest—were discussed in the preceding chapter. The survival of the species as a whole requires that its individual members multiply, that they produce new individuals to replace the ones killed by predators, parasites or old age. One of the fundamental tenets of biology, "omne vivum ex vivo" (all life comes only from living things), is an expression of this basic characteristic of all living things, their ability to reproduce their kind.

For centuries it was believed that many animals could arise from nonliving material by "spontaneous generation." For example, maggots and flies were thought to originate from dead animals, and frogs and rats to come from river mud. The classic experiments which disproved the theory of spontaneous generation were performed by Francesco Redi about 1670. By the simple expedient of placing a piece of meat in each of three jars, leaving one uncovered, covering the second with fine gauze and the third with parchment, he demonstrated that although all three pieces of meat decayed, maggots appeared only on the uncovered meat. Maggots do not come from decaying meat, but hatch from eggs laid on the meat by blowflies. With the development of lenses and microscopes, and the subsequent increase in knowledge of eggs and larval forms, we now know that no animal arises by spontaneous generation.

The process of reproduction varies tremendously from one kind of animal to another, but we can distinguish two basic types: asexual and sexual. In **asexual reproduction** a single parent splits, buds or fragments to give rise to two or more offspring which have hereditary traits identical with those of the parent. **Sexual reproduction** involves two individuals; each supplies a specialized reproductive cell, a **gamete.** The male gamete, the **sperm,** subsequently fuses with the female gamete, the **egg,** to form the **zygote** or fertilized egg. The egg is typically large and nonmotile and contains yolk which supplies nutrients for the embryo which results if the egg is fertilized. The sperm is typically much smaller and motile, adapted to swim actively to the egg by the lashing movements of its long, filamentous tail. Sexual reproduction is advantageous biologically for it makes possible the recombination of the best inherited characteristics of the two parents and provides for the possibility that some of the offspring may be better adapted to survive than either parent was.

6.1
Asexual Reproduction

Asexual reproduction occurs commonly in plants, protozoa, coelenterates, bryozoa and tunicates but may occur even in the highest animals. The production of **identical twins** by the splitting of a single fertilized egg is a kind of asexual reproduction. The splitting of the body of the parent into two more or less equal daughter parts, which become new whole organisms, is called **fission.** Fission occurs chiefly among single-celled animals and plants; the cell division involved is mitotic. Coelenterates typically reproduce by **budding;** a small part of the parent's body becomes differentiated and separate from the rest. It develops into a complete new individual and may take up independent existence, or the buds from a single parent may remain attached as a colony of many individuals.

Salamanders, lizards, starfish and crabs can grow a new tail, leg or other organ if the original one is lost. When this ability to regenerate the whole from a part is extremely marked it becomes a method of reproduction. The body of the parent may break into several pieces and each piece then develops into a whole animal by regenerating the missing parts. A whole starfish can be regenerated from a single arm.

One class of protozoa, the Sporozoa, characteristically reproduce asexually by means of **spores,** special cells with resistent coverings which withstand unfavorable environmental conditions. An interesting example of reproduction by spore formation is the parasitic protozoan, *Plasmodium,* which causes **malaria.** The organism has a complex life cycle in-

volving man and the *Anopheles* mosquito (Fig. 6.1). The malaria organisms enter the human blood stream when an infected mosquito bites a man. They enter the red blood cells and each *Plasmodium* divides into 12 to 24 spores which are released when the red cell bursts later on. The released spores infect new red cells and the process is repeated. The simultaneous bursting of billions of red cells causes the malarial **chill,** followed by **fever** as the toxic substances released penetrate to other organs of the body. If a second, uninfected mosquito bites the man, it will suck up some *Plasmodium* spores along with its drink of blood. A complicated process of sexual reproduction ensues within the mosquito's stomach and new spores are formed, some of which migrate into the mosquito's

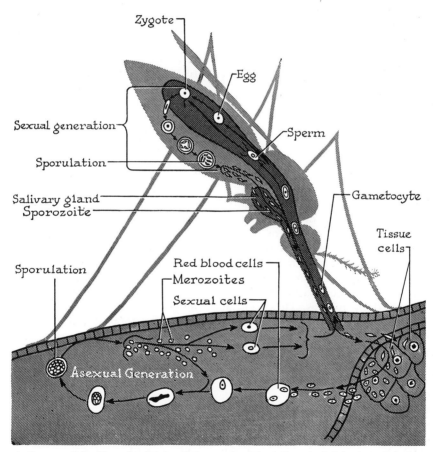

Figure 6.1 A diagram of the life cycle of the malaria parasite, *Plasmodium*. An infected mosquito bites a man and injects some *Plasmodium* sporozoites into his blood stream. These reproduce asexually by sporulation within the red blood cells of the host. The infected red cells rupture and the new crop of merozoites released then infects other red cells. The bursting of the red cells releases toxic substances which cause the periodic fever and chill. In time some merozoites become gametocytes which can infect a mosquito if one bites the man. The gametocytes develop into eggs and sperm and undergo sexual reproduction in the mosquito, and the zygote, by sporulation, produces sporozoites which migrate to the salivary glands.

salivary glands and are ready to infect the next man bitten.

6.2
Sexual Reproduction

Sexual reproduction is characterized by the development of a new individual from a zygote, or fertilized egg, produced in turn by the fusion of two sex cells, an egg and a sperm. Certain protozoa have a complicated process of sexual reproduction in which two individuals come together and fuse temporarily along their oral surfaces. The nucleus of each one divides several times before one of the resulting daughter nuclei migrates across to the other animal and fuses with one of its nuclei. Following this the two animals separate and each reproduces asexually by fission. Paramecia are not differentiated morphologically into sexes, but T. M. Sonneborn has shown that there are as many as eight distinct, genetically determined **mating types.** A member of one mating group will mate only with some member of another group.

6.3
Meiosis

The mitotic process is remarkably constant and ensures that the number of chromosomes per cell will remain unchanged through successive cell generations. The fusion of an egg and a sperm to form a fertilized egg would result in a doubling of the chromosome number in each successive generation if all cell divisions occurred by mitosis. However, at some point in the succession of cell divisions which constitute the life cycle of an individual—from the original fertilized egg through development, growth and maturation to the production of the fertilized egg in the next generation—there occurs a different type of cell division, called **meiosis.** In the higher animals, and in most of the lower ones, meiotic divisions occur during the formation gametes. Meiosis is essentially a pair of cell divisions during which the chromosome number is reduced to half (Fig. 6.2). Thus the gametes contain only half as many chromosomes as the somatic cells, and when two gametes unite at fertilization, the fusion of

their nuclei reconstitutes the normal number of chromosomes.

The reduction in chromosome number occurs in a very regular way. Chromosomes occur in *pairs* of similar chromosomes in somatic cells. As a result of meiosis, each gamete contains one and only one of each kind of chromosome, i.e., one complete set of chromosomes. This is accomplished by the **synapsis,** or longitudinal pairing, of like chromosomes and the subsequent separation of the members of the pair, one going to each pole. The like chromosomes which undergo synapsis during meiosis are called **homologous chromosomes.** They are identical in size and shape, have identical chromomeres along their length and contain similar hereditary factors. A set of one of each kind of chromosome is called the **haploid number** (n); a set of two of each kind is called the **diploid number** (2n). Gametes have the haploid number (e.g., 23 in man) and fertilized eggs and all the cells of the body have the diploid number (46 for man). A fertilized egg gets exactly half of its chromosomes (and half of its genes) from its mother and half from its father. Only the last two cell divisions which result in mature, functional eggs or sperm are meiotic; all other ones are mitotic.

Each of the meiotic divisions has the same four stages, prophase, metaphase, anaphase and telophase, found in mitosis. The chief differences between mitotic and meiotic divisions are seen in the prophase of the first meiotic division. Chromosomes appear as long thin threads which begin to contract and get thicker. The homologous chromosomes undergo synapsis, they pair longitudinally and come to lie side by side along their entire length, twisting around each other. Each then becomes visibly double, as in mitosis, so that it consists of two threads. By synapsis and doubling, a bundle of four homologous chromatids, called a **tetrad,** is formed. Each pair of chromosomes gives rise to a bundle of four, so there are as many tetrads as the haploid number of chromosomes (23 in man). The centromeres have not divided and there are only two centromeres for the four chromatids.

While these events are occurring the centriole divides, the two daughter centrioles go to opposite poles of the cell, a spindle appears between the centrioles, and the nuclear membrane dissolves. The tetrads

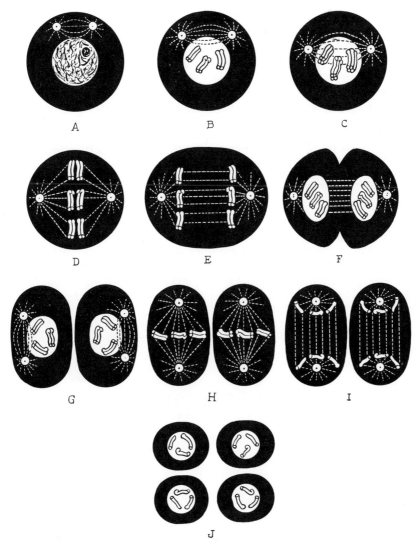

Figure 6.2 Meiosis in a hypothetical animal with a diploid chromosome number of six. It has three pairs of chromosomes, of which one is short, one is long with a hook at the end, and one is long and knobbed. *A,* Early prophase of the first meiotic division: chromosomes begin to appear. *B,* Synapsis: the pairing of the homologous chromosomes. *C,* Apparent doubling of the synapsed chromosomes to form groups of four identical chromatids, tetrads. *D,* Metaphase of the first meiotic division: the chromatids migrating toward the poles. *F,* Telophase of the first meiotic division. *G,* Prophase of the second meiotic division. *H,* Metaphase of the second meiotic division. *I,* Anaphase of the second meiotic division. *J,* Mature gametes, each of which contains only one of each kind of chromosome.

then line up on the equatorial plate; this constitutes the metaphase of the first meiotic division. In the anaphase the daughter chromatids formed from each chromosome, still united by their single centromere, move as a unit to the poles. Thus the homologous chromosomes of each pair, but not the daughter chromatids of each chromosome, are separated in the first meiotic anaphase. In mitosis, in contrast, the centromeres do divide and

the daughter chromatids pass to opposite poles. At telophase each pole has the haploid number of double chromosomes.

Typically, there is no interphase between first and second meiotic divisions, but the centrioles divide again, new spindles form (at right angles to the axis of the original spindle) and the haploid number of double chromosomes lines up on the equators of the spindles. Thus, the telophase of the first

meiotic division and the prophase of the
second are usually short and blurred together.
The lining up of the chromosomes on the
spindle constitutes the metaphase of the
second division. The metaphases of the first
and second meiotic divisions can be distinguished because in the first the chromosomes
are arranged in bundles of four and in the
second the chromosomes are arranged in
bundles of two. There is no further doubling
of the chromosomes; the centromeres divide and the daughter chromatids, now
chromosomes, separate and pass to the poles.

In the anaphase of the second meiotic
division a haploid set of single chromosomes
passes to each pole. In the telophase, the cytoplasm divides, the chromosomes become
longer, thinner and less easily seen, and a
nuclear membrane forms around them. The
net result of the two meiotic divisions is a
group of four nuclei, each of which contains
the haploid number of chromosomes, that is,
one and only one of each kind of chromosome. These cells are mature gametes and do
not undergo any further mitotic or meiotic
divisions.

The term **gonad** refers to the glands which
produce gametes, the **testis** of the male and
the **ovary** of the female. The meiotic process
is fundamentally the same in ovary and testis
but there are a few differences in detail.

6.4
Spermatogenesis

A typical testis consists of thousands of
cylindrical **sperm tubules,** in each of which
develop billions of sperm. The walls of the
sperm tubules are lined with unspecialized

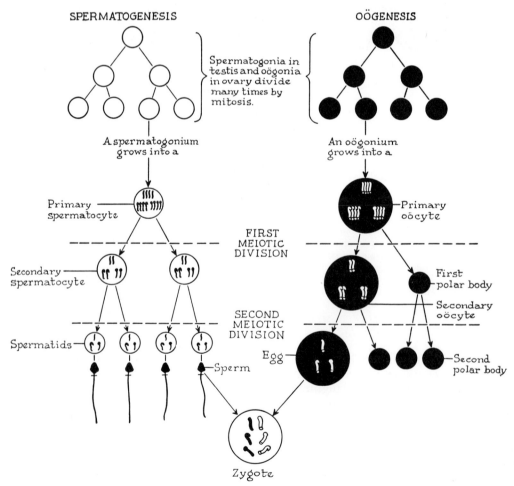

Figure 6.3 Comparison of the formation of sperm and eggs.

germ cells called **spermatogonia.** Throughout development, the spermatogonia divide by mitosis and give rise to additional spermatogonia to provide for the growth of the testis. After sexual maturity, some spermatogonia begin to undergo **spermatogenesis,** which includes the two meiotic divisions followed by the cellular changes which result in mature sperm. Other spermatogonia continue to divide mitotically and produce additional spermatogonia for spermatogenesis at a later time. In most wild animals, there is a breeding season, either in spring or fall, during which the testis increases in size and spermato-

genesis occurs. Between breeding seasons the testis is usually small and contains only spermatogonia. In other animals, including man and most domestic animals, spermatogenesis continues throughout the year once sexual maturity has been attained.

The first step in spermatogenesis is the growth of the spermatogonia into larger cells, the **primary spermatocytes** (Fig. 6.3). Each primary spermatocyte divides (first meiotic division) into two cells of equal size, the **secondary spermatocytes.** These, in turn, divide (second meiotic division) to yield four equal-sized **spermatids.** The spermatid,

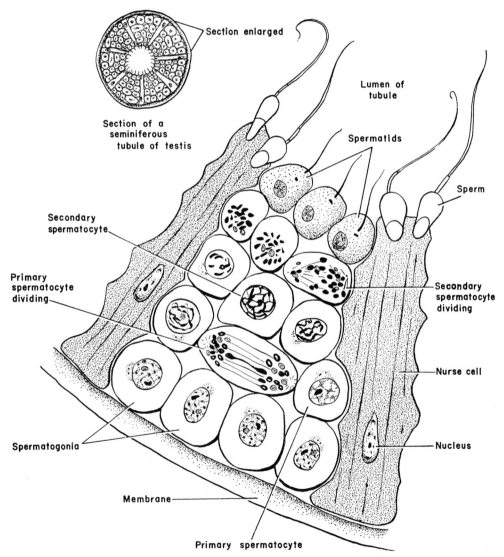

Figure 6.4 Diagram of part of a section of a human seminiferous tubule to show the stages in spermatogenesis and in the transformation of a spermatid into a mature sperm. (Villee: Biology, 5th ed.)

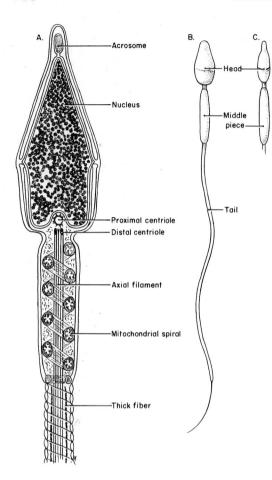

Figure 6.5 *A*, Diagram of the head and middle piece of a mammalian sperm, greatly enlarged, as seen in the electron microscope. *B* and *C*, Top and side views of a sperm seen by light microscopy. (Villee: Biology, 5th ed.)

Figure 6.6 Spermatozoa from different species of vertebrates, illustrating the differences in size and shape. *1*, Gastropod. *2*, Ascaris. *3*, Hermit crab. *4*, Salamander. *5*, Frog. *6*, Chicken. *7*, Rat. *8*, Sheep. *9*, Man. (Villee: Biology, 5th ed.)

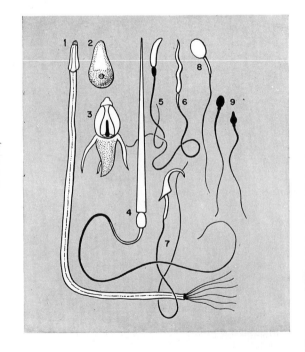

a spherical cell with quite a bit of cytoplasm, is a mature gamete with the haploid number of chromosomes. Further changes (but no cell division) are required to convert it into a functional **spermatozoan.** The nucleus shrinks in size, becomes more dense, and forms the head of the sperm (Fig. 6.4). Most of the cytoplasm is shed, but some of the Golgi bodies aggregate at the anterior end of the sperm and form a point (the acrosome) which may be of some value in puncturing the cell membrane of the egg.

The two centrioles of the spermatid move to a position just in back of the nucleus. A small depression appears on the surface of the nucleus and the proximal centriole takes up a position in the depression. The distal centriole gives rise to the axial filament of the sperm tail (Fig. 6.5). Like the axial filament of flagella, it consists of two longitudinal fibers in the center and a ring of nine pairs or doublets of longitudinal fibers surrounding the two.

The mitochondria move to the point where head and tail join and form a middle piece. This provides energy for the beating of the tail which drives the sperm forward. Most of the cytoplasm of the spermatid is discarded; only a thin sheath remains surrounding the mitochondria in the middle piece and the axial filament of the tail.

The mature spermatozoa of different species exhibit a wide range of sizes and shapes (Fig. 6.6). The sperm of a few animals, such as the parasitic roundworm *Ascaris*, lack tails and crawl along by ameboid motion. Crabs and lobsters have curious tailless sperm with three pointed projections on the head. These hold the sperm in position on the surface of the egg while the middle piece uncoils like a spring and pushes the sperm nucleus into the egg cytoplasm, thereby accomplishing fertilization.

6.5
Oögenesis

The immature sex cells in the ovary, **oögonia,** undergo successive mitotic divisions to form additional oögonia during development. When the individual reaches sexual maturity, some of the oögonia develop into large **primary oöcytes.** These are typically much larger than the corresponding

primary spermatocytes and contain **yolk,** which will serve as food in the event the egg is fertilized. Some of the "morphogenetic substances" which subsequently regulate the development of the fertilized egg are formed at this time. When it has completed its growth phase the primary oöcyte divides by the first meiotic division (Fig. 6.3). The two daughter cells, however, are not of equal size. One, the **secondary oöcyte,** receives essentially all the cytoplasm and yolk while the other, the **first polar body,** is essentially a bare nucleus.

The secondary oöcyte divides by the second meiotic division, again with an unequal division of cytoplasm, to yield a large **oötid,** with essentially all the yolk and cytoplasm, and a small **second polar body.** (The first polar body may divide at about the same time into two additional polar bodies.) The oötid undergoes further changes (but no cell division) and becomes a mature **ovum** (egg). The polar bodies disintegrate and disappear, so that each primary oöcyte forms a single ovum, in contrast to the four sperm derived from each primary spermatocyte. The formation of the polar bodies is a device to enable the maturing egg to get rid of its excess chromosomes, and the unequal division of the cytoplasm ensures the mature egg enough cytoplasm and yolk to survive and develop if it is fertilized.

The union of a haploid set of chromosomes from the sperm with another haploid set from the egg during fertilization re-establishes the diploid chromosome number. The fertilized egg, and all the body cells which develop from it, have the diploid number, two of each kind. Each individual gets half of his chromosomes (and half of his genes) from his father and half from his mother. Because of the nature of genic interaction, the offspring may resemble one parent much more than the other, but the two parents make equal contributions to its inheritance.

6.6
Reproductive Systems

In some of the simpler invertebrates, such as the coelenterates, the testes and ovaries are the only sex structures present, and eggs and sperm are released directly from the gonads into the surrounding water. Most animals, however, have a system of ducts and glands which serve to carry gametes from the gonad to the exterior of the body and to protect and nourish them during the process.

Many of the lower animals are **hermaphroditic;** both ovaries and testes are present in the same individual and it produces both eggs and sperm. Some hermaphroditic animals, the parasitic tapeworms, for example, are capable of **self-fertilization.** Since a particular host animal may be infected with but one parasite, hermaphroditism is an important adaptation for the survival of the parasitic species. Most hermaphrodites, however, do not reproduce by self-fertilization; in the earthworm, for example, two animals copulate and each inseminates the other. In certain other species, e.g., the oyster, self-fertilization is impossible because the testes and ovaries produce gametes at different times.

The reproductive systems of different species have a fundamentally similar plan, but many variations on the theme are evident. The gonads and their ducts may be single, paired or multiple, perhaps present in several segments of the body.

Sperm, produced in the coiled seminiferous tubules of the testis, are transported in a series of ducts to the exterior (p. 514), suspended in **seminal fluid,** secreted by glands associated with the reproductive tract. Seminal fluid contains glucose and fructose which the sperm metabolize, buffers which protect the sperm from the acids normally present in the urethra and female tract, and mucous materials which lubricate the passages through which the sperm travel.

In many vertebrates a number of accessory structures have developed to facilitate the transfer of sperm from the male to the female reproductive tract and to provide a place for the development of the fertilized egg. These structures have evolved either from or in close association with the urinary system, and the two together are frequently referred to as the **urogenital system.** In the male mammal, for example, the **vasa deferentia** empty into the **urethra,** which also carries urine from the bladder to the outside. The urethra of mammals is surrounded by the external reproductive organ, the **penis.** This consists of three columns of **erectile tissue**—spongy venous spaces which become filled with blood during sexual excitement to produce an erection of the penis.

Eggs are produced in the ovaries of the female and are typically surrounded and nourished by **nurse cells** during their development. At the time of ovulation, the eggs are released from the ovary into the abdominal cavity, whence they pass into the funnel-shaped end of the **oviduct** (p. 514). Eggs are moved along the oviduct by the peristaltic contractions of its muscular wall or by the beating of cilia lining the lumen of the duct. The yolk of the bird's egg is formed while the egg is still within the ovary, but the egg white and shell are added by glands in the wall of the oviduct. The oviducts may open directly to the exterior or they may expand into a terminal duct, the **uterus,** which is a thick-walled muscular pouch in which the young develop. In mammals the uterus is connected with the exterior by the **vagina,** which is adapted to receive the penis of the male during copulation. Female mammals have a **clitoris,** the homologue of the male penis, just anterior to the opening of the vagina; it contains sense organs and erectile tissue which becomes engorged with blood during sexual excitement.

6.7
Fertilization

The union of an egg and sperm is called **fertilization.** Most aquatic animals deliver their eggs and sperm directly into the surrounding water and the union of egg and sperm occurs there by chance meeting. This primitive and rather uncertain method of uniting the gametes is called **external fertilization.** Such animals usually have no accessory sex structures.

In other animals, fertilization occurs within the body of the female, usually in the oviduct, after the sperm have been transferred from the male to the female by copulation or by some other means. This method of **internal fertilization** requires some cooperation between the two sexes, and many species have evolved elaborate patterns of **mating behavior** to ensure that the two sexes are brought together, mate at the most appropriate time, and take care of the resulting offspring. The male salamander, for example, mounts and clasps the female, stroking her nose with his chin. He then dismounts in front of her and deposits a **spermatophore,** a packet of sperm. She picks up the spermatophore and stuffs it into her cloaca, where the packet breaks, the sperm are released, and fertilization follows.

Fertilization involves not only the penetration of the egg by the sperm, but the union of the egg and sperm nuclei and the activation of the egg to undergo cleavage and development (Fig. 6.7). The egg may be in any stage from primary oöcyte to mature ovum at the time of sperm penetration, but the fusion of the sperm and egg nuclei occurs only after the egg has matured. There is experimental evidence that the eggs of some species secrete a substance, **fertilizin**, which is an important constituent of the jelly coat surrounding the egg. Fertilizin causes the sperm to clump together and stick to the surface of the egg. Other extracts of the egg jelly, which may be identical with fertilizin, stimulate sperm motility and respiration and prolong sperm viability.

After the entrance of one sperm, a **fertilization membrane** forms around the eggs of some species which prevents the entrance of other sperm. This prevents polyspermy and the possibility of the fusion of more than one sperm nucleus with the egg nucleus. It can be shown experimentally that such fusion of two or more sperm nuclei with one egg nucleus leads to abnormal development.

Eggs can be stimulated to cleave and develop without fertilization. The development of an unfertilized egg into an adult is known as **parthenogenesis** (virgin birth). Some species of arthropods have been found which apparently consist solely of females which reproduce parthenogenetically. In other species, parthenogenesis occurs for several generations, then some males are produced which develop and mate with the females. The queen honeybee is fertilized by a male just once during her lifetime, in her "nuptial flight." The sperm are stored in a pouch connected with the genital tract and closed by a muscular valve. If sperm are released from the pouch as she lays eggs, fertilization occurs and the eggs develop into females—queens and workers. If the eggs are not fertilized they develop into males—drones.

Changes in temperature, in pH or in the salt content of the surrounding water, or chemical or mechanical stimulation of the egg itself will stimulate many eggs to parthenogenetic development. A variety of marine invertebrates, frogs, salamanders, and even rabbits have been produced parthenogenetically. The resulting adult animals are generally weaker and smaller than normal and are infertile.

The females of all birds, most insects, and many aquatic invertebrates lay eggs from which the young eventually hatch; such animals are said to be **oviparous** (egg-bearing). In contrast, mammals produce small eggs which are kept in the uterus and provided with nutrients from the mother's blood until development has proceeded to the stage where they can exist independently, to some extent at least. Such animals are said to be **viviparous** (live-bearing). In certain other forms—some insects, sharks, lizards and certain snakes—the female is **ovoviviparous;** she produces large, yolk-filled eggs which are retained within the female reproductive tract for a considerable period of development. The developing embryo forms no close connection with the wall of the oviduct or uterus and receives no nourishment from the mother.

The number of eggs produced by each female of a given species and the chance that any particular egg will survive to maturity are inversely related. In the evolution of the

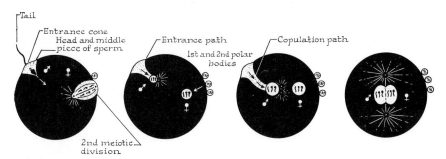

Figure 6.7　Diagram of the stages in the process of fertilization, the union of the egg and sperm.

vertebrates from fish to mammals, the trend has been toward the production of fewer eggs, and the development of better parental care of the young. Fish such as the cod or salmon produce millions of eggs each year, but only a small number of these ever become adult fish; in contrast, mammals have few offspring but take good care of them so that the majority attain maturity. Fish and amphibia generally take no care of developing eggs, which are simply deposited in water and left to complete development unaided. The eggs of reptiles are usually laid in earth or sand and develop there without parental care, warmed by the sun. Birds, in contrast, have a complex behavior pattern for nest-building, incubating the eggs by sitting on them and caring for the newly hatched youngsters. The mammalian egg develops within the mother's uterus, where it is safe from predators and from harmful factors in the environment. Most mammals have a strong "maternal instinct" to take care of the newborn until they can shift for themselves. This pattern of behavior is, to a large extent, controlled by hormones secreted by the pituitary gland and ovary.

Many animals have other special types of behavior, or "breeding habits" to ensure successful reproduction. A number of vertebrate and invertebrate species have characteristic courting and mating behavior patterns which may be dangerous or even fatal to the individual, yet ensure the continuation of the species. Salmon swim hundreds of miles upstream to spawn and die, male spiders are frequently eaten by the females they have fertilized, and so on.

6.8

Embryonic Development

The division, growth and differentiation of a fertilized egg into the remarkably complex and interdependent system of organs which is the adult animal is certainly one of the most fascinating of all biologic phenomena. Not only are the organs complicated, and reproduced in each new individual with extreme fidelity of pattern, but many of these organs begin to function while they are still developing. The human heart begins to beat, for example, during the fourth week of gestation, long before its development is completed.

The early stages of development of practically all multicellular animals are fundamentally similar; differences in development become evident somewhat later.

When fertilization has been accomplished, the zygote divides repeatedly by mitosis, forming a ball of smaller cells known as a **blastula.** These early cell divisions by which a many-celled embryo is formed are called **cleavage.** The pattern of cell division is determined largely by the amount of yolk present in the egg. An **isolecithal egg** has a relatively small amount of yolk distributed more or less evenly throughout the cytoplasm. **Telolecithal eggs** have a large amount of yolk which is more concentrated at the lower or **vegetal pole** of the egg; the metabolically active cytoplasm is concentrated at the upper or **animal pole.** The frog egg is about half yolk and a bird egg is more than 95 per cent yolk; the cytoplasm of the latter is restricted to a small disc at the animal pole. The insect egg is an example of a **centrolecithal** one; the yolk accumulates in the center of the egg and is surrounded by a thin layer of cytoplasm.

The line of the first division in the cleavage of an isolecithal egg passes through the animal and vegetal poles of the egg and forms two equal cells, called **blastomeres** (Fig. 6.8). The second cleavage division passes through animal and vegetal poles at right angles to the first and divides the two cells into four. The third cleavage division is horizontal. Its plane is at right angles to the planes of the first two divisions, and the embryo is split into four cells above and four below this line of cleavage. Further divisions result in embryos containing 16, 32, 64, 128 cells and so on until a hollow ball of cells, the **blastula,** results. The wall of the blastula consists of a single layer of cells, and the cavity in the center of the sphere, filled with fluid, is called the **blastocoele.** Each of the cells in the blastula is small, and the total mass of the blastula is less than that of the original fertilized egg, for some of the stored food was used up in the cleavage process.

The single-layered blastula is soon converted into a double-layered sphere, a **gastrula,** by the process of gastrulation. In isolecithal eggs, gastrulation occurs by the pushing in (**invagination**) of a section of one wall of the blastula (Fig. 6.9). This pushed-in wall eventually meets the opposite wall and the original blastocoele is obliterated. The new cavity of the gastrula is the **archenteron** (prim-

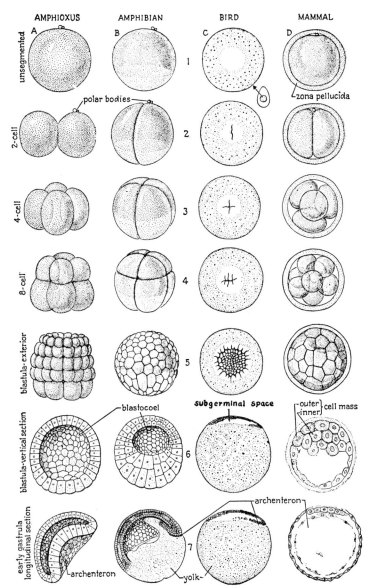

Figure 6.8 Stages in cleavage and early gastrulation in eggs of chordates. *A, Amphioxus* (holoblastic cleavage, isolecithal egg with little yolk). *B*, Frog (holoblastic cleavage, moderately telolecithal egg with much yolk). *C*, Bird (meroblastic discoidal cleavage, telolecithal egg with much yolk). *D*, Mammal (holoblastic cleavage, isolecithal egg with essentially no yolk). (From Storer and Usinger: General Zoology, 3rd ed. Copyright, 1957, by McGraw-Hill Book Co., Inc.)

itive gut), the rudiment of the digestive system. The opening of the archenteron to the outside is the **blastopore,** which marks the site of the invagination which produced gastrulation. The outer of the two walls of the gastrula is the **ectoderm,** which eventually forms the skin and nervous system. The inner layer, lining the archenteron, is the **endoderm,** which will form the digestive tract, liver, pancreas and lungs.

Cleavage and gastrulation are markedly modified in telolecithal eggs by the presence of the large amount of yolk. In the frog egg, which may be called moderately telolecithal, the cleavage divisions in the lower part of the egg are slowed by the presence of the inert yolk. The resulting blastula consists of many small cells at the animal pole and a few large cells at the vegetal pole. The lower wall of the blastula is much thicker than the upper one and the blastocoele is flattened and displaced upward. Only the small disc of cytoplasm at

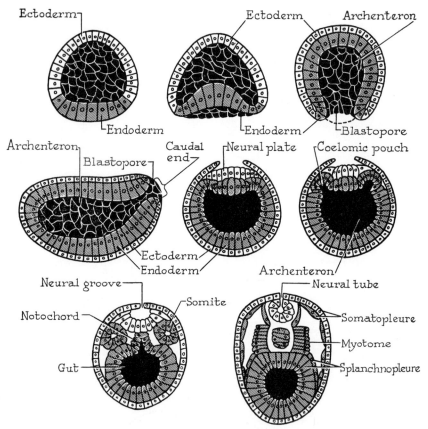

Figure 6.9 Stages in gastrulation and mesoderm formation in *Amphioxus*. Note that the mesoderm forms by the budding of pouches from the archenteron.

the animal pole of the hen's egg undergoes cleavage divisions; the lower, yolk-filled part of the egg never cleaves. The shallow cavity under the dividing cells is called the subgerminal space, since it is not homologous to the blastocoele of the frog egg. Gastrulation occurs in both frog and chick egg, and an archenteron is formed, but the process is greatly modified by the presence of the yolk. Gastrulation in the frog involves an invagination of the yolk-filled cells of the vegetal pole, a turning in of cells at the dorsal lip of the blastopore (**involution**), and a growth of ectoderm down and over the cells of the vegetal pole (**epiboly**) (Fig. 6.10).

In all multicellular animals, except sponges and coelenterates, which never develop beyond the gastrula stage, a third layer of cells, the **mesoderm,** develops between ectoderm and endoderm. In annelids, mollusks and certain other invertebrates, the mesoderm develops from special cells which are differentiated early in cleavage (p. 204). These migrate to the interior and come to lie between the ectoderm and endoderm. They then multiply to form two longitudinal cords of cells which develop into sheets of mesoderm between the ectoderm and endoderm. The coelomic cavity originates by the splitting of the sheets to form pockets and, hence, is called a **schizocoele.**

In primitive chordates the mesoderm arises as a series of bilateral pouches from the endoderm (Fig. 6.9). These lose their connection with the gut and fuse one with another to form a connected layer. The cavity of the pouches is retained as the coelom, which is called an **enterocoele** because it is derived indirectly from the archenteron. The mesoderm in amphibia is formed in part from the endoderm of the roof of the archenteron and in part from the ectoderm and endoderm at the dorsal lip of the blastopore (Fig. 6.10). In birds and mammals the **primitive streak** which develops on the surface of the developing embryo is homologous to the dorsal lip of the blastopore of lower forms. It is a thickened band of ectoderm and endoderm cells which marks the longitudinal axis of the embryo. At the primitive streak, cells migrate in from the surface, proliferate and form a sheet of mesoderm between ectoderm and endoderm. The primitive streak is a center of growth for ectoderm and endoderm as well as for mesoderm and plays a role in determining the position and order of appearance of the various parts of the embryo.

However the mesoderm may originate, it typically forms two sheets which grow laterally and anteriorly between the ectoderm and endoderm; one sheet becomes attached to the inner endoderm and the other to the outer ectoderm. The cavity between the two becomes the **coelom,** or body cavity. The layer of mesoderm associated with the endoderm forms the muscles of the digestive tract.

The primitive skeleton of the chordates, the **notochord,** is a flexible, unsegmented, longitudinal rod found in the dorsal midline of all chordate embryos. It is formed at the same time and in a similar way as the mesoderm—as an outgrowth of the roof of the archenteron, from the dorsal lip of the blastopore, or from the primitive streak. Later in the development of vertebrates the notochord is replaced by the **vertebral column,** derived from part of the mesoderm.

The nervous system of chordates is derived from the ectoderm overlying the notochord. This first forms a thickened plate of cells, the **neural plate;** the center of the plate becomes depressed while the lateral edges rise as two longitudinal neural folds. The folds eventually meet dorsally and form a hollow **neural tube.** The cavity of the tube becomes the central canal of the spinal cord and the ventricles of the brain.

The sheets of mesoderm grow ventrally and the ones from either side meet in the ventral midline; the coelomic cavities on the two sides then fuse into one. The mesoderm grows dorsally along each side of the notochord and neural tube and becomes differentiated into segmental blocks of tissue, the **somites,** from which the main muscles of the trunk develop. Other mesodermal cells become detached from the inner border of the somites, migrate inward, surround the notochord and neural tube, and develop into the **vertebrae.** The kidneys and their ducts, and the gonads and their ducts, are derived from the mesoderm originally located between the somites and the coelom.

The contributions of each germ layer to the development of a typical mammal are summarized in Table 6.1.

The details of vertebrate development will be given in Chapter 33.

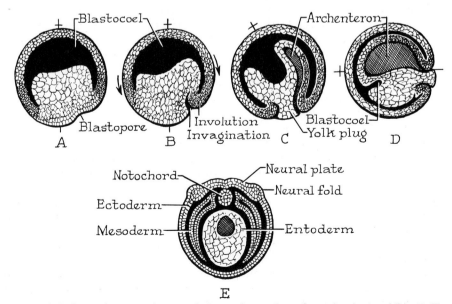

Figure 6.10 *A–D,* Successive stages in gastrulation and mesoderm formation in Amphibia. *E,* Transverse section of an early neurula stage.

Table 6.1 Derivatives of Germ Layers and Mammalian Development

Ectoderm	Endoderm	Mesoderm
Epidermis of the skin	Lining of gut	Muscles—smooth, skeletal and cardiac
Hair and nails	Lining of trachea, bronchi and lungs	Dermis of skin
Sweat glands	Liver	Connective tissue, bone and cartilage
Brain, spinal cord, ganglia, nerves	Pancreas	Dentin of teeth
Receptor cells of sense organs	Lining of gallbladder	Blood and blood vessels
Lens of the eye	Thyroid, parathyroid and thymus glands	Mesenteries
Lining of mouth, nostrils and anus	Urinary bladder	Kidneys
Enamel of teeth	Lining of urethra	Testes and ovaries

6.9

Protection of the Embryo

The egg and the developing embryo are, in general, very susceptible to unfavorable environmental conditions, and a variety of adaptations have evolved in invertebrates and vertebrates to tide the embryo over this critical period.

The eggs of many parasitic worms are covered with **shells** which enable them to survive exposure to heat, cold, desiccation and digestive juices. The skate egg is covered by a tough leathery case that protects the developing embryo within. The eggs of most fish and amphibia are surrounded by a **jelly coat** which is of some value in protecting against mechanical shock. The eggs of reptiles and birds are protected by tough leathery or calcareous shells. The developing chick embryo takes in oxygen and gives off carbon dioxide through its shell.

The eggs of fish and amphibia are fairly large and contain yolk which supplies the nutrients for the developing embryo. These eggs are laid and typically develop in water, whence the oxygen, salts and water required for development are obtained. The embryos develop a pouch-like outgrowth of the digestive tract, the **yolk sac,** which grows around the yolk, elaborates enzymes to digest it, and transports the products in its blood vessels to the rest of the embryo.

The eggs of reptiles and birds develop on land rather than in water, and further adaptations were required to permit development in the absence of the large body of water. These forms have three additional membranes, the **amnion, chorion** and **allantois,** which are sheets of living tissue that grow out of the embryo itself. The amnion and chorion develop as folds of the body wall and surround the embryo; the allantois grows out of the digestive tract and functions along with the yolk sac in nutrition, excretion and respiration. Each of these membranes is composed of two germ layers in close apposition.

The formation of the amnion is a complex process and its details differ in different animals. A bilateral, double-walled outfolding of the body wall of the embryo grows upward and medially to surround the embryo and fuse above it, enclosing a space, the **amniotic cavity,** between itself and the embryo (Fig. 6.11). This is filled with a clear watery fluid secreted in part by the embryo and in part by the amnion. The amnion develops from the inner part of the original fold; the outer part becomes the second fetal membrane, the chorion, which lies outside of and surrounds the amnion. The **chorionic cavity,** also known as the extraembryonic coelom (for the space is continuous with the coelomic cavity within the embryo), is the space between the amnion and chorion. The embryos of reptiles, birds and mammals develop in the liquid-filled amniotic cavity, their own private pond within the shell or uterus. This arrangement permits the embryo to move around to some extent but protects it from bumps and shocks.

The chorion of reptiles and birds comes to lie next to the shell and that of mammals is in contact with the maternal tissues of the uterus. The allantois is an outgrowth of the digestive tract which grows between the amnion and chorion and largely fills the chorionic cavity. The allantois of the bird and reptile typically fuses with the chorion to form a compound

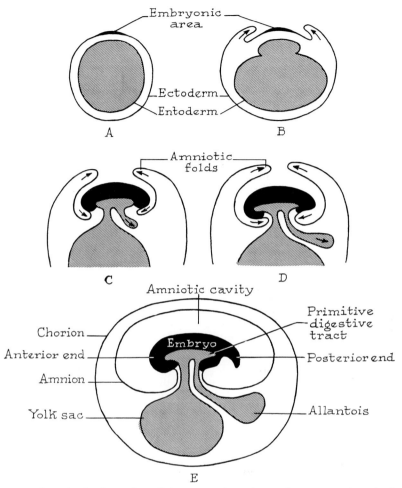

Figure 6.11 *A–E*, Steps in the formation of the extraembryonic membranes—amnion, chorion, yolk sac and allantois—in a typical mammal such as a pig. Arrows indicate direction of growth and folding.

membrane, equipped with many blood vessels, by means of which the embryo takes in oxygen, gives off carbon dioxide and excretes certain wastes.

The mammalian allantois is usually small and has no function as a membrane, but supplies blood vessels to the **placenta,** the organ formed from chorion, allantois and maternal tissue. Finger-like projections, or villi, of the chorion grow into and become embedded in the lining of the uterus. These villi, their blood vessels and the uterine tissues with which they are in contact are called the placenta. This organ, in which fetal blood vessels come in close contact with maternal blood vessels, provides the developing mammalian fetus with nutrients and oxygen from the maternal blood, and eliminates carbon dioxide and waste products into the mother's blood. The two blood streams do not mix at all; they are always separated by one or more tissues. However, substances can diffuse, or be transported by some active process, from mother to fetus or the reverse.

The form of the placenta, and the intimacy of the connection between maternal and fetal tissues, varies from one mammal to another. The placenta of the pig or cow has scattered villi over the chorionic surface and is said to be **diffuse.** The chorionic villi of the placenta of carnivores occur in a cylindrical band around the chorion; this is known as a zonary placenta. The primate and rodent placenta is disc-shaped and is called a discoidal placenta. The number of layers of tissues that intervene between maternal and fetal blood vessels varies from two in man and the rat to six in the sheep.

The growth of the embryo and of the amnion brings the edges of the amniotic folds together to form a tube which encloses the yolk sac (which is usually small or vestigial), the allantois, the two umbilical arteries and the umbilical vein which pass to the placenta. This tube, the **umbilical cord,** is composed of a peculiar, jelly-like material which is unique to the cord.

The amnion, chorion and allantois, together with the eggshell or placenta, are adaptations which permit the embryos of the higher vertebrates to develop on land; they are a substitute for the pond or sea water in which the embryos of the lower vertebrates develop.

6.10
The Control of Development

Biologists have been interested for many years in the nature of the factors which regulate the complex, orderly processes leading to the production of a new adult from a fertilized egg. How can a single cell give rise to many different types of cells which differ widely in their morphologic, functional and chemical properties?

Early embryologists believed that the egg or the sperm contained a completely formed but minute germ which simply grew and expanded to give the adult. This **preformation theory** explained development by denying that it occurred! An extension of this theory postulated that each germ contained within it the germs for all succeeding generations, each within the next. Some microscopists reported seeing this germ within the sperm or egg and described the "homunculus," a fully formed little man inside the egg or sperm! Others calculated the number of germs that were present in the ovaries of Eve, the mother of the human race, and suggested that when all of these were used up the human race would end.

The contrasting theory of **epigenesis,** first advanced by Wolff in 1759, stated that the unfertilized egg is not organized and that development involves progressive differentiation which is controlled by some outside force. We now know that development is not simply epigenetic, for there are certain potentialities localized in particular regions of the egg and the early embryo. The embryos of certain species, when separated into parts at an early stage, will develop normally; each part forms a complete, normal, though small, embryo. The embryos of other species show that certain potentialities are localized at an early stage, for neither of two parts can develop into a whole embryo. Each half develops only those structures it would have formed normally as part of the whole embryo. This localization of potentialities eventually occurs in the development of all eggs; it simply occurs at an earlier stage in some species than in others. It has been possible by experimental techniques to map out the areas of potentialities in the early amphibian gastrula and in the primitive streak stage of the chick (Fig. 6.12).

In the past, biologists have speculated that differentiation might occur (1) by some sort of segregation of genetic material during mitosis, (2) by the establishment of chemical gradients within the developing embryo, (3) by

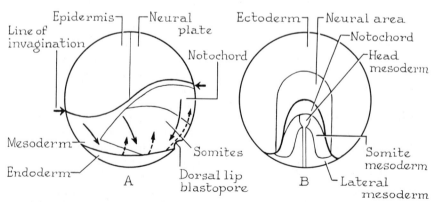

Figure 6.12   Embryo maps. *A,* Lateral view of a frog gastrula showing the presumptive fates of its several regions. *B,* Top view of a chick embryo showing location in the primitive streak stage of the cells which will form particular structures of the adult.

somatic mutations, (4) by the action of chemical organizers or (5) by the induction of specific enzymes.

Cellular differentiation might be explained if genetic material were parceled out differentially at cell division and the daughter cells received different kinds of genetic information. Although there are a few clear instances of differential nuclear divisions in animals such as *Ascaris* and *Sciara,* this does not appear to be a general mechanism of differentiation. The generalization that the mitotic process ensures the exact distribution of genes to each cell of the organism appears to be valid. Thus, the differences in enzymes and other proteins found in different cells must arise by differences in the *activity* of the same set of genes in different cells.

The induction of **adaptive enzymes** in bacteria has been used as a model system to provide an explanation for embryonic differentiation. Bacteria (and, to some extent, animals as well) can respond to the presence of some new substrate molecule by forming enzymes which will metabolize it. Jacques Monod, of the University of Paris, has suggested that extracellular or intracellular influences may initiate or suppress the synthesis of specific enzymes, thus affecting the chemical constitution of the cell and leading to differentiation. As an embryo develops, the gradients established as a result of growth and cell multiplication could result in quantitative and even qualitative differences in enzymes. As a result of the stimulation or inhibition of one enzyme, a chemical product could accumulate which would induce the synthesis of a new enzyme and thus confer a new functional activity on these cells.

Morphogenesis is probably too complicated a phenomenon to be explained in terms of a single phenomenon such as enzyme induction. Enzymes can indeed be induced in an embryo by the injection of a suitable substance. Adenosine deaminase, for example, has been induced by the injection of adenosine into a chick egg, but to date no enzyme has been induced which is not normally present to some extent in the embryo. Adult tissues show marked differences in their enzymatic activities, differences which might be the result of "adaptations" comparable to those seen in bacteria. Adaptive changes in enzymes, however, are temporary and reversible, whereas differentiation is a permanent, essentially irreversible process. Cells may lose some of their morphologic characteristics but they retain all of their biochemical specificities.

Some interesting data bearing on the problem of morphogenesis were obtained by Briggs and King of the Lankenau Institute. They have been able to transplant a nucleus from one of the cells of an early blastula of a frog into an enucleated egg. This egg will subsequently cleave, gastrulate, and develop normally. However, if a nucleus is taken from a cell of the late gastrula—from a chorda-mesoderm or midgut cell—and transplanted into an enucleated egg, abnormal development usually results. Development is arrested in the blastula or gastrula stage. Transplanted chorda-mesoderm nuclei result in embryos with deficient or absent nervous systems and transplanted midgut nuclei form embryos with thin or absent epidermis and no nervous system (Fig. 6.13). These experiments indicate some change in the intrinsic differentiative properties of the nuclei as cleavage and development proceed. The nature of this nuclear specialization is unknown, but the loss of differentiative potentialities bears some relationship to the site of the embryo from which the nucleus was derived.

Evidence of a different type of differentiation mechanism has been obtained from experiments in which microsurgical instruments are used to cut out a bit of tissue from one embryo and transplant it to another. For example, when a piece of the dorsal lip of the blastopore of a frog gastrula is implanted beneath the ectoderm of a second gastrula, the tissue heals in place and causes the development of a second brain, spinal cord and other parts at the site, so that a double embryo or closely joined Siamese twins results (Fig. 6.14). Many tissues show similar abilities to organize the development of an adjoining structure. The eyecup will initiate the formation of a lens from overlying ectoderm even if it is transplanted to the belly region, where the cells would normally form belly epidermis. Such experiments indicate that development is a coordinated series of chemical stimuli and responses, each step regularly determining the succeeding one. The term "organizer" is applied to the region of the embryo with this property and also to the chemical substance given off by that region which passes to the adjoining tissue and directs its development.

It had been widely accepted that organizers can transmit their inductive stimuli only when

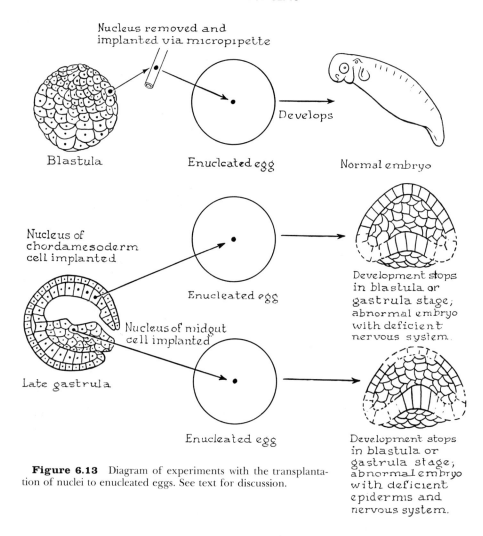

Figure 6.13 Diagram of experiments with the transplantation of nuclei to enucleated eggs. See text for discussion.

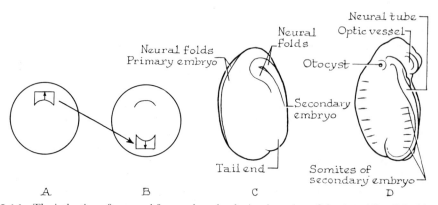

Figure 6.14 The induction of a second frog embryo by the implantation of the dorsal lip of the blastopore from embryo *A* onto the belly region of embryo *B*. Embryo *B* then develops through stage *C* to a double embryo, *D*.

in direct physical contact with the reactive cells. However, evidence from experiments by Victor Twitty of Stanford indicates that induction may be mediated by diffusible substances which can operate without direct physical contact of the two tissues. Twitty grew small groups of frog ectoderm, mesoderm and endoderm cells in tissue culture and found that ectoderm alone would never differentiate into nerve tissue. Ectoderm cells placed in a medium in which mesoderm cells had been grown for the previous week, did differentiate into chromatophores and nerve fibers. No comparable differentiation occurred when the ectoderm cells were placed in comparable cultures of endoderm cells. Twitty concluded that inductor tissues, such as chorda-mesoderm, contain and release diffusible substances which are capable of operating at a distance and inducing the differentiation of ectoderm. These substances appear to be nucleoproteins.

Additional evidence that morphogenetic substances can diffuse comes from the experiments of Clifford Grobstein at Stanford. Nephrogenic mesenchyme is normally induced to form renal tubules by the tip of the ureter. If the two rudiments are separated by treatment with trypsin and the dissociated cells are grown in tissue culture, they will reaggregate and form tubules. Certain tissues other than the ureter, and the ventral half of the spinal cord in particular, proved to be effective inducers of renal tubules. Grobstein carried out experiments in which the inducing and reacting tissues were separated by cellophane membranes of varying thicknesses and porosities. The inducing substance can pass through membranes up to 60 microns thick with pores 0.4 micron in diameter. Electron micrographs revealed that induction occurred even when there was no cellular contact through the fine pores: the inducing principle is diffusible. It appears to be a large molecule and is, at least in part, protein since it is inactivated by trypsin.

Evidence that steroids may play a morphogenetic role in development was obtained by Dorothy Price of the University of Chicago. When the reproductive tract of a fetal male rat is dissected out and grown in tissue culture, development occurs normally if the testis is left in place. If both testes are removed, there is no development and differentiation of the accessory organs—vas deferens, seminal vesicles and prostate gland. However, if both testes are removed and a pellet of **testosterone,** the male sex hormone, is implanted, development proceeds normally. Thus testosterone can diffuse across a limited space and induce the development of male characters; it is a morphogenetic substance.

The bonds holding cells together can be broken and the cells can be made to dissociate by treating a tissue with dilute trypsin solution. In this way a suspension of individual, healthy cells can be obtained. When the dissociated cells are grown in tissue culture medium, the cells can reaggregate and continue to differentiate. This occurs in conformity with their previous pattern of differentiation. The cells reaggregate not in a chaotic mass but in an ordered fashion, forming recognizable morphogenetic units. The cells appear to have specific affinities, for epidermal cells join with each other to form a sheet, disaggregated kidney cells join to form kidney tubules, and so on. Disaggregated cells growing in tissue culture can be treated with certain chemicals to measure their effects on differentiation. Dissociated epidermal cells grown in normal culture medium reaggregate to form a stratified squamous epithelium. If vitamin A is added to the culture medium, or if the dissociated cells are exposed to vitamin A for only 15 minutes, the cells reaggregate and differentiate into a columnar epithelium with mucus-secreting goblet cells.

Evidence that chemical differentiation precedes morphologic differentiation of a tissue has come from research using serologic and biochemical methods. The specific protein of the lens of the eye can be detected serologically in the chick embryo before the lens vesicle closes and before there is any evidence of morphologic differentiation. Cholinesterase is the enzyme which hydrolyzes acetylcholine and is believed to play an important role in the transmission of the nerve impulse. Edgar Boell of Yale showed by microchemical methods that the neural folds of the frog embryo, the parts which will form the central nervous system, have much more cholinesterase than the epidermis does. When epidermis is stimulated to form nervous system, by grafting a piece of chorda-mesoderm beneath it, the tissue becomes rich in cholinesterase.

In view of the extreme complexity of the developmental process it is indeed remarkable that it occurs so regularly and that so few malformations occur. About one child in 100 is born with some major defect, a cleft palate, clubfoot, spina bifida or the like. Some of these are inherited and others result from environmental factors. Experiments with fruit flies, frogs and mice have shown that x-rays, ultraviolet rays, temperature changes and a variety of chemical substances will induce alterations in development. The kind of defect produced is a function of the time in the course of development at which the environmental agent is applied and does not depend to any great extent on the kind of agent used. For example, x-rays, the administration of cortisone and the lack of oxygen will all produce similar defects in mice—harelip and cleft palate—if applied at comparable times in development. Such observations have led to the concept of **critical periods** in development, periods during which the development of a certain organ or organ system is occurring rapidly and hence is most susceptible to interference.

The property of reproduction, which we regard as one of the outstanding characteristics of living things, involves a great many complex and interdependent processes: the elaboration of hormones which regulate the development of gonads, secondary sex structures and the production of gametes in the parents; behavior patterns which bring the parents together and have them release their gametes at such a time and in such a place as to make their fusion probable; the union of male and female pronuclei followed by cleavage, gastrulation and morphogenesis; and devices for the care and protection of the developing young. Our descriptive knowledge of these phenomena is extensive but our understanding of the fundamental mechanisms involved in each of these processes is rudimentary. This is a fertile field for further investigation.

QUESTIONS

1. What are the advantages and disadvantages of asexual and sexual reproduction in animals?
2. What is accomplished by the process of meiosis?
3. Compare mitosis and meiosis.
4. Contrast spermatogenesis and oögenesis.
5. What is meant by the terms haploid, diploid, gamete, zygote, synapsis and tetrad?
6. Define and give an example of (a) hermaphroditism and (b) parthenogenesis.
7. What is accomplished by the process of fertilization? Contrast external fertilization with internal fertilization. What are the advantages of each?
8. Define and give an example of (a) oviparous and (b) viviparous animals.
9. Discuss the effect of the amount and distribution of the yolk on (a) the cleavage pattern of the egg and (b) gastrulation in the embryo.
10. Distinguish between an enterocoele and a schizocoele. In what animals are these found?
11. What is the evidence that the primitive streak of the chick is homologous to the dorsal lip of the blastopore of the frog?
12. Compare the adaptations for the protection and nourishment of the embryo during development in the shark, frog, chick and man.
13. Compare the current theories as to the factors which regulate development.
14. Define organizer, chorda-mesoderm, differentiation, adaptive enzyme.

ANNOTATED REFERENCES

Austin, C. R.: Fertilization. Englewood Cliffs, N.J., Prentice-Hall, Inc., 1965. A description of factors controlling the process of fertilization in various animals.

Balinsky, B. I.: An Introduction to Embryology, 2nd ed. Philadelphia, W. B. Saunders Co., 1965. A well-written and well-illustrated account of animal development with excellent accounts of gametogenesis, fertilization and early development.

Berrill, N. J.: Sex and the Nature of Things, New York, Dodd, Mead & Co., 1953. An interesting essay on the significance and nature of the sexual process in a variety of animals and plants.

Milne, L. J., and M. J. Milne: The Mating Instinct. Boston, Little, Brown and Co., 1954. A comparative account of the mating process in certain animals.

Part Two

THE
ANIMAL
KINGDOM

7 THE PRINCIPLES OF TAXONOMY

At present nearly one million species of animals have been identified. Probably several million more (mostly very small organisms) remain to be named. Such a variety makes it necessary to have a systematic method for naming and recording what is already known, lest species be named several times over, or the same name be assigned to different species. The accumulation of knowledge recorded in an unambiguous fashion is essential to scientific progress. Research upon an organism loses value just as surely if the author fails to record exactly what kind of animal he studied, as if he fails to describe adequately his experimental methods or results.

7.1
The Science of Taxonomy

The proper naming of organisms (plant and animal) is the province of the science of **taxonomy.** Biologic literature is so extensive today that only an expert on a particular group of species can hope to be informed of its taxonomy. If, for example, a zoologist should find a population of lizards that were new to him, he might first search the literature to see whether or not his lizards were already named. In order to do this he would have to be familiar with the details of many aspects of their structure, and with the usage of the descriptive terminology employed, so that he could compare them with the published descriptions. If he failed to locate any description that fitted his lizards, he might describe them and give them a name.

This description would have to be careful and precise so that others could use it. If this zoologist were not a specialist on lizards, he probably would be unable to make either an adequate search of the literature or a proper description of his new animals and would turn the job over to an appropriate specialist.

7.2
The Binomial System

Although the beginning student cannot, perhaps, appreciate the extreme exactness required in a proper description, he can understand that the naming of a new species must follow a set of rules. Scientific names are made of two words, the name of the **genus,** a group containing several closely similar kinds of organisms, and the name of the **species,** the particular kind in that genus. This **binomial system** performs a function similar to that of naming people, in which the use of both a surname and a given name facilitates the recording and cataloging of a population. The generic name is always a noun, such as *Canis* (dog), *Perca* (perch) or *Hymenolepis* (a genus of tapeworms), and is always capitalized. The specific name is (in zoology) never capitalized. It may be an adjective (such as Perch *yellow*), a noun in apposition (such as Dog *wolf*), a noun in the genitive (such as Mouse *of california*), or any of several other possibilities, always of course in Latin. The name of the species serves only to identify the particular species within its genus. Hence, the same specific name may appear many times in the animal kingdom, providing each time

125

it is in a different genus (*Cylichna alba,* a white snail; *Fredericia alba,* a white worm; etc.).

The generic name may be used only once in the entire animal kingdom, and duplication between the plant and animal kingdoms is discouraged. To facilitate the discovery and elimination of duplication, international lists of genera are maintained. When an instance of duplication is discovered, the earlier usage takes precedence. The author of the second usage is allowed time to rename his genus, but if he fails to do this, any other person may rename it. The same procedure applies when two species within the same genus receive the same specific name.

When a single species has been named more than once, again the earlier publication takes precedence. The person discovering the error establishes the first published name as the valid name, and places the second name as a synonym having no validity. Synonyms are a nuisance, since papers may have been published in which they were used as identification. They cannot be discarded, nor can they be used later to name new species.

These are just a few of the rules that govern the system of naming. They are spelled out in 36 articles in the *International Rules of Zoological Nomenclature,* a document accepted in 1901 by the Fifth International Zoological Congress. The system is administered by the International Commission on Zoological Nomenclature, which arbitrates disputes that arise and may offer interpretations or recommend modification of the rules to the congress. Adherence to the system is entirely voluntary, but the need for clarity and uniformity is so obvious that no responsible editor in any country of the world would knowingly publish scientific material that failed to follow these rules.

7.3

Higher Categories

The procedures of naming, and the grouping of species into genera, are but a part of the subject of taxonomy (literally, the law of arrangement). The number of genera is large, and for a number of reasons which will become apparent it is advantageous to arrange genera into higher groups, and these into still higher groups, etc. The full hierarchy of groups proceeds from the **kingdom,** the largest group, through **phylum, class, order** and **family** to the genus and species.

As an example, the **classification** (naming of all the grouping levels) for the tiger is as follows:

Kingdom: *Animalia* (including all animals)

Phylum: *Chordata* (including all vertebrates, sea squirts, Amphioxus, etc.)

Class: *Mammalia* (including animals that give milk)

Order: *Carnivora* (including bears, dogs, cats, weasels, otters, seals, etc.)

Family: *Felidae* (including cats, leopards, lions, jaguars, etc.)

Genus: *Panthera* (including leopards, lions and tigers)

Species: *tigris* (the tiger)

Additional categories may be interpolated by the use of prefixes. Thus, the phylum Chordata may be divided first into several **subphyla,** of which one is the subphylum *Vertebrata,* and the family Felidae may be combined with two other families in a **superfamily,** the superfamily *Feloidea.*

This hierarchy not only facilitates reference work in taxonomy but greatly reduces the volume of descriptive material necessary in a catalog of animals. As each major group is introduced, all the characters common to living and extinct members are stated once; they need not be repeated over and over for each species. The characters that separate the animals from the plants can be listed under the kingdom Animalia, and apply automatically to the million known species in that kingdom. Similarly, chordate characters can be defined once for 60,000 species, mammalian characters for 7000 species, and so on. At each lower level of the hierarchy only those additional characters common to all the members of that level need be discussed. When the species level is reached, it is necessary in a catalog to give only the distinguishing characters of each species in the genus. The catalog may also include for each species a reference to its original description, which would contain additional descriptive information and which may indicate why the author places his species in a particular genus and particular family.

7.4

Uses of Taxonomy

A good taxonomic system has several uses. It serves as a catalog of the information known to date, it makes this information more readily available, and it provides for economy in the length of descriptions. These are practical considerations and were the motivating forces behind the establishment of our present taxonomic system, which developed mostly during the eighteenth and nineteenth centuries.

Since the middle of the nineteenth century, however, taxonomy has had an additional and equally significant role. The grouping of animals is used not only as a matter of convenience but also in an attempt to indicate the **degree of evolutionary relationship** present. Thus, the species of one genus are considered to be more closely related to one another than to the species of other genera and to have evolved from a single original species. Similarly, the genera of a family are considered to form an evolutionary unit as well as a taxonomic unit, and so on. Taxonomy can never indicate evolution exactly, since of necessity the taxonomic boundaries between groups must be sharp, whereas evolutionary relationships form something closer to a continuum. Furthermore, taxonomy cannot describe the time dimension involved in any discussion of evolutionary paths. Nonetheless, the system has been revised continually to serve as well as possible as a framework from which evolutionary relationships can be discussed. The analysis of evolutionary relationships among organisms with taxonomy as the basic tool is the science of **systematics.**

Although the usages of genus and species are standardized by international rules and official lists of genera are maintained, the higher taxonomic categories are less well regulated. There is no universal agreement about either the number or the names of higher categories. Authors have different opinions, depending upon their conclusions regarding evolutionary relationship. The **chordates,** for example, are a group of animals (including the vertebrates) having a notochord and other characters in common and are a basic group having the rank of a phylum. In some organisms, e.g., the **acorn worms,** however, the existence of a notochord is debatable. Students who believe it is absent place such animals in a separate phylum (**Hemichordata** or **Enteropneusta**) from the others (**Chordata**), while those who believe it is present arrange these animals in one phylum (**Chordata**). Such differences of opinion persist, and are not arbitrated by the International Commission.

A partial classification of each animal phylum is given at the conclusion of the appropriate chapter. All phyla and most of the classes are included (arranged according to the views of these authors). Many of the orders of common animals are given, with a few examples of each.

7.5
Definitions

A discussion of taxonomy would be incomplete without definitions of the different grouping levels. In a formal sense the **species** is defined as a group of individuals capable of interbreeding under natural conditions and reproductively isolated from other such groups. In practice all of the necessary information is seldom available, and the species is considered to be a group of individuals that *could* fit this definition and which is recognizable as a distinct group by some dependable criterion (usually morphologic). Conceptually, the species is an evolutionary unit, regardless of the method by which actual species have been sorted out.

The **genus** is defined as a group of closely related species. This is not so satisfactory a definition as the formal definition of a species, since the word "closely" involves opinion. Actually, however, this does not appear to be a serious problem. A survey of the genera in many different taxonomic groups reveals that most taxonomists require about the same degree of closeness for the species of one genus.

The **family** is composed of related genera, the **order** of related families, and so on. Since at each level the degree of closeness must be evaluated, the definitions become less and less objective. It is apparent from comparisons that what is an order in one phylum may be comparable with a class or a family in another.

The classification system becomes more objective at the level of the **phylum.** This level is reached more directly, of course, by dividing the animal kingdom into a number of basic types. The phylum has been defined as an assemblage of organisms showing some degree of relationship among themselves and expressing as a whole a plan of existence that is unique, fundamentally different from that of all other organisms. Some people regard the phyla as *unrelated* and, therefore, as objective a category as the species. In practice, however, many of the phyla show some similarity to one another, and a value judgment is still involved, this time of distance rather than of closeness. Objectivity at the phyletic level should be about the same as that at the generic level.

7.6
The History of Taxonomy

The development of our taxonomic system is one of the more exciting chapters of biologic history. Taxonomy was started by the Greeks and Romans, most notably by Aristotle, but developed very little for 2000 years, until the end of the seventeenth century.

The first major break from this long era of stagnation is found in the works of **John Ray.** Although zoology was only one of his several interests, between 1676 and his death in 1705 he produced books on birds, fishes, quadrupeds and insects. Ray introduced a more complex grouping system than had been used before and improved greatly on the language of description. He rejected entirely the whole mass of superstition and medicinal folklore that had burdened earlier works. Ray developed the **key** by which students can identify a given animal, using only a few distinguishing characters. He also promoted the concept of the genus as a group of closely similar species (without the added concept of evolutionary relationship).

The work of John Ray opened a new era. Many students of history give him major credit for the development of a modern system of taxonomy. It remained for another, however, to bring the new approach into sharp focus and to initiate popular, worldwide activity in taxonomy. **Linnaeus** (Fig. 7.1) was the first taxonomist, in the sense that taxonomy was his career, his primary activity. Since Linnaeus made notable contributions to the taxonomic system and since his work was enormous, dwarfing that of all of his predecessors, Linnaeus, not Ray, is usually called the "father" of taxonomy.

The unique aspect of Linnaeus was his motivation. He wished to name and catalog *all* of the objects of nature, not as a tool for other studies, not as a means of compiling information, but for the sake of the process itself. He enjoyed taxonomy. His methods of classification, his system of naming and the keys he developed were even more simple to use than those of Ray. Others discovered that they could use his system and identify organisms themselves. Furthermore, his enthusiasm was

Figure 7.1 Karl Linnaeus (1707–1778), the father of modern taxonomy. In his day even the author's name was published in Latin, so that his name is more frequently seen as Carolus Linnaeus. His father was born before surnames were common, and adopted *Linnaeus* for himself and his family. Karl was establishing binomial nomenclature for the natural world at the same time that surnames were being required by law in Europe.

infectious. Linnaeus' first classification of nature (minerals, plants and animals) appeared in 1735 and was an immediate success. At the age of 28, Linnaeus had an international reputation, and within a short time he established at the University of Upsala in Sweden a center of taxonomic work to which students came from all over the world. His classification, the *Systema Naturae,* was revised and enlarged several times, and published in several countries. It was in its thirteenth edition when Linnaeus died in 1778, and was carried through several more editions during the next 50 years by his students.

The system used by Linnaeus was modified from edition to edition. He began by following Ray in the use of the genus followed by the name of the species, the latter being one or more descriptive words epitomizing the species. In successive editions more and more species were named, and in the interest of brevity the specific names became shorter and shorter. By the tenth edition, published in 1758, Linnaeus adopted a uniform system in which the genus and the species were each a single word. Since the specific name could no longer epitomize the species, Linnaeus suggested that it was sufficient if it merely identified the species among those of the genus. Thus, he established the **binomial system of nomenclature.**

Linnaeus also gave names to the groups larger than the genus. The largest groups (similar to those established by Aristotle) he called **classes,** and each class was divided into **orders,** which in turn were divided into genera and species. Before 1800, other workers introduced the **family** as a category between the order and the genus, and soon thereafter classes were grouped into higher categories, the **phyla.**

Since the tenth edition of the *Systema Naturae* is the first publication to adhere strictly to binomial nomenclature, one of the International Rules states that no name published prior to this is valid. Hence, the 4236 descriptions in this book include the earliest species names accepted as official.

The effect of Linnaeus on biology is difficult to measure. As with most giants, the world was ready for him, and without him someone else would certainly have done the work. But it is likely that taxonomy would never have enjoyed the popularity it had without the force and personality of Linnaeus behind it. Classification became an amateur as well as a professional "sport," which still persists in the activities of the many bird watchers and bug collectors.

Taxonomy, and the study of nature that taxonomic work stimulated, had between 1750 and 1850 an enormous influence upon the arts. To be sure, the attention that man turned toward nature was but one facet of his growing objectivity and curiosity, dwarfed beside the economic and political reforms of the period. Nonetheless nature was a prominent feature of literature, music and painting. The "new orderliness" of taxonomy gave nature a pleasing aspect. The fact that organisms could be neatly placed in groups and identified with labels lent a sense of security. Problems of grouping led to thought about their patterns, and this, in turn, developed into a search for harmony in nature. The foreboding, secret aspect of nature, intimately bound with medicine and magic and the devil, disappeared. The direct familiarity with nature initiated by the popularization of collecting and classifying organisms brought nature into the intellectual circles of the late eighteenth and early nineteenth centuries. The philosopher **Johann Wolfgang von Goethe,** who was a poet and a biologist among other things, more than any other person developed this emphasis upon harmony, upon the inherent goodness of nature. He established "nature-philosophy" as one approach to the understanding of life. In all the art forms, the works of this period are touched with his approach. Together with the new social philosophies and the rise of the common man they characterize the period known as nineteenth century romanticism.

If the highest external achievement of this generation of amateur naturalists following Linnaeus is echoed in the poetry of Keats and Shelley, it must be admitted that within the field of biology the "wonderful" era came to a less satisfactory end. The crescendo of taxonomic work reached its maximum in the early nineteenth century. At the same time that Goethe was court philosopher and biologist in the German city-state of Weimar, **Georges Cuvier** was court biologist in France, surviving both the French Revolution and Napoleon. Cuvier extended classification into the more complex area of **comparative anatomy,** a field which he established almost single-handed. He showed that reconstructions could be made from fossil bones and that they often represented animals no longer living. He began to give names to these **extinct species,** of which almost 100,000 have been identified since his time.

During this period the diversity among the lower animals was discovered, and the taxonomic system was expanded to provide for more and more phyla of invertebrates, while the several classes of vertebrates were joined together in a single phylum.

By 1830, however, the museums and laboratories of the world sagged under their collections, and the task of naming all the species appeared less complete than ever. Furthermore, many of the known species were discovered to vary in their characteristics from one region to another and species formerly considered distinct were found to have intergrades. Since the concept of evolution was not yet popular, and was denied vigorously by such authorities as Cuvier, all species were believed to have been created just as they were. The growing confusion over the boundaries between species and the apparent endlessness of the job of naming were discouraging indeed. Both Goethe and Cuvier died in 1832, at which time interest in taxonomy began to decline. The original goals set by Linnaeus have not yet been realized.

It was partly because taxonomy was already in difficulty that evolution was accepted so readily when Darwin presented his arguments in 1858. From that moment on, taxonomy was no longer an end in itself, and the taxonomic system was adjusted to serve the interest in evolution. The races and intergrades of species that had been taxonomic obstacles became interesting problems, evidence of evolution in action. Relationships among species became more important than ever, and a new question, the "why" of a species, could be asked. Finally, the definition of a species became more complete, establishing the species as an **evolutionary unit** as well as a taxonomic category.

A student of zoology in the time of Linnaeus had only the following groups of animals to learn: mammals, birds, reptiles, amphibians, fishes, insects and worms. Today, however, the beginning student may be dismayed and overwhelmed to discover that Linnaeus' category, "worms," includes most of the phyla (21 of 23 in this text). To facilitate matters the 23 phyla have been divided into 10 major and 13 minor phyla. The major phyla, ones containing many species, are described in 10 separate chapters and account for most of the material to be learned. The minor phyla are to some extent interspersed among the major groups, if it is especially convenient to do so, but most of them are considered together in Chapter 18.

The insistence that all animals, including the "lower" animals, should be studied was first expressed by Aristotle. In his treatise, *Of the Parts of Animals,* as he begins an analysis of animal structures he argues (from the translation by A. L. Peck):

So far as in us lies, we will not leave out any of them, be it ever so mean; for though there are animals that have no attractiveness for the senses, yet for the eye of science, for the student who is naturally of a philosophic spirit and can discern the causes of things, Nature which fashioned them provides joys that cannot be measured. If we study mere likenesses of these things and take pleasure in so doing, because then we are contemplating the painter's or the carver's Art that fashioned them, and yet fail to delight much more in studying the works of nature themselves, though we have the ability to discern the actual causes—that would be a strange absurdity indeed. Wherefore we must not betake ourselves to the consideration of the meaner animals with a bad grace, as though we were children; since in all natural things there is somewhat the marvelous.

QUESTIONS

1. List the grouping levels used in taxonomy between the species and the kingdom.
2. Give six of the international rules of nomenclature.
3. What did Ray and Linnaeus contribute to taxonomy?
4. What is a species?
5. What is taxonomy? What does it offer to zoology?

ANNOTATED REFERENCES

Linnaeus, K. von: Critica Botanica. (Translation.) London, The Ray Society, 1938. A thorough discussion of the principles and methods of classification, revealing both the humor and the incisiveness of the author.

Peattie, D. C.: Green Laurels. New York, Simon and Schuster, 1936. An informative, romanticized portrayal of the lives of early naturalists and taxonomists.

Simpson, G. G.: Principles of Animal Taxonomy. New York, Columbia University Press, 1961. A useful text for the serious student; includes chapters on the history and procedures of taxonomy and the interrelationships of taxonomy and evolutionary theory.

Wightman, W. P. D.: The Growth of Scientific Ideas. New Haven, Yale University Press, 1953. Chapter 28 (What's in a Name?) is both an excellent and a readable account of the growth of taxonomy.

8 THE PHYLUM PROTOZOA

The single-celled animals remained unknown until Antony van Leeuwenhoek, a Dutch lens maker of the seventeenth century, examined water droplets with a primitive microscope and discovered that diverse, very small forms of life existed. His work received international attention and these organisms were studied extensively. At that time, however, the cellular nature of organisms was not known and van Leeuwenhoek's "little animals" were considered by most investigators to be merely varieties of small worms or wormlike animals. It was not until 1845 that the unicellular nature of many of these microscopic animals was appreciated, and the phylum **Protozoa** was established to include them. Today this phylum includes all of the one-celled animals. Since all other animals are multicellular, the animal kingdom is often divided into the subkingdom Protozoa, including only the phylum Protozoa, and the subkingdom **Metazoa,** including all the other phyla.

The typical protozoan has a single nucleus and leads an independent existence. In some, however, the cell is multinuclear, while in others cells are attached together to form **colonies.** Colonies are distinct from multicellular animals because differentiation among cells is weak and does not include cells specialized for feeding. Most of the individuals in a protozoan population are produced by simple cell division of the parent, although sexual reproduction is by no means rare.

Protozoa are primarily aquatic, living in bodies of water of all kinds, fresh and salt, from puddles to oceans. Some live in damp soils, crawling in the thin film of water surrounding dirt particles. Others are parasitic and live in the fluids of animals and plants. Whatever their habitats, the surfaces of active protozoa must remain wet, for they cannot survive desiccation. Many species, however, form inactive spores or cysts that can be dried and distributed with dirt or dust from one habitat to another.

Variation in form is enormous. Some protozoans are shapeless "blobs" while others are as elaborate and as geometrically patterned as snowflakes. In some groups the cells may have internal skeletons, external skeletons, or protective houses cemented together from sand and other particles. Those with hard parts can be fossilized. Only two-thirds of the 25,000 described species of protozoa are living. The others are known from their remains found in rocks.

The phylum is divided into five classes: (1) *Flagellata,* the flagellates, having one or more long, whiplike flagella; (2) *Sarcodina,* in which pseudopods are formed for locomotion and feeding; (3) *Ciliata,* the ciliates, characterized by the presence of many short cilia for locomotion or feeding; (4) *Suctoria,* in which the young have cilia but the adults have tentacles; and (5) *Sporozoa,* parasitic forms that reproduce by multiple fission (division into more than two daughter cells) and in which adult forms lack obvious locomotor structures (Fig. 8.1).

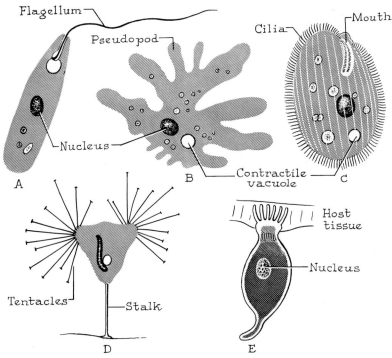

Figure 8.1 Classes of the phylum Protozoa. *A,* Flagellata. *B,* Sarcodina. *C,* Ciliata. *D,* Suctoria. *E,* Sporozoa.

8.1

Organelles

Each protozoan organism must carry on all the life processes of its species. These include the cellular activities described in Chapter 4, and also the physiologic activities described in Chapter 5. The metazoa have capitalized upon a **division of labor** among cells: some are nutritive, others excretory, and still others muscular. In the protozoa these various activities are accomplished by specialized structures within the single cell. Such structures, whose functions are comparable with those of the organs of higher animals, are called **organelles.** A few of these will be described as examples of **intracellular differentiation.**

Cilia and Flagella. Obvious in many protozoa are the locomotor organelles. Many ciliates are rapid swimmers, propelling themselves by the coordinated action of their many cilia. Flagellates may also move rapidly, pulling themselves forward by lashing the anteriorly located flagella. Each **flagellum** is a long, supple filament containing an **axial fiber** (Fig. 8.2). This fiber is found by electron microscopy to be composed of 11 filaments, a sheath of nine surrounding two in the center.

The latter give bilateral symmetry to the flagellum, influencing the plane of motion. The chemical structure of these 11 filaments is similar to that of actomyosin. In a typical swimming movement, the flagellum lashes stiffly to one side from an extended position and returns relaxed and bent. The flagellum may also undulate, with waves passing from tip to base, thus pulling the animal forward. Cilia are structurally similar to, but much shorter than, flagella.

Some protozoa can creep on a flat surface with wormlike movements. These animals have just beneath their surfaces a layer of **contractile fibrils** which form an organelle comparable to the muscular body wall of worms. Other protozoa "slide," moving along slowly with no apparent means of propulsion. These also have a surface layer of contractile fibrils, and it has been presumed (with no direct evidence) that they move by passing minute waves of contraction along the fibrils, after the fashion of a snail's locomotion. Finally there is locomotion by **ameboid movement,** described in Chapter 5.

Conductile Organelles. Other organelles are **conductile,** their functions being comparable to those of the nervous systems

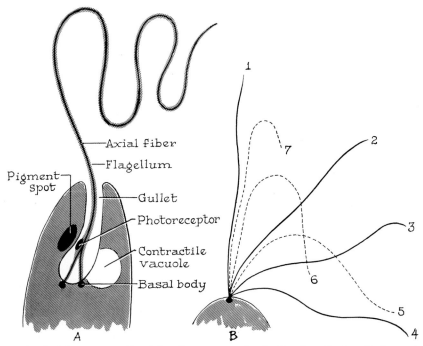

Figure 8.2   The flagellum. *A,* Details of flagellar structure in the flagellate *Euglena. B,* Successive positions of flagellum in a typical stroke.

of higher animals. The flagellates have, at the base of each flagellum, a **basal body** (Fig. 8.2). If flagellum and basal body are removed intact from the animal, flagellar activity continues, but as soon as the two are separated, movement usually stops. The basal body apparently stimulates and controls the movement of the flagellum. The flagellum may follow any of several different patterns of movement at different times, but nothing is known of the way in which this is controlled by the cell. The basal body is often joined by a filament to the centriole, from which it may be produced during development. It is considered to be a modified centriole, controlling the activity of the flagellum just as the centriole of the sperm during spermiogenesis (p. 106) gives rise to the axial filament of the sperm tail and presumably is important in controlling its movement.

The ciliates also have a basal body at the base of each cilium (Fig. 8.3). These have no connection with the centriole but are connected with each other by a network of slender fibrils, which can be made visible with a silver stain, the kind used to demonstrate nerve fibers in the metazoa. Each basal body activates its cilium, and coordination among the cilia is accomplished through the fibrillar net-

work. The basal bodies near the mouth initiate a wave of activity that passes over the body of the animal. Wave follows upon wave, as shown in the ciliary motion of the paramecium (see Fig. 8.12), producing a smooth, rapid motion. Microsurgical incisions that cut across the connecting fibrils produce a local asynchrony among the cilia and may seriously impair the animal's locomotor ability.

In many flagellates a **photosensitive organelle** is associated with the conductile and locomotor organelles. (Fig. 8.2). The photosensi-

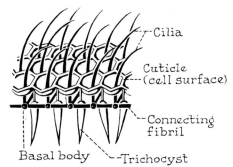

Figure 8.3   Cilia. A small bit of the surface of a ciliate, showing the cuticle, projecting cilia, and underlying structures. The trichocysts are discussed later in the text.

tive organelle of *Euglena* has two parts, a patch of red pigment beside the flagellum and a tiny, light-sensitive photoreceptor on the flagellar base. The shading of the photoreceptor by the pigment spot enables the animal to determine the direction from which the light comes. In other species the photoreceptor is seated in a pigment cup with the opening anterior. In a few species the thin cuticle covering the animal is swollen over the cup to produce an **optic lens.**

Organelles for chemoreception, heat perception, touch, etc., have not been recognized in the protozoa, although behavioral responses to such stimuli are easily demonstrated.

Contractile Vacuoles. A prominent structure in many protozoans is an excretory organelle, the **contractile vacuole** (p. 85). It is found in all fresh-water forms and in many marine species but is uncommon among the parasites. A fresh-water environment is hypotonic to the protozoan, and a method of removing water that enters through osmosis is needed. In marine forms (which are always isotonic with sea water) the contractile vacuole is used to excrete the water that accumulates in feeding. Many marine protozoa and most parasitic species do not ingest food, hence they do not tend to accumulate water and have little use for a contractile vacuole. The exact mechanism by which the contractile vacuole fills with water is unknown, but it is emptied by the contraction of the surrounding cytoplasm which shifts from a sol to a gel as it contracts and forces the water to the outside.

8.2

Class Flagellata

Flagellates are spherical to elongate protozoa with a simple, centrally located nucleus and from one to many flagella toward one end. The group is large, including half the known living protozoan species. Most of these are small and difficult to study but a few, such as members of the genus *Euglena,* are large and easily obtained (Fig. 8.4). A study of *Euglena* will introduce the class.

Euglena. Euglenas (*E. viridis* and *E. gracilis* are common species) are elongate flagellates 50 to 100 or more microns long. At the anterior end a deep depression forms the gullet. Although euglenas have never been observed to feed, members of the genus *Peranema* of the same family use the gullet for swallowing prey. The body is covered with a delicate **pellicle** showing spiral thickenings. Beneath the pellicle, invisible without special stains, is a layer of **contractile fibrils** with which the organism can change shape. Euglenas often creep upon the bottom in a wormlike fashion. A single **contractile vacuole** lies next to the gullet and empties into its base. The large **nucleus** is in the posterior third of the body.

Scattered in the cytoplasm are **chloroplasts** and **paramylum bodies.** Chloroplasts are bright green with their contained **chlorophyll;** in the light they are able to carry on photosynthesis, like the chloroplasts of other plants. The arrangement of chloroplasts is used in the identification of species. In *E. viridis* they are large and form a rosette (Fig. 8.4). In *E. gracilis* and in several other common species they are small and numerous, obscuring all other internal structures except the red pigment spot. The transparent, colorless paramylum bodies are a form of polysaccharide unique to the euglenas, different from both the glycogen of other animals and the starch of plants. The arrangement of these also varies among the species. They are formed during photosynthesis and, if they are so numerous as to obscure other structures, their numbers can be reduced by keeping the euglenas in the dark a day or two. A single long **flagellum** which protrudes from the gullet is used for swimming. It is formed by the fusion of two flagella that arise from two basal granules in the base of the gullet. At the point of fusion (Fig. 8.4) is a transparent swelling, the **photoreceptor.** Next to this in the wall of the gullet is a red **pigment spot.**

Swimming is a complex movement. The sideways lashing of a single flagellum is like one-armed swimming; the body is thrown forward but also to one side at each stroke. In *Euglena* the flagellum usually bends toward the side bearing the pigment spot, and if this stroke were merely repeated over and over the organism would move in a circle with the pigment spot facing outward. Each stroke is not a simple backward lash, however, but is directed obliquely to the long axis of the organism so that the body not only turns to one side but also rotates a little (Fig. 8.4). Successive lashes thus produce a spiral path in which the organism moves forward with the

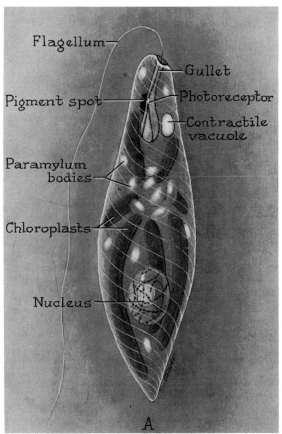

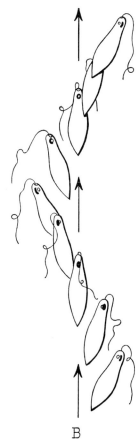

Figure 8.4 *Euglena. A,* A lateral view of *Euglena viridis. B,* A diagram showing successive positions in the spiral swimming pattern of *Euglena.* The position of the pigment spot shows the rotation that occurs.

pigment spot continually facing the outside of the spiral.

This swimming pattern makes optimal use of the visual organelle. As *Euglena* swims forward the pigment spot shades the photoreceptor from behind and from one side. When *Euglena* is swimming at right angles to the direction of light the photoreceptor is shaded once during each spiral loop. If the organism is seeking light it turns to one side more than usual at the moment that the photoreceptor is shaded, gradually turning the spiral path toward the light until the photoreceptor is never shaded. If it is avoiding light, it turns sideways more than usual during that part of the spiral in which the photoreceptor is illuminated, gradually turning the spiral path away from the light until the photoreceptor is continually shaded. In general, euglenas swim toward moderate light but avoid intense light. During the day

they usually swim to the surface of a pond where they form a green scum, exposing their chloroplasts to the light.

No *Euglena* is completely autotrophic. Healthy cultures can be maintained in light only if some organic substances, especially amino acids, are present. Growth is more rapid if a considerable variety of organic substances is present. In the absence of light, of course, the culture medium must be rich in all the basic foods. Some species, if cultured in the dark, gradually lose their chlorophyll. When the loss is complete, the organisms become obligatory saprophytes, for once chlorophyll is lost it cannot be regained. A few natural species of *Euglena* lack chlorophyll, which suggests that nature may have performed the same experiment in the past.

Euglenas belong to the order **Euglenoidida,** characterized by the gullet and pigment spot. Some members of the order are nearly

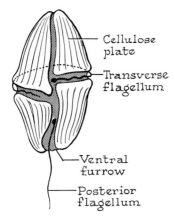

Figure 8.5 A typical dinoflagellate. The organism propels itself forward with undulations of the posterior flagellum, and rotates by activity of the transverse flagellum.

autotrophic, some are saprophytic, and some are holozoic. Of the remaining 15 to 25 flagellate orders, three will be mentioned here.

Dinoflagellates. The order **Dinoflagellida** is characterized by the presence of two flagella in **grooves,** one trailing posteriorly and the other wrapped around the "waist" (Fig. 8.5). Usually the body is covered

by a cellulose shell divided into upper and lower halves. Many species possess photosynthetic pigment and are able to synthesize some of their organic needs. None has been successfully cultured on a completely inorganic medium. Thus, like the euglenas, the dinoflagellates are not completely autotrophic. Some species can be cultured without light if all the necessary foods are supplied. Dinoflagellates have also been observed capturing other organisms and engulfing them by pseudopod formation from the **ventral furrow.** Is is now believed that most of the species combine autotrophic and holozoic nutrition. Some species lack photosynthetic pigment and live entirely by holozoic nutrition.

Dinoflagellates are abundant in the plankton of both marine and fresh waters. They often occur as "blooms," becoming extremely abundant for a short time and then disappearing. Although most species are harmless and form an important source of food for other organisms, a few produce deadly toxins. Most spectacular are the small reddish forms that color the water when they become abundant and produce "red tides." Such water is lethal to fish, killing them rapidly as

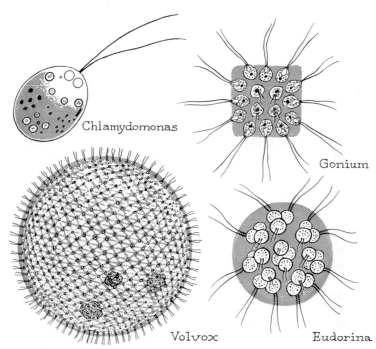

Figure 8.6 Examples of the order Phytomonadida showing solitary form (*Chlamydomonas*), simple colonies (*Gonium, Eudorina*), and a complex colony (*Volvox*). Colonial forms are embedded in a matrix of transparent jelly.

they enter the poisoned region. The dead animals decay and enrich the supply of nutrients so that a red tide, once started, tends to be self-perpetuating until water currents or storms break it up.

Many dinoflagellates are parasitic. Although the adult forms seldom resemble dinoflagellates, they can be identified by their young, which have the typical grooves and flagella.

Phytomonads. Certain more plant-like flagellates are included in the **phytomonads** (order Phytomonadida). They are all autotrophic but have visual organelles and swim about in a most animal-like fashion. Within the group is a series of colonial species, ranging in complexity from the one-celled *Chlamydomonas* to the highly integrated, spherical colony, *Volvox* (Fig. 8.6). *Volvox* represents the peak of protozoan colonial organization. The pigment spots are largest in the cells at one pole of the sphere, which is always the

anterior pole in locomotion, and decrease steadily in size around to the posterior pole. Reproduction is limited to the equatorial and posterior cells. All cells are connected with each other through **cytoplasmic bridges,** by which cellular activities can be synchronized. The superficial resemblance of *Volvox* to the embryonic blastula of metazoans has given this organism unwarranted prominence in zoology.

Most botanists believe that the higher plants evolved from the phytomonads. Many of the noncolonial species, able to swim with flagella, can also grow upon the bottom as round cells without flagella, in which case they take on a colonial appearance and resemble plants. Further kinship with the higher plants is suggested by certain similarities in their chemical structure.

Choanoflagellates. Most of the strictly animal flagellates are small, uncommon, or are inhabitants of foul water and thus are un-

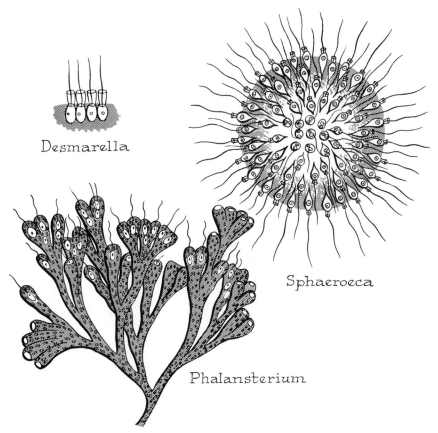

Desmarella

Sphaeroeca

Phalansterium

Figure 8.7 Examples of the order Choanoflagellida showing solitary and colonial forms. The matrix holding colonial individuals together is more pronounced than in the Phytomonadida.

pleasant to study. One order, prominent because of their resemblance to the sponges, are the **choanoflagellates** (order Choanoflagellida, Fig. 8.7). These are sedentary flagellates, attached to the bottom by a posterior **stalk.** The single flagellum is surrounded by a delicate cytoplasmic **collar.** The flagellum produces a water current over the animal, and small food particles brushing against the collar stick tightly and are carried to the collar base. Periodically, at the base, small pseudopods erupt and engulf the food in a food vacuole, where it is digested. This group includes a variety of colonial forms. Individuals tend to secrete a gelatinous material around their bases, which in colonial species may form a bulky structure. The more complex colonies include ones with branching patterns and one free-swimming spherical species, *Sphaeroeca volvox* (Fig. 8.7).

These are but a few of the flagellate groups. Many flagellates are parasitic; the most important of these are the **trypanosomes** that produce sleeping sickness. These and other parasitic protozoa are discussed in Chapter 42.

8.3
Class Sarcodina

Unlike other protozoa, the Sarcodina have no definite body shape. Because of their ameboid movement the shape changes from moment to moment. Nonetheless shape can be helpful in identifying species. Some species of amebas, for example, form several long narrow pseudopods at one time, while others form only one or two, or the pseudopods may be short and blunt (Fig. 8.8). It is possible to describe an "average shape" for a given species. The internal structures occupy no particular position. Nucleus, contractile vacuole and food vacuoles shift about as the animal moves.

Amebas. Amebas (order Amoebida) are common in all waters, move slowly, and are easily studied under the microscope. The **ectoplasm** (cytoplasm near the cell surface) is clear, while the **endoplasm** or inner cytoplasm is granular. From the behavior of the granules, it is apparent that the outer part of the endoplasm is in the gel state while much of the inner endoplasm is a sol. Where pseudopods are forming the outer endoplasm is also a sol, becoming a gel along the sides of the advancing lobes.

Amebas eat a wide variety of materials. They crawl slowly about, engulfing inactive food such as plant cells and debris by flowing slowly around them and enclosing them in **food vacuoles.** They may also capture active prey such as flagellates in a somewhat different manner (Fig. 8.9). When a swimming flagellate bumps into an ameba, it not only tends to slide into a crevasse between pseudopods but also stimulates the ameba to flow rapidly in its direction. If the anterior end of the flagellate becomes wedged, the ameba

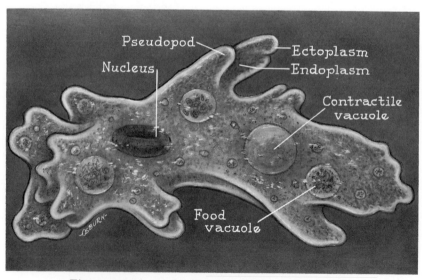

Figure 8.8   An ameba. The animal is flowing to the right.

Figure 8.9 An ameba capturing a large flagellate. The flagellate hits the side of the ameba and slips into the crevasse at the base of a pseudopod. The ectoplasm of this region erupts and rapidly engulfs the prey. Stages shown are at about one second intervals.

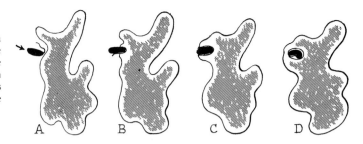

engulfs the entire prey in a second or two. If the flagellate is not wedged it is simply pushed away by the advancing cytoplasm. Sometimes the flagellate appears to become attracted to the ameba and returns again and again, so that the ameba may have several opportunities to be successful. Certain species of ameba are particular about their food and eat only flagellates or only plant cells.

The fate of food vacuoles has been studied closely. At first they become acid, owing to the secretion by the cytoplasm of inorganic acids (such as hydrochloric acid, secreted in our own stomachs). This kills the prey and initiates digestion. Later the vacuole becomes alkaline, enzymes are secreted into it, and digestion continues. Enzymes for the hydrolysis of proteins, fats and carbohydrates have been found in food vacuoles. The food particles swell, become indistinct, and the vacuole enlarges. As digestion is completed, both nutrients and water are absorbed by the ameba and the vacuole shrinks to a very small size. As the ameba continues its slow locomotion, the indigestible remnants are expelled and left behind. This digestive process in the food vacuole has been observed in all of the major groups of protozoa.

A few amebas, such as the genus *Difflugia*, cement sand particles together to make a protective case (Fig. 8.10). Other species secrete a membranous covering. Pseudopods project through a lower opening, and by means of these the animals move about.

Heliozoida. Related to the amebas is the order Heliozoida, a group of fresh-water sarcodinids with numerous delicate pseudopods projecting from a bubbly center (Fig. 8.10). They float in the water and capture small organisms that touch their pseudopods, first engulfing them in food vacuoles and then drawing them into the central mass. Although the prey are obviously paralyzed upon touching the pseudopods, the method of "stinging" is unknown.

Radiolarida and Foraminiferida. Members of the two marine orders **Radiolarida** and **Foraminiferida** are adapted to floating. Radiolarians resemble heliozoans but they possess an internal skeleton made of silica. These glassy frameworks combine porous spheres with radiating spines to produce intricate and beautiful patterns (Fig. 8.11). Silica is durable, and many deep-water marine sediments are composed largely of radiolarian fossils. Similar fossils are found in rocks that date from pre-Cambrian times, before fossils of metazoa occur.

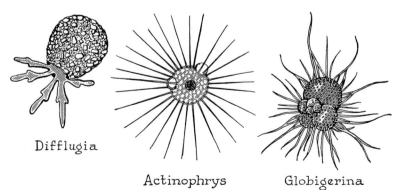

Difflugia   Actinophrys   Globigerina

Figure 8.10 Other sarcodinids. *Difflugia* is an ameba with a shell cemented from sand particles. *Actinophrys* is a member of the fresh-water order Heliozoida, and *Globigerina* belongs to the marine order Foraminiferida.

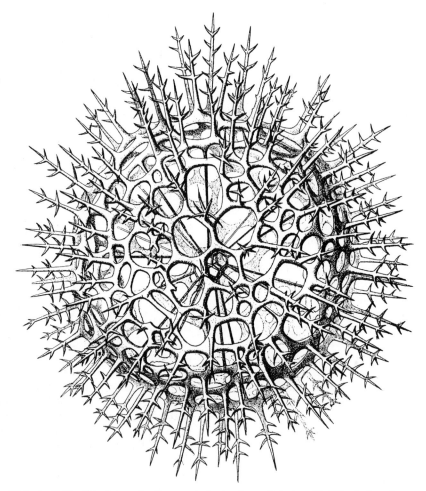

Figure 8.11 The internal, siliceous skeleton of a radiolarian. (E. Giltsch, Jena.)

Foraminiferans secrete an external porous capsule of calcium carbonate through which pseudopods project into the water. As the animal grows, it expands its home by adding new chambers. Many genera, such as *Globigerina,* are abundant (Fig. 8.10). Their skeletons rain continually upon the ocean floor, and in the more shallow seas where they are not dissolved they may form large deposits of **Globigerina ooze.** After compaction and elevation, they form such prominent structures as the chalk cliffs of Dover. While species of the genus *Globigerina* add new chambers in a somewhat irregular fashion, most species add them in a systematic pattern, often in a coiled sequence like a snail shell. The shape and arrangement of the chambers serves to identify the species. Although the Foraminifera are prominent members of the marine plankton, most of the species, especially those with heavy shells, live on or near the bottom in relatively shallow water.

During the coal age (later part of the Paleozoic era), when the major coal deposits were laid down, a family of foraminiferans, the **Fusulinidae,** flourished and died. In that brief space of geologic time (75 million years) thousands of species of fusulinids developed, most of which lived a very short time before becoming extinct. These were immense protozoa, up to 2.5 cm. in diameter, that lay upon the bottoms of the shallow seas. Their fossils are now found in deposits that have accumulated oil. As an oil well is drilled down into the rock, it passes, in rapid succession, these species of fusulinids. From these the driller can estimate just how far into the paleozoic deposit he has drilled. This is one of the few instances where an industry uses the services of a taxonomist—in this case a specialist on the classification of one family of extinct protozoa.

8.4

Class Ciliata

Ciliates can be distinguished from the flagellates and rhizopods not only by their cilia, but also by their nuclei. Each ciliate has two nuclei, a large **macronucleus** which governs the ordinary activities of the cell, and a small **micronucleus** which functions during sexual reproduction. Both nuclei divide at each mitosis, but at sexual repro-

duction the macronucleus disintegrates, and the micronucleus gives rise to both nuclei of the offspring. The details of this process will be described later.

Paramecia. The best known genus of ciliates is *Paramecium* (Fig. 8.12). Several of the species (such as *P. caudatum*) are large and easily cultured. They present many interesting biologic problems and are widely used in experimental work. Paramecia measure from 0.1 to 0.3 mm. in length. The body is blunt anteriorly, widest just behind the middle, and tapered posteriorly. They are rapid swimmers, revolving as they move forward in a spiral path. The **gullet** is located to one side, at the base of an **oral depression,** and is

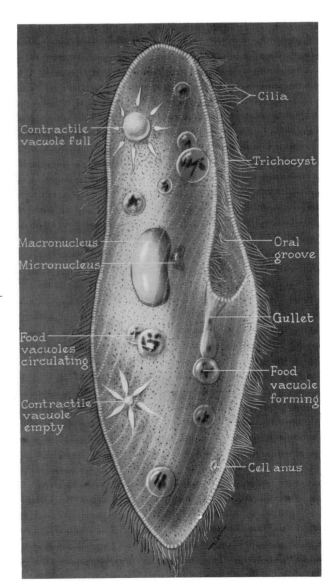

Figure 8.12 *Paramecium.* Generalized drawing combining features of several species.

usually kept to the inside of the spiral path. Food, which includes microscopic particles such as bacteria, yeast and algae, is swept into the gullet by ciliary action and is digested in food vacuoles. The cytoplasm circulates slowly in the body, so that each vacuole moves in a circle. The digestive processes are like those in the ameba, and the indigestible remnants are ejected through the **anus,** an organelle posterior to the mouth. Many of the experimental strains of this genus have been cultured for years on *Aerobacter aerogenes,* a bacterium cultured easily on boiled hay or alfalfa.

The movements of paramecia indicate highly coordinated activity. When a paramecium strikes a solid object, the waves of ciliary beating reverse and the animal backs up a short distance. Then it turns slightly and goes ahead again. The rapidity with which the animal changes direction is astonishing. Paramecia have no visible photoreceptors, but they do move toward or away from a light source under certain circumstances.

In addition to a network of **neurofibrils** (Fig. 8.3) beneath the cilia, paramecia have a layer of **trichocysts** (Figs. 8.3 and 8.12), spindle-shaped structures located between the basal bodies, that can be discharged to produce long **threads** projecting from the body surface. All paramecia and many other protozoa have them in abundance. They may be used for anchorage, or the capture of prey or for defense.

Mating Types. Paramecia may have more than two sexes, a condition found only in the ciliates. All the sexes look alike, but an individual of a given sex will mate only with an individual of some other sex. As many as eight sexes exist for a given species. Since "male" and "female" are inadequate terms, the sexes of paramecia are called **mating types,** numbered from I to VIII in the order in which they were discovered.

The study of paramecia is further complicated by the existence of **varieties,** groups of mating types that interbreed among themselves but which do not mate with other mating types that are morphologically similar. Thus, in *Paramecium bursaria* (Table 8.1), the 16 mating types found in the United States fall into three breeding groups of 4, 8 and 4, respectively. From a genetic point of view these three varieties are distinct species, since they do not interbreed. They can seldom be distinguished, however, except by breeding experiments, and for convenience the various morphologically similar varieties are given

Table 8.1   Breeding Relations in *Paramecium bursaria*

Variety	Mating Type	I				II								III			
		I	II	III	IV	I	II	III	IV	V	VI	VII	VIII	I	II	III	IV
I	I	−	+	+	+	−	−	−	−	−	−	−	−	−	−	−	−
	II	+	−	+	+	−	−	−	−	−	−	−	−	−	−	−	−
	III	+	+	−	+	−	−	−	−	−	−	−	−	−	−	−	−
	IV	+	+	+	−	−	−	−	−	−	−	−	−	−	−	−	−
II	I	−	−	−	−	−	+	+	+	+	+	+	+	−	−	−	−
	II	−	−	−	−	+	−	+	+	+	+	+	+	−	−	−	−
	III	−	−	−	−	+	+	−	+	+	+	+	+	−	−	−	−
	IV	−	−	−	−	+	+	+	−	+	+	+	+	−	−	−	−
	V	−	−	−	−	+	+	+	+	−	+	+	+	−	−	−	−
	VI	−	−	−	−	+	+	+	+	+	−	+	+	−	−	−	−
	VII	−	−	−	−	+	+	+	+	+	+	−	+	−	−	−	−
	VIII	−	−	−	−	+	+	+	+	+	+	+	−	−	−	−	−
III	I	−	−	−	−	−	−	−	−	−	−	−	−	−	+	+	+
	II	−	−	−	−	−	−	−	−	−	−	−	−	+	−	+	+
	III	−	−	−	−	−	−	−	−	−	−	−	−	+	+	−	+
	IV	−	−	−	−	−	−	−	−	−	−	−	−	+	+	+	−

A plus sign indicates the possibility of mating, and a minus sign indicates that mating does not occur. No mating type will mate with another individual of its own type, but it will mate with any other mating type of its variety. Three varieties are found in the United States, and no mating type of one variety will mate with any mating type of any other variety. (From Sonneborn, 1947.)

but one species name. Most of the species of paramecia and of many other ciliates are now known to be composed of several varieties.

The Killer Trait. T. M. Sonneborn, the protozoologist at Indiana University who discovered mating types, has found that several traits in paramecia are transmitted to offspring through the cytoplasm and not through the chromosomes of the nucleus, as is usually the case. The best known example of cytoplasmic inheritance concerns the **killer trait.** In some strains of *Paramecium aurelia,* certain individuals are able to produce and secrete into the medium small **killer particles** which, if they come in contact with a "sensitive" individual, cause death. All individuals that are unable to produce such particles are sensitive, whereas all the individuals that do produce killer particles are resistant to their effect and are not killed. These particles are manufactured in the cytoplasm from granules called **kappa particles,** present, of course, in killer animals but absent in sensitive ones. A killer may contain some 800 kappa particles and secrete one killer particle every five hours. Kappa particles are self-reproducing, multiplying in the cytoplasm independently of the division of the cell. When the paramecium divides, the kappa particles are divided randomly between the daughter cells. So long as each daughter cell receives at least one kappa particle, it remains a killer. Under certain culture conditions the paramecia divide more rapidly than the kappa particles,

and the number of particles per cell slowly decreases; ultimately, some cells are produced that lack particles. Such animals become sensitive to killer particles and are no longer able to produce either kappa or killer particles. Thus, an inherited characteristic may be lost. Occasionally, however, a sensitive animal may mate with a killer before it is killed through chance encounter with a killer particle, and during the mating process kappa particles may be transferred into the sensitive cell. These will subsequently survive and transform the cell into a killer. Furthermore, this trait will be transmitted to the offspring so long as reproduction of the particles keeps pace with that of the paramecia. Thus, a trait may be acquired and transmitted to the progeny. The ability to acquire the trait is absent in some strains, and Sonneborn has shown that this depends upon the presence in the nucleus of appropriate genes, indicating that this kind of cytoplasmic inheritance is ultimately influenced by the nucleus.

Tetrahymena. Related to *Paramecium* is a genus of smaller ciliates, *Tetrahymena.* These are similar in many respects, especially in the complexity of varieties and mating types that occurs. One species, *Tetrahymena pyriformis,* is of special interest because it can be cultured on a liquid medium in which the exact amounts and kinds of all the dissolved chemicals are known. By varying the chemical nature of some of the ingredients, scientists are discovering not only what materials are

Hypotrich

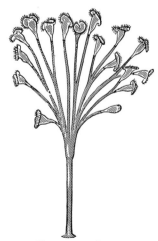

Peritrich

Figure 8.13 Other ciliates. The Hypotrichids run rapidly on the ventral cirri, formed by the fusion of cilia. The Peritrichida are mostly sessile and feed by sweeping food toward the mouth.

essential for growth and maintenance, but to what extent they may be converted into other materials, something of the steps involved in these transformations, and how genes control these steps. This may seem to be extravagant detail in the study of a mere protozoan, but it is now clear that the metabolic pathways in all organisms are essentially alike, and the study of this animal, in which information can be obtained rapidly and with relative ease, is shedding light on similar problems for all organisms, including man.

Other Ciliates. *Paramecium* and *Tetrahymena* belong to the subclass **Holotricha,** including ciliates completely or partially covered with simple cilia, and to the order **Hymenostomatida,** in which the cilia of the gullet or near the mouth are fused together to form small, flaplike **membranelles.** Another order in this subclass is the **Peritrichida,** in which the cilia are limited to a counterclockwise spiral leading to the mouth. The cilia are usually not fused to form membranelles. Most of the peritrichs are attached by **stalks,** and many species are colonial (Fig. 8.13). In the subclass **Spirotricha** the membranelles are large and are arranged in a clockwise spiral leading to the mouth. Examples are the common **hypotrichs** (Fig. 8.13) which lack cilia on the upper surface. On the lower surface, in addition to the adoral membranelles, are patches of cilia fused into **cirri** with which the animal scrambles over surfaces.

8.5
Class Suctoria

The **suctorians** (Fig. 8.1) are an offshoot of the ciliates which retain both macronucleus and micronucleus. The sedentary adults have no cilia but usually have stalks. The body bears a group of **tentacles** that are used for feeding. When prey such as other protozoa happen to strike the end of a tentacle, they adhere and are paralyzed by a toxic secretion. The contents of the prey are then sucked through canals in the tentacles and drawn into the body of the suctorian.

Although adult suctorians lack cilia, they do possess the **basal bodies** of cilia. During asexual reproduction the suctorian forms a bud in which the basal bodies multiply, become arranged in rows, and develop cilia similar to those of a holotrich. After nuclear division the bud separates and swims away. It later attaches to the bottom, the cilia disappear, and tentacles develop.

In view of the obvious ciliate affinities the suctorians are often considered to be an order in the class Ciliata. In recognition of the resemblance of the larvae to holotrichs the group is sometimes placed as a suborder in the order Holotricha. Another way to group the suctorians and ciliates is to place them in a subphylum, the **Ciliophora,** separate from the other protozoan classes.

8.6
Class Sporozoa

The **Sporozoans** are a large group of parasitic protozoa, some of which cause serious diseases such as **coccidiosis** in poultry and **malaria** in man (see Fig. 6.1). Neither locomotor organelles nor contractile vacuoles are present. Nutrition is saprozoic, nutrients from the host being absorbed directly through the cell wall. Most sporozoans live as intracellular parasites within the host cells during the growth phase of their life cycle.

The cycle of cell division indicated in Chapter 6 for *Plasmodium* is common in the class. The infective spore matures as a feeding animal or **trophozoite.** It then divides by **multiple fission** into a number of young that infect new cells of the same host and mature as more trophozoites. Eventually, however, some trophozoites fail to divide and instead undergo metamorphosis to sexual forms. The females become **eggs,** while the males divide by multiple fission into many **sperm.** In some sporozoans the females also divide to form a number of eggs. After fertilization the new individuals grow and divide by multiple fission into a number of spores—individuals able to infect new hosts. The spores of most sporozoans are encapsulated to withstand the dryness of the external world. In blood parasites, however, such as plasmodia, the spores are naked and must be transmitted directly into the blood stream of the new host.

Often, as in the malaria organisms, the formation of eggs and sperm, fertilization and the formation of infective spores take place in a different kind of host (e.g., a mosquito) from that in which trophozoite stages are found. Such two-host systems and other phenomena associated with parasitism are discussed in Chapter 42.

8.7

Reproduction in the Protozoa

Asexual Reproduction. Asexual reproduction is found in all of the protozoa. The nucleus divides mitotically, and the animal separates into two complete organisms. Such reproduction is commonly called **binary fission.** The origin of the additional set of organelles differs from group to group. In *Euglena* (Fig. 8.14), the centriole is the first to divide, then each centriole gives rise to a new basal body. In the meantime the old pair of basal bodies moves farther apart, and the new pair comes between them. The old flagellum separates, and each new flagellum growing out from the new basal bodies fuses with an old flagellum. The nucleus, which has gone through prophase and metaphase, divides next. Separation into two individuals begins anteriorly and ends at the posterior tip (Fig. 8.15).

In *Paramecium* the division is transverse (Fig. 8.15). The old gullet disappears and is replaced by two new gullets. (In most other ciliates the old gullet becomes the gullet of the anterior daughter.) The two contractile vacuoles become the posterior vacuoles of the

daughters and two new anterior vacuoles are formed. New cilia and basal bodies appear among the old. The micronucleus divides by mitosis. The macronucleus is apparently a compound structure formed by the amalgamation of many sets of chromosomes and merely pulls in half during asexual reproduction with no evidence of mitosis.

The ameba divides very simply by mitosis; the cytoplasm separates into approximately equal halves. The contractile vacuole passes to one daughter and a new one is formed in the other.

Sexual Reproduction. Sexual reproduction in free-living protozoa is known in detail for only a few groups: the phytomonads, the foraminiferans and the ciliates. In numerous other groups fertilization (i.e., the fusion of two gametes) has been observed, but the details of the cycle are not known. Wherever meiosis has been well studied, the process has been found to be the same as that described in Chapter 6, involving tetrad formation and two divisions. Variations concern the time relations of mitosis, meiosis and fertilization.

Phytomonads are **haploid** organisms, each possessing a single set of chromosomes. The

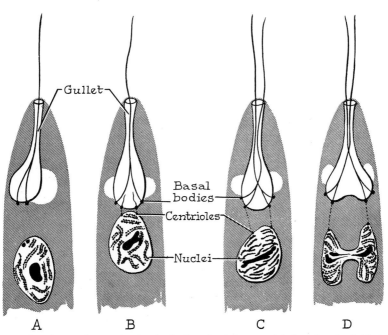

Figure 8.14 Details of asexual reproduction in *Euglena*. In *A* the centriole has already divided. *B*, Each centriole produces a new basal body and flagellum. The nucleus is in prophase and the contractile vacuole is double. *C*, The old pair of flagellar roots separate and fuse with the new roots. *D*, Mitosis proceeds and the gullet begins to divide. (Redrawn from Ratcliffe, 1927.)

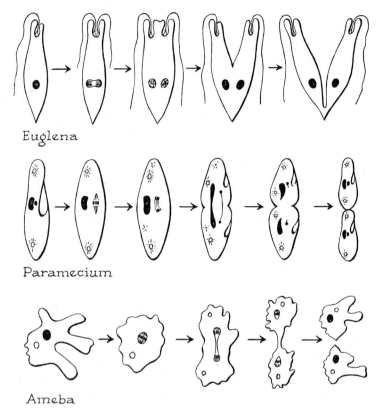

Figure 8.15 Asexual reproduction in several protozoa. For explanations see text.

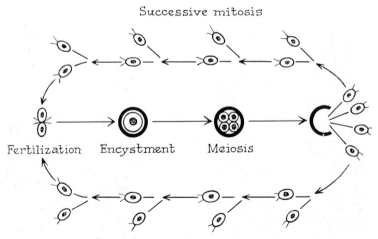

Figure 8.16 Sexual cycle in the Phytomonadida. Ordinary individuals are haploid (outsides of diagram) and reproduce asexually. Under certain conditions they unite in pairs (left) to form a zygote that encysts. Within the cyst meiosis occurs, so that when the individuals emerge (right) they are haploid again.

zygote never divides by mitosis to produce new cells, but immediately undergoes meiosis to produce active individuals (Fig. 8.16). These may divide mitotically to produce large populations of individuals. In the simplest case, at the time of sexual reproduction two individuals of opposite sex fuse together to form the zygote. In some species, especially in colonial forms like *Volvox*, individual cells undergo metamorphosis before functioning as gametes. In one sex the metamorphosing cell becomes large and egglike, while in the other sex the metamorphosing cell divides rapidly to produce a number of small spermlike gametes. In these species the sexes can be designated as male and female. Only the haploid stages are sexual, however; the zygotes are indeterminate as to sex, and in a given species the meiotic process is identical for all zygotes whether the ultimate gametes be eggs or sperm.

Ciliates are **diploid** organisms, each possessing a double set of chromosomes. Each zygote becomes an ordinary individual that may give rise to a whole population by mitosis. At sexual reproduction, two individuals of different sexes **conjugate** (Fig. 8.17), pressing together their oral surfaces. In each individual, the **micronucleus** undergoes meiosis. Three of the four meiotic products degenerate (notice that this is comparable to polar body formation in oögenesis), leaving only one viable **haploid nucleus.** This divides once by mitosis, producing two identical haploid nuclei. One of these from each cell crosses over through the oral region into the other individual and fuses with the haploid nucleus remaining in that cell. Thus, two fertilizations result from each conjugation, and the two new diploid nuclei are identical. The

old **macronucleus** disintegrates and the individuals separate. The diploid nucleus then divides several times and eventually gives rise to a new macronucleus and a new micronucleus.

Thus, mitosis in the phytomonads is limited to the haploid phase, whereas in the ciliates only a single mitosis occurs in this phase.

In the foraminiferans each generation of haploid animals is followed by a generation of diploid animals. After fertilization, the zygote develops into a typical foraminiferan, adding chambers as it grows. Throughout this period the nucleus divides by mitosis repeatedly, producing diploid, **multinuclear** adults. All of the nuclei subsequently go through meiosis, and the cytoplasm is divided up among the many haploid nuclei. These abandon the parent shell and begin life anew as the **haploid generation,** growing and adding chambers in much the same manner as the previous generation, except that they remain **mononuclear.** At maturity, haploid individuals of opposite sex come together in pairs and secrete a membrane around themselves. They then divide rapidly by mitosis, producing large numbers of gametes. The gametes of one individual unite with those of the other to form zygotes that break free from the membrane and begin the **diploid generation.** Thus, in this group mitosis occurs in both the diploid and haploid phases.

Sexual phenomena are virtually unknown in such familiar protozoa as the ameba and the euglenas. Apparently, some parasitic flagellates are diploid, and both haploid and diploid sporozoans have been described. At the present time our knowledge of the place of meiosis in the various cycles is insufficient to warrant general conclusions.

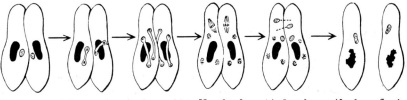

Pairing   1st meiotic   2nd meiotic   Haploid   Mutual   Nuclear fusion
division   division   mitosis   fertilization

Figure 8.17 Sexual cycle in *Paramecium.* Two individuals with diploid micronuclei unite in conjugation (left). After meiosis (second and third figures) three of the products degenerate and the fourth divides by mitosis (fourth figure). Mutual fertilization is followed by fusion of the haploid nuclei to form a new diploid nucleus (last figure). The old macronuclei disappear. The new diploid nuclei divide several times by mitosis, and eventually establish both the new macronuclei and the new micronuclei.

8.8

Relationships Among the Protozoa

The flagellates are usually considered to be a basic stock of organisms from which the other protozoa arose. They are thought by some to be the source of higher animals and higher plants as well. As a group they are difficult to exclude from either the plant or the animal kingdom, a problem that has prompted some biologists to erect a third kingdom (the **Protista**). Botanists usually claim all of the flagellates in which a photosynthetic pigment occurs, including closely related forms such as some of the euglenas and dinoflagellates that have lost the pigment. They do not include the larger, pigmentless groups such as the choanoflagellates and many of the parasitic groups. Zoologists generally claim all of the flagellates, even the groups that are completely autotrophic. Inclusion of the latter, with the Phytomonadida as an example, is probably not defensible but persists through custom. A good argument for keeping all of the flagellates together is that the transition from autotrophic to holozoic nutrition appears to have occurred independently in different groups.

Sarcodinids are related to the flagellates through several genera of ameboid organisms that have flagella and through several forms that resemble typical flagellates in open water but which lose their flagella and creep like amebas when they are next to solid surfaces. In fact, the existence of so many intergrades suggests that sarcodinids may have evolved several different times from the flagellates. A further tie relating the groups is found in the gametes of foraminiferans, each of which has two tiny flagella.

The ciliates are a distinct group and probably arose only once. Cilia are structurally like flagella and are considered to have evolved from them by extensive duplication and diminution. A significant step is the independence of the basal body from the centriole. The evolutionary origin of the macronucleus is unknown. During the conjugation of most ciliates a bit of cytoplasm is transferred along with the migrating nuclei. In one species, the spirotrich *Cycloposthium,* each migrating nucleus and its bit of cytoplasm separates in the mouth cavity as a distinct gamete with a long tail. The two gametes then move past each other to the opposite side. It has been suggested that this is similar to sperm formation in other organisms, and that it may reflect a flagellate ancestry. Suctorians are easily derived from the ciliates by a modification of the adult stage.

The sporozoa are probably a composite group. Some species show affinities with the flagellates while others more nearly resemble sarcodinids. Multiple fission may be regarded as an adaptation to parasitism and may well have developed independently in several groups of flagellates and sarcodinids. On the other hand, their life cycles suggest the possibility that sporozoans have evolved from the fungi.

It is, of course, a challenge to the systematist that the group divisions are not sharp and clear, either between plant and animal flagellates, between flagellates and sarcodinids, or between both of these and the sporozoans. Actually, the number of evolutionary changes necessary to develop one group from another is not great, and it is likely that the course of evolution is obscured as much by repetition as by the loss of intermediate forms.

SYNOPSIS OF PROTOZOA

PHYLUM PROTOZOA.   The protozoans; unicellular animals, sometimes colonial, abundant in water, in the soil, and as parasites in other organisms.

CLASS 1. FLAGELLATA.   Flagellates; with one to many flagella as locomotor organelles. A large group that is composed of both plants and animals. Many orders, including:

Order 1. Dinoflagellida.   One transverse and one longitudinal flagellum. Mostly marine.

Order 2. Euglenoidida.   Two flagella arising in a gullet. Primarily fresh-water. *Euglena, Peranema.*

Order 3. Phytomonadida.   Small cells, two flagella of equal length Many colonial forms. Largely fresh-water. *Chlamydomonas, Volvox,* etc.

Order 4. Choanoflagellida. Single flagellum surrounded by a collar. Many colonial forms. Not abundant. *Sphaeroeca, Codosiga,* etc.

Order 5. Trypanosomida. Parasitic. Includes such serious vertebrate parasites as *Trypanosoma* and *Leishmania.*

Order 6. Distomida. Two nuclei, parasitic. *Giardia.*

Order 7. Trichomonadida. Parasites with three to six flagella. *Trichomonas.*

CLASS 2. SARCODINA. The rhizopods, using pseudopodia for locomotion. The largest orders are:

Order 1. Amoebida. Naked forms that crawl actively about. Mostly free-living; includes some parasites such as *Entamoeba.*

Order 2. Foraminiferida. Chiefly marine, floating or creeping with reticulate pseudopods, usually with multichambered shells. *Globigerina,* fusilinids, etc.

Order 3. Heliozoida. Chiefly fresh-water, floating forms with a spherical body and radiating filamentous pseudopods.

Order 4. Radiolarida. Marine, floating, superficially similar to heliozoids, but with delicate skeletons of silica or strontium sulfate.

CLASS 3. CILIATA. The ciliates, typically using cilia as locomotor organelles; macronucleus and micronucleus both present. Numerous orders in two subclasses:

Subclass 1. Holotricha. With simple and uniform body cilia.

Order 1. Hymenostomatida. Cilia covering whole body, buccal cavity present. Abundant. *Paramecium, Tetrahymena.*

Order 2. Peritrichida. Usually attached, with a stalk, cilia confined to circumbuccal region. *Vorticella.*

Subclass 2. Spirotricha. Body cilia reduced or absent, buccal cilia prominent. Cilia often specialized. Hypotrichs, etc.

CLASS 4. SUCTORIA. Young with cilia, adults with tentacles. Often considered an order of ciliates.

CLASS 5. SPOROZOA. Parasitic. Reproduction by multiple fission, life cycle similar to some fungi. Several orders, including:

Order 1. Gregarinida. Gregarines, parasites of invertebrates, usually of the gut wall.

Order 2. Coccidida. Various hosts. Includes forms causing coccidiosis in birds and mammals.

Order 3. Haemosporidida. Blood parasites of vertebrates. Includes *Plasmodium,* which produces malaria.

QUESTIONS

1. Name the five classes of protozoans and make a sketch of an example from each.
2. Compare organs and organelles.
3. What is a basal body?
4. Compare movement, nutrition and asexual reproduction in *Euglena, Paramecium* and the ameba.
5. Describe sexual reproduction in *Paramecium.*
6. What is cytoplasmic inheritance?
7. Describe a typical sporozoan life cycle.

ANNOTATED REFERENCES

(See Chapter 13 for general references.)

Sonneborn, T. M.: Paramecium in modern biology. Bios *21*:31–43, 1950. An excellent account of the ways in which paramecia can be used in various areas of biological research.

Wenrich, D. H.: Protozoa as material for biological research. Bios *23*:124–145, 1952. A very good discussion of the same subject for various kinds of protozoa.

9

THE PHYLUM PORIFERA

The **Porifera,** the phylum of animals commonly called **sponges,** have porous body walls and internal cavities lined with choanocytes. The bulk of the body is composed of a jelly-like **matrix** that usually contains a proteinaceous, calcareous or siliceous skeleton. A nervous system appears to be lacking. Organization among the cells is best described as "loose," since cell relations can be disrupted without permanent damage to the organism. Because of their many distinct morphological features, the sponges are often considered to be a side branch in the evolution of the **Metazoa.** This branch is often called the **Parazoa** (animals to the side).

Sponges are sedentary organisms ranging in size from 1 to 200 cm. in height and varying in shape from flat, encrusting growths to balls, cups, fans and vases. Most sponges are marine; only the family **Spongillidae** occurs in fresh water.

The surface of the sponge is perforated with numerous small **incurrent pores** and a few large excurrent pores called **oscula.** These openings are connected internally by a system of **canals** that includes the cavities lined with choanocytes. Sponges circulate water through this system and filter out microscopic food particles. In the more complex sponges, which appear to have a more efficient pumping mechanism, an amount of water equal to the volume of the sponge is pumped through the animal each minute!

9.1

General Characteristics

The **choanocytes** (Fig. 9.1) are remarkably similar to the choanoflagellates (p. 137). Each cell has a single **flagellum** surrounded by a delicate, cytoplasmic **collar.** As in the choanoflagellates, undulations of the flagellum propel water away from the cell and occasionally bring food particles against the outside of the collar. Such particles are engulfed in food vacuoles and moved to the base of the cell. The layer of choanocytes forms the sponge **gastrodermis.**

In the extracellular matrix that forms the bulk of the sponge are numerous, wandering, ameboid cells, the **amebocytes.** The amebocyte is a jack-of-all-trades. It can differentiate temporarily to secrete gelatinous material, construct skeleton, or gather waste and debris. Some become **epidermal cells** and form a delicate membrane over the outer surface of the sponge or line the channels not already lined with choanocytes. Others become **muscle cells** arranged around the oscula and other openings to regulate their size. Amebocytes accept food vacuoles from the choanocytes and appear to play a dominant role in digestion (Fig. 9.1). As they crawl around, the

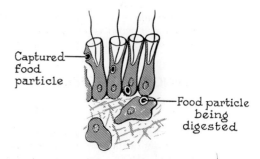

Figure 9.1 Choanocytes from a sponge. The choanocyte at the left has just captured a food particle. Adjacent cells show the movement of the food vacuole to the cell base and its eventual transfer to an amebocyte.

nutrients are distributed throughout the sponge.

Structural Types. The arrangement and complexity of the internal channels vary considerably in different sponges. For convenience sponges have been grouped in three structural types: (1) the **asconoid** sponges, having the simplest organization, exemplified by the genus *Ascon;* (2) the **syconoid** sponges, resembling in structure the genus *Sycon;* and (3) the **leuconoid** sponges, having the most complex organization, named after the genus *Leuconia* (Fig. 9.2).

Asconoid sponges have a single large chamber, the **spongocoel,** lined with choanocytes. The incurrent pores and osculum lead directly to and from this chamber. Incurrent pores develop as holes through tube-shaped cells, the **porocytes.** These cells develop from amebocytes, and may degenerate, leaving simple small holes in the body wall.

The body wall of syconoid sponges resembles a folded version of the asconoid wall. At least some syconoid sponges actually develop from asconoid-like juvenile forms. During development the body wall pushes out to form numerous finger-like projections, carrying the choanocytes in their internal cavities. Where the outer sides of the projections touch, they usually fuse. The arrangement is such that any four projections will enclose a space, the **incurrent canal.** The former incurrent pores are now internal, and are called **prosopyles.** Whether or not the prosopyles are formed in porocytes is debatable, but if they are, the porocytes soon disappear, for all prosopyles in the adult are simple holes in the body wall. At the outer surface of the body new **incurrent pores** open into the incurrent canals. The cavity of each finger-like projection is the **radial canal,** which opens into the spongocoel by an **internal pore.** All the choanocytes retreat into the radial canals, and a simple epidermis develops as the lining of the spongocoel. The excurrent pore is an osculum similar to the asconoid osculum.

The leuconoid type represents a further folding of the wall. The gastrodermis pushes out from the radial canals into the body wall to form a series of spherical **flagellated chambers.** Each chamber has a few inlets from the incurrent canal, the **prosopyles,** and a single outlet to the radial canal, the **apopyle.** Incurrent pores, incurrent canals and radial canals remain as in the syconoid type. The increased bulk given the body wall by this additional folding results in a shrinkage of the original main cavity. In leuconoid sponges the spongocoel is divided into confluent **excurrent channels** leading to the osculum. All the choanocytes are in the flagellated chambers, and the radial canals are lined with epidermis. The fresh-water sponges and most of the marine sponges are leuconoid.

Although the leuconoid structure is understandable as a modification of the syconoid type, it should be noted that many of the leuconoid sponges develop directly to the leuconoid type without passing through asconoid or syconoid stages.

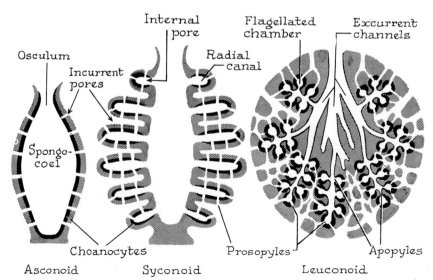

Figure 9.2 The three structural types of sponges. In each the choanocytes are shown in black.

The efficiency of the sponge as a pump is related to its structural plan. The only source of power is the beating of the choanocyte flagella, which are not coordinated in any one chamber. Choanocytes surrounding the incurrent pores or prosopyles propel water toward the interior, and the water escapes through the osculum. In the asconoid sponges the flagellated chamber is large and the force produced by the flagella is directed toward the middle, so that flow out of the osculum is passive. In the leuconoid type the flagellated chambers are small and the choanocytes are located so that they propel water toward the excurrent opening. Thus, they not only draw water in through the prosopyles but also actively direct it outward to the osculum, producing a more efficient pumping action.

9.2
The Classes of Sponges

The arrangement of channels in the sponge provides for a convenient structural classification, but this has not proved to be useful in separating the classes of the phylum. Instead, the classes are distinguished on the basis of the skeletal units present: (1) Calcarea, with a skeleton made of calcium carbonate spicules; (2) Hexactinellida, with a skeleton made of siliceous spicules, in which the basic spicule has six rays (Fig. 9.3); and (3) Demospongia, with a skeleton made either of siliceous spicules (never six-rayed) or spongin fibers, or both.

Calcareous Sponges. The calcareous sponges are marine, shallow-water forms of small size, including all the asconoid and syconoid and some leuconoid forms. The spicules have one, three or four rays (Fig. 9.3*A, B* and *C*). Spicules with three or four rays are interlaced in the body wall, forming a relatively rigid framework. The one-rayed spicules project from the body surface, especially around the osculum, and serve to keep other organisms away. The choanocytes are considerably larger than those of other sponges.

Hexactinellid Sponges. Hexactinellid sponges are marine, deep-water forms. The six-rayed spicules are usually cemented together to form rigid girders (Fig. 9.3*D* and *E*). Since the skeleton remains in one piece after the flesh has been removed, these **glass sponges** are often used as decorations. Even in the living glass sponge the tissue is scanty. Body structure is intermediate between syconoid and leuconoid, but the epidermis is lacking. *Euplectella* has a large spongocoel, and an osculum covered by a **sieve plate** that keeps out large objects (Fig. 9.4). Other glass sponges are flattened, fan-shaped structures, one side of which represents the spongocoel. These forms have no osculum but they are so placed in the deep ocean currents that the water flows through them continually.

Hexactinellids are especially common in the deep water off Japan, where large numbers of **Venus's flower baskets** may be gathered. Several species of shrimps live within the large spongocoel, entering through the

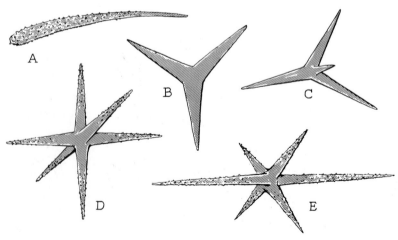

Figure 9.3 Sponge spicules. *A*, Monaxon. *B*, Triaxon. *C*, Tetraxon. *D* and *E*, Hexaxons. *A–C*, made of calcium carbonate, are found in the class Calcarea. The same shapes, made of silicate, are found in the class Demospongia. Hexaxons, made of silicate, occur in the class Hexactinellida.

Figure 9.4 Photograph of the skeleton of the glass sponge, *Euplectella*. The hexaxons are fused to form intersecting girders. (Courtesy of the American Museum of Natural History.)

sieve plate while young and unable to leave after they have grown. They are almost always found in pairs, one of each sex. A glass sponge with its imprisoned pair of shrimps is used as a wedding gift in Japan, and symbolizes a lifelong marriage.

Demospongia. The Demospongia include a family of fresh-water sponges and a large variety of marine forms found at all depths. The spicules have one, three or four rays. **Spongin fibers** are a protein secretion of the ameboid cells which form an anastomosing network in the body wall. They are resistant to digestion and decay, resembling hair and silk in these respects. All the members of this class have the leuconoid body plan.

Those that lack siliceous spicules have a soft pliable skeleton. The **bath sponges** (Fig. 9.5), whose skeletons are familiar objects, are found in warm shallow waters with a rocky bottom, including the Mediterranean Sea, the Gulf of Mexico and the Caribbean. They are hooked from the ocean bottom by poles having a pronged fork at the end. A short stay on shipboard is enough to kill them, after which they are left lying in shallow water until the

flesh is decayed. Then they are beaten, washed and finally bleached in the sun. All that remains is the spongin network, whose many tiny interstices permit it to soak up a large amount of water. The sponge fishery is limited by the rate of reproduction and growth of the sponges. Many of the grounds have been overfished, and the fishermen are beginning to experiment with the cultivation of sponges. Sponges are cut into many small pieces that are fastened to cement blocks and set out in the sea. They take many years to reach marketable size.

Some of the Demospongia live only upon other organisms. The **boring sponges** settle as larvae onto the shells of oysters or clams, into which the young sponge bores by dissolving the shell. It does not harm the host directly, but as the shell becomes honeycombed and weakened it eventually falls apart, and the host is rapidly consumed by predators. Another group, the **hermit crab sponges,** settle on snail shells inhabited by hermit crabs. They grow to a considerable size, eventually completely covering the shell. As time passes the shell dissolves, leaving a snail-shaped cav-

Figure 9.5   The common bath sponge. Only the spongin skeleton remains. (Courtesy of the American Museum of Natural History.)

ity in the sponge, still occupied by the hermit crab. Because the sponge is carried around it is never buried by silt (always a danger to attached organisms), and the disagreeable flavor of the sponge tends to protect the crab from predators.

Some of the spider crabs and other slow-moving crabs break off pieces of living sponge and hold them or glue them on their backs, where they may become permanently attached and grow. Such crabs also plant other attached organisms on their backs, and walk about like animated "gardens." They must repeat this operation each time they molt.

Most sponges apparently have an unpleasant taste to most animals, for few species eat them. Fish avoid sponges, and hence many smaller organisms seek refuge inside them. The canals of almost any large sponge shelter a number of such animals.

9.3

Reproduction

Sexual reproduction in the sponges, as in the protozoa, has been studied in too few species to permit generalizations. All sponges studied appear to be diploid and to have the usual metazoan processes of oögenesis and spermatogenesis described in Chapter 6.

Fertilization is internal. The eggs are retained just beneath the choanocytes, where they are fertilized by sperm brought in with the current. The origin of sex cells apparently varies; they may arise from choanocytes, from amebocytes, or from special **embryonic cells** identified by some investigators in the matrix.

The best studies of early development are in the genera *Sycon* and *Grantia* of the class Calcarea. In these the egg cleaves to form a blastula-like structure that is *inside out* when compared with the blastula stages of other animals (Fig. 9.6*A*). The nuclei lie toward the inner ends of the cells rather than the outer ends, and the flagella that appear on the cells toward the animal pole project *inward* instead of outward. The embryo is also peculiar in having a mouth at the vegetal pole through which food is taken from the parent. The food is utilized by the cells and in this way the embryo grows. When fully developed the embryo turns inside out (Fig. 9.6*B*) through its mouth and then penetrates through the maternal choanocyte layer to escape into the channels of the parent sponge. The flagellated cells, whose flagella now project outward, form the anterior half of the larva and the nonflagellated cells make up the posterior portion. This free-swimming stage is the **amphiblastula** (Fig. 9.6*C*) and is similar

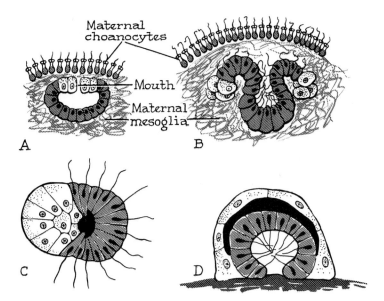

Figure 9.6 Development in the sponge *Sycon. A*, The embryo lies embedded beneath the choanocytes of the parent. *B*, Eversion. *C*, Free-swimming amphiblastula. *D*, Attachment and invagination. (*A* and *B* after Dubosq and Tuzet; *C* and *D* redrawn from Hyman.)

in appearance to the blastulae of a few other animals. The amphiblastula swims away and attaches to the bottom by its anterior end. As it becomes attached, the anterior, flagellated half invaginates into the posterior half to form a two-layered structure (Fig. 9.6*D*). The flagellated cells become the choanocytes while the outer layer forms all the rest of the sponge. This pattern of development is unlike that of any other metazoan.

The presence of flagella that project inward and the later inversion of the embryo through its mouth are unique to the sponges as features of sexual reproduction. A similar process is found in the colonial flagellate, *Volvox,* but is associated only with *asexual* reproduction.

The development of other sponges is less well known but they follow different developmental patterns. Free-swimming larvae of many species have been found, and in some of these a process similar to gastrulation in other animals takes place. An outer **flagellated layer** completely or partially surrounds an **inner cell mass** (Fig. 9.7). When such larvae attach and develop, the inner cell mass produces the bulk of the sponge. In some forms the flagellated cells migrate inward to become the choanocytes, while in others they are destroyed and the choanocytes develop from the inner mass.

Most sponges also reproduce asexually. Pieces of some sponges fall off, attach to a new substrate, and grow. In others, flagellated embryos are produced that resemble the sexually produced larvae. These swim away and attach. In still others, including fresh-water sponges, balls of cells embedded in the body are surrounded with a capsule. After the sponge dies (during the winter in fresh-water forms) and the body decays, these **gemmules** are released. Many of them are equipped with hooks that serve to anchor them to the bottom. When the environment is suitable (in the spring) the gemmules sprout into young sponges.

Sponges are simple animals, poorly coordinated, and it is not surprising that they can easily regenerate lost parts. Indeed, if the more complex sponges with several oscula are cut in half, there are no lost parts. The ability of sponge cells to reorganize was demonstrated by H. V. Wilson in 1907. Sponges squeezed into a dish through fine silk cloth are disaggregated into minute cell clumps. The choanocytes swim about on the

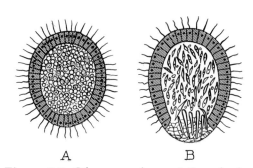

Figure 9.7 Other sponge larvae. *A*, From the class Calcarea. *B*, From the class Demospongia.

bottom by their flagella, and the amebocytes crawl. Whenever cells come in contact, they remain together. The bottom of the dish is soon covered with balls of cells, each of which develops into a tiny sponge if it includes both choanocytes and amebocytes. If the mass is very small, the choanocytes congregate on the outside and the organism resembles a colonial choanoflagellate. If the mass is large enough the choanocytes form chambers covered by the amebocytes.

Despite this low level of organization the cells are species-specific. If two kinds of sponge, one yellow and one orange, are disaggregated into one dish, the clumps that form are all yellow or all orange.

SYNOPSIS OF SPONGES

PHYLUM PORIFERA.   The sponges. Sessile aquatic animals with many small incurrent pores and a few large excurrent openings, connected internally by chambers lined with choanocytes.

CLASS 1. CALCAREA.   Spicules of calcium carbonate with one, three or four rays. Small, marine. Two orders. *Ascon, Sycon, Leuconia,* etc.

CLASS 2. HEXACTINELLIDA.   Glass sponges. Spicules of silica with six rays, often united to form girders. Two orders. *Euplectella,* Venus's flower basket.

CLASS 3. DEMOSPONGIA.   Skeleton various, not as above. Includes most of the large and common sponges.

Subclass 1. Tetractinellida.   No spongin, spicules of silica with four rays. Three orders.

Subclass 2. Monaxonida.   Simple one-rayed spicules of silica, spongin often present. Four orders. Includes the only fresh-water sponges, the family **Spongillidae.**

Subclass 3. Keratosa.   Spongin only, spicules absent. One order. Includes the bath sponges, family **Spongiidae.**

QUESTIONS

1. Diagram the three structural types of sponges.
2. Which sponges are found in fresh water?
3. How do the Demospongia differ from the Calcarea?
4. Discuss gastrulation in the sponges.

ANNOTATED REFERENCES

(See Chapter 13 for general references on invertebrates.)

10

THE PHYLA COELENTERATA AND CTENOPHORA

In addition to such animals as fishes and whales which swim actively through considerable distances, open water contains many organisms that are passive and float aimlessly with the water currents. They may swim, but not strongly enough to travel appreciably in a horizontal direction or to stay in one place against a current. This assemblage of organisms is the **plankton,** and their passive, floating way of life is called *planktonic.* The radiolaria and foraminifera described in Chapter 8 are planktonic protozoans, belonging to the marine plankton. The largest and most familiar of the plankton are **jellyfish,** often seen from shipboard as vast swarms in the upper few feet of water.

The common name, jellyfish, is applied to a heterogeneous group of organisms having a jelly-like consistency, members of the phylum **Coelenterata** and the phylum **Ctenophora** (Fig. 10.1). The coelenterate jellyfish usually have numerous **tentacles** with stinging cells and swim by muscular contractions of an umbrella-shaped body. The ctenophores usually have two tentacles with adhesive cells, and move by the beating of numerous **combs,** each of which is a row of fused cilia. In both phyla a simple epithelium, the **epidermis,** covers the body; another simple epithelium, the **gastrodermis,** lines a branched gut; and a jelly-like **mesoglea** between the epithelia forms the bulk of the body. Both groups are primarily carnivorous, catching other animals of appropriate size. Small jellyfish feed upon small worms, tiny shrimplike crustaceans and larval fish; larger

ones catch larger fish and sometimes other jellyfish. A single pelagic coelenterate is called a **medusa;** a ctenophore is called a **comb jelly.** The coelenterate phylum also includes a number of bottom-living forms such as **hydras, sea anemones** and **corals,** and floating colonies such as the **Portuguese man-of-war.** A few species of ctenophores creep on the bottom. As an introduction to these phyla we will first describe one of the medusae.

10.1
Gonionemus: General Behavior

Gonionemus is a genus of small medusae about 2 cm. in diameter when fully grown (Fig. 10.2). *G. murbachi* is a common species in Long Island Sound and *G. vertens* is found in Puget Sound. Like most medusae it does not merely float in the water, but moves rhythmically up and down through a span of a meter or more. The upward movement is active, produced by repeated, slow, graceful contractions of the body. The contracting muscle fibers are arranged circularly just beneath the epidermis of the lower or **subumbrellar** surface of the umbrella, and also in the **velum,** a delicate membrane extending inward from the lower edge of the umbrella. Contraction closes the umbrella, contraction of the velum reduces the size of the opening beneath the umbrella, and the downward jet of water produced pushes the animal upward. Between contractions elas-

157

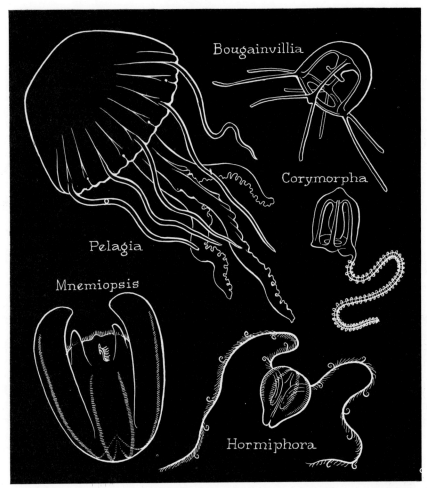

Figure 10.1 Jellyfish. The upper three are medusae, members of the phylum Coelenterata. The lower two are comb jellies, in the phylum Ctenophora. (Medusae redrawn from Mayer: Mnemiopsis from Hyman: Hormiphora from Chun.)

ticity of the body reopens the umbrella. Throughout the pulsing ascent the 60 to 80 **tentacles** on the umbrellar rim are usually shortened by the contraction of muscle fibers running lengthwise through them.

Downward movement is passive, for the jellyfish is slightly heavier than sea water and sinks slowly if it does not swim. As the velar and subumbrellar muscles relax completely the medusa opens wide. The muscle fibers in the tentacles relax and the tentacles slowly elongate. Probably as a result of its shape, the jellyfish usually turns over as it falls. The tentacles may trail behind, or be held out to the sides. By swimming up and drifting down in this way *Gonionemus* "nets" for food.

The medusa needs an orienting mechanism if it is to swim upward, rather than at random. The **statocysts** (Fig. 10.3) are sense structures that determine the direction of gravity. Each is a small concretion of calcium carbonate suspended on a flexible stalk in a cavity. The pressure of the stone against the cells in the wall of the cavity apparently provides the basis for orientation. Many statocysts are embedded in the margin of the medusa between the bases of the tentacles.

Although *Gonionemus* lacks eyes and does not orient its body to light, it sinks when the light is strong and rises when it is weak. Other species of medusae have eyespots, some of which provide directional information so that the jellyfish can swim toward or away from the light. The temperature and pH of the water may also influence the average depth at which the jellyfish stays. If

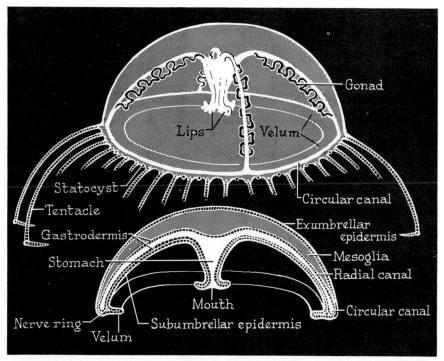

Figure 10.2 *Gonionemus.* Above, side view of whole animal, with many of the tentacles incompletely drawn. (Redrawn from Mayer.) Below, diagrammatic hemisection showing tissue layers; tentacles and gonads omitted.

the temperature or pH increases the medusae move to greater depths, whereas if the temperature or pH decreases they rise toward the surface. At night the light is greatly decreased and the pH of the water falls slightly so that the medusae are found closer to the surface than in the daytime. Similar **diurnal migrations** are performed by many pelagic organisms, and are especially marked in certain crustaceans that migrate as much as 100 meters vertically.

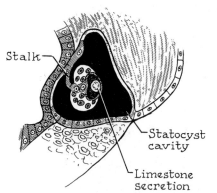

Figure 10.3 Detail of a statocyst, located in the margin of the bell between the circular canal on the left and the epidermis on the right. (After Hyman.)

Sense receptors for temperature and pH are probably scattered diffusely around the margin of the umbrella, a region known to be sensitive to certain chemicals. The activity of *Gonionemus* increases markedly when the juice of food organisms is added to the water. It swims horizontally as well as upward, keeping its tentacles extended in a random search for the prey.

Many other medusae have behavior patterns like those given above. Some, however, show adaptations for living where vegetation is abundant. *Gonionemus* and its close relatives can attach themselves to marine plants by means of adhesive pads on the tentacles (Fig. 10.2). They live primarily in shallow water where rooted vegetation is abundant and are often found in the daytime attached by a few of their tentacles with the rest outstretched in the netting position.

10.2

Gonionemus: Feeding and Digestion

Nematocysts. When a small organism brushes against an outstretched tentacle it is stung, and in its violent reaction to being stung it may throw itself against more tentacles. Further stinging paralyzes the prey, which is tightly held by the tentacles. Each tentacle has numerous rings of projecting **stinging cells** visible under the microscope (Fig. 10.4*A*). Within each of these is a shiny oval body, the **nematocyst** (Fig. 10.5), shaped like a tiny balloon with a very long tubular neck, the nematocyst **thread.** As the nematocyst develops within the stinging cell the thread appears in an inverted position, like a glove finger pulled inside out. To accommodate its length the thread is tightly coiled. On the outer surface of each stinging cell is a tiny projecting **trigger.** Upon suitable stimulation, which appears to include taste in addition to a touch on the trigger, the nematocyst fires its thread.

Firing is explosive. Water enters the nematocyst rapidly, the internal pressure increases and the thread is everted, just as a pulled-in glove finger can be everted by blowing into the glove. The diameter of the thread is so small and its eversion so fast that it easily penetrates the tissue of the prey. After discharge the everted thread is seen to bear recurved **hooks** on a swollen base and to be open at the tip (Fig. 10.5). The hooks hold the prey fast while the poisonous contents of the nematocyst are discharged through the thread into its body.

Gonionemus has just one kind of nematocyst. Other coelenterates have several distinct kinds, with marked differences in the details of hooks and thread.

Ingestion. Having caught its prey the medusa shortens its tentacles (sometimes only those holding the prey) and bends them toward the middle of the subumbrellar surface. The side of the umbrella holding the prey shrinks and bends inward. This movement brings the prey toward the **mouth,** an opening at the end of a short tube, the **manubrium,** that hangs down from the middle of the subumbrellar surface. As the prey is brought toward the mouth the manubrium extends and bends toward the prey. This synchronized activity involves the longitudinal muscle fibers of the tentacles, radial muscle fibers beneath the subumbrellar epidermis, and both circular and longitudinal fibers in the manubrium. Swimming muscles are not involved.

Surrounding the mouth are four **lips,** each folded longitudinally. The surface on the inner side of the fold, toward the mouth, is ciliated. Mucus is secreted on this surface and the ciliary activity moves the mucous sheet steadily into the mouth. As soon as the lips, which are weakly muscular, have folded over the prey, the tentacles release the bases of the discharged nematocysts and the medusa resumes its normal shape.

Digestion. The mouth opens into a large **stomach** in the middle of the medusa. When the prey has been swallowed, the mouth closes tightly and some of the gastrodermis cells secrete a digestive juice containing **proteases.** These enzymes initiate the breakdown of protein and reduce the prey to a broth.

Close to the subumbrellar surface the stomach extends laterally as four **radial canals** (Fig. 10.2), which are continuous at the margin with a **circular canal,** from which small branches extend into the tentacles.

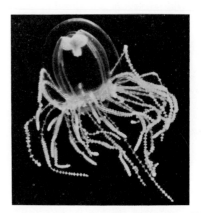

Figure 10.4   *A*, A portion of a tentacle from *Gonionemus,* showing rings of nematocysts. (After Hyman.) *B*, *Gonionemus vertens* actively swimming. (Courtesy of Douglas P. Wilson.)

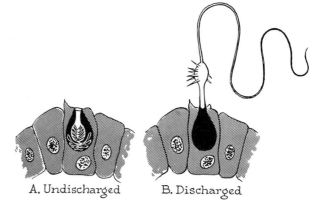

Figure 10.5 Diagrammatic view of a nematocyst. *A*, Before discharge. *B*, Everted.

A. Undischarged   B. Discharged

Both the stomach and the canals are lined with tracts of ciliated gastrodermis cells which set up currents to circulate the broth throughout the system. Other gastrodermis cells absorb dissolved nutrients and ingest the remaining small food particles. Ingestion is the same as in many protozoans. Particles are taken up in **food vacuoles** where digestion of fats and carbohydrates, and further digestion of proteins, take place. As among protozoans, the vacuoles become acid and then alkaline during digestion.

Since the stomach and canals perform both circulatory and digestive functions, digesting the food and distributing it to all parts of the body, they are properly called a **gastrovascular system.** Indigestible residues are eliminated through the mouth, which thus functions as both mouth and anus.

10.3
Gonionemus: Diffusion

The jelly-like mesoglea is present everywhere between the gastrodermis and epidermis. In the tentacles it is very thin but in the umbrella it is thick, providing bulk and determining the shape of the relaxed animal. In *Gonionemus* the mesoglea lacks cells and is nonliving. Since it is about 96 per cent water, dissolved materials diffuse readily in all directions. Diffusion is an adequate mechanism in jellyfish for the distribution of nutrients from gastrodermis to epidermis, and for respiration and excretion (cf. Chapter 5).

When a jellyfish is not digesting food the mouth usually remains open and fresh sea water is circulated through the gastrovascular system by the ciliated tracts. Hence, most of the time all the tissues are in direct contact with sea water, facilitating a direct exchange of gases and waste products by diffusion. In all probability the water in the gastrovascular system contains enough oxygen to supply the gastrodermis cells while the mouth is closed during digestion.

10.4
Gonionemus: Nervous System

Classically the nervous system of the coelenterate is described as a **nerve net,** a diffuse network of neurons each with several processes that synapse with those of other neurons. The system is distinguished from those of higher organisms by the transmission of impulses across synapses in either direction, rather than in one direction only. The concept of a generalized nerve net, however, does not adequately explain the specific coordinated behavior of the medusa. Detailed work has shown that the system is not this simple. On the upper or **exumbrellar** surface of the medusa, the neurons are sparse and their arrangement is indeed that of a simple net. Even here, however, preferred directions of impulse transmission have been observed. At the margin the nerve cells are concentrated to form circular fiber tracts, the **nerve ring.** On the subumbrellar surface the nerve fibers are arranged radially, extending from the margin toward the center with few if any circular fibers.

The nerve ring of *Gonionemus* is double (Fig. 10.6), with rings above and below the line where the velum is attached. The lower

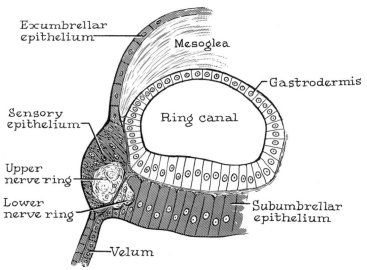

Figure 10.6 Section through the margin of the bell in *Gonionemus,* showing the nerve ring. It lies embedded in the double layer of epidermis at the base of the velum. (After Hyman.)

ring is primarily **motor** in function and sends fibers to the muscles. The upper ring is primarily **sensory** and integrates the information coming in from the several senses scattered around the umbrella margin. Notable exceptions are the nerves from the statocysts, which go to the motor ring. While the other senses influence the activity of the medusa, and may even reverse its direction of movement, the direction itself is related only to gravity. The intimate association of the gravity sense with the motor ring is therefore especially significant.

Locomotion is efficient only when the muscle fibers of the umbrella contract synchronously. Coordination is effected by the circular fibers of the nerve ring. If the ring is cut, coordination is lost and the medusa swims erratically with lopsided beats.

Feeding behavior requires coordination oriented radially rather than circularly. The shortening and bending of the tentacles, the bending of the umbrella, and the lateral bending of the manubrium must be in the right direction if the prey is to be successfully transferred to the mouth. The nerve ring is not important in this behavior and may be cut without serious effect if the cut is not exactly on the radius involved. The radial nerve fibers of the subumbrellar surface are involved, for this coordination disappears if they are cut. The manubrium may extend and bend but fails to bend in the right direction.

10.5
Gonionemus: Reproduction

Both male and female *Gonionemus* have four **gonads** that develop in the epidermis of the subumbrellar surface and hang downward as ruffles parallel to the four radial canals (Fig. 10.2). Since the canals are close to the subumbrellar surface, the gonads are close to a nutrient source. Eggs and sperm are shed into the surrounding water, where fertilization takes place.

The fertilized egg develops rapidly into a small ciliated larva, the **planula** (Fig. 10.7A). The planula is a swimming gastrula composed of a layer of ectoderm enclosing a solid core of large endoderm cells. Planulae are found in all classes of coelenterates. The planula of *Gonionemus* does not develop directly into a medusa, but attaches to some solid object and becomes a **polyp** (Fig. 10.7B).

The polyp is tube-shaped with an outer epidermis and inner gastrodermis separated by a very thin mesoglea. The tube is closed at the attached end, forming a **foot,** and the open free end is the **mouth.** The simple cylindrical cavity is the **stomach.** Surrounding the mouth is a ring of **tentacles** bearing nematocysts. Like the medusa, the polyp feeds by snaring prey with its outstretched tentacles and transferring it to the extensible mouth.

Structurally the polyp is simpler than the medusa. Circular and longitudinal muscle

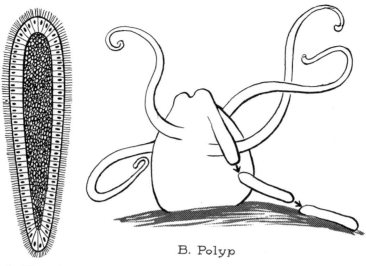

A. Planula

B. Polyp

Figure 10.7   Reproduction in *Gonionemus*. *A*, Planula larva that develops from the egg. *B*, The polyp, showing mouth and four tentacles. A frustule is forming on the side and is also shown in successive stages as it later creeps away. (*A*, after Hyman; *B*, modified from Hyman after Joseph.)

fibers are sparse and not arranged in layers or sheets as in the medusa. The nervous system lacks a nerve ring, and throughout its structure suggests a nerve net with neurons somewhat more numerous around the mouth. In many respects, the polyp is a juvenile stage, intermediate between the planula and the medusa.

The polyp of *Gonionemus*, only 1 mm. in diameter, is unusually small and squat. As it grows, the polyp reproduces asexually by budding. One side of the body thickens, becomes constricted as a separate tube, and very slowly creeps away. This bud or **frustule** has no mouth, tentacles or stomach cavity. Over the span of several days the frustule may move many centimeters, after which it settles down with one end attached and develops into a typical polyp.

Asexual reproduction by **budding** is common among the coelenterates. Most polyp stages are able to reproduce this way, but only a few kinds of medusae show the phenomenon. We have observed that sponges reproduce by asexual buds and, as we shall see later, many other animal groups do also. Coelenterates may pass through many generations of asexual budding before developing sexually mature individuals.

In the summer *Gonionemus* polyps produce spherical buds that develop into medusae. A well-fed polyp may produce several such buds, but a small or starved individual may produce only one. In the latter case the entire polyp may transform into a medusa.

While still attached, the medusa bud develops a velum, manubrium with mouth, and eight tentacles. It begins to pulsate and eventually breaks free by its own activity. As it grows, increasing its diameter from 1 mm. to 2 cm., new tentacles grow out between those already present on the umbrellar margin.

10.6

Classes of the Phylum Coelenterata

Differences in structure and life history are the criteria for grouping coelenterates in three classes. *Gonionemus* belongs to the class **Hydrozoa,** in which the medusa has a velum and the polyp has a simple unpartitioned gut. Medusa buds arise from the side of the polyp. The class **Scyphozoa** includes most of the larger jellyfish. The scyphozoan medusa lacks a velum, the stomach cavity of the polyp is subdivided by four longitudinal partitions, and medusae are formed by transformation of the end of the polyp so that the polyp mouth becomes the medusa mouth. The class **Anthozoa** includes sea anemones and corals. The polyps have a stomach cavity subdivided by 6, 8 or more partitions and become sexually mature without transformation into a free-swimming stage. Medusae are lacking.

10.7

Class Hydrozoa

The typical hydrozoan life history includes a juvenile polyp stage that reproduces asexually and an adult medusa stage that reproduces sexually. A full range of variations occurs, however, from species that lack medusae to species that lack polyps. Hydrozoans lacking polyps live in the open ocean, where an attached stage is impractical; the planula develops directly into a medusa. Polyps that lack medusae live near the marine shores or in fresh water. The gonads develop on the sides of the polyps, and a whole series of forms with various degrees of suppression of the medusa stage indicates that these gonads represent the last vestige of the medusa, appearing where medusa buds would otherwise develop.

Commonly, the polyp is larger and longer-lived than the medusa. In many hydrozoans most of the asexual buds of the polyp remain attached to the parent to produce a colony of many polyps. The few buds that creep off as frustules establish new colonies. Division of labor is frequent in the colonial forms. Some polyps catch and eat food while others are specialized for the production of medusae (Fig. 10.8). In a few species additional polyps are modified into long clubs covered with nematocysts which serve to protect the colony.

The genus *Obelia* is representative of hydrozoans with colonial polyps (Fig. 10.8). The branching stalk and terminal polyps are covered with a delicate horny sheath, the **perisarc,** secreted by the epidermis. It is annulated in many places to provide

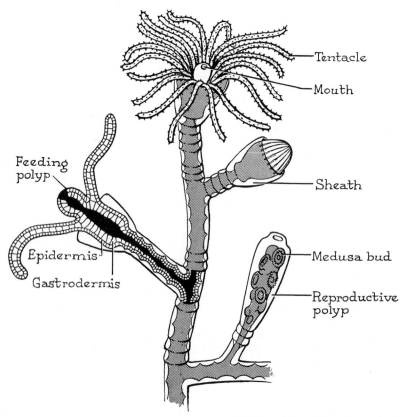

Figure 10.8 A hydroid, *Obelia*, showing a small portion of the branching colony. One polyp is shown in longitudinal section. (After Parker and Haswell.)

flexibility as well as support for the colony. The feeding polyps are typical. Polyps that produce medusae have neither mouth nor tentacles and develop many medusa buds along their sides. All polyps are connected through a common gastrovascular cavity. The medusae are about the size of polyps and do not grow after they become free-swimming. In related genera the medusae never become free of the polyp, but mature sexually and shed their gametes while still attached.

In the order **Siphonophora** of the class Hydrozoa the organisms are remarkably complex. The planula does not become attached, but develops into a polyp while swimming. The basal end of the polyp commonly develops an **air sac** to serve as a float. From this polyp a complex colony of polyps and medusae develops by budding. Some of the attached medusae are specialized for swimming. Some of the polyps have no mouths but are equipped with very long tentacles covered with powerful nematocysts. Other polyps have mouths but no tentacles and are used only for feeding. Still others develop as simple stalks that bear medusa buds along their sides. These buds produce eggs and sperm and are the only sexually reproductive individuals in the colony. Entire floating colonies of siphonophores may remain intact, or pieces including every kind of individual may break loose and lead independent lives.

A famous siphonophore is *Physalia*, the dreaded **Portuguese man-of-war** (Fig. 10.9). It has a large purple air float up to 12 cm. long that rides high out of the water and is carried by the wind across the oceans. Swimming medusae are absent. Tentacles of the stinging polyps may trail out 12 meters into the water, and their nematocysts easily penetrate the skin of man. The intense pain and occasional paralysis caused by many stings can result in drowning.

The four kinds of polyps in *Physalia* occur in groups, one of which is shown in Figure 10.10. Although the mouth of the feeding polyp can open very wide, the polyp is un-

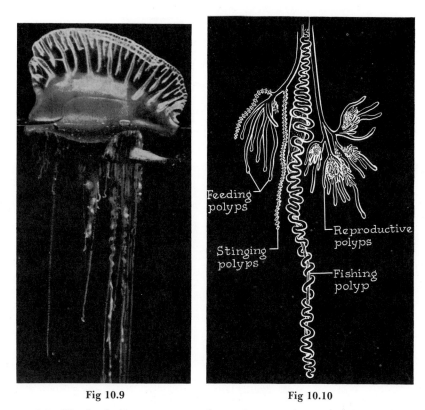

Fig 10.9   Fig 10.10

Figure 10.9 *Physalia*, the Portuguese man-of-war. (Courtesy of New York Zoological Society.)

Figure 10.10 A cluster of polyps from *Physalia*, showing the various modifications of the individual polyps. (After Hyman.)

able to swallow prey unless it is comparatively small. Larger prey are consumed in an ingenious fashion. Many feeding polyps become attached to the prey, each spreading its mouth as widely as possible over the prey. The edges of adjacent mouths meet and enclose the prey completely. Then digestive juices are regurgitated and the prey is disintegrated and swallowed.

Of the several thousand species of hydrozoans none is of economic importance. Usually the medusae are too small to be a nuisance to swimmers. A few kinds of polyps secrete limestone around the colonies and thus contribute slightly to the building of coral reefs.

10.8
Class Scyphozoa

The medusa, which may be as much as a meter in diameter, is the dominant stage in the class Scyphozoa. A common genus is *Aurelia* (Fig. 10.11), abundant in Atlantic and Pacific waters. Nematocysts of many of the larger forms can penetrate the human skin and produce intense pain.

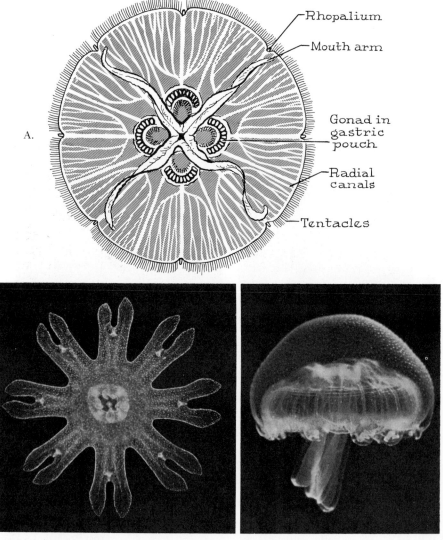

Figure 10.11 *A*, Ventral view of *Aurelia*. Compare with *Pelagia* on Figure 10.1, which differs primarily in having larger tentacles. (After Hyman.) *B*, Left, Ephyra larva of *Aurelia*. Right. Young *Aurelia* bell contracting (lateral view). (Courtesy of Douglas P. Wilson.)

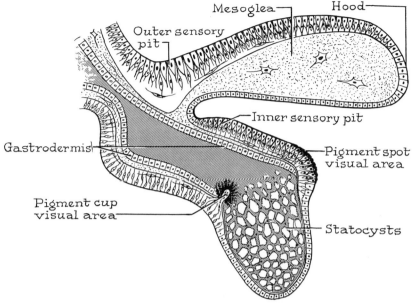

Figure 10.12   Section through a rhopalium showing the hood and the various sensory areas. (Modified from Hyman after Schewiakoff.)

The mesoglea of scyphozoan medusae contains numerous scattered ameboid cells of unknown function, and distinct fibers that stiffen the jelly-like matrix. The stomach is subdivided into a central chamber and four **gastric pouches,** each containing internal endodermal tentacles armed with nematocysts that can be used to reparalyze prey should it recover after being swallowed. The radial canals are much branched.

The sensory areas of the bell margin in this class are concentrated to form complex sense structures, the **rhopalia** (Fig. 10.12). These respond to gravity, light and chemicals in the water. Without them spontaneous activity of the medusa ceases.

The gonads of scyphozoans develop in the gastrodermis of the gastric pouches. Gametes are shed first into the pouches and then to the outside through the mouth.

In other respects the medusa of this class resembles that of the Hydrozoa. The scyphozoan polyp is an inconspicuous part of the life cycle. Asexual reproduction by frustule formation is common (Fig. 10.13A).

Medusae form by the direct transformation of the polyp head, rather than by lateral budding as in the Hydrozoa. In some species the entire polyp transforms into a single medusa. In others a series of medusae

may be produced. Successive medusae may overlap in development, so that new medusae begin to form beneath older ones that have

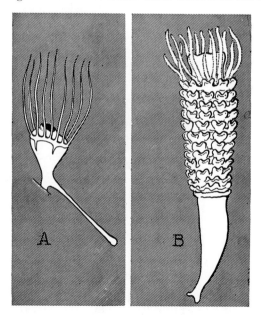

Figure 10.13   Reproduction in the Scyphozoa. *A,* The polyp. A frustule forming on its right will creep off and become another polyp. *B,* Strobila. Starting at the upper end, successively lower portions of the polyp transform into medusae. (*A* modified from Hyman after Perez; *B* after Hyman.)

not yet broken free. The result is a pile of partially formed medusae resembling a stack of plates. This stage, which is shown by *Aurelia,* is called a **strobila,** and the process is called **strobilization** (Fig. 10.13*B*).

Most of the 200 species of scyphozoans are similar and adhere to the simple jellyfish plan. They are of little interest to man except as nuisances to swimmers.

10.9
Class Anthozoa

In the third class, the **Anthozoa,** medusae are lacking and the polyps become sexually mature without metamorphosis. The polyps are usually short and stout with a large mouth and numerous internal partitions (Fig. 10.14). The mesoglea is packed with supportive elastic fibers. The gonads develop in the endoderm along the free edges of the partitions. In general, the structure of these polyps is closer to that of the Scyphozoa than that of the Hydrozoa. The anthozoan polyp also has a **stomodeum,** an inturned mouth lined with ectoderm.

The larger members of this class are the solitary **sea anemones,** which are flower-like

in appearance when their tentacles are spread in search of prey. Many of them are brightly colored and feed voraciously on fish. Others are adapted to living on shells containing hermit crabs and have behavioral adaptations for attaching to such shells.

The Anthozoa include the colonial **true corals,** which contribute greatly to the bulk of coral reefs along some tropical shores. The individual polyp may be only 1 cm. across, but the colony secretes an external supporting framework of calcium carbonate that may be of considerable size. This skeleton may be encrusting, arborescent or massive (Fig. 10.15).

Coral reefs are formed by large populations of many species of coral and other limestone-secreting organisms. They develop only in warm shallow water exposed to the ocean waves. At present the two major regions that offer these conditions and support reefs are: (1) the Caribbean area, including Florida, Bermuda, the Bahamas and the West Indies, and (2) the Indo-Pacific area known as the Coral Sea, extending from Australia to Hawaii and the Philippines.

The precious coral of commerce is not a true coral but a member of a third order of Anthozoa, the **alcyonarians.** These have an

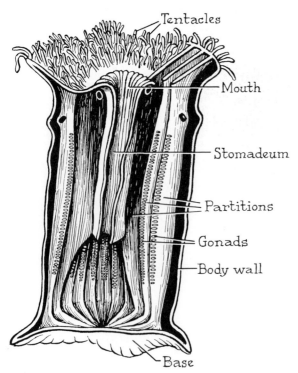

Tentacles

Mouth

Stomadeum

Partitions

Gonads

Body wall

Base

Figure 10.14 *Metridium.* Diagrammatic view of half a polyp. Several internal structures have been omitted.

Figure 10.15 *A*, Lace coral. *B*, West Indian coral. *C*, Polyps of the star coral. (Courtesy of the American Museum of Natural History.)

Figure 10.16 Sea fan. (Courtesy of the American Museum of Natural History.)

internal skeleton formed by the secretion of calcium carbonate and protein horny material into the mesoglea. In some species these secretions fuse into a rigid framework hard enough to resist wear. Precious corals form irregular branching colonies in the Mediterranean Sea and near Japan. Wooden frames with rope tangle mops are dragged over the sea bottom to break the brittle skeleton and gather the branches. Other alcyonarians are the yellow, red or purple sea fans (Fig. 10.16) of tropical waters. These colonies develop as flattened networks with a few main branches and numerous cross connections.

10.10
Fresh-water Coelenterates: Hydra

Only a few species of coelenterates, all members of the class Hydrozoa, occur in fresh water. The fresh-water forms include a colonial polyp found in a few eastern rivers of the United States, a jellyfish very similar to *Gonionemus* found sporadically in ponds and streams all over the world, and a number of species of solitary polyps, the **hydras.** Only the last are easily obtained in most bodies of fresh water.

The hydra is an unusual hydrozoan (Fig. 10.17, left). Medusae are lacking altogether, unless the gonads are considered to be their vestiges. Some species are hermaphroditic, others have separate sexes. The testes shed sperm into the water and each ovary produces one egg at a time which is retained and fertilized in the ovary (Fig. 10.18). The egg develops to the planula stage while still attached to the parent. The planula lacks cilia and secretes a surrounding shell. The encased larva then drops off the parent and hatches later as a young polyp.

The polyp feeds in typical fashion on small aquatic animals. It is no more complex than the polyp of *Gonionemus*, except that it is considerably larger and has four kinds of nematocysts. One kind is radically different (Fig. 10.17, right), having no spines, poison or opening at the tip of the thread. Instead the thread coils tightly after eversion, often encircling minute spines or hairs on the prey and holding it fast. The structural simplicity of hydra has suggested to some investigators that it is a juvenile form that becomes sexually mature without metamorphosis.

Asexual buds do not become frustules but develop mouths and tentacles while still attached to the parent. Later the base constricts and the offspring creeps away. A

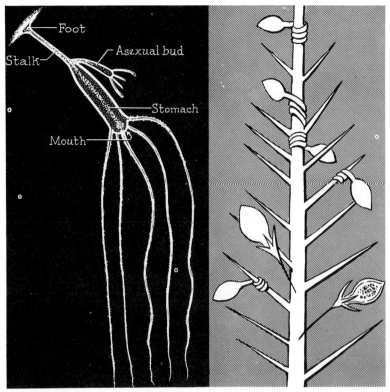

Figure 10.17 Left, *Hydra*. The tentacles hang in the water like a net, waiting for prey. (After Hyman.) Right, Spine of a crustacean that has brushed against the tentacles of a hydra. Two of the nematocysts shown are similar to those of *Gonionemus*. The others are of the coiling type. (After Hyman.)

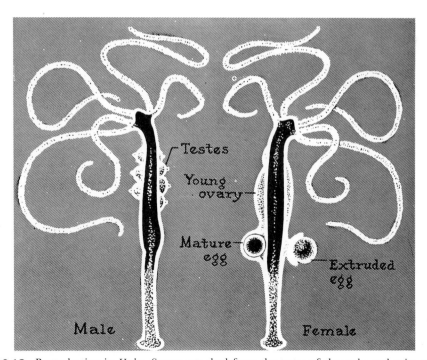

Figure 10.18 Reproduction in *Hydra*. Sperm are shed from the testes of the male, and swim to the females where they fertilize the mature eggs.

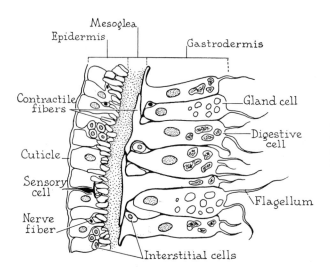

Figure 10.19 Diagrammatic view of a portion of a cross section through the body of *Hydra*. Combined from light microscopic and electron microscopic studies. Only the more obvious features are apparent under the light microscope.

parent may have several such buds and temporarily resemble a colonial hydrozoan (Fig. 10.17, left).

Unlike most hydrozoan polyps, which are permanently attached to one place, hydra moves from time to time. The polyp may slide slowly on its base at the rate of several centimeters a day, or it may somersault at a more rapid rate by alternately attaching tentacles and base.

The tissues of hydra, while comparatively simple among coelenterates, are difficult to analyze under the light microscope. The body shows an outer epidermis and a thick, vacuolated endodermis separated by an indistinct mesoglea (Fig. 10.19). Undifferentiated **interstitial cells** are seen in both layers. Those in the epidermis often occur in clusters. These may replace worn-out cells of all kinds but most frequently are found giving rise to stinging cells. Endodermal cells include at least two kinds: **glandular cells** that secrete proteolytic enzymes and **digestive cells** that take up food particles.

Careful teasing of the tissues shows that epidermal cells have, at their bases, **contractile fibers** running longitudinally on the outer surface of the mesoglea, whereas digestive cells have similar fibers running circularly on the inner surface of the mesoglea. Separated from the mesoglea by these muscle fibers are two networks of **nerve fibers,** very diffuse in the gastrodermis, including occasional **sensory cells** with processes extending to the surface of the body wall.

The electron microscope reveals additional features. The body wall of the hydra is covered with a very thin cuticle. The ends of contractile fibers are often intimately joined to the ends of adjacent fibers, and often the fibers are firmly rooted in the mesoglea. Gland cells lack fibers and do not reach the mesoglea. Both gland and digestive cells are flagellated, and the flagella have a normal construction although they are thicker than those of most organisms. Oddly, the electron microscope has not yet revealed the nervous system of hydra, although it is clearly evident in many previous studies.

10.11
The Phylum Ctenophora

Comb jellies have a spherical or vertically elongate body plan in contrast to the umbrella shape of medusae. Familiar representatives are the sea gooseberry, genus *Pleurobrachia,* and the sea walnut, genus *Mnemiopsis* (Fig. 10.1). The mouth is at one end, so that oral, aboral and lateral surfaces can be identified. Each ctenophore swims with eight columns of **combs** that radiate from the center of the aboral surface over the sides to the oral surface. Each comb is a row of fused cilia (Fig. 10.20). Just beneath the epidermis along each comb column is a tract of nerve fibers that coordinate the beating of the cilia. In the resting position each comb points toward the oral end. When the comb bends vigorously toward the aboral end the comb jelly moves through the water, mouth first. The combs beat in waves passing along the columns from aboral to oral ends.

Synchronized action of the eight comb columns produces a smooth gliding locomotion that may be as fast as 60 cm. per minute. Ctenophores usually swim up and down through a meter of water with the mouth always forward.

A comb jelly has but two **tentacles.** These are branched and can be retracted into **tentacle sheaths.** Each tentacle has an outer layer of epidermis surrounding a core of mesoglea. In the epidermis are numerous **colloblasts,** each one a modified epidermal cell containing a peripheral hemisphere of adhesive mucus and a basal coiled spring. The spring ejects the mucus against prey and anchors it to the tentacle.

The process of digestion is similar to that found in the coelenterates.

The sensory region of the comb jelly is concentrated at the aboral end where a **statocyst** is the primary sense organ. As in medusae, the statocyst is associated directly with motor nerves which, in the ctenophore, are the eight radiating nerves underlying the comb columns. If one of these nerves is cut,

the corresponding column is no longer coordinated with the others. If all the nerves are cut, coordination disappears and the comb jelly is unable to control its locomotion.

Like most jellyfish the ctenophores are transparent. The combs, however, reflect light and produce iridescent patterns. This shimmering color passing in waves from aboral to oral ends shows the waves of beating of the combs and is useful in studies of coordination.

At night many of the comb jellies are brightly luminescent when disturbed. The light is produced close to the nerve tracts beneath the comb columns. Like luminescence in most animals the light is blue-green in color. In ctenophores the luminescence is especially striking, since it becomes iridescent as it is reflected from the combs, flickering like colored fire up and down the comb columns.

The eggs and sperm are shed into the water where the embryos develop directly into the comb jelly form. Early divisions of the eggs follow an exact, rigid path of development. The first three divisions are vertical and produce a curved plate of eight cells. The fourth is horizontal and separates eight small upper cells from eight large lower cells. Later cleavages continue to be constant in all individuals, and each upper and lower cell of the 16-cell stage becomes the corresponding eighth of the ctenophore. Associated with this rigid pattern is an early chemical differentiation. The opposite is true of most coelenterates, in which early development appears to be unspecialized, with cell division preceding chemical differentiation.

10.12
The Regulation of Form

A fascinating and challenging area of biology is concerned with two problems associated with development: the extent to which an organism can repair injuries, and the extent to which it can correct disarrangements. Some of the coelenterates and ctenophores have remarkable abilities in these respects. If parts of the body are removed, they are usually replaced. If individuals are cut in half, each half may regenerate the missing half. Sometimes

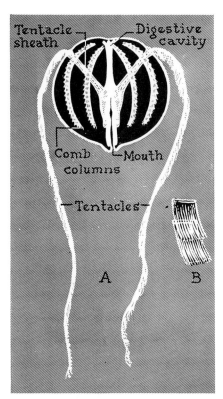

Figure 10.20 *Pleurobrachia. A,* Lateral view of whole animal. *B,* Detail showing two combs, each formed by the fusion of a row of cilia. (After Hyman.)

quarters or even smaller pieces of animals will regenerate into whole organisms.

Very often a remarkable regenerative ability is associated with natural reproduction by budding. In many sea anemones, for example, pieces of the base may break off spontaneously and develop into new individuals. Hence, when pieces are cut off, they regenerate well. Again, in the one genus of sea anemones in which a single, experimentally removed tentacle can regenerate all the missing parts, it is found that tentacles spontaneously do the same thing as a form of asexual reproduction.

The ability to correct disarrangements is usually not so marked as the regenerative ability. If an oral end of one hydra is grafted onto the side of another, the animal will eventually divide to form two normal individuals. If, however, the cut surfaces of two oral ends are placed together, they heal to form a single individual with two mouths and no base. Such monsters remain thus, apparently unable to achieve the normal form. If such a creature is then cut in half, each half may regenerate a base.

In the ctenophores, pieces put together in the original orientation with oral and aboral ends aligned will usually regulate into normal individuals, while opposed pieces such as two aboral ends with their cut surfaces placed together will not.

A most remarkable example of successful rearrangement is found in hydra. As in most polyps the mouth can open very wide, and it is possible to *turn a hydra inside out* through its mouth without tearing any of the tissues! Such an individual, with the epidermis inside and gastrodermis outside, is unable to turn inside out again to recover its normal form. In some cases, however, the normal form is recovered by a direct migration of the individual cells across the thin mesogleal layer to their former location.

These abilities to repair or replace parts and to rearrange disarrangements are two aspects of **form regulation,** the processes by which individual organisms come to have the morphology of their kind. Most coelenterates are able to regulate throughout their life. Injuries or disarrangements are as easily corrected by embryos as by adults. Among the ctenophores, however, the embryo has much less regulative ability than the adult. If the two-cell stage is divided into two separate cells, each becomes only half a ctenophore. One cell from the four-cell stage becomes one quarter of a ctenophore having only two comb columns. Later in life, however, those that survive will spontaneously regenerate the missing parts to become normal.

Not all coelenterates have good regulative abilities. The siphonophores, for example, usually fail to replace lost parts, and wounds are healed by a simple closure of the hole. In this group regulative ability is good in the embryos and larvae and becomes poor in the adults.

Many other animal groups, including the sponges already discussed and such complex animals as crabs, starfishes and salamanders, have a considerable ability to regulate form. The coelenterates and ctenophores are especially suitable for experimentation because the body plan, while relatively simple, is geometrically exact and provides an excellent frame of reference. Survival after operations is not difficult to achieve. The phenomena associated with form regulation are considered to be similar to those of embryologic development.

SYNOPSIS OF THE RADIATE PHYLA

PHYLUM COELENTERATA. Polyps and medusae. Aquatic, typically predaceous animals with radial symmetry and a ring of tentacles bearing nematocysts surrounding the mouth.

CLASS 1. HYDROZOA. Medusae with a velum, polyps without partitions in the gut.

Order 1. Trachylina. Small, primitive forms with the polyp stage reduced or absent. Includes *Gonionemus* and the fresh-water jellyfishes.

Order 2. Hydroidea. Mostly small, often common, forms, many of which have complex, branching polyp stages. *Obelia, Hydra.*

Order 3. Siphonophora. Complex floating colonies of polyps and medusae. Includes *Physalia,* the Portuguese man-of-war.

Order 4. Milleporina. Colonial polyps secrete massive external calcareous skeletons, may contribute to coral reef formation.

CLASS 2. SCYPHOZOA. The jellyfish. Medusae without a velum, polyps with four internal partitions. Includes many forms with large medusae. Five orders. *Aurelia.*

CLASS 3. ANTHOZOA. No medusa. Polyps with six, eight or more internal partitions.

Subclass 1. Alcyonaria. Eight feathery tentacles and eight internal partitions. Often with an internal skeleton. Six orders. Includes sea fans, precious coral.

Subclass 2. Zoantheria. Tentacles simple, six or more internal partitions. Five orders, including:

Order 1. Actinaria. The sea anemones. *Metridium.*

Order 2. Madreporaria. The true corals.

PHYLUM CTENOPHORA. Comb jellies. Marine animals with eight rows of ciliary combs and one pair of tentacles bearing colloblasts.

CLASS 1. TENTACULATA. One pair of branched tentacles. Four orders. *Pleurobrachia, Mnemiopsis, Coeloplana.*

CLASS 2. NUDA. Tentacles absent. Predaceous on large animals that are swallowed whole. One order.

QUESTIONS

1. Define "planktonic" and "plankton."
2. Describe mesoglea.
3. Draw a vertical section through a jellyfish and a sea anemone.
4. How does a nematocyst work?
5. Describe the role of diffusion in the physiology of coelenterates.
6. What is a strobila?
7. Distinguish between medusae and comb jellies.
8. What is "regulation of form"?

ANNOTATED REFERENCES

(See Chapter 13 for general references.)

Lenhoff, H., and Loomis, W. (Eds.): The Biology of Hydra. Miami, University of Miami Press, 1961. A fascinating collection of reports on recent work on *Hydra* and a few other coelenterates.

Rees, W. J. (Ed.): The Cnidaria and Their Evolution. New York, Academic Press, 1966. A collection of scholarly papers presented at a symposium sponsored by the Zoological Society of London. Papers on nematocysts, structure and function of mesoglea and receptors, and the coordination, locomotion and evolution of the various groups are included.

11 The Phylum Platyhelminthes

The flatworms or **Platyhelminthes** are wormlike animals with a single major opening to the gut, which functions as both mouth and anus. Between the gastrodermis and epidermis the body is filled with tissues, including layers of muscle, connective tissues and reproductive organs. Neither a body cavity (such as will be described in later chapters) nor a circulatory system is present.

Included in the flatworms are two major groups of animal parasites, the **flukes** (class **Trematoda**) and the **tapeworms** (class **Cestoda**), which will be discussed further in Chapter 42. The free-living forms (class **Turbellaria**) range in size from 0.1 to 600 mm. and are found in fresh water, in salt water and on land.

The phylum is best approached by a study of its free-living members. We will begin with an example of a turbellarian which is intermediate in size and complexity.

11.1
Dugesia: Habitat and Appearance

The most familiar free-living flatworms are the **planarians,** abundant in ponds and streams all over the world. This common name is used for an entire order, but only one genus has the scientific name *Planaria*. In the United States the more common planarians belong to the related genus, *Dugesia*. The species *D. dorotocephala* occurs in ponds and streams and is available from biologic supply houses.

Dugesia is about 1 cm. long, with a distinct head having what look like crossed eyes and pointed ears (Fig. 11.1). The surface of the

176

body is a single layer of cuboidal cells, the **epidermis** (Fig. 11.4). Planarians glide about on the ciliated ventral side of this surface. Slime glands among the ventral epidermis

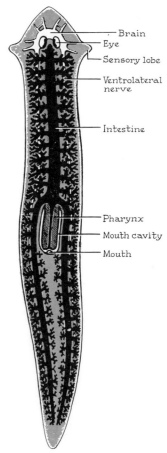

Figure 11.1 *Dugesia.* Dorsal view, showing the digestive and nervous systems. The mouth opens ventrally. (After Hyman.)

Figure 11.2 Hunting and feeding in *Dugesia*. A small crustacean (*Daphnia*) is captured and eaten, its tough exoskeleton remaining as an empty shell.

cells secrete a lubricating slime that smooths the path. The epidermis contains numerous small rods, the **rhabdites,** which upon ejection become a viscous mass. This may be a defense against adverse conditions.

11.2
Dugesia: Feeding and Digestion

As the animal glides along hunting for food, the anterior end is usually slightly elevated (Fig. 11.2). Should a small organism come close, the head turns quickly toward it. **Adhesive glands** along the edges of the body, and especially prominent in the head region, secrete a glue to which the passing organism adheres tightly, and the head of the planarian folds over the prey. After sliding around the prey once or twice, binding it tightly in slime and glue, the planarian comes to rest with the anterior half of its body on the bottom and the posterior half doubled over the prey.

The **mouth** of *Dugesia* is midventral (Fig. 11.1). The **pharynx** is a long extensible tube which can pass through the mouth. When not in use, the pharynx is withdrawn into a **mouth cavity** lined with ectoderm (Fig. 11.3). The pharynx itself is covered with ectoderm, and its wall is composed of several layers of muscle and connective tissue (Fig. 11.4). When withdrawn the pharynx is short and stout, but by contraction of the circular mus-

cle fibers it can be elongated greatly (Figs. 11.2 and 11.3). When feeding it is extended and used as a probe to search the prey for a tender spot. It then bores into the prey by, strong sucking movements and tears the soft parts to bits to be swallowed.

After a meal the planarian crawls off a short distance and rests, with the body rounded up and firmly attached to the bottom by glue from the marginal adhesive glands.

The pharynx opens into a **branched intestine,** one primary branch extending into the head, and two more extending toward the tail (Fig. 11.1). All have side branches so that in a cross section of the worm the intestine may be cut across several times. As in the coelenterates and ctenophores, the digestive organ is a simple gastrodermis of endoderm cells. In planarians these cells are very large, making the intestine the bulkiest structure in the body. Although no digestive enzymes have been found in the lumen of the intestine, it is obvious from the disintegration of large food particles that at least some proteolytic enzymes are secreted. Most of the digestion, however, is intracellular. The gastrodermis cells gather up food particles in food vacuoles. The food vacuoles have not been observed to become first acid and then basic, as they do in other phyla. Cilia are absent. Food is propelled through the intestine by muscular contractions.

Indigestible remains of food vacuoles are

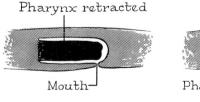

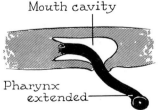

Figure 11.3 Diagrammatic side view of the pharynx of *Dugesia* retracted (left) and extended through the mouth (right).

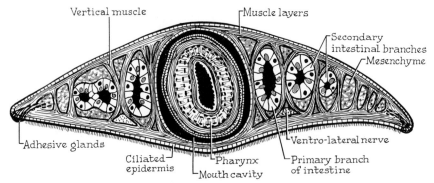

Figure 11.4   Diagrammatic cross section of *Dugesia* at the level of the pharynx.

released back into the intestine where, together with fragments that could not be taken up in food vacuoles, they are compressed into solid masses and eventually ejected through the mouth.

11.3

Dugesia: Sensation and Movement

Dugesia is well supplied with sense organs. The "nose," by which the animal explores the physical nature of the bottom on which it is crawling, contains numerous tactile nerve endings. Chemoreceptors (taste-smell) are located in other nerve endings scattered over the body, but are localized especially on the "ears." Each of these is held in a cupped position (Fig. 11.2). Cilia lining the cup beat more vigorously than elsewhere, drawing water from in front of the animal for analysis by the chemoreceptors.

Planarians capture small prey and are also quick to locate and feed upon dead organisms. When an individual first senses such food, it raises its head and turns from side to side. The two projections at the sides enable the worm to locate the food by chemoreception,

and the worm shortly lowers its head and slides off in the appropriate direction. At frequent intervals it will stop and raise its head again to get new bearings.

Dugesia is also sensitive to light, generally retreating from it. Each eye has a **pigment cup** facing laterally, in the hollow of which are rodlike extensions of **visual cells** (Fig. 11.5). These **rods** are arranged radially, and are believed to be stimulated maximally by light traveling along their length, since the direction of a light source is very accurately perceived. The bodies of the visual cells, containing the nuclei, lie outside the cup, and from them a bundle of nerve fibers proceeds to the brain. Such an eye, in which light must first traverse nerve fibers and visual cell bodies before reaching the sensitive rods, is an **inverted eye** (the human eye is also inverted). Eyes of planarians do not form images, but can detect roughly the relative amount of light and the general direction from which it comes.

In a water current planarians usually face or crawl upstream. Current direction is detected by tactile fibers, scattered along the sides of the animal, which are bent by the movement of the water.

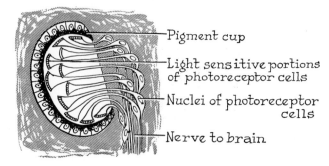

Pigment cup

Light sensitive portions of photoreceptor cells

Nuclei of photoreceptor cells

Nerve to brain

Figure 11.5   Diagrammatic section through the eye of a planarian. Light reaches the sensitive elements from the right.

All this sensory information, especially that from the head region, is relayed by nerve fibers to the **brain,** a bilobed white structure between the eyes (Fig. 11.1). Nerves branch out in all directions from the brain; the primary pair are the **ventrolateral nerve cords** (Fig. 11.4). If the brain is removed coordination is seriously impaired, and almost all the relation of sensory information to locomotion is lost.

The brain controls both ciliary and muscular action. If a planarian is bumped, ciliary locomotion ceases at once and the body contracts, withdrawing the end that was touched. If touched repeatedly on the tail, *Dugesia* will hasten forward by a series of wormlike body contractions. If touched repeatedly on the head, it will back up, turn to one side, and go forward again.

Ventral cilia are the primary means of locomotion. Their activity produces an even, gliding movement. Muscles which augment locomotion lie beneath the epidermis (Fig. 11.4). Outer circular fibers can constrict and lengthen the body, while deeper longitudinal fibers can shorten it. Other fibers are oblique and still others are vertical. The latter can flatten the body. Coordination among these fibers is such that the planarian can accomplish a number of maneuvers, turning, folding or stretching in all directions. When the organism is gliding smoothly along the bottom, successive waves of contraction of the longitudinal fibers may pass from the posterior end to the front, considerably increasing the rate of locomotion.

11.4

Dugesia: Water Balance and Excretion

The remainder of the flatworm body, the space between muscles and intestine, is filled with loosely organized mesodermal cells, the **mesenchyme.** Some of these cells are pigmented, giving the worm its characteristic brown or gray color. The mesenchyme forms a loose mesh containing a considerable amount of intercellular fluid that flows back and forth as the worm changes shape. The movement of this fluid probably aids in the distribution of nutrients from the intestine to other parts of the body.

Excess water from the body cells diffuses into the intercellular fluid and is picked up by excretory cells. These are the **protonephridia** or **flame cells** scattered throughout the body (Fig. 11.6*A*). Each flame cell surrounds a

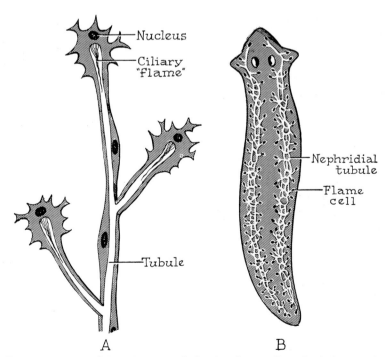

Nucleus

Ciliary "flame"

Tubule

Nephridial tubule

Flame cell

A   B

Figure 11.6 Excretory system of *Dugesia. A,* Detail showing flame cells and tubules. *B,* The tubule network.

blind tubule into which the water is excreted. A tuft of cilia in the blind end beats vigorously, propelling the fluid down the lumen. These tubules from the protonephridia empty into larger tubules that form an anastomosing system along each side of the body (Fig. 11.6B). These open to the surface through numerous small pores.

The number of flame cells in the body is adjusted to the salinity of the environment. Planarians grown in slightly salty water develop few flame cells but quickly increase the number if the amount of salt is later reduced.

Metabolic wastes other than water are believed to pass from the body simply by diffusion.

11.5
Dugesia: Reproduction

Throughout most of the year no reproductive organs are evident in *Dugesia*. If an individual is well fed, it grows and reproduces asexually by pulling itself into two pieces. The body becomes elongated posterior to the pharynx, then this region becomes stretched, attenuated, and finally ruptures. The anterior end moves off and in about one day a new tail begins to form. If it continues to be well fed, the process can be repeated. The posterior end rounds up and becomes quiescent. In a few days it will grow a head and pharynx. At first it is very small, but with feeding it soon becomes full size and may itself reproduce asexually.

In the spring a reproductive system develops from the mesenchyme in most populations. Each individual is hermaphroditic, having complete sets of male and female organs for the production, storage and transfer of the sex cells. When sexually mature, pairs copulate frequently. The initial step or "courtship" involves a series of repeated head and body contacts, obviously different from the casual way in which sexually undeveloped individuals pass by each other. The two individuals gradually assume a copulatory position, facing somewhat away from each other with the posterior regions elevated and their ventral surfaces pressed together (Fig. 11.7). On the ventral surface, posterior to the mouth, is the **genital pore.** Each individual protrudes a muscular **penis** through its pore and through the pore of its mate into a **copulatory sac** (Fig. 11.8). Sperm that have been produced in the many **testes** and stored in the **sperm ducts** leading from the testes to the **penis bulb** now pass into the bulb, where they are mixed with secretions of the bulb and are then forced by muscular contractions through the penis into the sac of the mate. Secretions of the penis bulb at the time of ejaculation activate the sperm, which begin to undulate. The mating process takes only a few minutes.

After mating the active sperm migrate from the copulatory sac through the **ovovitelline ducts** to the **seminal receptacles,** a pair of cavities next to the pair of **ovaries.** Mature eggs cross through a partition between the ovary and the receptacle, are fertilized, and then pass down the ovovitelline duct together with a group of yolk-packed cells from the **vitelline glands.** Several eggs are produced at one time. They gather with the yolk cells in the reproductive **atrium,** where secretions from the yolk cells form a membranous capsule surrounding them. As the capsule is released through the genital

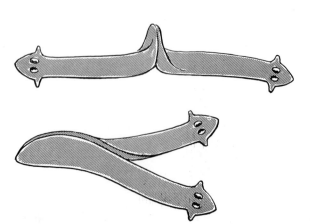

Figure 11.7 *Dugesia* copulating. (After Hyman.)

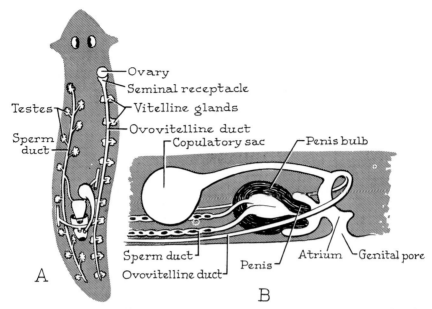

Figure 11.8 Reproductive system of *Dugesia*. *A*, A dorsal view showing the male organs on the left and the female organs on the right. *B*, A side view of the copulatory organs. (After Hyman.)

pore, it is covered with an adhesive secretion form **cement glands.** A portion of this secretion is drawn out into a stalk, which attaches the capsules to the under side of stones and other objects. The eggs develop into embryos that consume the yolk cells in the capsule, and emerge in two or three weeks as miniature flatworms similar to adults.

11.6
Dugesia: Regeneration and Polarity

Many flatworms (but not all) have marked powers of regeneration. These are especially good in *Dugesia* and in other genera that reproduce asexually. Cutting a *Dugesia* in two is, after all, little different from its natural form of division. If the worm is cut across, both pieces will survive and can regenerate a complete worm providing the cut falls somewhere between a line behind the brain and a line a similar distance from the posterior end. In fact, any piece of the worm that is about the size of the head may regenerate a complete worm. Successful regeneration depends upon the regeneration of a head; if this fails to appear, the rest of the body also fails to develop normal proportions and spatial arrangements.

A particular aspect of flatworm regenera-

tion that has been studied extensively is **polarity.** Polarity is a general phenomenon in organisms whereby the axes of symmetry tend to be established and maintained. Frequently, polarity correlates with metabolic gradients in the organism. The flatworms are used here as a convenient example in which a considerable amount of work has been done. Most of the experiments are concerned with the anteroposterior axis. C. M. Child, working with *Dugesia,* found that, in general, pieces taken from the middle of a worm regenerate heads at the original anterior ends and tails at the original posterior ends (Fig. 11.9). A more subtle expression of polarity is found in the ease with which the ends regenerate. Pieces from the forward part of the body regenerate heads rapidly, those from the middle portion of the body more slowly, and those from the posterior region very slowly or not at all. The readiness with which appropriate ends are formed is also seen in occasional errors. A head, if severed from the body, may regenerate a second head instead of a tail at its posterior end. Similarly, the tail end may sometimes produce a tail instead of a head at its anterior end. All the evidence suggests that there is a gradient in the worm, the head-forming tendency being strongest at the anterior end and weakest at the posterior end, with a reverse gradient for the tendency

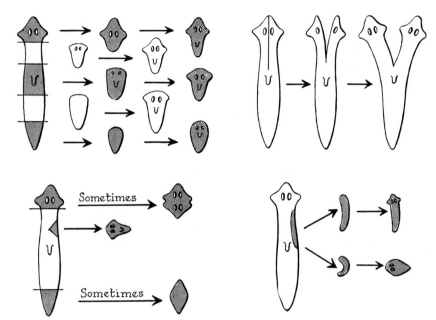

Figure 11.9   Polarity and regeneration in *Dugesia*. Top left, each of five pieces regenerates, but the rapidity with which the head develops depends upon the level of the piece. Lower left, occasional errors that occur, and an example of changed polarity. Lower right, preservation of polarity depends upon whether or not the piece bends. Upper right, a two-headed form produced by repeated splitting of the anterior end.

to form a tail. Such gradients predict that any piece of the worm will regenerate so as to retain its original polarity.

Polarity can be altered. If a triangular piece is cut from the side of the body, it usually regenerates a head at the inner end, forming a tail from the lateral edge (Fig. 11.9). A strip cut from the side of a worm will regenerate normally if it remains straight, but if it bends the head appears on the inner side.

Monsters can also be produced. If a worm is partially split (Fig. 11.9), and the split is kept open by continual recutting, the worm will eventually regenerate so as to produce

some double structures. Many of these monsters eventually solve their problems by splitting up and developing into several worms. If a two-headed worm is produced, for example, the split gradually deepens until the worms separate as two complete individuals.

11.7
Class Turbellaria

The platyhelminthes are divided into the three classes given at the beginning of the chapter. The **Turbellaria** are characterized

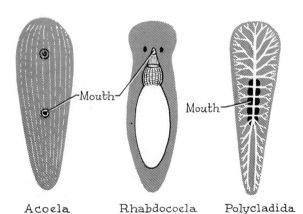

Acoela   Rhabdocoela   Polycladida

Mouth   Mouth

Figure 11.10   Other orders of the class Turbellaria. An example of the order Tricladida is shown in Figure 11.1.

by the presence of a ciliated epidermis, which is not found in any adults of the other two classes.

Turbellarians are divided into a number of orders (Fig. 11.10), according to the branching of the intestine. Planarians belong to the order **Tricladida,** in which the intestine has three primary branches. This is mainly a fresh-water group, but it also includes a few marine and terrestrial flatworms. In the order **Polycladida** the intestine has many primary branches. These worms are all marine. The **Rhabdocoela** have an anterior mouth and a simple, straight intestine, while the **Acoela** have no intestine at all. Rhabdocoels are common in all waters and include a large number of small species. Modern taxonomists recognize several distinct orders in this group. The acoels are marine and minute. They have a ventral mouth that opens directly into a mixture of mesenchyme and endoderm cells. Bits of food are swallowed and phagocytized by the endoderm cells.

11.8

Class Trematoda

Trematodes are parasitic flatworms that attach to the host by means of **suckers** (Fig. 11.11) and in which the entire adult epidermis has been replaced by a **cuticle** (Fig. 11.12). The digestive, excretory, muscular and reproductive systems are similar to those of the Turbellaria. The class is divided into two primary groups, the **Monogenea,** having a life cycle involving only a single host, and the **Digenea,** having a life cycle involving two or more kinds of host.

The Monogenea are mostly **ectoparasitic,** living on the external surface of the host. They have one or more **adhesive organs** next to the mouth and one or more **posterior suckers,** with which they creep about like inchworms (Fig. 11.11). This group includes the **gill flukes,** common on the gills of marine and fresh-water fishes. Following copulation, which is much like that in *Dugesia,* the hermaphroditic adults lay eggs, one to a capsule, at the rate of several to 150 per day. These have a thread on one end by which they become entangled on the surface of the host or in the vegetation. They hatch in a week to a month into small larvae that resemble the parent except that they are clothed in a **ciliated epidermis** and have less elaborate attachment organs. By means of the cilia the larvae swim to the appropriate host. Maturation involves modification of the suckers and replacement of the epidermis by a hard cuticle, apparently secreted by the underlying mesodermal tissue. They feed on the slime, on epithelial cells and on blood extruding from wounds they make in the skin of the host.

The Digenea include a number of medically important parasites, such as the **liver flukes, lung flukes** and **blood flukes.** In some regions of the world, especially in Asia and the Southwest Pacific, whole populations of people are kept in constant poor health by a single species of digenetic flukes. These are **endoparasitic** worms, living inside the body of the host. They have an anterior sucker surrounding the mouth (Fig. 11.11) and a large **midventral sucker.** Adults usually mate, but if one individual is alone in its host it can undergo self-fertilization by autocopulation. In one group, the blood flukes, the sexes are separate. These live in the circulatory system in pairs, the more slender but longer female nestled in

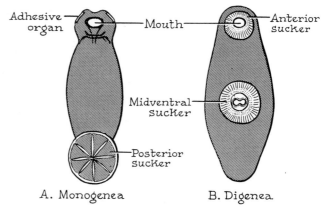

Figure 11.11 The two major groups of flukes, class Trematoda.

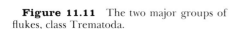

A. Monogenea   B. Digenea

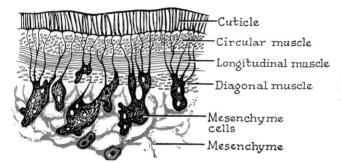

Cuticle
Circular muscle
Longitudinal muscle
Diagonal muscle
Mesenchyme cells
Mesenchyme

Figure 11.12 Part of the body wall of a trematode. Note that an epidermis is missing, and that the covering cuticle lies directly on tissue of mesodermal origin.

a ventral groove of the male. As in the Monogenea, digenetic eggs are laid one to a capsule, but the capsules are often retained in the parent until they are ready to hatch.

The life cycles of this group are complex. The egg hatches into a ciliated larva, the **miracidium** (Fig. 11.13), which invades the first host, usually a snail. The miracidium has a well-developed brain and a pair of eyes. It apparently has no digestive tract at all, although it has a typical set of flame cells. The anterior **rostrum** lacks cilia and is equipped with an **apical gland** that secretes corrosive juices for penetrating the tissues of the host. The body is filled with **reproductive tissue.**

The miracidium darts about rapidly in the water, and if it fails to find the proper species of snail in a few hours it will die.

As the miracidium penetrates the snail, it sheds its ciliated epidermis and rounds up as a **sporocyst** covered with a thin cuticle (Fig. 11.13). All miracidial structures disappear except some subepithelial muscle fibers and the flame cells, while the reproductive tissue develops by asexual reproduction into a variable number of embryos. Nutrients are absorbed from the host directly through the cuticular wall.

Each embryo develops into the next stage, usually a **redia** (Fig. 11.13). This escapes from

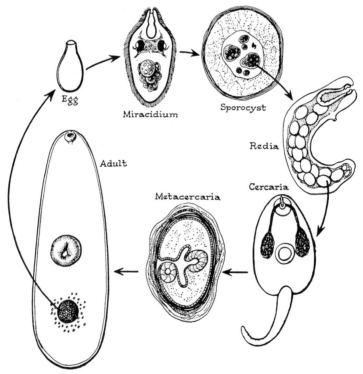

Egg

Miracidium

Sporocyst

Redia

Adult

Metacercaria

Cercaria

Figure 11.13 Life cycle of a digenetic fluke. The stages shown here belong to various species. The arrows indicate whether one stage becomes the next or whether it produces the next by reproduction. (After Hyman.)

the sporocyst and begins to feed upon the tissues of the host. The redia has an anterior **mouth,** a muscular **pharynx** by which host tissue is sucked up, and a short, saclike intestine. The body wall is made up of a cuticle, muscle and mesenchyme. A brain with nerve cords and a flame cell system are also present. The rest of the body is filled, as in the miracidium, with reproductive tissue. Again, this tissue develops asexually into a number of embryos.

Each embryo within the redia may develop into another redia, or into the next stage, a **cercaria** (Fig. 11.13), which escapes from the redia through a **birth pore.** Each cercaria is a miniature fluke with a tail. At the front end it has a **penetration stylet** equipped with an apical gland. The cercaria leaves the snail and swims through the water by lashing its tail, searching randomly for the next host, which varies considerably (crayfish, clam, fish, etc.), according to the species of fluke. The cercaria bores into the new host, sheds its tail, and becomes surrounded by a cyst.

Within the cyst the stylet and apical glands disappear, and the other structures develop further toward the adult pattern. This stage, the **metacercaria** (Fig. 11.13), must be eaten by the final host in order to mature. Thus, the fluke does not feed upon this second host, in which the cercaria becomes a metacercaria.

The second host serves as a means of gaining entry into the final host, which is usually some kind of vertebrate carnivore (fish, frog, cat, man, etc.). In some species the cercariae encyst and become metacercariae on aquatic vegetation and are thus able to parasitize a herbivore (sheep, cow, etc.) as the final host.

When the metacercaria is eaten by the appropriate final host, the cyst wall dissolves in the latter's intestine, and the young fluke emerges. It then migrates through the body to its final site (lungs, liver, etc.), feeding and growing as it goes, and finally maturing in a few days to several weeks.

One family of flukes live as adults in the host's blood vessels. An example is described on page 777.

11.9
Class Cestoda

Tapeworms are endoparasitic flatworms without epidermis, mouth or digestive tract. The front end of the body is a knoblike **scolex,** armed with hooks or suckers by which the animal attaches to the host (Fig. 11.14). Behind the scolex is a narrow **neck,** followed by a long chain of **proglottids.** Proglottids are produced by segmentation in the neck

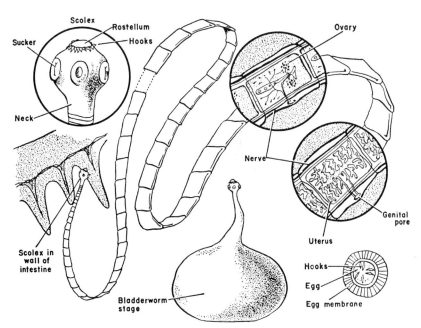

Figure 11.14   The pork tapeworm, *Taenia solium.* Insets show the head and an immature and a mature section of the body. (Villee: Biology, 5th ed.)

region, where rapid longitudinal growth takes place constantly. As each proglottid ages, it is found farther and farther back along the length of the worm. It widens and lengthens, and eventually becomes mature. Each proglottid has a complete set of reproductive organs, similar to those of the Turbellaria except that the genital opening is lateral. As each proglottid becomes filled with fertilized eggs it breaks off and passes out of the host.

Most tapeworms live in the intestine of vertebrates with the scolex buried in the intestinal wall. They do not feed upon the host itself, but soak up nutrients, competing with the host for food that the latter has digested.

The scolex contains a **brain** from which two **lateral nerves** extend posteriorly through all of the proglottids. Excretory tubules also extend the length of the body, opening posteriorly where the last proglottid dropped off. Flame cells connected with these tubules occur throughout the body. The body wall includes a cuticle and muscular tissue with which the tapeworm can make slow writhing movements.

When a proglottid becomes sexually mature it usually mates with itself by autocopulation, but mating between proglottids, either of the same or of different worms, has been observed. As in the trematodes, each fertilized egg is covered with a separate capsule. These are retained in the proglottid, which eventually becomes full, breaks off and bursts.

Most cestodes have more than one kind of host. The larva hatches from its capsule only after it is eaten by the appropriate first host, in whose digestive tract the capsular membrane is digested away. The first stage is the **oncosphere,** little more than a ball of cells containing a few hooks (Fig. 11.15). It bores through the intestinal wall and develops in various organs of the host. In some tapeworms it is covered with a ciliated epidermis, while in others it is covered with a cuticle. It also has a pair of flame cells.

In tapeworms with a three-host cycle, the oncosphere develops into a **procercoid** (Fig. 11.15). The body elongates and the hooks become located in a posterior tail. Anteriorly a rostrum with very large apical glands develops. When the first host, typically an arthropod, is eaten by the appropriate second host (fish, or other vertebrate), the procercoid sheds its tail, bores into the tissue of the new host, and develops into a **cercoid,** which varies in appearance in different tapeworms, but in general has a scolex and somewhat resembles a miniature tapeworm without proglottids. In tapeworms with a two-host cycle, the oncosphere develops directly into the cercoid stage.

When the host with its cercoid larva is eaten by the appropriate final host (usually a carnivorous fish, amphibian or mammal), the larva attaches to the intestinal wall by the scolex and matures into a tapeworm. Thus, the tapeworm cycle depends at each transition upon being eaten by the next host. In some species the cercoid stage is capable of asexual multiplication, but, in general, each tapeworm egg produces a single adult worm. The number of eggs produced is tremendous. For example *Taenia saginata,* a tapeworm that can infect man, sheds eight or nine proglottids daily, and each proglottid contains 80,000 eggs. The infective larvae of this tapeworm occur in beef.

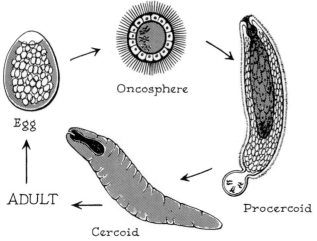

Egg

Oncosphere

ADULT

Cercoid

Procercoid

Figure 11.15 Life cycle of a tapeworm. All the stages are those of the fish tapeworm, *Diphyllobothrium latum.* (Modified from Hyman after Rosen.)

SYNOPSIS OF THE FLATWORMS

PHYLUM PLATYHELMINTHES. Flatworms. Well-developed mesoderm with nephridia, a single opening for mouth and anus.

    CLASS 1. TURBELLARIA. Free-living, epidermis ciliated in adult.

        Order 1. Acoela. No gut cavity.

        Order 2. Rhabdocoela. Simple tubular gut. Often subdivided into three suborders.

        Order 3. Alloeocoela. Gut has one main branch with small side branches. Often subdivided into five suborders.

        Order 4. Tricladida. Gut has three branches. *Planaria, Dugesia.*

        Order 5. Polycladida. Gut has many main branches.

    CLASS 2. TREMATODA. Flukes. Parasitic, with oral sucker, epidermis lacking.

        Order 1. Monogenea. Ectoparasitic with a one-host life cycle.

        Order 2. Aspidobothria. Endoparasitic with a one-host life cycle.

        Order 3. Digenea. Endoparasitic with at least a two-host life cycle. *Schistosoma.*

    CLASS 3. CESTODA. Tapeworms. Endoparasites with no epidermis, no gut.

      Subclass 1. Cestodaria. Body not segmented. Two orders.

      Subclass 2. Eucestoda. Body segmented into proglottids. Nine orders, of which the following two are found in mammals:

        Order 1. Bothriocephaloidea. Fish tapeworms (fish carry cercoid stage).

        Order 2. Taenioidea. Pig and beef tapeworms, etc.

QUESTIONS

1. What kinds of organs are found anteriorly in flatworms?
2. What influences the number of flame cells in the flatworm body?
3. Describe the path of sperm from the testis to fertilization in *Dugesia*.
4. What are the theories regarding the nature of polarity?
5. Characterize the classes of the phylum Platyhelminthes.
6. Describe the life cycle of a digenetic trematode.
7. Where does the life cycle of a tapeworm differ markedly from that of a digenetic trematode?
8. Define sporocyst, oncosphere and redia.

ANNOTATED REFERENCES

(See Chapter 13 for general references.)

Chandler, A. C., and Read, C. P.: Introduction to Parasitology. 10th ed. New York, John Wiley & Sons, Inc., 1961. A widely used text in parasitology, which includes the life cycles of many parasitic animals.

Willier, B. H.. Weiss. P. A., and Hamburger, V.: Analysis of Development. Philadelphia, W. B. Saunders Co., 1955. An excellent account of problems of regeneration and polarity in a variety of organisms.

12

THE PHYLA ASCHELMINTHES AND NEMERTEA

All the animals that remain to be considered have a body cavity or a circulatory system, or both. A circulatory system can be defined as a system of channels containing a fluid that is moved around by muscular activity. The walls of the channels are derived from mesoderm. Two kinds of body cavities can be distinguished. Both are fluid-filled spaces that permit the internal organs freedom of movement, unhampered by extensive connection with the body wall. If the space lies between the gastrodermis and tissues of mesodermal origin (i.e., if it surrounds a gut made only of endoderm), it is a **pseudocoelom.** If the space lies *within* tissues of mesodermal origin (if it surrounds a gut composed of gastrodermis covered with mesodermal tissues), it is a **eucoelom** or, simply, a **coelom.** A coelom is lined with a simple epithelium of mesodermal origin, the **peritoneum.** A pseudocoelom lacks an epithelium. None of the pseudocoelomates has a circulatory system.

The phylum **Aschelminthes** includes the pseudocoelomates whose bodies are largely covered with cuticle. They have an anterior mouth and a posterior anus. The phylum is large and includes groups of diverse appearance.

The **Nemertea** are acoelomate (have no body cavity) but have a circulatory system. The mouth is anterior and the anus posterior, and in front of the mouth is an eversible **proboscis.** The phylum is small and will be considered at the end of this chapter.

Most of the remaining phyla, to be considered in later chapters, have both a circulatory system and a eucoelom.

12.1

Classification of the Aschelminthes

The groups to be considered here have always been troublesome to taxonomists. They have been arranged in one, two, three and even six different phyla. In the face of so many diverse opinions any one position is necessarily arbitrary. It is largely for convenience, therefore, that the groups will be treated as six classes in one phylum. The classes are (Fig. 12.1):

  I. Rotifera. Aquatic microscopic animals with internal **jaws** and an anterior ciliated **wheel organ.**
 II. Gastrotricha. Aquatic microscopic animals with ventral portions of the epidermis ciliated, with posterior **adhesive tubes** and with a nematode-like pharynx.
III. Kinorhyncha. Marine microscopic animals with a segmented cuticle and a spiny head that can be withdrawn into the body.
 IV. Nematoda. Tapered cylindrical worms with a **triradiate pharynx,** a modified excretory system, and a very heavy cuticle covering the body.
  V. Gordiacea. Long, slender, cylindrical worms with a reduced digestive system and no excretory system. Parasitic as juveniles.

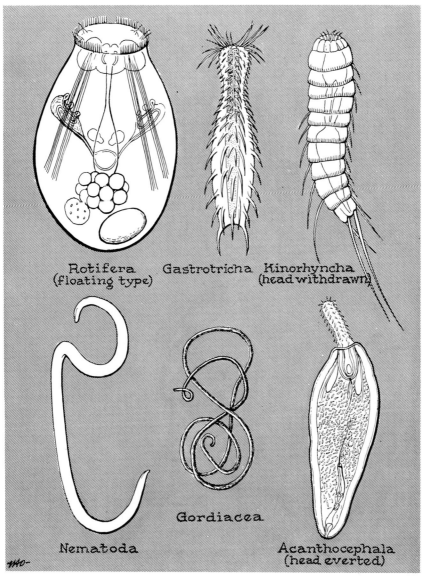

Figure 12.1 Classes of the phylum Aschelminthes. These are considered to be separate phyla by many authors. (Redrawn from Hyman.)

VI. Acanthocephala. Parasitic worms that (like the tapeworms) lack a digestive system. They have a retractile spiny head.

12.2

Class Rotifera

Rotifers, which are about the size of paramecia, are among the most abundant microorganisms in ponds, lakes and streams. Some 1500 species are known. A few of these live in moss or wet sand, others live in the oceans, but the majority live in fresh water. Some rotifers float in the water, others are attached to the bottom or to other animals, and still others creep about with leechlike movements. Most of the familiar rotifers, common in temporary ponds and puddles, are of the creeping variity.

A characteristic structure of the rotifers is the **wheel organ,** a circlet of cilia extending around the front end of the head from the anteroventral **mouth** (Fig. 12.2). It may be a simple circle, or it may be elaborated by outfoldings from the body. A common plan is

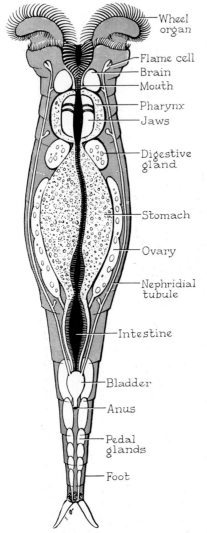

Wheel organ

Flame cell

Brain

Mouth

Pharynx

Jaws

Digestive gland

Stomach

Ovary

Nephridial tubule

Intestine

Bladder

Anus

Pedal glands

Foot

Figure 12.2 Ventral view of a rotifer, *Philodina roseola,* showing many of the internal structures. (Redrawn from Hyman.)

they are usually in motion. In spite of their small size the jaws are elaborate, being composed of seven pieces of varying shape. In different species, they may be used for grinding, biting or piercing. When used for biting or piercing, the jaws are everted through the mouth.

The body, which is clothed in a thin cuticle, usually ends posteriorly in a **foot** (Fig. 12.2). The foot is equipped with **pedal glands** that secrete adhesive mucus, by which the rotifer can attach to objects temporarily or permanently. The foot is missing in many of the planktonic species.

12.3

Philodina

The genus *Philodina* includes a number of common species of creeping rotifers, of which *P. roseola* (Fig. 12.2) is representative. Its wheel organ is divided into two whorls, with the funnel-shaped mouth located midventrally between them. *Philodina* is usually attached by its foot and creates water currents with the wheel organ that bring minute food particles (algae, bacteria, etc.) to the mouth.

The mouth leads to a muscular **pharynx** containing hard cuticular **jaws.** The jaws of *Philodina* are stout and ridged for grinding the food particles into a soft pulp. They chew constantly while feeding. The pharynx leads to a large **stomach** by way of a short **esophagus** surrounded by **digestive glands.** These glands have been observed to secrete into the stomach material that is assumed to be enzymatic. Digestion takes place rapidly in the stomach cavity and the nutrients are quickly absorbed into the gastrodermis cells. The stomach opens into a short **intestine,** which leads to the **bladder.**

A pair of **nephridial tubules** opening into the bladder drain a series of **flame cells** that extend forward in the body. The bladder fills and empties every few minutes, suggesting that the primary function of the rotifer excretory system is water balance. A pair of **ovaries** lateral to the stomach also open into the bladder by paired **oviducts.** The bladder opens dorsally at the base of the foot.

Philodina may detach itself and swim away. The action of the wheel organ, which pulls water toward the animal in feeding, is equally suitable for locomotion. Rotifers often swim off in this fashion when they are disturbed.

that of a double circle (Fig. 12.2). When observed under the microscope the wheel organ appears to rotate, an illusion so convincing that Leeuwenhoek believed rotifers possessed wheels. The illusion is the result of a coordinated rhythm of the ciliary beating. The cilia beat in waves, which pass circularly around the rim. At any given moment some cilia are relaxed while the adjacent ones are bending, producing a momentary aggregation of cilia. It is these aggregations of cilia moving with the waves around the circle that are seen and not the motion of the individual cilia.

Most rotifers are transparent, and the internal **jaws** are easily seen, especially since

When a rotifer creeps on the bottom or on vegetation, its entire wheel organ is retracted into the body by its **retractor muscles** (Fig. 12.3). The **rostrum** is everted and forms a new anterior end to the body, dorsal to the wheel organ. At its tip are cilia, spines and plates by which it can attach. Like a leech or bloodsucker (Chapter 15) with its anterior and posterior suckers, *Philodina* creeps by alternately attaching rostrum and foot. When it finds a place suitable for feeding, the rostrum is retracted by means of the **rostral retractor** muscles as the wheel organ is everted. In a sense *Philodina* has two anterior ends which it can use alternately. The retractor muscles are part of the body wall musculature, which also includes a number of circular and longitudinal strands (Fig. 12.3). The remainder of the body wall is made of a simple ectodermal epithelium covered by the cuticle. In the creeping rotifers this cuticle is segmented to facilitate movement.

The nervous system of rotifers, like that of the flatworms, includes a bilobed **brain** dorsal to the pharynx, and several pairs of nerves, of which the ventrolateral pair are the largest. Additional nerve cell **ganglia** are located on the pharynx, bladder and foot.

Sense organs include bristles for touch and chemoreception on the body, especially around the wheel organ and rostrum. Most rotifers have a **dorsal antenna** (Fig. 12.3), a short projection rich in sensory endings. **Eye-**spots are light-sensitive cells containing pigment that screens out the light except from one direction. These are found in many rotifers embedded in the brain, on the wheel organ or on the rostrum.

In addition to all of the complex structures found in these tiny animals, they have a cavity between the body wall and the digestive tract. The pharynx and bladder, which have muscles, are formed as ectodermal invaginations during development. The rest of the digestive tract is a simple gastrodermis, without mesoderm, so that the body cavity is a true pseudocoel, lying between endoderm and mesoderm.

12.4
Reproduction in Rotifers

The creeping rotifers (including *Philodina*) are **parthenogenetic;** young are produced from eggs that have not been fertilized by sperm. In oögenesis, the meiotic process is much modified, with the result that the eggs remain diploid. Such eggs hatch in a day or two and mature within a week into adults, all of which are female. Each adult produces only from 10 to 50 eggs.

Males are occasionally found in the other groups of rotifers, but much of the reproduction is exclusively by parthenogenesis. Under certain environmental conditions the new generation of females matures as somewhat different organisms. The eggs they produce are smaller, and follow through the normal meiotic process to become haploid. The first of these eggs are laid and hatch quickly as males. The males are haploid, often remain very small, and mature rapidly. They mate only with members of their mother generation, the females that are producing small haploid eggs. The small eggs that are fertilized, restoring diploidy, are retained until they become very large, when they are laid in a heavy shell, usually as a **resting egg** for overwintering. These resting eggs later hatch into females that produce only female offspring, completing the reproductive cycle.

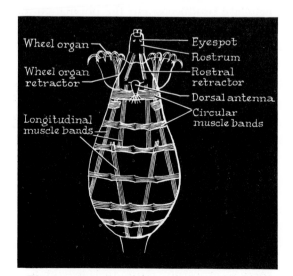

Figure 12.3 Dorsal view of the rotifer, *Rotaria*, showing external structures and many of the muscle strands in the body wall. Similar structures occur in *Philodina*.

Wheel organ
Wheel organ retractor
Longitudinal muscle bands
Eyespot
Rostrum
Rostral retractor
Dorsal antenna
Circular muscle bands

12.5
Cell Constancy

Associated with rotifers are several interesting phenomena, one of which is **cell**

constancy. In a given species, each part of the body is made of a precise number of cells arranged in a fixed pattern. Many of the body parts are syncytial (cell boundaries disappear), but it is evident from the number and positions of the nuclei that cell constancy is maintained. The total number of nuclei in the rotifers studied ranges from 900 to 1000. The exact number in each organ has been counted for several species. These numbers are fixed during embryologic development, and mitosis then stops completely. Even the eggs that the female will produce after maturity are all present early in development.

It has been impossible to induce mitosis in adult rotifers experimentally. If a piece of the body containing nuclei is removed, no regeneration takes place. Often the wound does not heal over and the individual dies. Young rotifers are able to replace bits of cytoplasm, and sometimes even replace a piece containing nuclei, but the replacement lacks nuclei. Thus, rotifers are extremely specialized at the cellular level, to the extent that further growth and repair are impossible. One of the challenging unsolved problems of biology concerns the possible differences which may distinguish such nondividing cells from those of other animals.

12.6
Interspecies Induction

A remarkable example of morphological induction in one species induced by a second species has been found in rotifers. The genus, *Asplanchna*, is predaceous on other rotifers, including the genus, *Brachionus*. When the predator is scarce in the environment of the prey, *Brachionus* has very short spines protruding from the body. Such forms are readily consumed by *Asplanchna*. If the predators become numerous, however, the following generation of prey are born with long spines. Experiments show that such forms can be eaten only with difficulty. This response in development is mediated by a chemical given off into the water by *Asplanchna*, which induces brachionid eggs to alter the path of development, producing rotifers with long spines.

The role of such a mechanism in the ecology of *Brachionus* is obvious. The biochemical basis through which it operates remains to be elucidated. It is also not obvious why the predator continues to supply such a stimulus to the prey.

12.7
Senescence

An individual rotifer lives an active life for only a few days, and yet toward the end of this period it shows several of the characteristic features of old age. Egg production ceases, the animal becomes sluggish, and portions of the body begin to degenerate. Lansing has found that during these few days the amount of calcium in the body increases, just as it increases with age much more slowly in the bodies of man and other animals. He also found that if the calcium was removed every day by immersing the rotifers in sodium citrate for one minute, the average life span was considerably lengthened. If the aging of rotifers is found to be similar to that of man, they will be used widely in research, for mere days rather than years are required for the completion of experiments with rotifers.

A decline in vigor in successive parthenogenetic generations has been reported in some rotifers. In certain species the appearance of males is not related to external factors but seems to be inherent. After a certain number of female-producing generations, the male-producers appear, resting eggs are produced, and the population disappears for the season. In some, there is a continual decrease in activity and longevity from generation to generation of parthenogenetic females before the sexual phase appears. Little is known of the mechanism by which an aging factor can be transmitted or accumulated through successive generations. Many rotifer populations do not show this kind of aging and can be kept as parthenogenetic strains indefinitely.

12.8
Resistance to Desiccation

Perhaps the most interesting aspect of rotifer physiology is the ability of some species, especially those that live in temporary puddles or moss, to resist adverse circumstances. A dry, tarred roof in a hot summer sun, when the tar is bubbling hot,

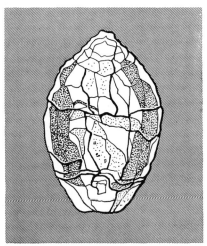

Figure 12.4 A desiccated rotifer from a dried-up puddle. It can absorb water and become active again in a few minutes.

is an unlikely place to find delicate animals, yet if a bit of dried scum is taken from a spot where the last rain puddle dried up and placed in some fresh water, the dish may be swarming with rotifers within minutes. These are not newly hatched but are full grown adults. They are visible in the dry scum as rotifer mummies (Fig. 12-4), shrunken bodies with retracted wheel organs. When water is added they simply swell, stretch out and begin to move. To see them open out the delicate wheel organ only minutes after baking in the sun is truly astonishing.

If well-fed rotifers are dried slowly they may survive several years of desiccation. The longest known record is 59 years. In the dry state they can survive extremes of temperature, from well above the boiling point of water to well below zero. They have even survived eight hours in liquid helium, where the temperature is −272° C., just one degree above absolute zero, where molecular activity ceases. Rotifers, then, can achieve a state of suspended animation by the mere loss of water. While a few other groups of animals can also survive desiccation in this way, such a water loss is usually lethal unless a special resistant stage (cyst or egg) develops beforehand. The properties of rotifers that enable them to survive desiccation are entirely unknown.

12.9
Class Nematoda

The **Nematoda** are mostly cylindrical worms tapered toward both ends and commonly called **roundworms.** The class includes many parasites and a very large number of small free-living species. They are common wherever there is water, even though it be but a thin film. The nematode body is covered by a thick **cuticle** that is elastic and tends to hold the body straight if all the muscles are relaxed (Fig. 12.5). Beneath the cuticle is a simple ectodermal epithelium, and beneath this a single layer of longitudinal muscle fibers. Roundworms are unique among all animals in having longitudinal muscles but no circular muscles. The only motion possible is bending of the body, which may result in simple curvature or in sinuous movements. The opposing tension in the cuticle completes a muscular-cuticular system of movement. Roundworms crawl easily, like snakes, but swim very poorly despite an extremely vigorous thrashing of the body. The anterior **mouth** leads through a

Figure 12.5 Cross section through the pharynx of a nematode, showing the body wall and the peculiar cell structure of the pharyngeal wall.

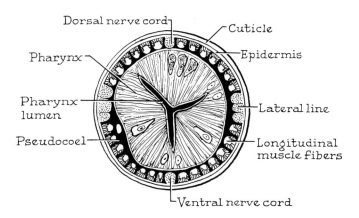

mouth cavity to a muscular **pharynx** of unusual structure (Fig. 12.6). During development the pharynx arises as an ectodermal invagination together with surrounding mesoderm cells, which form epithelial cells and muscle fibers respectively. In the completed pharynx, however, the two elements are intermingled to form a single layer of tissue. The result is a **triradiate pharynx,** named for the shape of its lumen, which is due to the uneven thickness of the wall. It is surrounded by a membrane and lined with a continuation of the external cuticle. Between these are epithelial cells and interspersed radial muscle fibers (Fig. 12.5). When the muscle fibers contract, the lumen is enlarged, producing a sucking action at the mouth.

12.10
The Vinegar Eel, Turbatrix aceti

A free-living nematode common in older vinegar is the vinegar eel, *Turbatrix aceti,* about 2 mm. long (Fig. 12.6). Under the microscope many of its general anatomic features are visible. The pharynx ends in a posterior enlargement, the **bulb,** which leads directly into a long simple **intestine.** The intestine ends in a short **rectum** that opens at a posteroventral **anus.** The vinegar eel, like many free-living nematodes, feeds primarily on bacteria.

A **nerve ring** is the only visible part of the nervous system; it surrounds the pharynx just in front of the bulb.

The sexes are separate. Males have a single thin **testis** that passes forward from just in front of the anus, then doubles back on itself and continues as a **sperm duct** to a storage expansion, the **seminal vesicle,** that opens into the rectum. Instead of a penis the male has a pair of **copulatory spines** mounted in the dorsal wall of the rectum. These can be protruded through the anus and into the vagina of the female by the contraction of **protractor muscles.**

A single **ovary** lies in the middle third of the female (Fig. 12.6). From its anterior end an **oviduct,** widened to form a **uterus,** leads back to the **vagina,** just posterior to the middle of the body. The vagina opens ventrally. Posterior to the uterus a diverticulum serves as a **seminal receptacle** for receiving sperm at copulation. Eggs produced in the ovary are fertilized as they pass into the uterus by sperm that migrate forward from the re-

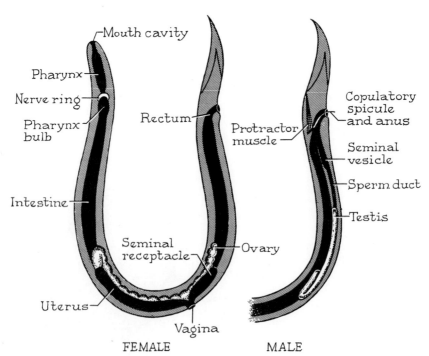

Figure 12.6   Lateral view of the vinegar eel, *Turbatrix aceti.* (After De Man, 1910.)

ceptacle. Eggs are retained in the uterus until they hatch, and the young worms escape through the vagina. Thus, the vinegar eel is ovoviviparous.

12.11
The Pig Roundworm, Ascaris lumbricoides

Further details of nematode anatomy are more easily seen in the few large species, all of which are parasitic. *Ascaris lumbricoides* is 30 cm. long and may be obtained from pig intestines at slaughterhouses. This species differs from the free-living species primarily in having more prominent reproductive organs. The mouth and pharynx are somewhat reduced.

As *Ascaris* is cut open, the large **pseudocoelom** (Fig. 12.7) is evident. In it the long intestine and much-folded reproductive organs lie loosely. On the wall are lateral, dorsal and ventral lines, and the inner surface is covered with small transparent sacs. These represent some of the more bizarre cell structures in nematodes.

The lateral lines are internal ridges, each containing an **excretory canal** that runs the length of the worm. The two canals join beneath the pharynx and a short common tube runs forward to open just behind the

mouth as an **excretory pore.** The entire excretory system, often 30 cm. long, is made from a single cell, whose nucleus is located where the two tubes join together. At their inner ends the tubes are closed. Flame cells are lacking, and little is known of the physiology of this system.

The dorsal and ventral lines are the **nerve cords** that extend back from the **nerve ring** around the pharynx. The brain in most nematodes is located in the swollen sides of this ring, connected above and below the pharynx by many nerve fibers. In *Ascaris* the brain is scattered out as several pairs of ganglia associated with the ring.

The small transparent sacs lining the body wall, easily visible to the naked eye, are the **cell bodies** of the muscle fibers. Each fiber extends longitudinally 0.6 to 1.2 cm. beneath the epidermis. At its middle is the sac hanging into the pseudocoelom. The cell body contains the nucleus and is not contractile. The muscle cells of nematodes are not innervated by nerve fibers coming from the nerve cords as in most animals. Instead, each muscle cell sends a **conductile process** to the nerve cord (Fig. 12.7). Thus, each muscle cell has three portions and is structurally unique in the animal kingdom.

The life cycle of *Ascaris* involves only a single host. The pig roundworm may lay as many as 200,000 eggs per day. These pass

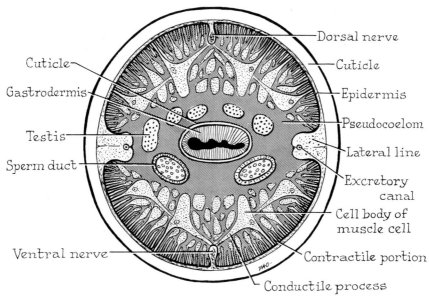

Cuticle
Gastrodermis
Testis
Sperm duct
Ventral nerve

Dorsal nerve
Cuticle
Epidermis
Pseudocoelom
Lateral line
Excretory canal
Cell body of muscle cell
Contractile portion
Conductile process

Figure 12.7 Cross section through the middle region of a male *Ascaris lumbricoides.* The testes are sectioned several times because they lie folded in the body.

out of the pig in its feces, in which the egg develops into a small worm within its shell. If these contaminate the food of pigs and are eaten, they hatch in the intestines. They then go through a seemingly unnecessary cycle. The young worms burrow through the intestinal wall into the blood stream, whence they are carried through the heart to the lungs. Here they burrow into the air spaces, crawl up the trachea to the pharynx, and are swallowed again. They finally mature in the intestines. During the burrowing phase, if large numbers are involved, hemorrhage, infection or pneumonia may result.

Ascaris lumbricoides is a species complex of a number of morphologically indistinguishable strains that variously infect pigs, sheep, squirrels, apes and man. Each strain can temporarily infect other hosts but can mature and reproduce only in its own host.

Roundworms also show the phenomenon of cell constancy in most of their organs. Mitotic divisions continue throughout life only in the epidermis, gastrodermis and gonads. In large nematodes, the organs with cell constancy increase in size entirely by the growth of the cells, and not by an increase in their numbers. This explains why the individual cell bodies of *Ascaris* muscle fibers are so easily visible. In many parts of the body the tissues tend to become syncytial. As in the rotifers, the ability to regenerate is very poor.

12.12
Molting

The growth of the young nematode into an adult, when contained in a heavy cuticle, presents a problem that is solved by periodically shedding the cuticle and expanding rapidly before the new cuticle hardens. This process is called **molting.** Each nematode molts four times in becoming adult. When the external cuticle is shed, the cuticle lining the mouth cavity, pharynx and rectum is also shed. This indicates that these structures are also of ectodermal origin.

12.13
Parasitism

The roundworms have exploited endoparasitism more fully than any other metazoan group. Practically all metazoa have roundworm parasites that produce a wide variety of diseases. These include such human diseases as hookworm (p. 775), elephantiasis (p. 778) and trichinosis (p. 778). These and other parasites are treated more fully in Chapter 42.

12.14
Class Gastrotricha

The microscopic **gastrotrichs** (Fig. 12.1) are common, but seldom abundant, in quiet fresh and salt water. A few can be found in almost any sample of pond debris. Gastrotrichs are very active, darting about on the two longitudinal bands of cilia on their ventral surface, clambering rapidly over vegetation and debris. They feed on bacteria and algae, sucking them into the anterior mouth with a triradiate pharynx very similar to that of the nematodes. Cell constancy is as rigid in this class as in the rotifers. In some gastrotrichs all growth is limited to the embryonic stage; the parent produces enormous eggs, one at a time, that later hatch into full grown individuals. The fresh-water species have only females, which reproduce parthenogenetically.

12.15
Class Kinorhyncha

These small marine worms, less than 5 mm. long (Fig. 12.1), are seldom found. They live in soft sand and mud at the bottom of shallow or deep seas. Kinorhynchs resemble nematodes in two ways. They grow by molting, and they have a pharynx similar to the nematodes except that the muscle and epithelial layers remain distinct. The muscle fibers are radially arranged, however, and produce suction by contraction. Kinorhynchs have a body musculature reduced to separate strands as in the rotifers. The cuticle is segmented into 13 or 14 joints, and internal structures such as the muscles and nerve cells are segmentally arranged.

12.16
Class Gordiacea

The Gordiacea are the **hairworms** that often appear in spring water (Fig. 12.1). The body is extremely long and slender and tapers little if at all at either end. Hairworms are parasitic as juveniles, free-living as adults. The adults live near or in water, in which they lay long strings of eggs. These hatch into short fat larvae that infect grasshoppers, crickets and other insects. They bore through the digestive tract into the body cavity where they grow to adult size, following a single molt. After the adult leaves the host it apparently does not feed and its digestive tract may become closed and degenerate. The adult is often much tangled with itself, suggesting a Gordian knot.

12.17

Class Acanthocephala

Adult spiny-headed worms (Fig. 12.1) live in the digestive tracts of vertebrates. The head is retractile, and may be withdrawn as the worm crawls about, or everted and thrust into the intestinal wall as an anchor. The head bears rows of **recurved spines** and the wounds produced by them may become seriously infected. Large numbers of eggs, usually well advanced in development, pass out in the host feces and hatch only if they are eaten by an arthropod. The young larva bores through the digestive tract of this first host into the body cavity, where it develops into a miniature adult. If the arthropod host is eaten by the vertebrate host, the worm matures in the intestine of the latter. Most species are small, not more than 2.5 cm. long. The spiny-headed worm of the pig, however, which parasitizes beetle grubs as the arthropod host, grows to a length of 65 cm.

The pseudocoelom of this group is not well developed, and biologists are not agreed that the Acanthocephala belong in the Aschelminthes. The total absence of a digestive tract in both larva and adult and the many other specializations for parasitism make comparisons difficult. Unlike the nematoda, the Acanthocephala have circular muscles in the body wall and ciliated excretory organs.

12.18

Phylum Nemertea

The nemerteans are a small group numbering 550 species, most of which are marine. They are predaceous but sluggish, creeping slowly or burrowing deep into mud in search of prey by the contraction of muscles and by the beating of the cilia on the surface.

In several respects nemerteans resemble the turbellarians: they lack a body cavity, they tend to be flattened, the epidermis is ciliated, the excretory system includes flame cells, and the nervous system and sense organs such as eyes and chemoreceptors are similar in construction. Nemerteans also differ from the turbellarians in several respects: the mouth and anus are separate openings, a proboscis may be everted through a pore just above the mouth, a circulatory system is present, and the reproductive organs are simple. Because nemerteans tend to be flattened and long, they are called **ribbon worms** (Fig. 12.8).

Although the circulatory system and separate anus are important characteristics for locating the Nemertea among the other phyla, the eversible **proboscis** is their most characteristic feature, for nothing quite like it is found elsewhere in the animal kingdom. It consists of a **proboscis pore, vestibule, proboscis, proboscis cavity** and **proboscis sheath** (Fig. 12.9). When the muscular sheath constricts it exerts pressure

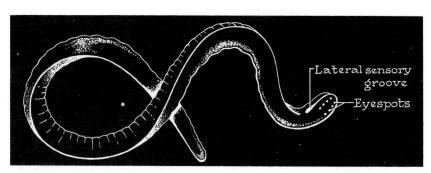

Figure 12.8   A ribbon worm, member of the phylum Nemertea. (Modified from Coe, 1905.)

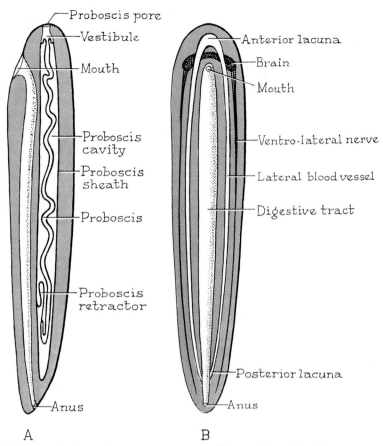

Figure 12.9   Diagrammatic views of nemertean structures. *A*, Lateral view of the digestive tract and the proboscis. *B*, Dorsal view of the digestive, circulatory and nervous systems.

on the fluid in the cavity, forcing the hollow proboscis to turn inside out through the vestibule and pore. The proboscis never everts all the way because its inner end is anchored to the sheath by a band of muscle. This muscle is the **proboscis retractor.** Its contraction helps pull the proboscis back inside the sheath. When everted, the proboscis is sticky, and it coils tightly around the prey, drawing it to the mouth.

In its simplest form the circulatory system (Fig. 12.9) consists of two **lateral vessels** connected anteriorly by an **anterior lacuna** above the proboscis vestibule, and posteriorly by a **posterior lacuna** below the posterior end of the gut. Each lacuna is an enlarged space. Additions that are found in some nemerteans include a **middorsal vessel** and numerous circular connections. The longitudinal vessels are contractile, keeping the colorless blood and many corpuscles in constant motion. In some species the corpuscles contain respiratory pigment.

The nemertean circulatory system lacks capillaries, and while it does not form an intimate association with many of the body tissues it probably aids in the distribution of nutrients. Even in species with respiratory pigment it is doubtful whether the system has much to do with ordinary respiration when oxygen is available in the environment. It is more likely that the blood serves as an oxygen reservoir for use when the worm burrows into anoxic mud.

The reproductive organs are simple saclike structures scattered along each side of the body. The sexes are usually separate, and fertilization is external. Eggs and sperm may be shed through short tubes that develop from each gonad to the body surface, or they may merely burst through the body wall. Most nemerteans have excellent powers of regeneration, and some of them reproduce asexually by fragmenting into a number of pieces, each of which becomes a whole worm.

SYNOPSIS OF ROUNDWORMS AND RIBBON WORMS

PHYLUM ASCHELMINTHES. Pseudocoelomates with tendencies toward extreme cellular differentiation and loss of regenerative powers. Body covered by a cuticle.

> **CLASS 1. ROTIFERA.** Rotifers. Wheel organ around mouth, and jaws in pharynx. Three orders. *Philodina, Rotaria.*
>
> **CLASS 2. GASTROTRICHA.** Gastrotrichs. Cilia on ventral surface, pharynx nematode-like. Two orders.
>
> **CLASS 3. KINORHYNCHA.** Body segmented with eversible spiny head. One order.
>
> **CLASS 4. NEMATODA.** Roundworms. Triradiate pharynx and modified nephridia. About 17 orders, including:
>
>> *Order 1. Rhabditoidea.* Vinegar eel.
>> *Order 2. Ascaroidea. Ascaris,* other large intestinal roundworms.
>> *Order 3. Oxyuroidea.* Pinworms.
>> *Order 4. Strongyloidea.* Hookworms. *Ancylostoma, Necator.*
>> *Order 5. Filarioidea. Loa, Wuchereria.*
>> *Order 6. Trichuroidea. Trichinella* and whipworms.
>
> **CLASS 5. GORDIACEA (or NEMATOMORPHA).** Hairworms. Reduced digestive tract and no nephridia. Two orders.
>
> **CLASS 6. ACANTHOCEPHALA.** Spiny-headed worms. Endoparasitic aschelminths with no mouth or digestive tract. Three orders.

PHYLUM NEMERTEA. Ribbon worms. With a circulatory system but no body cavity. An eversible proboscis lies in a special cavity in front of the mouth. Two subclasses and four orders.

QUESTIONS

1. Give examples for the six classes of the phylum Aschelminthes.
2. Explain the illusion of rotation in rotifers.
3. What do *Philodina* and *Turbatrix* eat?
4. What is cell constancy and what is its apparent relation to regenerative capacity?
5. How do roundworms move?
6. Compare the excretory systems of rotifers and roundworms.
7. Describe the life cycle of *Ascaris.*

ANNOTATED REFERENCES

(See Chapter 13 for general references. Further information on parasitic forms is available in numerous texts—cf. Chapter 11.)

Donner, J.: Rotifers (Translated by H. G. S. Wright.) London, Frederick Warne & Co. Ltd., 1966. This important German study on the biology of these fascinating organisms has recently been made available to English readers.

Lee, D. L.: The Physiology of Nematodes. San Francisco, W. H. Freeman & Co., 1965. Written for the University Reviews in Biology, this book is a very readable synthesis of the biology of this important but often neglected group of organisms.

13 INTRODUCTION TO THE HIGHER INVERTEBRATES

The preceding chapters describe those animals usually referred to as the "lower" invertebrates. These are lower in the sense that they lack some of the structural complexity of the remaining or "higher" invertebrates, and lower also in the sense that they are often thought to represent the lower limbs of the evolutionary "tree." The Metazoa are believed to have evolved from the Protozoa, and the sponges, jellyfish and flatworms are considered to be living representatives of groups that appeared early. The roundworms and ribbon worms represent groups that arose somewhat later, possibly from the flatworms. The higher invertebrates are usually considered to have evolved still later.

13.1

Origin of the Metazoa

It is most commonly held that the Metazoa arose from the Protozoa as a single evolutionary unit. They share a number of traits not known to occur together in any protozoan or plant: (1) metazoans are typically diploid; (2) meiosis immediately precedes fertilization, usually with no mitotic divisions of the haploid stages (gametes); and (3) all four products of meiosis are functional in spermatogenesis, whereas only one (the egg) is functional in oögenesis. In addition, Metazoa differ from colonial protozoa by having a division of labor among cells with respect to nutrition. Some of the cells, specialized for this purpose, take up food that is later dis-

tributed among the other cells. In contrast, each cell of a colonial protozoan is responsible for its own nutrition.

While the unitary origin of the Metazoa is a matter of only minor controversy, their origin from the Protozoa remains very speculative. A search for evolutionary links between these groups reveals only one that will withstand close scrutiny: choanoflagellates (see Fig. 8.7). The collar cells of sponges (see Fig. 9.1) are remarkably similar. In both, each cell has a single flagellum surrounded by a cytoplasmic collar. In both kinds of cell the collar is easily lost and replaced. Both feed on microscopic material, using the flagellum to propel water past the collar and catching food on the surface of the collar. Both cells have a jelly-like matrix as their substratum.

Differences are also obvious. In a crude sense a sponge is a very large choanoflagellate colony turned inside out, with the collar cells lining cavities, with differentiation into more than one kind of cell, with additional skeletal support, and with a complicated development of embryos and larvae. Unfortunately, choanoflagellates are difficult to study. Little is known of their reproduction or life history, so that a meaningful comparison with the life cycle of sponges cannot be made.

Although sponges can be linked strongly with the choanoflagellate protozoa, they are related only remotely with the rest of the metazoa. None of the traits they share with choanoflagellates are shared with other metazoans. Their cell types are not easily related to those of other metazoa. Their gross morphologies are not at all comparable. For such reasons, sponges are often isolated in a subdivision of the Metazoa, the **Parazoa,** with all the remaining phyla combined in the **Eumetazoa.**

Many workers have searched elsewhere among the protozoans for ancestors of the Eumetazoa, on the premise that they have an origin separate from that of the sponges. In general, such searches have not been rewarding. Although *Volvox* (see Fig. 8.6) is superficially interesting as an ancestral blastula-like organism, it is entirely a plant, haploid, autotrophic, and not at all suited as an ancestral animal. Similarly, although large ciliates (see Fig. 8.12) resemble planula larvae (see Fig. 10.7), the specializations of their nuclei, of their ciliary apparatus, and of their methods of reproduction raise difficult issues.

If one looks outside the Eumetazoa for forms most like the planula, which is essentally a free-swimming solid gastrula, it is difficult to by-pass some types of sponge larvae (see Fig. 9.7) in favor of any other group of organisms. Thus, as possible ancestors of the Eumetazoa, sponges are at least as difficult to avoid as they are to claim.

13.2

Origin of a Digestive Tract and Nervous System

Above the Porifera on the evolutionary scale, the Coelenterata, Ctenophora and Platyhelminthes share a number of traits suggesting the next stage of metazoan evolution. In all three, the typical animal has a baglike body with a large mouth and a simple but effective nervous system and lives as a predator capturing relatively large prey. The origin of these groups appears to be bound intimately with the development of a predaceous habit, which in turn favors the development of a simple saccular gut for protein digestion and a nervous system for the pursuit of prey (comparable organelles are found in predaceous protozoans).

Although most of the species of these phyla are large enough to feed on higher metazoans, such as worms, shrimps and fish, they could not have evolved earlier than their prey. The first forms must have been small predators that fed on the larger protozoa. A

number of the smaller species feed this way today.

The embryonic development of the nervous system from the ectoderm, and the general method of forming the gut from the endoderm, are similar in all phyla above the porifera. Thus, the Eumetazoa appear to be a single evolutionary unit. It is fascinating to consider the chain of events that was started, over half a billion years ago, when the first planula-like animal swallowed another organism whole.

The coelenterates and ctenophores are usually considered to be the simplest metazoa other than sponges. They lack mesodermal tissues and excretory organs. To a considerable extent they can be regarded as organisms made of two layers, folded and warped in various ways. A jelly-like matrix between the two layers usually contains additional cells that have a diffuse embryonic origin from the outer and inner cell layers. Most students believe that these groups are primitively simple, but a few prefer the possibility that they once had a bulky mesoderm that has been lost.

13.3

The Evolution of Three Germ Layers

The flatworms appear to lie close to the stock that produced all the remaining phyla. They are relatively simple in the sense that the gut lacks a separate mouth and anus, and neither a body cavity nor a circulatory system is present. They are more complex than the preceding, however, in that all three germ layers (ectoderm, mesoderm, endoderm) are present and well defined. They have protonephridia, and they have muscle layers added to the body wall. These latter characters link the remaining phyla, suggesting strongly that from the flatworms up, at least, all metazoa have a common origin.

The nemertean body plan can be derived from the flatworm type by the addition of the proboscis and a circulatory system, a separation of the mouth and anus, and minor elaborations of other structures. The resemblance of the nemertean epidermis and sense organs to those of the flatworms is very striking.

The aschelminthes are difficult to relate to any of the other groups. The degree to which their cells are specialized gives them a different appearance. Some zoologists believe they are derived from a flatworm type by the separation of mouth and anus and the addition of a pseudocoelom. Although the aschelminthes are simpler than the higher invertebrates in the sense that they lack both a circulatory system and muscles around the gut, they are complex from the point of view of such features as cell constancy and cellular differentiation.

13.4
The Evolution of the Coelom

The major groups of higher invertebrates, including the mollusks, annelids, arthropods and echinoderms, together with the chordates, all have a separate mouth and anus, a muscular gut, a true coelom and a well-developed circulatory system. In some of the minor groups one or another character is absent, but such cases are believed to represent losses during their evolution from ancestors in which the characters were present.

The distinctive characteristic of these animals is the **coelom** (or eucoelom), a cavity within the mesoderm lined with a delicate epithelium, the **peritoneum.** These phyla are often grouped together as the **Eucoelomata.**

The coelom may appear during development by either of two methods, depending on the species. The mesoderm may form first as solid masses and the coelom later by cavitation within the mesoderm (Fig. 13.1). Such a coelom is a **schizocoelom** (cavity by splitting). In other eucoelomates the mesoderm and coelom are formed together as pouches from the original gut cavity of the gastrula (Fig. 13.1); the wall becomes the mesoderm and the separated cavity persists as the coelom. Such a coelom is an **enterocoelom** (cavity from the gut or enteron). In either method the coelom usually appears first as one or more pairs of cavities beside the digestive tract. The result is similar, regardless of method of origin. The paired cavities are usually enlarged until they meet above and below the gut, where the two lining epithelia come together and often persist as a supporting membrane, a **mesentary.**

A coelom divides the mesoderm into an

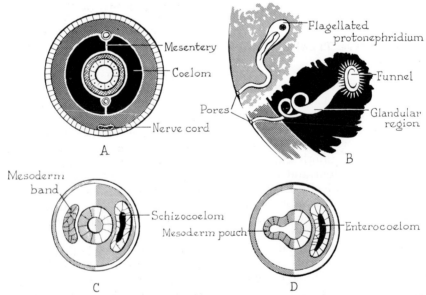

Figure 13.1   Coelom formation in the Eucoelomata. *A,* A diagrammatic cross section showing the fully developed coelom and mesenteries. *C,* The schizocoelom. On the left side is shown a solid band of mesoderm. A later stage is shown on the right *(C),* in which a cavity has appeared. *D,* The enterocoelom. The mesoderm and pouch are shown forming on the left side. A later stage is shown on the right after complete separation from the gut. *B,* Nephridia found in the eucoelomates. Protonephridia with one flagellum are common in larvae, while adults often have the metanephridium, which opens into the coelom (lower part of *B*).

outer layer that contributes to the body wall, and an inner layer that contributes to the gut wall. This permits the development of two independent sets of musculature, one in the body wall adapted for locomotion and other activities, and another in the gut wall specialized primarily for mechanical churning of the contents of the gut. These two sets of muscles may differ not only in their gross morphology, but also in their physiology. This is readily seen in the vertebrates in a comparison of skeletal muscle, found in the body wall, and smooth muscle, found in the gut wall (p. 50). In acoelomates the single musculature is inextricably involved in both locomotion and mechanical digestion. Thus, a flatworm usually is quiescent after feeding, while peristaltic waves of contraction distort the entire body as food is distributed throughout the digestive tract.

The basic excretory organ of the lower invertebrates is the **protonephridium,** described in the chapter on flatworms. In the eucoelomates a different kind of excretory organ is common, the **metanephridium.** This is a tubule open at both ends, the outer end opening as a nephridiopore and the inner end opening into the coelom (Fig. 13.1*B*). The inner opening is a ciliated funnel that sweeps coelomic fluid into the tubule. Within the tubule useful components of this fluid are reabsorbed by a glandular region of the tube wall while the waste is left and eventually ejected. In some forms additional waste may be excreted by the glandular region, and if the metanephridium is intimately associated with the circulatory system the funnel may be absent.

Although metanephridia are the common adult excretory organs of eucoelomates, many larval eucoelomates have protonephridia, usually with the tuft of cilia replaced by a single long flagellum (Fig. 13.1). This supports the idea that the higher invertebrates arose from the lower.

13.5

Spiral Cleavage and Its Evolutionary Importance

The acoelomate Platyhelminthes and Nemertea, and several eucoelomate phyla including the Mollusca and Annelida, share a pattern of early embryonic development

called **spiral cleavage.** This pattern combines a precise system of cell division and a fixed, or predetermined, fate of the subsequent cells. Within any one species the pattern is constant, while from one species to another variations occur. Such variations are found both between and within the phyla. Following is a description of the early stages of spiral cleavage as it is found in several of the phyla for eggs containing only a modest amount of yolk:

The first and second cell divisions are *meridional* and at right angles to each other, forming four cells of nearly equal size (Fig. 13.2).

The third division is *oblique* in the sense that the mitotic spindles are neither vertical nor horizontal, but inclined to one side. (One of them is indicated by the solid line in the eight-cell stage, Fig. 13.2.) As a result, the upper four cells are displaced circularly so that each upper cell touches two lower cells. The third division is also *unequal*, separating four upper, small **micromeres** from four lower, large **macromeres.** The four micromeres are called the **first quartette.**

The fourth division is also oblique but always in the opposite direction from the third (Fig. 13.2). The first quartette forms eight cells. The macromeres divide unequally, producing again an upper tier of small cells, the **second quartette,** and a lower tier of four macromeres.

The fifth division continues the pattern. The axes of division are oblique in the direction of those of the third division. The progeny of the first quartette become 16 cells, the second quartette becomes eight cells, and the macromeres divide unequally to form a **third quartette** of micromeres and a lower tier of four macromeres.

Divisions continue to be oblique, alternating to one side and then the other. If the eight-, 16- and 32-cell stages are studied carefully, it should be evident that the embryo is twisted by this process first one way and then the other (Fig. 13.2). This is particularly evident to an observer looking down on the top of the embryo when the macromeres are resting firmly on the bottom of a dish. It is this phenomenon that gives the pattern its name.

It should also be evident that the progeny of each cell of the four-cell stage remain together in one quadrant of the embryo.

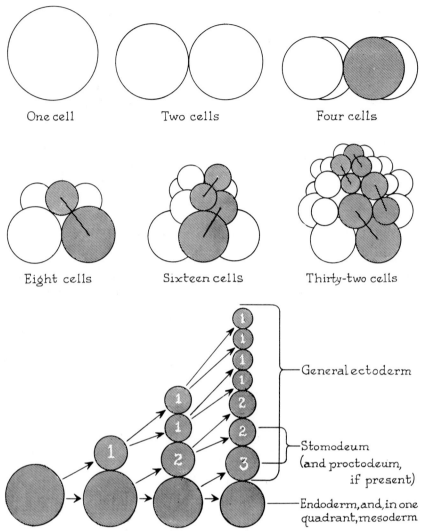

Figure 13.2 Spiral cleavage. One quadrant (the progeny of one cell of the four-cell stage) is shaded. Lines indicate the axes of the preceding mitoses. The lower diagram shows the fates of the cells of one quadrant. Numbers indicate the three quartettes or their progeny.

Gastrulation usually begins after the sixth or seventh cleavage. In all the phyla showing spiral cleavage, the macromeres of the 32-cell stage or all their progeny pass into the interior. Usually, all the mesoderm develops from one of the macromeres, which may be slightly larger than the others, while the other three become endoderm. The three quartettes form all of the ectoderm and its derivatives. A more detailed example of the fate of the quartettes and macromeres is given at the end of Chapter 15.

The occurrence of spiral cleavage in so many phyla suggests that it is a basic pattern of development in three-layered animals and additional evidence relating coelomates to acoelomates. The concept of a "main line" of evolution arises, proceeding from the flatworms and nemerteans to the mollusks and annelids. In relation to this concept some phyla, such as the Aschelminthes, show further specialization and modification toward rigid embryonic fate and cell constancy, while others, including the chordates and echinoderms, show simplification and loss of rigidity in early development.

13.6
Evolution Within the Eucoelomata

Looking forward to the remaining chapters, the student will find that the eucoelomates are presented in two series, one including the mollusks, annelids and arthropods, and another including the echinoderms, hemichordates and chordates. These are distinct evolutionary units. In the first series spiral cleavage is found, unless obscured by the presence of very large amounts of yolk, as in the arthropods. The body cavity is usually a schizocoelom, and the embryonic blastopore is more or less ventral and usually contributes to the mouth. In the second series spiral cleavage is absent (after the first two divisions, the spindle axes usually alternate between horizontal and vertical orientations or show no set pattern). The body cavity is frequently an enterocoelom, and the blastopore is posterior, contributing nothing to the formation of the mouth. The first series, together with the lower metazoa except the sponges, are grouped together as the **Protostomia,** indicating that the blastopore is the definitive mouth. The second series form the **Deuterostomia,** indicating that the adult mouth forms as a new structure unrelated to the blastopore.

Some authors find these differences so profound that they consider the two series to have evolved independently from the acoelomates. This deep division is based on two major arguments: the fate of the blastopore and the method of coelom formation.

In deuterostomes the blastopore becomes the anus, and it is at first difficult to visualize how a coelomate protostome, which already has a separate anus, can become a deuterostome. Actually, however, in many coelomate protostomes the blastopore elongates ventrally and contributes to both mouth and anus. Thus, the evolution of the deuterostome condition can be regarded as a restriction, rather than a complete change, in the fate of the blastopore.

The two methods of coelom formation also may not be so divergent as they appear. Although arthropods have a schizocoelom, the housefly and the tardigrades have an enterocoelom. In the phylum Brachiopoda both methods of coelom formation occur. Other exceptions are also known. Thus, the view held here is that the deuterostomes evolved from coelomate protostomes and that all eucoelomates are a single evolutionary unit.

In the following chapters, between those

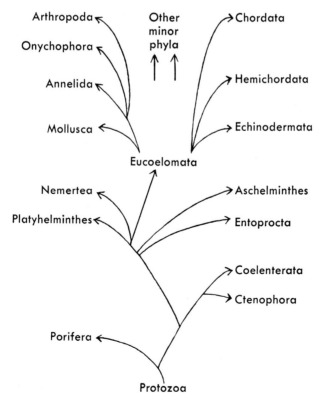

Figure 13.3 A suggested phylogeny of the Metazoa, showing all the major phyla and some of the minor phyla. The Entoprocta and other minor phyla will be discussed in Chapter 18.

presenting the two series of coelomate phyla, lies one chapter (Chap. 18) on minor phyla. Some of these can be related to one series and some to the other. Other minor phyla cannot be easily related to either series. It is sufficient at the introductory level to recognize that there are two major groups of eucoelomates and that some minor groups do not fit into either.

This discussion of possible evolutionary relationships among phyla can be summarized in a phylogenetic tree (Fig. 13.3). This is, of course, only a guess based on available evidence. Various other schemes can also be proposed.

A very simplified *key* to the phyla of the animal kingdom is appended to this chapter. It will be meaningful to the student only after he has completed the survey of the animals. He should, however, begin to use it now, and return to it after each new chapter. It is intended as a simple framework within which to organize concepts of the animal kingdom. It is only with such an organization that the phyla will become other than a dreary sequence of too many kinds of animals.

QUESTIONS

1. In what ways do sponges differ from all other metazoa?
2. List the characteristics of flatworms that are not found in coelenterates.
3. Compare the pseudocoelom and the eucoelom.
4. Distinguish an enterocoelom from a schizocoelom.
5. What is a mesentery?

ANNOTATED REFERENCES

Barnes, R. D.: Invertebrate Zoology. Philadelphia, W. B. Saunders Co. 1963. One of the very few modern texts written for the scholarly undergraduate. An excellent treatment that includes all invertebrates except the insects.

Borradaile, L. A., F. A. Potts, L. E. S. Eastham, and J. T. Saunders: The Invertebrata. 3rd ed. Cambridge, Cambridge University Press, prepared by G. A. Kerkut, 1958. A discussion of all the invertebrates, written for the honor student. Readable and thought-provoking. Beware of differences in definitions of words.

Buchsbaum, R.: Animals Without Backbones. 2nd ed. Chicago, University of Chicago Press, 1948. An immensely popular, richly illustrated summary of the invertebrates, containing many excellent photographs.

Bullock, T. H., and G. A. Horridge: Structure and Function in the Nervous System of Invertebrates. San Francisco, W. H. Freeman & Co., 1965. An important review of the serious student of the status of our knowledge of the receptors, nervous system and neurosecretion of invertebrates.

Hyman, L.: The Invertebrates. New York, McGraw-Hill Book Co., Vol. I, 1940; Vol. II, 1951; Vol. III, 1951; Vol. IV, 1955; Vol. V, 1959; Vol. VI, 1967. Although this treastise by the world's authority on invertebrates is incomplete, these volumes are the best references available on the groups covered. All aspects of invertebrates are covered, with special sections devoted to problems of phylogeny, comparative embryology, the regulation of form, behavior, reproduction, etc. Intended as reference works, they include a series of lively and provoking discussions.

MacGinitie, G. E., and N. MacGinitie: Natural History of Marine Animals. New York, McGraw-Hill Book Co., 1949. A wealth of general information on the habits, behavior, learning ability, etc., of a variety of marine animals, with emphasis on west coast species. Very good on the larger invertebrates.

Meglitsch, P. A.: Invertebrate Zoology. New York, Oxford University Press, 1967. An important and carefully written textbook on invertebrates.

Parker, T. J., and W. A. Haswell: A Text-Book of Zoology. 6th ed. Vol. I. Revised by C. Forster-Cooper. London, Macmillan & Co. Ltd., 1947. Intended as an introductory text, the coverage of invertebrates is better than in many texts on invertebrates. Concise and informative.

Shrock, R. R., and W. H. Twenhofel: Principles of Invertebrate Paleontology. 2nd ed. New York, McGraw-Hill Book Co., 1953. Especially good on those groups that have fossils (some of which are poorly treated in standard invertebrate texts). Living representatives are discussed whenever possible.

Yonge, C. M.: The Sea Shore. London. William Collins Sons & Co. Ltd., 1949. A richly illustrated account of the larger animals inhabiting the seashore. Particularly good on the major invertebrate phyla.

Zim, H. S., and L. Ingle: Seashores. New York, Simon and Schuster, 1955. A paperback picture guide to the identification of the common organisms of the seashore.

A KEY TO THE ANIMAL KINGDOM

Unicellular: *Phylum 1, Protozoa.*
Uncertain status: *Phylum 2, Mesozoa.*
Multicellular: *The subkingdom Metazoa.*
  No nervous system: *Phylum 3, Porifera.*
  Nervous system: All remaining phyla.
    Little or no mesoderm and radial symmetry: the radiate phyla.
      Ciliary locomotion, colloblasts: *Phylum 4, Ctenophora.*
      Muscular locomotion, nematocysts: *Phylum 5, Coelenterata.*
    Well-developed mesoderm with nephridia.
      Mouth-anus as a single opening: *Phylum 6, Platyhelminthes.*
      Mouth and anus separate openings.
        Pseudocoelom, no circulatory system.
          No asexual budding, poor powers of regeneration, never with ciliated tentacles: *Phylum 7, Aschelminthes.*
          Asexual budding, good powers of regeneration, with a ring of ciliated tentacles: *Phylum 8, Entoprocta.*
        No coelom, circulatory system present: *Phylum 9, Nemertea.*
        Eucoelom, circulatory system usually present: *Superphylum Eucoelomata.*
          Protostomous and primarily schizocoelous.
            Reduced coelom and no segmentation: *Phylum 10, Mollusca.*
            Well-developed coelom, usually segmented at least as larvae: *Phylum 11, Annelida* and the related *phyla 12, Echiuroidea; 13, Sipunculoidea;* and *14, Priapuloidea.*
            Reduced coelom and segmented: *Phyla 15, Onycophora* and *16, Arthropoda.*
          Minor phyla that are protostomous but not closely related to the preceding; some are enterocoelous: The lophophore-bearing *phyla 17, Phoronida; 18, Brachiopoda;* and *19, Bryozoa,* and the *phylum 20, Chaetognatha.*
        Deuterostomous and primarily enterocoelous.
          Hydraulic coelom and secondary radial symmetry: *Phylum 21, Echinodermata.*
          Hydraulic coelom and gill slits: *Phylum 22, Hemichordata.*
          Gill pouches and notochord: *Phylum 23, Chordata.*

14 _____ THE PHYLUM MOLLUSCA

14.1

General Features of the Mollusks

The **Mollusca,** which includes snails, clams, squids and others, are a group of soft-bodied animals that usually secrete external protective **shells.** The ventral portion of the body is elaborated as a muscular organ, called the **foot,** used in locomotion. Many of the molluscan groups have in the mouth a unique rasping organ, the **radula.** These structures will be described later.

Mollusks have both a eucoelom and a circulatory system. The coelom is small and is associated with the heart, gonads and excretory organs. The portion surrounding the heart, the **pericardial cavity,** is the most obvious.

The circulatory system is well developed. It is modified variously in the different groups, but typically includes a single dorsal

heart composed of one anterior **ventricle** and a pair of posterior **auricles** (Fig. 14.1). The auricles receive blood from **veins** and pump it into the ventricle while the latter is relaxed. Then the ventricle, a heavily muscled organ, pumps the blood out through **arteries** to all parts of the body. The blood may pass through capillaries to the veins but usually passes into **venous sinuses,** spaces among the various organs that are difficult to observe. Most of the returning blood passes through the excretory organs and then either directly to the auricles or through the gills to the auricles. The amount passing through the gills determines the amount of freshly oxygenated blood returning to the heart and varies from mollusk to mollusk according to its level of activity.

The excretory organs are a single pair of **nephridia,** intimately associated with the circulatory system. In each a large glandular

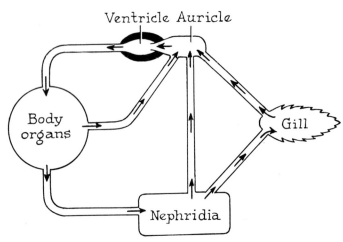

Figure 14.1 A diagram showing the principal features of the molluscan circulatory system. Auricles, gills and nephridia are usually paired.

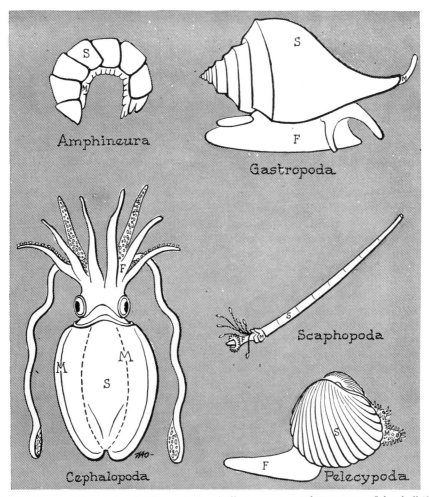

Figure 14.2 Classes of the phylum Mollusca. Letters indicate structures that are part of the shell (*S*), mantle (*M*) and foot (*F*). (Gastropoda after Kline in Curtis and Guthrie, 1938; Scaphopoda, original; others after Lankester, 1906.)

region is bathed in blood, and from this a tubule opens externally at a **nephridiopore.** In many mollusks the inner ends of these tubules open into the pericardial cavity as nephrostomes.

The phylum includes three large classes having species of economic importance and two additional small classes (Fig. 14.2). The classes are:

I. Amphineura. A small group with a shell, if any, located dorsally and made of many spicules or of a longitudinal series of plates. Includes the chitons.

II. Gastropoda. A large group with a single dorsal shell, if present, that is usually spiral in shape. Includes snails, slugs, whelks and abalones.

III. Pelecypoda. A large group with a pair of lateral shells, hinged dorsally. In-

cludes the bivalves, such as clams, oysters and scallops.

IV. Scaphopoda. A small group with a conical shell open at both ends. These are called the tooth shells.

V. Cephalopoda. A large group in which part of the foot forms arms or tentacles surrounding the mouth. Includes the squids and octopuses.

14.2

Class Amphineura

The chitons, which are common on the west coast of the United States, are the most primitive class in the phylum and illustrate the generalized molluscan plan. They are found only in the oceans, where they creep slowly over the rocks. Many live between high and low tide lines. Some species remain in one place all the time, where they gradually wear a depression in the rock. These feed upon the debris that settles into their hole. Often, after the hole has become deep, encrusting growths may obstruct the opening to such an extent that the chiton can no longer get out.

Chitons creep upon a broad foot, moving by a succession of small waves of muscular contraction that pass forward from the posterior end. The broad surface with its slimy secretions enables the chiton to cling tenaciously. The mantle extends out over the foot on all sides, enclosing a circular mantle cavity below. Dorsally the mantle secretes a shell usually made of eight segments. Because of the segmental structure of the shell, a chiton is able to roll into a ball, shielding the vulnerable ventral surface, if it is torn loose from its substratum (Fig. 14.2).

In the anterior part of the mantle cavity is the **head,** no more than a tubular extension of the body, bearing a mouth at its end. Well-developed sense organs such as eyes or tentacles are lacking.

In the floor of the mouth cavity lies the **radula,** with which the chiton scrapes up its food. The radula is a thin flexible strip of toothed skin that can be pulled around the end of a stiff tongue. In a typical scraping movement the tongue is pushed out of the mouth with the radula on its anterior and lower surface (Fig. 14.3). The radula is then pulled around the end of the tongue onto the upper surface, scraping whatever the mouth is pressed against. Finally the tongue is withdrawn, and the debris on the radula is swallowed. Chitons feed primarily on encrusting algae.

The mouth leads to a long coiled **intestine** that ends posteriorly at a short **rectum** and **anus** opening into the posterior part of the mantle cavity. Anteriorly the intestine receives ducts from a pair of **digestive glands,** presumed to secrete digestive enzymes.

The sides of the mantle cavity have several pairs of small **gills** that hang freely in the water of the cavity. Beneath the edge of the projecting mantle this water is continuous with the environment.

The amphineuran nervous system is poorly developed. In most mollusks the central nervous system consists of a brain and several pairs of ganglia connected by nerve cords. In the chiton the nerve cells are spread out along cords forming a diffuse system. Such poor centralization of the nerve cells only reflects the sluggish habit of these animals, and does not necessarily indicate the ancestral pattern of the central nervous system in the phylum.

Recently, dredges operating in deep water off the west coast of Mexico brought up sev-

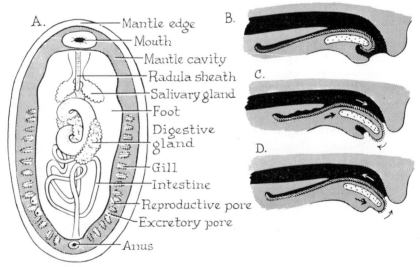

A. — Mantle edge
— Mouth
— Mantle cavity
— Radula sheath
— Salivary gland
— Foot
— Digestive gland
— Gill
— Intestine
— Reproductive pore
— Excretory pore
— Anus

B.

C.

D.

Figure 14.3   *A,* Ventral view of a chiton, with the digestive tract indicated. *B,* Longitudinal section through the mouth showing the radula extending forward over the end of the stiff cartilaginous tongue. *C,* The tongue is pushed out and the radula is pulled as far as possible onto its lower surface. *D,* The radula is pulled posteriorly while the tongue is pressed against the food. After this maneuver both tongue and radula are withdrawn into the mouth.

eral specimens of a new type of mollusk, *Neopilina*. Although probably most closely related to the **Amphineura,** it shows some affinities to the **Gastropoda,** but more remarkable still shows evidence of segmentation. *Neopilina* has five pairs of gills, five pairs of nephridia, five pairs of muscles to the broad ventral foot, and several pairs of auricles. The body is covered by a single shell, which shows evidence of being coiled in a larval stage. The development of *Neopilina* is unknown, so that it cannot yet be decided whether the segmentation is primary (and possibly homologous with segmentation in the annelids) or secondary (like the paired gills of chitons). For the present this mollusk can be considered a member of the class **Amphineura.**

14.3
Class Gastropoda: General Features

Snails are the only class of mollusks found on land. They also occur in fresh water and in the oceans. Both herbivorous and carnivorous species are found, with appropriate modifications of the radular teeth. Most snails creep like chitons upon a broad muscular foot, but a few use the foot as a lever for jumping while others use it as a fin for swimming.

The basic feature that distinguishes gastropods from other mollusks is the result of an embryologic event, known as **torsion** (Fig. 14.4). The gastropod embryo develops to a stage known as the **veliger.** This early embryo is symmetrical, with an anterior mouth and a posterior anus, but at a particular point in its development parts of the body twist or rotate as much as 180 degrees, bringing the anus around (usually to the right) to lie over the mouth. This twist is abrupt and permanent. Following this, development is asymmetrical, with the structures of one side often suppressed. The body elongates dorsally, growing up in a spiral pattern. The enclosing spiral shell forms a structure characteristic for the class.

14.4
Busycon

The familiar large whelks of the eastern seaboard belong to the genus *Busycon,* of which *B. canaliculatum* (Fig. 14.5), about 20 cm. long, is the most common. *Busycon* lives on sand and mud, where it can plow about with its large powerful foot searching for small clams and other prey. The mouth is borne on a long, retractile **proboscis** which is usually kept withdrawn into the head but may be shot out quickly to capture food. The teeth of the radula are long, sharp and recurved so that *Busycon* can not only pierce the flesh of its prey but also draw it into the mouth.

Food is swallowed through a long esophagus to a curved **stomach** lying in the lower whorl of the body (Fig. 14.5). From the stomach an **intestine** bends dorsally and down the anterior surface of the whorl to a short wide **rectum** that opens at an **anus** in the mantle cavity over the head. A pair of **salivary glands** beside the esophagus secrete juices (probably containing enzymes for digesting carbohydrates) into the anterior end of the esophagus. The stomach lies between a pair of large **digestive glands** that occupy most of the space in the upper body whorls. Ducts from these glands open into the stomach. They are not known to secrete digestive juices but do take

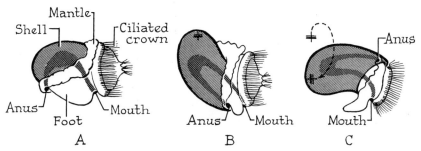

Figure 14.4 Torsion in the gastropod *Acmaea* (a limpet). *A,* Young larva, showing beginning of shell and foot. *B,* Just before torsion, with a U-shaped digestive tract. *C,* Just after torsion (arrow indicates movement that has occurred). All these stages swim with the ciliated crown uppermost in the water. They are shown here in positions comparable with that of the adult snail. (After Boutan, 1899.)

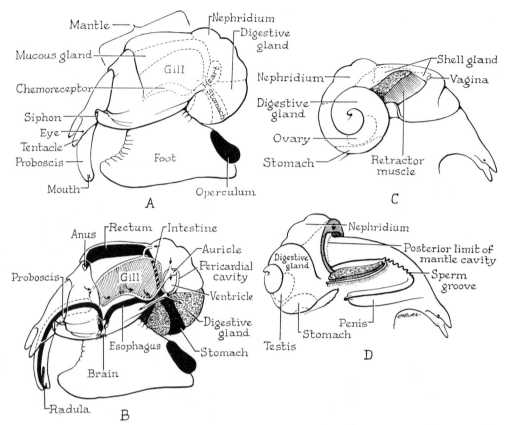

Figure 14.5   Anatomy of *Busycon canaliculatum* (shell removed). *A*, Left side, showing external organs and internal organs visible through the integument. *B*, Same view with digestive, respiratory, circulatory and nervous systems indicated. *C*, Female, showing portion of the right side. *D*, Male, portion of the right side with mantle and retractor muscle cut short. In *C* and *D* the proboscis is withdrawn. Adult with shell is shown in Figure 14.2.

up food particles from the fluid that flows up the ducts into the glands and digest them in food vacuoles.

The mantle cavity formed by the fleshy mantle that lines the inner surface of the shell surrounds the anterior part of the body. On the left side both shell and mantle are drawn out into a long **siphon,** a tubular fold through which water is drawn into the mantle cavity. A large **chemoreceptor** at the base of the siphon samples the incoming water before it passes over the single **gill,** a flat, oblong, feathery structure richly supplied with blood vessels. Along the upper edge of the gill numerous glands secrete mucus that passes over and cleanses the gill. Water leaves the mantle cavity through the slit between the anterior edge of the mantle and the head.

Blood passing through the capillaries of the gill is collected in a large vein that empties into the single **auricle.** The heart, which lies close to the intestine, is reversed during torsion so that the ventricle lies posterior to the auricle. In *Busycon canaliculatum,* which twists to the right during development, only the left gill and the left auricle develop.

The single left **nephridium** lies over the heart, opening dorsally into the mantle cavity. Most of the blood passing through the nephridium goes through the gill, but a small portion goes directly to the auricle, so that the final mixture is not completely oxygenated.

Most of the nervous system is centralized anteriorly. Except for one pair on the intestine, the ganglia are located close to the brain, forming an irregular ring around the esophagus (Fig. 14.5). The several elements can be distinguished by careful dissection. The **visceral ganglia** on the intestine were reversed during torsion, so that their connectives with the rest of the system are crossed, a persistent feature characteristic of many snails.

The head bears a pair of sensitive **tentacles,** and halfway out on each tentacle is a small **eye.** The eye is well developed and probably forms crude images. It is spherical, lined with a **retina** and a layer of light-sensitive cells, and contains a large globular **lens** (Fig. 14.6). The outer surface, except where the light comes through, is pigmented to screen out extraneous light.

In *Busycon* sexes are separate. A single **gonad** lies in an upper whorl of the body, between the digestive glands. From the ovary an **oviduct** passes down through the mantle, opening near its anterior edge to the right of the anus. Near its end the oviduct is surrounded by a yellow **shell gland.** A **sperm duct** from the testis opens on the right side into the posterior limit of the mantle cavity. From there a ciliated **sperm groove** leads across the body to the base of a large **penis** just behind the right tentacle (Fig. 14.5). The groove continues along the penis to its tip. Fertilization is internal.

The fertilized eggs are laid in cases secreted by the shell gland, a dozen eggs to the case. The cases are arranged in a row along a connecting strand that is attached to the bottom (Fig. 14.7). The young pass through all of their larval stages within the cases, emerging

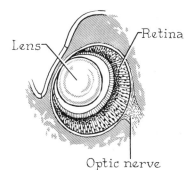

Figure 14.6 Section through the eye of a whelk. (After Helger.)

as small whelks. The cases are tough, lasting long after the young have emerged, and are often washed ashore; they are known as "mermaids' necklaces."

14.5
Other Gastropods

Prosobranchia. Snails are divided into three large subclasses. *Busycon* beongs to the subclass **Prosobranchia,** in which torsion brings the originally posterior gills, anus, etc., around to the anterior side. Although *Busycon* has only the left nephridium, gill and auricle, other members of the group, such as the prized **abalone** of the west coast, have these organs in pairs. It is reasonable to sup-

Figure 14.7 The egg case of *Busycon.* (Photo by Hugh Spencer.)

pose that the abalone represents the primitive condition and that the loss of organs in such snails as the whelk is an adaptation to the twisted shape of the body. Most of the Prosobranchia are marine, although a number of small forms are found in fresh water. On isolated tropical south Pacific islands some have become terrestrial.

Opisthobranchia. In a second large subclass torsion as an embryologic event is less extreme and may not occur at all. The gills (if present) remain posterior, or at most are moved to the right side, giving the subclass its name, the **Opisthobranchia.** In certain species the original gills have disappeared entirely. Since all members of this group have a single nephridium, gill and auricle, their incomplete torsion is believed to be secondary. These are almost entirely marine and include some strange forms.

One group has left the bottom and swims as plankton in the upper water of the open oceans. Each side of the foot is expanded as a muscular flap suggesting wings (Fig. 14.8*A*). Hence their name, the **pteropods.** Pteropods hang shell down in the water, swimming upward by flapping the "wings," and falling more gently while gathering food from the water. They sometimes form immense swarms and serve as food for whales.

A second group of opisthobranchs have lost the shell. With it the mantle cavity and original gill have also disappeared, to be replaced by new gills on the back. These are the **nudibranchs** or sea slugs (Fig. 14.8*B*). Many of them, particularly those on the west coast, are brightly colored, crawling with great agility over the hydroids and algae upon which they feed. Nudibranchs that feed on hydroids do so without discharging the nematocysts. In the stomach, the nemato-

cysts are digested free, and afterward are picked up by ameboid cells and carried to the epidermis, where they protect the sea slug in much the same way that they were supposed to protect the hydroid.

Pulmonata. The third large subclass of gastropods is the **Pulmonata,** or airbreathers. This includes most of the terrestrial and fresh-water species. They show full torsion and have a single nephridium and auricle. No gill is present. Air is circulated through the mantle cavity, which is lined with a richly vascular epidermis that serves as the respiratory surface. These are the familiar garden snails (Fig. 14.8*D*). Included also are the **slugs,** in which the shell is reduced to fragments buried in the mantle or is completely absent (Fig. 14.8*C*). The mantle is still present, providing a cavity for respiration.

Most of the prosobranchs have **opercula,** horny lids borne on the upper surface of the posterior part of the foot, by which the opening to the shell is tightly closed when the animal is withdrawn inside the shell. In the pulmonates, which are the most susceptible to desiccation, the operculum is lacking. When the environment becomes dry, pulmonates bury themselves in the soil and secrete a thick mucus in the shell opening that hardens to form an effective seal. When rain returns moisture to the soil the seal softens and the snails become active again.

Most prosobranchs have separate sexes, but most of the opisthobranchs and pulmonates are hermaphroditic. Cross fertilization is the rule. Either individuals are temporarily active as males or as females, or simultaneous cross fertilization, as in the flat worms, will occur. Self-fertilization is known to occur in a few species.

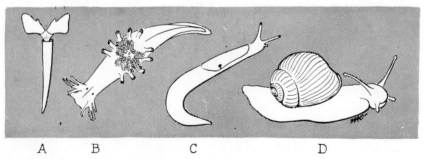

Figure 14.8 Opisthobranchia: *A*, a pteropod; *B*, a nudibranch. Pulmonata: *C*, a slug; *D*, a garden snail. (*A* and *C* after Parker and Haswell; *B* and *D* after Lankester.)

Figure 14.9 Diagrammatic cross sections showing different gill types in the Pelecypoda. *A,* Order Protobranchiata. Gills short and simple. *B,* Order Filibranchiata. Gills long and folded back. *C,* Order Eulamellibranchiata. Like *B,* but with the folds fused with many bridges. *D,* Order Septibranchiata. Gills modified to form horizontal partitions. (After Lang.)

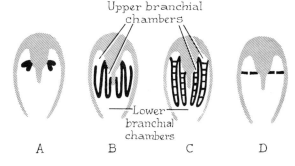

14.6
Class Pelecypoda: General Features

The pelecypods include all the bivalves. In these forms the foot is bilaterally compressed to form a muscular spade for digging and the head is greatly reduced, lying well within the mantle cavity. In most species the shell, composed of two **valves** hinged together dorsally, can completely enclose the body. Strong muscles, the **adductors,** can close the shells and hold them tightly shut against enemies (Fig. 14.10).

The mantle cavity and gills are elaborated to serve both respiration and feeding. Typically, the edges of the mantle around the free margins of the valves are kept together, forming a closed cavity, except posteriorly where they separate to form two openings, a ventral **incurrent siphon** and a dorsal **excurrent siphon.** These openings may be extended as a long double tube which can be projected up into the water while the clam lies buried in the sand. The mantle cavity extends all around the body. The two gills on each side are large and are attached to the body along the whole length of each side and around the posterior end. The inner gill of each side extends medially against the foot, and each outer gill extends laterally against the mantle, thus dividing the mantle cavity into upper and lower chambers that connect with the excurrent and incurrent siphons, respectively. The lining of the cavity and the surfaces of the gills are ciliated. The beating of the cilia creates water currents inward through the incurrent siphon, upward through many small slits in the gills, and outward through the excurrent siphon. The water brings oxygen for respiration at the gill surface and many small food particles (algae and bacteria) that are trapped on a mucous sheath secreted on the gills. Special tracts of cilia move this mucus toward the mouth, where it is eventually swallowed. Thus, most pelecypods feed by filtering water and have little need for locomotion. The head is reduced to a mouth between a pair of **palps,** long folds of ciliated skin that collect food from the anterior edges of the gills and transfer it to the mouth. In this class of mollusk the radula is lacking.

The Pelecypoda are divided into orders according to the detailed structure of the gills (Fig. 14.9). In the most primitive group the gills are plumes in the posterior part of the mantle cavity resembling those of the chitons and snails. The palps are correspondingly enlarged to serve in feeding. In other groups the gills are large and lamellated, with numerous slits as described above. Still other modifications occur, but most of the familiar bivalves, such as mussels, clams, oysters and scallops, have the lamellated type.

14.7
Venus mercenaria

Quahog, hardshell clam, littleneck and cherrystone are common names for *Venus mercenaria,* a heart-shaped bivalve found on the east coast of the United States (Fig. 14.10). The young (cherrystones) are eaten alive on the half-shell and the adults make excellent chowder. *Venus* lives buried head down in the sand anywhere from low tide to depths of 30 meters, with the short siphons projecting to obtain and filter sea water.

The shell valves are thick and strong. The **hinge ligament,** which opens the valves, is anterodorsal, next to the **umbo,** a prominent swelling on each valve. Anterior to the ligament are several prominent **teeth** and several

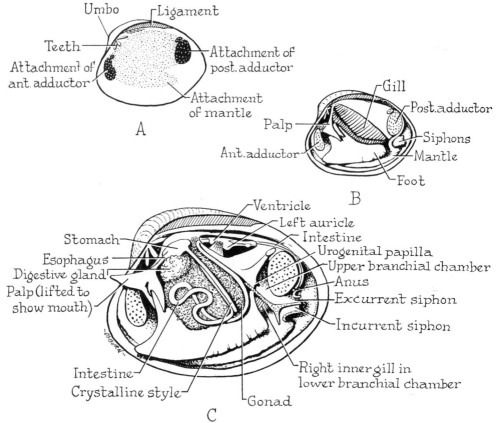

Figure 14.10 Anatomy of *Venus mercenaria. A,* Interior of the right valve. *B,* Left side with shell and mantle removed. *C,* Partial dissection, showing some of the internal organs.

more appear below the ligament as long ridges. These differ on the two valves to form a rigid interlocking mechanism. The valves can be shut by the adductor muscles so completely that *Venus* will live for days out of water, a convenience for shipping them inland. Live healthy specimens can be purchased in almost any seafood market.

The foot can be extended some distance out of the shell and is usually thrust anteriorly (downward) into the sand as an anchor. *Venus* can also move slowly by movements of the foot.

As in many clams, each of the four gills is attached along the dorsal limit of the mantle cavity, hangs down toward the ventral limit, and then folds back dorsally (Fig. 14.9*C*). Each inner gill is attached to the base of the foot, while each outer gill attaches to the mantle, forming a total of four longitudinal **upper gill chambers** that come together posteriorly at the excurrent siphon. Bridges of tissue between the folds of each gill keep the folds

slightly apart and create channels leading from the many tiny slits in each fold up to the upper gill chambers. While *Venus* is feeding the shells are slightly open and the siphons extended. Water passes in the lower siphon, through the several gill folds into the upper branchial chambers, and out through the upper siphon. On the free surface of each gill fold the mucous sheath is swept ventrally to the lower edge of the fold, and then forward to the palps. If accepted, the mucus and food are carried up the folds of the palps into the mouth. Sometimes, however, dirt or distasteful material may enter the mantle cavity, collect on the mucous sheath, and arrive at the palps as though it were food. This is rejected, and transferred to the mantle where the cilia move it ventrally and then posteriorly to accumulate just below the incurrent siphon. Periodically these pseudofeces are ejected through the incurrent siphon as the clam suddenly closes the valves, squirting water out of both siphons.

From the mouth a short **esophagus** leads to a small **stomach.** A long looped **intestine** eventually turns dorsally and runs posteriorly *straight through the ventricle of the heart,* around the posterior adductor muscle, and ends at an **anus** over the excurrent siphon. The stomach is buried in a **digestive gland** that opens into it, and the intestine is buried in the **gonads.** All four organs are bound tightly into a rounded **visceral mass** at the base of the foot.

The first portion of the intestine is divided longitudinally to form right and left channels. The right channel functions as the intestine and is continuous with the rest of the intestine. The left channel forms a tubular, blind sac that contains the **crystalline style,** a structure unique to the pelecypods and a few gastropods. In many pelecypods the sac is completely separate from the intestine. The crystalline style is a gelatinous rod secreted by the wall of the diverticulum which moves slowly into the stomach where the end wears away. Its function is similar to that of the salivary glands in snails, since it contains enzymes for the digestion of carbohydrates. Little is known of the function of the digestive gland. Although its cells may secrete digestive enzymes into the stomach, it is more likely that they function as in the snail, phagocytizing small food particles.

The paired gonads open through small ducts ending on **urogenital papillae,** one on each side of the posterior part of the foot. Sexes are separate. Eggs and sperm are released throughout the summer into the sea, where fertilization takes place. The embryo develops into a larva known as a **trochophore** that settles to the bottom by autumn as a tiny clam. It matures in about three years.

The circulatory and excretory systems are similar to those of the snails, except that two auricles and two nephridia are present. The pericardial cavity surrounds not only the heart but also a small part of the intestine. The tubular portion of each nephridium opens internally into the pericardial cavity as well as externally on the urogenital papilla.

The heart of *Venus* is used extensively in physiologic research. If one valve is removed from a live specimen, the beating heart can be seen in the dorsal part of the body. The only further dissection necessary is the removal of a portion of the mantle and one wall of the pericardial cavity. A small hook can then be inserted into the ventricle and attached by a string to a lever, so that both strength and frequency of the beat may be recorded. After a "normal" record is obtained, various drugs are dripped onto the heart and the results observed. Since the molluscan heart has been found to respond to the same kinds of drugs that affect the human heart, the heart of *Venus* is used in some laboratories as a means of measuring the strength of various drug extracts. The response is very closely related to the concentration of the drug administered.

The nervous system follows the typical molluscan plan. The **brain** and some ganglia are located over the esophagus. A pair of large **visceral ganglia** can be easily distinguished on the anterior surface of the posterior adductor muscle, below the intestine. An additional pair of **pedal ganglia** (which in the gastropods have moved forward to join the brain) are deeply embedded in the foot of pelecypods. Nerve cords connect these various components. Sense organs are limited to scattered chemoreceptors on the palps and siphons. Touch and temperature sense endings are probably present along the mantle edges. A few pelecypods have eyes but they are at the mantle edge, never on the head.

14.8

Other Pelecypoda

Many clams, including the steaming clam, *Mya arenaria* (Fig. 14.11), live buried in the sand and mud like *Venus.* Others, such as the cockle, *Cardium edule* (Fig. 14.2), jump over the bottom with quick movements of the foot. Mussels and oysters are attached to rocks and pilings. The common mussel, *Mytilus edulis,* attaches by a cluster of strong threads secreted by a gland at the base of the foot. Oysters cement one valve to the bottom.

The edible oyster (several species of the genus *Crassostrea*) is harvested by the most intensive and thoroughly regulated fisheries in the world. Along the eastern seaboard of the United States, for example, wherever the bottom is especially suitable for oysters it has been surveyed and rented to various fishermen by the states. Once a fisherman rents a given area, he is entitled to rent it for the rest of his life and to pass on the privilege to his heirs. Each oysterman manages his own "land" to produce as many oysters as possible. Every year boatloads of old shells are scattered about to serve as possible sites for the

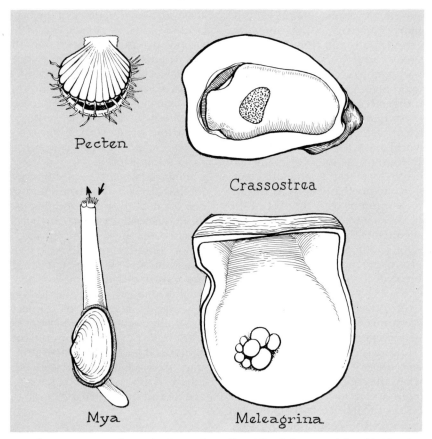

Figure 14.11 Some common pelecypods. *Pecten*, the scallop (after Johnson and Snook). *Mya*, the steaming clam (after Verrill, 1873). *Crassostrea*, the oyster (drawing by Hairston). *Meleagrina*, the pearl oyster (after Fischer, 1887), showing pearly "warts" in a shell.

attachment of larval oysters. Once larvae are attached to these loose shells, they may be moved about several times, inshore each summer for maximum growth, offshore in winter for protection, and finally to premium spots where they develop the best flavor for marketing. Oysters mature in three to five years. Curiously, most of the young are not produced by the older oysters of the fishery but come from scattered populations along the rocky shores and especially in the mouths of rivers, where the water is a little less salty. These "wild" oysters produce enormous numbers of young that drift offshore and eventually settle to the bottom.

Oysters are hermaphroditic; an individual may be a male for a few years, and then become a female, but it is never both sexes at once. The American oysters shed both eggs and sperm into the water, where fertilization occurs. The gametes shed by one individual enter the siphons of other oysters, stimulating them to release their gametes also, and soon the entire bed has been triggered.

The pearl oysters (species of the genus *Meleagrina*) are found in warm seas, especially around Japan (Fig. 14.11). Theoretically, any pelecypod can produce pearls, and many species such as the common mussels and oysters often do, but only the pearl oysters produce pearls of consistently high quality. The formation of a pearl is a reaction of self-defense. If a small foreign body should become lodged between the mantle and the shell, a layer of shell is secreted around it to seal it off. If the foreign body should be buried in the flesh of the mantle, shell is secreted all the way around it in concentric layers. The edge of the mantle, which makes the growing edge of the shell, secretes a chalky kind of shell, but the inner part of the mantle that thickens the shell secretes a harder, pearly material. The quality of the pearl depends upon the quality of the shell lining normally produced. The common mussel produces a lustrous, irridescent shell lining, and is sometimes infested with parasites around which pearls are secreted. Although there are often dozens in every mussel, none of them becomes larger than a tiny sand grain.

The Japanese have mastered the technique of culturing pearls. Pearl oysters are collected, small particles are introduced into the mantle, and then they are put out to sea in cages for several years. When the pearls have had time to reach a suitable size, the oysters are taken in and opened.

The large fresh-water bivalves are a group of mussels that live buried in the sand like clams. They are adapted for life in lakes and rivers where floating larvae would be swept away. Eggs are retained in the adult until they become miniature bivalves called **glochidia** (Fig. 14.12), mostly shell and adductor muscle with very little else. These clamp tightly onto the fins or gills of fish, where they gradually become buried and actually receive nourishment. In this way they are carried about, upstream as well as down. In a few weeks the glochidium assumes an adult form and ends its parasitic phase by dropping off and burrowing into the bottom.

The fresh-water mussels of the Mississippi River system support a pearl button industry. The buttons are cut from the inner, pearly layers of the shells. At present the industry is considerably reduced in size, both because many of the fisheries have been depleted and because competition with substitutes has

driven the pearl button into a semiluxury category. In recent years pollution has eliminated many mussel populations. Several species have become extinct. So far plastics have failed to imitate the unique luster of pearl, which results from the structure of its crystals, and not from the material of which it is made.

A few pelecypods lie loosely on the ocean bottom and are able to swim by flapping the shells. An example is the **scallop,** a species of the genus *Pecten* (Fig. 14.11). The familiar scalloped shells are closed by an enormous adductor muscle, the only part of the scallop that is eaten. The free edges of the mantle are set with bright blue eyes and numerous short tentacles. Scallops are easily frightened and violently clap their shells as they swim away on erratic courses. A frequent stimulus is the detection, through chemoreception, of an approaching starfish.

14.9

Class Scaphopoda

The tooth shells are a small group of marine mollusks that burrow in mud and sand. They have a funnel-shaped shell open at both ends (Fig. 14.2). The foot is conical and used for digging. Around the head are a number of prehensile **filaments** that are presumed to be used to bring food particles to the mouth. A radula is present. The smaller opening of the shell remains above the mud and is used for water circulation. Gills are absent; the mantle lining is suffcient for respiration. Strings of tooth shells, which are 5 to 7.5 cm. long, were formerly used by west coast Indians as money.

14.10

Class Cephalopoda: General Features

Cephalopods are active, fast-moving mollusks. The **chambered nautilus** (Fig. 14.13) is the most primitive of living species, with relatives that are abundant as fossils dating all the way back to the beginning of the known fossil record. The nautilus floats by secreting gas (resembling air, but with less oxygen) into its shell. The shell is chambered, and the animal lives only in the most recently added chamber. A **stalk,** which secretes the gas, extends back through the other cham-

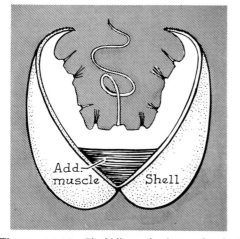

Figure 14.12 Glochidium, the larva of a fresh-water mussel.

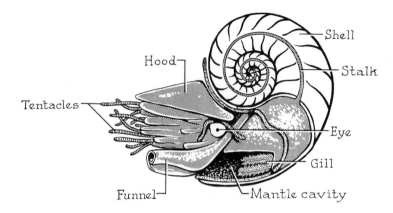

Figure 14.13 Lateral view of *Nautilus*. A diagrammatic section of the chambered shell is shown. The mantle of the left side is cut away to show the mantle cavity and two of the gills. When the animal retracts, the leathery hood protects the shell opening. Combined from several sources.

bers. The shell covers the animal dorsally and is secreted by a mantle as in other mollusks.

The nautilus has modified the foot for both feeding and locomotion. The anterior part grows forward on each side of the head in a series of lateral lobes, at the edges of which are numerous **tentacles.** The tentacles, annularly ridged, are able to grasp objects tightly. With these the nautilus may attach to rocks while resting or may grasp prey and carry it to the mouth. The posterior part of the foot is folded longitudinally to form a large **funnel.** The posterior end fits against the opening into the mantle cavity, while the smaller anterior end is supplied with a flaplike **valve.** When the funnel enlarges, water enters between mantle and foot, but when the funnel constricts, the posterior edge of the foot closes against the mantle and the water is squirted out the anterior end. By this form of jet propulsion the nautilus is able to swim. Two pairs of gills lie in the mantle cavity, where they are continually flushed with water.

A stout pair of horny **jaws** assists the radula in tearing prey to bits. The lower jaw closes outside the upper jaw, resembling the reverse of a parrot's beak. The nautilus also has a pair of large, protruding **eyes** that form images. Each eye is a simple cavity with a

small hole opening to the exterior (Fig. 14.16). Water is free to enter the cavity, which is lined with a retina differentiated from the ectoderm. Images are formed on the principle of the pinhole camera, a lensless system that requires only a very small opening to a dark chamber with a light-sensitive back surface.

The nautilus and its relatives, including the extinct ammonites, dominated the seas for many millions of years, but dwindled nearly to extinction at the end of the Mesozoic era. Throughout this time various cephalopod groups showed tendencies to reduce the size of the shell and make it an internal structure. Today most of the living members belong to such groups. The squids are the most highly developed in the direction of an active, swimming predator (Fig. 14.14). The tentacles are fewer in number, longer, and bear numerous **suckers.** The funnel is closed into a complete tube, while the mantle, no longer confined within the shell, has become a muscular pump that draws water in around its free edge and expels it through the siphon. The squids can match fish in speed and agility. The octopuses (Fig. 14.17) have gone back to the ocean bottom, where they crawl rapidly over the rocks and swim only when chased.

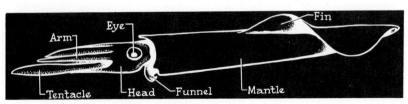

Figure 14.14 Lateral view of *Loligo.*

14.11

Loligo

The common squids, *Loligo pealei* of the east coast and *L. opalescens* of the west, grow to 20 to 30 cm. in length and are frequently netted in large numbers by fishermen and sold at market. A glance at their streamlined shape and compact organs suggests that the changes initiated by the nautiloids have been carried much farther in the squid (Figs. 14.14 and 14.15).

The squid is elongated like the gastropods, but in this case the elongation remains straight. The body is covered by a thick muscular **mantle** that tapers to a point. The shell

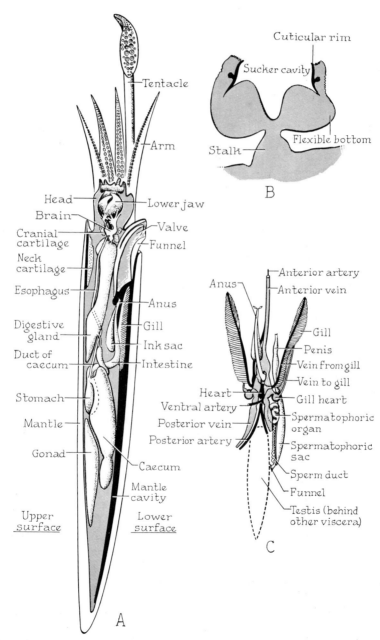

Figure 14.15 Anatomy of *Loligo. A*, Lateral view with body wall removed, showing digestive and nervous systems. *B*, Section through a sucker. *C*, Ventral view of part of the circulatory system and of the male reproductive system (drawn to the same scale as *A*, so that it can be turned on edge and fitted into *A*). (After Williams.)

is reduced to a **pen,** buried in the upper portion of the mantle. The anterior part of the foot is completely dissociated from the rest and is intimately fused with the head, forming a complete ring of eight tapered **arms** and two elongate **tentacles.** The posterior part of the foot, much smaller than in the nautilus, is fused into a tubular **funnel** attached to the lower side of the head. The head is carried on a slender neck and fits snugly into the opening of the mantle. In life it is locked in place by three articulations: the end of the pen fits into a cartilaginous groove on the upper side of the head, and two cartilaginous rods at the mantle rim fit into corresponding grooves on the funnel.

By changing the direction of its funnel the squid can swim forward or backward in the water. When the mantle cavity enlarges, the funnel valve shuts and water is sucked in along the sides of the head. When the mantle constricts, flaps of skin close all openings between mantle and head, and the water is forced out the funnel. The funnel is flexible and is turned backward when the squid wishes to swim head foremost. For the most rapid locomotion, however, the funnel is held straight, pointing forward, and the squid shoots away with its head trailing. For slow movement jet propulsion may be assisted or replaced by the undulations of a pair of lateral **fins** near the apex of the mantle. These can undulate in either direction and in rapid movement are used for steering.

A spectacular feature of the living squid is its changing color. Just beneath the skin are numerous **chromatophores,** cells packed with pigment that may be black, yellow or red. When a chromatophore is spherical and contracted it is barely visible to the naked eye, but attached around its sides are numerous muscle fibers that can stretch it out into a flat disc as much as 3 mm. in diameter. These muscle fibers are controlled by the nervous system and can act rapidly. A squid can change color in less than a second, or pass waves of color along its body by expanding differently colored sets of chromatophores.

The arms are covered along their oral surfaces with numerous stalked **suckers** (Fig. 14.15*A*). The arms are relatively short and tapering, with the suckers arranged in two longitudinal rows. The tentacles are long, with cylindrical bases and expanded ends having four rows of suckers. If the arms are counted from the upper surface, the tentacles

lie between the third and fourth pairs, and can be retracted into pouches formed by fleshy webs between these two pairs of arms. The tentacles are shot out suddenly to capture prey. The arms serve primarily to hold and manipulate the food after it is caught.

Each sucker is a rigid cup with a finely toothed rim and a flexible bottom attached to a slender stalk (Fig. 14.15*B*). When the tentacle is pressed against a surface the cup is pushed back upon its stalk, obliterating the cavity beneath. When the tentacle pulls, the force is transmitted through the stalk to the middle of the flexible bottom of the cup, creating suction that holds the cup tight. The squid can release a sucker by contracting small muscles between cup and stalk, pulling in the bottom to eliminate the suction. Thus, the suckers are attached automatically and can be released only by positive action of the squid, unless sufficient external force is applied to overcome the suction.

Food is shredded by a pair of jaws and a radula similar to those of the nautilus. The slender **esophagus** (Fig. 14.15*A*) traverses the neck to a muscular **stomach** in the body. Next to the esophagus, at the anterior end of the stomach, an **intestine** leads forward to an **anus** just behind the inner end of the funnel. A very large delicate sac, the **caecum,** opens into the stomach. Salivary glands open into the esophagus and digestive glands into the stomach. In the cephalopods both of these secrete enzymes and the absorption of food appears to be limited largely to the caecum. Enzymes rapidly liquefy the meat that is eaten, and it is only the liquid hydrolysate that passes into the caecum.

The **ink sac** opens just behind the anus into the end of the intestine. The glandular lining of this sac secretes a black liquid that is expelled when the squid is alarmed. The defensive action of this ink has been much debated. It is commonly thought to act as a "smoke screen" behind which the squid can swim rapidly away. It may also serve as a distracting dark object that momentarily holds the attention of the pursuer. The ink of deep sea squids is luminescent, producing a bright splotch in the otherwise black water. The ink of the octopus is known to have an additional function. MacGinitie has shown that if a pursuer swims into the ink its sense of smell is paralyzed for as much as two hours. During that time it will continue to hunt for the octopus, but even if it touches it the pursuer seldom recognizes that the octopus is there. We do not know whether squid ink has a similar effect.

A single pair of gills hangs in the lower part of the mantle cavity. Associated with these are a pair of auricles, nephridia and a single ventricle, as in most mollusks. The circulatory system is closed, however, unlike that of other mollusks. Arteries end in networks of capillaries all over the body that come together in veins leading back to the nephridia. Furthermore, all the blood passing through the nephridia goes on through the gills. Between each nephridium and gill is an auxiliary **gill heart** that pumps blood through the capillary network of the gill to the auricle (Fig. 14.15C).

Most of the central nervous system is grouped into a large ring around the esophagus. This structure, the fused brain and ganglia, is as large as the brain of a fish of similar size. It is also encased in a kind of "skull," formed by several **cranial cartilages.** Many nerves run from this central mass to all parts of the body. The only large ganglia outside of this center are the star-shaped **stellate ganglia** on the inner side of the mantle. From these ganglia, giant axons extend the length of the mantle. Their function will be discussed in the following chapter.

The large lateral eyes appear during development as simple pits that resemble the pinhole eyes of the nautilus. Later, however, a lens, iris, cornea and focusing mechanism develop, producing an eye remarkably like that of the vertebrates (Fig. 14.16). The **lens** is supported on a flexible membrane between the inner and outer chambers. Contraction of the muscles around the inner chamber squeezes it and forces the lens outward for near vision. The squid eye is "direct," since light reaches the retina without having to traverse nerves and cell bodies. The retina is ectodermal in origin and is reached from behind by nerves from the **optic ganglia,** large lateral outgrowths from the brain. As shown in the figure, the lens is composed of two pieces. A unique feature of the squid eye is that these two pieces form at different times during development. The inner half develops along with the retina, while the outer half forms later along with the iris.

The apex of the body is occupied by the **gonad.** In the female, eggs are released into a part of the coelom surrounding the ovary and collected in a ciliated funnel to be stored in the **oviduct.** This loops back and forth and ends to the left of the anus. Near the end a glandular region of the oviduct secretes a capsule around each individual egg, and at the end a pair of large glands secretes a gelatinous matrix around the entire mass of eggs.

In the male, the sperm are released into the coelom and collected by a funnel (Fig. 14.15). The **sperm duct** is convoluted and passes

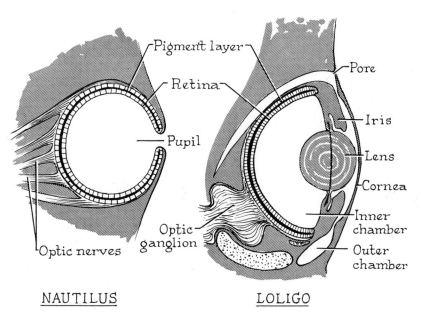

NAUTILUS   LOLIGO

Figure 14.16 Cephalopod eyes. *Left,* The pinhole camera type in *Nautilus.* (After Borradaile et al.) *Right,* The lens type complete with shutter (iris) in *Loligo.* (After Williams.)

forward on the left side of the body to an expanded, coiled portion, the **spermatophoric organ,** which wraps the sperm into packets called **spermatophores.** The duct then continues backward as a straight narrow tube and turns forward again as a large sac, the **spermatophoric sac,** where the spermatophores are stored. The sac opens anteriorly on a penis-like projection to the left of the anus.

The left fourth arm of the male is modified to serve as a copulatory organ. A short distance from its tip the sucker cups are very small or absent, but the stalks are enlarged. During courtship, the male moves excitedly around the female, holds the copulatory arm in his mantle cavity against the male opening, and the stored spermatophores are ejaculated onto the specialized region. He then thrusts this arm toward the female, and either inserts it into her mantle cavity or presses it against the **sperm receptacle,** a horseshoe-shaped depression on the posterior side of the mouth. In either case the spermatophores are glued to the female.

The eggs are laid soon after. They are fertilized either in the mantle cavity or as they cross the sperm receptacle. The whole mass is gathered by the female in her arms, and after all the eggs are laid she finds a suitable place for attachment. The gelatinous matrix hardens slowly to form a protective coat, and young squids hatch in two or three weeks. Development in the cephalopods is direct, the yolky eggs producing young that resemble the adults.

14.12
Other Cephalopods

The nautiluses, with four gills, belong to the order **Tetrabranchiata,** which is presumed to include most of the fossil cephalopods. All other living cephalopods have two gills, and belong to the order **Dibranchiata.** In addition to the common squids and octopuses, the group includes the **cuttlefish** (Fig. 14.2), whose internal shell is used as a source of lime for canaries, and the deep-sea **giant squids.** The latter are the largest living invertebrates, having bodies at least 6 meters long with tentacles more than 10 meters long. They were first known from the marks of their suckers on the skin of the sperm whale, which were often several centimeters

Figure 14.17   A "small" relative of the giant squid, the oceanic squid, *Ommastrephes caroli.* This remarkably intact specimen was stranded. A meter ruler gives the scale. (Courtesy of Douglas P. Wilson.)

Figure 14.18 Octopus pursuing a crab. (Fritz Goro—Courtesy of LIFE Magazine. Cop. 1955 Time Inc.)

in diameter, and from their jaws in the whale's stomach. These squids are the major food of the sperm whale, which dives to great depths to hunt them. Rarely, a dying giant squid may come to the surface or be washed ashore (Fig. 14.17).

Octopuses (Fig. 14.18) lack the tentacles present in squids and cuttlefish. They also differ from the other Dibranchiata in having suckers that lack stalks and teeth, and in having no shell whatsoever.

Small octopuses survive well in aquariums, where observers are discovering that they have a surprisingly high order of intelligence. They are able to make associations among stimuli and, in general, show an adaptability of behavior that more closely resembles that of the vertebrates than the more stereotyped patterns of other invertebrates. Octopuses feed on crabs and other arthropods. They catch their prey and first kill it by a poisonous secretion from the salivary glands. Then all the flesh is delicately picked out, leaving the hard parts uneaten. Octopuses live among rocks, seeking shelter in small caves that they may partially excavate. The motion of octopuses is incredibly fluid, with no suggestion of the strength that lies in the eight arms. Their ferocity, however, has been overrated. Octopuses hide during the day and come out in the evening. They are by nature timid and flee from animals as large as man. The largest individuals, which may have arms 4 meters long, are certainly to be respected from a distance, but these are rare. Most octopuses have arms less than 30 cm. long.

SYNOPSIS OF MOLLUSKS

PHYLUM MOLLUSCA. With a ventral foot and dorsal shell. Coelom reduced, circulatory system with extensive sinuses.

CLASS 1. AMPHINEURA. Foot flattened, shell flat, in one to several pieces.
Order 1. Polyplacophora. Chitons. Shell a dorsal row of eight plates.
Order 2. Aplacophora. Shell reduced to buried spicules, body wormlike.
Order 3. Monoplacophora. Neopilina, shell a low conical plate.
CLASS 2. GASTROPODA. Snails. Foot broad and flat, shell single and usually coiled.
Subclass 1. Prosobranchia. Abalone, *Busycon.*

Subclass 2. Opisthobranchia.   Pteropods, nudibranchs.

Subclass 3. Pulmonata.   Garden snails, slugs.

CLASS 3. SCAPHOPODA.   Tooth shells. Foot conical, shell tubular. One order.

CLASS 4. PELECYPODA.   Foot spadelike, shell hinged dorsally with two lateral valves.

Order 1. Protobranchiata.   Gills plumose, palps large.

Order 2. Filibranchiata.   Marine mussels and scallops.

Order 3. Eulamellibranchiata.   Clams, oysters, fresh-water mussels.

Order 4. Septibranchiata.   Gills form horizontal partitions in mantle cavity.

CLASS 5. CEPHALOPODA.   Foot forms tentacles and siphon.

Subclass 1. Tetrabranchiata.   Four gills, chambered external shell, no suckers on tentacles.

Order 1. Nautiloidea.   The chambered nautilus.

†Order 2. Ammonoidea.   Ammonites. Partitions in shell wrinkled.

Subclass 2. Dibranchiata.   Two gills, shell internal or absent, arms with suckers.

†Order 1. Belemnoidea.   Belemnites. Shell straight, slender, heavy.

Order 2. Sepioidea.   Cuttlefish.

Order 3. Teuthoidea.   Loligo; deep-sea squids.

Order 4. Octopoda.   Octopuses.

---

† Extinct

QUESTIONS

1. Distinguish among the five classes of mollusks.
2. Compare the chiton with a generalized mollusk.
3. Describe the radula.
4. What is torsion?
5. Give examples of gastropods that (a) swim, (b) have no shell, (c) breathe air.
6. How does *Venus* feed?
7. Describe sexual phenomena in the oyster and the squid.
8. Why are the tentacles and siphon of the squid considered to be parts of the foot?
9. How does the squid sucker work?

ANNOTATED REFERENCES

(See Chapter 13 for general references. In addition, a variety of manuals are available for the identification and study of shells [conchology].)

Abbot, R. T.: American Seashells. Princteon, D. Von Nostrand Co., 1954. One of several good manuals for identifying shells written for the amateur conchologist. Abbot is a recognized authority on shells, and he discusses their biology and collection as well as the identification of the commoner species along our entire coast line.

Wilbur, K. M., and C. M. Young (Eds.): Physiology of Mollusca. New York, Academic Press, Vol. I, 1964; Vol II, 1966. This valuable source book, written by 27 of the world's authorities includes chapters on most aspects of the classification, ecology, physiology, and behavior of this large phylum.

15 _____ PHYLUM ANNELIDA

The **Annelida** are segmented worms, the body wall and coelom of which are divided into a longitudinal series of rings or **segments.** The epidermis, circular muscle, longitudinal muscle, coelom and peritoneum are all arranged in segments.

Some of the phyla considered previously have structures that look like segments. The tapeworms, for example, might be said to be segmented, with new segments forming in the scolex and the older segments moving to the posterior end as proglottids. Each segment of the tapeworm is eventually shed, however, and is only a temporary part of the body. Many rotifers and a few nematodes have a superficial segmentation, which involves only the cuticle and a part of the musculature. Most of the musculature of the kinorhynchs is segmented and their cuticle is deeply segmented. Young kinorhynchs have few segments, and add new ones at the posterior end as they grow. Most zoologists do not consider these animals to be truly segmented as are the annelids, arthropods and chordates.

15.1
General Features of the Annelid Worms

True segmented animals exhibit **metamerism,** a repetition of a structure or organ from segment to segment. The annelid body is made of a series of **metameres** or segments, each of which has the same fundamental structures as all the others. The nervous, circulatory, excretory and reproductive systems of the annelids are metameric in structure. In fact, only the digestive tract of annelids shows little or no metamerism. Thus,

segmentation is much more fully developed in the Annelida than in any of the other groups that have been considered. Young annelids usually have few segments, and add new segments as they grow by subdividing the terminal segment.

In annelids the mouth lies between the first and second segments, forming one preoral segment or **prostomium.** The brain originates in the prostomium, and develops a pair of **circumpharyngeal commissures** that reach around the pharynx to join the ventral cord, which appears as a chain of **ganglia,** one pair in each segment. The first segment behind the mouth is often different from the rest, and is called the **peristomium.** In counting segments, the prostomium is ignored, and the peristomium is counted as segment one.

Annelids are covered with a thin **cuticle** secreted by a simple epidermis. Each segment has a ring of circular muscle fibers that can constrict and thereby elongate the segment, and beneath this are several bands of longitudinal muscles that can produce shortening and thickening. Various oblique fibers may also be present. Between the body wall and the digestive tract is a spacious **coelom** divided by thin muscular **septa** between segments into a series of annular (ringlike) cavities. Each of these originates as a pair of lateral cavities lined with a delicate mesodermal **peritoneum.** The cavities become enlarged until they fill the segment, but the two peritoneal sacs remain intact, lining (1) the body wall on each side, (2) the septa before and behind, and (3) the digestive tract between them. Above and below the digestive tract the two membranes meet to form the **dorsal** and **ventral mesenteries.** These may persist in the adult, but in most species one or both later disappear.

15.2

Classification of the Annelids

Polychaetes. Most of the marine annelids have eyes, tentacles and palps on the prostomium, and lateral appendages on the body segments. The latter are flaps of the body wall, the **parapodia,** bearing tufts of many bristles, the **chaetae.** These annelids are placed in the class **Polychaeta** (Fig. 15.1).

Most polychaetes live near the shore and on the bottom of shallow seas. A few species live in brackish or fresh water. They are extremely diverse in their habits. Some live in tubes and filter water for microscopic food, while others scrape up the thin film of organic debris that settles on the bottom. Most members of the class are predaceous and have stout jaws or denticles on an eversible pharynx that can be used to grasp prey.

The sexes are separate and fertilization is external. Both eggs and sperm are shed through tubules that connect each coelomic cavity with the outside. In some species the segments producing gametes merely burst to release them. Typically, the eggs develop into planktonic larvae called **trochophores** that swim about and feed, eventually metamorphosing into worms and sinking to the bottom. In some, however, the eggs are heavily yolked and hatch directly into small worms.

Oligochaetes. Most of the fresh-water and terrestrial annelids belong to one of two other classes. Those that are wormlike and usually lack eyes or appendages on the prostomium belong to the class **Oligochaeta** (Fig. 15.1). Parapodia are also absent, but each segment bears small tufts of a few chaetae.

The oligochaetes include the large earthworms and smaller aquatic worms. Earthworms burrow in soil or leaf-mold, eating their way through the world, or they live in temporary burrows from which they emerge at night to feed on the surface of the ground. Aquatic worms burrow in mud or clamber on the vegetation, eating whatever debris they can find.

All oligochaetes are hermaphroditic. The testes are located in a few anterior segments, with the ovaries in a few following segments. Pairs copulate and the eggs are fertilized while they are on the outer surface of the parent. Development is direct.

Hirudinea. The other class of freshwater and terrestrial annelids, the **Hirudinea** (Fig. 15.1), includes the leeches or bloodsuckers, which have one large sucker surrounding the mouth and another at the posterior end of the body. Leeches share

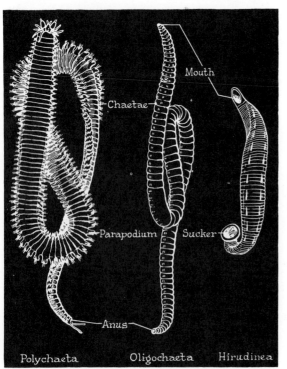

Figure 15.1 Classes of the phylum Annelida. Polychaeta: *Nereis virens,* the clamworm. Oligochaeta: *Lumbricus terrestris,* the earthworm. (After Lawson et al.) Hirudinea: *Hirudo medicinalis,* the medicinal leech. (After Hegner.)

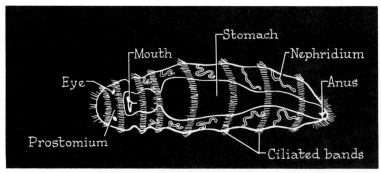

Figure 15.2 An example of the class Archiannelida. *Dinophilus*, a diminutive (0.5 to 2.0 mm. long) annelid that lacks external segmentation but has a metameric arrangement of body organs typical of the phylum. Most of the ventral surface is ciliated, and the animal has a superficial resemblance to a flatworm. (After Meyer.)

many characteristics with the oligochaetes, especially in their reproductive systems, but have no appendages or chaetae. A few oligochaetes are ectoparasitic and have a posterior sucker for attachment to the host. It is generally believed that the leeches evolved from the oligochaetes through such transitional forms. Years ago leeches were used in medical treatment.

Archiannelida. A few marine annelids are very small and reduced in their complexity, sometimes with no external segmentation, or no chaetae, or with the body surface covered with cilia instead of a cuticle. These were formerly thought to be primitive forms, indicating that the annelids evolved either from the flatworms or from trochophore-like ancestors, and they were placed in a fourth class, the **Archiannelida.** These worms are of particular interest as examples of simplification from a more complex ancestor. Of the several genera the most markedly simplified is *Dinophilus* (Fig. 15.2), which has only five or six segments and no chaetae or parapodia. Its general structure resembles that of some young polychaete larvae, and it is generally concluded that the archiannelids are "reduced" polychaetes. It is probable that the group includes genera that evolved independently from the polychaetes. At the present time the class is maintained as a matter of convenience and not because it is thought to have evolutionary significance in the origin of annelids.

15.3

Nereis and Lumbricus: Habitat and Habit

Several species of the polychaete genus *Nereis* are called clamworms (Fig. 15.1). The common east coast form, *N. virens*, is 10 to 15 cm. long and has a metallic green sheen on the body. On the west coast the common species is the somewhat smaller, metallic blue-green or brown *N. vexillosa*. They live in sand and gravel, constructing mucus-lined, semi-permanent tunnels from which they forage at dusk. Nereids are omnivorous, gobbling down plant and animal debris and whatever animals they can capture. The single pair of large **jaws** in the eversible pharynx are adapted for capture but not for chewing. Food is swallowed whole.

The many species of earthworms are difficult to distinguish. The common European earthworm, *Lumbricus terrestris* (Fig. 15.1), is now common in the United States also and is the favorite species for study. It remains in its burrow by day, coming out on damp nights when it can be collected easily. It is largely herbivorous, but acts as a scavenger, eating whatever organic debris is available.

These two representatives of the polychaetes and oligochaetes will be treated comparatively. In their gross appearance they are more similar than most polychaetes and oligochaetes, but in their detailed anatomy each is a good example of its class.

15.4

Nereis and Lumbricus: External Morphology

The **prostomium** of *Nereis* (Figs. 15.1 and 15.3) bears a pair of small tactile **tentacles** and a pair of stout **palps.** The palps are used for exploratory probing and their tips are very sensitive to touch and chemicals. On the dorsal surface of the prostomium are two pairs of black **eyes** lying directly over the

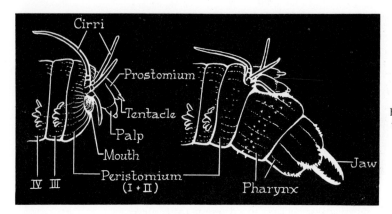

Figure 15.3 Lateral view of the head of *Nereis* with the pharynx withdrawn (left) and everted (right).

brain. Each eye is a cup of modified epidermal cells, the ends of which extend through a black **pigment layer** to form a retinal lining of light-sensitive **rods.** The cavity is filled with a **lens,** protruding from the cup as a spherical swelling covered by a transparent layer of skin, the **cornea.** The eyes are directed upward and outward, and are probably defensive in function, warning *Nereis* when a fish or other large predator approaches from above. Behind the eyes are a pair of small ciliated pits believed to function as chemoreceptors.

The prostomium of *Lumbricus* lacks special sense organs and appendages (Figs. 15.1 and 15.4). It is richly supplied with nerve endings for touch and chemoreception, and is used as a muscular probe in burrowing. Although *Lumbricus* lacks eyes it responds to light, generally moving away from it. Certain large epidermal cells scattered over the back and sides of the body have been shown to be sensitive to light.

The **peristomium** of *Nereis* is actually two segments fused together (Fig. 15.3). Four pairs of **tentacular cirri,** used as tactile organs, are located at its anterior margin. The uppermost are the longest, and they are longer in males than in females. The peristomium of *Lumbricus* lacks appendages.

The body may be divided into as many as 200 segments in *Nereis,* 180 in *Lumbricus.* Young worms have fewer segments and apparently new ones are added posteriorly throughout life. A middorsal line indicates the underlying dorsal blood vessel, and a midventral line indicates the position of the ventral nerve cord. These lines are faint in *Lumbricus.* Both species are more heavily pigmented above than below.

Every body segment of *Nereis* except the peristomium bears a pair of **parapodia,** each of which is divisible into a dorsal **notopodium** and ventral **neuropodium** (Fig. 15.5). Each portion has several lobes and bears a tuft of many chaetae. A slender, tactile **dorsal cirrus** projects up from the notopodium, and a **ventral cirrus** extends down from the base of the neuropodium. The upper lobes of the notopodia are large and richly vascularized, serving as **gills.** Internally, each tuft of chaetae clusters around a single stout **aciculum** to which numerous small muscles are attached. The chaetae and acicula are made of **chitin,** which resembles the material that forms the exoskeletons of arthropods.

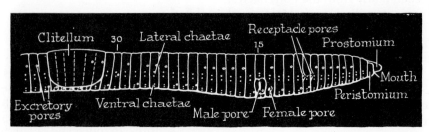

Figure 15.4 Lateral view of the anterior 40 segments of *Lumbricus.* Reproductive openings are found on segments 9, 10, 14 and 15. On each segment the excretory pore is either ventral, near the ventral chaetae, or lateral, above the lateral chaetae, with much variability between worms.

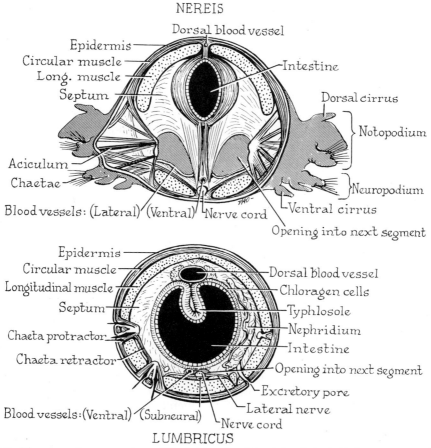

NEREIS

Dorsal blood vessel
Epidermis
Circular muscle
Long. muscle
Septum
Intestine
Dorsal cirrus
Notopodium
Aciculum
Chaetae
Neuropodium
Blood vessels: (Lateral) (Ventral) Nerve cord
Ventral cirrus
Opening into next segment

Epidermis
Circular muscle
Longitudinal muscle
Septum
Chaeta protractor
Chaeta retractor
Dorsal blood vessel
Chloragen cells
Typhlosole
Nephridium
Intestine
Opening into next segment
Excretory pore
Lateral nerve
Blood vessels: (Ventral) (Subneural)
Nerve cord

LUMBRICUS

Figure 15.5 Diagrammatic cross sections of *Nereis* (above) and *Lumbricus* (below). Each is a segment viewed from in front, with the septum behind. In *Nereis,* on the left side the body wall has been cut back to show the internal structure of the parapodium. In *Lumbricus* the body wall is cut at the level of the excretory pore on the right side, and further back at the level of the chaetae on the left side.

For walking, each parapodium is extended forward and downward, moved backward, withdrawn, then moved upward and forward again. In walking, the movements of the parapodia of each segment are slightly ahead of those on the next anterior segment, producing the appearance of waves of motion that pass forward along the sides.

In *Lumbricus* every body segment except the peristomium bears four pairs of **chaetae** (Fig. 15.5), each of which has small muscles that can move it out or in, and slant it forward or backward. The location of pairs corresponds with the location of the notopodia and neuropodia of the polychaete. These chaetae are used for gripping the sides of the burrow, to assist locomotion. They can be slanted forward or backward to help the worm resist being pulled from the burrow.

The anus is located on the terminal seg-

ment, which always remains the terminal segment as new segments are formed from its anterior edge. In *Nereis* the parapodia of this segment are reduced to a pair of **ventral cirri** which are longer than those of other segments and function as a pair of posterior tentacles (Fig. 15.1).

15.5

Nereis and Lumbricus: Body Wall

The body wall is made of the same layers in both species (Fig. 15.5). The epidermis of *Lumbricus* has more sensory cells than that of *Nereis,* a reflection, perhaps, of the lack of sense organs. The musculature is better developed in *Lumbricus.* In *Nereis* the circular layer thins out dorsally and ventrally, while in *Lumbricus* it remains relatively thick. The longitudinal muscles in *Nereis* are restricted to four bands, whereas in *Lumbricus* they form a nearly continuous layer. The two musculatures are, however, very similar in general plan.

The muscles are used differently in the two species. *Nereis* walks with its parapodia, but often assists them with lateral undulations of the body that pass as waves forward along the body. *Nereis* can also swim, and then these undulations simply become more vigorous. In its burrow *Nereis* circulates water by *vertical* undulations of the body, the waves passing *backward* along the body to draw water in from the front. All these sinuous movements involve the longitudinal muscles, which act alternately within a given segment, contracting first on one side and then on the other. The circular muscles are used to increase the length of the body and are used with the other muscles in digging.

Lumbricus crawls forward by extending the body, gripping the surface with its chaetae, and then shortening the body. As it moves, coordinated waves of extension and contraction pass posteriorly along the body. The pattern can be reversed so that the waves pass forward, in which case *Lumbricus* crawls backward. Movement in the burrow is similar but more efficient, since the entire circumference of the worm can be used for gripping. In all these movements the muscles of a given segment act together. All the longitudinal muscles, or all the circular muscles, contract at a given moment. Independent movement of the muscles on one side occurs only as the worm turns.

Movement depends upon the integrity of the body cavity, which functions as a hydrostatic mechanism. The total volume of the body fluid is held constant as the muscles contract and relax, and pressure is continually redistributed along the body as coelomic fluid passes slowly through septal openings between segments.

15.6

Nereis and Lumbricus: Nervous System

The large bilobed **brain** is in the prostomium of *Nereis*, but migrates posteriorly in the *Lumbricus* embryo to lie in the third segment. Many small nerves extend to all parts of the anterior end of the body. Paired **circumpharyngeal commissures** pass down around the anterior end of the pharynx to join the **subpharyngeal ganglion.** This is also bilobed; it is formed in *Nereis* by the ventral ganglia of the peristomium (two fused segments), and in *Lumbricus* by a fusion of the ganglia of the first three segments. The whole ventral nervous system arises as a pair of longitudinal cords, but these fuse together to make an apparently unpaired ventral cord. In each segment behind the peristomium the cord thickens to form a ganglion, from which nerves emerge to supply that segment. In most segments an additional pair of nerves passes forward to the body wall of the next anterior segment.

Locomotor activity, indeed all activities that pass in waves along the body, are coordinated locally by the ventral ganglia. A series of reflexes coordinates movements so that what happens in one segment will occur a moment later in the next. This coordination is achieved both by direct neural connections and by the tensions produced in one segment by movement in the adjoining one. The entire system is so constructed that an activity beginning at one end of the body will pass automatically along its length. Hence adding more segments does not noticeably increase the complexity of movement.

Annelids may respond to an alarm with a sudden violent shortening of the entire body. Both *Nereis* and *Lumbricus* keep the posterior end of the body in their burrows as they forage, and this sudden shortening is sufficient to pull the entire body back into the hole. Such a response cannot be handled by the usual ventral nervous system with its numerous ganglia and many synapses along the length of the body. Conduction is very slow in this system; an impulse requires as much as 10 seconds to travel the length of a worm 25 cm. long. For the alarm response annelids have **giant axons,** nerve fibers of large diameter that run the length of the ventral cord. *Nereis* has three central fibers and a pair of larger lateral fibers; *Lumbricus* has one very large central fiber and a pair of smaller laterals. The speed of conduction along a nerve fiber has been found to depend upon its diameter. These fibers are not only large, but some of them extend the full length of the body without synapses. Conduction along the giant fibers requires only a hundredth of a second to travel 25 cm. In the earthworm, T. H. Bullock has found that the median fiber, which is the fastest, is activated by sensory information from the first 40 segments of the body, whereas the lateral fibers respond to sensations from segments posterior to this.

Giant fibers are excellent material for physiologic research, and have been used extensively in studies of the nerve impulse. They are found in the mantle of the squid and in arthropods and certain other animals as well as in the annelids.

The brain and subpharyngeal ganglion govern the nervous system, initiating and controlling bodily activities. If the brain is removed the worm becomes *more active* than before, and moves about ceaselessly. This indicates that the brain functions in part as an inhibitory center. If the subpharyngeal ganglion is destroyed, all spontaneous activity stops, and the worm moves momentarily only if it is touched. This ganglion originates the impulses responsible for such activity. Separation of inhibitory and stimulatory centers in the central nervous system is typical of the coelomate phyla.

15.7
Nereis and Lumbricus:
Digestive System

The mouth opens into a muscular **pharynx** which occupies several segments. In *Nereis* muscles extending from the prostomium to the back of the pharynx can pull it forward, everting it through the mouth (Figs. 15.3 and 15.6). Muscles from the gut to the body wall several segments back can pull it in again. In the middle of the nereid pharynx are numerous small **denticles** and one pair of large **jaws.** The jaws lie open at the anterior limit of the everted pharynx. To attack prey the pharynx is everted by its muscles and by a constriction of the body until the jaws open. As the pharynx is retracted the jaws close scissorswise and the denticles grip the prey, dragging it back into the middle of the pharynx by the time it is fully withdrawn.

The pharynx in *Lumbricus* is more bulbous and is attached to the body wall by numerous radiating muscles (Fig. 15.6). When these muscles contract, the cavity of the pharynx is suddenly enlarged, producing suction at the mouth.

The pharynx leads to a tubular **esophagus** into which a pair of glandular **digestive pouches** open. These pouches apparently secrete digestive enzymes. In *Lumbricus* two pairs of **calciferous glands** open behind the pouches. Their function is not definitely known.

The rest of the digestive system in *Nereis*

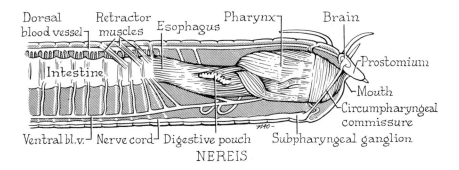

NEREIS

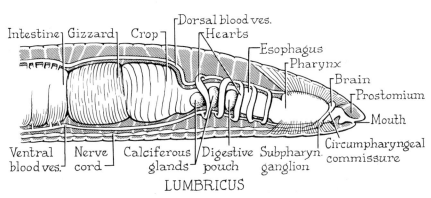

LUMBRICUS

Figure 15.6 Lateral views of *Nereis* (above) and *Lumbricus* (below) with the right body wall removed. The digestive, circulatory and nervous systems are shown.

is a simple long **intestine** ending at a short **rectum** in front of the anus. The diameter of the intestine is smallest in the middle of each segment and sharply expanded at each septum. The moderately muscular walls have a lining of simple gastrodermis, a layer of circular muscles, longitudinal muscles, and a covering peritoneum. During digestion food is moved posteriorly by peristaltic waves of contraction in the two muscle layers. The intestine is suspended in the coelom at each septum. The mesenteries have largely disappeared, remaining as bands of delicate muscle fibers dorsally and ventrally in the posterior part of each segment.

In *Lumbricus* the esophagus ends in an expanded storage chamber, the **crop.** Behind the crop a muscular **gizzard** mills the food to a fine pulp before it is passed on to the intestine, where it is digested. The intestinal wall has the same layers as that of *Nereis,* but with much thinner musculature. The intestinal diameter is greatest in the middle of each segment, with moderate constrictions at each septum. The intestine is infolded dorsally, forming externally a groove and internally a ridge, the **typhlosole** (Fig. 15.5), which increases the absorptive surface. The intestine terminates in a short rectum and anus. The peritoneum surrounding the intestine in *Lumbricus* is modified to form a glandular layer, the **chloragen cells.** These extract wastes from the blood, and later become detached and float in the coelom. Ultimately, much of their substance is engulfed by ameboid cells and carried to the skin, where it is deposited as pigment.

As in most animals, the mouth, pharynx and rectum are lined with an epidermis of ectodermal origin. In the annelids this epidermis secretes a cuticle which is continuous with that covering the body.

15.8
Nereis and Lumbricus:
Circulatory System

The annelid circulatory system is well developed. A system of large vessels pumps the blood through capillary beds that invade all the tissues. The blood is collected into a longitudinal **dorsal vessel** (Fig. 15.6) and distributed from a longitudinal **ventral vessel.** At the anterior end several pairs of commissures around the pharynx and esophagus

connect the two vessels. Waves of contraction force the blood forward through the dorsal vessel, down the commissures, and posteriorly through the ventral vessel. In *Nereis* the dorsal vessel is the most powerful pump, while in *Lumbricus* the commissures are enlarged and muscular, functioning as **"hearts."** Beneath the ventral vessel small longitudinal vessels parallel the nerve cord and carry blood posteriorly.

The system includes three major capillary beds. One of these lies in the intestinal wall and has connecting vessels in every body segment with the ventral and dorsal vessels. Blood passing upward through these capillaries picks up nutrients. Another lies in the body wall and is especially well developed just beneath the epidermis. Paired vessels in each segment bring blood from the ventral vessel, and paired lateral vessels carry it away to the dorsal vessel. Blood passing through these capillaries is oxygenated (especially that passing through the parapodia of *Nereis*). The third capillary bed lies in the glandular regions of the nephridia. Paired vessels bring blood from the ventral vessel, and it continues through the same lateral vessels that serve the body wall. Waste is removed from blood passing through these capillaries. Direct connectives from the ventral to the dorsal vessels also occur, so that not all the blood is forced to flow through capillaries. These are more prominent in *Nereis* than in *Lumbricus*. All the blood is mixed together in each segment in the dorsal vessel.

The blood contains hemoglobin dissolved in the plasma. In *Lumbricus* it aids in respiration (p. 83). In *Nereis* such evidence is lacking, and it is thought that oxyhemoglobin may serve primarily as a reservoir while the worm is burrowing.

The major advance of the annelid system over that of the nemerteans is the addition of the capillary networks, a much more finely branched system which is an efficient mechanism for distribution.

15.9
Nereis and Lumbricus:
Excretory System

Each segment except the first and last contains a pair of metanephridia, convoluted tubules lying in a vascularized, glandular mass of tissue. The mass lies at the base of each neuropodium in *Nereis* and against the anterior septum in *Lumbricus*. From each nephridium the tubule extends forward through the septum to open as a ciliated **funnel** in the coelom of the next anterior segment. The other end of the tubule opens to the exterior at the minute **excretory pore.**

The funnel collects coelomic fluid, including some debris from the chloragen cells, and passes it down the tubule. Along the way the fluid is modified so that only waste remains in the portion excreted. In *Lumbricus* a terminal expansion of the tubule forms a **bladder.**

15.10

Nereis and Lumbricus: Reproduction

The reproductive systems of polychaetes and oligochaetes are very different. Gonads appear in *Nereis* only during the breeding season, developing from the peritoneum lining the ventral body wall in many of the segments. Eggs or sperm accumulate in the coelomic cavities and are eventually shed through temporary ruptures of the body wall. Fertilization is left to chance in the open sea water.

In some species of *Nereis*, and in many other polychaetes, the gonads appear in the posterior half of the body, which becomes considerably modified as the gametes accumulate. The parapodia develop foliaceous outgrowths and the chaetae become larger and often flattened. The eyes may become temporarily enlarged. On the night of breeding the individuals leave their borrows and swim to the surface, the enlarged parapodia serving not only as better oars but as better gills for increased activity. After the body wall ruptures and the gametes are shed, the worms settle to the bottom again and recover their former morphology and habits.

Reproduction in *Lumbricus* is considerably more complex (Figs. 15.4 and 15.7). Segments 10 and 11 each contain a pair of **testes** in isolated median cavities of the coelom, the **testis sacs.** These two sacs have three pairs of prominent lateral pouches, the **seminal vesicles,** that extend into the ninth, tenth and eleventh segments. Sperm elaborated in the testes are shed into the sacs and vesicles, where they mature and are stored in large numbers. From the sacs two pairs of **sperm funnels** collect sperm and pass them posteriorly through a pair of **sperm ducts** to the **male pores** on the ventral side of the fifteenth segment.

The single pair of minute ovaries are in the thirteenth segment, where eggs are shed into the coelomic cavity. At oviposition the eggs are collected by a pair of **egg funnels** and passed through short **oviducts** to the ventral **female pores** on the fourteenth segment. Two pairs of **seminal receptacles** in the ninth and tenth segments open laterally at the posterior septa. Sperm received during copulation are stored here.

The female system also includes a **clitellum,** a swollen glandular region of the epidermis (segments 32–37). During copulation two worms facing in opposite directions press their ventral surfaces together so that the clitellum of one is opposite segment 10 of the other (Fig. 15.8). The chaetae of one may pierce the body wall of the other, and they are also glued together by thick mucous secretions of the clitellum and skin. These secretions form grooves between the worms so that sperm extruded on the fifteenth segment pass posteriorly along the mucus to the level of the clitellum, where they enter the seminal receptacles of the other worm.

Soon after copulation the clitellum secretes a membranous **cocoon** and beneath this an albuminous secretion. The worm may then lay several eggs that pass back into the cocoon, or the cocoon may slip forward along the

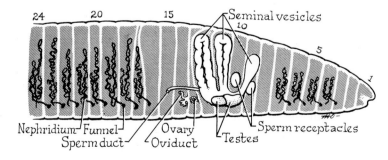

Figure 15.7 Lateral view of *Lumbricus* (see Fig. 15.6) with many of the viscera removed. Reproductive and excretory systems are shown. The testes lie inside the sperm reservoirs. Compare with Figure 15.4 for the external openings.

Figure 15.8 Two earthworms copulating. (Photograph of living animals made at night, courtesy of General Biological Supply, Chicago, Ill.)

body so that the eggs are laid directly into it as it passes. The cocoon is then moved forward (or the worm slips backward) and the eggs are fertilized as they pass the sperm receptacles. Finally, the cocoon is slipped off the head, and the openings in it constrict to produce a spindle-shaped capsule. The eggs develop into tiny worms which later emerge from the cocoon. This complex reproductive pattern is an adaptation to terrestrial or freshwater environments.

15.11
Reproductive Periodicity and Palolo Worms

External fertilization like that of the polychaetes is usually accompanied by a coordinating behavioral mechanism that will ensure fertilization. Many such organisms respond to rhythms in the environment to achieve this coordination. In the oceans three such rhythms are dominant. Seasonal cycles produce variations in temperature, length of day and food. Lunar cycles produce variations in the height of tides, strength of currents, the relation between tide and the hour of the day, and the amount of night light. Diurnal cycles produce the obvious great variation in light from day to night. Several species of *Nereis*

use all three of these rhythms to achieve reproductive periodicity.

In a common Atlantic nereid (*Platynereis*) the adults become sexually mature only in the summer months, some individuals breeding several times in one season. During this season they reach sexual maturity only during the second and third weeks after the new moon, possibly because during this time the moon is bright and shines much of the night, providing the dim light in which nereids will feed. The actual moment of breeding depends upon the diurnal cycle. They will breed only after dark, but only if the moon is not yet risen. Thus, worms reaching maturity during the second week will not breed unless the night is cloudy, and usually are forced to wait some time. In the third week, after the full moon, a period of darkness separates sunset and moonrise, and nightly during this period of darkness large numbers of nereids swarm to the surface to breed. By compressing the shedding of gametes into this hour or so in the third week of each lunar month, enough worms breed at the same time to guarantee fertilization of the eggs. Other nereids have different lunar cycles.

Other worms may use the same external rhythms but respond differently to them and thus have different behavioral rhythms. A remarkable example of periodic reproduction is found in the **Palolo worms,** a species of polychaete living on coral reefs in the south Pacific. Over 90 per cent of the population breeds within a single two-hour period of the entire year. The seasonal rhythm limits the reproductive period to about a month, the lunar rhythm to a day, and the diurnal rhythm to a couple of hours after complete darkness. The major swarm occurs in November during the last quarter of the moon when the low tide is unusually low. This is the spring rainy season in this region. A smaller swarm usually occurs four weeks earlier, at the previous neap tide, and a different species of annelid always swarms the night before the Palolo.

The posterior half of the Palolo worm not only becomes different from the anterior half, but actually breaks off. On the night of breeding, individuals back out of their holes and the posterior half twists counterclockwise until it breaks free. It then swims backward to the surface. Each segment has a pair of eyes beneath the parapodia, so that broken pieces will still swim appropriately. After swimming at the surface for a few minutes they burst, shedding eggs or sperm and leaving a rapidly disintegrating body.

These posterior halves packed with gametes are frantically collected in dip nets by the island natives during the brief period when they are available. They are made into a thick soup said to taste like spinach. The natives have learned to predict when the Palolo will swarm and lookouts camp on the shores at the right season to watch the water daily. When the water is suddenly full of spume and debris, apparently because extreme tides produce severe wave action on the reefs, swarming will follow in two days.

Reproductive periodicities are found in many other animals. The oysters described earlier are also coordinated by the integration of seasonal and lunar rhythms, and several arthropods and fishes follow tidal cycles in their behavior. A Bermudan annelid that swarms in a fashion similar to that of the Palolo is also luminescent. Females swim along a straight path as males gyrate around them, both flashing brightly.

15.12
Earthworms and the Soil

Although earthworms usually forage on the surface from temporary burrows, they also dig extensively, as much as 30 to 60 cm. beneath the surface. Much of the dirt is eaten and later deposited on the surface as castings. They also pick up debris while foraging and carry it below the ground and, at dawn, may pull sticks and leaves into their burrows for concealment.

Darwin noted the abundance of earthworms in fields and estimated that there are some 64,000 earthworms per acre. He then speculated on the effect that so many worms would have, and concluded that they are possibly the most important organism influencing the soil. According to his calculations, earthworms will bring to the surface a layer of dirt 5 cm. thick every 10 years. This not only mixes the soil, but slowly buries rocks and other large objects. While such claims are now challenged, it cannot be doubted that earthworms are an important agent in the conditioning of soil. Their burrows help to aerate the soil and permit water to enter easily during rain. The constant mixing of soil and organic debris contributes to the development of good humus.

15.13
Other Annelid Worms

One of the largest annelids (40 cm. or more long) is the **lugworm,** a polychaete that burrows in muddy sand at the level of low tide. The pharynx is everted into the sand and then withdrawn with its load. Organic debris in the sand serves as food which is removed as the sand passes through the digestive tract. Although the body is long and thick, it is composed of relatively few segments. The parapodia are variously modified, and they are missing from the first two and the last several segments. The notopodia and neuropodia are separated widely. The last several notopodia bear feathery gills.

The small polychaete *Hydroides* builds twisted calcareous tubes on shells and rocks. The prostomium bears a pair of large ciliated feathery "gills" that are not only respiratory, but also serve as a device for catching food particles.

Some fresh-water oligochaetes have more chaetae than the earthworm, but otherwise they tend to have simplified organ systems. *Tubifex* is a small red worm that lives in the mud beneath standing or running water. Large numbers often form red patches. Each worm lives head down, foraging deeply for food, while the posterior end is waved cease-lessly above the mud for respiration. The amount of worm projecting from the mud re-flects inversely the amount of oxygen dis-solved in the water.

Aeolosoma is a microscopic oligochaete 1 to 5 mm. long. The body wall contains numerous red, yellow and green globules that give it a clownlike appearance. It clambers about on fresh-water vegetation, gathering minute de-bris with its ciliated prostomium.

A number of worms can reproduce asexu-ally like the planarians. New individuals are budded posteriorly, usually forming the head before detachment. The polychaete *Autolytus* may have several offspring budding at one time. Many of the fresh-water oligochaetes, including *Aeolosoma,* reproduce in this way.

15.14

Class Hirudinea

Bloodsuckers are annelids modified for an ectoparasitic existence. The body is stout and bears a large, powerful sucker on each end for attachment to the host. They creep by moving the posterior sucker up close to the anterior one and then stretching the anterior sucker forward. They also swim well by verti-cal undulations of the flattened body. Their powerful suction is known to anyone who has tried to pull a leech off his skin. Most leeches live in fresh water, feeding on fish, amphibi-ans and other animals. In the absence of blooded prey most leeches can subsist in-definitely on small worms and arthropods, which they capture and swallow whole. Once leeches find blood, however, they take enough to last for weeks.

The suckers are not used for sucking blood but only for attachment. In the mouth are three cutting teeth that make a Y-shaped in-cision in the skin. Numerous small **salivary glands** around the mouth secrete a substance that prevents the coagulation of blood. This substance, **hirudin,** is commercially extracted from leeches and used medicinally when anti-coagulants are indicated. Once assured of a continuing flow of blood, the leech sucks with a powerful **pharynx** built like that of the earthworm with radiating muscles to the body wall. The esophagus, which in the earthworm forms a modest crop, in the leeches is ex-panded into an enormous, branched **crop** that fills much of the body and which can be greatly distended. Blood is stored here dur-ing feeding, and over the following weeks trickles slowly into the small **stomach** and on into the **intestine** that ends in a short **rectum** and **anus.**

The other organ systems are similar to those already described for *Nereis* and *Lum-bricus,* except that the coelom is secondarily reduced by the invasion of loose connective tissue to a series of sinuses that become con-nected with the circulatory system. The circu-latory system includes longitudinal vessels and networks of capillaries, but the capillaries of the skin, containing oxygenated blood, drain into the sinuses. These sinuses parallel the digestive tract and the ventral nerve cord.

The body is composed of a fixed number of segments (36 in the large medicinal leech), each of which is superficially subdivided into several rings, giving the external appearance of many more segments.

The male reproductive system, comparable to that of the oligochaetes terminates at a single median duct that opens on the eleventh segment through a curved, muscular, eversi-ble **penis.** Seminal receptacles are absent from the female system. The oviducts termi-nate at a single median duct that opens on the twelfth segment as a **vagina.** Mutual cross fertilization is followed by the secretion of a cocoon (by the ninth to eleventh segments) into which eggs, sperm and albuminous fluid are placed. The cocoon is slipped off the head and attached to a rock. The fertilized eggs de-velop into tiny leeches which eventually hatch from the cocoon. Some of the larger leeches attach the cocoons to the ventral surface of the body, and after the young emerge they re-main attached to the parent for some time.

In moist tropical forests leeches are ter-restrial. They climb up the vegetation and stand with the posterior sucker attached and the anterior end held over a pathway, waiting for some mammal to go by. They sometimes occur in such numbers as to pose a serious threat to animals because of the amount of blood they can remove in a short time.

15.15

The Relationships of Annelids, Mollusks and Arthropods

Adult annelids and mollusks differ mark-edly in appearance (compare Figs. 14.2 and 15.1). Even if diagrammatic representations of the phyla are compared (Fig. 15.9*A* and *C*), they have little in common. The annelid coelom is spacious (Fig. 15.9*B*), whereas that of the mollusks is small. The annelid "heart" is not a distinct organ; it includes the dorsal blood vessel and often other vessels, whereas the molluscan heart is compact. The annelid circulatory system is closed; that of the mollusks includes extensive sinuses. Their nephridia, though basically similar, are as different from each other as from the nephridia of many other coelomate groups. The dorsal shell and ventral foot of the mollusks have no counterpart in the elongate, annulated annelid. In short, a comparative study of adult structures yields little evidence that these phyla are at all related.

A comparison of annelid and arthropod morphology yields quite different results. Although the arthropods will be described in the next chapter, it is convenient to indicate some of their general features here. An extremely diagrammatic representation of an arthropod (Fig. 15.9*D*) shows many structures in common with the annelids. In both phyla the body is segmented, and each segment usually has a single pair of appendages. Many arthropods have a long, tubular dorsal heart that is more like that of the annelids than is the molluscan heart. Annelids and arthropods both have a ventral chain of nerve ganglia with metameric, lateral nerves to the body segments. Several basic differences also exist, of course. Arthropods have a chitinous exoskeleton and jointed appendages, their circulatory system is completely open, and the

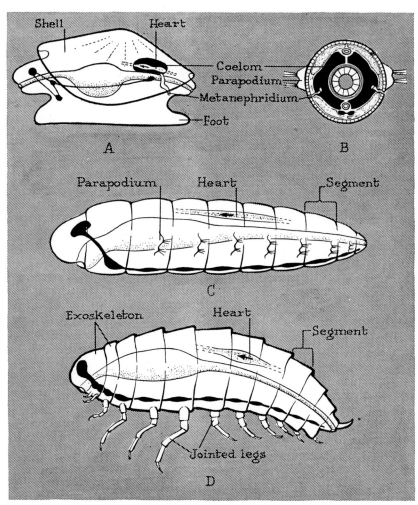

Figure 15.9 Diagrammatic representations of the Mollusca (*A*), Annelida (*C*), and Arthropoda (*D*), including a cross section of an annelid (*B*).

body cavity is a hemocoel rather than a coelom. The similarities are such, however, as to suggest a close relationship between the two phyla.

If the early development of these three phyla is compared, it is found that both the annelids and the mollusks have spiral cleavage, whereas the arthropods (almost all of which have heavily yolked eggs) do not. Gastrulation is similar in the annelids and mollusks, and further development in many species of both phyla results in a free-swimming larva, the **trochophore** (Fig. 15.10*A*). Although the structure of the trochophore varies considerably from species to species in both phyla, no characteristic will completely separate those of the Annelida from those of the Mollusca. Hence, development from the egg through the trochophore is strikingly similar in these two phyla. Arthropods do not have larvae of this type; all arthropod larvae, even in their youngest stages, have jointed legs and other characteristics that readily identify them as arthropods.

The later development of the annelids and mollusks is quite different. Molluscan trochophores develop a foot and a shell gland and become **veligers** (Fig. 14.4). By further metamorphosis the veliger is transformed gradually into the adult form. The general relation between the trochophore anatomy and that of the the adult is indicated by diagrams (Fig. 15.10*B*) that for the sake of clarity do not indicate the actual course of development for a mollusk but do indicate general body relationships. Annelid trochophores develop directly into the adult form (Fig. 15.10*C*). In both phyla the upper half of the trochophore becomes only the extreme anterior end of the body, and most of the adult body develops from the lower half. In both phyla the brain develops by ingrowths of ectoderm from the upper half of the trochophore, and the other ganglia develop from ventral ectoderm. Many mollusks do not hatch until they have developed to the veliger stage, and others hatch with the adult morphology. Trochophores occur, however, in all of the classes

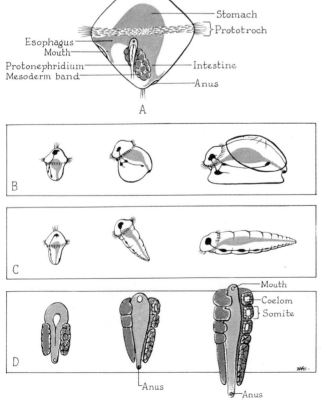

Figure 15.10 Development in annelids and mollusks. *A*, A typical trochophore. *B*, Diagrammatic representations of the development of a mollusk from a trochophore. *C*, The same for an annelid. *D*, Ventral views of the gut and mesoderm bands of an annelid from the trochophore stage (left) through the formation of a few anterior segments.

except the Cephalopoda. Many annelids do not hatch until later stages of development, and then emerge as small worms. Trochophores are found only in marine annelids, the Polychaeta and the Archiannelida.

A comparison of later development in the annelids and arthropods indicates that the similarities of adult structure are associated with similarities in development. In the annelids the mesoderm, which remains as a pair of bands in the trochophore, elongates and becomes divided into pairs of **somites** (Fig. 15.10D). Within each somite a coelomic cavity appears. The somites of each pair expand dorsally and ventrally around the gut, eventually forming a ring with dorsal and ventral mesenteries. To complete the process of segmentation the body wall constricts between adjacent rings. The body elongates during this process, and segmentation begins at the anterior end. In arthropods the mesoderm follows a similar pattern of development, starting as a pair of longitudinal bands that become divided into somites, with coelomic cavities appearing in each somite. Later the cavities disappear, but the somites correspond with the segments of the adult body. In both phyla the ventral nerve cord arises from the midventral line as a pair of longitudinal cords that later become metameric. In both phyla the paired nature of the ventral cord often disappears by fusion, producing a single adult nerve cord.

Thus, the early development of these forms indicates a close relation between annelids and mollusks, whereas later development and adult morphology indicates a close relation between annelids and arthropods. Hence, the three phyla are considered to form a natural group within the eucoelomates.

15.16
The Trochophore Larva

The trochophore larva has been the subject of a considerable amount of embryologic research. In a given species the cleavage pattern from egg to trochophore tends to follow an exact pattern (which is somewhat less exact in those with much yolk). This pattern is termed a **cell lineage.** The cell lineages of some of the invertebrates have been described previously (p. 203). These patterns differ in detail from species to species but are similar in many general features. A comparison of cell lineages in annelids and mollusks reveals that the patterns of development are as similar as the results; i.e., the trochophores not only look alike but also develop in similar ways.

The trochophore is biconical, with a ring of cilia, the **prototroch,** around the equator (Fig. 15.10A). At the upper apex there is usually a sensory **apical organ** bearing a tuft of cilia. Brain rudiments are usually evident beneath the apical organ. The **mouth** is just beneath the prototroch and the **anus** is near the lower apex. Often (especially if yolk is plentiful) the digestive tract is less well developed than shown here; an intestine and anus may be lacking at this stage of development. The mesoderm is a pair of undifferentiated masses in the lower cone, lying beside a pair of protonephridia that develop from the ectoderm. At this early stage of development the trochophore lacks a coelom; its body is composed primarily of an outer ectoderm, with ectodermal derivatives such as nervous tissue and scattered ectomesodermal elements, and an inner endoderm forming a gut.

If cell lineage is followed from the 16-cell stage to the trochophore (Fig. 15.11) in a number of species, it is found that, in general, the upper cone and prototroch develop from the first quartette (upper eight cells). Of these the upper four cells become the apical organ and most of the cone surface, and the lower four cells become the prototroch and the lower part of the upper cone surface. Most of the surface of the lower cone is derived from the second quartette (middle four cells). The four large cells become a part of the ectoderm between the mouth and anus (this portion is formed by the cells of the third quartette, which separate from the large cells at the next division), and all of the mesoderm and endoderm. The mesoderm develops from one of these cells while the endoderm comes mostly from the other three. This general pattern of development is found in both the annelids and the mollusks.

An interesting problem in embryology is whether or not particular cells are able to develop into structures other than those they become in *normal* development. You will recall (p. 174) that isolated coelenterate embryo parts usually become *whole* organisms, whereas isolated parts of the ctenophore embryo become only *portions* of adults. The annelid-mollusk trochophore is a classic example of the second type, in which development is a mosaic. Each piece is able when isolated to

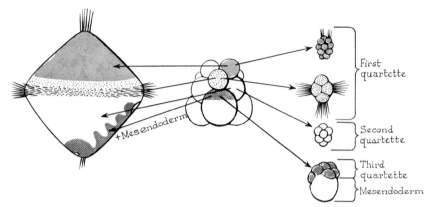

Figure 15.11 Development of the trochophore. The contribution of each tier of four cells in the 16-cell stage (center) to the trochophore (left) is shown. The wavy boundary between the ectoderm of the second and third quartettes is intended to show interdigitation between these components and a degree of variability. When the cells of the 16-cell stage are isolated, each produces a structure of the kind shown at the right (four of each kind, 16 in all). (Drawings on the right are after Costello.)

produce only those structures that it produces under normal conditions.

E. B. Wilson, a pioneer in experimental embryology, separated the cells of a cleaving mollusk egg in 1904 and found that each cell gave rise to only a portion of a trochophore. In 1945 D. P. Costello did the same with an annelid egg (Fig. 15.11, right). In his experiments Costello separated the cells of the two-cell stage as soon as they formed, and continued to separate cells as cleavage occurred until he had 16 cells in 16 separate dishes. Thus, none of the cells had any opportunity to influence any of the others. The 16 cells were then allowed to develop, without further separation of cells. Sixteen groups of cells, four of each of the varieties shown, resulted. Four dishes each had a cluster of small cells, some of which had cilia similar to those of the apical organ. Another four dishes each had a cluster of four large cells, three of which had cilia like those of the prototroch. In the trochophore of the species Costello studied, the prototroch is formed by a circle of 12 large cells, and just above the prototroch are four more large cells. Thus it appears that the isolated cells formed exactly the number and kinds of cells they form in the normal larva. Another four dishes each contained a cluster of small cells which were identified as the progeny of the second quartette. The four

large cells of the 16-cell stage each became a single large cell with a cluster of small cells. In each case the small cells were spread out over the surface of the large cell, suggesting the only attempts at gastrulation found in the 16 isolates. From this observation Costello concluded that the macromeres are necessary for gastrulation and that none of the other cells are able to produce mesoderm or endoderm.

The work of Wilson, Costello and many others leads to the same general conclusions: In the early development of annelids and mollusks the abilities of the parts of the embryos are limited to the functions they serve in normal development (with a few exceptions in which some portions are able to form a few additional structures). Such development is called determinate or mosaic. A second and equally significant conclusion is that in some cases these abilities can be realized in isolation, without interaction among the parts. Examples are the cilia of the apical organ and of the prototroch that developed in Costello's isolates. It should be added that the development of other structures appears to require the integrity of the embryo, since the macromeres in Costello's experiments showed no tendencies to form mesoderm bands or digestive tract, and none of the ectomesodermal structures appeared in any of his isolates.

SYNOPSIS OF ANNELIDS

PHYLUM ANNELIDA. Segmented worms with a large coelom and a closed circulatory system. Protostomous.

CLASS 1. POLYCHAETA. With parapodia and numerous chaetae.
Order 1. Errantia. Nereis, Autolytus, Palolo worm.
Order 2. Sedentaria. Hydroides, lugworm.

CLASS 2. ARCHIANNELIDA. Small marine annelids with simplified body. Once thought to be ancestral to other annelids, now believed to have come from the polychaetes. One order.

CLASS 3. OLIGOCHAETA. Parapodia absent, chaetae few per segment. One order. *Lumbricus, Tubifex, Aeolosoma.*

CLASS 4. HIRUDINEA. Leeches. Parapodia and chaetae absent. With suckers.
Order 1. Rhynchobdellida. No jaws, pharynx eversible, blood colorless.
Order 2. Gnathobdellida. Three jaws, blood red. *Hirudo.*

QUESTIONS

1. Discuss segmentation in the animal kingdom.
2. Draw cross sections of a polychaete and an oligochaete.
3. Compare the sense organs of *Nereis* and *Lumbricus.*
4. Describe a parapodium.
5. Discuss the role of giant axons in annelids.
6. How can a population achieve reproductive coordination so that all individuals breed at one time in the year?
7. How do leeches feed?
8. Compare reproduction in *Nereis, Lumbricus* and a leech.
9. Draw and label a trochophore.

ANNOTATED REFERENCES

(See Chapter 13 for general references.)

Laverack, M. S.: The Physiology of Earthworms. New York, Macmillan, 1963. Major advances in annelid physiology are reviewed.

Willier, B. H., P. A. Weiss, and V. Hamburger: Analysis of Development. Philadelphia, W. B. Saunders Co., 1955. Includes a discussion of the development of the trochophore and other larval forms.

16

PHYLUM ARTHROPODA

Arthropods are segmented animals whose epidermis secretes an exoskeleton of stout rings corresponding with the segments; the rings are connected by flexible membranes that act as joints. Many of the segments bear paired lateral appendages, each of which has a similar chitinous skeleton of jointed rings. The phylum takes its name from these jointed appendages (Gr. *arthron* joint + *podos* foot). The exoskeleton is a chemical complex which includes **chitin,** a nitrogenous polysaccharide made of hexoses, some of which contain amino or acetyl groups. The body includes a **head, thorax** and **abdomen,** each composed of several segments which may be fused in various ways. The body musculature is made up of numerous small muscles extending across joints to form an intricate mechanism capable of precise complex movements.

The evolutionary potentialities of such a structural system would appear to be tremendous. The exoskeleton not only forms a protective cover that has been successful in all the habitats of the world, but its division into numerous parts makes possible many different morphologic adaptations to particular habitats. For example, the mouth parts of an insect may be modified for biting, chewing, scraping or sucking. The specialization of the skeletal parts of many arthropods has adapted them beautifully for some particular habitat; they are so precisely adapted, in fact, that they are severely limited in their ecologic distribution. This may explain the enormous number of species of arthropods, for many species can coexist in the same geographic region if each has different ecologic requirements. At the present time, the known species of all other phyla add up to about 130,000,

while those of the arthropods alone add up to 870,000! The majority (800,000) of these are insects, most of which are terrestrial.

16.1
Classification of the Arthropods

Arthropods can be divided into four subphyla according to the structures of the appendages of the first six segments. In all arthropods the first segment, believed to correspond with the annelid prostomium, appears in the embryo but is never distinct in the adult. It never has appendages. In most arthropods the mouth opens ventrally between the third and fourth segments.

The four subphyla are the **Trilobita, Chelicerata, Crustacea** and **Labiata** (Fig. 16.1). The first includes only one class, Trilobita, now extinct. The trilobites (Fig. 16.2) were marine bottom scavengers with the skeleton extended laterally to form a three-lobed shield. The second segment bore a pair of **antennae** and all remaining segments bore **biramous** (two-branched) limbs. The inner branch or ramus of each limb was used for walking while the outer ramus apparently served as a gill. The single base of each limb was enlarged medially as a toothed jaw or **gnathobase.** Debris was chewed by this long row of gnathobases as it was passed forward to the mouth. The abundance of their fossils suggests that trilobites were dominant organisms of the Cambrian period, over 500 million years ago. During the rest of the Paleozoic era they were gradually replaced by the Crustacea and became extinct 225 million years ago.

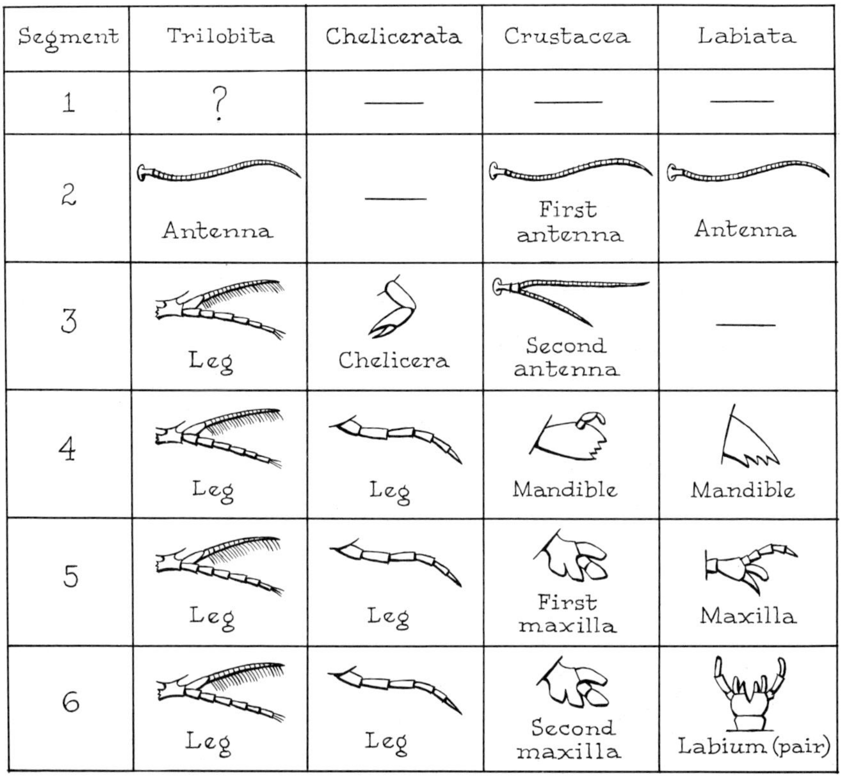

Segment	Trilobita	Chelicerata	Crustacea	Labiata
1	?	——	——	——
2	Antenna	——	First antenna	Antenna
3	Leg	Chelicera	Second antenna	——
4	Leg	Leg	Mandible	Mandible
5	Leg	Leg	First maxilla	Maxilla
6	Leg	Leg	Second maxilla	Labium (pair)

Figure 16.1 Appendages of the first six segments in the four subphyla of the Arthropoda. Except for the labium (lower right) only one member of a pair is shown. The chelicera illustrates a chelate appendage, in which the next to last segment is prolonged as a hand against which the last segment closes as a thumb.

The subphylum **Chelicerata** includes a variety of both living and extinct groups such as horseshoe crabs, eurypterids, scorpions, spiders and mites. In these forms the second segment has no appendages. Those of the third are **chelate** (tipped with pincers) (Fig. 16.1). This particular pair of chelate appendages is small, located in front of the mouth, and called the **chelicerae.** The first three pairs of appendages behind the mouth usually serve together with others as walking legs, but they are sometimes modified as grasping or tactile limbs. While the posterior limbs are usually biramous, the anterior limbs are always uniramous. Most of the living species are carnivores, although horseshoe crabs are scavengers and many mites are herbivorous.

The subphylum **Crustacea** includes the single class Crustacea, the dominant living aquatic arthropods (Fig. 16.2). The second and third segments each have a pair of **antennae.** The first pair of postoral appendages are short, stout **mandibles,** or jaws. The appendages of the fifth and sixth segments are **maxillae,** modified to aid the jaws by holding and manipulating the food. Many of these appendages are biramous. Crustaceans have invaded a variety of aquatic habitats; some crawl over the bottom while others swim or drift with the current. Many of the species are extremely abundant. The crustaceans as a group probably comprise a larger mass of living material than any other single class of animals.

The fourth subphylum, **Labiata,** includes millipedes, centipedes and insects. Their second segment has antennae and the third segment lacks appendages. The fourth has mandibles, the fifth has maxillae and, on the sixth, appendages comparable to maxillae are fused together to form a lower lip, the **labium,** from which the subphylum takes its name. All the appendages are uniramous. This group apparently arose on land, although so many insects have developed aquatic young that labiates now challenge the supremacy of crustaceans among fresh-water arthropods.

A fragmentary record of the appearance and spread of these subphyla is shown by

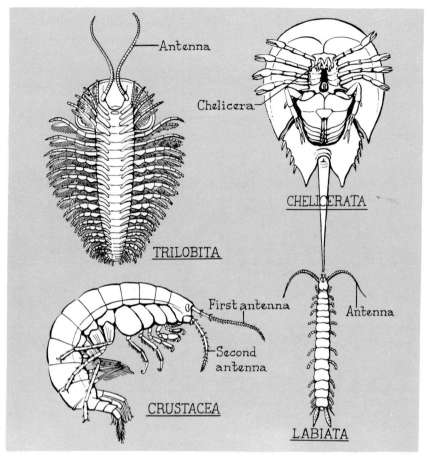

Figure 16.2   Representatives of the four subphyla of the Arthropoda. (After Parker and Haswell.)

their fossils. At the beginning of the fossil record, 585 million years ago, Cambrian seas already contained numerous species of trilobites. Within 60 million years, before the end of the Cambrian period, the seas also contained chelicerates and crustaceans. Trilobites never left the ocean, but chelicerates appeared in fresh water by the Ordovician period (505 million years ago), and crustaceans followed by the Devonian (375 million years ago). Certain chelicerates (scorpions) became terrestrial by the Silurian (425 million years ago), leaving for us the oldest known terrestrial fossils. The labiates appeared as a terrestrial group during the coal age (Pennsylvanian period, 275 million years ago). Among the earliest of these are winged insects, indicating that the air had already been conquered 50 million years before flying reptiles and 110 million years before birds appeared. Terrestrial crustaceans exist today, but all of their known fossils are of recent

origin. Thus terrestrialism developed independently at least three times within the phylum. The insects now form a dominant terrestrial group, their myriad species scattered from the arctic to the equator, from the swamps to the deserts.

There is no general agreement on the origin of labiates. It is equally difficult to derive them from trilobites, crustaceans or an unknown pre-arthropod stock. Their embryology shows no trace of a biramous limb pattern, nor any evidence of an aquatic ancestry.

The phylum can be subdivided in other ways. Subphyla may be omitted, and the phylum is then divided into several or more classes. The trilobites and chelicerates may be placed in one subphylum. The trilobites have also been grouped with the crustaceans, and it is not uncommon to find all the antennate groups in one subphylum. The arrangement used here is a combination of views current in zoology and paleontology.

16.2

Class Crustacea

Crustaceans have two distinguishing features, the two pairs of antennae already described, and a **nauplius larva** (Fig. 16.3). This larva has an externally unsegmented body, a simple, median eye, and only three pairs of appendages, the first pair uniramous and the other two biramous. Its mouth is ventral between the second and third pairs of limbs and the anus is terminal. This minute creature floats in the water feeding upon microscopic plants and debris. As the larva grows and undergoes several molts, additional limbs appear on segments added in front of the anus, and the organism gradually assumes its adult shape. The uniramous limbs of the larva become the first antennae of the adult, the first biramous limbs become the second antennae, and the third pair of limbs become the adult mandibles. Since the additional limbs are usually biramous when they first appear, the basic limb plan in crustaceans is similar to that of the trilobites: one pair of uniramous antennae followed by a series of biramous limbs. The nauplius larva is found in all the major groups of crustaceans, which suggests that the common ancestor of the class may have had a similar larva.

Crustaceans are traditionally divided into the large and the small. Large members form a natural subclass, the **Malacostraca.** In this group the order **Decapoda** (10 walking legs) includes the familiar shrimps, crayfish, lobsters and crabs. The crayfish will be described as an example of the subclass. Similarities among malacostracans are close enough so that knowledge of one form is a key to the understanding of others. Small crustaceans are grouped in several orders that form sev-

eral subclasses. Of these the water flea will be described as an example. Unfortunately, the orders of small crustaceans are so diverse that one example is not an adequate introduction to the others.

16.3

Astacus, A Crayfish

Crayfish of the genus *Astacus* are common in this country west of the Rockies. To the east the slightly different genus, *Cambarus,* is abundant. Crayfish are found in or near ponds, lakes and streams. Those in the water excavate holes beneath logs and stones to serve as temporary shelters, while those on the banks may dig deep burrows. They are most active at dusk and after dark, scavenging the neighborhood for plant or animal debris and occasionally capturing unwary insects, tadpoles and fish.

16.4

External Morphology of the Crayfish

The crayfish body is divided into a solid **cephalothorax** and a jointed **abdomen** (Fig. 16.4). If we include the embryonic first segment, the cephalothorax represents the fusion of six cephalic and eight thoracic segments. All except the first have appendages. The back extends laterally as a pair of skeletal folds that bend down over the sides of the body forming the **carapace.** The same skeleton extends forward over the head as a **rostrum.** The tapered abdomen is composed of seven segments, of which the first six have appendages. The last, called the **telson,** is often not counted as a segment. The anus is located on its ventral side but it lacks appendages. The abdomen is flattened and has broad dorsal and ventral surfaces. The rigid portion of the ventral skeleton is reduced to narrow transverse rings joined together with broad areas of flexible chitin. This enables the abdomen to flex sharply beneath the body.

The appendages are modified in a variety of ways (Fig. 16.5). In many of them a base **(protopodite),** an inner ramus **(endopodite)** and an outer ramus **(exopodite)** can be recognized.

The last appendages (on the twentieth segment) are extremely flattened **uropods.** When extended, the exopodites, endopodites and

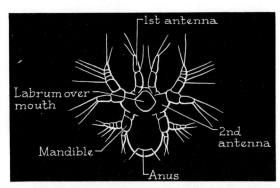

Figure 16.3 Nauplius larva. (After Dietrich.)

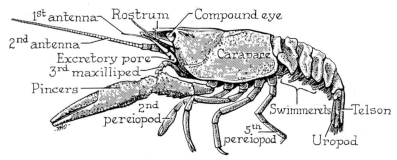

Figure 16.4　Lateral view of a crayfish. (After Howes.)

the telson between form a **tail fan.** The crayfish spreads this fan and flexes the abdomen rapidly, pulling itself backward with startling speed.

The other abdominal appendages are the much more delicately built swimmerets or **pleopods,** with bristly endopodites and exopodites. The continual gentle beating of these limbs produces a water current backward beneath the animal, probably of use beneath rocks or in burrows where the water

would become devoid of oxygen if not circulated. In the male the first pleopods (fifteenth segment) are modified as copulatory organs (Fig. 16.5). The female deposits her eggs on the pleopods, to which they are glued by secretions from the limbs. Constant motion then keeps the eggs well aerated. If the pleopods beat vigorously, the current produced helps the crayfish to walk forward, and in small individuals may actually produce a gentle forward swimming.

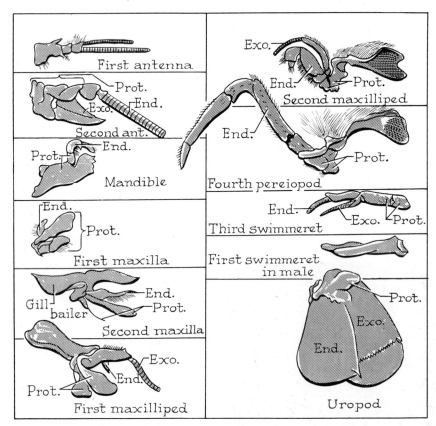

Figure 16.5　Appendages of the crayfish. Prot. = protopodite; end. = endopodite; exo. = exopodite. Those on the left are drawn to a larger scale than those on the right. (After Howes.)

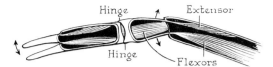

Figure 16.6 Dissected pereiopod of *Astacus* showing muscle arrangement. The terminal joint moves up and down, the next joint fore and aft, and the third joint up and down. (After Parker and Haswell.)

The last five pairs of appendages on the cephalothorax (segments 10 to 14) are the large walking legs or **pereiopods.** These are uniramous in the adult. Each is formed of seven segments, of which the first two represent the protopodite and the last five the endopodite. Each joint (Fig. 16.6) can move in a single plane, but the planes of succeeding joints are rotated so that the limb as a whole can move with considerable flexibility. The first three pairs of pereiopods are chelate, and the first pair have large pincers. The jaws of the pincers are made of the two distal segments of the leg, which are hinged one upon the other. The pincers are used for fighting and for occasional food capture and may assist in walking over rough terrain. They are also used as plows for digging. The other chelate legs are used for grooming and for picking up bits of food and handing them to the mouth parts. The last four pairs of pereiopods are the primary walking legs. Crayfishes cannot run, but they use the tail fan for swift escape.

The anterior three pairs of thoracic appendages (segments 7 to 9) and the posterior three pairs of cephalic appendages (4 to 6) form the mouth parts. These overlap each other so that the most posterior pair covers those in front. The thoracic legs are three pairs of **maxillipeds,** with endopodites modified as small arms to hold, manipulate and tear the food, and exopodites modified as tactile **palps.** The two pairs of cephalic **maxillae** have much flattened protopodites expanded medially to serve as plates for holding food against the jaws. Endopodites are similarly flattened. The first maxillae lack exopodites, but those of the second are expanded laterally with part of the protopodites to form large flaps, the **gill bailers.** The **mandibles** (segment 4) are deeply seated under the mouth. Each is a stout protopodite expanded medially to form teeth, which bears a small tactile endopodite, the **mandibular palp.** These jaws chew the food which is brought by chelate pereiopods, shredded by maxillipeds, and held against the mouth by maxillae. The simultaneous activity of all these pieces is bewildering to the observer!

Anterior to the jaws are two pairs of **antennae.** In the posterior second pair each antenna has a very long, many jointed endopodite, the **flagellum,** and a flat exopodite, the **scale.** While the crayfish is scooting backward the scales are held outward to serve as rudders. Each first antenna has a base with two flagella, producing an apparent biramous condition in what is embryologically a uniramous limb. The flagella of both pairs of antennae are used for exploration of the environment. Those of the second antennae are primarily tactile, while the others have many small chemoreceptors.

In addition to appendages the crayfish has several sense organs. **Compound eyes** are borne on stalks at the front of the cephalothorax. Each is a cluster of 10,000 or more **ommatidia** arranged radially, with the outer facets forming the eye surface (Fig. 16.7*A*). Each ommatidium functions as a complete eye looking out at a restricted part of the world. The visual fields of adjacent ommatidia overlap considerably, but all together provide a kind of mosaic view of the world.

Chemoreceptors are small blunt bristles, usually found in groups of three or four (Fig. 16.7*B*). They are especially abundant on the first antennae and on the mouth parts. Tactile bristles (Fig. 16.7*B*) are small bristles jointed to the body surface and supplied with nerve cells at the base. These are scattered all over the body and are especially abundant on the second antennae.

The basal segment of each first antenna contains an ingenious **statocyst** (Fig. 16.7*C*). During development the dorsal surface invaginates to form a sac lined with numerous tactile bristles. The opening remains as a slit concealed by a tuft of surface hairs. The crayfish pushes its head into the sand until each sac contains a group of sand grains, which then provide stimuli for the sense of balance by the way they lie against the sensory bristles.

The sides of the carapace, arching over the body, enclose a pair of **gill chambers.** Numerous gills (20 in *Astacus*) lie in each chamber, projecting upward from their origins on the limbs and body wall (Fig. 16.8). Each gill resembles a bottle brush, having a central axis and numerous radiating filaments. On each side six gills (podobranchiae) arise from the

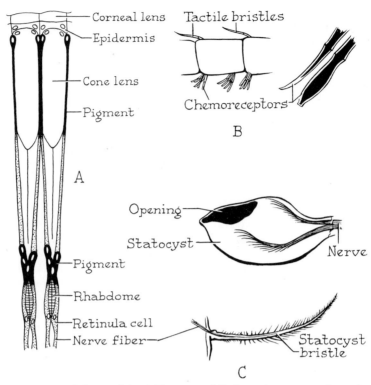

Figure 16.7 Sense organs of the crayfish. *A*, Two ommatidia from the compound eye. In each, light passing through the two lenses is focused on the outer end of the rhabdome, which is made of seven fused rods or rhabdomeres, striated thickenings along the inner edges of seven retinula cells. Pigment screens out stray light. *B*, Sensory bristles on the antenna. A chemoreceptor is enlarged at the right, viewed from two directions. *C*, The statocyst (above) and a still greater enlargement of one of the sensory bristles inside the statocyst (below). (*B* and *C* from Huxley, 1880.)

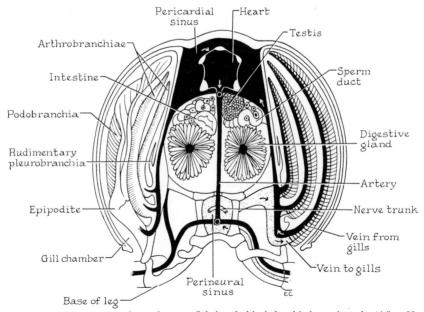

Figure 16.8 Cross section through a crayfish just behind the third pereiopods. (After Howes.)

basal segments of the second and third maxillipeds and first four pairs of pereiopods. Eleven more (arthrobranchiae) emerge from the joint membrane between these legs and the body. Three additional pairs of gills (pleurobranchiae) originate on the sides of the body above the last three pairs of pereiopods. Gills of adjacent body segments are separated by flattened plates, the epipodites, attached to the bases of the legs (Fig. 16.8).

The carapace fits snugly against the bases of the legs, leaving sizable openings only at the posterolateral edge and anteriorly beside the mouth parts. The gill bailers of the second maxillae (Fig. 16.5) extend back over the gills and undulate to produce a water current. Most of the time water is drawn in posteriorly and expelled anteriorly, but occasionally the direction is reversed to flush out debris that may have collected on the gills.

16.5
Internal Anatomy of the Crayfish

Muscles extend between various parts of the body but are prominent only in the abdomen and legs. The abdomen is nearly filled with muscle, including straplike dorsal **extensors** (Fig. 16.9C) and very stout complex ventral **flexors.** Obviously, flexion is a much more powerful movement than extension. In the floor of the thorax, muscles to the pereiopods are attached to infolded lamina of the

skeleton which form an internal framework. In the limbs each joint is crossed by a pair of antagonistic muscles (Fig. 16.6). These attach to the side wall of one segment and insert at the base of the next, which may be extended internally to form a lever. The muscles between the "hand" and "thumb" of the pincers claw fill the large hand. The extensor is relatively small, but the flexor that closes the pincers is enormous, inserting on a large flat plate that extends into the hand from the inner side of the base of the thumb. Little force is needed to hold the pincers shut against the effort of the crayfish, but great effort is required to hold it open.

The digestive system includes an ectodermal foregut and hindgut lined with chitin, and an endodermal midgut (Fig. 16.9A). The foregut includes a short ascending **esophagus** and a large **stomach** over the mouth. The stomach is divisible into anterior **cardiac** and posterior **pyloric** portions. The cardiac stomach contains a **gastric mill,** including one dorsal and two lateral teeth operated by some 13 sets of muscles (Fig. 16.9B). The pyloric stomach contains several **filters** formed by bristles that permit only liquids and very small food particles to pass through. The anterior wall of the cardiac stomach may have a pair of large calcareous discs, the **gastroliths.** These appear and disappear as they play a role in the molting process (p. 276).

The midgut and hindgut form a straight narrow **intestine** from stomach to anus. The

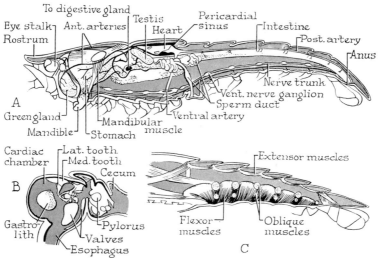

Figure 16.9 Internal anatomy of the crayfish. *A,* Digestive, circulatory, reproductive and nervous systems. *B,* Stomach (enlarged). *C,* Musculature of the abdomen. (After Howes.)

midgut portion, lying in the thorax, has a short dorsal **caecum** extending forward over the stomach and a pair of large, yellowish green **digestive glands** that open into it by large lateral ducts. As in the mollusks, these glands not only secrete digestive enzymes but also serve as regions of absorption.

As the mill grinds food to a pulp, juices from the digestive glands are passed forward through the pyloric stomach so that chemical digestion also takes place in the cardiac stomach. Particles too large to pass through the pyloric filters are regurgitated through the mouth, while the rest filters through into the midgut. Absorption occurs through the linings of the midgut, dorsal caecum and digestive glands.

The nervous system is similar to that of the annelids, except that the original brain and the following two ganglia are fused together to form the arthropod **brain** (Fig. 16.9*A*). During development it arises as three pairs of ganglia, and in the nauplius the third pair are postoral. They later move around the mouth and the three pairs fuse. Circumesophageal connectives join the brain with the **subgastric ganglion,** formed by the fusion of the six pairs of ganglia associated with the mouth parts. Beginning with segment 10 bearing the large pincers, each body segment has a bilobed ventral ganglion joined with that in front by nerves to form a ventral cord. As in many annelids the cord is paired in the embryo and fused in the adult. This ventral cord has four giant fibers. Stimulation of these fibers produces rapid strong abdominal flexures. Hence, as in the annelids, the giant fibers are associated with the escape mechanism.

The circulatory system of arthropods is unique. The coelom, which arises early in development as paired pouches like those of the annelids, later regresses. It is replaced by a system of blood sinuses that appears around the ventral nerve cord and spreads into the space formerly occupied by the coelom. Eventually, the sinuses extend throughout the body, even into the limbs and sides of the carapace, forming a **hemocoel.**

In the crayfish a dorsal part of this cavity is separated off by a partition, the **pericardial membrane,** to form a **pericardial sinus** around the heart. When the heart contracts, blood is pumped anteriorly, posteriorly and

ventrally through arteries that branch out to all parts of the body. Eventually, the arteries end, and the blood is poured into the hemocoel. It then drains ventrally into the perineural sinus from which **veins** carry it to the gills. After passing through sinuses in the gills, the blood continues in veins toward the heart and is emptied into the pericardial sinus. It enters the heart during relaxation through slitlike valves in its sides. The blood is nearly colorless but becomes bluish when exposed to air because of the presence of the oxygen-carrying pigment **hemocyanin,** a copper-containing protein. Hemocyanin is also found in some arachnids and mollusks.

The excretory system of the crayfish is the **green glands** at the base of the second antennae. Each consists of a ventral green glandular part bathed in blood and a dorsal bladder. Wastes removed from the blood in the glandular part pass through ducts and are stored in the bladder. A duct from the bladder opens on the ventral surface of the basal antennal segment.

Paired gonads lie beside the midgut and fuse together over it (Fig. 16.9*A*). In the female a straight **oviduct** passes ventrally on each side to open on the basal segment of the middle pereiopods (segment 12). In the male a pair of **sperm ducts** follows a similar but convoluted course, opening on the basal segment of the last pereiopods (segment 14). The sperm are peculiar in lacking flagella and are gathered into bundles or **spermatophores** by secretions of the ducts.

At copulation the male turns the female on her back, holding her with pincers and other chelate pereiopods. The first pleopods, which otherwise lie forward against the body between the bases of the pereiopods, are then depressed against the female. Spermatophores issuing on the last pereiopods pass down grooves on the modified pleopods to the female, where they adhere tightly between the bases of the posterior pereiopods. In the lobster and in some crayfishes the females have a small hollow, the **seminal receptacle,** between the bases of the fourth and fifth pereiopods, where spermatophores are fastened.

Some days or weeks later the eggs are laid. The female lies on her back with the abdomen folded tightly against the thorax. As the eggs emerge they are fertilized and glued to the pleopods. They hatch after several weeks into miniature crayfish that remain attached for a while to the mother.

16.6

Daphnia, The Water Flea

The crayfish is a good example of a large crustacean, but many of this class are small and reduced in their complexity. The water fleas (order Cladocera), 1 to 3 mm. long, are described here as an example of small crustaceans because they are transparent and can be studied easily without dissection (Fig. 16.10). They live primarily in open fresh water as part of the plankton. The genus *Daphnia* is represented all over the world by numerous species. A large species, *D. magna,* can often be obtained from fish hatcheries or from tropical fish stores where they are raised as fish food.

The head of *Daphnia* bears minute first antennae bristling with chemoreceptors and very large biramous second antennae, which are locomotor organs (Fig. 16.10). On the very rapid downstroke the antennae are extended laterally, while on the slower upstroke the joints bend, curving them close to the body. Behind the head and continuous with it, the carapace extends posteriorly and ventrally to enclose the rest of the body.

Within the carapace are all the mouth parts and trunk limbs. Small blunt mandibles are followed by two pairs of minute maxillae and five pairs of flattened biramous legs. The legs are used both for respiration and for filtering microscopic food from the water. The last four body segments bend ventrally and lack appendages. The body is made of six head segments and nine trunk segments in all.

By the beating of the trunk limbs and an intricate arrangement of bristles, food filtered from the water is passed forward along the limbs and pressed against the body behind the mouth. The mandibles chew the front end of the food mass, pushing pieces of it into the mouth. A short esophagus extends dorsally to open into the **midgut,** a long tube that curves through the length of the body to a short **rectum** (hindgut) and **anus** on the terminal segment. From the anterior end of the midgut a pair of curved **digestive pouches,** comparable with the digestive glands of the crayfish, extend into the head.

A spacious **hemocoel** fills the body and limbs. Dorsally a portion is separated off, as in the crayfish, to form a **pericardial sinus** containing the **heart.** *Daphnia* lacks arteries and veins. The heart pumps blood forward, where it streams among the head organs, curves ventrally, and flows posteriorly through the body organs. As in the crayfish

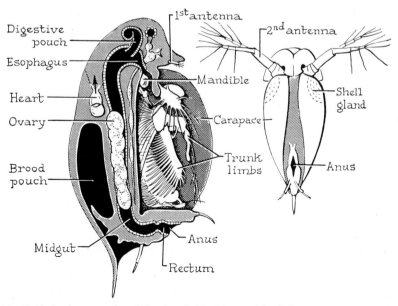

Figure 16.10 *Daphnia,* the water flea. Side view (left) with one side of the carapace removed to show enclosed body and organs. (Modified from Lockhead.) Ventral view (right) with trunk appendages omitted.

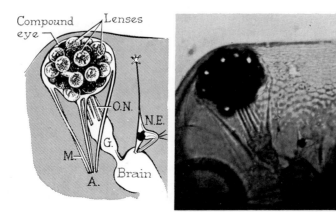

Figure 16.11 Part of the head of *Daphnia* showing compound eye with protruding lenses and muscles (*M.*) of the right side attached to the side of the head (at *A.*). Also shown are the optic nerves (*O.N.*), optic ganglion (*G.*) and brain. The nauplius eye (*N.E.*) is described in the text.

the hemocoel also extends into the carapace. A coiled tubule on the anteroventral part of each side of the carapace is the **shell gland,** believed to be an organ of excretion.

Compound eyes arise embryologically as paired structures that later fuse to form a single eye (Fig. 16.11). As it develops it sinks into the head and is covered over by the exoskeleton, enclosing a cavity. Three pairs of muscles from the sides of the head to the rim of the eye can turn it in various directions. These muscles also keep the eye in constant motion, jiggling it several times a second. Since the eye is composed of only a few ommatidia, each of which gathers light from a relatively wide area, this jiggling may improve vision (the human eye has a microscopic jiggle, and our visual acuity is better than the spacing of retinal cells alone would predict). Ommatidial lenses are large and protruding. From the eye a bundle of **optic nerves** passes to a large **optic ganglion** connected with a still larger brain. The circumesophageal connectives, subesophageal ganglion and the few ventral ganglia are seldom visible.

Attached to the anteroventral margin of the brain is another unpaired median eye, the **nauplius eye** (Fig. 16.11). This eye is found as the only eye in nauplii, where it typically has a central pigment mass with one anterior and two lateral groups of visual cells. It frequently persists in adult crustaceans. In *Daphnia* the anterior group is reduced and divided into a single **anterior cell** and two **ventral cells.** Each lateral group is reduced to a single **posterolateral cell.** This eye is suspended in the blood, its cells anchored by

delicate fibers. The outer ends of the cells turn back as nerves to the brain. This is the only *inverted* eye found in the phylum Arthropoda, and is another distinguishing feature of the class Crustacea.

Most daphnias are females which reproduce parthenogenetically. Paired ovaries lie beside the midgut. Eggs are laid through ducts that open dorsally into a **brood pouch,** an enlarged cavity between the back of the body and the carapace. The eggs remain here until they develop into small daphnias resembling their parents. When the environment becomes unfavorable (too cold, no food, etc.) some of the young mature as males while the females produce "resting eggs." These are fertilized and shed to the bottom, where they may last for years without hatching. The same females produce both parthenogenetic and resting eggs, depending upon whether the environment is favorable or unfavorable.

16.7
Other Crustaceans

Small crustaceans are usually considered to be the more primitive crustacea. Of these a natural group is formed by the orders **Anostraca** (brine shrimps and fairy shrimps), **Notostraca, Conchostraca** and **Cladocera** (water fleas) (Fig. 16.12), in which the trunk limbs are biramous, flattened, and used for both respiration and feeding. These orders form the subclass **Branchiopoda.** They are mostly fresh-water organisms, and are especially abundant in temporary ponds.

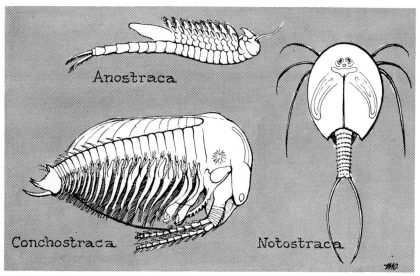

Figure 16.12   Other members of the subclass Branchiopoda. (After Borradaile et al.)

Other small crustaceans include the orders **Ostracoda, Copepoda** and **Cirripedia** (Fig. 16.13). The first two are common in both fresh and salt water. The last are the barnacles, found only in the seas. Copepods are the most abundant of all crustaceans, forming dominant organisms of salt- and fresh-water plankton. The evolutionary relations of these groups to each other, to the Branchiopoda, and to the Malacostraca are somewhat obscure.

The Malacostraca are divided into eight orders, of which five will be mentioned here (all eight are listed in the synopis at the end of the chapter). The **Mysidacea** (Fig. 16.14) are abundant, delicate, shrimplike animals living near the bottoms of shallow seas and arctic fresh water. They usually rise into the upper water as plankton at night. The **Euphausiacea** are similar, living deep in the open ocean by day and coming near the surface at night. They are remarkable for their light organs and for the amplitude of their daily migration. Schools of them are a major food for the filtering whales.

The **Isopoda** are dorsoventrally flattened

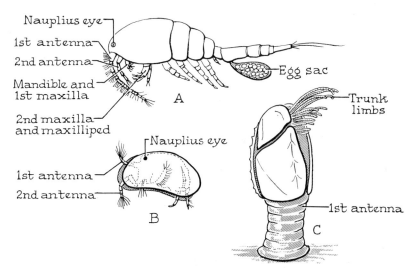

Figure 16.13   Additional orders of small Crustacea. *A,* Order Copepoda. *B,* Order Ostracoda, with a hinged carapace enclosing head and body. *C,* Order Cirripedia, the barnacles, attached by an enormous first antenna, with the body enclosed in calcareous plates. (From various sources.)

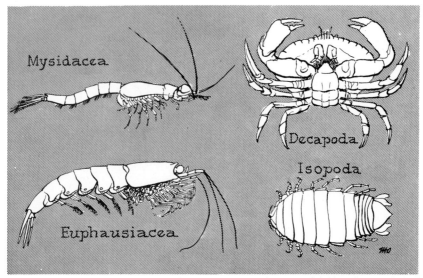

Figure 16.14 Some of the orders of the subclass Malacostraca. (The first three are after Borradaile et al., the fourth after Parker and Haswell.)

crustaceans without carapaces. They are found in both salt and fresh water. This order also includes the only truly terrestrial crustaceans, the pill-bugs and sow-bugs (Fig. 16.14). The **Amphipoda** (shown in Fig. 16.2) also lack carapaces, but they are compressed laterally rather than dorsoventrally. They are common in all waters, forming an important fish food. Finally, the order **Decapoda** includes a variety of familiar forms such as shrimps, crabs and lobsters.

16.8
The Subphylum Labiata

All labiates have a distinct head enclosed in a **head capsule,** which usually bears eyes, a pair of many-jointed antennae, mandibles,

maxillae, and a **labium** formed by the embryonic fusion of the second maxillae. Trunk appendages are uniramous and usually seven-jointed, ending in terminal claws. The subphylum can be divided into two superclasses, the **Myriapoda,** in which most of the trunk segments have walking legs, and the **Hexapoda,** in which only the first three trunk segments have walking legs. Hexapod embryos usually develop limb buds on many trunk segments, revealing their origin from myriapod ancestors.

Myriapods are simpler and less specialized. They lack compound eyes, having instead aggregates of ommatidia clustered on the sides of the head. The trunk segments are similar to one another like those of the annelids. Behavior patterns are simple.

Of the myriapods, centipedes and milli-

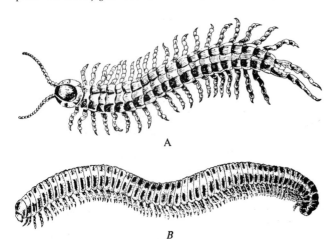

A

B

Figure 16.15 Examples of the Myriapoda. *A*, Order Chilopoda, the centipedes. *B*, Order Diplopoda, the millipedes. (Villee: Biology, 5th ed.)

Figure 16.16 Primitive wingless insects (Apterygota), showing a silverfish (left) and a springtail (right). (After Lubbock [left] and Carpenter and Folsom [right].)

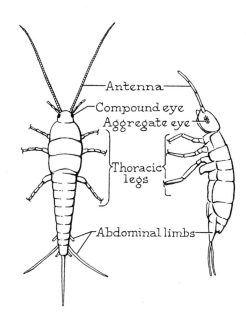

pedes are the only familiar groups. Centipedes, class **Chilopoda** (Fig. 16.15*A*), are predaceous animals, hunting down insects and killing them with their **poison claws,** which are the modified legs of the first body segment. Each of the remaining body segments except the last has a pair of long walking legs. The total number of legs ranges from 15 to 173 pairs in different species. Centipedes can run rapidly, the legs moving in waves from rear to front. Coordination follows the annelid pattern, with reflex pathways between adjacent segments.

Millipedes, class **Diplopoda** (Fig. 16.15*B*), are herbivorous scavengers, feeding primarily on decayed and living plant material. The first maxillae appear in the embryo but later disappear. The labium is well developed, and its segment is fused ventrally with the first body segment. The next three body segments remain single, but beginning with the fifth and sixth every two segments fuse together during development. Since each embryonic segment has a pair of legs, most of the apparent segments of the adult body bear two pairs of legs, giving the order its name. Millipedes may have from 13 to nearly 200 pairs of legs, manipulated like those of the centipedes. The legs are short, and millipedes cannot move fast.

The superclass **Hexapoda** includes only the class **Insecta,** although there is a growing tendency to separate the primitive wingless insects such as the silverfish and springtails (Fig. 16.16) from the winged groups. These wingless forms have small appendages on the abdominal segments, suggesting a relationship with the myriapods. Silverfish do, however, have compound eyes like the winged insects.

The insects proper are the winged forms, including all hexapods lacking abdominal appendages except those at the posterior end used in reproduction. Typically, they have two pairs of membranous wings, on the second and third thoracic segments. It is beyond the scope of this book to represent adequately an invertebrate class that is divided into 26 orders. The cockroach will be presented as a generalized insect and some distinguishing features of the larger orders will be described later. Finally, the honeybee will be described as an example of a specialized insect. All 26 orders are listed in the synopsis.

16.9
Periplaneta americana, A Cockroach

Cockroaches are the only order of living insects that have a fossil record extending back into the Pennsylvanian period, 250 million years ago. Other orders of insects existing then have either become extinct or evolved sufficiently to warrant separation into new orders. Cockroaches have also been conservative in their habits, shifting only from the steaming swamps of the coal age to the steaming jungles and steam-heated buildings of today. They require both moisture and warmth for survival.

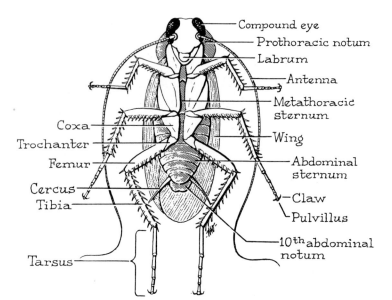

Compound eye
Prothoracic notum
Labrum
Antenna
Metathoracic sternum
Coxa
Trochanter
Femur
Wing
Abdominal sternum
Cercus
Tibia
Claw
Pulvillus
10th abdominal notum
Tarsus

Figure 16.17 Ventral view of the cockroach. (After Comstock.)

The large native cockroach *P. americana* (Fig. 16.17) is found in greenhouses and institutional buildings. Adults are a dark reddish brown color, 25 to 35 mm. long. Like all cockroaches these have flattened bodies with long legs on which they can run rapidly and escape into narrow crevices.

16.10
External Morphology of the Cockroach

The head has dorsolateral **compound eyes,** anterior **antennae** and ventral mouth parts (Fig. 16.18). The head is usually bent beneath the body so that the eyes actually look anteriorly. The front of the head extends down as a movable upper lip or **labrum** behind which are **mandibles, maxillae** and **labium,** which are suited to an omnivorous habit (Fig. 16.18). Each mandible is a single segment with sharp cutting and grinding teeth along the medial edge. Each maxilla has seven segments, of which the last five form a tactile palp. The second segment is large and bears two processes. The labium is similarly constructed, except that the two basal segments are fused and the palps are four-jointed. The processes on maxillae and labium, together with the labrum, manipulate and hold food for the mandibles.

A short **neck** joins the head to the thorax. The latter is formed of three fused seg-

ments, the **prothorax, mesothorax** and **metathorax.** The back or **notum** of the prothorax is expanded as a shield, partially covering the head and mesothorax. The nota of the other two segments are covered by the wings. On the ventral side oblique lateral plates or **pleura** join the three nota to the **sterna,** three triangular plates in the midline. Each sternum bears a pair of legs, while the nota and pleura

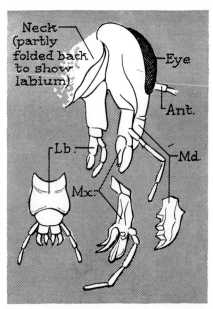

Neck (partly folded back to show labium)
Eye
Ant.
Lb
Md.
Mx.

Figure 16.18 Head and mouth parts of the cockroach (mouth parts viewed from behind). (Combined from Comstock, and Parker and Haswell.)

of the last two segments articulate with the wings.

Each leg is composed of a large flattened **coxa,** small **trochanter,** long stout **femur,** long slender **tibia,** and five small segments collectively called the **tarsus** (Fig. 16.17). Many of these segments are beset with spines. Each tarsal segment ends ventrally in a small adhesive pad. The last, called the **pulvillus,** is the largest and is flanked by a pair of **tarsal claws.** Joints between coxae and body permit only a slight movement, and the trochanters are fused immovably onto the femurs. Most of the locomotion is derived from movements between coxae and trochanters, and between femurs and tibias. The claws and pulvilli provide for a grip on any kind of surface, and the several small tarsal joints allow freedom between the position at which a grip is best maintained and the direction of the tibia.

The anterior wings at rest are folded over the body, covering the posterior wings (Fig. 16.19). They are slender and leathery, protecting the hind wings when the animal passes beneath objects. The posterior wings are pleated and fold fanwise when not in use. In flight all four wings are held out to the sides and flapped dorsoventrally. Cockroaches seldom fly and do so primarily in search of new habitats. Each wing is strengthened by a number of hollow **veins** which are continuous with the hemocoel of the body. Their arrangement or venation is a prominent characteristic in insect classification.

The abdomen is made of 11 segments, each slightly overlapping the segment behind and divisible into a dorsal notum and ventral sternum (Fig. 16.17). Nota of the eighth and ninth segments are telescoped completely

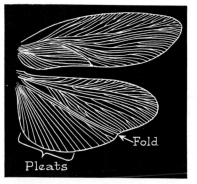

Figure 16.19 Wings of the cockroach, showing the numerous veins characteristic of the more primitive insects.

out of sight beneath that of the seventh, and the tenth extends posteriorly as a notched plate. From the sides of the tenth segment emerge a pair of **cerci,** antenna-like structures sensitive to air currents and low frequency sounds. The anus opens posteriorly on the tenth segment, with the reproductive openings beneath it.

Between the prothorax and eighth abdominal segments are 10 pairs of **spiracles,** openings to the respiratory system, between adjacent segments just beneath the nota.

16.11

Internal Anatomy of the Cockroach

The digestive tract (Fig. 16.20) includes fore-, mid- and hindguts as in the Crustacea. The mouth opens into a **mouth cavity** that receives ducts from a pair of large, bilobed **salivary glands** in the mesothorax. Their secretion digests starches. The mouth cavity continues as a long narrow **esophagus** to a

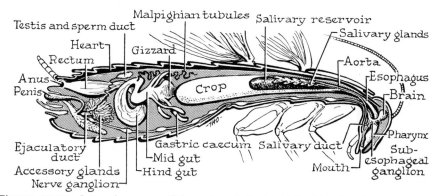

Figure 16.20 Internal anatomy of the cockroach (male). (After Metcalf, Flint and Metcalf.)

posterior enlargement, the **crop.** The crop opens into a small muscular **gizzard** containing six strong teeth and numerous bristles. All of these organs are part of the foregut and are lined with chitin.

The gizzard opens into the midgut, a narrow **stomach.** Anteriorly the stomach has eight **digestive pouches.** The stomach curves around to the anterior end of the abdomen, where it joins the hindgut. This includes a long **intestine** and a short **rectum,** lined with chitin. The stomach is lined with a simple gastrodermis, surrounded by thin circular and longitudinal muscle layers. The gizzard projects into the stomach, and the posterior cells of the foregut secrete chitin continuously, forming a tubular **peritrophic membrane** that surrounds the food as it passes through the stomach and intestine. This remarkable structure is found in many insects.

Digestion occurs primarily in the crop. Secretions from the digestive pouches are passed forward as in the crayfish. Mechanical breakdown is aided by the gizzard, and the finely pulverized and digested food is then passed into the stomach. Water and dissolved nutrients diffuse through the peritrophic membrane to be absorbed by the lining of the stomach and digestive pouches. The remaining water is absorbed in the intestine, leaving dry fecal pellets to be eliminated through the anus.

At its anterior end the intestine receives six groups of delicate **malpighian tubules.** These are blind tubules lying in the hemocoel. They pick up waste from the blood and excrete it into the intestine. Nitrogenous wastes are excreted as uric acid, an adaptation which conserves body water (p. 85). Each tubule has a muscular coat and its slow writhing aids the passage of wastes down its lumen. These are the excretory organs of all labiates.

The **brain,** formed from three parts as in the crustacea, is a bilobed structure lying over the esophagus (Fig. 16.20). The **subesophageal ganglion** is formed by fusion of the remaining three pairs of head ganglia and lies beneath the esophagus. These are connected by stout **circumesophageal connectives** forming a nerve ring around the esophagus. The ventral cord continues posteriorly with three thoracic and six abdominal pairs of ganglia. The last pair supplies all of the remaining abdominal segments.

The compound eyes of insects are remarkably like those of crustaceans. Each ommatidium of the cockroach has the same general parts, all of ectodermal origin except the optic nerve itself. Compound eyes are widespread in the arthropods, being found in the trilobites, crustaceans, horseshoe crabs and insects. They are lacking in the other groups of living chelicerates and labiates.

Most insects also have **ocelli,** small eyes on the top of the head. Typically, three of these are arranged in a triangle. Each ocellus is a group of **retinuli,** comparable to the lower portions of ommatidia, underlying a single large **lens** (Fig. 16.21). In most insects the retinuli lie too close to the lens for an image to be formed. The function of these eyes is not understood. They are believed to monitor light intensity and to influence the insect's general level of activity rather than to provide spatial information on light distribution. In *Periplaneta* the ocelli are degenerate.

Organs of touch are special **tactile bristles** scattered over the body and especially prominent on the antennae, palps and cerci. On the cerci they vibrate in response to wind or low

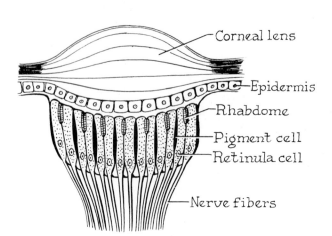

Corneal lens

Epidermis

Rhabdome

Pigment cell

Retinula cell

Nerve fibers

Figure 16.21 Diagrammatic section through an insect ocellus. (After Comstock.)

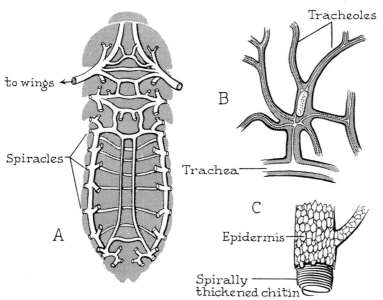

Figure 16.22   Tracheal system of the cockroach. *A,* The major tracheal trunks. (After Parker and Haswell.) *B,* Diagrammatic view of the tracheoles of a single cell. *C,* Detailed structure of a trachea. (*B* and *C* adapted from Wigglesworth.)

sounds. Smell and taste are mediated by chemoreceptors clustered on these same organs. The chemoreceptors are projecting cones with a very thin exoskeleton kept moist by glandular secretions. Those on the antennae and cerci are olfactory, those on the palp are gustatory. The distinction between smell and taste depends upon whether the chemical sensed is airborne or dissolved in liquid.

The **tracheal tubes** found in all labiates are a respiratory system of air ducts leading in from the **spiracles** to all the tissues of the body (Fig. 16.22). The larger tubes anastomose, forming a network from which smaller tubes ramify. Each is a cylinder of epidermal tissue lined with a thin layer of chitin thickened spirally to provide strength. The smallest branches end blindly in **tracheoles** (Fig. 16.22), minute branching tunnels within the cytoplasm of **end cells.** End cells are applied closely to the surfaces of other cells. The cockroach flushes air in and out of the system by respiratory movements, or **breathing,** in which the abdomen is alternately flattened and relaxed by the contraction and relaxation of stout vertical muscles within it.

The hemocoel of insects is a single large branched space without a separate pericardial sinus. In the cockroach the **heart** is a long dorsal tube, expanded in each segment of the thorax and abdomen. In each segment a pair of valves admits blood from the hemocoel. Anteriorly, the heart continues as a short artery that ends behind the brain. Contraction usually proceeds forward along the heart and can be seen through the body wall of an uninjured roach. Relieved of respiratory duties by the tracheal system, the blood in labiates serves primarily to distribute nutrients to the body and to transport wastes to the malpighian tubules.

The male cockroach has a terminal complex of copulatory organs (Fig. 16.20) formed from the sternum of the last segment and the much modified appendages of the eighth and ninth abdominal segments. Except for a pair of ventral **styles** on the ninth segment these organs are usually retracted into the body. Small **testes** lie dorsally in the fourth and fifth abdominal segments from which a pair of **sperm ducts** lead to **seminal vesicles,** clusters of delicate tubules in the sixth and seventh segments where the sperm are stored. At copulation sperm are passed through a single stout **ejaculatory duct** that opens among the copulatory organs.

The female has a pair of large **ovaries,** each composed of eight lobes in segments 4 to 6. Within each lobe the smallest eggs are anterior, the larger and more mature eggs posterior, giving it a beaded appearance. Paired **oviducts** from the ovaries join to open ventrally on the eighth segment. The ninth segment has a ventral opening to a **seminal receptacle** where sperm are received. The last sternites and appendages are greatly modified to aid in copulation and in carrying the eggs. As the eggs are laid and fertilized they are covered with secretions from a pair of **accessory glands.** The two glands secrete dissimilar materials that react in the presence of air to produce a tanned protein cover. The case thus formed is carried about until the eggs hatch. Young cockroaches resemble adults but lack wings; they mature in seven molts.

16.12

Classification of the Insecta

Insects are divided into a wingless group, **Apterygota,** and a winged group, **Pterygota.** The former includes the silverfish (order **Thysanura**) and springtails (order **Collembola**) (Fig. 16.16).

The **Pterygota** are divided by paleontologists into the **Paleoptera,** in which the wings are held permanently at right angles to the body, and the **Neoptera,** in which the wings are folded back over the body when not in use. Paleopterans were abundant in ancient times, and included many orders now ex-

tinct. Surviving are the dragonflies and damselflies (order **Odonata**) and mayflies (order **Ephemerida**) (Fig. 16.23), groups that have aquatic young. The adults are forced to stay out in the open to avoid breaking their wings, and have flight as the only means of escape. Neopterans, with hinged wings, not only can escape by flight but also may run fast or hide in crevices. It is interesting in this respect that, although wingless species are found in all of the neopteran orders, none of the living or extinct paleoptera are wingless.

Neopterans are divided into the **Exopterygota** and **Endopterygota.** In the former, as in the Paleoptera, the wings appear in juvenile forms as external **wing buds** that become larger at each molt, finally becoming full-sized wings (Fig. 16.24). Such development is part of a pattern called **incomplete metamorphosis** and the young are called **nymphs.** The group includes many orders, such as the **Orthoptera** (grasshoppers, crickets, mantids and roaches), **Isoptera** (termites) and **Hemiptera** (the true bugs). Representatives are shown in Figure 16.25. The Endopterygota are the so-called "higher" insects. The young have internal wing buds that later evert suddenly in a resting stage, the **pupa** (Fig. 16.24), and become full-sized wings on the following molt. This is associated with marked changes in appearance, so that the young seldom re-

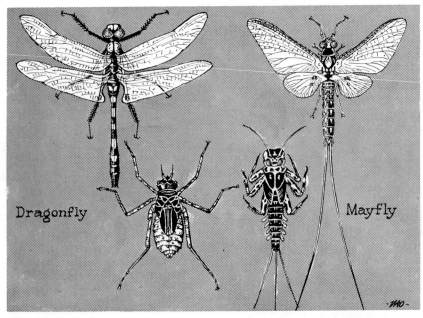

Figure 16.23 Living Paleoptera. Orders Odonata (left) and Ephemerida (right). Adults above, and nymphs below. (After Borror and DeLong.)

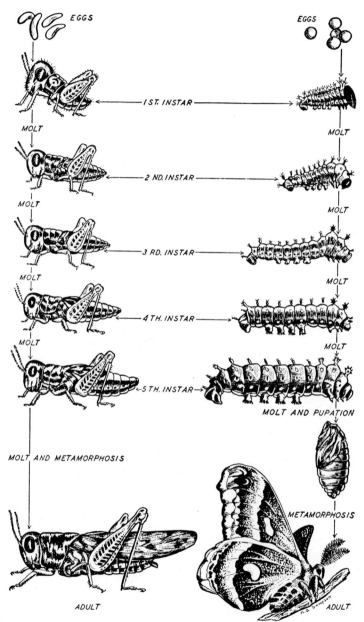

Figure 16.24 Metamorphosis in the insects, showing a comparison of an exopterygote (grasshopper) and an endopterygote (cecropia moth). (Turner: General Endocrinology.)

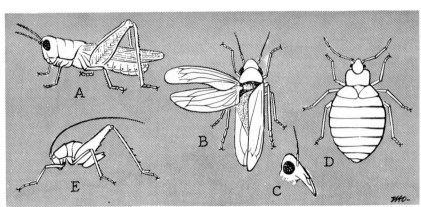

Figure 16.25 Representative orders of the Exopterygota. *A,* Orthoptera (grasshopper). *B,* Hemiptera (leaf-hopper). Hemipterans have sucking mouth parts (*C*). Wingless forms in each order include the camel cricket (*E*) and the bedbug (*D*). Other orders include the Blattaria (cockroach, Fig. 16.17) and the Isoptera (termite, Fig. 17.18).

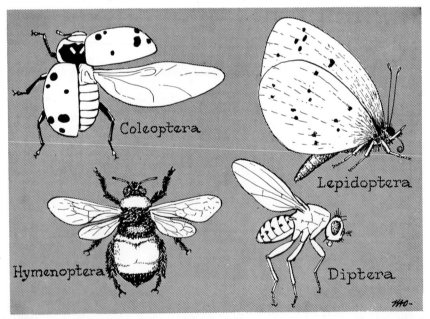

Figure 16.26 The major orders of the Endopterygota. The coleoptera (beetles) have thick, rigid forewings. The Lepidoptera (butterflies and moths) have scales on the wings and sucking mouth parts. The Hymenoptera (bees, ants, etc.) have membranous wings with few veins. The Diptera (flies) have two wings, the hindwings being reduced to balancing organs.

semble the adults. Such development is called **complete metamorphosis** and the young are called **larvae.** The Endopterygota also includes many orders (Fig. 16.26) such as the **Lepidoptera** (butterflies and moths), **Coleoptera** (beetles), **Hymenoptera** (bees, ants, wasps), and the **Diptera** (flies, mosquitoes). Most of the species of insects are included in these four orders, which are further described with the illustrations. Although the butterflies and some moths cannot fold the wings flat upon the body, the wing articulations and muscles indicate that this represents an evolutionary loss, and that these insects are properly grouped with the Neoptera.

16.13

Metamorphosis

A change in the shape or relative size of body parts during growth is called **metamorphosis.** In organisms such as man and other mammals the young resemble adults and little metamorphosis takes place. In other organisms metamorphosis may be marked. We have already described a number of examples, such as the coelenterate polyp and medusa, and the larval and adult tapeworms, flukes, mollusks and annelids.

The apterygote insects show very little metamorphosis. Young hatch as miniatures of their parents, easily recognizable as to species. In the living Paleoptera the young are aquatic and often have a very different appearance from their parents (Fig. 16.23). They not only lack wings but have a different body shape so that the species cannot be identified unless they are reared to maturity. Although the young differ from the adults, their bodies are complete with jointed legs and compound eyes. Metamorphosis in the Exopterygota is similar except that, since both young and adults are terrestrial, they do not differ so much in appearance. Young grasshoppers, for example, are easily recognized as grasshoppers.

In the Endopterygota the young not only show little resemblance to the adults, but often lack such structures as compound eyes, jointed legs, and wings. Some larvae have no appendages at all. As the larva grows, wing buds develop inside the body but are not evident externally. Finally, in a single molt the appearance changes markedly as the animal pupates. The **pupa** is a nonfeeding stage in which all the adult appendages become visible as external buds (Fig. 16.24). Internally, whole organ systems may be dissolved and replaced as the adult form is developed. The pupa molts to become a full-grown adult.

Metamorphosis is considered to involve the same phenomena that appear in the formation and development of embryos. Gastrulation, the formation of limbs and development of organ systems in the embryo are actually forms of embryonic metamorphosis. Similarly, the metamorphosis of young into adults is a kind of delayed embryonic development. As yet very little is known of the causes and forces involved in metamorphosis. The role of hormones in insect metamorphosis will be discussed in the next chapter.

16.14

Apis mellifera, The Honeybee

As an example of a highly specialized insect the honeybee offers interesting contrasts to the cockroach. Sense organs, mouth parts, wings, legs and many internal organs are more diversified and specialized than in the cockroach. The worker bee, a sterile female, shows most of these specializations (Fig. 16.27).

The most striking modifications on the head concern the mouth parts. Labial palps and maxillae are fused into a **sucking tube** containing a **tongue** formed from the middle portion of the labium. When this tube is folded back against the body the short **mandibles** can still be used as jaws, and the bee is thus one of the few insects that can both suck and chew.

The wings are small in relation to body size and have a much modified and reduced venation. The rear wing bears a row of minute hooks that fasten to the front wing, forming a single flight blade. The round and compact thorax houses powerful flight muscles.

The legs have numerous modifications. The first tarsal segment of each leg has a patch of bristles on its inner surface. Those of the first and second pairs of legs are **pollen brushes.** The bristles on the tarsi of the third pair of legs are arranged in regular rows forming **pollen combs.** The tibias of the third pair of legs have a concave surface fringed with curved hairs which forms a pair of **pollen baskets.** The lower inner edge of each tibia has a row of stout bristles, the **pecten,** be-

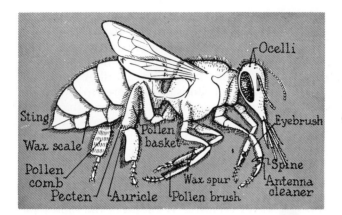

Figure 16.27 The worker honeybee. (Adapted from Casteel.)

neath which the upper end of the first tarsal segment is expanded and flattened to form an **auricle.**

As the bee visits flowers, pollen sticks to its hairy body. This pollen is a major source of protein in the bee diet and must be collected carefully. The anterior pollen brushes collect pollen from the head, the middle brushes gather it from the thorax and the anterior brushes, while the combs collect it from the abdomen and the second pair of brushes. Each pair of legs is drawn between those behind to effect transfer. Finally the pollen on one comb is scraped off by the pecten of the opposite leg and it falls onto the auricle. The tarsus is then bent so as to force the pollen up the outer surface of the tibia into the pollen basket. The pollen adheres through its own moisture and may become a sizable mass. Although this sounds like a very complex process, the bee actually does it all in midflight with very little loss of pollen.

The base of the first tarsal segment of each front leg has a bristled notch overlapped by a movable spine at the end of the tibia. This is the **antenna cleaner.** The base of the antenna is fitted into the notch and locked in place by the spine. It is then drawn through the bristly hole. Above the spine each anterior tibia has a row of short, evenly spaced bristles, the **eyebrush,** used for brushing off the compound eyes. Each middle tibia has a terminal **wax spur** for removing plates of wax secreted on the abdomen.

The abdomen shows two specializations. Paired, ventral **wax glands** secrete wax as plates that are used for building the honeycomb. The reproductive apparatus is modified at the posterior end to form a **stinger**

(Fig. 16.27). The tube is formed of a dorsal **sheath** and two ventral **darts** that slide on ridges of the sheath. The tips of all three are barbed. The sheath initiates a puncture, after which a seesawing movement of the darts drives the stinger deep into the flesh. Two secretions are mixed as they are extruded through the central canal. That from a pair of **acid glands** is stored in a **poison sac** and, during extrusion, the secretion of a single **alkaline gland** is added. The mixture is more poisonous than either secretion alone. When the worker bee stings a mammal and then flies away, the stinger with its glands and muscles is pulled from the insect's body. The bee later dies, but the stinger remains in the mammal's flesh with all of its parts still working, the darts driving it deeper and the glands pumping in their poison.

Connected with the esophagus are large salivary glands which for the first 10 days of adult life secrete "royal jelly," the food of young bee larvae. After 10 days, however, these glands secrete ordinary saliva containing enzymes to digest starch. The crop serves as a **honey-stomach** where nectar is temporarily stored as the bee collects it. Salivary enzymes convert the disaccharide, sucrose, of the nectar into the monosaccharides glucose and fructose. In the hive the nectar is regurgitated, concentrated by evaporation in the cells of the honeycomb, and thus converted to honey.

The life history of a worker reveals additional specializations. Life begins as a fertilized egg laid by the queen in a comb cell (Fig. 16.28). For the first two days after hatching the grublike larva is fed royal jelly by young adult workers, and for the next four days it receives **beebread,** a kneaded mixture of pollen and honey. The larva molts several times and then spins a delicate **cocoon** within which it pupates. Adult workers cover the cell with a thin wax cap. After 12 days (three weeks from the day the egg was laid) the pupa molts to form a full-grown adult that cuts off the cap and emerges.

First the new bee busies herself cleaning out newly vacated cells to prepare them for a new generation of larvae. After a few days the salivary glands begin to secrete royal jelly and the major duty of the bee is to feed larvae. Young adult workers feed heavily upon protein-rich pollen to produce this jelly. The worker also "weans" the two-day old larvae, feeding them the beebread that she has chewed thoroughly. Groups of young workers care for a whole brood of young, feeding each of them two or three thousand times during the six days of their larval life. Calculations show that one worker working full time can take care of the needs of only two or three larvae!

Toward the end of this period of caring for the larvae, the young worker begins to fly short distances from the hive. After the tenth day the secretion of royal jelly stops and the wax glands begin to function. The worker then becomes a builder of new honeycomb. In addition she receives nectar and pollen brought to the hive. Pollen is stored in cells next to the brood cells, while nectar is placed peripherally. Many of the bees sit over the nectar cells fanning the air with their wings to increase the rate of evaporation. When cells are filled with honey or pollen they are capped with wax.

At this age the worker also carries debris and dead bees out of the hive, taking them off some distance and dropping them. Toward the end of this period a certain number of wax-secreting bees guard the entrance of the nest, inspecting all incomers to be sure that they are bees of their colony (which they recognize by smell). Raiding bees, wasps, beetles and flies are stung mercilessly by these guards. Curiously, the stinger does not pull off after stinging such brittle-skinned enemies, so that the guards live to sting again. They also fly out to sting large animals that approach too closely.

After three weeks of adult life the wax glands cease to function and the bee becomes a forager. For the rest of her life her primary function is to collect nectar and pollen. On the average workers will live four or five weeks after reaching this stage.

It has been found that these successive stages of activity in the adult are not rigid. If the age structure of the colony is experimentally altered by the removal of one or more age classes, remaining bees shift their schedule of development to compensate.

The queen bee has functional ovaries and uses the reproductive apparatus both for oviposition and stinging. Her legs lack the pollen-collecting apparatus. Other characteristics

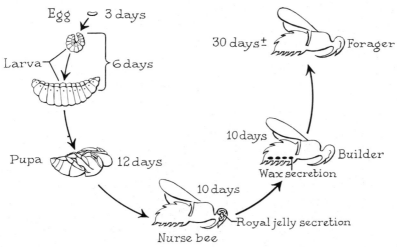

Figure 16.28 Life cycle of the worker honeybee. The first 21 days are spent in a cell of the comb. All growth takes place during the six days of larval life. Adults are drawn in diagrammatic section to show the glandular activities. (Combined from Curtis and Guthrie, and von Frisch.)

of the queen and the drones will be discussed in Chapter 42, where insect societies are considered.

16.15
The Subphylum Chelicerata

Chelicerates have a long and varied evolutionary history. They appeared first in the ocean, then in fresh water and, finally, on land. Of the five or more classes only three will be mentioned here. The **Xiphosura** (horseshoe crabs) are marine, the **Eurypterida** are believed to have lived in both fresh and salt water, and the **Arachnida** (scorpions, spiders, etc.) are terrestrial.

Xiphosura. The class **Xiphosura** was common, although never abundant, during the Paleozoic era. It survives today as a single genus, *Limulus,* shown in Figure 16.2. The only American species is *L. polyphemus* found on the east coast. The superficial resemblance between horseshoe crabs and trilobites is striking. The body is flattened, with anterior segments fused dorsally to form a shield. In trilobites this **prosoma** bore dorsally a pair of compound eyes and ventrally one pair of antennae and four to six pairs of legs. Horseshoe crabs are generally similar but lack antennae. The prosomal legs of horseshoe crabs lack exopodites, which were the gills of trilobites. The remaining body segments of trilobites were free and each bore limbs like those of the prosoma. In horseshoe crabs the remaining segments are fused into an **opisthosoma** and have much modified appendages.

The anterior appendages of horseshoe crabs are the **chelicerae** (segment 3) hanging in front of the mouth in the typical chelicerate position. The next four pairs of walking legs are also chelate. The last legs end in several stout spines and are used for pushing in sand. On the opisthosoma the limbs are biramous and fused medially to form flat plates. The first plate is an **operculum** which overlaps and protects the others. Each of the remaining five plates is delicate and bears a pair of **book gills** formed of many thin lamellae. The **telson** projects as a long movable spine. It is not a true segment, but a posterodorsal extension of the opisthosoma.

Eurypterida. Eurypterids were abundant in Paleozoic times and included a few species as much as 3 meters long. They had a prosoma with dorsal compound eyes and six pairs of ventral appendages (Fig. 16.29). The first appendages were chelicerae, the next four pairs were walking legs, and the sixth were large paddles for swimming.

The remaining segments of eurypterids were unfused and divisible into two regions, a middle **mesosoma** and a posterior **metasoma**. The mesosoma was of six segments and bore ventrally an **operculum** on the first, and five pairs of flattened plates, believed to

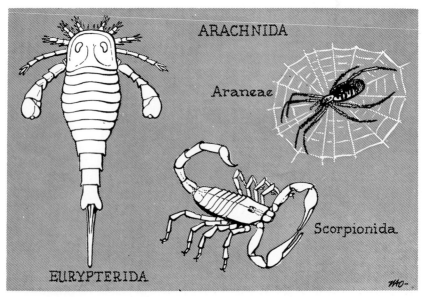

Figure 16.29 Representative classes of the subphylum Chelicerata. Two of the arachnid orders are shown. A third class (Xiphosura) is shown on Figure 16.2. (Combined from various sources.)

have been **gills,** on the others. The metasoma of seven segments lacked appendages, and ended in a telson spine.

Although eurypterids are believed to have been primarily a fresh-water group, the evidence for this is not conclusive. The best deposits of fresh-water organisms are usually found where they have been washed into the sea at the mouths of rivers. Although many of the fossils in such deposits are obviously of fresh-water origin, others are just as clearly marine.

Arachnida. In the class **Arachnida** the most primitive order, **Scorpionida,** shows many similarities with the preceding classes. The scorpion has a prosoma with six pairs of appendages, the first of which are the chelicerae (Fig. 16.29). The second pair are large and chelate, forming pincers comparable with those of the crayfish. The remaining four pairs are walking legs.

The scorpion mesosoma has six segments, of which the first has a small bilobate appendage now part of the reproductive apparatus and thought to be a vestigial operculum. The second segment bears a pair of **combs,** modified tactile limbs. The third to sixth segments each bear a pair of ventral slits that open into air chambers containing **book lungs** formed of many delicate lamellae. Embryologic evidence suggests that these lungs are borne on limb vestiges that have sunk into the body, protecting the lamellar respiratory organs from desiccation.

The scorpion metasoma is made of one tapered segment and five narrow segments forming a long tail. These lack appendages. The telson is modified as a powerful sting.

Although no arachnids have compound eyes, most of them have ocelli resembling those of the insects (Fig. 16.21). Ocelli are also found in horseshoe crabs and eurypterids.

The class Arachnida is divided into 11 or more orders. Only two forms are discussed here, the scorpions, above, and the spiders, order **Araneae,** below. The other scorpion-like and spider-like orders are listed in the synopsis at the end of this chapter.

16.16
Argiope, An Orb Spider

Of the many species of spiders only a few build geometrically regular webs. These are the orb spiders, about 25 mm. long. Both the golden (*Argiope aurantia*) and the banded (*A. trifasciata*) orb spiders are common in gardens and marshes (Fig. 16.29).

The prosoma bears four anterior **ocelli** that look forward, upward and to the side. Below them are the **chelicerae,** no longer chelate but modified as poison fangs. The second pair of appendages are small **pedi-palps,** tactile in function and used to manipulate prey. The remaining four pairs are typical walking legs, each composed of seven segments. The prosoma is joined to an **opis-thosoma** by a slender waist. The opisthosoma is a large soft bag formed embryologically by the fusion of 10 segments. A pair of ventral slits opens to the one pair of **book lungs** and posteriorly are three pairs of **spinnerets** and one pair of small **anal papillae.** The anus is terminal. Just anterior to the spinnerets is a single median opening, the **spiracle.**

The mouth, just behind the chelicerae, opens into a narrow esophagus that leads to a **sucking stomach** (Fig. 16.30). This is fol-

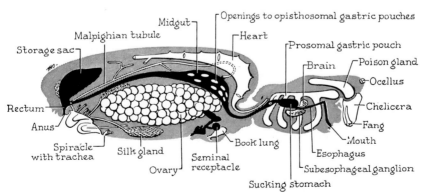

Figure 16.30 Internal anatomy of the orb-spider, *Argiope*. The body wall, appendages, and some of the internal organs of the right side have been removed. The much branched gastric pouches in the opisthosoma are removed, leaving their openings into the midgut. Only a few of the silk glands are shown. (After Buck and Keister.)

lowed by a midgut. After traversing the waist the midgut expands dorsally and continues posteriorly to join the hindgut, a short **rectum** with a dorsal **storage sac** leading to the anus. The midgut has the usual pouches. The first pair extend forward in the prosoma and send branches into the bases of the legs. In the opisthosoma are several more highly branched pouches. As in other arthropods these not only secrete enzymes but also absorb nutrients.

A pair of **malpighian tubules** are located at the junction of the midgut and hindgut. The dorsal heart lies in a separate part of the hemocoel as in the crustaceans. The nervous system is condensed into a brain and a large subesophageal ganglion with connectives and nerves to all parts of the body.

Argiope has two respiratory systems. The book lungs are continually flushed with blood that is oxygenated as it passes through. Since the blood is not known to contain any respiratory pigment, however, not much oxygen can be carried. The single spiracle opens into a **tracheal system.** The tubes are small and do not branch as much as in the insects, but they are structurally identical and have the same spirally thickened, chitinous lining.

A pair of **poison glands** fills the dorsal part of the prosoma, opening on the tips of the chelicerae by way of slender ducts. Prey is first killed with poison from these glands, then wrapped tightly in silk from the spinnerets. The spider applies its mouth to the prey, and secretions containing proteolytic enzymes from glands behind the mouth begin digestion. The resulting broth is sucked into the midgut where digestion is completed and the nutrients are absorbed.

The **ovary** lies in the opisthosoma beneath the midgut, opening anteroventrally by way of an **oviduct** through a **genital pore** between the openings to the book lungs. Associated with the oviduct is a **seminal receptacle** where sperm are received. The male is much smaller than the female, with **testes** and a **sperm duct** in the opisthosoma. Before copulation the male transfers the sperm to specialized cavities in the tips of his pedipalps. At copulation the pedipalps are thrust into the female opening and the sperm are expelled into the receptacle. The whole maneuver is remarkably like that of the cephalopod mollusks. The eggs are fertilized as they are laid and are put in a cocoon spun by the spinnerets. They hatch later into miniature spiders.

Associated with the three pairs of spinnerets are five kinds of **silk glands** in the ventral part of the opisthosoma. The different secretions yield different kinds of silk, including the nonsticky radial fibers of the web, the sticky circular fibers, and the brownish fibers of the cocoon. Silk is emitted as a fluid that instantly hardens into tough protein threads.

16.17

The Phylum Onychophora

The **Onychophora** are about 70 species of wormlike, segmented, terrestrial animals with metameric legs. All the living species found in very damp regions of the tropics belong to one family, and possibly to one genus, *Peripatus* (Fig. 16.31).

During development, segmentation appears in *Peripatus* in a manner very similar to that in the arthropods and annelids (especially in the heavily yolked eggs of the latter). The coelomic cavities neither form the main body cavity as in the annelids nor disappear as in the arthropods, but persist as small cavities associated with annelid-like, metameric nephridia. The adult body cavity is a hemocoel like that of the arthropods. The embryonic first segment persists and bears a pair of **preantennae.** The mouth opens on the second segment whose appendages become **jaws.** The appendages of the third segment lie beside the mouth as **oral papillae** which can shoot out slime to entangle an enemy. The rest of the paired appendages are short *unjointed* legs ending in terminal **claws.** The body covering is a thin, soft cuticle like that of the annelids, but contains numerous small **spiracles** from which **tracheal tubes** branch into the body.

These characteristics are sufficient to differentiate the Onychophora from both the Annelida and the Arthropoda as a separate phylum. Although the group is often used as a possible ancestral type for the Arthropoda, linking them to the Annelida, a second look shows that *Peripatus,* a terrestrial organism itself, forms a rather awkward tie between trilobites and annelids. A view which is now winning acceptance is that the first segmented, pre-annelid, pre-onychophoran, pre-arthropod animals probably radiated into a number

Figure 16.31 *Peripatus,* a member of the Onychophora, a "missing link" between the Annelida and the Arthropoda. (Courtesy of Ward's Natural Science Establishment.)

of groups, of which three exist today. There is some speculation that the Onychophora may once have been more widespread and may have included a wider variety of forms. This view is supported by the discovery in 1930 of *Aysheaia,* a Cambrian fossil. The particular rocks in which 11 specimens were found are remarkable for the perfection of their fossils and contain clear prints of many soft-bodied animals otherwise unknown from that ancient period. *Aysheaia* appears to have been a marine, peripatus-like animal.

If this current view proves correct, then although the Onychophora share characteristics with both the annelids and the arthropods and are often intermediate structurally, they would not be considered an evolutionary link but a third surviving branch of an ancient and possibly much diversified group of segmented organisms.

SYNOPSIS OF ARTHROPODS AND ONYCOPHORANS

PHYLUM ARTHROPODA. Segmented protostomous eucoelomates with a hemocoel and jointed legs.

†**Subphylum 1. Trilobita.** Antennae on second segment, biramous limbs on all succeeding segments. One class with five orders.

Subphylum 2. Chelicerata. Chelicerae on third segment, no antennae.

†CLASS 1. AGLASPIDA. Limbs on opisthosoma small but leglike. One order.

CLASS 2. XIPHOSURA. Horseshoe crabs. One order. Book gills on opisthosoma. *Limulus.*

†CLASS 3. EURYPTERIDA. Opisthosoma divided into mesosoma and metasoma. Appendages of mesosoma gill-like. One order.

CLASS 4. PYCNOGONIDA. Sea spiders. Body greatly reduced, opisthosoma rudimentary. One order.

CLASS 5. ARACHNIDA. Respiration by book lungs or trachea or both. Appendages of the fourth segment often specialized as pedipalps.

Subclass 1. Latigastra. Mesosoma broadly joined to prosoma.

Order 1. Scorpiones. Scorpions. Poison sting on telson, pedipalps chelate.

Order 2. Pseudoscorpiones. Like scorpions but very small, no sting.

Order 3. Opiliones. Daddy-longlegs or harvestmen. Pedipalps tactile, legs very long, opisthosoma very short.

Order 4. Acari. Mites and ticks. *Sarcoptes, Dermacentor.*

Additional orders of uncertain taxonomic affinities:

† Extinct.

Order 5. Myzostomida. Parasites with a much simplified adult morphology, usually considered to have evolved from the mites.

Order 6. Tardigrada. The water bears. Small aquatic or semiterrestrial arthropods with a simplified morphology. Usually considered to have evolved from the mites.

Subclass 2. Cauligastra. Constriction between mesosoma and prosoma.

Order 1. Palpigradi. Minute, legs long, metasoma long and threadlike.

Orders 2, 3. Schizomida and Thelyphonida. Whip scorpions. Pedipalps large and chelate, metasoma long and whiplike.

Order 4. Phrynichida. Pedipalps large but not chelate, opisthosoma rounded.

Order 5. Araneae. Spiders. Poison sting in chelicerae. *Argiope.*

Order 6 Ricinulei. Rare tropical spider-like forms.

Order 7. Solifugae. Chelicerae short but very stout, pedipalps leglike.

Subphylum 3. Crustacea. Antennae on second and third segments. One class. If another class is included (see doubtful groups at the end of this phylum) the class of Crustacea would be defined further as having mandibles on the fourth segment.

CLASS 1. CRUSTACEA.

Subclass 1. Branchiopoda. Thoracic limbs leaflike, respiratory.

Order 1. Anostraca. Brine shrimps and fairy shrimps.

Order 2. Notostraca. Tadpole shrimps, *Apus.*

Order 3. Conchostraca. Clam shrimps.

Order 4. Cladocera. Water fleas, *Daphnia.*

Subclass 2. Ostracoda. Body without segmentation and entirely enclosed in a bivalved carapace. Five orders, including:

Order 1. Podocopa. Includes most of the fresh-water species.

Order 2. Myodocopa. Includes several common marine species.

Subclass 3. Cirripedia. Sedentary, compound eyes lacking, carapace forms a mantle covering body and often secreting a shell.

Order 1. Thoracica. Acorn and gooseneck barnacles.

Order 2. Acrothoracica. Barnacles commensal on mollusk shells.

Order 3. Ascothoracica. Parasites of corals with enlarged mantle.

Order 4. Apoda. Parasites of barnacles; mantle and limbs lacking.

Order 5. Rhizocephala. Parasites of crabs, shrimps, etc., largely internal.

Subclass 4. Copepoda. Small, one pair of maxillipeds, no abdominal appendages.

Order 1. Branchiura. Fish lice. Ectoparasites, with compound eyes.

Order 2. Eucopepoda. No compound eyes. The copepods.

Subclass 5. Cephalocarida. Small, intermediate between the Copepoda and Malacostraca, possibly ancestral to both. One order.

Subclass 6. Mystacocarida. Similar to copepods but with different segmentation. By broadening the definition of subclass 4, subclasses 5 and 6 can be included as orders equal in rank to the fish lice and true copepods.

Subclass 7. Malacostraca, the large crustaceans. Thorax of eight segments.

SUPERORDER 1. LEPTOSTRACA. Abdomen of eight segments including telson (all others have seven). One order. *Nebalia.*

SUPERORDER 2. PERACARIDA. Incomplete carapace, abdomen narrow.

Order 1. Mysidacea. Mysid shrimps. Short carapace present.

Order 2. Cumacea. Mud-inhabiting relatives of the mysids.

Order 3. Amphipoda. No carapace. Beach fleas, scuds.

Order 4. Isopoda. No carapace. Gribbles, sow-bugs, pill-bugs.

SUPERORDER 3. HOPLOCARIDA. Short carapace, abdomen wider than cephalothorax. One order. The mantis shrimps.

SUPERORDER 4. EUCARIDA. Carapace covers entire thorax.

Order 1. Euphausiacea. Krill.

Order 2. Decapoda. Shrimps, lobsters, crabs, crayfish (*Cambarus, Astacus*).

Subphylum 4. Labiata. Antennae on second segment, nothing on third, mandibles on fourth. Second maxillae form lower lip.

Superclass 1. Myriapoda.   Adults with more than three pairs of legs.

CLASS 1. CHILOPODA.   Centipedes. First legs are poison fangs. Five orders.

CLASS 2. DIPLOPODA.   Millipedes. Every other body segment reduced, especially dorsally. About eight orders.

CLASS 3. PAUROPODA.   Similar to millipedes. Small, eyeless, with branched antennae. Two orders.

CLASS 4. SYMPHYLA.   Small, eyeless. Mouth parts and legs similar to those of insects. One order.

Superclass 2. Hexapoda.   Adults with three pairs of legs. One class, Insecta.

CLASS 1. INSECTA.

Group 1. Apterygota.   Primitively wingless, very little metamorphosis. Orders 1 and 2 are often placed in a separate class.

Order 1. Thysanura.   Silverfish, firebrats.

Order 2. Entotrophi.   Similar to the Thysanura but lack scales on body.

Order 3. Protura.   Lack both eyes and antennae. Often considered to be a class.

Order 4. Collembola.   Springtails, snowfleas. Often considered to be a class, sometimes a superclass.

Group 2. Pterygota.   With wings, although numerous species have secondarily lost the wings. When the above groups are separated as three classes, this group forms a fourth and is usually called Insecta.

Subclass 1. Paleoptera.   Wings held stiffly out at the sides. Five extinct orders and:

Order 1. Odonata.   Dragonflies and damselflies.

Order 2. Ephemeroptera.   Mayflies.

Subclass 2. Neoptera.   Wings fold back when at rest.

SUPERORDER 1. EXOPTERYGOTA.   Wingbuds external, metamorphosis incomplete. Five extinct orders and:

Order 1. Plecoptera.   Stoneflies.

Order 2. Orthoptera.   Praying mantis, walking sticks, grasshoppers, crickets and katydids.

Order 3. Blattaria.   Cockroaches.

Order 4. Isoptera.   Termites.

Order 5. Dermaptera.   Earwigs.

Order 6. Embioptera.   Somewhat like termites and earwigs.

Order 7. Thysanoptera.   Thrips.

Order 8. Psocoptera.   Book lice.

Order 9. Mallophaga.   Bird lice or biting lice.

Order 10. Anoplura.   Sucking lice. *Pediculus, Phthirus,* etc.

Order 11. Hemiptera.   True bugs, plant lice, cicadas, *Rhodnius.*

SUPERORDER 2. ENDOPTERYGOTA.   Wing buds internal, metamorphosis complete.

Order 1. Neuroptera.   Lacewings, ant lions, etc.

Order 2. Mecoptera.   Scorpion flies.

Order 3. Trichoptera.   Caddis flies.

Order 4. Lepidoptera.   Butterflies and moths.

Order 5. Coleoptera.   Beetles.

Order 6. Strepsiptera.   Small, with vestigial anterior wings.

Order 7. Hymenoptera.   Sawflies, ants, bees (*Apis*), wasps, etc.

Order 8. Diptera.   True flies, gnats, mosquitos, *Dermatobia,* etc.

Order 9. Siphonaptera.   Fleas. *Xenopsylla.*

Of several extinct arthropod groups of uncertain affinities, the Archaeostraca (four orders) are probably a subclass of the class Crustacea. The Homopoda (four orders), with two pairs of antennae followed by biramous limbs, can be considered a separate class in the subphylum that includes the Crustacea. The Xenopoda (one order) are intermediate between trilobites and the chelicerates. Since they have antennae they should probably be placed as a class in the subphylum containing the class Trilobita.

PHYLUM ONYCOPHORA.   Segmented, with a hemocoel, one pair of unjointed limbs per segment. One order. *Peripatus.* Often considered to be a class of the Arthropoda.

QUESTIONS

1. Compare diagrammatic body segments of an arthropod and a polychaete annelid.
2. Which limbs put food into the mouth in each of the four arthropod subphyla?
3. When did each of the subphyla develop terrestrial forms?
4. Describe the nauplius larva.
5. What is a pleopod?
6. List the sense organs of a crayfish and give their locations.
7. Describe what happens to food from the time it is captured until its nutrients are absorbed in the crayfish.
8. Compare the circulatory systems of arthropods and annelids.
9. What are the locomotor organs of *Daphnia*?
10. Contrast centipedes, millipedes and insects.
11. What is a pulvillus?
12. Compare the excretory systems of *Cambarus* and *Periplaneta*.
13. What is the functional significance of the characteristic that separates the Neoptera from the Peleoptera?
14. Describe complete metamorphosis.
15. What is a pollen basket?
16. Give the life cycle of the honeybee.
17. What animal has two respiratory systems?
18. Discuss the relation of the Onychophora to the arthropods.

ANNOTATED REFERENCES

Crompton, J.: The Life of the Spider. Boston, Houghton Mifflin Co., 1954. A readable and informative account of the natural history of spiders.

Imms, A. D.: Insect Natural History. London, William Collins Sons & Co. Ltd., 1947. A remarkable text by one of our foremost entomologists, written for the nonspecialist.

Maeterlinck, M.: The Life of the Bee. Boston, Houghton Mifflin Co., 1954. A detailed account of the complex life history of the bee.

Zimm, H. S., and C. Cottam: Insects. New York, Simon and Schuster, 1956. One of many manuals intended for insect identification. This paperbound is adequate for the beginner and contains pictures of many common species.

17 _____ PHYSIOLOGY OF THE ARTHROPODA

In this large and varied phylum, a number of physiological problems have been studied extensively. Some of these studies have revealed mechanisms different from their analogues in the vertebrates. In this chapter, some of the better known and more interesting ones—molting, hormones, innervation patterns, flight and compound eye vision—will be discussed.

17.1
Molting

All arthropods periodically shed their chitinous exoskeleton as a part of growth and metamorphosis. The length of the period between molts is variable, depending on both irregularities in the growth sequence of a species, the amount of food available and other environmental factors. The hardness of the exoskeleton limits any change in size or shape until the time just around molting. The actual shedding of the old skeleton and the hardening of the new, which may take a few seconds (daphnia) or several hours (lobster), is only the visible culmination of the elaborate process of **molting** or **ecdysis.** Before shedding occurs, the new skeleton is preformed and some of the materials of the old skeleton are salvaged. Salvage measures are even more extensive when the molt is coincident with a change in shape, i.e., metamorphosis.

The exoskeleton is composed of three layers (Fig. 17.1). The outermost is a thin, flexible, colorless **epicuticle** composed of wax and **cuticulin,** a lipoprotein containing a large amount of fatty material. The middle layer is the **primary chitinous layer,** composed of chitin and cuticulin, sometimes impregnated with calcium carbonate or other salts. The inner **secondary chitinous layer** is made almost entirely of chitin and protein. The epidermis lies beneath this as a single layer of cells with numerous filamentous extensions into the two chitinous layers.

During the **intermolt period,** numerous metabolic processes are carried out by the arthropod which produce the necessary materials for the next ecdysis. The first step toward a molt is a separation of the epidermis from the old skeleton by the secretion of a **molting fluid** (Fig. 17.1). Glandular cells in the epidermis add to the fluid enzymes capable of digesting protein and chitin but not cuticulin. While the epidermis lays down a new epicuticle, the molting fluid begins to erode the old secondary chitinous layer.

Formation of a new skeleton and salvage of the old go on simultaneously. All of the secondary chitinous layer and some of the primary layer are ultimately digested, although the amount of cuticulin in the latter may prevent its complete digestion. If growth is to take place at the next molt, the epidermis with its new epicuticle grows and becomes wrinkled within the confines of the old skeleton. It begins to secrete a soft, pliable primary chitinous layer.

At the time of molting the new epicuticle and the primary chitinous layer are complete, although they are still soft and flexible. The molting fluid and its digested products are completely absorbed into the body. The old epicuticle and much of the primary chitinous layer remain as a loose covering. At various

275

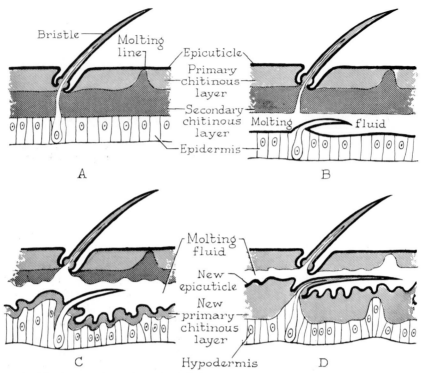

Figure 17.1 Molting in an arthropod. *A,* The fully formed exoskeleton and underlying epidermis between molts. *B,* Separation of the epidermis and secretion of molting fluid and the new epicuticle. *C,* Digestion of the old secondary chitinous layer and secretion of the new primary chitinous layer. *D,* Just before molting. (Modified from Wigglesworth.)

places, especially along the back, the old primary layer is thin so that, after the secondary layer is digested away, a line appears along which the old skeleton will break (Fig. 17.1).

The arthropod must then swell up to burst the old exoskeleton. It may contract the abdomen, forcing blood into the head and thorax, or it may swallow water or air. Once the old exoskeleton has been split open, the organism extricates itself, shedding not only the covering of the body and legs, with all their fine bristles, but also the lining of the foregut and hindgut and, in the labiates, the lining of the tracheal system. The molt period is a dangerous time for an arthropod, dangerous because of the physiological difficulties of completing the molting process and because of the lack of protection against predators and abiotic elements during the time its exoskeleton is still soft. Many arthropods "go into hiding" just before the molt to avoid the added dangers posed by predation and desiccation (in the case of land dwellers). The land hermit crab buries itself deep in the sand prior to molting, as it is subject both to desiccation and to attack by nonmolting fellow hermits when it is soft.

If the arthropod grows during the molt, it must swell rapidly to stretch the wrinkled new exoskeleton out to its full size. Most arthropods swallow water or air to do this and may double their volume. Even if the organism is not growing at some particular molt, it may be necessary to compress some parts of the body in order to force blood into others so as to achieve whatever metamorphosis is taking place. A newly emerged adult moth, for example, contracts the abdomen to force blood into the wrinkled wings and expand them to full size. After the skeleton is adjusted to its new size and shape, the epidermis secretes enzymes which oxidize and harden the epicuticle and primary chitinous layers. Usually the primary layer, which at first is pale, darkens during this process. In some cases, special areas harden quickly before the main part of the exoskeleton; these are parts that are required to help finish the molting process. In the crayfish and many other hard-shelled forms, calcium carbonate is deposited as an additional stiffening agent. The crayfish has previously absorbed much of this lime from the old skeleton and has stored it on the sides of the stomach between epidermis and chitinous lining as **gastroliths** (p. 251). In the spiny lobster, the needed materials are stored in the hepatopancreas and the blood; in this marine crustacean, however, the supply of calcium carbonate is not as critical as in a fresh-water species, owing to the presence of large amounts of this chemical in sea water. After the molt the gastroliths are exposed to digestive fluids and dissolve rapidly, providing an immediate supply for the new skeleton.

The final event of molting occurs later. The epidermis secretes the secondary chitinous layer as a permanently elastic portion of the exoskeleton. The desired flexibility of any part of the exoskeleton is achieved to a considerable extent by the thickness of the two chitinous layers. Where rigidity is required, the outer layer is thick; where a tough but flexible skeleton is required, the inner layer is thick; and where great flexibility is needed, both layers are thin.

17.2
Arthropod Hormones

The molting of both crustaceans and insects is under endocrine control. Arthropods produce a number of other hormones that regulate metabolism, reproduction and changes in pigment. As the glands secreting these hormones are discovered and studied, it is becoming apparent that arthropods have an endocrine system functionally similar in many ways to that of the vertebrates. Both are intimately related to the brain. In both phyla antagonistic hormones are known, and in both some of the glands have reciprocal effects on each other which provide for a system of "feedback" control. However, arthropod and vertebrate endocrine systems evolved independently.

An important contribution to the field of physiology made by investigators of arthropod function was the discovery of **neurosecretion**, the secretion of physiologically active substances by nerve cells. In a narrower and more usual sense, neurosecretion refers to the production of hormonal materials in the cell body of a neuron which then travel the length of the axon to be stored and ultimately released at the tip (Fig. 17.2). These are specialized nerve cells whose primary function is the production and release of hormonal substances, and not the conduction of nerve impulses.

The primary endocrine organs of crustaceans, for example, were once believed to be the **sinus glands** found on the optic ganglia of the eyestalks (Fig. 17.3). Extracts of these glands contain a variety of hormones, including one that affects the distribution of pigment in the compound eyes, two that control pigmentation of the body, one that affects molting, and several that influence metabolism and reproduction. It was later recognized that the sinus glands are composed of the expanded tips of nerve axons surrounding a blood sinus, thus forming a **neurohaemal organ.** The cell bodies of these axons lie some distance away and form the **X organs** (Fig. 17.3). The cell bodies making up the X organs are the site of production of the hormones; the sinus gland is simply a storage area. It has been shown that granules produced in the nerve cell bodies of the X organs travel through the axons and are stored in the expanded terminals in the sinus glands. A number of different kinds of cell bodies can be recognized in the X organs, each presumably producing a distinctive hormone.

Neurosecretory organs are also well known in insects. The major organ initiating physiological activity is the **intercerebral gland** on the surface of the brain (Fig. 17.4). Axons

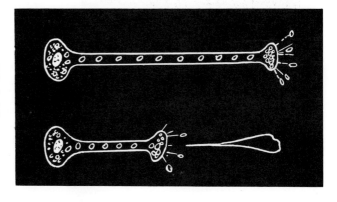

Figure 17.2 Neurosecretion. The neuron produces secretion granules in the cell body (left) that are stored in the expanded tip of the axon, from which they may also be released (right). If the axon is cut, material accumulates at the cut (below).

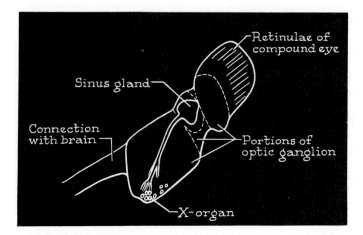

Figure 17.3 Eyestalk of the crab with the skeleton removed, showing sinus gland and X organ. (After Passano.)

from these neurosecretory cells pass posteriorly to the **corpora cardiaca** which, like the crustacean sinus glands, are composed primarily of the expanded terminals of axons. The corpora cardiaca also contain cells which play a role in the endocrine system. Although a number of hormones are elaborated by the intercerebral gland, the one that has been studied most extensively is that related to molting.

The hormonal control of molting in insects is now well understood. The process is initiated by the intercerebral gland with the release of a **prothoracicotropic hormone** through the tips of the axons in the corpora

cardiaca. This hormone stimulates another endocrine gland, the **prothoracic** or **ecdysial gland,** and sets in motion an irreversible chain of events. In some insects, the conditions which lead to the activity of the intercerebral gland have been studied. For example, in the bloodsucking bug *Rhodnius,* stretch receptors in the abdomen are stimulated following a large meal of blood, and this in turn stimulates the intercerebral gland cells to become active. *Rhodnius* feeds infrequently, but one large meal is sufficient to support the metabolism associated with a molt.

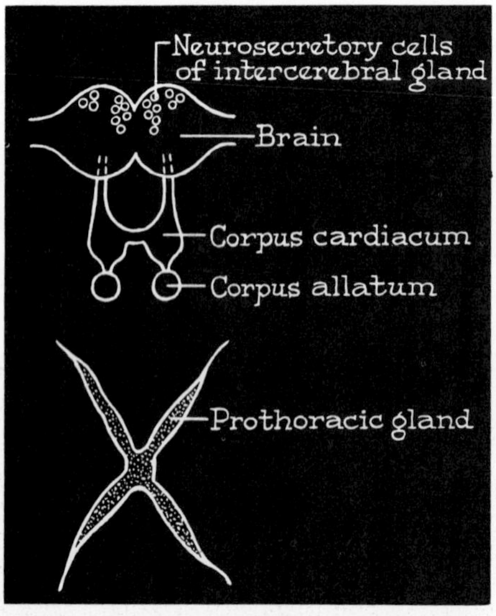

The prothoracic gland is a diffuse set of strands of large ectodermal cells in the ventral part of the prothorax. Upon stimulation, this gland produces a hormone which induces a molt. The prothoracic gland hormone has been extracted, purified, crystallized and named **ecdyson.** Ecdyson is a powerful hormone, since very small amounts injected into an insect will induce an immediate molt. It is a steroid, probably derived from cholesterol.

Ecdyson appears to exert its effect by directly affecting certain genes. In the larvae of the dipteran *Chironomus,* the formation of puffs in restricted regions of chromosomes has been associated with a high level of synthetic activity by the DNA triplets of those regions. Injection of ecdyson is followed within 15 minutes by the formation of these chromosomal puffs. The hormone appears to affect a number of DNA sites independently. Other hormones produced by the intercerebral gland control the laying down of the wax layer in the epicuticle and the tanning of the new cuticle.

Figure 17.4 Endocrine glands of the cockroach. The upper group lie above the esophagus in the head. The lower gland is ventral in the prothorax, strung among the muscle cells. (After Bodenstein.)

Associated with molting in insects is the

Figure 17.5 Effect of the removal ot the corpora allata in the silkworm. Moth at left is normal. Moth at the right developed from a young caterpillar whose corpora allata were removed. It pupated at the next molt after the operation. (After Bodenstein from Fukuda.)

phenomenon of metamorphosis. A caterpillar, for example, may molt several times with little morphologic change and, at the next molt, become transformed into a pupa. A grasshopper nymph after several molts will, at the last molt, acquire wings. The control of metamorphosis involves a third set of endocrine organs, the **corpora allata** (Fig. 17.4). These are small glands in the head, just behind the corpora cardiaca. Neurosecretory material from the brain is stored in the corpora allata. If these glands are removed from a young larva or nymph, metamorphosis proceeds at the next molt, even though this may be several molts early (Fig. 17.5). Conversely, if corpora allata from young individuals are implanted in insects scheduled to undergo metamorphosis, the juvenile form is retained (Fig. 17.6). Apparently, a **juvenile hormone** is elaborated by these glands which tends to prevent metamorphosis. Normally, in insects with complete metamorphosis, the glands are active at each larval molt, secrete at a reduced rate at the pupal molt, and show little or no activity at the adult molt. Perhaps the most spectacular experiment involves the injection of an extract of corpora allata into a pupa. Such a pupa may molt to produce another pupa!

The juvenile hormone and ecdyson interact to control the normal course of events. When both are present, the growth of larval tissues is promoted while the growth of future adult structures is inhibited. When juvenile hormone is absent, ecdyson promotes the growth of adult tissues. The juvenile hormone also helps to maintain the prothoracic gland, thus making further molts of any kind possible. In many of the insects that do not molt after reaching maturity, the prothoracic gland degenerates and disappears, apparently owing to a lack of the juvenile hormone.

The changes that take place during insect metamorphosis are of special interest, due to the common occurrence of what has been termed "programmed cell death." As the animal changes from one form to another, many tissues and organs disappear as others are formed. For example, in the abdomen of *Bombyx*, a silkworm, special intersegmental muscles are necessary to force fluid into the thorax and assist in the rupture of the old cuticle. But the adult moth does not molt again, and these muscles are useless. Within 48 hours after the pupal-adult molt, these muscles have disappeared completely, their substance broken down ,by enzymes and

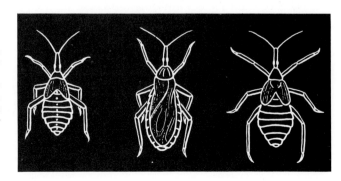

Figure 17.6 The effect of adding corpora allata in *Rhôdnius*. The last stage nymph (left) normally molts to form an adult (center). When corpora allata from young nymphs are added to a last stage nymph, it molts to form an oversized nymph (right). This later molts again to become an oversized adult. (After Wigglesworth.)

taken up by phagocytic cells. This loss is initiated by the presence of ecdyson coupled with the absence of juvenile hormone. As a consequence, as soon as the final molt is complete, neural activity in the motor nerves leading to these muscles ceases. This cessation of neural activity appears to be responsible for the breakdown of the muscles. Artificial stimulation of the nerves prolongs the life of the muscles.

The corpora allata also contain hormones that affect other phenomena in some groups of insects. The deposition of yolk in the eggs and the secretions of the accessory sex glands are under the control of the corpora allata. In addition, in some cockroaches the male is attracted to the female by a chemical secreted by the female, the production of which is controlled by the corpora allata.

Molting in the crustaceans involves a somewhat different pattern of endocrine interaction. When the eyestalks (containing the X organs and sinus glands) are removed, a molt usually occurs, indicating that the hormone involved tends to prevent molting. As in the insects, however, the effect appears to be indirect, since the hormone influences another gland and not the molting process directly. In crustaceans this is the **Y organ,** composed of diffuse strands of ectodermal cells at the base of the large muscles of the mandibles. The Y organ produces a hormone that induces molting. This hormone has not yet been extracted and purified, but ecdyson

prepared from insects will readily induce molting when injected into crustaceans, and it is likely that the hormone produced by the Y organ is similar to ecdyson.

Apparently, the hormone of the X organ prevents secretion by the Y organ, which has been shown to contain and possibly to accumulate granules throughout the intermolt period. When X organ activity decreases or stops, the Y organ rapidly empties of granules and the molting process is initiated. Recent studies of larval crustaceans have indicated some hormonal control of metamorphosis, and raise the possibility that a hormone akin to juvenile hormone may be involved in the process.

In many crustaceans, the production of eggs by the female, copulation and the later release of larvae are associated with distinct phases of the molting cycle. Thus the hormonal systems controlling the reproductive cycle and molting are in some way connected. Hormones produced by the ovaries not only promote the development of mature eggs but also the formation of secondary sex characteristics such as specialized setae for the attachment of fertilized eggs. In males, a specialized gland, the **androgenic gland,** found at the base of one pair of walking legs, secretes a hormone which controls the development of the testis and of male secondary sex characteristics. Implantations of androgenic gland can almost completely reverse the sex of a female crustacean.

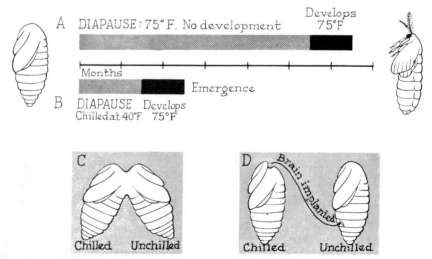

Figure 17.7 Diapause in the pupae of the cecropia moth. *A,* Normal development at 25° C. (75° F.). *B,* Normal development with diapause broken by six weeks (or more) of chilling at 4° C. (40° F.). *C,* When chilled and unchilled pupae are joined, diapause is broken in both individuals. *D,* The brain of a chilled pupa, implanted in an unchilled pupa, induces immediate development in the latter.

Further interactions among the endocrine organs are evident in the control of diapause in moths. Diapause is a state of arrested development which occurs in many eggs, insect pupae and plant seeds. The large moth, *Platysamia cecropia* (Fig. 16.24), overwinters as a pupa formed in the middle or late summer. If newly formed pupae are kept at 75° F., they remain inactive for five or six months. Eventually, however, development does proceed, and the moths emerge four weeks later. If new pupae are chilled to 40° F. for six weeks and subsequently placed at 75° F., development proceeds at once. Hence chilling leads to an end of diapause and shortens the period of pupal life. Carroll Williams, finding that both a chilled and an unchilled pupa will develop if grafted together (Fig. 17.7), suggested that diapause is under hormonal control. He found further that the brain of a chilled pupa implanted in an unchilled pupa will end its diapause. By combining chilled and unchilled organs in various ways, he showed that only the chilling of the brain is important. Upon being chilled the brain releases the prothoracicotropic hormone to which the prothoracic glands respond (whether they were chilled or not) by releasing ecdyson, which ends the diapause. Once the brain acts upon the prothoracic glands, its continued presence is not needed to produce the molt. In one experiment, Williams implanted a chilled brain in an unchilled pupa, then transferred it to a second unchilled pupa. Both pupae ended diapause promptly and developed into adults. In other insects, differences in photoperiod are the environmental variables that stimulate the end (or beginning) of diapause.

17.3

Patterns of Muscular Innervation

The individual motor axons of vertebrates each innervate a few muscle fibers of a single muscle, forming a **motor unit** (p. 90). The strength of any given muscular contraction is a function of the number of motor units active, and the duration of contraction is controlled by the duration of stimulation from the nerves.

In arthropods the anatomic relations of nerve and muscle fibers are different. A single axon may not only innervate all the fibers of one muscle but may innervate those of an-

other muscle as well. Furthermore, most muscles receive just two or a few axons. However, each of these has a different effect upon muscular contraction. Usually in a three-axon system, one axon produces a strong brief contraction, another a weak sustained contraction, and the third inhibits the action of the other two. By varying the frequency of stimulation among the axons, the strength and duration of muscular contraction can be varied considerably.

Muscular contraction may be inhibited by one of two ways in crustacean systems. More commonly, an inhibitory neuron releases a chemical substance (the inhibitory neurotransmitter) which directly affects the conductance of the muscle and thus prevents or decreases its response to the release of the excitatory neurotransmitter. In a second possible mechanism, termed **presynaptic inhibition,** the inhibitory neuron affects the excitatory neuron, decreasing the probability that it will release its excitatory transmitter. Both of these effects are mimicked by gamma-aminobutyric acid (GABA), but final proof that this is the neurotransmitter is lacking.

A study of the innervation pattern for several muscles shows how precision can be achieved, even when one axon innervates more than one muscle. The four muscles of the hand and claw of the crayfish are represented diagrammatically in Figure 17.8. The claw opener and hand extensor share a single excitor axon but have different inhibitory

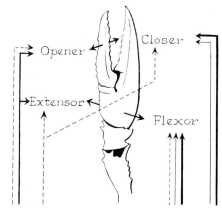

Figure 17.8 Nerve supply to the last four muscles of the crayfish pincers. Each vertical line represents a single axon, which supplies all the fibers of the indicated muscle(s). Dotted lines show inhibitory axons; heavy lines show rapid, strong excitors; and thin lines show slow, sustained excitors. Arrows on the pincers indicate the directions of movement.

axons. The hand extensor muscle shares its inhibitor with the claw closer. The claw closer has two excitor axons, one for rapid strong contraction and one for slow sustained contraction. The hand flexor has three axons, one of each type, unshared by other muscles being considered. It is important to remember that most arthropod motor axons have many endings on the surface of a muscle and that the contraction of such a muscle is the summation of many small, relatively nonconducted local contractions of the muscle. A variety of strengths of contraction can be obtained by the rate of action potentials coming from the neurons involved. A **graded response** to stimulation occurs even though only a few neurons may be involved in the stimulation.

In the behavior of the crayfish pincers, only one activity requires the instantaneous activity of two muscles: a sudden thrust or reach toward an adversary. Analysis of the nerve pattern shows that only one axon need be active to produce this response; it stimulates both the extension of the hand and the opening of the claw in a single operation. At the end of the thrust, the claw can be clamped shut by stimuli in the rapid excitor axon of the claw, whether or not the claw opener is inhibited, since the closer is a much more powerful muscle. Hence, the whole maneuver of thrust and grab can be accomplished by activity in two axons.

In more gentle manipulatory movements an opener inhibitor is probably useful, to permit gentle and sustained activity in the claw closer. Obviously, if the claw is to be opened during manipulation, the much stronger muscle that closes the claw must be relaxed. Interestingly enough, the inhibitor of the claw closer also inhibits the extensor, so that opening of the claw can be accomplished as a simple unhampered motion by activity in two axons.

This pattern of connections between nerves and muscles, which is comparatively simple anatomically by vertebrate standards, permits remarkably fine control and rapid activity. This is accomplished with very few neurons, a feature seen at all levels of the arthropod nervous system. This simplicity in numbers makes analysis of the system much more feasible than in the vertebrates, where the number of units to be analyzed in order to understand even the simplest movements, is staggering. The student who looks in dismay at the crayfish and says "It will never work, it has too many moving parts," does not appreciate the underlying simplicity of the system associated with all those parts.

17.4
The Flight Mechanism in Insects

Unlike birds and bats, insects do not have large flight muscles attached to the wings. Instead, the wings are articulated with the thorax in such a way that very slight changes in the shape of the thorax cause the wings to beat up and down. The flight muscles are located entirely within the thorax and are not attached to the object moved.

The thorax can be compared to a box having an undersized cover (Fig. 17.9). The inner end of each wing is attached by a movable joint to the upper edge of the sides of the box. When the **vertical muscles** of the thorax contract, the notum is depressed and the wings flip upward. When **longitudinal muscles** contract, the notum arches upward and the wings flip down. The flight muscles are very stout and undergo little change in length during contraction. The two major sets of muscles are opposed and pull alternately against each other. The thoracic box and articulating mechanism are actually made up of a number of parts of the exoskeleton, and there are a number of muscles

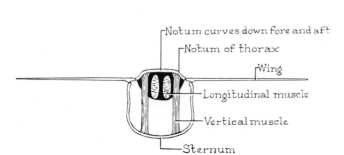

Notum curves down fore and aft

Notum of thorax

Wing

Longitudinal muscle

Vertical muscle

Sternum

Figure 17.9 Diagram of the primary flight muscles. Vertical muscles extend between the notum and the sternum. Longitudinal muscles extend between the downturned ends of the notum.

involved in flight. But the system works in the general manner described above.

In many insects (all the Exopterygota and Lepidoptera and most Coleoptera), the frequency of the wing beat is closely correlated with the frequency of the nerve impulses to the muscles. The impulses are evenly spaced in time and staggered in the nerves to the two sets of muscles, so that rhythmic up and down movements of the wings result. The rate varies with the rate of the nerve impulses, from eight wing beats per second in large moths to 75 or more in the smaller insects.

In many of the Diptera and Hymenoptera, and possibly a few Coleoptera, the wing beats are not correlated with the frequency of the nerve impulses. Low frequency nerve impulses have little or no effect, but when the frequency rises above 100 or so per second the flight muscles begin to contract rapidly but at a higher frequency. J. W. Pringle has studied this phenomenon and found that not only are the nerve impulses not correlated with the wing beats, but their frequency is irregular and not staggered in nerves to opposing muscles. Hence, although the frequency of the nerve impulses must exceed a certain threshold, once this is exceeded the rhythm of muscular contraction originates within the muscles. Such **myogenic rhythms,** as opposed to the **neurogenic rhythms** in other insects, produce frequencies that may reach 300 or 400 wing beats per second. Standard neurogenic systems could not maintain such frequencies because of limitation of the nerve in its ability to conduct action potentials in rapid succession.

A critical feature of such myogenic rhythms is the tension in the system. If one set of flight muscles is cut, the other will not develop its rhythm. The two must act together, each alternately stretching the other. The frequency of contraction depends upon the tension in the flight muscles, and this tension is caused not only by the opposing flight muscles but can be increased by other smaller muscles in the thorax. If these smaller muscles contract steadily, they increase the tension and raise the frequency of wing beat. The hum of a mosquito, fly or bee is an accurate indicator of this frequency, since changes in tone indicate changes in frequency.

Pringle has recently shown that a single muscle can develop rhythmic contractions if it is suspended with a weight hung on one end. As he predicted, the frequency of contraction is a function of the magnitude of the weight. He has also shown that the rhythm is myogenic, being independent of the frequency of nerve stimulation. Rhythmic contractions of isolated stretched myofibrils will continue indefinitely if ATP is supplied; they can be switched on or off by altering the concentration of calcium ions in the surrounding medium.

In the evolution of these small, fast-flying, higher insects the coordination of the flight muscles has been taken from the nervous system and built into the muscles themselves. The ability to contract repeatedly under tension is apparently a result of adjustment in the internal physiology of the muscle cells, perhaps at the level of the interaction of actin and myosin molecules.

In many insects with slow neurogenic rhythms, the path traced by the wing tip as it moves up and down shows that the wing moves evenly from the up or down position

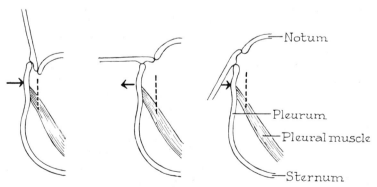

Figure 17.10 The "click" mechanism. A comparison of the three figures, using the dotted line as a reference line, shows that the sides of the thorax are pushed out when the wings are horizontal, and closer together when the wings are up or down. Oblique muscles to the sides of the thorax produce tension to enhance the "click," which is a rapid conclusion of the wing beat upward or downward.

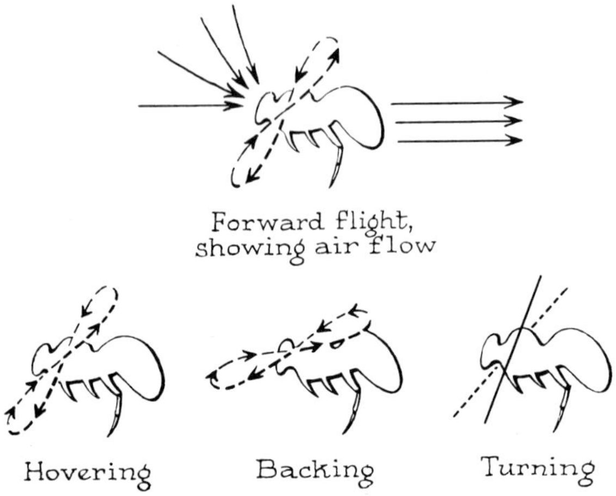

Forward flight, showing air flow

Hovering

Backing

Turning

Figure 17.11 Flight maneuvers in the honeybee. The figure eight in the first three diagrams traces the path of the left wingtip. The lines on the last diagram show the positions of the two wings during a full beat. (After Stellwaag.)

to the horizontal, and then "clicks" suddenly the rest of the way down or up. Until recently the "click" mechanism was not understood. It has turned out to be a marvel of simplicity: Some of the small muscles of the thorax attach to the inner upper edge of the elastic thoracic box, just below the point where the wings articulate (Fig. 17.10). The steady contraction of these muscles tends to pull the sides of the box together. A study of the figure shows that the distance between the upper edges of the box is least when the wings are up or down and greatest when the wings are horizontal. Hence, as the wings begin to move they do so against the force of these small muscles until they reach the half-way point, when they move with the force and are suddenly accelerated. This guarantees full amplitude to the wing beat and a sudden, rapid stretching of the relaxing set of muscles just before their next contraction. Such stretching improves the stength of contraction of many kinds of muscles, including those of the vertebrates.

In all winged insects, smaller muscles in the thorax attached to the sides and wing bases are used to alter the posture of the wings as they move up and down. Suitable contraction of these muscles enables the insect to turn, hover or back up (Fig. 17.11). While the details of these processes are too intricate to present here, the general pattern of ordinary flight is such that the wings act as propeller blades, drawing air from above, in front, and the sides, and propelling it posteriorly as a sharply driven column of air. The details are modified endlessly in the various groups of insects.

17.5
Vision

The functioning of the compound eyes is a most intriguing physiologic problem. It was recognized at an early time that images formed by such eyes must be very different from those formed in our eyes. Their structure (Figs. 16.7 and 17.12) suggests that each ommatidium records the amount of light received from a particular direction and that all of them together provide a **mosaic** impression of the world. This theory received considerable support when Exner, in 1891, sliced off the compound eye of a firefly and used it as a lens for making a photograph. The image on the film was a single large one and was erect rather than inverted as in our eye.

More recent work shows that, in addition to receiving the light from directly in front, each ommatidium transmits light less and less effectively as the incident light arrives more and more obliquely. Eyes with few ommatidia gather light from wide angles. All the light transmitted through the cornea and cone is brought to a point at the internal tip of the cone, where it enters the ends of the seven to 15 **rhabdomes** (Fig. 17.12) which form a single **retinula.** In the horseshoe crab, *Xiphosura*, each retinula unit contains a central **eccentric cell,** surrounded by the rhabdomeres. In this animal, it appears that the rhabdomeres act as the **sensory transducers** which in some way produce a nonpropagated change in membrane potential, called the **generator potential,** upon receiving light energy. This generator potential affects the eccentric cell in such a way that it produces

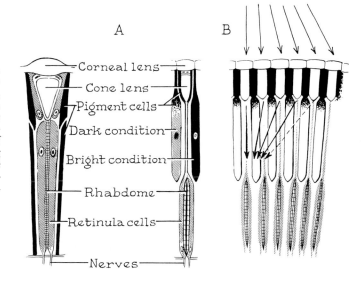

Figure 17.12 *A*, Insect ommatidia, showing a diurnal type (left) and a nocturnal type (center). In the nocturnal type, the pigment is shown in two positions, adapted for very dark conditions on the left side, and for relatively bright conditions on the right. *B*, Nocturnal type of eye adapted for dark conditions, showing how light can be concentrated upon one rhabdome from several lenses. If the pigment moved downward, light from peripheral lenses would be screened out.

the propagated action potential, which carries information toward the central nervous system.

The curtains of pigment separating adjacent ommatidia vary from arthropod to arthropod and, in many species, from day to night. Diurnal species usually have a complete curtain formed by two sets of pigment cells (Fig. 17.12) so that each retinula can receive light only from its own lens system. In nocturnal species, however, the pigment is restricted to the outer layers, and the retinulae are separated some distance from the inner ends of the cones. In such eyes, light from a distant point can pass through several adjacent lenses to be superimposed on a single underlying retinula.

In both kinds of eyes the pigment may migrate, usually under hormonal control, according to the intensity of the light. The pigment of the nocturnal eye (Fig. 17.12) spreads inward under bright light, reducing the number of facets that can superimpose an image. In this way the total light reaching the light-sensitive regions is reduced to avoid glare.

The visual acuity (ability to perceive detail) of arthropods has been studied extensively. A common method is to take advantage of a reflex by which many animals attempt to maintain a constant orientation with respect to the environment. The animal is placed in a circular, glass-walled container around which is rotated a drum with vertical black and white stripes on the interior (Fig. 17.13). If the

animal sees only a mixed gray it remains quiet. If, however, it can distinguish the stripes, the rotational impression is very strong and the animal turns or walks in circles to stay with the drum. By varying the width of the stripes, the discriminative limit can be tested.

Two general conclusions can be derived from such studies: (1) Visual acuity varies according to the excellence of the lens system in the ommatidia, which admit light through wider incident angles in some arthropods

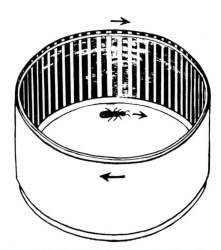

Figure 17.13 A device for estimating the visual acuity of an arthropod. A drum with internal vertical stripes is rotated slowly around a circular glass dish. If an arthropod inside can distinguish the stripes, it tends to move with them and maintain a fixed relation with the surroundings.

than in others. (2) Acuity varies inversely with the number of ommatidia. Even the best visual acuity of the arthropods tested is only about one-sixtieth as good as that in the human, and the acuity of most of them is much worse than this. The compound eye is generally considered to be a much better detector of movement than it is a former of images.

Neurophysiological studies of compound eyes were the first to elucidate the phenomena of contrast enhancement by **lateral inhibition.** By recording the action potentials in the interneurons between the retinula and the brain, it was shown that when one ommatidium was stimulated the nerve activity of the adjacent ones was decreased, thereby increasing the difference in the level of neuronal activity of adjacent interneurons.

Recently more complex "discriminatory interneurons" have been investigated in certain crabs. Just as in the frog's visual system, some interneurons in the optic tract fire only when something moves across the crab's eye in a specific way. Some report to the brain on the general level of light intensity, others on when there is a sudden increase or decrease in light intensity, and still others on various types of movement. Such **peripheral filtering** of sensory information is common in the arthropod nervous system.

Von Frisch has extended his study of vision to an investigation of the honeybee's ability to discriminate among various shapes. If a group of white cards is placed on the ground with a glass dish on each (Fig. 17.14) and syrup is placed in only one dish, bees discovering the syrup will load up, return to the hive, and come back for more. Others come too, and soon many may be coming and going. The bees are marked with paint as they feed so that they can be recognized when they return. If all the cards look alike to the bees, they alight on all the dishes. If, however, the card with the syrup is recognizably different, once each bee has found it she will return only to that dish.

By using cards marked in various ways, von Frisch found that bees did not discriminate among squares, circles or triangles (Fig. 17.15), nor did they distinguish two lines from a cross. They did, however, distinguish between solid and open figures and between one line and two lines. While they did not distinguish between a bar and a solid square,

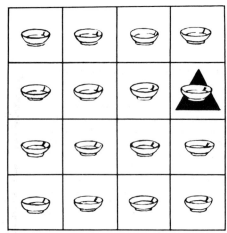

Figure 17.14 Design for studying discrimination in bees. All 16 cards had dishes, but only a few dishes had syrup. By varying background (as on one card above), the ability of the bees to discriminate could be observed. This design was also used to study color vision. (After von Frisch.)

they easily distinguished one bar from two that occupied less space than the square.

Obviously, form discrimination in insects and in man utilizes different criteria to different degrees. Later work supports these early experiments by von Frisch and shows that important criteria for insects are the contrast in brightness or color between design and background, complexity of the contours of the design, and the extent to which the pattern is subdivided. A condition which enhances the ability to discriminate, and which may be necessary to it, is movement either of the insect or the pattern so that the image moves rapidly across the mosaic of retinulae in the compound eye. It is suggested that patterns of visual stimulation in time, rather than in space, are the primary

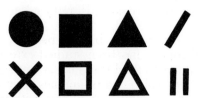

Figure 17.15 In feeding experiments, bees did not distinguish among the figures of the top row, or among those of the bottom row. They did distinguish between the members of any pair including one upper and one lower figure. (After von Frisch.)

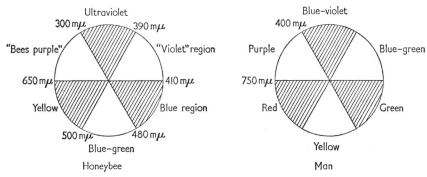

Figure 17.16 Color wheel of the honeybee compared to man's. (After Burkhardt.)

basis of form discrimination in insects. Thus a single black bar produces a single wave of darkening across the compound eyes of a flying bee, while two black bars, or an open square, produce two waves of darkening.

These results indicate the risk involved in drawing negative conclusions from experiments with behavior. If only solid figures had been used, von Frisch might well have concluded that bees discriminate very poorly if at all. Actually, the choices presented to the bees simply would not have provided stimuli appropriate for the response being studied.

A more dramatic case of this kind occurred earlier in experiments with color vision. Men have long wondered whether other animals perceive color, and many early experiments were negative. Again, the critical factor turned out to be whether or not the stimulus used was an appropriate cue for the situation. Kupelweiser stated in 1913 that bees were color-blind. Discovering that captured bees released in a dark room invariably flew to windows, he performed a variety of excellent experiments in which bees could choose between two windows of varying brightness and color. He showed without a doubt that only brightness is involved in the choice. The same year, however, von Frisch did his classic experiments on color vision in bees, using groups of colored cards some of which had syrup. He found proof of good color vision, with what we call orange, yellow and green seen as one color, blue-green another, blue and violet a third, and ultraviolet a fourth (Fig. 17.16).

These two sets of experiments are not contradictory. Both have been repeated successfully. They illustrate that in its escape reactions the bee uses only brightness cues, whereas in feeding it uses color cues. Man is handicapped to the extent that he cannot ignore color in an attempt to evaluate brightness. Ordinarily man does very poorly in judging the relative brightness of dissimilar colors.

Color vision has now been demonstrated in a wide variety of insects and crustaceans, and in some cases two visual pigments have been extracted from the eyes of animals showing color vision. Microelectrode recordings of the spectral sensitivity of single units in the eye of the drone bee have shown units that are maximally sensitive in the ultraviolet, another the blue, and a third in the yellow region. Even the tiny daphnia with a single compound eye distinguishes between orange-yellow-green and blue-green–blue-violet. Probably most compound eyes distinguish color to some extent. Butterflies, as a final example, are easily trained to feed at blue or yellow cards among other colors and grays, but cannot be trained to visit green. The conclusion that they cannot distinguish green is shown to be false by the demonstration that, when laying eggs, they visit only green cards.

An interesting phenomenon which has been observed in a number of higher crustacea, is the presence of a **caudal photoreceptor.** This is not an eye in any sense, but it does respond to light stimulation, presumably reporting only the presence or absence of light. The spectral sensitivity of these receptors on the sixth abdominal ganglion is similar to that of the compound eye. How the individual crustacean utilizes this information or how this group of nerves operates in the intact animal is not known.

QUESTIONS

1. How does an arthropod escape from its old exoskeleton?
2. What are gastroliths?
3. Describe the role of the sinus glands in the crustacean endocrine system.
4. Define neurosecretion.
5. How was the role of the corpora allata in insects determined?
6. Describe the general features of the innervation of muscles in arthropods.
7. What is a myogenic rhythm?
8. Draw a diagram of an ommatidium in a day-flying insect.
9. How did von Frisch discover color vision in bees?

ANNOTATED REFERENCES

Prosser, C. L., and F. A. Brown: Comparative Animal Physiology. 2nd ed. Philadelphia, W. B. Saunders Co., 1961. This general source of information on all animals is particularly good on the arthropods.

Roeder, K. D. (Ed.): Insect Physiology. New York, John Wiley & Sons, Inc., 1953. This collection of papers comprises an exhaustive and authoritative account of insect physiology.

Waterman, T. H. (Ed.): The Physiology of Crustacea. New York, Academic Press, Vol. I, 1960; Vol II, 1961. Thirty-one of the world's experts have contributed chapters to this important reference work on the physiology and behavior of crustaceans.

Wigglesworth, V. B.: The Principles of Insect Physiology. 3rd. ed. London, Methuen & Co. Ltd., 1947. One of the best of a variety of texts on this subject, by one of the world's foremost authorities.

18 MINOR PHYLA

The major phyla, the ones composed of many and diverse kinds of animals, are each discussed in separate chapters. The animal kingdom contains, in addition, a number of forms which are not related closely enough to any of these major phyla to be a class within one of them and so are classified as separate phyla. This emphasizes that a phylum is not a *large* assemblage of organisms but a group of organisms which are so unique in structure and function that they are not closely related to any other group. Some of these minor phyla (Ctenophora, Nemertea, Onychophora and Hemichordata) are treated elsewhere; the remaining ones are described briefly here.

18.1
Mesozoa

The **Mesozoa** (Fig. 18.1A) are minute parasites found in the body cavities of certain invertebrates; one is found in the kidney of the octopus. The body structure is the simplest of any multicellular animal. Each is composed of a ciliated outer cell layer and an inner mass of reproductive cells. While the group itself is well defined, it cannot be related easily to other animals. Two views on the origin of these animals are current: that they arose directly from the Protozoa and that they represent extremely degenerate flatworms. They

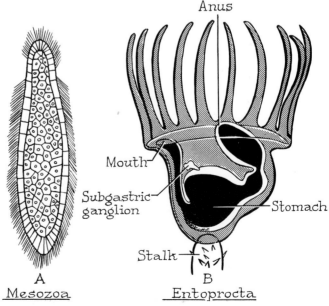

Figure 18.1 Mesozoa (*A*), showing the ciliated epithelium surrounding an inner mass of reproductive cells, and Entoprocta (*B*), showing some of the internal organs.

Anus

Mouth

Subgastric ganglion

Stomach

Stalk

A
Mesozoa

B
Entoprocta

have complex life cycles with asexual as well as sexual reproduction.

18.2
Entoprocta

The **Entoprocta** (Fig. 18.1*B*) are small, sedentary, stalked animals with a complete digestive tract and a pair of protonephridia. Although the larva has a brain, this is lost in metamorphosis and the central nervous system of the adult consists of a subesophageal (actually subgastric in position) ganglion. The gut is U-shaped, and both mouth and anus are surrounded by a circle of ciliated tentacles. Water is swept upward through the tentacles, and food particles are passed from the sides to the upper surfaces of the tentacles, where short cilia carry them down to the mouth. The digestive tract is a simple gastrodermis without musculature except on the stomodeal and proctodeal portions. Between the gut and the body wall is a space filled with a few scattered cells and a viscous fluid. This structure resembles closely the pseudocoelom of the Aschelminthes.

Entoprocts are primarily marine, with one family occurring in fresh water. Many of the species form branching colonies by asexual budding from the stalk. In several species the upper portions or **calyces** of the individuals die during the winter or other adverse circumstances, but the stalks remain alive and regenerate new calyces in the spring or when suitable conditions return. In sexual development the egg follows a modified spiral cleavage to produce a ciliated free-swimming larva. The larva attaches by its ventral surface, but the organs rotate 180 degrees so that in the adult the "ventral" surface is directed upward.

The taxonomic position of this phylum is uncertain. The body structure is that of a pseudocoelomate, and much of the body is clothed in cuticle as in the Aschelminthes. But the entoprocts adhere more closely to typical spiral cleavage than the Aschelminthes, and at the cellular level they show none of the extreme specializations of the Aschelminthes. The entoprocts have good powers of regeneration. Asexual budding is common in the entoprocts but is unknown in the Aschelminthes. It seems reasonable, therefore, to suppose that the two groups have evolved independently from a flatworm stock, but have independently reached comparable levels of structural complexity.

18.3
Sipunculoids and Echiuroids

The **Sipunculoidea** and **Echiuroidea** (Fig. 18.2) are relatives of annelids in which seg-

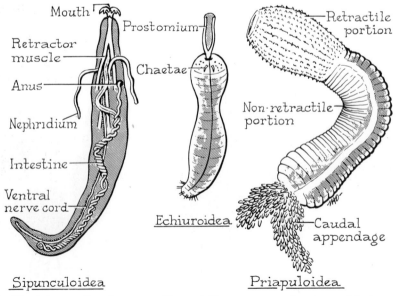

Figure 18.2   Three groups of marine worms. Sipunculoidea, cut open to show some of the internal organs. (After Brown.) Echiuroidea (after Parker and Haswell) and Priapuloidea (after Theel) shown in side view.

mentation has been lost. In both phyla the egg follows spiral cleavage to produce a trochophore larva. In the further development of the trochophore, segmentation begins to appear (three pair of somites in sipunculoids, 15 in echiuroids) but then disappears. Both groups are marine.

Echiuroids are sausage-shaped worms that move about very little and lie buried in the mud or within cavities of shells, with a greatly developed, mucus-covered prostomium projecting. The prostomium is ciliated and is used for gathering detritus from the bottom surface and passing it to the mouth. Neither a distinct brain nor sense organs are present; the esophagus is surrounded by a nerve ring continuous with the ventral nerve cord.

In the genus *Bonellia,* which has a very long, forked prostomium, an interesting case of sexual dimorphism is found. Each larva can develop into either sex. If it settles by itself on the bottom it becomes a female, which is a sizable, fully developed worm. If the larva lands on a female, however, it becomes a male, which remains microscopic in size and simplified in morphology and lives in the mouth or nephridia of the female.

Sipunculoids are elongate flexible worms with a retractile anterior end used for burrowing in sand. They swallow the sand and digest the debris and small organisms it contains. The mouth is surrounded by a ciliated, tentacled disc. The digestive tract includes a long intestine that doubles back from the posterior end to a dorsal anus well forward on the body. The nervous system is well developed and is similar to that of the annelids, but the circulatory system is reduced and restricted to the anterior end of the body. The coelom is large and undivided.

18.4

The Priapuloids

The **Priapuloidea** (Fig. 18.2) is another phylum of sizable marine worms that lack segmentation. The anterior end is retractile and carries a large mouth that opens into a muscular pharynx lined with teeth. Priapuloids plow through mud and swallow whole whatever prey they can seize. The nervous system resembles that of the echiuroids, and a circulatory system is lacking. Young priapuloids have a sheath of cuticular plates enclosing the posterior, nonretractile portion

of the body. Their early development is unknown.

For many years these animals have been allied with the sipunculoids and echiuroids. Then notice was taken of the fact that although the body cavity is lined with a membrane it did not appear to be cellular, and the possibility arose that the cavity is a pseudocoelom. Comparisons have been made between the young and some of the rotifers (although they differ greatly in size). The poorly developed nervous system and absence of a circulatory system are further evidence for grouping the priapuloids with the Aschelminthes. The digestive tract, however, is completely muscularized, and the large size and general appearance of these worms do not suggest a pseudocoelomate affinity. More recently, the cellular nature of the peritoneum has been demonstrated. Until their early development is learned, the true relations of this group probably will not be known. For the present they will be placed as a group related to the annelids.

18.5

The Phoronids and Brachiopods

The **Phoronida** and **Brachiopoda** (Fig. 18.3) include medium-sized sessile marine animals with a **lophophore,** a circle of ciliated tentacles surrounding the mouth. Typically, the lophophore in these phyla is drawn out to each side into whorls. The cilia draw water toward the animal and food particles are passed down a ciliated tract at the tentacle bases to the mouth. In both phyla the eucoelom, circulatory system and metanephridia are well developed, so that they are obviously eucoelomates. Each group contains few living species.

Phoronids live in membranous tubes in the sand or cemented to rocks. They have a long body with a U-shaped gut, the anus opening just behind the lophophore. During feeding, the lophophore is extended from the tube into the open water. Brachiopods are encased in a bivalved shell, the ventral shell being slightly larger than the dorsal shell. They have a superficial resemblance to the bivalved mollusks. In some species a stalk projects through the hinge to attach the animal to rocks; in others the stalk is absent and the animals lie free on the bottom. Either the anus opens to one side of the lophophore

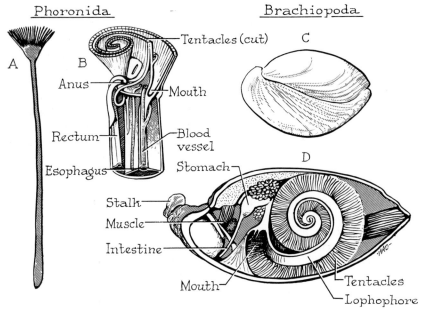

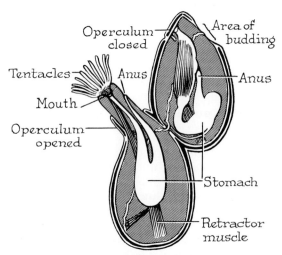

Figure 18.3   Phoronida: *A*, Whole animal in side view. *B*, Half of anterior end showing internal organs. (After Parker and Haswell.) Brachiopoda: *C*, Side view of shell. *D*, Side view showing internal structure. (After Borradaile et al.)

or the gut ends blindly without an anus. During feeding the shells are opened slightly and water is drawn in. Most brachiopods have shells composed of calcium carbonate, as in many other groups of animals. In some, calcium phosphate is used.

Although the Brachiopoda are a minor phylum today, they were a major group in the past. Throughout the Paleozoic era they were abundant, with thousands of species in all the oceans of the world. Most of the fossil shells that can be found today in shale and slate deposits are not those of clams, but of brachiopods.

The relation of these phyla to other eucoelomates is obscure. Their early development is variable, but in all cases shows a wide departure from the spiral cleavage—trochophore pattern. Cleavage follows a simpler pattern. Some species are schizocoelous while others are enterocoelous. In some the mouth forms from the blastopore (characteristic of the mollusk-arthropod series) while in others it is a new opening (characteristic of the echinoderm-chordate series). In the light of these variations the two phyla are sometimes considered to represent survivors of an intermediate group between the two major series, a group that possibly was involved in the evolution of the echinoderm-chordate series from the "main line" with its spiral cleavage.

18.6
The Bryozoa

The **Bryozoa** are minute colonial animals that also have a lophophore (Fig. 18.4). They are common in both salt and fresh water. They have a long fossil record but, apparently, were never a dominant group. Although they have no circulatory system or excretory organs, they have a well-developed

Figure 18.4   Diagrammatic view of two individuals in a colony of Bryozoa. The upper individual is retracted. (After Twenhofel and Schrock.)

eucoelom. The absence of some structures is probably an adaptation to small size. The lophophore is circular or U-shaped, and the cilia draw water toward the animal. Food particles are swirled into the mouth. The tentacles bend actively and are somewhat selective, knocking large debris to one side and sometimes hitting smaller particles toward the mouth. The colonies are formed by asexual budding, and often a particular individual in the colony will degenerate, to be replaced by the development of a surviving bud of tissue.

The position of bryozoans in the animal kingdom is debatable. They are usually grouped with the brachiopods and phoronids to form an assemblage of animals with lophophores. Bryozoans also show some similarities with the pterobranchs, a class in the phylum Hemichordata (Chapter 19). It seems best to leave this phylum in an indefinite position between the two major series of eucoelomates.

18.7

The Chaetognatha

The **Chaetognatha** (Fig. 18.5) or arrowworms are a phylum of a few species that may be extremely abundant in the marine plankton. These small worms prey voraciously on other small animals, grasping them with the anterior spines and swallowing them whole. They float motionless in the water and move in sudden jerks by flips of the body. Arrowworms are transparent, revealing much of their internal anatomy without dissection. They lack both circulatory and excretory systems but have a spacious coelom divided into a head cavity, a pair of trunk cavities and a pair of postanal tail cavities. The paired cavities are separated by vertical mesenteries. The worms are hermaphroditic, with ovaries in the trunk cavities and testes in the tail cavities. The nervous system is composed of a well-developed brain and a single large ventral ganglion.

Development is direct. The egg undergoes simple cleavage and the coelom is enterocoelous. The mouth forms as a new opening considerably in front of the blastopore. In its early embryology, therefore, the arrowworm resembles the echinoderm-chordate series. In other respects, however, they show no resemblance whatsoever. The phylum is usually grouped with the echinoderm-chordate se-

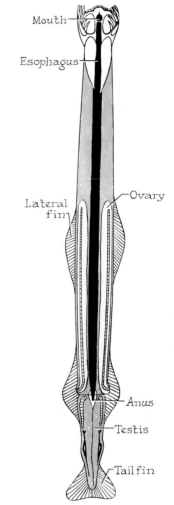

Figure 18.5 Chaetognatha. A ventral view of a mature specimen. (Modified from Parker and Haswell.)

ries, but it seems preferable to place a gap between them. It is possible that this phylum evolved from the same stock that produced the chordates but diverged early and then followed a somewhat parallel course of evolution.

The minor phyla include animals of interest primarily to the zoologist, who is interested in any animal that presents a unique way of life. These phyla represent life forms that have failed to dominate the scene, and this, in itself, is a challenging problem. They are of special interest to the student of phylogeny, for among them may be found intermediate stages that will reveal how the major groups arose. It is evident from the foregoing (and from the discussions of minor phyla in other chapters) that in some cases a study of minor groups has helped our understanding of phylogeny. In other cases, new and interesting situations are revealed that are of little use in the understanding of other groups and, in some instances, the result is more confusion rather than less. Although they offer no simple solution to the problem of phylogeny, the minor phyla enrich the subject considerably.

SYNOPSIS OF MINOR PHYLA

PHYLUM MESOZOA.   Parasitic. A single layer of outer cells surrounds a few reproductive cells. Two orders. Uncertain whether they arose from the Protozoa or by simplification from the Platyhelminthes.

PHYLUM ENTOPROCTA.   Pseudocoelomates with a circle of ciliated tentacles surrounding both mouth and anus. One order in one class.

PHYLUM ECHIUROIDEA.   Adults not segmented, larvae with up to 15 segments. One pair of ventral chaetae. One order. *Bonellia.* Often considered to be a class of the Annelida.

PHYLUM SIPUNCULOIDEA.   Adults not segmented, larvae with up to three segments. No chaetae, anus dorsal, head retractile. One order. Often considered to be a class of the Annelida.

PHYLUM PRIAPULOIDEA.   Adults not segmented, larvae unknown. No chaetae, anus posterior, head retractile. No circulatory system. One order. Often considered to be a class of the Annelida and sometimes a class of the Aschelminthes.

PHYLUM PHORONIDA.   With a lophophore. No skeleton. One order.

PHYLUM BRACHIOPODA.   With a lophophore. Dorsal and ventral shells.

    CLASS 1. INARTICULATA.   Shells without hinge, anus present. Two orders. *Lingula.*

    CLASS 2. ARTICULATA.   Shells hinged, anus absent. Two or three orders. Lampshells.

PHYLUM BRYOZOA.   Moss animals, with a lophophore surrounding the mouth. Circulatory system and nephridia absent. Two orders. *Bugula.*

PHYLUM CHAETOGNATHA.   Arrowworms. Enterocoelous, with lateral fins. One order.

QUESTIONS

1. List the 10 major phyla.
2. Compare an entoproct and a bryozoan.
3. Compare sipunculoids and echiuroids with the annelids.
4. What is a lophophore?
5. Sketch and label a chaetognath.

ANNOTATED REFERENCES

(See Chapter 13 for general references on invertebrates.)

19 THE PHYLA HEMICHORDATA AND ECHINODERMATA

Hemichordates and echinoderms are sedentary or slow-moving inhabitants of the ocean floor. Most of them feed on debris and microscopic organisms, although a few echinoderms are predaceous. Both phyla are entirely marine. They range from the shoreline to the ocean depths, and from the tropics to the poles. Echinoderms are conspicuous and common everywhere, but the hemichordates are seldom noticed, although they may be locally abundant in the sand and mud. Echinoderms have a predominantly radial symmetry which is not so well developed, however, as that of the coelenterates. The hemichordates are of special interest to the zoologist because they show affinities with both the echinoderms and the chordates.

19.1

The Phylum Hemichordata

Hemichordates are bilaterally symmetrical animals with a body divided into three regions (Fig. 19.1): the **proboscis,** the **collar** and the **trunk.** The proboscis contains an anterior projection of the gut, the **stomochord.** The collar has a well-developed dorsal **collar nerve** and numerous **gill slits** open into the pharynx along the sides of the trunk.

Each body region contains a separate portion of the eucoelom. The portion in the proboscis (coelom$_1$) opens to the outside through one or two dorsal pores. The muscular proboscis can expand or contract, flushing sea water in and out of its cavity. The portion in the collar (coelom$_2$) opens to the outside through a pair of lateral pores; it can also be filled with and emptied of sea water. The third portion (coelom$_3$) forms a typical body cavity in the trunk, lying between the viscera and the body wall.

The phylum is divided into three classes. The largest class is the **Enteropneusta** which includes the wormlike form shown in Figure 19.1C. Its 60 species vary in length from 2 to 250 cm. The second class, **Pterobranchia,** includes a few minute species, some of which are colonial. In the pterobranchs the collar with its coelomic cavity is expanded dorsolaterally as a pair of branched tentacles used for gathering food (Fig. 19.2). The trunk is folded so that the anus lies just behind the mouth. Despite their small size the pterobranchs show all the hemichordate characteristics except the gill slits, which are reduced to a single pair in some species and are absent altogether in others. They live mostly at considerable depths and have seldom been studied alive.

The third class, the **Pogonophora,** has been poorly known until recently. At first thought to be restricted to great depths, they are now known to be common over wide areas of ocean bottom. They are usually placed in a separate phylum, but their em-

295

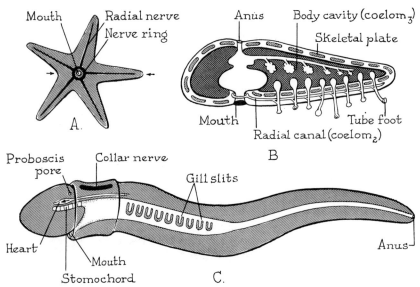

Figure 19.1 Diagrammatic representations of the Echinodermata and the Hemichordata. *A*, Ventral view of a starfish (echinoderm). *B*, Vertical section through a starfish at the position of the arrows in *A*. *C*, Lateral view of an acorn worm (hemichordate) showing a few internal structures.

bryology and body plan relate them strongly to hemichordates. They are very slender, long worms living in membranous tubes in the bottom ooze. The proboscis and collar regions are externally fused and bear long tentacles whose coelomic cavities apparently connect with the proboscis cavity, not the collar cavity as in the pterobranchs. Mouth, anus, gill slits and digestive tract are absent. The nervous system, circulatory system and general trunk anatomy are similar to those of other hemichordates. Apparently, in life the tentacles form a long cylinder pro-

jecting anteriorly. Many minute branches on the tentacles line this cylinder. It is probable that digestion and absorption occur here.

Saccoglossus. Enteropneusts, many of which live in shallow water, have been studied extensively. A familiar species is *Saccoglossus kowalenski* (Fig. 19.3) of the Atlantic coast. These burrow in sandflats near the low tide line, living in semipermanent tunnels lined with a mucous secretion. The **mouth,** which apparently cannot be closed, lies ventrally between the proboscis and the collar. As the worm burrows, much of the sand is swallowed.

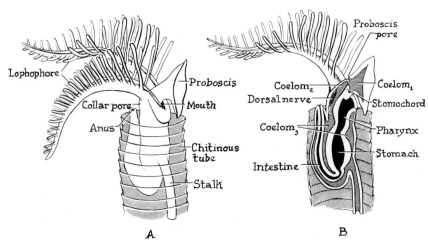

Figure 19.2 Class Pterobranchia (genus *Rhabdopleura*). *A*, Lateral view of one animal in its case (lower portion of case and stalk omitted), showing external features. *B*, Diagrammatic section showing some of the internal organs.

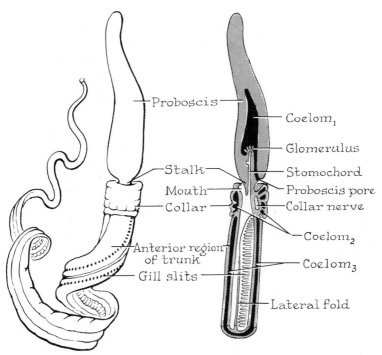

Figure 19.3 Class Enteropneusta (genus *Saccoglossus*). *Left,* External view showing external features (after Bateson). *Right,* A diagrammatic section through the anterior part of the body showing some of the internal organs. A lateral fold subdivides the pharynx into a ventral channel along which the sand passes and a dorsal channel containing the gill slits.

In the **pharynx** excess water passes out through the **gill slits** and the sand passes down a long **intestine.** All the nourishment of *Saccoglossus* comes from organic debris in the sand. Eventually, the sand is eliminated through a terminal **anus,** often piling up in long coils around openings to the burrows.

The yellowish pink **proboscis** of *Saccoglossus* is longer than that of most enteropneusts. The junction of proboscis to collar is a narrow **stalk.** The **proboscis pore** that opens into the coelomic cavity of the proboscis is located dorsally at the posterior margin of the proboscis. The reddish **collar** overlaps the stalk in front and the trunk behind. Its coelomic cavity opens on the sides through a pair of ducts that end at the first pair of gill slits in the trunk. *Saccoglossus* burrows by inflating the collar against the tunnel wall, pushing the deflated proboscis forward, inflating the proboscis, deflating the collar, and pulling the body forward.

The **trunk** is divisible into three regions. In the anterior part numerous pairs of gill slits open externally near the middorsal line. The middle part of the trunk contains the gonads, which are gray in the female and yellow in the male. The posterior region contains only the posterior part of the intestine and tapers gradually to the anus.

Although each gill slit first appears as a simple slit, later in development the internal aperture, the opening into the pharynx, becomes U-shaped (Fig. 19.4). The fleshy **tongue bar** that grows down from the dorsal margin is primarily a respiratory organ and contains a capillary network in which blood is oxygenated as it passes from the ventral blood vessel to the dorsal blood vessel.

Blood is carried forward in a dorsal vessel of the trunk and collar to the **heart,** which lies in the proboscis (Fig. 19.1). It is then pumped through the **glomerulus** (Fig. 19.3), a tortuous knot of vessels projecting into the coelomic cavity of the proboscis, and passes posteriorly through a ventral vessel. The coelomic epithelium covering the glomerulus is glandular, and waste products are believed to be removed from the blood at this point. The waste is excreted into the coelom and flushed out with the sea water as the cavity is filled and emptied. Branches from the ventral vessel in the trunk lead not only to the gills but also to the gonads, intestine and

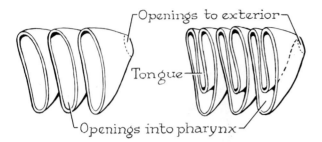

Openings to exterior

Tongue

Openings into pharynx

Figure 19.4 Diagram showing how simple gill slits (*left*) become U-shaped (*right*) by the down-growth of tongue-bars from the roof of each slit. The external opening remains simple.

body wall. Collecting vessels from these organs return all blood to the dorsal vessel, where it is mixed as it passes forward again. All the major vessels are contractile. The **stomochord** (Fig. 19.3) is an outgrowth of the pharynx that extends into the proboscis. The cells of this diverticulum are large and vacuolated, resembling the cells of the chordate notochord. On the ventral surface of the stomochord the mesoderm secretes a chitinous plate which, together with the stomochord, supports and stiffens the proboscis. A notochord-like tissue is also found along the ventral margin of the intestine in some enteropneusts.

The nervous system is very poorly centralized and is more primitive in most respects than that of the flatworms. The proboscis is underlaid with a thin continuous layer of neural tissue. Most of the collar lacks this layer but, dorsally, a longitudinal strip of

ectoderm constricts off to form a tubular **collar nerve.** The trunk has a layer of neural tissue similar to that of the proboscis and, in addition, the nerve fibers tend to concentrate dorsally and ventrally to form **longitudinal nerves.** The collar nerve appears to function primarily as a pathway for nerve fibers between the proboscis and trunk and cannot be considered to be *the* central nervous system. Except for the collar nerve the entire system is at the body surface and is covered only with epidermis.

19.2
Classification of the Echinoderms

Living echinoderms are divided into five classes (Fig. 19.5): (1) **Crinoidea,** the sea lilies and feather stars; (2) **Holothuroidea,** the sea cucumbers; (3) **Echinoidea,** the sea urchins

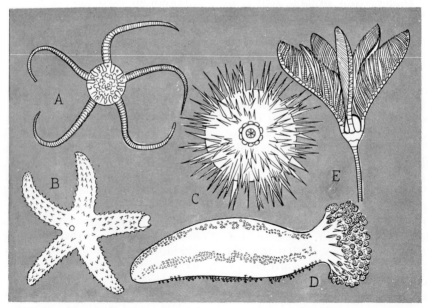

Figure 19.5 The five living classes of the Echinodermata. *A,* Ophiuroidea, brittle stars. *B,* Asteroidea, starfishes. *C,* Echinoidea, sea urchins. *D,* Holothuroidea, sea cucumbers. *E,* Crinoidea, sea lilies. (*C* after Hunter and Hunter, others after Hyman.)

and sand dollars; (4) **Asteroidea,** the starfish; and (5) **Ophiuroidea,** the brittle stars and basket stars. In addition, a number of extinct echinoderms have been identified that are placed in some five additional classes. Most echinoderms are large and have skeletons, and many of the species are or have been abundant. This phylum has a rich fossil record, probably the best known of any phylum, that reaches back to the early part of the Paleozoic era. The number of known extinct species greatly outnumbers the number of known living species.

The five living classes are so different in their structural features that space does not permit an adequate description of each one. The general aspects of the classes will be given following a detailed description of a member of the Asteroidea.

19.3
Asterias forbesi, A Typical Five-rayed Starfish

Asterias lives on rocky or shell-covered bottoms, where it preys extensively on shellfish. The common species of the east coast, *A. forbesi* (Fig. 19.6), is at times abundant and may seriously deplete whole populations of oysters. Because of its economic importance this starfish has been studied extensively.

Its color is variable, including shades of brown, yellow, orange, pink and purple. The five arms or **rays** are joined at the center to form a **disc.** On its upper surface the disc bears a bright orange or yellow **madreporite,** a fine-meshed sieve that opens into a part of the coelom. The eccentric location of the madreporite is the only obvious departure from radial symmetry in the starfish.

Asterias is protected from predators by a spiny skeleton in the mesoderm just beneath the epidermis. A layer of calcareous plates connected by short bands of connective tissue and muscle forms a tough barrier (Fig. 19.6*D*). In addition, many of the plates bear **tubercles** and **spines.** The former are mere bumps, whereas the latter are jointed at the base and supplied with muscles so that they can be pointed in various directions. Spines bordering the ambulacral grooves are especially long and numerous and can be closed over the grooves to protect them if the starfish is torn loose from the bottom. Each skeletal piece is secreted as a single crystal of calcium carbonate. Although the entire skeleton is originally covered with epidermis, that on the spines is often worn off.

The settling mud and the larvae of various organisms seeking places to attach are threats to a slowly moving creature. In echinoderms the epidermis is ciliated, and the ciliary currents continually sweep the fine debris that settles on the starfish out to the sides, where it falls off. The larvae of mollusks, barnacles, bryozoans and others that might attach to the naked spines are discouraged by the **pedicellariae** (Figs. 19.6*E* and 19.8*A*), each a microscopic pincers. These snap vigorously when stimulated and any pedicellaria that catches anything remains shut for several days. These are scattered over the body surface and clustered in rosettes at the bases of spines. Occasionally, the tissue around the base of a spine contracts, lifting the rosette so that the pedicellariae reach to the tip of the spine, snapping all the way up and down to clean its surface. In this way the starfish does not become a traveling home for attached organisms.

Asterias creeps slowly on a multitude of **tube feet,** delicate projections ending in suckers. These project from deep **ambulacral grooves** radiating from the disc along the lower surface of each ray. The tube feet are arranged in two longitudinal rows, each of which is staggered so as to look like a double row. Their epidermis is not ciliated.

Each tube foot operates as an independent hydraulic mechanism (Fig. 19.8*B*). Its cavity, which is a part of the coelom, extends inward through the body wall and expands inside the body as a bulb or **ampulla.** When the muscular coat of the ampulla contracts, the fluid in the cavity is forced into the foot. Since the wall of the foot contains connective tissue rings that prevent expansion of the tube diameter, the foot elongates as it fills. The end of the foot forms a suction cup, and once it is pressed against a smooth surface it will stick tightly. Suction is improved by a sticky secretion from the end of the foot, and it can be increased further by the contraction of small muscles attached to a connective tissue "spray" that pulls on the middle of the suction cup. To release the foot, longitudinal muscle fibers in the tube contract and lift the edges of the sucker. When these longitudinal fibers contract completely, the tube foot is drawn up close to the body and its fluid is forced into the ampulla. In creeping,

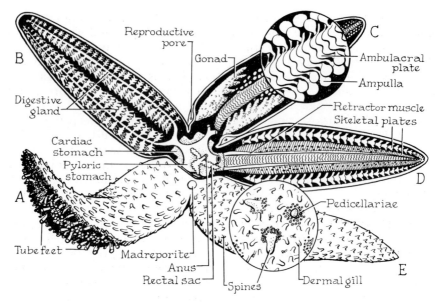

Figure 19.6 *Asterias* viewed from above with the arms in various stages of dissection. *A,* Arm turned to show lower side. *B,* Upper body wall removed. *C,* Upper body wall and digestive glands removed, with a magnified detail of the ampullae and ambulacral plates. *D,* All internal organs removed except the retractor muscles, showing the inner surface of the lower body wall. *E,* Upper surface, with a magnified detail showing surface features.

the tube feet work asynchronously. Each foot elongates in the direction of motion, attaches to the bottom, and then is swung beneath the body so as to propel the body forward.

A small **lateral canal** joins each tube foot with a **radial canal** (Fig. 19.8*B*). The lateral canal is valved so that it can be closed or opened to adjust the amount of fluid in the tube foot and ampulla. The five radial canals join a circular **ring canal** in the lower part of the disc, and from this a single **stone canal** leads upward to the madreporite. All of these cavities together are the **water vascular system,** which is a unique echinoderm feature derived from one portion of the coelom.

The tube feet at the tips of the rays are long and slender, acting as tentacles to explore the bottom as the starfish moves. No one or two rays are permanently anterior, but temporary anteroposterior axes are established.

The only sense organs in addition to the tactile tube feet are small **eyespots** at the tips of the rays (Fig. 19.8*C*). Each eyespot is composed of about 100 pigment cups, each lined with a layer of retinal cells. The starfish, however, shows no evidence of form vision and has only general movements toward or away from light. The tips of the arms are curved so that the eyespots face outward or upward.

Scattered throughout the epidermis are numerous cells that act as chemoreceptors. Starfish have been observed to move toward dead fish and are often caught in baited traps such as those used for crabs and lobsters.

The **mouth** is in the center of the lower surface surrounded by a membranous area, the **peristome.** The mouth opens directly into a large **cardiac stomach** which, in turn, opens upward into a smaller **pyloric stomach.** The digestive tract continues upward as a small **intestine** that ends at an **anus** in the middle of the upper surface of the disc. Five large, hollow, branched **digestive glands** that extend out to the tips of the rays open into the pyloric stomach. The intestine has a lobulated diverticulum, the **rectal sac,** of unknown function. In feeding, the cardiac stomach

Figure 19.7 *A,* The common starfish, *Asterias,* eating a fish. Transparent lobes of the cardiac stomach can be seen surrounding the body of the fish. A number of tube feet are being used to hold the starfish to the side of the aquarium. (Courtesy of Robert S. Bailey.) *B,* A Caribbean brittle star, shown in repetitive flash photographs, pulls itself along with its two anterior arms and shoves with the other three. It is far more agile and flexible than its sluggish, stiff-armed cousin, the common starfish. (Fritz Goro—Courtesy of LIFE Magazine. Cop. 1955, Time, Inc.)

A

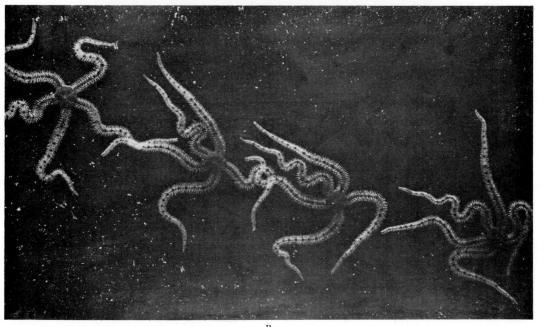

B

Figure 19.7 *See opposite page for legend.*

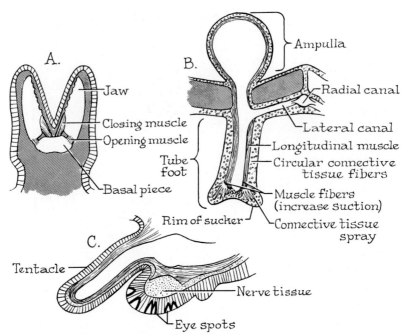

Figure 19.8 *A,* One of the several varieties of pedicellariae. *B,* The tube foot and associated apparatus. *C,* Section through a terminal tentacle (suckerless tube foot) showing the eyespots at its base. (All figures diagrammatic, modified from Hyman.)

everts through the mouth and spreads over the food (Fig. 19.7*A*). A copious fluid containing powerful enzymes is secreted by the digestive glands and poured over the food, rapidly reducing it to a broth. The digested material is then swallowed, and the nutrients are absorbed by the gastrodermis lining the pyloric stomach and digestive glands. Five pairs of **retractor muscles** (Fig. 19.6*D*) from the cardiac stomach to the ventral body wall of the rays contract to pull the cardiac stomach back inside the disc.

Asterias feeds mostly on live bivalves whose shells close tightly. The starfish can open these easily in a few minutes, although the mechanism is not entirely understood. Apparently, the starfish grips the two shells with its many tube feet and pulls slowly and steadily. As soon as the bivalve opens the least bit, the cardiac stomach is slipped inside and digestion begins. Some of the larger starfish, such as the genus *Pisaster* of the west coast, are so powerful that they will break the shells of bivalves that are wired shut.

The nervous system of *Asterias* is composed of a **nerve ring** encircling the mouth and five radial nerves adjacent to the lower epidermis (Fig. 19.1). Other fibers have been identified in the walls of the digestive tract and inside the upper body wall. The separated rays of a

starfish, each with a pie-shaped piece of the disc, will continue to creep for a few minutes in the same direction as they were creeping before being separated. After a few minutes, however, all the rays will creep with the tip forward as though all were acting as anterior rays. These pieces retain a part of the nerve ring and its junction with the radial nerve. If the radial nerve is severed at its junction with the nerve ring, then the ray will creep with its base forward, as though it were a posterior ray. This suggests that the part of the nerve ring near each radial nerve is a center from which stimuli pass along the arm and cause it to advance with the tip forward. In the intact animal the centers on one side temporarily inhibit those on the other, permitting the animal to move in a coordinated manner in one direction.

The large body cavity of *Asterias* surrounds all the digestive organs and extends to the tips of the rays. Although the coelom appears in the embryo as a pair of lateral cavities, these migrate and come to lie one above the other after metamorphosis. In *Asterias* the horizontal mesentery dividing this pair of cavities disappears except for the five pairs of **retractor muscles** of the cardiac stomach.

All over the top and sides of the starfish the body cavity projects through the body wall as numerous tiny **papillae** covered with epidermis. The ciliated epithelium lining the body cavity circulates the coelomic fluid rapidly in and out of these papillae; they probably function in respiration. The coelomic fluid contains numerous wandering cells that gather up waste. When carmine particles are injected into the body cavity they are picked up by these cells. After a few minutes the cells can be seen in the papillae, and many of them leave the body cavity by crawling through the wall to the outside, thus removing the carmine from the body. Whether this is a usual or major method of eliminating wastes is not known.

The circulatory system of *Asterias* is composed of circular and radial vessels filled with a fluid similar to that of the body cavity which, in turn, is not very different from sea water. The vessels lie above the nervous system enclosed in a body cavity of their own, derived embryologically from a part of the coelom. Contractions have been observed in some of the vessels.

A pair of gonads are located one on each side of the gastric gland in the base of each ray (Fig. 19.6C). They hang free in the body cavity except where each is attached by a short duct to a **reproductive pore** opening externally between the bases of adjacent rays. In the spring the gray testes or orange ovaries are prominent, and large numbers of gametes are released in June. Fertilization is external. The release of gametes by one individual stimulates others to do likewise, as in the oyster.

19.4

Class Asteroidea, The Starfish

Asterias forbesi is a member of this class. Most starfish have five rays and a relatively small disc. In some, however, the disc is large relative to the rays and the body is pentagonal rather than star-shaped (Fig. 19.9). In one genus, *Leptasterias* (Fig. 19.9), the animals have six rays. In other starfishes the number of rays may be as high as 25 or 50. Usually, the number of rays in a species is variable if it is greater than seven. In all cases studied where the number exceeds five, the embryo first develops five rays and adds the others later.

Many starfish live and feed like *Asterias*. Some eat only small bivalves and other organisms which are swallowed whole into the cardiac stomach. Many of the large species 30 to 90 cm. in diameter feed primarily upon other echinoderms.

19.5

Class Crinoidea, The Sea Lilies

Sea lilies are echinoderms attached to the bottom by a **stalk** (Fig. 19.5E). The mouth is directed upward, with the anus located to one side on a small projection. The five rays are usually branched to form a graceful pattern. Ciliated grooves in the epidermis extend out from the mouth along the upper surfaces of all the rays and branches. Each groove is flanked on both sides by tube feet, but these lack suckers and are covered with numerous tiny sensory papillae. The movement of the tube feet pushes tiny organisms and food particles against the ciliated groove, which is covered with a mucous secretion that is continually swept toward the mouth. In this way food is trapped and swallowed. Movement in sea lilies is limited to postural changes of the body and the spreading or folding together of the branches. Although 5000 extinct species have been described, only 80 living species of attached crinoids are known.

Figure 19.9 Other members of the Asteroidea. A pentagonal starfish, *Culcita* (*left*). A starfish with six rays, *Leptasterias* (*center*). A starfish with 12 or more rays, *Crossaster* (*right*). (After Hyman.)

Figure 19.10   The feather star, a crinoid that lacks a stalk as an adult. (Austin H. Clark: in Smithsonian Misc. Coll., Vol. 72, No. 7.)

The sea lilies were first known as fossils. In the nineteenth century, shortly after evolution became an accepted theory, a number of scientists suggested that living representatives of extinct groups might still be found in the ocean depths. When the first dredging explorations into these depths yielded living sea lilies, there was much excitement and hope that other "living fossils" would be found. The failure to find animals such as trilobites was a disappointment; although a number of survivors of groups that are mostly extinct have been found in deep water, the number is not much greater than that found in other regions.

Another 550 living species of crinoids occur in a recently evolved family that are free-living as adults. These are the **feather stars** in the family **Comatulidae** (Fig. 19.10). They attach as larvae and grow a short stalk like that of the sea lilies, but later break loose. Their general anatomy and method of feeding are unchanged. Feather stars differ from the sea lilies primarily in locomotion. They can crawl through the vegetation, using the rays as prehensile organs, and they can swim. In swimming the 10 arms are raised and lowered as fast as 100 times a minute. The two primary branches of each of the five rays alternate, so that while arms 1, 3, 5, 7 and 9 are moving up, arms 2, 4, 6, 8 and 10 are moving down. The many tiny branches are folded against the arm as it is raised, and are spread out during the down swing. A feather star may swim 5 meters in one minute.

19.6
Class Holothuroidea, The Sea Cucumbers

Sea cucumbers (Fig. 19.5D) creep or burrow in the sand and mud. The calcareous plates beneath their epidermis are microscopically small and the body wall is soft and flexible. The body is elongated between mouth and anus, and usually one side becomes the permanent lower side so that the radial symmetry is imperfect. Five rows of tube feet extend from mouth to anus, indicating the five **ambulacral areas.** Often only the tube feet of the three lower rows have suckers and are used for creeping. The tube feet surrounding the mouth are modified to form a circle of branched **tentacles.** The tentacles in most species are covered

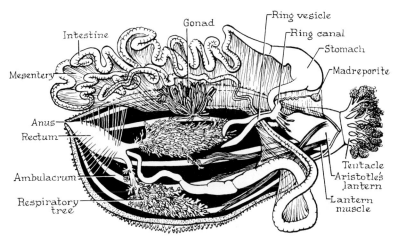

Figure 19.11   The sea cucumber, *Thyone briareus,* cut open along one side. The digestive tract has been moved to one side to show the respiratory trees, retractor muscles of the anterior end, and the internal surface of the body wall with its five ambulacra. In holothurians the madreporite lies in the body cavity, so that the water vascular system is not filled with sea water but with coelomic fluid.

with mucus and extended into the water as a trap for small organisms. Periodically each tentacle is bent into the mouth and wiped clean. A few species use the tentacles for shoveling mud and debris into the mouth.

In many sea cucumbers (Fig. 19.11) the rectum has a pair of large, much branched diverticula that extend into the body cavity. These are the **respiratory trees.** Rhythmically the anus opens and water is drawn into the rectum. Then the anus closes and the rectum contracts, forcing water into the trees. This may be repeated several times, filling the trees more and more. Finally the anus opens and the whole body contracts, expelling all the water.

Holothurians are remarkable for the ease with which they will throw away their viscera. Whenever conditions are unfavorable, whether this be caused by lack of oxygen, high temperatures or excessive irritation, the sea cucumbers contract violently and eject the entire digestive tract. In different species it may be thrown out through the mouth, through the anus, or rupture through the side of the body. Later a new digestive tract is regenerated. Spontaneous evisceration has been suggested to be a device by which the sea cucumbers offer a distraction to a potential predator. When evisceration is found in nature, however, it is usually associated with unfavorable environmental conditions. Possibly by throwing out the viscera sea cucumbers can close up tightly and live at a reduced metabolic level until favorable conditions return.

When larval sea cucumbers settle to the bottom, the first tube feet to develop are five around the mouth and a single pair near the anus on the lower side. These tiny holothurians clamber about actively, often walking on the pair of posterior tube feet (Fig. 19.12). This is the only example of "bipedal" locomotion known in the invertebrates.

Figure 19.12   Larvae of the sea cucumber, *Cucumaria frondosa. Left,* "sitting," and *right,* "walking." (After Runnström and Runnström.)

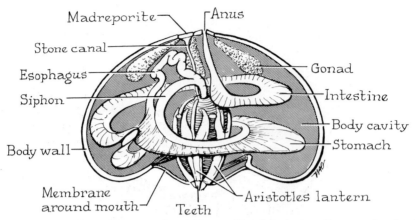

Figure 19.13 A sea urchin, *Arbacia punctulata,* with one side of the body wall removed and only some of the structures shown. The teeth protrude from Aristotle's lantern, of which only the outer structures are indicated. The digestive tract circles twice around the body, once in each direction. A second tube, the siphon, by-passes the esophagus and stomach. Each of the five gonads opens above, near the anus.

19.7

Class Echinoidea, the Sea Urchins, Heart Urchins and Sand Dollars

The body skeleton of the echinoids forms a rigid box (Fig. 19.5C). Five ambulacral grooves with tube feet radiate from the mouth up around the sides to end near the anus. The tube feet on the lower surface usually have suckers and are used in locomotion, whereas the lateral and upper tube feet are often long and filamentous, apparently used for respiration.

Sea urchins have numerous long spines, some of which aid the tube feet in walking. The urchins creep slowly about, using their five sharp teeth to scrape and chew whatever they pass over. The skeleton and musculature associated with the teeth form a distinctive structure known as **Aristotle's lantern** (Fig. 19.13).

Some urchins live on coral reefs where waves are continually breaking over them. Their spines are as thick as pencils and are used as props to hold the urchins tightly in shallow crevices. They remain for long periods in one place and often carve out a depression in which they sit, feeding upon the debris brought to them by the waves.

Some urchins are ovoid and have lost much of their radial symmetry. These, known as **heart urchins** (Fig. 19.14), plow through the sand just beneath the surface. Ciliated grooves along the ambulacral areas collect fine debris which is eaten, and the long upper tube feet project above the sand for respiration.

A group of much-flattened echinoids are the **sand dollars** (Fig. 19.14). These creep almost entirely by the action of numerous short spines. They usually move slowly just under the surface of the sand, and use the upper spines to keep a thin layer of sand moving over the top as they creep on their lower spines. The sand dollars also have ciliated grooves that collect fine debris for food.

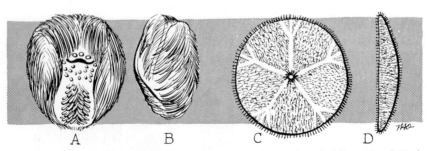

Figure 19.14 Ventral and lateral views of heart urchins (*A* and *B*) and sand dollars (*C* and *D*), showing modifications for burrowing and for creeping through sand. (After Hyman.)

19.8

Class Ophiuroidea, The Brittle Stars

Brittle stars have slender rays attached to a circular **disc** (Fig. 19.5A). Each ray is composed, in part, of a row of large cylindrical skeletal pieces called **vertebrae** joined together with short but powerful muscles. Each ray as a whole is very supple, and brittle stars move by pushing and pulling on surrounding objects, "slithering" like a snake (Fig. 19.7B). The tube feet are poorly developed and lack suckers. They function primarily as tactile sense organs. The delicate ciliated epidermis that covers most of the skeleton in other echinoderms is replaced in this class by a tough cuticle. Pieces of the rays are easily broken off but are easily regenerated.

Some ophiuroids, such as *Gorgonocephalus* (Fig. 19.15) of the west coast, are called **basket stars** because the arms branch and intertwine repeatedly. One wonders how basket stars are able to keep track of all the branches as they clamber through vegetation and, indeed, they have been observed to leave behind pieces that are hopelessly entangled.

Most ophiuroids feed on debris and mud. Some capture prey with their prehensile rays and bring it to the mouth. The mouth opens into a simple saclike **stomach** where food is digested and absorbed. Indigestible remains must be eliminated through the mouth, for no other digestive organs are present.

19.9

Relationships Among Echinoderm Classes

The most primitive echinoderms of which we have any record are believed to be members of the extinct class **Heterostelea** (Fig. 19.16), bilaterally symmetrical echinoderms of the early Paleozoic. These were attached by a stalk like the crinoids, but apparently held the body in a horizontal position. All the other echinoderm classes have radial symmetry.

Three more of the extinct classes were attached by stalks like the crinoids. All of these attached forms (including the feather stars) are placed together in the subphylum **Pelmatozoa.** Within this subphylum the bilateral symmetry of the Heterostelea gave way to the radial symmetry of the other classes, presumably as an adaptation to an attached existence. Except for the feather stars, which are attached only when young, the Pelmatozoa appear to be on the verge of extinction.

The unattached echinoderms, which include the Holothuroidea, Echinoidea, Asteroidea, Ophiuroidea and one extinct class, are placed in the subphylum **Eleutherozoa.** In a few species of starfish the larva attaches to the bottom briefly during its metamorphosis into the adult form, but in most asteroids and in all other eleutherozoans that have been studied, the individuals are never attached. While it is generally concluded that the Eleutherozoa evolved from the Pelmatozoa, it is not known whether they evolved once or whether some of the classes arose separately from attached forms. The Eleutherozoa apparently did not evolve from the Crinoidea, but arose from some extinct and possibly unknown pelmatozoan.

Evolutionary relations among the four living classes of the Eleutherozoa are obscure. A comparison of the adult anatomy suggests that the Asteroidea and Ophiuroidea are the most closely related and that the Echinoidea and Holothuroidea form two distantly related groups. The fossil record supports this arrangement. The Holothuroidea, Echinoidea and Asteroidea are found as fossils in the early part of the Paleozoic era, 350 million

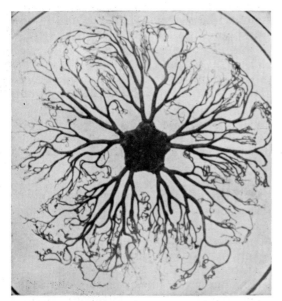

Figure 19.15 The basket star, *Gorgonocephalus,* showing the branched arms. (Courtesy of the American Museum of Natural History.)

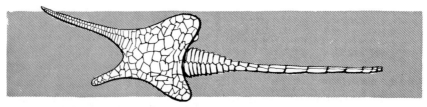

Figure 19.16 An extinct class, *Heterostelea*, view of upper side. This is one of several bilaterally symmetrical genera of early Paleozoic echinoderms. (After Bather.)

years ago. The Ophiuroidea begin as fossils only 275 million years ago. During the 75 million years between the first asteroids and the first ophiuroids, there were a number of species intermediate in morphology between these two classes. They can be arranged in a series suggesting many steps in the evolution of the Ophiuroidea from asteroid-like ancestors, particularly in the skeletal modification of the rays.

Fossil evidence as convincing as this for the origin of a class is rare and should be conclusive. Other evidence, however, contradicts the conclusion that ophiuroids are close to the asteroids. Ophiuroid larvae are different from those of the Asteroidea, but resemble echinoid larvae closely (Fig. 19.19). Analyses of two different chemical constituents, sterols and phosphagens, revealed that ophiuroids differ from asteroids and are identical with echinoids, whereas asteroids resemble holothurians and crinoids. These embryologic and chemical studies suggest that the ophiuroids are more closely related to the echinoids than to the asteroids.

Obviously both theories cannot be correct. The echinoids existed long before the ophiuroids, so the ophiuroids cannot be both closely related to the echinoids and yet descendants of the asteroids. Other chemical studies tend to negate the evidence from the sterol and phosphagen analyses.

19.10
Relationships Among the Hemichordata, Echinodermata, and Chordata

From the study of adult structure given in this chapter there is little evidence for relating the hemichordates and echinoderms. Both have a poorly developed nervous system with few sense organs, a negative characteristic that can also be found in other animal groups. In both groups a portion of

the coelom opens to the outside, filling that portion with sea water to serve as a hydraulic mechanism. This is most remarkable, since such a device is not found in other animals. The similarity, however, appears to be functional rather than structural, for the morphological bases of the two mechanisms are very different.

The close relationship of these phyla is suggested by their development. Not only are the early stages of some hemichordates and some echinoderms very similar, but the development of the hydraulic mechanisms shows that they are essentially homologous.

In both phyla the eggs usually divide in simple fashion into two, four, eight, etc., cells with no evidence of a specialized pattern such as spiral cleavage. Gastrulation (Fig. 19.17) is accomplished by simple invagination, followed by a concentric ingrowth of the blastopore rim. In both phyla the blastopore becomes the anus, and the mouth forms as a new opening some distance away. On this account these phyla are called **deuterostomous** ("second mouth").

In both phyla the coelom usually forms as pouches from the archenteron of the gastrula. The coelom (Fig. 19.17) typically has three portions, one which is usually unpaired and two that are paired. The unpaired portion (coelom$_1$) forms as a pouch from the anterior end of the archenteron. The paired portions (coelom$_2$ and coelom$_3$) may form as posterior growths from coelom$_1$ or as separate pouches from the sides of the archenteron. Other variations also occur. Since several variations are found in both phyla, it is concluded that the final result (three portions) is of more significance in a study of relationship than is the particular way in which they are formed.

In both phyla the embryos develop into larvae that have a tuft of **sensory cilia** at the anterior end, a tract of **locomotor cilia** on the body, a ventral mouth and a posterior anus (Fig. 19.18). The anterior coelomic

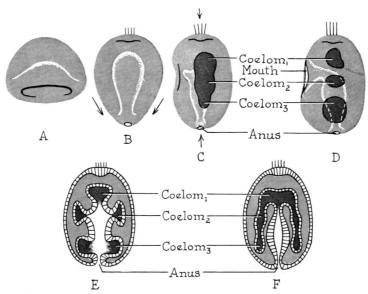

Figure 19.17 Diagrammatic representation of early development in the hemichordates and echinoderms. The lower figures are sections through the embryo indicated by arrows in *C*, and show two different methods of coelom formation, both of which are found in each phylum.

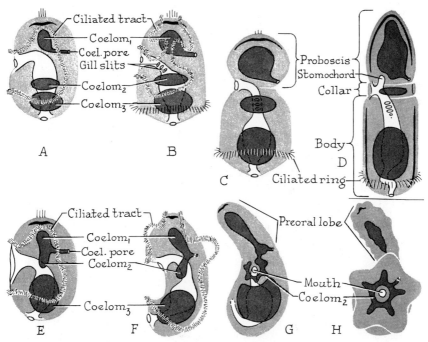

Figure 19.18 Diagrammatic side views of larvae of the Hemichordata (*A* to *D*) and of the Echinodermata (*E* to *H*). Although the early stages (*A* and *E*) are similar, after different patterns of metamorphosis (*B*, *C*, and *F*, *G*), the end results are strikingly different (*D* and *H*). The ciliated tract has been omitted from *G*, where it is somewhat more lobulated than in *F*. It has disappeared in *C*, *D* and *H*.

cavity opens dorsally through a **pore** (in a very few instances both the cavity and the pore are paired). In the echinoderms the first and second portions of the coelom are connected.

Only a few hemichordates become free-swimming at this stage of development. They develop rapidly to the next stage, which has a posterior ring of stout locomotor cilia. The ciliated tract becomes more elaborate and extends anteriorly on both sides, finally meeting to form two tracts: a **preoral circle** between the mouth and the sensory tuft, and a **postoral circle** behind the mouth and dorsal to the tuft. The rudiments of several gill slits appear in the walls of the pharynx. This is the **tornaria larva.** In some species

the ciliated tracts are greatly folded over the surface of the larva.

Some of the echinoderms become free-swimming before gastrulation, whereas others emerge at various times from gastrulation to metamorphosis. Development varies enormously in this phylum, depending in part upon the amount of yolk in the eggs and, in part, upon the taxonomic group. Those with little yolk usually pass through larval stages comparable with those of the hemichordates. As in the hemichordates, the ciliated tract usually extends anteriorly and fuses to form two loops. Meanwhile, the body becomes concave ventrally and the ciliated tract becomes lobulated, extending out from the body surface on **body folds.** A larva of this sort, the

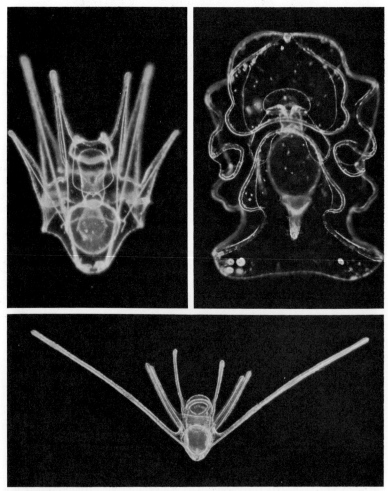

Figure 19.19 Echinoderm larvae. *Upper right,* Ventral view of an *auricularia* of the sea cucumber, *Labidoplax digitata* (compare with Fig. 19.18F). *Upper left, Pluteus* larva of the sea urchin, *Psammechinus milaris. Lower, Pluteus* larva of the brittle star, *Ophiothrix fragilis.* (Courtesy of Douglas P. Wilson.)

auricularia, is found in many holothurians. In the asteroids the lobulation of the ciliated tracts becomes much more pronounced, while in the echinoids and ophiuroids the lobes become extremely long and slender with skeletal supporting rods inside (Fig. 19.19).

The tornaria metamorphoses by a straight-forward fashion into an adult hemichordate. The ciliated tracts disappear, and a constriction separates the proboscis from the rest of the body. The pharynx elongates while the middle coelomic pouches move anteriorly. A second constriction separates the collar from the trunk, and the gill slits in the pharynx open through the sides of the trunk. The anterior coelomic pouch becomes the proboscis cavity with its dorsal pore. The pair of middle cavities become right and left collar cavities, with dorsal and ventral mesenteries separating them above and below the pharynx. Each half later develops an opening into the first gill slit. The posterior coelomic pouches form the right and left cavities in the trunk, also with dorsal and ventral mesenteries between them. The ciliated ring disappears, and the swimming tornaria becomes a burrowing worm. (See Fig. 19.18).

Metamorphosis in the echinoderms involves not only a drastic alteration of body parts but also a change in symmetry. The details vary considerably, and only a simplified course of events in some of the starfish will be followed here. One of the first events of metamorphosis is the migration of the mouth around to the *left* side of the body, where the left middle coelomic pouch surrounds it to form the ring of the water vascular system. At the same time the anus begins to migrate to the *right* side. The region anterior to the mouth becomes a prominent **preoral lobe** and may be used for temporary attachment to the ocean bottom.

The ring canal develops five branches which will become the radial canals, and the body around the mouth begins to grow out in the five-part radial symmetry of the adult. The pore of the anterior coelomic pouch migrates to the original right side and the anterior pouch becomes constricted to form two portions. The preoral lobe with its sensory tuft and coelomic cavity degenerates and is absorbed, while the pore and a portion of the anterior pouch become the madre-porite and stone canal (and associated structures) of the adult. Thus, the lower side of a starfish develops from the left side of the larva, while the upper side develops from the larval right side. The third pair of coelomic pouches, which lie left and right in the larva, become upper and lower in the adult, with a horizontal mesentery between them. All that remains of this mesentery in the adult is the five pairs of retractors of the cardiac stomach.

The steps in this metamorphosis that are general for echinoderms include (1) the development of an adult oral surface from the larval left side and an aboral surface from the larval right side, (2) the development of most of the water vascular system from the left middle coelomic pouch, (3) the development of the adult madreporite from the pore of the anterior pouch, (4) the loss of the preoral region, and (5) the development of lower and upper body cavities from the left and right posterior pouches.

Thus, if a comparison between the hemichordates and echinoderms is valid, the proboscis pore is homologous with the madreporite, the collar cavity with the ring canal and radial canals, and the trunk cavity with the echinoderm body cavity.

Chordates, like the hemichordates and echinoderms, are deuterostomous. The development of the blastopore is slightly different, however. As it closes, the lips are drawn together dorsally and elongated, with the anus forming at the posterior end. Among primitive chordates the method of coelom formation is enterocoelous as in other deuterostome phyla. The later development of chordate embryos and larvae differs markedly from that of echinoderms and hemichordates, however.

Chordates can be related to the hemichordates through a comparison of the adults. Both groups have gill slits, and in some members of both groups the slits become U-shaped through the development of **tongue bars.** The details of structure in the tongue bars of hemichordates and chordates are so similar that they become the strongest evidence for relating the groups. Formerly, much stress was placed on the possible homology of the stomochord of hemichordates and the notochord of chordates, and on the hemichordate collar nerve and chordate nerve cord, but as more is learned of the details of structure and function in these organs, more doubt is cast on the validity of their homology. Even so, such structures represent similar experiments in evolution and, as such, do not argue against a relationship of the two groups.

The hemichordates, echinoderms and chordates are reminiscent of the annelids, mollusks and arthropods, in which two of the phyla can be related through similarities of larvae while another two are related through a comparison of adult structure. These relationships are much more obvious in the annelids, mollusks and arthropods.

SYNOPSIS OF HEMICHORDATES AND ECHINODERMS

PHYLUM HEMICHORDATA. Deuterostomes with bilateral symmetry, stomochord, and usually with gill slits. Marine.

   CLASS 1. ENTEROPNEUSTA. Acorn worms. Burrowing, wormlike animals with numerous gill slits. One order. *Saccoglossus.*

   CLASS 2. PTEROBRANCHIA. Sedentary animals with a dorsal anus, collar expanded as a lophophore around mouth.

   Order 1. Rhabdopleuridea. No gill slits, lophophore of two branching arms.

   Order 2. Cephalodiscoidea. One pair of gill slits, lophophore of several branching arms.

   CLASS 3. POGONOPHORA. Digestive system absent; tentacles on proboscis possibly digestive organs. Tube-dwelling.

PHYLUM ECHINODERMATA. Deuterostomes with subepidermal calcareous plates and usually radial symmetry on a plan of five. Marine.

   Subphylum 1. Pelmatozoa. Attached in youth or throughout life by an aboral stem.

   †CLASS 1. HETEROSTELEA. Bilaterally symmetrical, possibly ancestral to others.

   †CLASSES 2–4. CYSTIDEA, BLASTOIDEA, EDRIOASTEROIDEA. Radial symmetry, no arms.

   CLASS 5. CRINOIDEA. Sea lilies and sea feathers. Well-developed arms, anus on oral surface. One living and three extinct orders.

   Subphylum 2. Eleutherozoa. Stemless unattached echinoderms.

   CLASS 1. HOLOTHUROIDEA. Sea cucumbers. Armless, elongate, with secondary bilateral symmetry, skeleton reduced to microscopic spicules. Five orders, all living.

   CLASS 2. ECHINOIDEA. Sea urchins, sand dollars. Armless, skeleton well developed and usually rigid with numerous mobile spines. About three living and five extinct orders.

   CLASS 3. ASTEROIDEA. Starfishes. With arms, skeleton well developed but flexible, locomotion by tube feet. Three living and two extinct orders. *Asterias, Leptasterias.*

   CLASS 4. OPHIUROIDEA. Brittle stars. With arms and flexible skeleton, locomotion by prehension. Two orders, both living.

   †CLASS 5. OPHIOCISTIOIDEA. Armless. Body heavily armored, with a few pairs of very large scaly tube feet. One extinct order.

---

†Extinct.

QUESTIONS

1. What characteristics link the hemichordates and echinoderms? The hemichordates and chordates? The chordates and echinoderms?
2. Characterize the five living classes of echinoderms.
3. How do tube feet function?
4. Describe the skeleton of *Asterias.*
5. Compare feeding in sea lilies and sea cucumbers.
6. What is Aristotle's lantern?
7. What was unique about the Heterostelea?

8. Discuss conflicting evidence concerning evolutionary relationships among the Echinoidea, Asteroidea and Ophiuroidea.
9. What is a tornaria?

ANNOTATED REFERENCES

(See Chapter 13 for general references.)

Barrington, E. J. W.: The Biology of the Hemichordata and Protochordata. Edinburgh, Oliver and Boyd, 1965. The anatomy, physiology and behavior of the curious hemichordates are thoroughly discussed.

Boolootian, R. A. (Ed.): Physiology of the Echinodermata. New York, Interscience, 1966. An advanced and valuable source book on the physiology and ecology of echinoderms written by 31 leading authorities.

20 THE CHORDATES

20.1

Chordate Characteristics

The chordates are perhaps more familiar than the invertebrates described in the preceding chapters; the phylum includes the backboned animals or vertebrates—man and his domestic creatures, birds, frogs, fishes, and the like. The **Vertebrata,** however, is but one subphylum of the phylum **Chordata.** Two others, the **Urochordata** and **Cephalochordata,** contain less conspicuous, soft-bodied, marine species often collectively called the lower chordates. The urochordates are represented by the sea squirts (*Molgula*), and the cephalochordates by the lancelet (*Amphioxus*, Fig. 20.1C). One may well ask, what do such diverse groups have in common that all are placed in the same phylum? Certainly the adults do not look alike, but at some

stage in their life history these animals share three unique features.

First, a dorsal, longitudinal rod known as the **notochord** is present in the embryos of all and sometimes in the adults. It is composed of a fibrous sheath encasing many vacuolated cells, whose turgidity make it firm yet flexible. It is generally assumed that the notochord provides support for the body, but it can be argued that the small marine chordates, which first acquired a notochord, did not need this extra support. A more plausible suggestion is that it prevents the body from shortening in the manner of an earthworm when the longitudinal muscle fibers in the body wall contract. Since telescoping is prevented, the contraction of muscle fibers first on one side and then on the other causes the animal to bend from side to side and move through the water with fishlike lateral undu-

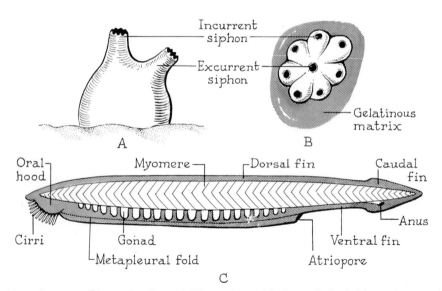

Figure 20.1 A group of lower chordates. *A,* The tunicate *Molgula*, partly buried in sand; *B,* a portion of the colonial tunicate *Botryllus*, viewed from above; *C,* a lateral view of *Amphioxus*. *Molgula* is natural size; the others are enlarged.

314

lations. Undulatory movements are possible without a rod of this type—certain marine worms, for example, swim in this fashion—but the notochord may increase the efficiency and precision of this type of locomotion.

Secondly, a longitudinal **nerve cord** lies dorsal to the notochord. It differs from the ventral nerve cord of certain nonchordates, both in position and in structure, for it is a single rather than a double cord and is tubular rather than solid.

Finally, chordates differ from most nonchordates in having **pharyngeal pouches** that extend laterally from the anterior part of the digestive tract toward the sides of the body, often breaking through as **gill slits.** All chordates have gill slits, or at least pharyngeal pouches, at some stage of their life cycle. Certain hemichordates (p. 295) also have gill slits. This arrangement appears to have served originally as a means of letting the water taken into the mouth escape from the digestive tract, thereby concentrating the small food particles that were in the water. The lower chordates and the larvae of the most primitive vertebrates are filter-feeders and live upon minute organic matter gathered in this way.

Chordates share many other characters with certain of the more advanced, nonchordate groups. They are bilaterally symmetrical; they are triploblastic; their general plan of body organization is a tube within a tube, for in most chordates a coelom separates the digestive tract from the body wall; the gut tube is complete—i.e., there is a separate mouth and anus. Diffusion is adequate for gas exchange and excretion in the simpler chordates, but special respiratory and excretory organs are present in the vertebrates. The vertebrates are active animals, with a high degree of **cephalization** (accumulation of nerves and sense organs in the head) and segmental muscular and related systems.

20.2

Subphylum Urochordata

The first chordate subphylum, the **Urochordata,** includes the marine tunicates and their allies. Most urochordates belong to the class **Ascidiacea** and are sessile organisms that are frequently seen attached to submerged rocks and wharf pilings, or are found partially buried in sand and mud in coastal waters. They may be either solitary or colonial (Fig. 20.1). *Molgula* ia a familiar example of the former type occurring along the Atlantic coast.

A solitary adult ascidian is a sac-shaped creature that is enclosed in a leathery **tunic,** which has been secreted by the underlying body wall, or **mantle** (Fig. 20.2*A*). A considerable amount of cellulose, a complex carbohydrate characteristic of the cell walls of plants but rarely found in animals, is present in the tunic. The animal is attached to the substrate by its base, and two tubular openings are present near the upper surface. The uppermost one, or **incurrent siphon,** leads into a large, barrel-shaped **pharynx,** which occupies most of the space within the body. The **gill slits** in the pharyngeal wall do not open directly to the body surface but into a specialized, ectodermally lined chamber, called the **atrium,** lying on each side of the pharynx and along its dorsal edge. The atrium opens at the surface through an **excurrent siphon.** Ciliated cells in the pharynx maintain a flow of water into the incurrent and out of the excurrent siphon.

Gas exchange occurs between the water passing through the pharynx and blood channels in the pharyngeal wall, but the pharynx is also a food-gathering mechanism. Mucus produced in the **endostyle** (a longitudinal groove in the floor of the pharynx) is moved across the lateral walls of the pharynx to its dorsal surface. Minute food particles are entrapped in this sheet of mucus, which is then carried along a dorsal band into the more posterior parts of the digestive tract (Fig. 20.2*B*). The **intestine** finally opens into the atrium.

A tube-shaped, muscular **heart** is enclosed in a reduced coelom, and a vessel leads out from each of its ends into open channels in the wall of the pharynx and other organs. Capillaries are absent. The beating of the heart is unique in that waves of contraction move from one end of the heart to the other for a while, and then the beat reverses and the contractions move in the opposite direction. The heart and blood vessels have no valves.

A solid nerve **ganglion,** from which nerves extend to various parts of the body, lies in the mantle between the siphons, and a peculiar **neural gland** lies beside the ganglion. The latter opens into the pharynx by means of a short ciliated duct. Its function is un-

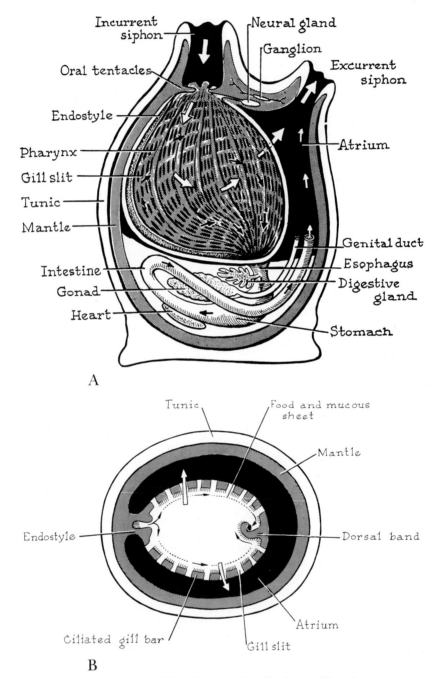

Figure 20.2 Diagrammatic lateral view (*A*) and cross section (*B*) of an ascidian showing major internal organs. Large arrows represent the course of the current of water; small arrows that of the food and mucous sheet. The stomach, intestine and other visceral organs are embedded in the mantle.

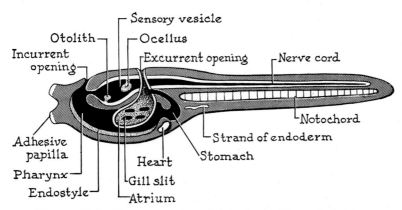

Figure 20.3 Diagrammatic lateral view of an ascidian tadpole larva.

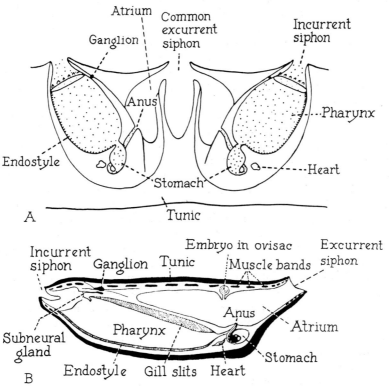

Figure 20.4 Types of urochordates. *A,* Vertical section through the colonial ascidian, *Botryllus; B,* lateral view of the pelagic thaliacian, *Salpa.* (From Borradaile. *A* after Delage and Herouard; *B* after Herdman.)

certain, but some investigators consider it to be an endocrine gland and have compared it to the pituitary gland of vertebrates.

Ascidians are hermaphroditic, part of the gonad being **ovary** and part **testis.** One or more ducts lead from the gonad to the atrium. Certain ascidians are self-fertilizing— that is, the eggs of one individual can be fertilized by sperm from the same individual —but in others the sperm must come from a different individual. Asexual reproduction by budding also occurs.

Pharyngeal gill slits are well developed in the adult, but one must examine a tunicate larva to find the other diagnostic chordate characteristics (Fig. 20.3). The larva is tadpole-shaped, with an expanded body and a long mobile tail equipped with longitudinal muscle fibers. A **notochord** supports the tail (whence the term urochordate), and a distinct tubular **nerve cord** lies dorsal to it. The anterior end of the nerve cord expands to form a brainlike **sensory vesicle** containing a light-sensitive **ocellus** and an **otolith** concerned with equilibrium. The pharynx and other digestive organs develop within the body but do not function in most larvae. A pair of dorsal, ectodermal invaginations, which soon acquire a common external opening, grow down beside the pharynx to form the **atrium.** Within a day or two the tadpole finds a favorable substrate to which it attaches by its anterior adhesive glands. It loses it tail and is transformed into an adult. Notochord and nerve cord are resorbed, only the ganglion and neural gland remaining as traces of the latter. Motile larvae are of great importance in the life history of sessile organisms, for they are responsible for finding a suitable substrate for the particular species and for the dispersal of the organism.

Many other ascidians are colonial. Some colonies are little more than loose aggregates of individuals which have developed by budding; others, including *Botryllus,* consist of individuals embedded in a common tunic and often sharing certain organs such as the atrial cavity (Fig. 20.4*A*).

In addition to the ascidians, the urochordates include two less conspicuous classes. Members of the class **Thaliacea** are barrel-shaped, pelagic types with incurrent and excurrent siphons located at opposite ends of the body (Fig. 20.4*B*). Rhythmic contraction of muscular bands in the body wall cause

water to be ejected from the pharynx and atrium with sufficient force to propel the organism. In effect, the feeding current is now also used for locomotion. Least conspicuous of urochordates are members of class **Larvacea.** All are minute pelagic forms that retain the larval tail as a propulsive organ, yet acqurie sexual maturity. Organisms that acquire sexual maturity while retaining many larval features, and subsequently fail to lose these larval features, are said to be **neotenic.**

20.3
Subphylum Cephalochordata

Amphioxus and a related genus of small, superficially fish-shaped chordates constitute the subphylum **Cephalochordata.** Species occur in United States coastal waters south from Chesapeake (*Amphioxus virginiae*) and Monterey (*A. californiense**) Bays. They usually lie buried in sand with only their anterior end protruding, but they can also swim fairly well.

The body of *Amphioxus* (Fig. 20.1*C*) is elongate, tapers at each end, and is compressed from side to side. A dorsal, a caudal and a ventral **fin** lie in the median plane of the body, and a pair of long finlike **metapleural folds** are present ventrolaterally. Dorsal and ventral fins are supported by blocks of connective tissue, but these fins and folds are apparently not large or strong enough to keep the animal on an even keel, for *Amphioxus* spirals as it swims. Swimming is accomplished by the contraction of longitudinal muscle fibers in the body wall that are arranged in segmental, <-shaped muscle blocks, or **myomeres.** These can easily be seen through the thin skin. Successive myomeres are separated by connective tissue septa to which the muscle fibers are attached. Shortening of the body is prevented by an unusually long **notochord** (Fig. 20.5) that extends farther anteriorly than in any other chordate, an attribute after which the subphylum is named.

Water and minute food particles are taken

---

*Branchiostoma Costa, 1834, has priority over *Amphioxus* Yarrell, 1836, as the generic name for these animals, but there is some question as to the adequacy of Costa's description and hence as to the validity of his name.

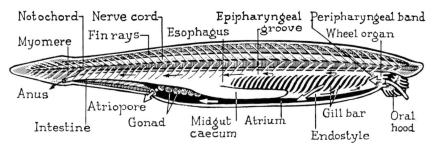

Figure 20.5   A diagrammatic lateral view of *Amphioxus*. White arrows represent the course of the current of water; black arrows that of the food. Further details of the course of food particles in the gut are shown in Figure 20.7.

in through the **oral hood,** whose edges bear a series of delicate projections, the **cirri,** that act as a strainer to exclude larger particles (Fig. 20.6). The inside of the oral hood is lined with bands of cilia called the **wheel organ,** which, together with cilia in the pharynx, produce a current of water that enters the mouth. The mouth proper lies deep within the oral hood and is surrounded by 12 **velar tentacles.**

Food is entrapped within the **pharynx** in mucus secreted by an endostyle just as it was in urochordates. Water in the pharynx escapes into an ectodermally lined **atrium** through nearly 200 gill slits. **Gill bars,** supported by delicate skeletal rods, lie between the slits. At one stage in development the gill slits are U-shaped and resemble those of hemichordates (Fig. 19.4), a detail that may point to an affinity between these animals, but in *Amphioxus* the tonguelike process that causes the slit to be U-shaped subsequently continues its downward growth and completely subdivides the slit. Some gas exchange occurs in the pharynx, but the skin is the main respiratory surface. The pharynx, therefore, is primarily a food-gathering device.

After leaving the pharynx, the food enters a short **esophagus,** a **midgut** and finally an **intestine,** which opens at the surface through an **anus.** The intestine terminates before the end of the body, so there is a postanal tail as in vertebrates. A prominent **midgut caecum,** which produces digestive enzymes, extends from the floor of the midgut forward along the right side of the pharynx.

Many of the cells of the midgut, midgut caecum and intestine are ciliated, and complex ciliary currents sort out food particles for digestion and absorption (Fig. 20.7). Particles pass from the esophagus back into the midgut. Here they are joined by material and enzymes being carried out along the floor of the midgut caecum. This entire mass then rotates for a considerable period of time in the midgut. Food and enzymes are mixed, some extracellular digestion takes place, and particles break from the rotating food mass and are carried forward. Larger particles are deflected by a lateral ciliated tract and are returned to the rotating food mass; smaller particles enter the dorsal part of the midgut caecum and drift down along its lateral walls. As they do so, they are ingested by caecal cells, and digestion is completed intracellu-

Figure 20.6   An enlarged view of the anterior end of *Amphioxus*, cleared and stained to show internal structures. (Modified after Young.)

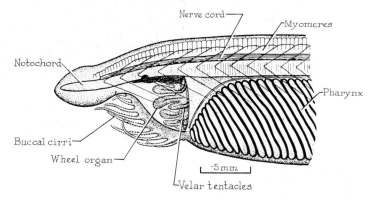

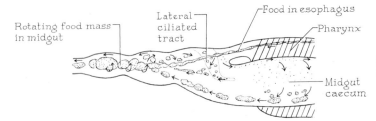

Figure 20.7 Diagram of food particle movements in the intestine and midgut caecum. (From Barrington.)

larly. Doubtless, soluble products pass from the caecal cells into the circulatory system, but the undigested residue finally is discharged from the cells into the lumen of the caecum, from which it is carried, along with the enzymes secreted by certain caecal cells, back into the midgut. As time goes on, certain material escapes from the rotating mass and continues posteriorly through the intestine. Presumably this is largely undigestible detritus, but some additional digestion and absorption probably occur here. This elaborate mechanism is an extremely effective way to process and digest the stream of food particles on which the animal feeds.

Absorbed food and other substances are distributed by a circulatory system. A series of **veins** returns blood from the various parts of the body to a sinus which is located ventral to the posterior part of the pharynx and may be comparable to the posterior part of the vertebrate heart. A muscular heart, however, is not present, and the blood is propelled by the contraction of the arteries. A **ventral aorta** extends from the sinus forward beneath the pharynx and leads into **branchial arteries** that travel dorsally through the gill bars into a pair of **dorsal aortas.** The dorsal aortas, in turn, carry the blood posteriorly to spaces within the tissues. True

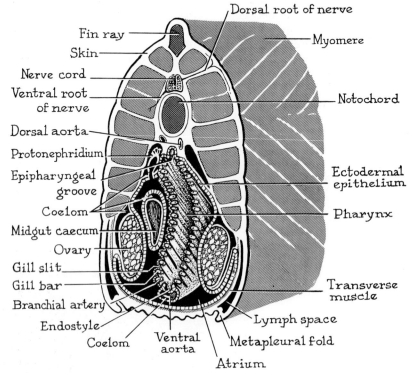

Figure 20.8 A diagrammatic cross section through the posterior part of the pharynx of *Amphioxus*. Branchial arteries extend from the ventral aorta through the gill bars to the dorsal aortas. The portion of the coelom ventral to the endostyle is connected through alternate gill bars with the pair of coelomic canals lying dorsal to the atrium. Other parts of the coelom are associated with the midgut caecum and gonads.

capillaries are absent, but the general direction of blood flow, i.e., anteriorly in the ventral part of the body and posteriorly in the dorsal part, is similar to that of a vertebrate and different from that of other animals.

The excretory organs are segmentally arranged, ciliated **protonephridia** (p. 179) that lie dorsal to certain gill bars and open into the atrium.

The nervous system of *Amphioxus* consists of a tubular **nerve cord** located dorsal to the notochord. Its anterior end is differentiated slightly but does not expand to form a brain. Paired, segmental **nerves,** consisting of **dorsal** and **ventral roots,** extend into the tissues. The roots remain separate and do not unite. The ventral roots go directly into the myomeres, and the dorsal roots pass between myomeres to supply the skin, gut wall and ventral parts of the body. *Amphioxus* is sensitive to light and to chemical and tactile stimuli, but elaborate sense organs are not present. The cirri on the oral hood and a flagellated pit in the skin near the front of the nerve cord appear to be chemoreceptors. Photoreceptive cells, which are partly masked with pigment, lie in the nerve cord. The prominent pigment spot at the anterior end of the cord apparently does not function in light reception.

Numerous gonads, which are either all **testes** or all **ovaries** since the sexes are separate in *Amphioxus,* bulge into the atrial cavity. Actually, they lie within a portion of a highly modified coelom (Fig. 20.8). The gametes are discharged into the atrium upon the rupture of the gonad walls. Fertilization and development are external.

20.4

Subphylum Vertebrata

The Vertebrata is by far the largest and most important of the chordate subphyla, for all but about 2000 of the approximately 41,000 living species of chordates are vertebrates. The subphylum, in turn, is divided into eight classes. The oldest and most primitive vertebrates, which lack jaws and paired appendages, are placed in the class **Agnatha.** Most of these are extinct, heavily armored fishes known as ostracoderms, but the lamprey is a living representative of this group. The ostracoderms gave rise to the class **Placodermi,** a group of primitive jawed

fishes, all of which are extinct. Placoderms, in turn, gave rise to the large groups of living fishes — the class **Chondrichthyes** and the class **Osteichthyes.** The Chondrichthyes are the fishes with cartilaginous skeletons such as the sharks and rays; the Osteichthyes are the more familiar fishes with bony skeletons such as salmon, minnows and perch. The first terrestrial vertebrates evolved from certain of the bony fishes and are placed in the class **Amphibia.** Adult frogs, salamanders and other amphibians are more or less terrestrial, but they generally return to the water to reproduce. Amphibians gave rise to the class **Reptilia,** a group that includes turtles, alligators, lizards and snakes. Reptiles are better adapted to the terrestrial environment and reproduce on land, but they resemble all the lower vertebrates in being cold-blooded. The remaining two classes, the birds (class **Aves**) and mammals (class **Mammalia**), evolved from the reptiles, and the members of both groups have become very active and warm-blooded. Birds are clothed with feathers and lay eggs; most mammals are covered with hair and give birth to living young, which are nourished by milk secreted by the mammary glands.

Vertebrates share with the lower chordates the three diagnostic characteristics of the phylum. These are clearly represented at some state in the life history of the various groups. A dorsal tubular **nerve cord,** which has differentiated into a **brain** and **spinal cord,** is present in the embryos and adults of all (Fig. 20.9). Embryonic vertebrates have a **notochord** lying ventral to the nerve cord and extending from the middle of the brain nearly to the posterior end of the body, but a vertebral column replaces the notochord in most adults. All embryonic vertebrates have a series of **pharyngeal pouches** that grow out from the lateral walls of the pharynx, but these pouches break through the body surface to form gill slits only in fishes and larval amphibians.

Vertebrates evolved as a group of chordates that became more active and soon gave up the sessile, filter-feeding mode of life for more aggressive ways of food gathering. Most of the distinctive characteristics of vertebrates are related to these changes in mode of life. Their greater activity is reflected in the replacement of the notochord by a **vertebral column,** in the continued elaboration of the segmented muscular system seen beginning

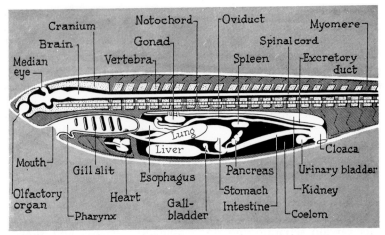

Figure 20.9 A diagrammatic sagittal section through a generalized vertebrate to show the characteristics of vertebrates and the arrangement of the major organs.

in *Amphioxus,* in an aggregation of elaborate **sense organs** and nervous tissue (the **brain**) at the anterior end of the body, and in the protection of these organs by a brain case or **cranium.** An alternate name for the subphylum, the Craniata, emphasizes this last feature.

Early vertebrates probably continued a filter-feeding mode of life but used muscular movements of their pharynx, and not just ciliary currents, to draw in water and food. This was certainly more efficient and it made possible an increase in size. Larger size, and the eventual evolution of jaws, permitted a yet more active and aggressive mode of life. A simple epithelium no longer sufficed for protecting the body surface, and a layer of **skin** with a stratified epithelium evolved. The general body surface, or pharyngeal surface, was no longer adequate for gas exchange. **Gills** developed in the gill slits, which were the sites of a steady stream of water originally associated with filter-feeding. Later, in terrestrial vertebrates, **lungs** replaced the gills. A **liver** serving as a site for food storage and conversion evolved. As size and metabolic complexity increased, the circulatory system became closed. **Capillaries** now connected arteries and veins, and blood is propelled by the action of a muscular **heart** lying ventral to the digestive tract. Excretion is now performed by a pair of **kidneys** composed of numerous kidney tubules (Fig. 5.6D) that remove both water and excretory products from the blood, although in many vertebrates much of the water is later reabsorbed by other portions of the kidney. Vertebrates

have become the most successful and the dominant group of chordates.

20.5
The Origin of Chordates

Ever since the general acceptance of the theory of organic evolution, man has been interested in the origin of the chordates. But this problem does not have an easy solution, for chordates are a distinctive group separated by a wide morphologic gap from other phyla.

The segmentation of cephalochordates and vertebrates early drew attention to a possible evolutionary relationship between chordates and the annelid-arthropod stock. Annelids and arthropods are segmented, but they differ from chordates in so many basic characters that this view has been abandoned. Their nerve cord, for example, is not a single dorsal tubular cord, but a solid, essentially double cord, lying ventral to the digestive tract. It would be necessary to turn an annelid or arthropod upside down, evolve a completely new nerve cord, and make many other radical transformations in order to derive a chordate from these animals. A continuity of structure and function must be maintained in any evolutionary transition, and viable intermediate stages in such a transformation are difficult to visualize. Moreover, the urochordates, generally considered to be the most primitive chordates, are not segmented and are a source of embarrassment to those who would derive chordates from segmented ancestors.

Other evidence indicates that the chordates

may have evolved from the echinoderm-hemichordate stock (Fig. 20.10). The presence in certain hemichordates and chordates of pharyngeal gill slits and the unusual tongue bar that causes the slits to become U-shaped suggest an evolutionary relationship between these groups. Indeed, some authors include the hemichordates as a subphylum of the chordates. Some have concluded that the radial symmetry of echinoderms negates a relationship with the bilaterally symmetrical hemichordates and chordates but, as we have learned (p. 307), the radial symmetry of the adult, present-day echinoderms has been secondarily superimposed upon a basically bilateral organization. Both the primitive, extinct echinoderms and the early echinoderm larvae are bilaterally symmetrical. Many features of the early development (cleavage, origin of mesoderm and coelom, fate of the blastopore) of echinoderms, hemichordates and chordates are similar and suggest an evolutionary relationship (see section 19.10). Moreover, there is a closer similarity between the body fluid proteins of the chordates, hemichordates and echinoderms than between those of chordates and annelids or arthropods, and the degree of resemblance of the proteins of live animals has been shown to be a good measure of

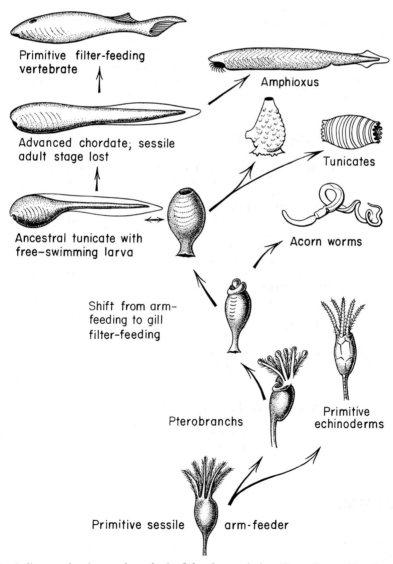

Figure 20.10 A diagram showing one hypothesis of chordate evolution. (From Romer: Vertebrate Body, 3rd ed.)

their evolutionary relationship. The serologic technique by which the degree of protein similarity is determined is described in Chapter 37.

Professor Berrill of McGill University has proposed that primitive chordates were sessile, filter-feeding marine organisms not unlike present-day ascidians. Gill slits presumably evolved in this group as a means of concentrating food; a respiratory function for gill slits was a secondary development. The tadpole-type larva, with its sensory vesicle and mobile tail supported by a notochord, evolved as a means of selecting a suitable habitat for permanent settlement. Berrill postulates that at a later time, and as an adaptation for exploiting the rich pasture of oceanic surface waters, certain of these larvae became neotenic. Contemporary pelagic tunicates of the class Larvacea have unquestionably evolved through neoteny, so this is a reasonable proposal. Certain of these neotenic tadpoles came to exploit the rich detritus at river mouths. An increase in size

and in powers of locomotion, particularly the evolution of a segmented muscular system, would have enabled them to overcome the current and ascend the rivers. The segmentation of certain chordates and of annelids and arthropods is, therefore, attributed to the independent evolution of increased activity in unrelated lines of descent. Berrill believes that vertebrates gradually evolved in this way as a fresh-water adaptation of neotenic tunicate larvae. He considers *Amphioxus* to be a relic of a phase in which chordates were becoming more active and entering fresh water but suggests that it has subsequently readapted to the life of a marine filter-feeder. The discovery in Silurian deposits of Scotland of the impression of an amphioxus-like creature known as *Jamoytius,* which is interpreted by some as an early vertebrate, lends some support to Berrill's hypothesis. But if vertebrates evolved from soft-bodied neotenic tunicates, it seems unlikely that many intermediate fossils will ever be found.

SYNOPSIS OF CHORDATES

PHYLUM CHORDATA.   The chordates. Deuterostomes having at some stage of their life a notochord; pharyngeal gill pouches; a single dorsal tubular nerve cord.

Subphylum 1. Urochordata.   The tunicates and their allies. Notochord and nerve cord are present only in the tail of the tadpole-like larval stage; adults are filter-feeders and have a well developed pharynx; exclusively marine.

CLASS 1. ASCIDIACEA.   Ascidians, or sea squirts. Adults sessile; solitary or colonial; encased in a well developed tunic. *Molgula.*

CLASS 2. THALIACEA.   Pelagic tunicates without a tail; propel themselves by a jet of water passing through the body; muscular "straps" or "hoops" in body wall. *Salpa.*

CLASS 3. LARVACEA.   Appendicularians. Small neotenic tunicates; larval tail retained as a propulsive organ. *Appendicularia.*

Subphylum 2. Cephalochordata.   The lancelets. Active fusiform chordates; notochord extends the length of the body; muscles segmented; filter-feeders that burrow into sand; exclusively marine. *Branchiostoma (Amphioxus).*

Subphylum 3. Vertebrata.   The vertebrates. Most active of chordates; notochord usually replaced in adult by vertebral column; muscles segmented; well-developed sense organs (nose, eye, ear) and brain encased in a cranium; marine, freshwater, terrestrial. These are classified further in Chapters 22 to 25.

QUESTIONS

1. How does the nerve cord of chordates differ from that of nonchordates?
2. What is the function of the notochord?
3. What was the primitive function of the gill slits?

4. Briefly characterize each of the chordate subphyla.
5. Compare the method of feeding of *Molgula* and *Amphioxus*.
6. List the eight classes of vertebrates and give an example of an animal that belongs to each one.
7. How does the mode of life of a vertebrate differ from that of other chordates? Which distinctive vertebrate features are correlated with this change in mode of life?
8. To which group of nonchordates are chordates believed to be most closely related? What is the evidence?

ANNOTATED REFERENCES

Barrington, E. J. W.: The Biology of the Hemichordata and Protochordata. Edinburgh, Oliver and Boyd, 1965. Written for the University Reviews in Biology, this is a thorough and updated account of the biology of all the lower chordate groups.

Berrill, N. J.: The Origin of the Vertebrates. London, Oxford University Press, 1955. Theories of vertebrate origin are reviewed and the urochordate theory of vertebrate origin is presented.

Berrill, N. J.: The Tunicata. London, The Ray Society, 1950. A definitive treatise on the biology of the largest group of lower chordates.

Meglitsch, P. A.: Invertebrate Zoology. London, Oxford University Press, 1967. A section on urochordates is included in this recent textbook of invertebrate zoology.

Young, J. A.: The Life of Vertebrates. 2nd ed. London, Oxford University Press, 1962. Lower chordate groups are included in this useful textbook of vertebrate biology.

Part Three

**VERTEBRATE
LIFE
AND
ORGANIZATION**

21

THE FROG—
A REPRESENTATIVE
VERTEBRATE

The vertebrates will be considered more fully than any other group of animals because a knowledge of their biology is particularly important for an appreciation of human form and function. The frog is selected to introduce the vertebrates because of its availability, ease of study and importance in zoologic research. It is not the most representative of vertebrates; indeed, no single type can be truly representative of so diverse a subphylum. As a member of the class **Amphibia,** it occupies an evolutionary position between the primitive ancestral fishes and the advanced terrestrial mammals. A frog retains certain of the primitive features of fishes, yet it has also evolved certain of the features characteristic of the more advanced terrestrial vertebrates.

21.1
Frogs and Other Amphibians

Amphibians live both in water and in moist places on land. The eggs and immature individuals are normally aquatic, and the adults never get far from the water, for their ability to prevent excessive loss of body water in a terrestrial environment is rather rudimentary. The adults are found on the land close to ponds, streams and other bodies of fresh water to which they can retreat, or in other moist places such as beneath stones and logs in damp woods. The most terrestrial of the amphibians, the **toads,** are particularly active at night, when the humidity is relatively high.

Contemporary members of the class are grouped into three orders. The frogs and toads are placed in the order **Anura.** The other orders consist of the lizard-shaped, scaleless **salamanders** (order **Urodela**), and the legless, wormlike caecilians of tropical continents (order **Apoda**). The several orders of extinct amphibians are discussed in Chapter 23.

Anurans differ from the others in having powerful hind legs that enable them to jump on land and swim in water. Their short trunk, the absence of a tail, and the enlarged hind legs with webbed feet are among the many features which adapt them to their mode of life.

Approximately 100 species of frogs and toads occur in the United States and Canada. The most widespread is the leopard frog, *Rana pipiens* (Fig. 21.1). This species is found throughout North America except for the more northern parts and the west coast of the continent. The following description applies specifically to *Rana pipiens,* but most of what follows applies to other anurans as well.

329

Figure 21.1   The leopard frog. *Rana pipiens.*

21.2

External Features

The body shape of vertebrates is closely correlated with their methods of locomotion. All vertebrates are actively moving creatures with bilateral symmetry, and with a mouth and a concentration of sense and nervous organs at the anterior end, or **head.** Immediately posterior to the head in fishes is a **trunk,** and a powerful propulsive **tail** lies posterior to the termination of the digestive tract. No neck is present in fishes; indeed, motion between the head and trunk would be disadvantageous in their type of locomotion. In contrast most terrestrial vertebrates have a neck, which permits independent motion of the head, but frogs retain the fishlike absence of this body region. Aquatic tadpoles have a propulsive tail, but this is lost during metamorphosis to the adult frog, and the legs become the propulsive organs.

A large **mouth** is located at the anterior end of the head and a pair of external nostrils, or **external nares,** is dorsal to the front of the mouth. The large and protruding **eyes** are protected by **eyelids.** The upper one is a simple skin fold; the lower one is a translucent membrane. When the eyeball is retracted into the eye socket, the lower lid spreads over its surface. Between and in

front of the eyes on the top of the head is a light-colored spot about the size of a small pinhead. It is known as the **brow spot** and is a vestige of the median eye of very primitive vertebrates. A round eardrum, or **tympanic membrane,** lies posterior to each eye. It is noticeably larger in the males than in the females of some common frogs such as the green frog (*R. clamitans*) and bullfrog (*R. catesbeiana*), but not in *R. pipiens.*

The forelegs **(pectoral appendages)** are much shorter than the hind legs **(pelvic appendages)** and do little more than hold up the front of the body; the powerful hind legs are the main organs of locomotion. Comparisons can easily be made between the frog's appendages and our own, for they consist of the same parts; however, several differences in details will be observed. Only four fingers **(digits)** are present on the hand of the frog, the first digit, i.e., the thumb, is missing. The most medial digit (which phylogenetically is the second) bears a **nuptial pad** in the males of many species of frogs, especially during the breeding season, and helps the male to grasp the female. Five digits are present in the foot, the most medial being the first, the equivalent of our own big toe. A membranous **web** extends between the toes. A small spurlike digit known as the **pre-hallux** is located medial to the base of the first typical toe. Two of the ankle bones are elongated, so the foot is very long and more efficient in jumping and swimming.

An anus, or **cloacal aperture,** is located at the posterior end of the trunk. This opening is best called a cloacal aperture in the frog, for a cloaca (a chamber receiving the products of the digestive, excretory and genital tracts) is present. Strictly speaking, the anus is the posterior opening of the digestive tract only.

21.3
Skin and Coloration

The soft, smooth, moist skin, or **integument,** is more complex than one might suspect. It serves for protection, sensory reception and also as one site for gas exchange between the organism and its environment. The integument consists of two layers of tissue—a superficial **epidermis** and a deeper and much thicker **dermis** (Fig. 21.2). The epidermis is composed of stratified squamous epithelium whose basal cells are columnar in shape. These cells proliferate actively by mitosis and this portion of the epidermis is known as the **stratum germinativum.** Newly formed cells move outward, are flattened through various pressures, accumulate some

horny material (only a small amount in frogs), eventually die, and are finally sloughed off in large sheets. The outer, somewhat horny layer of the epidermis is known as the **stratum corneum.**

The dermis consists of fibrous connective tissue. The fibers in the deep portion are more regularly arranged and more tightly packed than those immediately beneath the epidermis. The deeper layer of the dermis, which commonly contains a few smooth muscle fibers, constitutes the **stratum compactum,** whereas the more superficial layer is known as the **stratum spongiosum.** Blood vessels, nerves and simple sense organs are found throughout the dermis. They come close to the epidermis, but only a few naked nerve processes actually enter this layer.

The stratum spongiosum contains many **alveolar glands,** which consist of simple round sacs of cells that have pushed into the dermis from the epidermis. They have an epithelial wall and a cavity or **lumen** which remains connected to the surface by a duct. The most numerous glands are **mucous glands,** whose secretion is a slimy mucus that is discharged over the surface of the body where it helps to protect the frog against desiccation and excessive water entrance. A few **poison glands** are found in certain areas

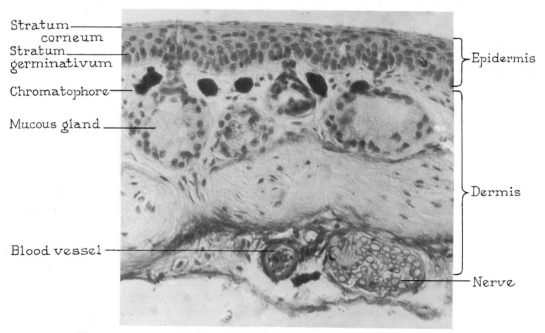

Figure 21.2 A photomicrograph of a vertical section through the skin of a frog.

of the skin, notably in the dorsolateral folds in *Rana pipiens.* These are larger and produce a watery secretion that is presumed to be distasteful and irritating to certain of the frog's predators.

Frog skin is richly colored. In *Rana pipiens,* the general greenish tone blends with the surroundings, while the darker spots and blotches tend to obscure the form of the animal. This concealing coloration presumably helps the frog to elude its predators and to lie unseen as it awaits its prey.

Most of the pigment and refractive granules responsible for the coloration are contained within stellate cells known as **chromatophores,** which are concentrated just beneath the epidermis. Some chromatophores **(melanophores)** contain a brown to blackish pigment, some **(lipophores)** a yellowish to reddish pigment, and some **(guanophores)** refractive granules of guanine. There is no green pigment in frog skin. The lipophores reflect yellow light back through the epidermis. Much of the remaining light penetrates to the guanophores and is dispersed, and blue light is reflected back. The rest of the light rays are absorbed by the melanophores. Yellow and blue light reflected back together result in a greenish color.

Changes in the general color tone of the skin are effected by the migration of pigment within the melanophores. When the skin darkens, pigment streams out into the processes of these cells, some of which mask the guanophores; when it becomes paler, the pigment concentrates near the center of the melanophores. It is the pigment that migrates; the processes of the malanophores remain extended. The movement of the pigment is controlled in part by the hormone **intermedin** secreted by the pituitary gland (p. 563).

21.4
Skeleton

The skeleton of vertebrates forms the supporting framework of the body, provides a point of attachment for most of the muscles, and encases and protects much of the delicate nervous system.

The **somatic skeleton** is the skeleton of the "outer tube" of the body and is located in the body wall and appendages. It includes an **axial portion** lying in the longitudinal axis of the body (vertebral column, sternum and most of the skull), and an **appendicular portion** supporting the paired appendages girdles and limbs). The **visceral skeleton** is the skeleton of the "inner tube" of the body and is associated with the anterior part of the digestive tract. It is prominent in fish, where it supports the gills and helps to form and support the jaws. In terrestrial vertebrates it is reduced, but parts of it usually remain associated with the jaws, and parts become associated with the ear, tongue and larynx.

Skull and Hyoid. The anterior end of the axial skeleton, together with certain parts of the visceral skeleton, forms the **skull,** a complex of bone and cartilage encasing the brain and major sense organs and forming the jaws. The central portion of the skull surrounding the brain is known as the **cranium;** its more peripheral parts constitute the **facial skeleton** (Figs. 21.3 and 21.4). The nasal cavities are situated near the front of the skull; a pair of large openings for the eyes, **orbits,** lie lateral to the middle of the cranium; and the inner part of the ears, containing the receptive cells, lie in posterolateral extensions of the cranium known as the **otic capsules.** A slender bony rod, the **stapes,** extends laterally from each otic capsule. In most terrestrial vertebrates it is a part of the visceral skeleton which has become modified in such a way that it can transmit vibrations from the tympanic membrane to the inner ear. In frogs, however, it develops embryonically from a part of the otic capsule; hence it is not comparable to a gill arch. The spinal cord passes through a large hole, **foramen magnum,** at the posterior end of the cranium. A pair of rounded bumps, **occipital condyles,** lie ventrolateral to the foramen and articulate the skull with the vertebral column.

The upper jaw bears small **teeth** along its margin and two patches of vomerine teeth are borne by the vomer bones in the roof of the mouth, but the lower jaw lacks teeth. The jaw joint lies between a **quadrate cartilage** of the upper jaw and **Meckel's cartilage** of the lower jaw; both are parts of the visceral skeleton. Most other skull bones are of axial origin. The names of major ones are shown in Figures 21.3 and 21.4.

The greater part of the visceral skeleton is incorporated in the **hyoid apparatus** — a plate of cartilage and bone that supports the floor of the mouth and the base of the tongue.

Vertebral Column. The vertebral col-

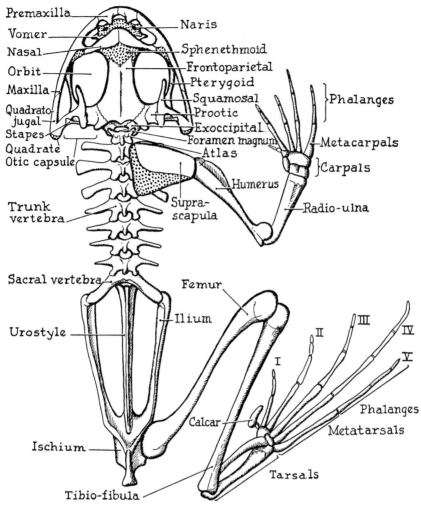

Figure 21.3 A dorsal view of the frog's skeleton. Major cartilaginous areas are stippled in this and in other drawings of the skeleton. Roman numerals refer to digit numbers. (After Parker and Haswell.)

umn, which forms a firm yet movable support for the trunk, is a part of the axial skeleton. It is unusually short in frogs, consisting in most species of only nine **vertebrae,** plus an elongate terminal piece known as the **urostyle** (Fig. 21.3). The urostyle appears to represent two caudal vertebrae fused together and specialized for the attachment of powerful pelvic muscles. The short compact vertebral column is adapted for the frog's jumping mode of progression.

A representative vertebra consists of a ventral, cylindrical block of bone, the **centrum,** and a dorsal **neural arch** enclosing the **vertebral canal,** in which the spinal cord lies. The neural arch bears a pair of prominent, broad, lateral extensions called **transverse processes,** a small middorsal **neural spine,** and an articular process, or **zygapophysis,** on each dorsal corner. The transverse process represents a true vertebral process fused with a short rudimentary rib. Free ribs articulating movably with the vertebrae are absent in the adults of all but a few very primitive species of frogs. Foramina for the passage of the spinal nerves are found laterally between successive vertebrae.

The most anterior vertebra, known as the **atlas,** is modified for articulating with the skull and lacks transverse processes. The vertebra preceding the urostyle, the **sacral vertebra,** is also modified with unusually large transverse processes that articulate with the pelvic girdle.

Appendicular Skeleton. The sternum, though a part of the axial skeleton, is in-

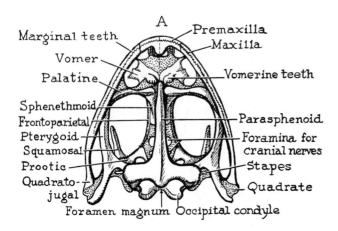

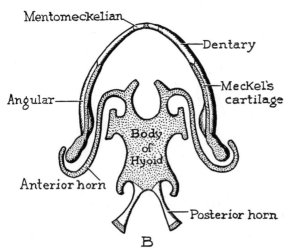

Figure 21.4 *A,* A ventral view of the frog's skull; *B,* a ventral view of the lower jaw and hyoid apparatus. (After Gaupp.)

timately associated with the pectoral girdle. Sternum and girdle together form an arch of bone and cartilage that nearly encircles the front of the trunk and supports the pectoral appendages. Each half of the **pectoral girdle** (Fig. 21.5) consists of two bones extending laterally from the midventral line, an anterior **clavicle** and a posterior **coracoid.** Clavicle and coracoid of opposite sides are connected by a narrow strip of cartilage. Another bone, the **scapula,** extends dorsally from the lateral end of these. The concavity where these three meet, known as the **glenoid cavity,** articulates with the humerus, the bone of the upper arm. A partly ossified **suprascapula** lies dorsal to the scapula and folds over the back of the animal. Only muscles bind the pectoral girdle to the trunk, for there is no direct connection between the girdle and the vertebral column.

The **sternum** is divided into four mid-ventral pieces, two of which extend anteriorly from the clavicles and two posteriorly from the coracoids.

The forelimb is composed of a **humerus** extending from the shoulder to the elbow joint; a **radio-ulna** (fusion of a radius and ulna) continuing to the wrist joint; a series of small wrist bones, the **carpals,** lying in the proximal part of the hand; four long **metacarpals** in the region of the palm; and a series of small segments known as **phalanges** in each of the four digits. Although the first finger is not apparent in an entire frog, its vestigial metacarpal can often be seen in the skeleton.

The **pelvic girdle** is attached to the sacral vertebra so that the body weight can be transferred directly by way of bone from the axis of the body to the hind legs (Fig. 21.5). Each side of the girdle consists of a long **ilium** extending posteriorly from the sacrum to the **ischium** and **pubis.** The ventral pubis is un-

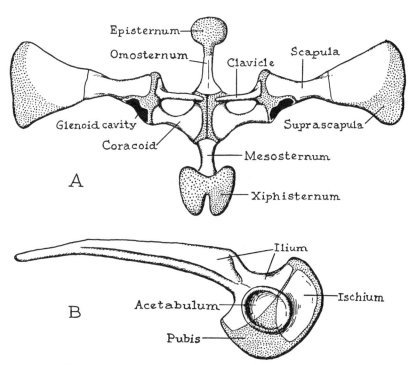

Figure 21.5 Girdles of the frog. *A*, A ventral view of the sternum and pectoral girdle; *B*, a lateral view of the pelvic girdle. (Modified after Gaupp.)

Figure 21.6 Three stages in the leap of a bullfrog. (Courtesy of Mr. Earle R. Edmiston.)

ossified. A concavity, the **acetabulum,** is situated where the three join and serves for the articulation of the hind limb.

The **femur** extends from the acetabulum to the knee, and a fused **tibio-fibula** from the knee to the ankle joint. Ankle bones, the **tarsals,** form the proximal part of the foot. These are followed by five **metatarsals** in the region of the sole, and a series of **phalanges** in each digit. The frog foot is unusual in that the two proximal tarsals are elongated and form, in effect, an extra segment to the limb. These elongated tarsals are followed distally by too small and inconspicuous ones. A bone called the **calcar** supports the prehallux.

When a frog is at rest, its powerful hind legs are folded up (flexed) beside the frog and the pelvic girdle and urostyle are rotated forward slightly so that there is a conspicuous bump in the back at the sacroiliac and sacrourostyle joints (Fig. 21.6). During a leap, all segments of the powerful legs are extended and, during a strong leap, the pelvic girdle and urostyle also rotate posteriorly and provide an additional thrust. The initial shock of the landing is taken up by the front legs. Many features of the appendicular skeleton are clearly related to this pattern of locomotion. The long hind legs and elongation of certain tarsals increase the thrust of the hind legs in jumping; the elongation of the urostyle and ilium permit the pelvic girdle to take part in the thrust; fusion of the tibia and fibula and of the radius and ulna has reduced the capacity of the hand and foot to rotate, but has increased the strength of these parts of the limbs.

21.5
Muscular System

Smooth muscles are found in the walls of many visceral organs, cardiac muscles in the wall of the heart, and striated muscles attached to the skeleton. The striated muscles, which are generally under voluntary control, form the bulk of the muscular system. Most of these are attached to bones by tendons. The **origin** of the muscle is its fixed end; the **insertion** is the end attached to the structure that moves when the muscle contracts. For

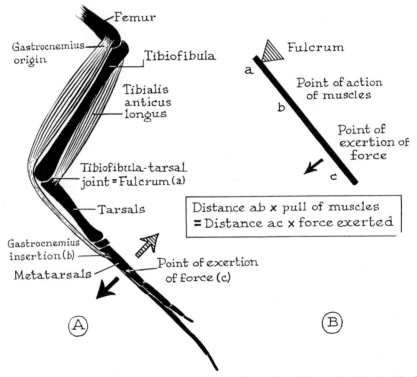

Figure 21.7 *A,* A diagram to illustrate the antagonistic action of muscles on the frog's right hind foot. The gastrocnemius moves the foot in the direction of the solid arrow; the tibialis anticus in the direction of the shaded arrow *B,* A comparable lever system.

limb muscles, the origin is the proximal end, the insertion the distal end.

Muscles can induce movement only by contracting or shortening; hence, the muscles of the body are grouped into antagonistic sets. One set of muscles is responsible for moving a part in one direction, whereas movement in the opposite direction entails the relaxation of the first set of muscles and the contraction of an antagonistic set on the opposite side of the part. Various terms are used to describe movement in different directions. For example, **flexion** is the bending of a joint with a consequent diminishing of the angle between the bones, as occurs at the knee or elbow; **extension** is the opposite movement, i.e., a straightening. The forward movement

of the entire limb at the hip or shoulder is sometimes also called flexion, but **protraction** is a more appropriate term. **Retraction** is the opposite movement. **Adduction** is a movement that brings the distal end of an appendage toward the midventral line of the body; **abduction,** away from the midventral line.

Most of the muscles are attached to the bones in such a way that the fulcrum is at one end of the lever, and the muscle attachment is nearer the fulcrum than the point at which the lever exerts its force (Fig. 21.7). Such levers are mechanically inefficient, but this arrangement provides for compactness and speed of movement.

The superficial skeletal muscles of the frog

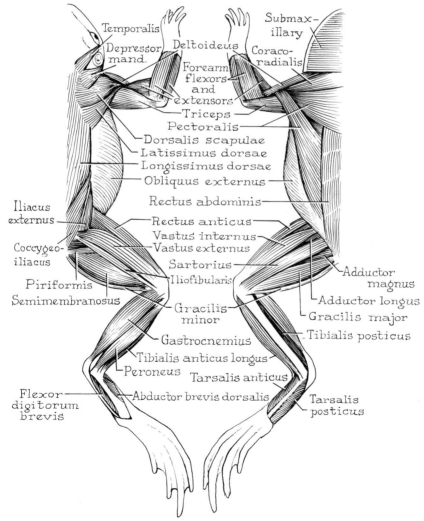

Figure 21.8 Superficial skeletal muscles of the frog in a dorsal (left side of figure) view and a ventral (right side) view.

Table 21.1   Major Attachments and Actions of Important Frog Muscles

Muscle	Origin	Insertion	Action
Jaw Muscles			
Temporalis	Dorsal surface of skull	Mandible anterior to jaw joint	Closes jaws
Depressor mandibulae	Dorsal surface of skull, connective tissue of back	Mandible posterior to jaw joint	Opens jaws
Submaxillary	Medial surface of mandible	Longitudinal connective tissue septum between submaxillaries of opposite sides	Raises floor of mouth and pharynx during breathing and swallowing
Trunk Muscles			
Obliquus externus	Connective tissue of back	Longitudinal midventral connective tissue septum	Supports abdomen, helps compress lungs during breathing
Rectus abdominis	Sternum	Anteroventral surface of pelvic girdle	Supports abdomen, flexes back
Longissimus dorsi	Posterior end of skull, dorsal surface of vertebrae	Urostyle and ilium	Extends back
Coccygeoiliacus	Urostyle	Ilium	Helps extend back
Foreleg Muscles			
Dorsalis scapulae	Surface of scapula and suprascapula	Proximal end of humerus	Abducts arm, helps protract arm
Latissimus dorsi	Dorsolateral surface of trunk	Proximal end of humerus	Abducts arm, helps retract arm
Triceps	Base of scapula, shaft of humerus	Proximal end of radio-ulna	Extends forearm
Deltoideus	Base of scapula, clavicle	Proximal end of humerus	Adducts arm, protracts arm
Pectoralis	Ventral surface of trunk and sternum	Proximal end of humerus	Adducts arm, retracts arm
Coracoradialis	Ventral surface of coracoid	Proximal end of radio-ulna	Flexes forearm
Hindleg Muscles: Thigh			
Triceps femoris (rectus anticus, vastus internus and externus)	Ilium and capsule of hip joint	Proximal end of tibio-fibula	Extends shank
Iliofibularis Semimembranosus Gracilis major and minor	Posterodorsal part of pelvic girdle	Proximal end of tibio-fibula	Flexes shank, during shank extension helps retract and abduct thigh
Sartorius	Anteroventral part of pelvic girdle	Proximal end of tibio-fibula	Flexes shank, helps adduct and protract thigh
Adductor magnus Adductor longus	Ventral part of pelvic girdle	Distal portion of femur	Adducts thigh
Hindleg Muscles: Shank			
Gastrocnemius	Distal end of femur	Planar aponeurosis and terminal segment of each toe	Extends foot
Tibialis posticus Peroneus	Shaft of tibio-fibula	Proximal end of tarsals	Helps extend foot
Tibialis anticus longus	Distal end of femur	Proximal end of tarsals	Flexes foot, helps extend shank

are shown in Figure 21.8, and the attachments and actions of important ones are listed in Table 21.1. As in most terrestrial vertebrates the limbs, rather than the trunk, are the important organs for locomotion. Their muscles are numerous, complex and powerful. The trunk musculature is considerably reduced as compared with that of a fish, and most of it has lost the primitive segmentation.

21.6
Body Cavity and Mesenteries

The internal organs of the frog protrude into the body cavity, or **coelom,** which contains a small amount of watery **coelomic fluid.** The space and fluid facilitate the expansion, contraction and slight movement of the organs in relation to one another. The coelom is divided into an anterior **pericardial cavity** containing the heart and a posterior **pleuroperitoneal cavity** containing the other visceral organs. The coelom is lined with a thin layer of epithelium. The internal organs have pushed into the coelom and are covered by a layer of coelomic epithelium called the **visceral peritoneum** (Fig. 21.9). The visceral peritoneum is continuous with the **parietal peritoneum** lining the body wall by way of thin double-layered **mesenteries** which support the internal organs. Blood vessels and nerves pass through the mesenteries in going from the body wall to the visceral organs. Relations in the pericardial cavity are much the same, but mesenteries are absent in the adult.

The coelomic epithelium here is called the **visceral** and **parietal pericardium.**

21.7
Digestive System

Adult frogs are carnivorous and feed upon any animal small enough for them to catch and swallow—worms, crustaceans, insects and the like. Many of these are captured by a flick of the **tongue,** which is covered by a sticky secretion produced by glands in the roof of the mouth. As the tongue flicks out, the back of the tongue vaults over the front, for the tongue is attached anteriorly (Fig. 21.10). Tongue protrusion is very fast, on the order of 0.05 second. It is now considered to result from muscular action rather than from the filling of a lymph sac at its base. Food is held in the mouth by the teeth and then swallowed whole. A lubricating mucous secretion, the tongue, and an inward movement of the eyes all aid in swallowing. Mucus is carried back into the throat by the beating of microscopic cilia on the cells lining the mouth cavity, and this helps keep the mouth free of debris.

From the **mouth,** or buccal, cavity proper the food passes through the **pharynx** (back of the apparent mouth cavity where food and air passages cross) into a narrow **esophagus.** The esophagus is a short tube leading to the **stomach,** where food is temporarily stored and its digestion initiated. The stomach terminates in a muscular valve, the **pyloric**

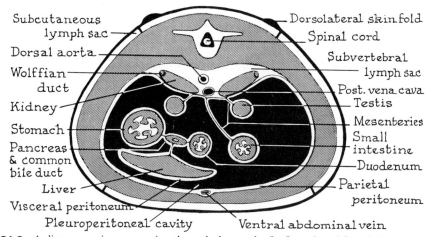

Figure 21.9 A diagrammatic cross section through the trunk of a frog viewed from behind. At a more anterior level, a mesentery would pass to the stomach rather than to the intestine.

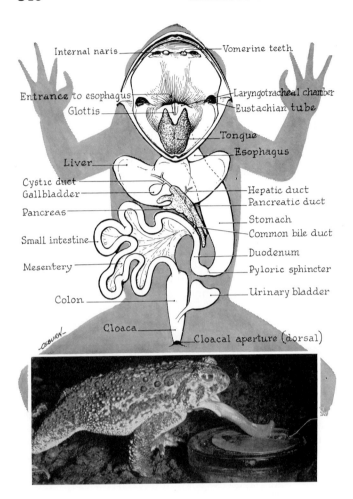

Internal naris — Vomerine teeth
Entrance to esophagus — Laryngotracheal chamber
Glottis — Eustachian tube
Tongue
Esophagus
Liver
Cystic duct — Hepatic duct
Gallbladder — Pancreatic duct
Pancreas — Stomach
— Common bile duct
Small intestine — Duodenum
Mesentery — Pyloric sphincter
Colon — Urinary bladder
Cloaca
Cloacal aperture (dorsal)

Figure 21.10 A ventral view of the frog's digestive system. The liver lobes have been turned forward to show the gallbladder. Tongue action is shown in the inset. Notice that the tongue is stretched to over half the length of the body. (Inset from Van Riper in Natural History, Vol. LXVI, No. 6)

sphincter. From the stomach a segment of the small intestine known as the **duodenum** passes anteriorly, receiving secretions from the liver and pancreas by way of a common bile duct. The remainder of the small intestine continues posteriorly in a number of convolutions, finally emptying into the large intestine, or **colon.** Digestion is completed in the small intestine, and the food is absorbed into the circulatory system. Water and certain ions and vitamins are absorbed from the large intestine, and residue is temporarily stored as fecal material. The large intestine narrows posteriorly before entering the **cloaca** — a chamber receiving the products of the digestive, excretory and genital systems. The cloaca opens on the body surface through the **cloacal aperture.**

The basic histology of the alimentary canal can be seen to advantage in a cross section through the anterior part of the stomach (Fig. 21.11). Progessing from the coelom to-ward the lumen there is (1) the visceral peritoneum, or **serosa,** consisting of a single layer of squamous epithelium supported by fibrous connective tissue; (2) two layers of smooth **muscle** — a much reduced (in the stomach) outer longitudinal layer in which the fibers more or less parallel the long axis of the gut, and a thick inner circular layer with fibers nearly at right angles to the preceding; (3) a layer of highly vascular, fibrous connective tissue known as the **submucosa;** and finally (4) the **mucosa,** or mucous membrane. Movement of the food within the stomach and along the intestine is accomplished by rhythmic waves of contraction of the muscle layers, which are known as **peristalsis.**

The mucosa consists of thin layers of longitudinal and circular muscles **(muscularis mucosae)** next to the submucosa, plus connective tissue and the simple columnar epithelium lining the lumen. The epithelium

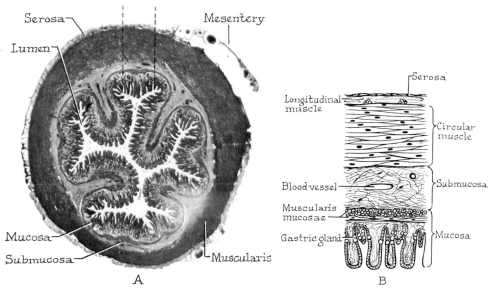

Figure 21.11 Diagrams of cross sections through the frog's stomach. *A*, Low magnification; *B*, an enlargement of the segment of the preceding lying between the dotted lines.

contains numerous mucus-secreting **goblet cells** and is invaginated to form many **gastric pits.** From the base of each pit one or two narrow tubular **gastric glands** continue toward the muscularis mucosae. These glands contain several large, clear, mucus-producing cells and other secretory cells filled with granules. In frogs the protein-splitting enzyme **pepsin** is secreted by these glands in the anterior part of the stomach and the adjacent portion of the esophagus, but hydrochloric acid, needed to activate pepsin, is secreted by glands in more posterior parts of the stomach.

Multicellular glands are absent from the mucosa of the frog's intestine. The intestine receives digestive juices from the liver and pancreas. Chemical breakdown, or digestion, of food is completed in this region, and the products of digestion are absorbed. The intestinal mucosa is thrown into many longitudinal and transverse folds which slow up the passage of the food and increase the digestive and absorptive surface.

The **pancreas** and **liver** are large glands that develop embryonically as outgrowths from the intestine. The pancreas produces a variety of enzymes that are discharged through a **pancreatic duct** into the common bile duct. Certain of its cells also produce the hormones insulin and glucagon (p. 558). The liver's secretion, known as **bile,** leaves the liver through **hepatic ducts,** is stored tem-

porarily in the **gallbladder,** then is discharged into the intestine through the **cystic** and **common bile ducts.** Bile contains no digestive enzymes, but its bile salts emulsify fats and aid in their absorption. In addition, the liver has an important role in determining the concentration of glucose and certain other constituents of the blood.

21.8
Respiratory System

Any moist, vascular semipermeable membrane exposed to the external environment can serve as a respiratory membrane for the exchange of gases between the blood and environment. In a frog, the skin and the mucous membrane lining the mouth and pharynx, as well as the lungs, fulfill these requirements. It has been estimated that in a typical semi-aquatic frog on the land, about one-third of the gas exchange occurs through the skin (**cutaneous respiration**) and two-thirds through the lungs (**pulmonary respiration**); only a small amount occurs through the mouth and pharynx lining (**buccopharyngeal respiration**). But when the frog is submerged in water for an extended period, all exchange must be through the skin and lining of the mouth and pharynx.

Air is taken into the body through the paired **external nares,** traverses the short

nasal cavities and enters the front of the mouth through the paired **internal nares** (Fig. 21.12). It then passes through the **glottis,** a slit-shaped opening in the floor of the pharynx, and into a **laryngotracheal chamber** (comparable to the larynx and trachea of higher vertebrates). Small cartilages, which are homologous with parts of the visceral skeleton of fish, support this chamber, and a pair of **bronchi** lead from its posterior corners to the **lungs.** The lungs of frogs are simple, ovoid sacs in external shape, but their internal surface is increased by numerous pocket-shaped folds that give them a honeycomb appearance.

Air is moved into the lungs by the pumping action of the floor of the mouth (Fig. 21.13). Four main stages can be recognized. (1) The floor of the mouth and pharynx is lowered and fresh air is drawn into the buccopharyngeal cavity through the nasal passages. (2) The external nostrils close. A continued lowering of the floor of the mouth, assisted by the contraction of the elastic tissue in the lungs and muscles in the flanks, forces stale air from the lungs through the now opened glottis into the buccopharyngeal cavity, where it mixes with the fresh air. (3) Much of this mixed air is pumped into the lungs by a raising of the floor of the mouth and pharynx. (4) The glottis now closes, the external nares

open, and the rest of the mixed air is expelled. Air does not enter the lungs with each set of throat movements, however. The glottis is closed most of the time and throat movement then simply moves air back and forth through the nasal passages, where the olfactory epithelium is located.

Voice.   A mechanism for sound production is closely associated with the respiratory system. Two longitudinal elastic bands, the **vocal cords,** are situated in the laryngotracheal chamber near the glottis (Fig. 21.12). Air forced from the lungs sets the free edges of these cords in vibration, and they, in turn, vibrate the column of air in the pharynx and mouth. The pitch of the sound is controlled by muscular tension on the vocal cords. Some of the expelled air inflates the **vocal sacs,** which serve as resonating sacs and considerably increase the volume of the sound. In some species the vocal sacs are paired evaginations from the lateral walls of the pharynx; in other species there is a single median vocal sac ventral to the floor of the pharynx. Contraction of muscle fibers in the wall of the vocal sac returns the air to the lungs, and the same air can be used repeatedly. Some frogs, such as the bullfrog, can even call from beneath water.

The vocal cords are more prominent in males than in females, and only the males

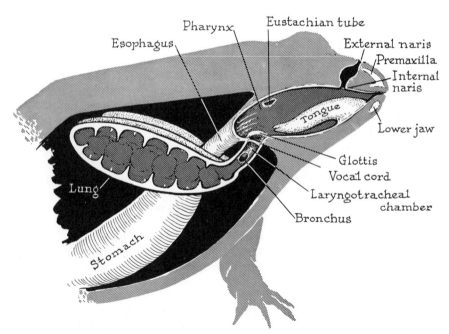

Figure 21.12   A diagrammatic longitudinal section of the respiratory system of the frog.

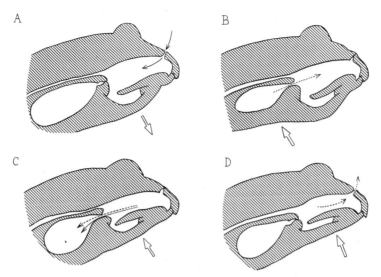

Figure 21.13   Diagram of four stages in the ventilation of the frog's lungs. Black arrows indicate the course of fresh and stale air; white arrows the movements of the floor of the pharynx and flanks. (Modified after Hughes.)

have vocal sacs. The males gather first in the breeding ponds during the spring, and their familiar croaking attracts the females of the appropriate species.

21.9
Circulatory System

The circulatory system is the transport system of the body. It consists of the circulating fluids, chiefly blood, and of the heart and a series of vessels that carry the fluids. As explained in Chapter 3, blood is composed of a liquid plasma, in which red cells, white cells and thrombocytes are suspended. The thrombocytes are spindle-shaped cells essential for blood clotting. The exchange of materials between the blood and the tissues occurs in the microscopic, thin-walled **capillaries** situated between the arteries and veins. Food, oxygen and water leave the capillaries, and carbon dioxide and other wastes enter them to be removed by the veins. A volume of water nearly equal to the amount that left the capillaries also re-enters them. Some liquid remains in the tissues and is returned by **lymph vessels,** which usually parallel the veins and eventually empty into them. Before connecting with the veins, some of these vessels lead into **lymph sacs.** Unusually large lymph sacs lie ventral to the vertebral column and beneath the skin, separating it

from most of the underlying musculature (Fig. 21.9).

Arteries. The pattern of the major blood vessels of the frog is shown in Figure 21.14. Many, though not all, of these vessels are also present in the higher vertebrates, including man. A pair of arteries, each known as the **truncus arteriosus,** leave the front of the heart. Each soon divides into three vessels—**carotid arch, systemic arch** and **pulmocutaneous arch.** Each carotid arch extends anteriorly and divides into an **external carotid,** supplying the tongue and adjacent parts, and an **internal carotid,** supplying the upper parts of the head and the brain. The function of the swelling at the base of the internal carotid artery, the **carotid gland,** is not certain. There is some evidence that it contains stretch receptors and helps to regulate blood pressure and flow; other evidence suggests that it contains chemical receptors sensitive to the partial pressure of oxygen in the blood.

Each systemic arch curves dorsally and posteriorly, giving off an artery to the back (the **occipitovertebral**) and one to the arms (the **subclavian**). The left and right systemic arches then unite to form a median **dorsal aorta** that continues posteriorly, ventral to the vertebral column. The aorta supplies the abdominal viscera (except for the lungs), trunk and hind legs (Fig. 21.14). Among the structures supplied is the **spleen,** an organ

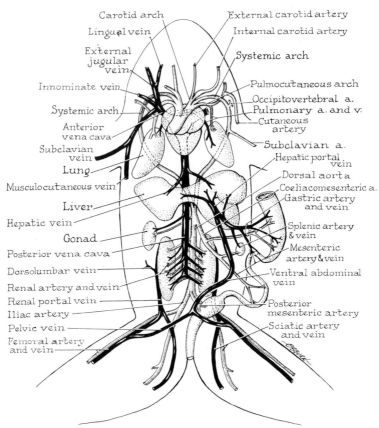

Figure 21.14 A ventral view of the major arteries and veins of the frog. Veins are shown in black; arteries are white. Certain of the anterior veins have been omitted from the right side of the drawing and certain of the anterior arteries from the left side.

in which blood cells are produced, stored and destroyed.

The pulmocutaneous arch carries blood to organs where gas exchange with the external environment occurs. Each vessel soon divides into a **pulmonary artery** to the lungs and a **cutaneous artery.** The latter supplies not only the skin but also much of the lining of the mouth and pharynx.

Veins. The veins returning blood to the heart have a more complex pattern. The digestive tract and associated organs are drained by the hepatic portal system. Various tributaries from the viscera unite to form a large **hepatic portal vein,** which enters the liver and breaks up into many capillary-like spaces among the liver cells. Absorbed materials, therefore, pass directly from the gut to the liver, which, as explained in Chapter 5, has an important role in the metabolism of food. The liver also receives blood from the aorta by the **hepatic artery.** It is drained by

hepatic veins, which empty into the large **posterior vena cava.**

Much of the blood from the hind legs and the back enters a pair of **renal portal veins** leading to capillaries within the kidneys. The kidneys are drained by **renal veins** which enter the posterior vena cava. As the vena cava continues forward it also receives veins from the reproductive organs and the liver. Some blood from the legs passes through **pelvic veins** to the **ventral abdominal vein.** This vessel continues forward, draining the urinary bladder and ventral body wall, and finally joins the hepatic portal as the latter enters the liver. Blood from the hind legs thus moves forward via two routes: some flows through the kidneys and then into the posterior vena cava, and some flows through the ventral abdominal vein and liver before entering the posterior vena cava. The functional significance of this complex arrangement is not understood, but it does ensure a larger volume of blood flow through the kidneys and liver than would otherwise be the case. In higher vertebrates, all the blood from hind legs enters the posterior vena cava directly, without going through the kidney or liver.

Blood from the head, shoulders and arms returns to the heart through a pair of **anterior venae cavae** (Fig. 21.14). Certain of the tributaries of the anterior venae cavae, e.g., the **musculocutaneous vein** from the skin and the tributaries of the **jugulars** from the mouth lining, come from respiratory membranes and carry blood with a relatively high oxygen content.

The lungs are drained by a separate pair of vessels, the **pulmonary veins,** which unite and enter the heart independently of the anterior venae cavae.

Heart. The frog's heart consists of a series of chambers having muscular walls that force the blood along and valves that prevent its backflow (Fig. 21.15). A thin-walled **sinus venosus** receives blood from the posterior and anterior venae cavae, and passes it into the **right atrium.** The right atrium receives blood low in oxygen content from the body, and blood high in oxygen content from the skin and lining of the mouth. The pulmonary veins bring additional oxygen-rich blood brom the lungs to the **left atrium.** Both atria lead into a single **ventricle** having a thick muscular

wall. The ventricle forces the blood through a final chamber, the **conus arteriosus,** and into each truncus arteriosus. A peculiar spiral valve is found in the conus, and each truncus is partitioned internally into separate channels leading to the three vessels to which it gives rise.

Some mixing of blood from the two atria takes place in the ventricles, but how much is uncertain. According to the classic view, a slight difference in the time of entrance of the blood from the two atria, the spongy ventricular wall, and the deflective effect of the spiral valve in the conus result in most of the blood from the left atrium passing into the carotid and systemic arches, while most of the blood from the right atrium passes into the pulmocutaneous arch. Others believe there is a thorough mixing. In recent years, blood has been traced through the heart using various methods to distinguish between the blood streams. One investigator finds that there is always some mixing of the two blood streams, yet the pulmocutaneous arch receives primarily right atrial blood relatively low in oxygen content, the systemic arch a rather complete mixture of blood, and the carotid arch primarily left atrial blood high in oxygen content.

Lungless fish have a single atrium and ventricle; blood low in oxygen content is received by the atrium and continues through the ventricle to the gills, where it is aerated

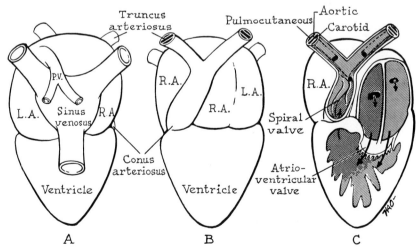

Figure 21.15 The frog's heart. *A,* Dorsal view of the surface of the heart; *B,* ventral view of the surface; *C,* ventral view of a dissection of the heart. L.A., left atrium; P.V., pulmonary vein; R.A., right atrium. In *C,* blood entering the ventricle from the right atrium is more darkly shaded than the blood entering from the left atrium, and the classic hypothesis of the separation of the blood within the single ventricle is shown.

and then distributed to the body. Gas exchange in mammals takes place only in the lungs, and mammals have a completely divided atrium and ventricle. The right chambers of the heart receive blood low in oxygen content and send it to the lungs; the left chambers receive aerated blood from the lungs and send it to the body. At one time it was believed that the frog heart represented a necessary but inefficient intermediate stage in the evolution of the mammalian double circulation. However, lungfish have a nearly completely divided heart and a double circulation. It is possible that their heart reflects the ancestral terrestrial vertebrate situation and that contemporary frogs have lost the interventricular septum as an adaptation for cutaneous respiration. When on land some aerated blood is entering the right atrium from the skin, and some mixing of this blood with even richer blood from the left atrium in the single ventricle is not critical. When a frog is submerged, the only aerated blood it receives is from the skin and buccopharyngeal membrane. The absence of an interventricular septum permits much of this blood to be distributed directly to the body without an unnecessary trip through the lungs.

21.10
Excretory System

The skin and the lungs remove some waste products of metabolism, but the **kidneys** are the major excretory organs and remove most of the nitrogenous wastes. They also help to maintain the constancy of the internal environment by removing from the blood substances in excess and by conserving those in short supply.

The frog's kidneys are a pair of elongate organs lying in the subvertebral lymph sac

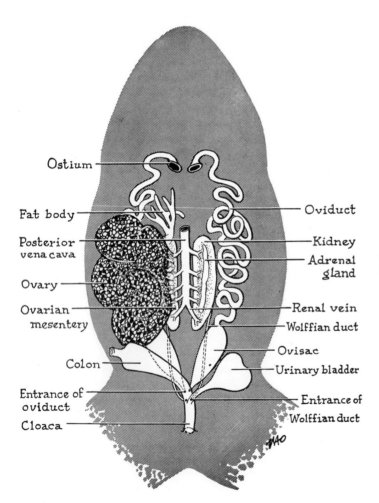

Figure 21.16 Ventral view of the urogenital system of a female frog. The left ovary has been removed.

Ostium

Fat body

Posterior vena cava

Ovary

Ovarian mesentery

Colon

Entrance of oviduct

Cloaca

Oviduct

Kidney

Adrenal gland

Renal vein

Wolffian duct

Ovisac

Urinary bladder

Entrance of Wolffian duct

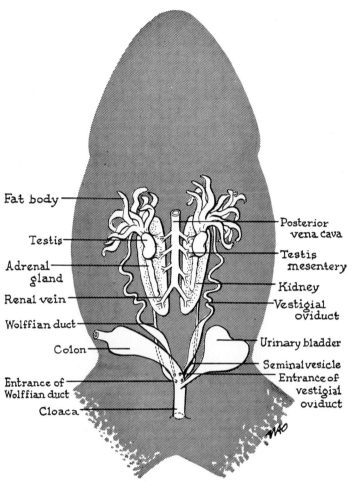

Figure 21.17 Ventral view of the urogenital system of a male frog. The vestigial oviduct shown in this figure tends to be absent in the southeastern members of the species.

dorsal to the pleuroperitoneal cavity (Figs. 21.9, 21.16, and 21.17). They are composed of several thousand microscopic **kidney tubules** that are intimately related to blood entering the kidneys in the renal arteries and renal portal veins. These tubules are described more fully in Chapter 29; briefly, they remove waste products from the blood along with a great deal of water and carry them as urine to the **wolffian ducts.** A wolffian duct, which is functionally but not structurally comparable to the ureter of higher vertebrates (section 29.1), extends along the lateral border of each kidney and continues to the dorsal surface of the cloaca. The urine may be discharged directly through the cloaca, or it may cross and enter the **urinary bladder** attached to the ventral surface of the cloaca.

Since frogs normally spend much time in the water, they must eliminate a great deal

of water that diffuses into the body through the skin. The production of copious and dilute urine is therefore adaptive. Under conditions of dehydration, however, frogs have less control over loss of body water than do truly terrestrial vertebrates. But some water can be conserved by a decrease in the rate of urine production and by an increase in the reabsorption of water from the kidney tubules and the urinary bladder. The terrestrial toads, in particular, can reabsorb a great deal of water from the urinary bladder. The frog's rudimentary ability to conserve water is one factor that restricts it to the amphibious environment.

The **adrenal glands** are endocrine glands that appear as a pair of irregular, light-colored bands, one on the ventral surface of each kidney. They produce a variety of hormones which will be considered in the chapter on endocrine glands.

21.11
Reproductive System

The reproductive system includes the gonads, which produce the gametes (eggs and sperm), and the reproductive ducts, which transfer the gametes to the exterior (Figs. 21.16 and 21.17). A pair of gonads, **testes** in the male and **ovaries** in the female, are suspended by mesenteries from the kidneys, and a finger-like **fat body** is attached to the anterior end of each gonad. The fat bodies contain a reserve of food, some of which is used during hibernation and the rest during the spring breeding season, when frogs become very active. These organs, therefore, are largest in the fall just before hibernation and smallest after reproduction in the spring.

In the breeding season, the ripe eggs are forced out of the ovary by the contraction of smooth muscles in the wall of a saclike **follicle** which surrounds each egg within the ovary. These muscle fibers are stimulated by a hormone from the pituitary gland (section 21.14). This mechanism for discharging eggs from the ovary is quite different from that in mammals, in which an accumulation of liquid within the follicle causes it to rupture. The eggs pass into the pleuroperitoneal cavity and are carried anteriorly by the action of peritoneal cilia (present only in females) toward the openings **(ostia)** of the paired

oviducts. As the eggs are carried down these highly coiled tubes by muscular contraction and the beating of cilia within the ducts, they are covered with several layers of a jelly-like albumin secreted by certain oviducal cells. Just before entering the cloaca, each oviduct expands to form a thin-walled **ovisac** where the eggs are stored for a short time until mating takes place.

Sperm are produced in numerous microscopic **seminiferous tubules** within the testes. During the breeding season, under the stimulus of a pituitary hormone, the mature sperm leave the testis through minute ducts, the **vasa efferentia,** which cross to the anterior portion of the kidney in the mesentery supporting the testis. The vasa efferentia connect with certain of the kidney tubules through which the sperm pass to the wolffian duct. The sperm may be stored briefly until mating in a slight enlargement of the wolffian duct known as the **seminal vesicle.** Certain of the kidney tubules and the wolffian duct thus have a dual function in the male—the production and transport of urine and the transport of sperm.

Male frogs often have vestigial oviducts lying beside the wolffian ducts. These are remnants of a sexually indifferent stage of the embryo when rudiments for both male and female systems are present.

During mating, the male grasps the female about her trunk with his forelimbs, an em-

Figure 21.18 Leopard frogs in amplexus.

brace termed **amplexus** (Fig. 21.18). Then, as the female discharges eggs into the water, the male sheds sperm. Fertilization is external. As the eggs are laid, the protective layers of jelly imbibe water and swell. The jelly layers protect the delicate eggs from abrasion and fungus infections, and they help to conserve heat produced by the metabolism of the developing embryos.

21.12
Sense Organs

The survival of an organism requires that it respond suitably to changes in the environment. This entails the perception of changes in the internal and external environments, the integration of this information, and the stimulation and coordination of appropriate effectors—muscles, glands, cilia and chromatophores. Stimuli are received by special cells or groups of cells called sense organs or **receptors,** and sometimes also by free nerve endings.

Receptors for touch, pressure, temperature changes, and the like are widely scattered, but those for smell, taste, light, sound and equilibrium are usually aggregated. The receptors for smell are collected in a special **olfactory epithelium** lining part of the nasal cavities. Those for taste are gathered in **taste buds** located on the tongue and in other parts of the lining of the mouth and pharynx.

The **eyes** of frogs are very similar in basic structure to those of mammals, which are described in Chapter 30, but the method of accommodation is different. A frog focuses on near objects by moving the lens of the eye forward, thereby increasing the distance between the lens, which is located near the front of the eye, and the light-sensitive **retina,** located at the back of the eye. The same thing is done to focus a camera on near objects. In the mammalian eye, the shape of the lens is changed in focusing. A frog's eyes are well adapted to the animal's mode of life. The position of the eyes high on the head and the relatively large lens give the animal a wide-angled visual field. The components of the retina are so organized that the receptive cells are particularly sensitive to images of moving objects. A frog will ignore an insect in front of it unless the insect is moving.

The **ears** receive sound vibrations which set a **tympanic membrane** in vibration. The vibrations are transmitted across a **middle ear cavity** by a rod-shaped bone known as the **stapes** (Fig. 21.19). This cavity is comparable to a gill pouch of a fish, which is connected to the pharynx, so it is not surprising that it is connected to the pharynx by a **eustachian tube.** The inner end of the stapes fits into an opening in the otic capsule known as the oval window **(fenestra ovalis).** An **inner ear,** consisting of a series of liquid-filled canals and sacs, lies within the otic capsule. Vibrations of the stapes are transmitted to a specific group of cells within the inner ear, which are stimulated and initiate impulses

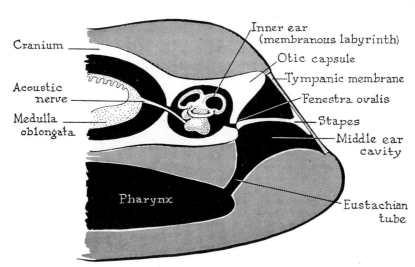

Figure 21.19 A diagrammatic cross section through the head of a frog to show the ear and its relation to surrounding parts.

in the acoustic nerve. By this means the vibrations are perceived as sounds. Other cells in the inner ear are stimulated by the motion of the liquid in the canals and sacs that is brought about by changes in the position of the body. Thus, the inner ear is concerned with equilibrium as well as sound detection.

21.13

Nervous System

The various parts of the nervous system are commonly grouped into a **central nervous system,** which includes the **brain** and **spinal cord,** and a **peripheral nervous system,** which includes the **nerves** connecting the brain and cord with the receptors and effectors of the body. Both the brain and the spinal cord, which lie respectively within the cranium and the neural canal of the vertebral column, are hollow. A single, dorsal, tubular nerve cord, you will remember, is a diagnostic characteristic of chordates. Within the brain, parts of the central cavity are expanded to form large chambers known as **ventricles.** All parts of the nervous system are composed largely of specialized, elongate cells, the **neurons,** described earlier (Chapter 3).

The structure of the brain is shown in Figure 21.20. It can be divided into five major regions: (1) An anterior **telencephalon** bears the paired **olfactory bulbs** and rather small **cerebral hemispheres,** the latter containing the first and second ventricles. (2) An indented region, the **diencephalon,** lies posterior to the cerebral hemispheres. Its lateral walls constitute the **thalamus.** The pituitary gland is attached to a part of the floor of the diencephalon known as the **infundibulum.** An inconspicuous **pineal body** extends from the roof of the diencephalon toward the brow spot. Most of the roof of the diencephalon is thin and vascularized, forming a **choroid plexus** which dips into the third ventricle. This region is followed by (3) the **mesencephalon** bearing the paired **optic lobes** containing optic ventricles; (4) the **metencephalon** with a small, dorsal, transverse ridge known as the **cerebellum;** and (5) the **myelencephalon,** consisting of the **medulla oblongata.** The medulla also has a thin roof which forms a choroid plexus dipping into the large fourth ventricle. The choroid plexuses secrete a **cerebrospinal fluid** which fills the ventricles and central canal. Some of this fluid escapes via pores in the roof of the medulla to circulate between the brain and cord and certain of

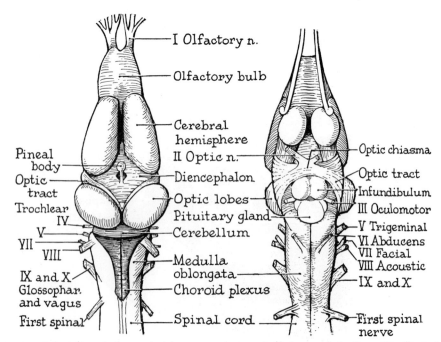

Figure 21.20 *Left,* A dorsal view and *right,* a ventral view of the brain of the frog. (Modified after Gaupp.)

their **meninges,** or connective tissue sheaths. It forms a protective liquid cushion and helps to nourish the central nervous tissue.

Ten pairs of cranial nerves extend from the brain to various parts of the body. The first pair are the **olfactory nerves** (I), which bring impulses from the olfactory epithelium to the olfactory bulbs and cerebral hemispheres. Fibers in the **optic nerves** (II) come from the retina, cross to the opposite side of the brain, forming an **optic chiasma** on the ventral surface of the diencephalon, then continue as **optic tracts** to end chiefly in the optic lobes. The **oculomotor** (III), **trochlear** (IV) and **abducens** (VI) nerves contain motor fibers to the muscles that move the eyeball. The third also includes motor fibers to muscles within the eye that move the lens. The **trigeminal nerve** (V) brings in sensory impulses from the skin of the head and carries motor impulses to the jaw muscles. The **facial nerve** (VII) is also mixed, supplying motor fibers to certain of the throat muscles and to the tear glands, and sensory fibers to the mouth and pharynx. Many of the latter innervate taste buds. The **acoustic nerve** (VIII) brings impulses from the inner ear to the anterior portion of the medulla. The **glossopharyngeal nerve** (IX), like the facial, conducts sensory impulses from the mouth and pharynx and carries motor impulses to a few throat muscles. The last of the frog's cranial nerves, the **vagus** (X), is attached to the side of the medulla in common with the glossopharyngeal nerve. It supplies motor and sensory fibers to the posterior part of the pharynx, certain of the shoulder muscles and most of the abdominal viscera (heart, lungs, digestive tract).

Like the entire trunk region of the frog, the spinal cord is short, and the number of spinal nerves is reduced to 10 pairs. Each of the spinal nerves is attached to the cord by a **dorsal** and a **ventral root** (Fig. 31.4). The former contains sensory fibers and an enlargement, the **dorsal root ganglion,** in which the cell bodies of these neurons are located; the latter, motor fibers. The roots join peripherally and the spinal nerves are mixed. As the spinal nerves emerge from the vertebral column, they are surrounded by calcareous bodies, which are reservoirs of calcium salts. Some of this calcium is used for bone formation during the late stages of metamorphosis from tadpole to adult when the animal is not feeding. The spinal nerves are then distributed to the trunk and limbs in the manner illustrated in Figure 21.21. The first spinal nerve supplies the tongue muscles. This nerve is actually comparable to the second spinal nerve of other vertebrates, for a more anterior spinal nerve is lost during embryonic development. The spinal nerves to a limb first unite and then rebranch, forming a network or **plexus.** Many of the peripheral nerves arising from a plexus contain neurons from more than one spinal nerve. Each spinal nerve has one or more ventral branches, the **rami communicantes,** which pass to a ganglionic enlargement on the **sympathetic cord**—a pair of longitudinal nerve tracts lying on each side of the dorsal aorta. A pair of **splanchnic nerves** extends from the sympathetic cords along the coeliacomesenteric artery to the abdominal viscera. The motor fibers in the sympathetic cords and splanchnic nerves, together with certain of the motor fibers in several of the cranial nerves, constitute a special part of the peripheral nervous system known as the **autonomic nervous system.** The autonomic system, which innervates visceral organs, blood vessels and glands, will be considered more fully later.

The nervous system receives impulses from the sense organs, integrates them, and sends out impulses to appropriate effectors. This is often accomplished by simple **reflexes**—stereotyped, subconscious responses to specific stimuli. For example, when one pinches the toe of a frog, a **sensory neuron** carries the impulse into the spinal cord. Here it is transferred by a short **internuncial neuron** (or perhaps directly by the sensory neuron) to a **motor neuron** that transmits it to the leg muscles, and the frog retracts its leg. The response to this kind of a stimulus is always the same, it happens very rapidly, and need not involve much, or any, passage of impulses up and down the central nervous system. Much of the integration of bodily functions is achieved by reflexes occurring subconsciously, either in the cord or in the brain.

Some regions of the brain have evolved as integration centers for impulses coming in from major sense organs. The telencephalon and diencephalon of frogs are concerned primarily with the integration of olfactory impulses. When these regions are destroyed, the frog does not move spontaneously, pre-

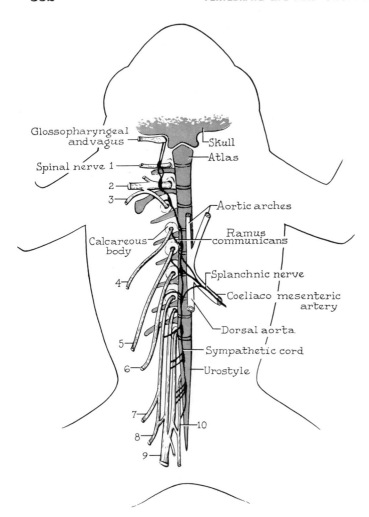

Glossopharyngeal and vagus

Spinal nerve 1

2

3

Calcareous body

4

5

6

7

8

9

Skull

Atlas

Aortic arches

Ramus communicans

Splanchnic nerve

Coeliaco mesenteric artery

Dorsal aorta

Sympathetic cord

Urostyle

10

Figure 21.21 A ventral view of the spinal nerves and sympathetic cord lying on the right side of the vertebral column. (Modified after Gaupp.)

sumably because it cannot respond to olfactory or visual stimuli. (Generally, optic tracts also are destroyed in this operation.) However, the frog does maintain its posture and can feed, jump and swim upon proper stimulation. The optic lobes integrate impulses of sight, but some other sensory impulses are projected to the optic lobes in frogs and other lower vertebrates, so this region has, to a limited extent, the over-all integrative function assumed by the cerebral hemispheres in higher vertebrates. Electrical stimulation of the area can, for example, induce movement of the limbs. Its destruction prevents response to optic impulses and also removes a dampening or inhibiting effect upon spinal reflexes. The cerebellum and medulla receive impulses from the ear and also sensory impulses from most muscles which indicate their present state of activity. In addition,

respiratory movements and some other vital activities are controlled reflexly in the medulla. When these regions are destroyed, the frog loses its ability to maintain its posture or to right itself when turned over. Muscular coordination is impaired, though not so much as in birds and other vertebrates with a larger cerebellum. Feeding is impossible and respiratory movements stop. Spinal reflexes continue for a while, but the animal eventually dies.

21.14
Endocrine Glands

Some of the integration of metabolic processes and other vital activities is controlled by the secretions (hormones) of the endocrine glands. Although chemical integration in the vertebrates is discussed more fully later (Chapter 32), two major endocrine glands of the frog may be briefly considered.

The **pituitary gland,** which is attached to the floor of the brain, is often regarded as the master endocrine gland because it produces a variety of hormones, including some that regulate the activity of many other endocrine glands. Among its hormones are **intermedin,** which helps to control skin coloration; a **gonad-stimulating hormone,** which stimulates amplexus and the release of the gametes; and a **growth-stimulating hormone,** which controls growth of the larvae.

The **thyroid gland** is paired in frogs and located on each side of the posterior part of the hyoid apparatus. Its hormone, **thyroxin,** is necessary for metamorphosis from larva to adult and for an adequate level of metabolism in the adult.

21.15
Life Cycle

A look at certain aspects of the frog's development is no less important than studying the adult, for the continuation of the species requires its reproduction and the development of a reasonable proportion of the fertilized eggs into adults of the next generation. Great numbers of eggs must be laid by frogs and other animals that do not care for them, because the mortality of such eggs and young is very high. The leopard frog lays from 2000 to 3000 eggs, and the bullfrog can lay up to 20,000 per year.

Eggs are laid in the spring, often in rather cold water. However, development can proceed, for the pigmentation of the upper hemisphere of each egg absorbs some heat, metabolic activity produces more, and the jelly coats provide some insulation. The fertilized egg, or **zygote,** cleaves systematically into progressively smaller cells during the early stages of development, finally attaining the **blastula** stage, at which time the embryo is a hollow sphere of cells (Fig. 21.22). Since its lower cells contain more yolk and are larger, the cavity of the blastula, the **blastocoele,** is excentric in position.

This stage is followed by **gastrulation,** a dynamic process during which the cells of the blastula that are destined to form the major organs of the body are moved to appropriate regions of the embryo. This involves the inward movement of many cells

(p. 112), the elimination of the former blastocoele and the formation of the primitive gut cavity, the **archenteron.** The last temporarily opens to the surface through the **blastopore,** an opening which is occluded to some extent in frogs by a plug of yolk-laden cells, the **yolk plug.**

Shortly after this, the embryo begins to elongate. A pair of longitudinal **neural folds,** destined to meet dorsally and close to form the tubular nervous system, appears along its back, and the embryo begins to acquire a distinct head, trunk and tail. A pair of **oral suckers,** for later attachment, and primordia for the eyes and gills are evident upon the head. Embryonic muscle segments **(myotomes)** form along the trunk and tail, and the heart begins to beat.

About this time the embryo wiggles out of its jelly capsule and hatches into a free-swimming **larva,** or tadpole. Nasal cavities, finger-like **external gills,** and mouth and cloacal openings soon appear, and the larva can take care of itself. Most frog tadpoles feed upon minute plant material, scraping it up with **horny teeth.** The younger tadpoles attach onto the plants on which they are feeding by means of their oral suckers. Plant material is more difficult to digest than animal matter, and plant-eating vertebrates generally have longer intestines, which provides more digestive and absorptive surface, than their carnivorous relatives. The intestine of a tadpole is many times the length of the body and is coiled like a watch spring.

Later in larval life the external gills become covered by the growth of a fold known as the **operculum,** and **gill slits** develop that lead from the pharynx to the opercular chamber. About this time the external gills are lost and the larvae respire by **internal gills** that develop within the gill slits. Water containing oxygen enters the mouth and pharynx, and crosses the internal gills on its way out of the gill slits into the opercular chamber. It leaves this chamber through a small opening on the left side, the **spiracle.** Late tadpoles also have lungs and may be seen surfacing to gulp air. Hind limbs appear at the base of the tail, and forelimbs develop within the opercular chamber.

After two and one-half to three months, leopard frogs undergo a **metamorphosis,** a period of rapid differentiation during which larval features are lost and those of the adult are acquired. The front legs burst

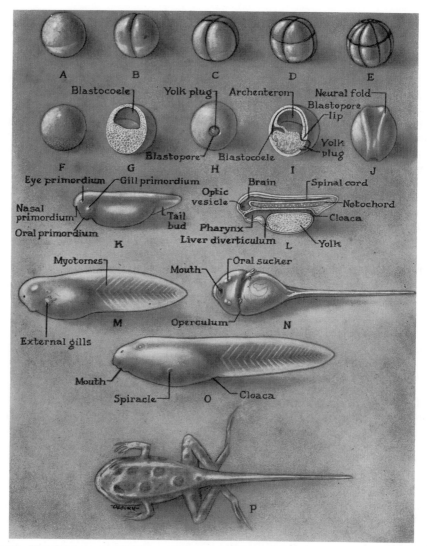

Figure 21.22   The development of the frog. *A*, Zygote; *B–E*, cleavage; *F, G*, blastula; *H, I*, late gastrula; *J*, neural folds; *K, L*, late embryo; *M*, early larva; *N*, opercular folds; *O*, late larva; *P*, metamorphosis. (*A–H, J* and *K*, and *M–O* after Shumway; *G, I* and *L* from Rugh after Huettner; *P* after Rugh.)

through the operculum, the left one first, gills and gill slits are lost and the tail is resorbed. The mouth widens, the horny teeth are lost, a tongue develops, and the digestive tract shortens. A tympanic membrane and eyelids appear, and even the shape of the lens changes, thereby providing for good vision in air, which has a different refractive index than water. Finally gonads develop and differentiate into testes or ovaries.

QUESTIONS

1. How can the sexes of frogs be distinguished externally?
2. What makes a frog's skin appear green? What is the advantage to the frog of its greenish color and dark spots?
3. What parts of the frog's skeleton are classified as visceral skeleton, axial skeleton, appendicular skeleton?
4. In what ways is the frog's skeleton well adapted for jumping?

5. Describe one pair of antagonistic muscles. Indicate their origins and insertions and the way they interact to move a part of the body in opposite directions.
6. Make a diagram of a cross section of a frog showing the relationship of the internal organs to the coelom, peritoneum and mesenteries.
7. How do frogs catch their food?
8. List in correct sequence the parts of the digestive tract of a frog.
9. Describe the route that air takes in going to the lungs of a frog. How is the air moved in and out of the lungs?
10. How do frogs produce sound? What is the purpose of their croaking?
11. List in correct sequence the vessels through which blood can pass in traveling from the hind leg of a frog to the heart.
12. Where does the blood of a frog become aerated? How does the structure of the heart correlate with this?
13. Briefly discuss the problem of water balance in a frog. What effect does this have on the environment in which a frog lives?
14. Trace the route of sperm from the testis of the frog to the outside. Do eggs have a comparable route?
15. List the five regions of the frog's brain and the major structures that are present in each.
16. Are the cerebral hemispheres important integration centers in the frog? What happens if they are destroyed?
17. What is the value of the jelly layers that surround frogs' eggs? Where are these layers added to the egg?
18. Briefly describe the main features of frog development.

ANNOTATED REFERENCES

Gaupp, E.: Anatomie des Frosches. Braunschweig, Friedrich Vieweg and Sohn, 1896–1904. An old, yet very valuable, reference on the anatomy of frogs. It is still the point of departure for research on frog morphology.

Holmes, S. J.: Biology of the Frog. 4th ed. New York, Macmillan, 1934. A standard reference on frog biology, it includes a good summary of Gaupp's classic work.

Moore, J. A. (Ed.): Physiology of the Amphibia. New York, Academic Press, 1964. A very valuable source book covering most aspects of frog physiology.

Rugh, R.: The Frog, Its Reproduction and Development. Philadelphia, Blakiston, 1951. An excellent book on the development of the frog from gamete formation through metamorphosis.

Walker, W. F., Jr.: Dissection of the Frog. San Francisco, W. H. Freeman and Co., 1967. Discussions of function are interwoven with descriptions of anatomy in this laboratory manual on the frog.

Wright, A. H., and A. A. Wright: Handbook of Frogs and Toads of the United States and Canada. 3rd ed. Ithaca, Comstock Publishing Co., 1949. The standard reference for the taxonomy and natural history of frogs.

22 A HISTORY OF VERTEBRATES: FISHES

22.1
Methods of Determining the History of Animals

Homologous and Analogous Organs. The vertebrates have had a long and fascinating evolutionary history, much of which can be inferred from a careful analysis of contemporary species. To make inferences about evolutionary relationships from a study of structure, one must distinguish between various types of resemblances and have a clear understanding of the implications of each. There are two broad categories of resemblance: homology and analogy. **Homologous organs** are organs in different animals which share a structural similarity. By definition this similarity is due to an inheritance from a common ancestor. Homologous organs may resemble each other closely, as the bones of the forelimb of a man and a monkey, or they may be superficially quite unlike, as the scales of a snake and the feathers of a bird. Whether superficially alike or unlike, homologous organs share certain deep-seated, basic similarities in structure that derive from their common ancestry. This includes such features as positional relationships to other parts of the body, similarity in vascular and nerve supply, and a common mode of embryonic development. The scales of a snake and the feathers of a bird resemble each other closely in their early stages of embryonic development. It should also be clear from these examples

that homologous organs may, or may not, have similar functions.

Analogous organs are organs in different animals that have a functional similarity that is in no way related to a community of ancestry; that is to say, analogous organs are nonhomologous organs with a similar function. Often analogous organs have little gross structural resemblance to each other; for example, the gills of a crayfish and the lungs of a man. But sometimes they may have a superficial structural resemblance, as in the case of the wings of an insect and those of a vertebrate (Fig. 22.1). In this case the common function, flight, has only one structural solution, the evolution of some sort of an airfoil. Analogous organs with a structural resemblance are said to be **homoplastic.**

Evolutionary relationships must be traced through a careful identification of homologous organs, for, by definition, they imply descent from a common ancestor. A potential source of error, however, is to confuse homoplastic organs, which have evolved independently, with homologous ones. Usually, homoplastic resemblances are superficial and not basic. In the wing example, it is clear that the bones supporting the wings of the bird and the bat have a basic resemblance, i.e., are homologous, whereas the veins supporting the insect wing are an entirely different sort of structure. The implication is that the bird and the bat had a common ancestor in which the pattern for the bones in the pectoral appendage had already been established; the insect evolved a wing quite independently

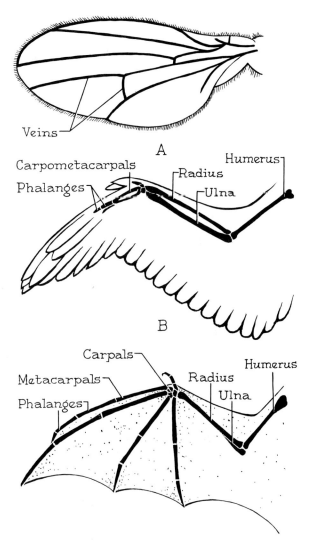

Figure 22.1   Wings of a (*A*) fly, (*B*) bird and (*C*) bat. The bones of the wings of the bird and bat are homologous to each other. The fly's wing is similar to the vertebrate wings in function, but it has only a superficial structural resemblance to them. It is, therefore, analogous and homoplastic to them.

and from different materials. Another source of confusion is that the same organ may be homologous at one level of comparison and homoplastic at another. Although supported by homologous bones, the flying surface of the bird wing is composed of feathers, while that of the bat is composed of a skin membrane. At this level of comparison the two wings are homoplastic. All of this suggests that birds and bats had a remote common ancestor with a certain arrangement of bones in the pectoral appendage, but that the wings of birds and bats evolved independently in the two groups; bats did not evolve from birds.

Fossils.   Since difficulties are sometimes encountered in inferring vertebrate history solely from a study of the structure of contemporary species, it is fortunate that we have other methods with which to supplement and verify our conclusions. The most direct evidence comes from the records that early vertebrates have left of themselves. Organisms that have left such records usually became buried in silt or other water or windborne sediments. Certain of their parts, ordinarily hard parts such as the skeleton, (1) were preserved as such, (2) were gradually replaced with mineral salts, i.e., **petrified,** or (3) left impressions or molds **(external casts)** in the sediments before they decayed. Some of these molds persisted as such and others became filled with some hardened material, thus making **internal casts** of the original parts. The sediments in which the organisms became buried commonly hard-

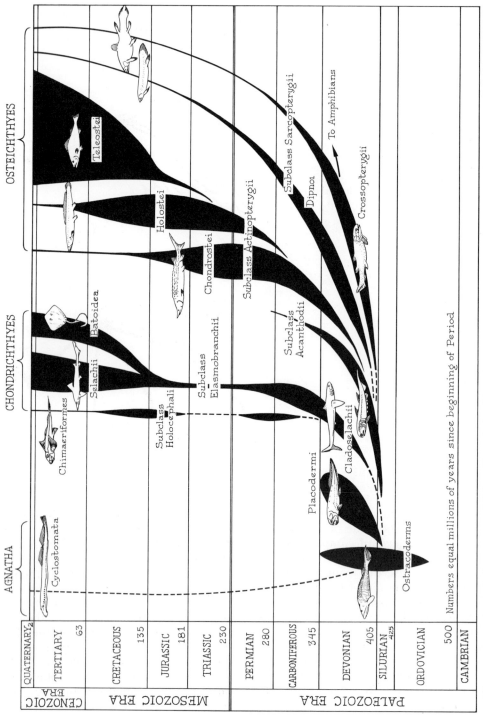

Figure 22.2 An evolutionary tree of fishes. The relationships of the various groups, their relative abundance and their distribution in time are shown.

ened and formed sedimentary rock such as shale, limestone and sandstone. Records of these types, together with footprints and other indications of the activity of organisms of past geologic ages, are known as **fossils.**

From the fortuitous ways in which fossils are formed, uncovered (and sometimes destroyed) by erosion, and finally discovered, it follows that the fossil record is far from complete. It is also a somewhat biased sample of the life of the past, because organisms living in or near water, or on plains where their remains can be covered by wind-blown sand, are more likely to be fossilized and preserved. Forest-dwelling species in particular leave few fossils, for decay is very rapid on the forest floor. Nevertheless, the study of fossils (the science of **paleontology**) and earth history **(geology)** can provide us with much information concerning the history of organisms. Earth history will be considered more fully in Chapter 37. For our present purposes it is sufficient to realize that geology can tell us the sequence of the fossils, can give us estimates (based on radioactive decay of certain isotopes of uranium and argon) of their age and can help to tell us something of the environment in which the organisms were living. Geologists divide earth history into eras, periods and sometimes smaller units of time. Those that pertain to a history of vertebrates, together with an indication of their age, are shown in the diagram of vertebrate evolution (Fig. 22.2).

22.2
Vertebrate Beginnings

Although vertebrate origins are obscure, we have a reasonably complete fossil record of their subsequent evolution. The most primitive are jawless types placed in the class **Agnatha.** This group flourished during the middle Paleozoic era, when it was represented by several orders collectively known as the **ostracoderms** (Fig. 22.2). These ancestral vertebrates were small bottom-feeding animals that were fishlike in general proportions but somewhat flattened dorsoventrally, especially near the front of the body (Fig. 22.3). They had an extensive armor of thick bony plates, and scales developed, for the most part, in the dermis of the skin. These were very similar to the **cosmoid scales** of some other primitive fishes (Fig. 22.4), for beneath a thin layer of enamel-like **ganoine** there was a thick layer of dentine-like **cosmine.** The rest of the scale consisted of a layer of **spongy bone** containing many vascular spaces, and a layer of more compact **lamellar bone.** These heavy scales certainly offered some mechanical protection, possibly against aquatic scorpion-like euryp-

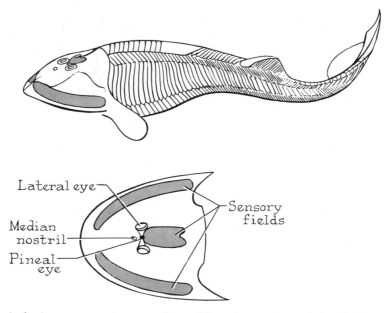

Figure 22.3 *Hemicyclaspis,* a representative ostracoderm of the early Devonian period. This fish was about 20 cm. long. (Modified after Stensiö.)

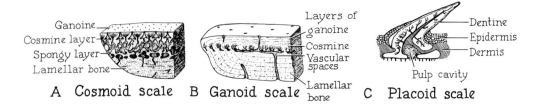

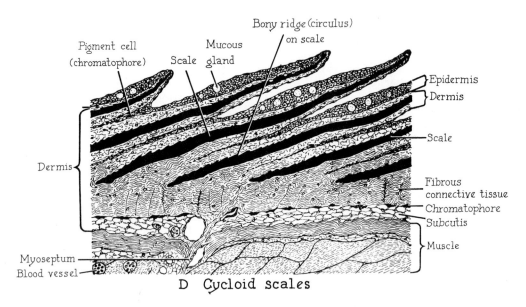

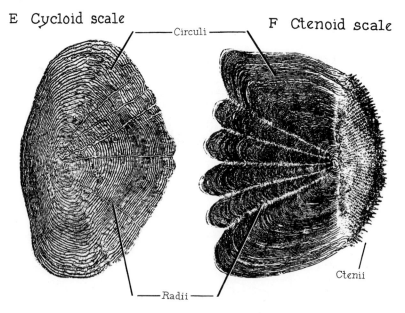

Figure 22.4 Types of fish scales. Vertical sections through (*A*) a cosmoid scale of the type seen in certain ostaco-derms and sarcopterygians, (*B*) a ganoid scale of the type seen in acanthodians and primitive actinopterygians, (*C*) a placoid scale of a shark, (*D*) the skin and cycloid scales of a teleost. Surface view of (*E*) the cycloid scale of a primitive teleost and (*F*) the ctenoid scale of an advanced teleost. (*A−C* from Romer; *D* courtesy of General Biological Supply House; *E* and *F* from Hubbs and Lagler.)

terids of the period; in addition the layers of ganoine and cosmine may have offered some protection against an excessive inflow of water from the fresh-water environment in which these fishes probably lived.

The ostracoderms had median fins but (with the possible exception of pectoral flaps in a few genera) no paired fins equivalent to the paired appendages of other vertebrates. The upper portion of the caudal fin was larger and more rigid than the lower because it included an extension of the body axis. This **heterocercal tail** is characteristic of both fossil and living primitive fishes (Fig. 22.9).

The ostracoderm head was rather unusual. A single **median nostril** was present on the top of the head in the best known species. There was a pair of lateral eyes and a single, median **pineal eye** on the top of the head posterior to the nostril. Professor Young of University College, London, has removed the pineal eye from primitive living fishes (lampreys) and finds that they no longer undergo the rhythmic color changes (light at night and dark in the day) observed in the usual diurnal cycle. These color changes are known to be controlled by the hypothalamic portion of the brain and by the pituitary gland; hence, the pineal eye must affect these organs. The hypothalamus and pituitary gland also control many other physiologic activities, so it is possible, as Young has postulated, that the pineal is an organ that in these animals adjusts the rate of activity to changing conditions of illumination. Three regions of the ostracoderm head, one dorsomedial and a pair of dorsolateral areas, contained small plates beneath which were enlarged cranial

nerves. These peculiar areas may have been sensory fields, or areas beneath which lay muscles modified for the production of electric shocks. Much of the ventral surface of the head was covered with small plates forming a flexible floor to the gill region, or pharynx. Movement of this floor presumably drew water and minute particles of food into the jawless mouth. The water then left the pharynx through as many as 10 pairs of small **gill slits,** but the food particles were somehow trapped in the pharynx. It seems likely that the ancestral vertebrates, like the lower chordates of the present day, were filter-feeders.

22.3
Living Jawless Vertebrates

Ostracoderms became extinct by the end of the Devonian, but the living lampreys and hagfishes of the order **Cyclostomata** are a specialized remnant of the class Agnatha (Figs. 22.5 and 22.6). They are jawless, have more gill slits than other living fishes, lack paired appendages, retain a pineal eye, and have a single median nostril. Besides leading to an olfactory sac, this nostril opens into an **hypophyseal sac** that passes beneath the front of the brain. Much of the pituitary gland of higher vertebrates is derived from an embryonic hypophysis. Cyclostomes differ from ostracoderms in several respects: they have an eel-like shape and a slimy scaleless skin, and they are predators or scavengers. Many lampreys, like the ostracoderms, live in fresh water, but some spend their adult

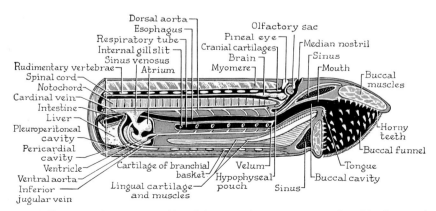

Figure 22.5 A diagrammatic representation of the more important organs found in the anterior part of the lamprey.

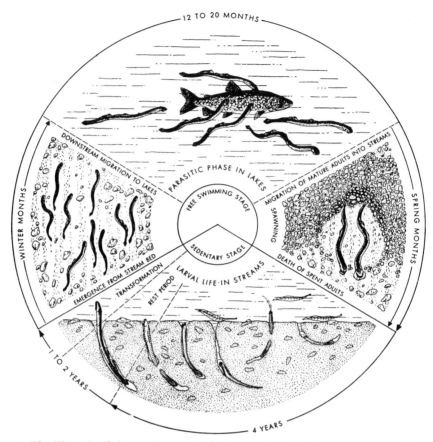

Figure 22.6 The life cycle of the sea lamprey in the Great Lakes. The lamprey spends all but a year or two of its six and one-half to seven and one-half years of life as a larva. (From Applegate and Moffett: Scientific American, April, 1955.)

life in the ocean and return to fresh water only to reproduce. The hagfishes are exclusively marine.

A familiar example of the group is the sea lamprey, *Petromyzon marinus.* The chief axial support for the body is a **notochord** which persists throughout life and is never replaced by vertebrae. Rudimentary vertebrae are present, however, on each side of the notochord and spinal cord. The brain is encased by a cartilaginous **cranium,** and the gills are supported by a complex, cartilaginous lattice-work known as the **branchial basket,** which may be homologous to the visceral skeleton of other fishes.

The **mouth** lies deep within a **buccal funnel,** a suction-cup mechanism with which the lamprey attaches to other fishes (Fig. 22.6). The mobile **tongue** armed with horny "teeth" rasps away at the prey's flesh, and the lamprey sucks in the blood and bits of tissue. It has special **oral glands** that secrete

an anticoagulant which keeps the blood flowing freely. From the mouth cavity, the food enters a specialized **esophagus** that by-passes the pharynx to lead into a straight **intestine.** There is no stomach or spleen. A **liver** is present, but the adult has no bile duct. The intestine does not receive bile from the liver, but the liver functions as site for the storage and conversion of much of the absorbed food brought to it by the circulatory system. A separate pancreas is not present, but **pancreatic tissue** is embedded in the wall of the intestine and liver.

Since a lamprey is often attached to another fish by its buccal funnel, water cannot pass into the mouth and out of the gill slits in respiration, as it does in most fishes. Instead, a pumping action of the pharyngeal region moves water both in and out of the seven **gill pouches** through as many **external gill slits.** Each pouch is lined with highly vascular gills and connected with the pharynx through an internal gill slit. The mixing of food and water is prevented, however, by the separation of the pharynx from the digestive passages. The pharynx is a blind sac posteriorly and is separated anteriorly from the mouth cavity by a small flap of tissue. Because of its isolation, the pharynx is often called a respiratory tube. The pumping of the pharyngeal region also changes the pressure in the hypophyseal sac in a way that resembles the compressing and relaxing of the bulb of an eye dropper, and water is thereby circulated across the olfactory sac.

The kidneys, as in the frog, are drained by wolffian ducts. These ducts carry only urine, for sperm or eggs pass from the large median (embryonically paired) testis or ovary into the coelom. A pair of genital pores leads from the coelom into a urogenital sinus, formed by the fused posterior ends of the wolffian ducts, and thence to the cloaca and outside. The absence of genital ducts may be a very primitive feature. The sexes are separate in the adult lamprey, though sexual differentiation occurs rather late in development, and the gonads of young individuals may contain both developing sperm and eggs.

The eggs are laid on the bottom of streams in a shallow nest, which the lampreys make by removing the larger stones with their buccal funnels (Fig. 22.6). During mating the female attaches to a stone on the upstream side of the nest, and the male to the female, each by its buccal funnel. As the eggs are laid, the sperm is discharged over them. The adults die after spawning.

Developing sea lampreys pass through a larval stage that lasts five to six years. The larva is so different in appearance from adult lampreys that it was originally believed to be a different kind of animal and was named Ammocoetes. The ammocoetes larva is eel-shaped but lacks the specialized feeding mechanism of the adult. It lies within burrows in the mud at the bottom of streams and sifts minute food particles from water passing through the pharynx. Like the lower chordates, it has a mucus-producing endostyle that aids in trapping food.

Adult lampreys injure and kill many other fishes. In recent years the sea lamprey has passed the Niagara barrier, presumably through the Welland Canal, and extended its range from Lake Ontario into the other Great Lakes. The lake fishing industry has been harmed greatly. For example, the lake trout catch in Lake Michigan was 6,860,000 pounds in 1943 and was worth $3,430,000. It began to decrease markedly in 1945 and by 1958 only stray catches were made in this lake. Research by Dr. Applegate and his colleagues on a chemical larvicide that will kill larval lampreys, but not game fish or important larval insects, gives promise of being effective, and the industry can look forward to a brighter future.

The hagfishes resemble the lampreys in major respects, though differing, of course, in certain details. Hags are believed to be primarily scavengers feeding upon dead fish along the ocean bottom, but they also attack disabled fish of any sort, including those hooked or netted. They burrow into the fish and eat out the inside, leaving little but a bag of skin and bone. They are a commercial nuisance, but their over-all damage is not great, since they are abundant in only a few localities.

22.4
Jaws and Paired Appendages

During the Silurian and Devonian periods, certain descendants of the sluggish ostracoderms acquired paired appendages and jaws and become more active and predaceous. The earliest fishes of this type are placed in the class Placodermi. Most were small freshwater forms, but the best known genus is *Dunkleosteus*, a 9 meter long monster of the upper Devonian seas of Ohio (Figs. 22.2 and 22.7C). The head and anterior part of the trunk were incased in bone, but the rest of the body was naked. The primitive heterocercal tail was retained, and well developed pectoral and pelvic fins were present. Such fins, which give a fish greater stability in the water, are necessary for an actively swimming mode of life.

Of particular importance was the presence of jaws, for they enabled these animals to feed upon a wider variety of food than the jawless ostracoderms. Jaws have evolved from a part of the visceral or gill arch skeleton. Jawless fishes have a series of cartilaginous or bony gill arches that lie between the gill slits and serve as a supporting framework for the gills and pharynx (Fig. 22.7A). Typically, each gill arch is a >-shaped structure with the apex of the > hinged and pointing pos-

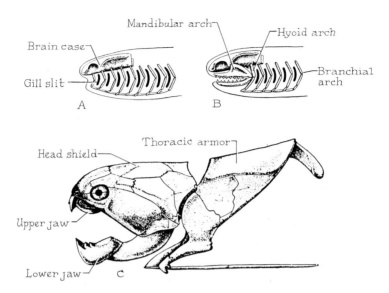

Figure 22.7 Evolution of jaws. Diagrammatic lateral views of (*A*) a primitive jawless fish and (*B*) a shark in which a modified gill arch forms the jaws. *C*, A lateral view of the anterior end of the ancient armored fish *Dunkleosteus*. The dermal plates comprising the upper and lower jaws were attached to the mandibular arch.

teriorly. All arches are interconnected ventrally, but unattached dorsally. Jawless fishes have a greater number of gill slits and arches than jawed fishes. This suggests that during the evolution of jaws, certain of the anterior arches were lost, but that the most anterior remaining arch became enlarged and, together with dermal bones developed in the skin adjacent to it, formed the jaws (Fig. 22.7*B* and *C*). This first arch is known as the **mandibular arch;** the next posterior arch, as the **hyoid arch;** the remaining arches, as typical gill or **branchial arches.** In most early fishes, the upper portion of the mandibular arch was movably articulated with the brain case and was also supported posteriorly by the upper part of the hyoid arch, which extended as a buttress from the posterior part of the brain case to the angle of the jaw. The most conspicuous parts of the jaws of *Dunkleosteus* are sharp-edged plates of dermal bone, but in a few fossils there is evidence that these were attached to an underlying mandibular arch. The development of jaws was an important step in the evolution of vertebrates, for their presence enabled vertebrates to adapt to many modes of life. The success of jawed vertebrates must have contributed to the extinction of the ostracoderms and to the limitation of cyclostomes to rather specialized ecological niches.

22.5
Characteristics of Cartilaginous Fishes

Although a few ostracoderms and some of the later placoderms entered the sea, most of these early vertebrates were fresh-water animals. The first fishes to achieve lasting success in the ocean were the sharks, skates and their relatives of the class **Chondrichthyes.** The earliest members of this class appeared during the Devonian period. They were marine, and the group has remained marine except for a few species that have secondarily entered fresh water.

Cartilaginous fishes, as the common name implies, have an internal skeleton that is entirely cartilaginous. Calcium salts may be deposited in the cartilage and strengthen it, but there is never any internal ossification. A skeleton composed of cartilage is believed to represent the retention by the adult of the embryonic skeletal material. It is not regarded as the primitive adult condition, for at least parts of the skeleton were ossified in most early fishes. The only bonelike materials present in cartilaginous fishes are teeth and the small, spiny **placoid scales** embedded in the skin (Fig. 22.4) and giving to the surface of the fish the feel of sandpaper. Placoid scales are structurally comparable to the enamel-like and dentine-like outer parts of the heavy bony scales of more primitive fishes. The triangular teeth of sharks closely resemble enlarged placoid scales, and have doubtless evolved from them (Fig. 22.8).

Most cartilaginous fishes are highly streamlined fishes that propel themselves through the water by means of lateral undulations of the trunk and tail (Fig. 22.9). As the tail moves from side to side, it pushes diagonally backward upon the water, and the water, in turn, has an opposite and equal reaction upon the tail. This force can be resolved into lateral and forward components. The lateral components cancel each other out, but the forward components drive the fish forward. The large head has considerable inertia and so does not move from side to side as much as the tail. Well developed pectoral and pelvic fins are present. They are fan-shaped organs supported internally by an appendicular skeleton. The paired fins give stability against the body's pitching and rolling; the median fins give stability against rolling and yawing (the tendency of the front of the body to move from side to side) as shown in Figure 22.9B. In early cartilaginous fishes, each paired fin had a broad attachment to the body, but in modern sharks the base of the fin is rather narrow, so that the fins are more mobile and effective in stabilizing the body and in steering. The medial part of each pelvic fin of the male is modified as a clasper, or copulatory organ (Fig. 22.10A).

Cartilaginous fishes resemble more primitive fishes in being heavy bodied and denser than water, for they lack air-filled lungs or a swim bladder—features found in more progressive fishes. The heterocercal tail, which is retained in sharks, is related to the tendency of these heavy-bodied fishes to sink under the pull of gravity. As the fish moves through the water, the large pectoral fins provide a lift component near the front of the body; the heterocercal tail, with its large, flexible lower lobe, has a skulling action and gives a compensatory lift to the rear end (Fig. 22.9C).

A **lateral line** sensory system is well developed. It consists of a canal in the skin that extends along the side of the tail and trunk and ramifies over the head. This canal may be an open groove, as in the chimaeras (Fig. 22.10D), or it may be closed, opening to the surface only through small pores. It contains minute sensory organs that enable the fish to detect low frequency vibrations, movements, and perhaps pressure changes in the water. Such a system is found in all fishes but is rather inconspicuous in cyclostomes.

The cartilaginous skeleton of these fishes (see Fig. 26.4) consists of a brain case, or cranium, a vertebral column bearing short ribs, an appendicular skeleton, and a set of visceral arches. The upper and lower jaws are formed entirely by the mandibular arches, for there are no dermal plates associated with them as there are in placoderms. The

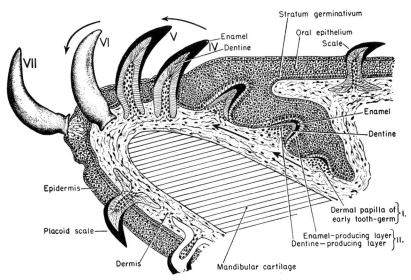

Figure 22.8 A vertical section through the lower jaw of a shark. Teeth, which are structurally very similar to placoid scales, are continually developing, moving to the surface, and sloughing off. (From Rand.)

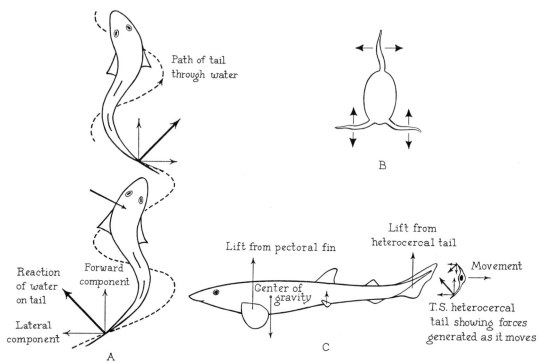

Figure 22.9 Locomotion of a dogfish. *A,* Undulatory movements and forces generated by the tail; *B,* cross section of the body showing stabilizing effect of median and paired fins; *C,* lift of the pectoral fins and heterocercal tail. (Modified from Marshall and Hughes.)

upper jaw is suspended from the brain case entirely by the upper section of the hyoid arch, the **hyomandibular** cartilage (Fig. 22.7). There is space for only a reduced gill slit, or **spiracle,** between the mandibular and hyoid arches. Five branchial arches lie behind the hyoid in most species, and five typical gill slits open independently to the surface.

The visceral organs of the dogfish, *Squalus acanthias* (Fig. 22.11), are in many ways more characteristic of primitive fishes than are those of the specialized cyclostomes. The **mouth cavity** is continuous posteriorly with the **pharynx.** A spiracle, containing a vestigial gill, and the gill slits, containing functional gills, open from the pharynx to the body surface. A wide **esophagus** leads from the back of the pharynx to a J-shaped **stomach.** A short, straight **valvular intestine** continues back to the **cloaca.** The valvular intestine receives secretions from the **liver** and **pancreas.** It contains an elaborate spiral fold known as the **spiral valve;** this helical fold serves both to slow the passage of food and to increase the digestive and absorptive surface of the intestine.

The **heart** consists of a series of chambers arranged in linear sequence. Blood from the veins, low in oxygen content, enters the posterior end of the heart and is pumped out the anterior end into an artery that leads to capillary beds in the gills. Aerated blood from the gills is collected by a **dorsal aorta** and carried to the body wall and visceral organs. Such a circulatory system is a sluggish, low-pressure system, for the pressure built up by the beating of the heart is immediately reduced by friction in the gill capillaries.

The **kidneys** are elongate organs drained, as in the frog, by **wolffian ducts.** These ducts also carry sperm in the male. The kidneys play a major role in water balance and excretion (p. 509). Excess salt, taken in with the food, is eliminated by the **rectal gland,** which is a salt-excreting organ.

At the time of reproduction, eggs are discharged from the ovary, pass through a part of the coelom, and enter the **oviducts.** The male cartilaginous fish uses a clasper to deposit sperm in the oviducts, and fertilization is internal. A horny protective capsule is secreted around the fertilized eggs by certain oviducal cells and, in all of the skates, the eggs are laid and develop externally.

Skates are **oviparous,** but there is no free larval stage as there is in frogs and many other oviparous animals. The eggs are very heavily laden with yolk, and the embryos develop within the protective capsule. Some sharks are also oviparous, but most have departed from this primitive egg-laying habit. A few are truly **viviparous,** for the fertilized eggs develop in a modified portion of the oviduct known as the **uterus,** an intimate association is established between each embryo's yolk sac and the uterine lining, forming a **yolk sac placenta,** and the embryos have a greater dependence for their nutrient requirements upon the mother than upon food stored in the yolk. However, most sharks, including our common dogfish, are **ovoviviparous;** the eggs also develop within a uterus, but there is a greater dependence upon food stored in the yolk. In some cases,

Figure 22.10 A group of cartilaginous fishes. *A,* A male dogfish, *Squalus acanthias; B,* the sawfish, *Pristis; C,* the stingray, *Dasyatis; D,* the ratfish, *Chimaera.* (*A* modified after Bigelow and Schroeder; *C* courtesy of Marine Studios; *D* from Romer after Dean.)

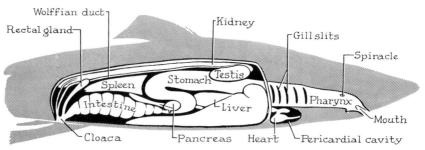

Figure 22.11 The visceral organs of the dogfish.

a portion of the nutritional requirements is derived by the absorption of materials secreted by the mother into the uterine fluid, but an intimate placental relationship is not established. It is frequently difficult to make a sharp distinction between viviparous and ovoviviparous reproduction, for the degree of dependence of the embryo for its nutrients upon the mother ranges along a continuum, and the young are born at an advanced stage of development as miniature adults in both cases.

22.6
Evolution of Cartilaginous Fishes

The ancestral Chondrichthyes were essentially sharklike, but in their subsequent evolution the cartilaginous fishes have diverged widely and have become adapted to many modes of life within the aquatic environment. One line of evolution (subclass **Holocephali**) has led to our present-day, rather rare, deep-water ratfish (*Chimaera*) (Fig. 22.10*D*). In these fishes, the gill slits are covered by an operculum, so there is a common external orifice, and the tail is long and ratlike. The other line of evolution (subclass **Elasmobranchii**) is distinguished by having separate external openings for each gill slit. Elasmobranchs have been far more successful and have diverged into two contemporary orders—**Selachii** (sharks and dogfish) and **Batoidea** (skates and rays).

Sharks. Most selachians are active fishes that feed voraciously with their sharp, triangular-shaped teeth upon other fishes, crustaceans and certain mollusks. The largest sharks, such as the whale shark (*Rhincodon*), which may reach a length of about 15 meters, have minute teeth and feed entirely upon small crustaceans and other organisms that form the drifting plankton of the surface layers of the ocean. They gulp mouthfuls of water and as the water passes out of the gill slits, the food is kept in their pharynx by a branchial sieve. Whale sharks are the largest living fishes.

Although rare, shark attacks on man receive considerable notoriety. In order to obtain reliable data as to their frequency and the circumstances of their occurrence, the Shark Research Panel of the American Institute of Biological Sciences has been maintaining a world-wide "Shark Attack File." There seem to be some 30 unprovoked attacks per year, occurring mostly between latitudes 35°N and 35°S, where the waters are warm and the more dangerous species live. It is well established that sharks are attracted to fresh blood, even in small quantities, coming from injuries to a swimmer or from speared fish a skin diver may be towing. Most sharks circle their intended victim several times before attacking, so if the victim is aware of their presence and he does not attract undue attention by splashing, there is a fair chance of his avoiding or warding off any attack.

Skates and Rays. Most skates and rays are bottom-dwelling fishes that are flattened dorsoventrally and have enormous pectoral fins whose undulations propel the fish along the bottom (Fig. 22.10*C*). Their mouth is often buried in the sand or mud, and water for respiration enters the pharynx via the pair of enlarged **spiracles.** A spiracular valve in each one is then closed, and the water is forced out the typical gill slits. Most skates and rays have crushing-type teeth and feed upon shellfish, but others are adapted for other methods of feeding. The sawfish (*Pristis*) has an elongated, blade-shaped snout armed with toothlike scales. By thrashing about in a shoal of small fishes, it can disable many and eat them at leisure. As in the sharks, the largest members of the group (the devilfish, *Manta*) have reduced teeth and are plankton feeders. Some devilfish have a "wing spread" of 6 meters and can easily upset small boats. Harpooning these is an exciting sport!

22.7
Lungs and Swim Bladders

While early sharks were becoming dominant in the ocean, another offshoot of primitive fishes, the bony fishes of the class **Osteichthyes,** became dominant in fresh water. They subsequently entered the ocean and became the most successful group there as well. Most of the familiar present-day fishes (gar, herring, minnows, perch, cod, lungfish) belong in this group.

The Osteichthyes, like the Chondrichthyes, are highly evolved, advanced fishes with efficient paired appendages and jaws. An obvious way in which they differ from the cartilaginous fishes is in having an ossified internal skeleton and in retaining more of the primitive bony scales and plates. The internal skeleton consists of **cartilage replacement bone** that has developed embryologically in association with cartilaginous rudiments, which it gradually replaces. The bone in the scales and plates, although histologically similar to the preceding type, is **dermal bone.** It develops in the dermis of the skin and is not preceded by cartilage. The deeper portions of the dermal plates in the head and shoulder region become intimately associated with the internal skeleton; thus, the skull and pectoral girdle of these fishes, and of the terrestrial vertebrates which have descended from them, contain both types of bones.

The jaws are formed partly by the ossified mandibular arch of the visceral skeleton (cartilage replacement bone) and partly by dermal bone encasing this arch. The hyoid arch lies close behind the mandibular, and its hyomandibular usually takes part in the suspension of the jaws. There is no room for a postmandibular gill slit, and even the spiracle, when present, rarely opens to the surface. Typical branchial arches lie behind the hyoid, but the gill region is covered by a flap containing dermal bone (the **operculum**), so the gill slits have a common opening just anterior to the pectoral fin.

The soft parts of most bony fishes, the perch for example (Fig. 22.12), show a peculiar mixture of primitive and highly specialized characters. Most need not concern us, but one of great interest is the **swim bladder.** In the perch, this is a median membranous sac lying in the dorsal portion of the coelom. The bladder is filled with gases similar to those dissolved in the water (nitrogen, oxygen, carbon dioxide). It functions primarily as a hydrostatic organ, adjusting the density of the body so that the fish can stay at various depths with a minimum of effort. Gases may be secreted into the bladder or absorbed from it, as conditions warrant, through specialized capillary networks in its wall. Under conditions of oxygen deficiency, some fish can utilize the oxygen in the bladder, so the organ also functions as a temporary storage site for this gas.

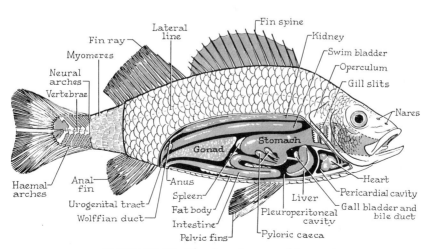

Figure 22.12 The visceral organs of the perch.

In some bony fishes, the swim bladder is connected to the digestive tract by a pneumatic duct and, in a few, functional **lungs** are present instead. This led many to postulate that the swim bladder was the precursor of lungs. At present, however, lungs are considered to be the precursor of the swim bladder, for the organ is most lunglike in the most primitive bony fishes.

It is believed that the ancestral bony fishes had lungs similar to those of the living African lungfish (*Protopterus*). In the lungfish a pair of saclike lungs develops as a ventral outgrowth from the posterior part of the pharynx (Fig. 22.13). The lungs enable the fish to survive conditions of stagnant water and drought. The rivers in which the African lungfish live may completely dry up, but the fish can survive curled up within a mucous cocoon that it secretes around itself in the dried mud. A small opening from the cocoon to the surface of the mud enables the fish to breathe air during this period. The African lungfish has become so dependent upon its lungs that it will die if it cannot occasionally reach the surface to gulp air.

Air breathing probably evolved in fishes as a supplement to gill respiration. Presumably, early bony fishes, or perhaps their placoderm ancestors, evolved lungs as an adaptation to the unreliable fresh-water conditions of the Devonian period. Geologic evidence indicates that the Devonian was a period of frequent seasonal drought. Bodies of fresh water undoubtedly either became stagnant swamps with a low oxygen content or dried up completely. Only fishes with such an adaptation could survive these conditions. The others became extinct or migrated to the sea, as did many later placoderms and the cartilaginous fishes. Groups of bony fishes that have remained in fresh water throughout their history tended to retain lunglike organs, but those that went to sea no longer needed lungs, for ocean waters are rich in oxygen. Their useless lungs evolved into useful hydrostatic organs. What are presumed to be intermediate stages in this shift can still be seen in certain species. Later, when conditions were more favorable, many salt-water bony fishes re-entered fresh water but retained their swim bladders. The fresh-water perch has such a history. Its ancestors first evolved lungs in a fresh-water environment, then went into the ocean, where the lungs changed into swim bladders; later the fish re-entered fresh water and retained the swim bladders.

22.8
Evolution of Bony Fishes

Bony fishes can be traced back to the early Devonian and late Silurian (Fig. 22.2). At that time three lines of evolution within the class were already established—subclasses **Acanthodii**, **Actinopterygii** and **Sarcopterygii**. Since all share at least a partly ossified skeleton and well developed bony scales, it is assumed that they had a common

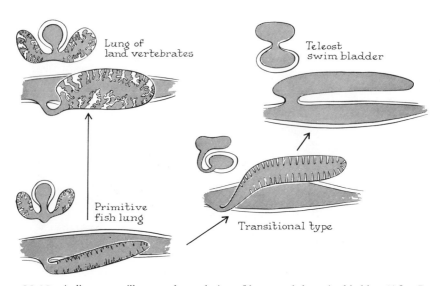

Figure 22.13 A diagram to illustrate the evolution of lungs and the swim bladder. (After Dean.)

evolutionary origin from some early placoderm, or possibly they evolved directly from ostracoderms.

Acanthodians. Acanthodians, often referred to as "spiny sharks," were the oldest and most primitive. Until recently they have been classified as placoderms. *Climatius* is a typical genus (Fig. 22.14). These were fusiform fishes with a heterocercal tail, well developed dorsal and anal fins, and pectoral and pelvic fins of a primitive type. In many species, additional paired fins were present between the pectoral and pelvic fins. The paired fins consisted of a web of flesh supported primarily by a large anterior spine, but occasionally traces of an internal fin skeleton are found. The trunk was covered by small but thick bony scales of the **ganoid** type (Fig. 22.4), for thick layers of enamel-like ganoine formed their surfaces. Larger bony plates covered the head and gills. A well developed mandibular arch can be seen in specimens in which the superficial dermal bones have been removed. The group formed a conspicuous part of fish fauna in the Devonian, but was replaced by more progressive fish types by the end of the Paleozoic era.

Actinopterygians. The actinopterygians are the familiar ray-finned fishes such as the perch. Their paired fins are fan-shaped. Skeletal elements enter their base, but most of the fin is supported by numerous dermal rays which evolved from rows of bony scales. Their paired olfactory sacs connect only with the outside and do not lead into the mouth cavity.

Actinopterygian evolution presents a good example of a succession in which early dominant groups became replaced by more successful types. Three infraclasses are recognized and each, in turn, had its day (Fig. 22.2). Currently, the infraclass **Chondrostei** has dwindled to a few species, of which the Nile bichir (*Polypterus*) and the sturgeon (*Scaphirhynchus*) are examples (Fig. 22.15). The infraclass **Holostei** has also dwindled and is represented today by such relict species as the gar (*Lepisosteus*) and bowfin (*Amia*). The infraclass **Teleostei,** in contrast, has been continuously expanding since its origin in the Mesozoic era. It is to this group that the minnows, perch and most familiar fishes belong.

Various evolutionary tendencies can be traced through this succession. The functional lungs of early actinopterygians (still retained in *Polypterus*) became transformed into swim bladders with little respiratory function. Correlated with increased buoyancy and better streamlining, we find that the primitive heterocercal tail of most chondrosteans (*Polypterus* is an exception) became superficially symmetrical in teleosts, but the caudal skeleton still shows indications of the

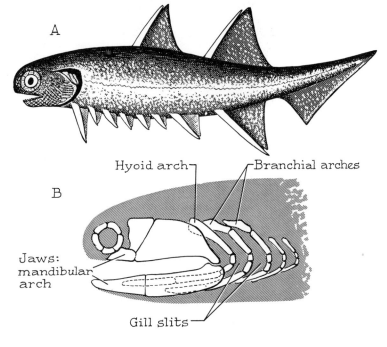

Figure 22.14 *A,* The "spiny shark," *Climatius,* was among the first jawed vertebrates. This fish was about 8 cm. long. After removal of the gill covering and superficial bony scales and plates on the head of a related genus (*Acanthodes, B*), it can be seen that the jaws are modified gill arches. (*A* after Watson; *B* modified after Watson.)

Figure 22.15 A group of primitive ray-finned fishes that have survived to the present day. *A,* The Nile bichir, *Polypterus; B,* the shovel-nosed sturgeon, *Scaphirhynchus platorhynchus; C,* the longnose gar, *Lepisosteus oseus; D,* the bowfin, *Amia calva.* (*A* after Dean; *B, C* and *D* courtesy of American Museum of Natural History.)

upward tilt of the vertebral column. The caudal fin rays attach to **hypural bones,** which are modifications of the haemal spines that attach to the ventral surface of the tail vertebrae (Fig. 22.16). Such a tail is said to be **homocercal.** Holosteans have an intermediate **abbreviated heterocercal** tail. Early actinopterygians were clothed with thick bony scales of the ganoid type. During subsequent evolution the superficial layers were

lost, and the bone was reduced to a thin disc which develops in the dermis of the skin (Fig. 22.4*D*). Such a scale is termed **cycloid** if its surface is smooth, **ctenoid** if the posterior portion bears minute spiny processes, or ctenii. As the fish grows, increments of bone are added to the scale and these appear as rings, or **circuli.** In some fish, in which the rate of growth slows down in the winter, the circuli are much closer together and form a

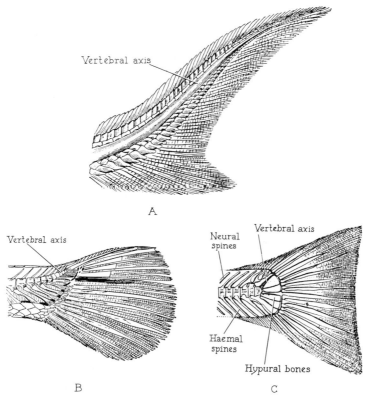

Vertebral axis

A

Vertebral axis

Neural spines

Vertebral axis

Haemal spines

Hypural bones

B   C

Figure 22.16 Caudal fin types of bony fishes. *A,* The primitive heterocercal tail seen in the sturgeon, *Acipenser; B,* the abbreviated heterocercal tail of the garpike, *Lepisosteus; C,* the homocercal tail of a teleost. (*A* and *B* from Jordan; *C* from Romer.)

check mark. By counting such marks, and not the circuli themselves, estimates of a fish's age can be made. The anterior part of a bony scale is always embedded in the skin, but the posterior part, which extends out into a fold of the skin, may be exposed as the overlying epidermis wears off.

Teleosts are an exceedingly large and diverse infraclass, for there are 30,000-odd species. The evolutionary relationships between the various groups is far from certain, but certain evolutionary trends are quite apparent. The more primitive teleosts include the tarpons and herrings (Fig. 22.17). These fishes are characterized by having elongate, streamlined bodies; a single dorsal fin; pelvic fins located near the posterior part of the trunk; fins supported by flexible and branching bony rays rather than by spines; cycloid scales covering the tail and trunk, but not extending onto the head; an air, or pneumatic, duct connecting the swim bladder and digestive tract. The most advanced are the spiny-finned teleosts such as the sunfishes and perch. These are often rather short and deep-bodied (from dorsal to ventral) fishes.

There is a tendency for the dorsal fin to split into two parts; the anterior being supported by spines, the posterior by flexible bony rays. The pelvic fins have shifted forward to a point beneath the pectoral fins, and spines are present in the anterior border of these fins. The scales have become ctenoid and have extended onto the head and gill covering. The pneumatic duct is lost.

Teleosts between these two extremes show a mixture of primitive and advanced characteristics and often certain distinctive features of their own. Eels, for example, have long snakelike bodies and have lost their pelvic fins and usually their scales (Fig. 22.18*F*). Although bizarre in many ways, a relationship between eels and the more primitive tarpon is suggested, for both have a similar, ribbon-shaped, transparent larval stage known as the **leptocephalus** (Fig. 22.19). Most of our common fresh-water teleosts such as minnows, suckers and catfish (Fig. 22.20*C*) resemble primitive teleosts in the various parameters discussed, but are distinctive in having a small set of bones, the **weberian ossicles,** extending from the an-

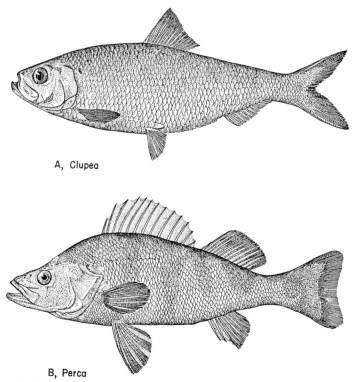

A, Clupea

B, Perca

Figure 22.17 *A*, A primitive teleost, the herring; *B*, an advanced teleost, the perch. Differences in body proportions and fins are apparent. (From Romer: Vertebrate Biology, 3rd ed.)

terior end of the swim bladder to the inner ear (Fig. 22.21). This mechanism apparently acts as a hydrophone, for the acoustical sensitivity of these fishes is considerably greater than that of any other group. Other groups of teleosts are defined in the synopsis at the end of this chapter.

The more primitive teleosts, such as the herring and tarpon (Fig. 22.18*A*), are active, predaceous, streamlined fishes of the open waters. But there have been many interesting departures from these generalized types, for teleosts have spread out into all parts of the aquatic environment and have become adapted to nearly every conceivable ecologic niche. This phenomenon of **adaptive radiation** is seen in all large groups. Apparently, the resources of the environment can be utilized more fully if subgroups become specialized for certain parts of the environment than if all compete with one another in the total environment.

The halibut, soles and flounders have become specialized for a bottom-dwelling life. Like the skates and rays, they are flattened and glide along the bottom with up-and-down undulatory movements. But instead of being flattened dorsoventrally, they are greatly compressed from side to side, and swim turned over on one side (Fig. 22.18*B*). During larval development, the eye that would be on the "ventral" side migrates to the top surface, but the mouth does not change position. The skates and flounders present a good example of **convergent evolution,** by which animals that are widely separated in the evolutionary scale independently adapt to similar modes of life. They acquire similar adaptive features, in this case a flattened body shape, though in different ways.

Other teleosts have adapted to a life among seaweeds and in coral reefs. The sea horses with their monkey-like, prehensile tails, the sargassum fish with its camouflaging color and weedlike protuberances, and the elongate, snakelike moray eels are examples (Fig. 22.18).

A few teleosts have adapted to life in the ocean depths. Such fish often have light-producing luminescent organs presumably for species recognition, and large mouths and greatly distensible stomachs that enable

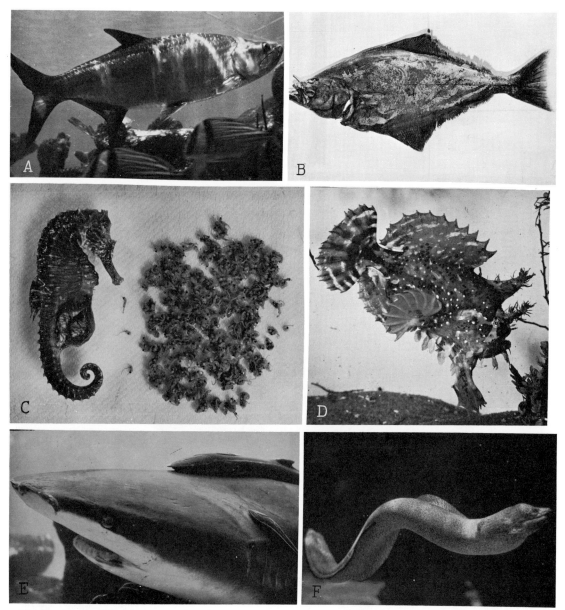

Figure 22.18 Diversity among the teleosts. *A,* A tarpon, *Tarpon,* one of the more primitive types of teleosts; *B,* a halibut, *Hippoglossus,* one of the flatfish that feeds along the bottom; *C,* a male sea horse, *Hippocampus,* with the brood pouch in which the female deposits her eggs, young shown at right; *D,* the sargassum fish, *Histrio,* appears very bizarre out of its natural environment, but is well concealed among seaweed; *E,* the sharksucker, *Remora; F,* the moray eel, *Gymnothorax,* normally lurks within interstices of coral reefs. (*A, C, D, E* and *F* courtesy of Marine Studios; *B* courtesy of the American Museum of Natural History.)

Figure 22.19 The transparent leptocephalus larva of the eel. A similar larval stage occurs during the development of the tarpon. (From Jordan after Eigenmann.)

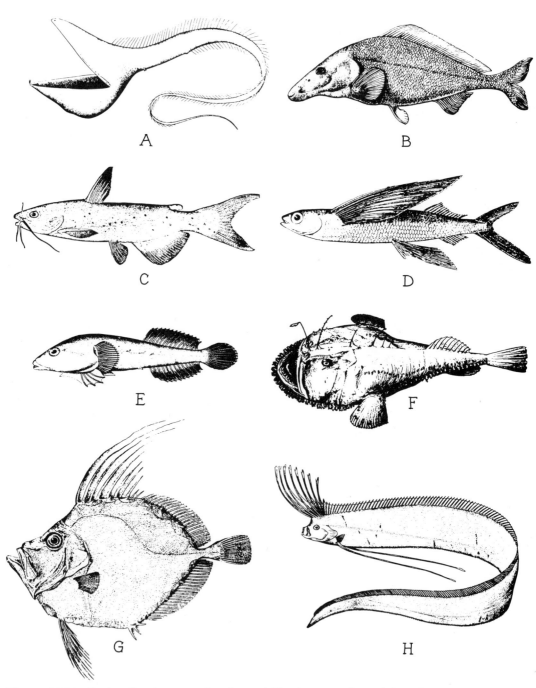

Figure 22.20 Further diversity among the teleosts. *A*, The deep-sea gulper eel, *Saccopharynx; B, Mormyrus,* one of the primitive fresh-water osteoglossomorphs; *C*, the catfish, *Ictalurus*, one of the ostariophysians; *D*, the flying fish, *Exocoetus*, a specialized top minnow; *E*, the clingfish, *Caularchus*, with pelvic fins modified as a sucking disc; *F*, the angler, *Lophius*, with its tassel-like lure; *G*, the John Dory, *Zeus; H*, the oarfish, *Regalecus*. (*C* and *E* from Jordan; others from Romer.)

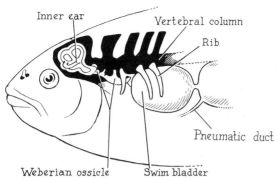

Figure 22.21   A lateral view of the head of a carp to show the connection between inner ear and swim bladder made by the weberian ossicles. (From Portman.)

them to take full advantage of the occasional meal that comes their way (Fig. 22.20*A*).

Some teleosts live in intimate association with other fishes. The remora has an anterior dorsal fin that is modified as a suction cup and is used to attach to sharks. It feeds upon crumbs of the larger fish's meals, or obtains free rides to favorable feeding grounds. Relationships of this type, in which one organism benefits and the other receives neither benefit nor harm, are known as **commensalism** (Fig. 22.18*E*).

A few teleosts have become amphibious. The Australian mudskipper frequently hops about on the mud flats of mangrove swamps at low tide in search of food, and may even bask in the sun. It has unusually muscular pectoral fins with which it pulls itself along the land, and it can close its opercular chamber and extract oxygen from the air with its gills.

A number of fishes, both cartilaginous and bony, have evolved (from muscular tissue) electric organs capable of discharging pulses of electrical energy. In such fishes as the electric ray (*Torpedo*) of the North Atlantic and the electric eel (*Electrophorus*) of the Amazon basin the pulses are strong enough to stun prey or predator. *Electrophorus* can put out pulses in excess of 500 volts! In other fishes, the pulses are very weak and their biologic significance was long unknown. Researchers have found that they are part of an electric guidance system. Dr. H. W. Lissmann of the University of Cambridge has found that *Gymnarchus,* a nocturnal freshwater fish of West Africa, gives off a continuous stream of weak electric pulses that set up an electric field in the surrounding water, resembling a dipole. Objects having an electrical conductivity different from that of the water distort the field, and these changes can be detected by the fish by way of modified portions of its lateral line system. Dr. Lissmann has postulated that electric organs of this type represent an intermediate evolutionary stage between typical muscle with its action potential measured in millivolts and the stunning electric organs. Darwin could not explain how natural selection could favor the evolution of stunning electric organs for, at the lower levels of efficiency, they would be useless. Probably they had a different function when they were first evolving. After a certain threshold of power was reached, the function could change.

Many other fascinating adaptations are found among teleosts, but we must not dwell upon them for these fishes are only a side issue in the total picture of vertebrate evolu-

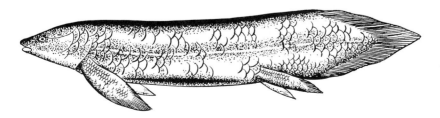

Figure 22.22   The Australian lungfish, *Epiceratodus.* (After Norman.)

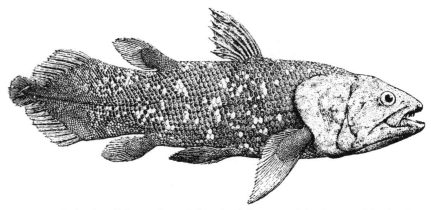

Figure 22.23   *Latimeria*, a living coelacanth found off the coast of the Comoro Islands. (From Millot.)

tion. The branch toward the higher vertebrates passed through the less spectacular Sarcopterygians of ancient Devonian swamps.

Sarcopterygians. The sarcopterygians include the lungfishes and crossopterygians (Figs. 22.22 and 22.23). Their paired appendages are typically elongate and lobe-shaped and are supported internally by an axis of flesh and bone. In many species, each of the olfactory sacs connects to the body surface through an **external nostril** and to the front part of the roof of the mouth cavity through an **internal nostril.** Sarcopterygian evolution diverged at an early time into two lines—the lungfishes (order **Dipnoi**) and the crossopterygians (order **Crossopterygii**). The primitive crossopterygians were the less specialized, having a well-ossified internal skeleton and small conical teeth suited for seizing prey. It is from this group that the amphibians arose. Lungfishes early in their evolution developed specialized crushing tooth plates, which enabled them to feed effectively upon shellfish, and showed tendencies toward reduction of the internal skeleton and paired appendages. In certain other features lungfishes and crossopterygians have paralleled actinopterygian evolution. They evolved symmetrical tails, though of a type that is symmetrical internally as well as externally **(diphycercal),** and their primitive, thick bony scales, which were characterized by having a thick layer of dentine-like **cosmin** (Fig. 22.4), have tended to thin to the cycloid type.

Both crossopterygians and lungfishes were successful in the fresh waters of the Devonian, but have dwindled to a few relict species today. Lungfishes retained their lungs and have survived in the unstable fresh-water environments of tropical South America, Africa and Australia. It was long believed that all crossopterygians had become extinct, as indeed the primitive freshwater ones have. However, a few specimens of a somewhat specialized side branch (the coelacanths) have been found in recent years near the Comoro Islands between Africa and Madagascar (Fig. 22.23).

*SYNOPSIS OF FISHES

CLASS 1. AGNATHA. Jawless fishes. The oldest and most primitive class of vertebrates; all members lack jaws; most lack paired appendages.
    †OSTRACODERMS. Four orders of small, heavily armored Paleozoic fishes are collectively called the ostracoderms. *Hemicyclaspis.*
    ORDER 5. CYCLOSTOMATA. Lampreys, hagfishes. Body eel-shaped; round

---

*All synopses of vertebrates are based on the classification in A. S. Romer: Vertebrate Paleontology, 3rd ed. Chicago, University of Chicago Press, 1966. The classification is taken down to orders, and in a few cases suborders. All living groups are included, but only the more important extinct groups are mentioned.

†Extinct groups.

mouth without jaws; no paired appendages; scaleless slimy skin. The sea lamprey, *Petromyzon.*

†**CLASS 2. PLACODERMI.** Five orders of primitive jawed fish of the Paleozoic; paired appendages present. *Dunkleosteus.*

CLASS 3. CHONDRICHTHYES. Cartilaginous fishes. Skeleton entirely of cartilage; placoid scales usually present; lungs or swim bladder absent; nearly all are marine.

> **Subclass 1. Elasmobranchii.** Gill slits open independently on the body surface; placoid scales present; lateral line system imbedded in the skin.

>> †ORDER 1. CLADOSELACHII. Ancestral sharks with broad-based paired fins. *Cladoselache.*

>> ORDER 2. SELACHII. Modern sharks with narrow-based paired fins; streamlined bodies; heterocercal tail; most with sharp triangular teeth. The dogfish, *Squalus*; whale shark, *Rhincodon.*

>> ORDER 3. BATOIDEA. Sawfish, skates, rays. Body dorsoventrally flattened; pectoral fins enlarged; trunk and tail reduced; teeth usually in the form of crushing plates. Common skate, *Raja*; devilfish, *Manta*; sawfish, *Pristis.*

> **Subclass 2. Holocephali.** Gill slits covered by an operculum; scales absent; lateral line system in the form of open grooves.

>> ORDER 1. CHIMAERIFORMES. The ratfish, *Chimaera.*

CLASS 4. OSTEICHTHYES. Bony fishes. Skeleton includes considerable bone; various types of bony scales, other than placoid, usually present; lungs or swim bladder usually present; abundant in fresh and salt water.

> †**Subclass 1. Acanthodii.** Three orders of Paleozoic fishes. At one time classified as placoderms, they are now provisionally considered to be an ancestral group of bony fishes. The "spiny shark," *Climatius.*

> **Subclass 2. Actinopterygii.** Ray-finned fishes. Ray fins fan-shaped, supported by radiating bony rays or spines; each nasal cavity has an entrance and exit on snout surface.

>> **Infraclass 1. Chondrostei.** Two extinct and two living orders of primitive ray-finned fishes. Scales usually ganoid; mouth opening large; tail usually heterocercal.

>>> ORDER 3. POLYPTERIFORMES. The bichir. Body slender; numerous dorsal fins; lungs present; tropical Africa. *Polypterus.*

>>> ORDER 4. ACIPENSERIFORMES. Sturgeon and allies. Long sharklike snout; subterminal mouth; several rows of heavy bony scales. Common sturgeon, *Acipenser*; paddlefish, *Polydon.*

>> **Infraclass 2. Holostei.** Three extinct and two living orders of intermediate ray-finned fishes. Scales ganoid or cycloid; mouth opening smaller than in chondrosteans; abbreviated heterocercal tail.

>>> ORDER 4. SEMIONOTIFORMES. Garpikes. Elongated trunk and snout; scales ganoid. *Lepisosteus.*

>>> ORDER 5. AMIIFORMES. The bowfin. Snout rounded; scales cycloid; long dorsal fin. *Amia.*

>> **Infraclass 3. Teleostei.** Advanced ray-finned fishes. Scales cycloid or ctenoid; mouth opening small; tail homocercal; a hydrostatic swim bladder usually present.

>>> †*Superorder 1. Leptolepimorpha.* One order of primitive herring-like teleosts still retaining some holostean characters, including traces of ganoine on scales.

>>> *Superorder 2. Elpomorpha.* Primitive teleosts with a "leptocephalous" larva.

>>>> ORDER 1. ELPOIFORMES. Tarpons. Often large, rapidly swimming oceanic fishes; much prized for sport. *Tarpon.*

>>>> ORDER 2. ANGUILLIFORMES. Eels. Body elongate; scales rudimentary or absent; pelvic fins usually absent. American eel, *Anguilla.*

>>>> ORDER 3. NOTACANTHIFORMES. Gulper eels. Deep-sea, somewhat eel-shaped fishes; large mouths. *Saccopharynx.*

>>> *Superorder 3. Clupeomorpha.*

>>>> ORDER 1. CLUPEIFORMES. Herring, sardines, shad and their allies. Primitive teleosts; scales cycloid; head and operculum not scaled; fins with-

out spines; trunk not greatly shortened; single dorsal fin; pelvic fins abdominal; a duct connects swim bladder and digestive tract; most marine. Common herring, *Clupea*.

Superorder 4. *Osteoglossomorpha*.

ORDER 1. OSTEOGLOSSIFORMES.   Primitive fresh-water teleosts of the Old and New World tropics. The elephant-snouted fish, *Mormyrus*.

Superorder 5. *Protacanthopterygii*.   Primitive teleosts, some of whom are beginning to acquire certain of the advanced features of acanthopterygians.

ORDER 1. SALMONIFORMES.   Salmon, trout, pike. A fleshy adipose fin is often present on the back. The salmon, *Salmo*.

ORDER 2. CETOMIMIFORMES.   A few unusual deep-sea fishes.

ORDER 3. CTENOTHRISSIFORMES.   Possibly ancestral spiny-finned teleosts; most are extinct.

ORDER 4. GONORHYNCHIFORMES.   Milkfishes.

Superorder 6. *Ostariophysi*.   A large group of primarily fresh-water teleosts; primitive in most respects, but have webberian ossicles.

ORDER 1. CYPRINIFORMES.   Carp, minnows, suckers and their allies. Primitive ostariophysians; usually retain cycloid scales; most lack spines in fins. Carp, *Cyprinus*; shiner, *Notropis*; sucker, *Catostomus*.

ORDER 2. SILURIFORMES.   Catfish. Specialized ostariophysians; scales usually lost; a large spine in dorsal and pectoral fins; long sensory barbels on head. Channel catfish, *Ictalurus*.

Superorder 7. *Atherinomorpha*.

ORDER 1. ATHERINIFORMES.   Top minnows, flying fishes and their allies. Teleosts with a mixture of primitive and advanced characters; scales usually cycloid; scales beginning to spread onto head and operculum; some spines present in fins; pelvic fins abdominal in position. Killifish, *Fundulus*; silverside, *Atherina*; flying fish, *Exocoetus*.

Superorder 8. *Paracanthopterygii*.   Several small orders of specialized teleost fishes with advanced characteristics. Scales usually ctenoid; spines usually present in fins; pelvic fins located far forward.

ORDER 1. AMBLYOPSIFORMES.   Pirate perch. Anus located far forward under gill region. Pirate perch, *Aphredoderus*.

ORDER 2. BATRACHOIDIFORMES.   Toadfishes. Bizarre teleosts with large, somewhat flattened heads and long tapering trunks. *Batrachoides*.

ORDER 3. GOBIESOCIFORMES.   Clingfishes. Pelvic fins located far forward and modified as a sucking disc; often found in tidepools. *Caularchus*.

ORDER 4. LOPHIIFORMES.   Anglers. First dorsal spine carries a tassel that dangles as a lure over large mouth; most deep sea. Common angler, *Lophius*.

ORDER 5. GADIFORMES.   Cod, haddock. Elongate and subdivided dorsal and anal fins. Cod, *Gadus*; burbot, *Lota*.

Superorder 9. *Acanthopterygii*.   Spiny-finned teleosts. Advanced teleosts; scales ctenoid; head and operculum usually scaled; spines present in fins; trunk often short; often two dorsal fins; pelvic fin thoracic in position; swim bladder without a duct.

ORDER 1. BERYCIFORMES.   Squirrelfish. Moderately deep-bodied fishes; retain 18 or 19 rays in the tail fin in contrast to 17 in more advanced acanthopterygians.

ORDER 2. ZEIFORMES.   John Dory, *Zeus*.

ORDER 3. LAMPIDIFORMES.   Ribbonfish, oarfish. Elongate oceanic fish; some species 6 meters long. The oarfish, *Regalecus*.

ORDER 4. GASTEROSTEIFORMES.   Sticklebacks, pipefish, sea horses. Trunk encased in bony armor; small mouth at end of tubular snout. The sea horse, *Hippocampus*.

ORDER 5. CHANNIFORMES.   Snakeheads. Small Asiatic coastal fish with lung-like extensions from gill chambers; can live out of water. *Channa*.

ORDER 6. SYNBRANCHIFORMES.   Eel-like, tropical coastal fish. Swamp eel.

ORDER 7. SCORPAENIFORMES.   Scorpion fish, sculpins. Enlarged heads and pectoral fins; projecting spines from gill covering. The sculpin, *Acanthocottus*.

ORDER 8. DACTYLOPTERIFORMES. Enlarged pectoral fins; glide in a manner similar to the more familiar flying fishes.

ORDER 9. PEGASIFORMES. Dragonfishes. Small marine fishes of tropical seas; trunk and tail encased in a bony box or rings. *Pegasus.*

ORDER 10. PERCIFORMES. The largest order of spiny-finned teleosts; includes perch, bass, mackerel, gobies, barracuda and their allies. A relatively unspecialized group of spiny-finned teleosts. The perch, *Perca.*

ORDER 11. PLEURONECTIFORMES. Flatfishes. Body highly compressed; fish lie on ocean bottom on one side of body; both eyes on upper side of body. Halibut, *Hippoglossus;* flounder, *Paralichthys.*

ORDER 12. TETRAODONTIFORMES. Triggerfish, trunkfish, puffers. Strong jaws with a sharp beak; scales often spiny; some inflate by swallowing water. Porcupine fish, *Diodon.*

Subclass 3. Sarcopterygii. Fleshy-finned fishes. Paired fins lobe-shaped with a central axis of flesh and bone; internal nostrils usually present; primitive members had cosmoid scales.

ORDER 1. CROSSOPTERYGII. Crossopterygians. Primitive fleshy-finned fishes; conical teeth present; median eye usually present.

†Suborder 1. Rhipidistia. Primitive fresh-water crossopterygians; includes the ancestor of amphibians. *Osteolepis.*

Suborder 2. Coelacanthini. More specialized fresh-water and marine crossopterygians; one genus has survived to present day. *Latimeria.*

ORDER 2. DIPNOI. Lungfishes. Specialized fleshy-finned fishes; teeth forming crushing tooth plates; median eye usually absent, three genera confined to Australia (*Neoceratodus*), Africa (*Protopterus*) and South America (*Lepidosiren*).

QUESTIONS

1. Distinguish between homology and homoplasty. Can it be assumed that organisms having homologous organs are closely related?
2. What factors prevent the fossil record from giving us a complete and unbiased picture of the life of the past?
3. Briefly describe the general nature and mode of life of the ostracoderms. What living vertebrates are most closely related to them?
4. Discuss the evolution of jaws and the importance of this evolutionary step.
5. Discuss the method of locomotion of a primitive fish, such as the dogfish. What effect does a swim bladder have on a fish? What changes in fins are correlated with the presence of a swim bladder?
6. How do members of the class Chondrichthyes differ from members of the class Osteichthyes?
7. How have a typical shark, a whale shark, a skate and a sawfish diverged in their method of feeding?
8. Under what conditions did lungs probably evolve? Is the swim bladder more primitive than lungs?
9. How do actinopterygians differ from sarcopterygian fishes?
10. What morphologic changes occurred during actinopterygian evolution?
11. From which group of fishes did tetrapods evolve?
12. Define and give an example of adaptive radiation.
13. Define and give an example of convergent evolution.

ANNOTATED REFERENCES

Vertebrates

The following references contain useful information on many aspects of the biology of fishes and other groups of vertebrates.

Colbert, E. H.: Evolution of the Vertebrates. New York, John Wiley & Sons, Inc., 1955.

An excellent and thorough account of vertebrate evolution; all groups, both living and extinct, are considered briefly.

Florey, E.: An Introduction to General and Comparative Animal Physiology. Philadelphia, W. B. Saunders Co., 1966. An excellent undergraduate textbook of general physiology of all animal forms.

Gregory, W. K.: Evolution Emerging, A Survey of Changing Patterns from Primeval Life to Man. New York, Macmillan, 1951. A valuable and superbly illustrated source book on vertebrate evolution; includes much original material.

Orr, R. T.: Vertebrate Biology. 2nd ed. Philadelphia, W. B. Saunders Co., 1966. A valuable text and reference on many aspects of vertebrates; a chapter is devoted to each major group of vertebrates and to such general topics as territory, dormancy and population dynamics.

Prosser, C. L., and F. A. Brown, Jr.: Comparative Animal Physiology. 2nd ed. Philadelphia, W. B. Saunders Co., 1961. Many aspects of the physiology of fishes and other vertebrates are included in this useful source book.

Romer, A. S.: The Vertebrate Story. 4th ed. Chicago, University of Chicago Press, 1959. A very well written and nontechnical account of the evolution of vertebrates.

Romer, A. S.: The Vertebrate Body. 3rd ed. Philadelphia, W. B. Saunders Co., 1962. This standard and widely used textbook of comparative anatomy is, at the same time, a valuable reference on vertebrate structure.

Romer, A. S.: Vertebrate Paleontology. 3rd ed. Chicago, University of Chicago Press, 1966. The most recent edition of a standard text and source book.

Young, J. Z.: The Life of Vertebrates. 2nd ed. Oxford, Clarendon Press, 1963. A fascinating account of the evolution and adaptations of vertebrates. One or more chapters are devoted to each group; morphological and physiological perspectives are skillfully interwoven.

Fishes

Breder, C. M., Jr.: Field Book of Marine Fishes of the Atlantic Coast from Labrador to Texas. 2nd ed. New York, S. P. Putnam's Sons, Inc., 1948. A useful guide for the identification of the more common fishes of our Atlantic Coast.

Brown, M. E. (Ed.): The Physiology of Fishes. New York, Academic Press, 1957. A valuable source book; chapters on various aspects of fish physiology have been written by leading investigators.

Herald, E. S.: Living Fishes of the World. Garden City, N. Y., Doubleday & Co., 1961. A very well written, nontechnical account of the biology of the various groups of fish. As with other books in this series, the photographs are superb; many are in color.

Hubbs, C. L., and K. F. Lagler: Fishes of the Great Lakes Region. 2nd ed. Bloomfield Hills, Mich., Cranbrook Institute of Science, 1958. The definitive guide to fishes of the Great Lakes Basin, this book would also be useful, though not infallible, for adjacent parts of the United States.

Jordan, D. S.: A Guide to the Study of Fishes. New York, Henry Holt and Co., 1905. An old but still very valuable two-volume account of most aspects of the biology of fishes and of the various groups. David Starr Jordan was one of the great men of ichthyology.

Lagler, K. F., J. E. Bardach, and R. R. Miller: Ichthyology. New York, John Wiley & Sons, Inc., 1962. A very useful text covering the basic anatomy, physiology, systematics and ecology of fishes.

Marshall, N. B.: The Life of Fishes. Cleveland, World Publishing Co., 1966. A very readable account of the biology of fishes written by a senior investigator at the British Museum of Natural History.

Norman, J. R.: A History of Fishes. 2nd ed. Revised by P. H. Greenwood. New York, Hill and Wang, Inc., 1963. A recent edition of a classic on the biology of fishes.

Tee-van, J., H. B. Bigelow, and G. W. Mead (Eds.): Fishes of the Western North Atlantic. New Haven, Sears Foundation for Marine Research, Yale University Press, 1948, 1953, 1963, 1964, 1966. Five parts of this definitive treatise on the taxonomy and biology of Atlantic fishes have been published.

23

A HISTORY OF VERTEBRATES: AMPHIBIANS AND REPTILES

23.1

The Transition from Water to Land

The transition from fresh water to land was a momentous step in vertebrate evolution that opened up vast new areas for exploitation. It was an extremely difficult step because the physical conditions on land are so very different from those in water. Air neither affords so much support nor offers so much resistance as water. The terrestrial environment provides little of the essential body water and salts. Oxygen is more abundant in the air than in water, but it must be extracted from a different medium. The ambient temperature fluctuates much more on the land than in the water. Air and water have different refractive indices.

Successful adaptation to the terrestrial environment necessitated changes throughout the body. Stronger skeletal support and different methods of locomotion evolved. Changes occurred in the equipment for sensory perception and changes in the nervous system were a natural corollary of the more complex muscular system and altered sense organs. An efficient method of obtaining oxygen from the air evolved, as did adaptations to prevent desiccation. The delicate, free-swimming, aquatic larval stage was suppressed, and reproduction upon land became possible. Finally, the ability to maintain a fairly constant and high body temperature was achieved, and terrestrial vertebrates could then be active under a wide range of external temperatures.

In view of the magnitude of these changes, it is not surprising that the transition from water to land was not abrupt but took millions of years and involved the participation of many groups. Indeed, a main theme in the evolution of the terrestrial vertebrates, or **tetrapods,** has been a continual improvement in their adjustment to terrestrial conditions.

The crossopterygians unwittingly made the first steps in this transition. Their lungs, as we have seen, were probably an adaptation to survive conditions of stagnant water or temporary drought. Their relatively strong, lobate paired fins may have enabled them to squirm from one drying and overcrowded swamp to another more favorable one. Crossopterygians were not trying to get onto the land but, in adapting to their own environment, they evolved features that made them viable in a new and different environment. That is, they became **preadapted** to certain terrestrial conditions. Given this preadaptation, an abundance of food (various invertebrates, stranded fishes, plants) upon the land or the shores of swamps, little competition upon the land, and overcrowding and intense population pressure in the swamps, it is not hard to imagine some of the crossopterygians

Figure 23.1 A restoration of life in a Carboniferous swamp 345 million years ago. The labyrinthodont amphibians were the first terrestrial vertebrates. (Courtesy of American Museum of Natural History.)

making the adaptive shift from water to land and becoming the amphibians (Fig. 23.1). No one knows how long the transition from crossopterygians to amphibians took, but the first amphibian fossils are found in strata that were formed nearly 50 million years later than those containing the first crossopterygians.

Amphibians, in turn, acquired additional terrestrial features, and reptiles still more. But the pinnacle of terrestrial adaptation is achieved only by the reptiles' descendants—the birds and mammals.

23.2
Characteristics of Amphibians

During the evolution of the amphibians, many fishlike characteristics of their ancestors were lost, and many features evolved that enabled them to spend considerable time on land. The vertebral column is stronger with more thoroughly ossified vertebrae, and the vertebrae interlock securely by means of overlapping **articular processes** on the neural arches (Fig. 23.2). These features help provide the necessary support on land. The paired fins of fishes are transformed into **legs,** but the limbs are in a somewhat sprawled position, and the humerus and femur move back and forth in the horizontal plane. Fishlike undulations of the trunk and tail help to advance the limbs to a position favorable for placing them on the ground, and may help in developing the thrust of the limb on the ground (Fig. 23.3). The footfall pattern seen in amphibians, and even in slower moving higher vertebrates that do not undulate their trunk, follows naturally from the positions assumed by the fins of a fish as a result of the undulations of the trunk. First the left front foot is advanced, and this is followed in turn by the right rear foot, right front foot and left rear foot. Usually just one foot is advanced at a time, leaving a tripod of three feet to support the body.

Important changes have occurred in the respiratory system. Larval amphibians retain gills, but these are lost in adults; **lungs,** supplemented by the skin and buccopharyngeal membrane, become the sites of gas exchange. The loss of bony scales, of course, is a pre-

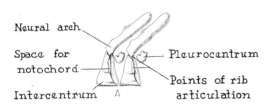

Neural arch

Space for notochord

Intercentrum   A

Pleurocentrum

Points of rib articulation

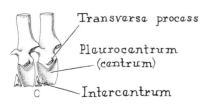

Transverse process

Pleurocentrum (centrum)

Intercentrum

C

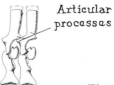

Articular processes

B

Figure 23.2 Lateral views of a trunk vertebra of (*A*) a crossopterygian, (*B*) an early labyrinthodont and (*C*) a primitive reptile. Anterior is toward the left. (From Romer: Vertebrate Biology, 3rd ed.)

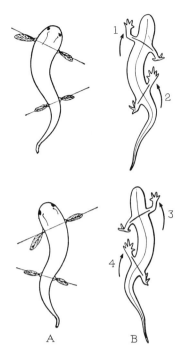

Figure 23.3 A comparison of locomotion in (*A*) a fish and (*B*) a salamander. Fish-like undulations of trunk and tail continue in the salamander and help to determine the placement of the limbs upon the ground. Numbers indicate the sequence of limb movements. (*A* after Marshall and Hughes; *B* after Romer.)

requisite for the skin to serve as a respiratory membrane. As explained earlier (p. 342), air is pumped in and out of the lungs by movements of the floor of the mouth and pharynx. These are very similar to the movements which in a fish circulate water through the pharynx and across the gills. In the evolution of the respiratory system, we see a good example of the continuity of structure and function which must exist in any evolutionary transition. Lung ventilation by rib and diaphragm movements evolved much later.

The substitution of lungs for gills as the major site of gas exchange has important consequences in the circulatory system. Two types of blood, depleted blood from the body and oxygen-rich blood from the lungs, return to the heart. As discussed in the chapter on the frog (p. 345), these two blood streams are kept separate to some extent as they flow through the heart. Depleted blood for the most part is sent to the lungs and skin, and rich blood is distributed to the body. Since blood leaving the heart on its way to the body does not first go through the gills, as it would

in a fish, there is little loss of blood pressure. Blood pressure in the dorsal aorta of a frog is nearly double that in the dorsal aorta of a dogfish. In this respect, terrestrial vertebrates have a more efficient circulatory system than do fishes.

Catching and swallowing food on land is somewhat more complex than in the water, and amphibians have evolved a muscular **tongue** and **oral glands** that aid in these processes.

Many changes occur in the sensory apparatus, for problems associated with perception on land are quite different from those in the water. The lateral line sensory system is retained by larval amphibians but is lost in the adult. Also, at the time of metamorphosis **eyelids** and **tear glands** develop, which protect and cleanse the eye in the aerial environment, and an **ear** sensitive to air- or ground-borne vibrations also appears. A number of changes occur in the nervous system correlated with changed patterns of locomotion and changes in the sensory apparatus.

Although well adapted to the terrestrial environment in many ways, amphibians have retained several features from their piscine ancestors that restrict most of them to a rather moist habitat and prevent them from fully exploiting the terrestrial environment. First, most amphibians are unable to prevent a large loss of body water when on land. Since their skin is a thin, moist, vascular membrane, considerable evaporation takes place through it. There has been some shift in the nitrogen metabolism of amphibians so that less of the waste products are removed as highly toxic ammonia, and more is removed as **urea,** than is the case in fresh-water fishes (Table 23.1). Amphibians do not need such a large water turnover as these fishes, yet a fairly large volume is still needed to flush these products from the tissues and body.

Table 23.1 Types of Nitrogen Excretion in Representative Vertebrates*

Animal	Ammonia	Urea	Uric Acid	Other
Fresh-water				
minnow, *Cyprinus*	60.0	6.2	0.2	33.6
Bullfrog, *Rana*	3.2	84.0	0.4	12.4
European tortoise,				
Testudo	4.1	22.0	51.9	22.0
Hen	3.0	10.0	87.0	0.0
Adult man	3.5	85.0	2.2	9.3

*Data from Prosser and Brown. Figures in per cent.

The structure of their kidney tubules is not yet modified for the reabsorption of a large volume of water from the urine during the process of urine formation.

A second restricting feature is that all amphibians are cold-blooded, or **poikilo-thermic;** their body temperature is close to that of the environment and fluctuates with it. They cannot maintain a constant and rather high body temperature. Since the rate of metabolic processes fluctuates with temperature changes, they cannot be active at low temperatures. This is not too serious for a fish for, in most bodies of water, temperatures, even beneath the ice, remain above freezing. But terrestrial poikilotherms living in temperate regions must move during the winter to areas that do not freeze and enter a dormant state known as **hibernation.** Amphibians bury themselves in the mud at the bottom of ponds or burrow into soft ground below the frost line. During hibernation metabolic activities are at a minimum. The only food utilized is that stored within the body; respiration and circulation are very slow. Some tropical amphibians during the hottest and driest parts of the year go into a comparable dormant state known as **aestivation.**

Finally, amphibians are unable to reproduce under truly terrestrial conditions. Like the common leopard frog (*Rana pipiens*), most of them must return to the water to lay their eggs. Even the terrestrial toad returns to this medium, for it has no means of internal fertilization and sperm cannot be sprayed over eggs upon the land. Neither has it suppressed the free larval stage in development, and these larvae cannot withstand the rigors of the terrestrial environment.

23.3

Evolution of Amphibians

The best known of the early amphibians are the **labyrinthodonts,** a group that finally diverged from the crossopterygians during the late Devonian period (Fig. 23.4). An interesting detail they shared with the crossopterygians was a peculiar labyrinthine infolding of the enamel in their teeth. The name labyrinthodont is derived from this feature. All were fairly clumsy, salamander-shaped creatures with rudimentary necks and heavy, muscular tails inherited from their piscine ancestors (Fig. 23.1). All became extinct during the Triassic. However, the group is important, for it included not only the ancestors of other amphibians but also those of reptiles and, hence, of all higher tetrapods.

A key to the relationships among many early terrestrial vertebrates is seen in their vertebral structure. The labyrinthodonts are characterized by having a vertebral column in which the centra of the individual vertebrae were composed of arches of bone that surrounded, and in some cases replaced, the notochord. In the first labyrinthodonts, an **intercentrum** (U-shaped in end view) formed the anterior part of the centrum, and a pair of smaller chunks of bone, the **pleurocentra,** formed the posterior part (Fig. 23.2B). This type of centrum is very similar to the type seen in crossopterygians and, by a decrease in size of the intercentrum and an increase in size and fusion of the pleurocentra, could easily give rise to the type found in ancestral reptiles. Another group of extinct amphibians, the **lepospondyls,** although probably derived from the labyrinthodonts, had a centrum that was a unitary, somewhat spool-shaped structure perforated by a narrow longitudinal canal for a persistent notochord. The vertebral structure of living amphibians appears to be closer to that of this group, so that their most likely ancestors seem to be the lepospondyls.

Living amphibians are grouped into three orders. Salamanders (order **Urodela**) retain the primitive body form with short legs, long trunk and well developed tail. Caecilians (order **Apoda**) are legless, burrowing, wormlike forms confined to the tropics (Fig. 23.5). Frogs and toads (order **Anura**), as described in Chapter 21, with their short trunk and powerful, enlarged hind legs are specialized for a hopping and jumping mode of life. The fossil history of all these groups is fragmentary, but we do have one curious frog fossil from the early Triassic (Fig. 23.6) that is intermediate between specialized contemporary frogs and more primitive types of amphibians. Its skull shape, shortened trunk, elongated ilia in the pelvic girdle,

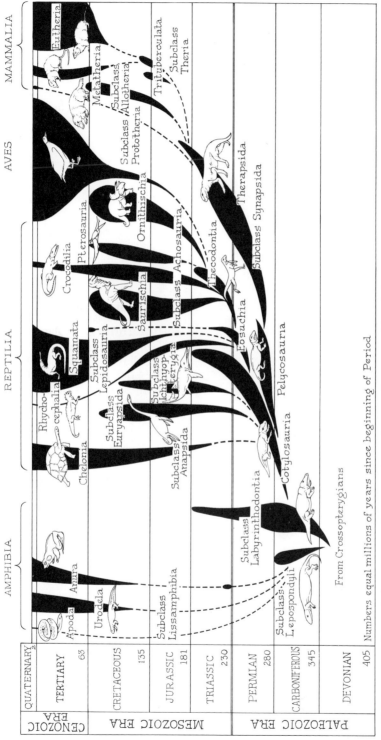

Figure 23.4 An evolutionary tree of terrestrial vertebrates. The relationship of the various groups, their relative abundance and their distribution in time are shown.

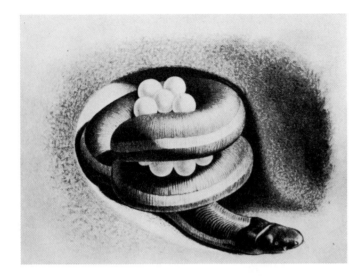

Figure 23.5 A burrowing caecilian, *Ichthyophis*, with her egg mass. (From Romer after the Sarasins.)

and slightly enlarged hind legs are suggestive of a frog. But the trunk is not as short as in modern frogs, there is a bit of a tail, and there has been no fusion of the bones of the lower arm and lower leg.

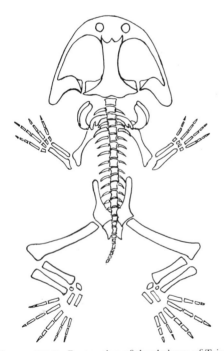

Figure 23.6 Restoration of the skeleton of *Triandobatrachus*, a Triassic frog-like amphibian possibly ancestral to modern frogs. (From Romer: Vertebrate Paleontology.)

23.4
Amphibian Adaptations

Salamanders. Salamanders are not such familiar amphibians as frogs and toads, for most have secretive habits. They may be found beneath stones and logs in damp woods or beneath stones along the side of streams, and some are entirely aquatic. A rather generalized type is Jefferson's salamander, *Ambystoma jeffersonianum* (Fig. 23.7), of the eastern United States. This species is terrestrial as an adult, but returns to the water in early spring to reproduce. Breeding is sometimes preceded by a nuptial dance in which many individuals writhe about in the water, rubbing and nosing one another. The males deposit sperm in clumps called **spermatophores** on sticks and leaves in the water. Later the females pick these up with their cloacal lips. Fertilization occurs inside the cloaca, and the fertilized eggs are deposited in masses attached to sticks submerged beneath the surface of the water. This habit is adaptive, for these salamanders reproduce very early in the spring, at a time when the surface of the water may freeze over. The larvae of salamanders differ from those of frogs and toads in retaining external gills throughout their larval life and in having true rather than horny teeth.

There have been many special adaptations among salamanders. The most abundant of our American species are woodland types

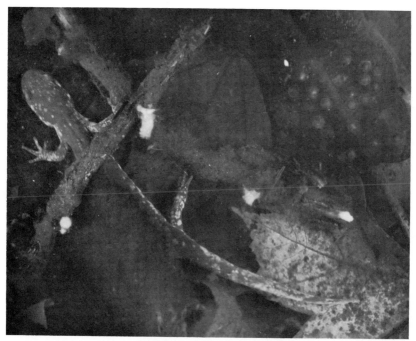

Figure 23.7 Jefferson's salamander, *Ambystoma jeffersonianum*, reproduces in the water. The four white structures attached to sticks are spermatophores. A clump of eggs can be seen in the upper righthand corner.

like the red-backed salamander (*Plethodon cinereus*), which belongs to the family Plethodontidae. A particularly interesting feature of plethodonts is their complete loss of lungs; gas exchange occurs entirely across the moist membranes lining the mouth and pharynx and the skin. The skin is a more effective respiratory organ than in frogs because the epidermis is very thin and capillaries come close to the surface. Loss of lungs may seem to be a curious adaptation for a terrestrial vertebrate, but it has been postulated that early in their evolution plethodonts became adapted for life in rapid mountain streams. The oxygen content of cold water is rather high, and the low temperature reduces the general rate of metabolism of the animals. Air in the lungs would be disadvantageous under these conditions, for the animals would float and be washed away. Lungs may have been lost in adapting to this habitat. Subsequently many plethodonts entered different environments but never regained the lost lungs.

Several groups of salamanders, including the mudpuppy (*Necturus maculosus*, Fig. 23.8*A*), have become entirely aquatic. The development of the reproductive organs has been speeded up in relation to development of other parts of the body. Sexual maturity is achieved in the larval stage and metamorphosis is never completed. This is another example of **neoteny,** a phenomenon encountered earlier in the lower chordates. The hormone of the thyroid gland, thyroxin, is necessary for metamorphosis. The failure of *Necturus* to metamorphose appears to result from the inability of the tissues to respond to thyroxin rather than from an absence of this hormone. Thyroxin is produced, for the thyroid of *Necturus* hastens metamorphosis when transplanted to frog tadpoles. In some other neotenic salamanders, the failure to metamorphose may result from an inhibition of the mechanism that releases thyroxin. The tiger salamander, *Ambystoma tigrinum* (Fig. 23.8*B*), metamorphoses under most conditions, but those living at high altitudes in the Rocky Mountains fail to do so and remain permanent larvae known as **axolotls.** Apparently, cold inhibits the release of thyroxin, for when axolotls are fed thyroxin or when they are brought to warmer climates, metamorphosis is normal.

Frogs and Toads. Most anurans are

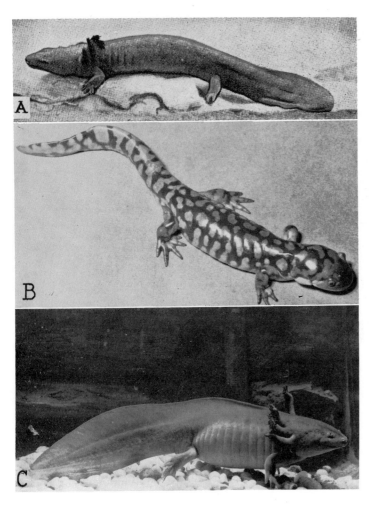

Figure 23.8 Neotenic salamanders. *A,* The mudpuppy, *Necturus maculosus,* is a permanent larva. *B,* The tiger salamander, *Ambystoma tigrinum,* metamorphoses in most environments, but fails to do so in certain mountain lakes. *C,* The axolotl, or neotenic form of *Ambystoma tigrinum.* (*A* courtesy of Shedd Aquarium, Chicago; *B* and *C* courtesy of the Philadelphia Zoological Society.)

amphibious as adults, living near water to which they frequently go to feed or escape danger, but some are more terrestrial in habits, and others have become adapted to an arboreal life. The terms frog, toad, and tree frog or tree toad ordinarily imply amphibious, terrestrial and arboreal modes of life, not natural evolutionary groups. Members of several distinct families of anurans, for example, have become adapted independently to an arboreal life.

Toads have adjusted to a terrestrial life by evolving structures and patterns of behavior that reduce water loss. The epidermis of their skin is more horny and less pervious to water than that of frogs. A thick dry skin reduces cutaneous respiration, but this is compensated for by an increase in the respiratory surface of the lungs. The lining of toad lungs is more complexly folded than that of frogs. Much of the water lost through the kidneys is reabsorbed in the urinary bladder. Toads are crepuscular in habits; they burrow or take shelter by day and come out in the moist evening to feed upon insects.

The chief adaptation to arboreal life has been the evolution of **digital pads** upon the tips of the toes (Fig. 23.9). The surface epithelium of the pads is rough and grips the substratum by friction. The gripping action is enhanced by the discharge of a sticky mucus from numerous glands within the pads.

A particularly fascinating aspect of anuran biology is the evolution of methods by which development can proceed elsewhere than in the open water. This has occurred primarily among tropical frogs and probably as a protection against seasonal drought and numerous aquatic enemies such as predaceous in-

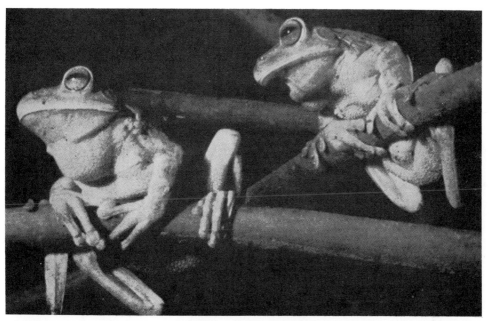

Figure 23.9 The tree frog *Hyla faber* clings to trees by means of its expanded digital pads. (Courtesy of G. A. Lutz, Natural History, Vol. LXX, No. 1.)

sect larvae. A Brazilian tree frog (*Hyla faber*) protects its young by laying its eggs in mud craters which the male builds by circling in shallow water and pushing up mud (Fig. 23.10*A*). A more striking means of protection is seen in a small Chilean frog, *Rhinoderma darwinii*. The male of this species stuffs the fertilized eggs into his vocal sacs where they remain until metamorphosis is complete. In the completely aquatic Surinam toad, *Pipa pipa*, of tropical South America, the male pushes the fertilized eggs into the puffy skin on the back of the female. The eggs gradually sink deeper into the skin, and the outer membrane of each one forms a protective cap over its temporary skin pocket. The young emerge as little froglets. The eggs and larvae of all these frogs are equipped with a large supply of yolk, but in other respects the larvae are fairly typical and simply develop in a sheltered environment.

In certain species the vulnerable larval stage is omitted, and the embryo develops directly into a miniature adult. Anurans with **direct development** include the marsupial frog, *Gastrotheca*, and *Eleutherodactylus*—both of the New World tropics (Fig. 23.10*C*). The former carries her eggs in a dorsal brood pouch; the latter lays eggs in protected damp places such as beneath stones or in the axil of leaves. The jelly layers about the egg of *Eleutherodactylus* help to prevent desiccation; sufficient yolk is stored within the egg for the nutritive requirements of the embryo; such larval features as horny teeth, gills and opercular fold are vestigial or absent; the fins of the larval tail are expanded, become highly vascular and form an organ for gas exchange (Fig. 23.10*D*); and the period of development is accelerated.

Something similar to what has taken place among these frogs today may have occurred among the amphibians which were ancestral to reptiles. Ancient amphibians were certainly no more consciously trying to improve upon their terrestrial adaptation than crossopterygians were trying to get onto the land. If the aquatic larvae of the ancestral amphibians were subjected to a very high predation, any variation that tended toward the suppression of the defenseless larval stage and toward the direct development of their embryos in a less vulnerable environment would have a selective advantage. It is possible that the amphibians that gave rise to the reptiles developed means of terrestrial reproduction before the adults completely left the water to live on the land.

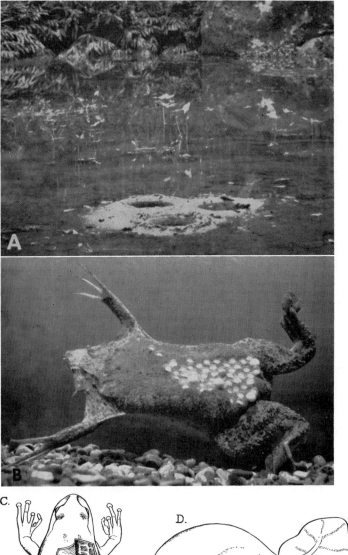

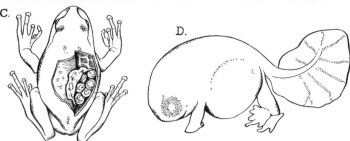

Figure 23.10 Adaptations of frogs that protect the larvae from aquatic predators. *A,* The circular mud crater nests of the Brazilian tree frog, *Hyla faber; B, Pipa pipa,* the female's back is covered with eggs which by the third day have begun the process of sinking into the skin; *C,* the brood pouch of the marsupial frog, *Gastrotheca,* cut open to show the eggs; *D,* the modified embryo of *Eleutherodactylus.* (*A* from G. A. Lutz, Natural History, Vol. LXX, No. 1; *B* from G. Rabb, Natural History, Vol. LXX, No. 5; *C* after Noble; *D* after Lynn.)

23.5
Characteristics of Reptiles

As we have seen, most amphibians are prevented from fully exploiting the terrestrial environment by three factors: (1) poor means of conserving body water, (2) inability to reproduce on the land, and (3) inability to maintain their body temperature and metabolic processes at a fairly constant level. Reptiles, as a group, evolved means of con- serving body water and reproducing upon the land, and certain reptiles achieved some measure of control over their body temperature by their behavior and regulation of their exposure to the sun. A small median eye on the top of the head of many reptiles plays an important role in the responses to light. Reptiles also improved upon the means of locomotion and gas exchange and other terrestrial attributes of their amphibian ancestors.

A lizard, such as the collared lizard (*Crotaphytus collaris*, Fig. 23.11) of the southwestern United States, is a typical reptile. The surface of the skin is covered with dry **horny scales** that prevent water loss by this route. These scales develop through the deposition of considerable **keratin** (a very insoluble and hence waterproofing protein) in the superficial layers of the epidermis. Some lizards and crocodilians also have small plates of dermal bone imbedded in the dermis of the skin beneath many of the horny scales.

The kidney tubules of reptiles are modified in such a way that less water is initially removed from the blood than in amphibians, and much of the water that is removed is later reabsorbed by other parts of the kidney tubule and by the urinary bladder. In reptiles, a large proportion of the nitrogenous waste products is excreted as **uric acid** (Table 23.1). Uric acid is much less toxic and water soluble than ammonia or urea, hence it does not have to be flushed out of the tissues so rapidly nor with such a large volume of water. The urine of animals excreting uric acid typically has a pastelike consistency. The reptilian kidney also differs from that of lower vertebrates in being drained by a duct called the **ureter** instead of by the wolffian duct. The latter becomes a genital duct in males and is lost in females.

The reptilian body shape is better adapted to land life than the amphibian. The neck is longer and the first two cervical vertebrae are specialized to permit the head to move independently of the rest of the body as the animal feeds. The tail is more slender than in the labyrinthodonts and salamanders. This reflects the decreasing importance of fishlike lateral undulations of the trunk and tail in locomotion, and the increasing importance of the limbs. Well-formed **claws,** which are basically modified horny scales, are borne upon the toes. The more powerful hind legs require a pelvic girdle that is attached more firmly onto the vertebral column. Reptiles typically have two sacral vertebrae, whereas amphibians have only one.

Improved locomotion and increased agility also involve a more elaborate muscular system, nervous system and sense organs. The delicate tympanic membrane is protected by its position deep within a canal, the **external auditory meatus,** and the eye is further protected through the evolution of a third, transparent eyelid known as the **nictitating membrane.**

The dry horny skin of reptiles reduces cutaneous respiration to a negligible amount, but an increase in the respiratory surface of the lungs not only compensates for this, but also provides for the increased volume of gas exchange necessitated by a general increase in activity. Mechanisms for moving air into and out of the lungs are also more efficient. Instead of pumping air into the lungs by

Figure 23.11 The collared lizard, *Crotaphytus collaris*. (Courtesy of the New York Zoological Society.)

froglike throat movements, reptiles decrease the pressure within their body cavity, and atmospheric pressure drives in air. A subatmospheric pressure is created around the lungs during inspiration by the forward movement of the ribs and the concomitant increase in size of the body cavity. The contraction of abdominal muscles and the elastic recoil of the lungs force out air. Circulatory changes, discussed in a later chapter, further separate the oxygenated and unoxygenated blood leaving the heart and make the oxygen supply to the tissues more effective.

Major changes have come about in the method of reproduction. Male reptiles have evolved **copulatory organs** which introduce the sperm directly into the female reproductive tract. Fertilization is internal, and the delicate sperm are not exposed to the external environment. A large quantity of nutritive **yolk** is stored within the egg while it is still in the ovary. As the eggs pass down the oviduct after ovulation, they are fertilized, and additional substances and a **shell** are secreted around each one by certain oviducal cells. **Albumin** and similar materials around the egg provide additional food, ions and water. The leathery or calcareous shell serves for protection against mechanical injury and desiccation, yet it is porous enough to permit gas exchange. Such an egg, which contains, or has the means of providing, all substances necessary for the complete development of the embryo to a miniature adult, is called a **cleidoic egg.** Reptiles lay fewer eggs than lower vertebrates, but the eggs are larger, better equipped, and laid in sheltered situations, so the mortality is low. A collared lizard lays only four to 24 eggs in contrast to the 2000 or 3000 of the leopard frog.

As the embryo develops, it separates from the yolk, which becomes suspended in a **yolk sac** (Fig. 23.12). Protective layers of tissue fold over the embryo. The outermost of these is the **chorion.** An **amnion** lies beneath it and forms around the embryo a fluid-filled chamber, which serves as a protective water cushion and provides an aquatic environment in which the embryo develops. These two membranes appear to be derived phylogenetically from something similar to the superficial layers covering the yolk sac of certain large yolked fish embryos. Another membrane, the **allantois,** is a saclike outgrowth from the embryo's hindgut. It is homologous to the urinary bladder of the frog but extends beyond the body wall, passing between the amnion and the chorion. Its highly vascular wall unites with the chorion, and gas exchange with the external environment occurs there. Nitrogenous excretory products, largely in the form of crystals of uric acid, accumulate in the cavity of the allantois. It has been postulated that the evolution of the cleidoic egg necessitated a shift in nitrogen metabolism so that most nitrogenous wastes are converted to uric acid. Little water is available to carry off ammonia and urea in the terrestrial environment in which the eggs are laid, and nitrogen cannot be eliminated in gaseous form; consequently much of it must be converted to an inert product which can be stored.

Yolk sac, chorion, amnion and allantois are collectively called the **extraembryonic membranes.** These adaptations for terrestrial

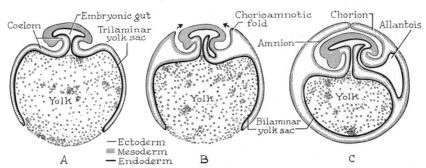

Figure 23.12 Sections of vertebrate embryos to show the extraembryonic membranes. *A,* The trilaminar yolk sac of a large yolk fish embryo consists of all three germ layers. *B,* The chorioamniotic folds of an early embryo of a reptile appear to have evolved from the ectoderm and part of the mesoderm of a trilaminar yolk sac. *C,* A later reptile embryo in which the extraembryonic membranes are complete. Notice that the yolk sac is bilaminar. The albumin and shell, which surround the reptile embryo and extraembryonic membranes, have not been shown.

reproduction are found in the embryos of all reptiles, birds and mammals. These groups of vertebrates are often called **amniotes,** after one of these membranes. In contrast, the various fish groups and amphibians are called the **anamniotes.**

23.6

Evolution and Adaptations of Reptiles

Stem Reptiles. Having "solved" the essential problems of terrestrial life at a time when there were few competitors upon the land, the reptiles multiplied rapidly, spread into all of the ecologic niches available to them, and became specialized accordingly. Much of their divergence has involved adaptation to different methods of locomotion and feeding. Different feeding patterns have entailed, among other things, modification of the jaw muscles, and this in turn has affected the structure of the temporal region of the skull. Skull morphology, therefore, provides a convenient way to sort out the various lines of reptile evolution. As can be seen in a posterior view of a skull (Fig. 23.13*A*), only a small part of the skull of a primitive tetrapod actually surrounds the brain. A large space lies lateral to the brain case and posterior to the eyes, and it is largely filled with jaw muscles which extend down to the lower jaw. In ancestral terrestrial vertebrates (the

labryinthodonts, and the earliest reptiles, the cotylosaurs of the order **Cotylosauria**), a solid roof of dermal bone covered these muscles dorsally and laterally (Fig. 23.13*A* and *B*). This is referred to as the **anapsid** condition. As a consequence of some brain enlargement, and an enlargement of jaw muscles, various types of openings have evolved in the temporal roof of most later reptile groups. Jaw muscles arise from the brain case and from the periphery of the temporal fenestrae, and they can bulge through the opening when they contract.

Turtles. Turtles (order **Chelonia**) are believed to be direct descendants of cotylosaurs (Fig. 23.4), for most have retained the anapsid skull, but they are specialized by being encased in a protective shell composed of bony plates overlaid by horny scales. The bony plates have ossified in the dermis of the skin, but they have also fused with the ribs and some other deeper parts of the skeleton.

The portion of the shell covering the back is known as the **carapace;** the ventral portion, the **plastron.**

Ancestral turtles were stiff-necked creatures, unable to retract their heads, but modern species can withdraw theirs into the shell. This is accomplished by bending the neck in an S-shaped loop in either the vertical plane (North American species such as the red-eared turtle, *Pseudemys scripta elegans*) or in the horizontal plane (Australian side-necked turtle, *Chelodina longicollis*, Fig.

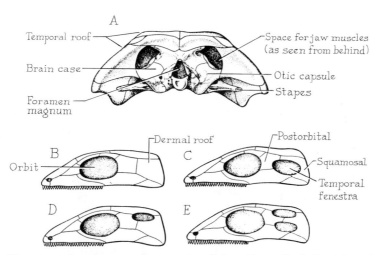

Figure 23.13 Diagrams to show the types of temporal roofs found in reptile skulls. *A*, Posterior view of the skull of a cotylosaur to show the relationship between temporal roof and brain case; *B*, the anapsid condition; *C*, the synapsid condition; *D*, the euryapsid condition; *E*, the diapsid condition. (*A* from Romer after Price; *B–E* from Romer.)

23.14*D*). Sea turtles belong to the former group. They have also adapted to an aquatic mode of life, swimming about by means of oarlike flippers. They come ashore only to lay their cleidoic eggs in holes which they dig on the beaches.

Marine Blind Alleys. Sea turtles are not the only reptiles that have returned to the ocean. In the Mesozoic, two lines of reptilian evolution adapted to marine conditions. Plesiosaurs (order **Sauropterygia,** Fig. 23.15) were superficially turtle-shaped (though they lacked the shell), with squat, heavy bodies and long necks. Some species reached a length of 12 meters. They propelled themselves by means of large paddle-shaped appendages. Members of the other line, the ichthyosaurs (order **Ichthyosauria,** Fig. 23.15), were porpoise-like in size and shape, and probably in habits. They moved with fishlike undulations of the trunk. Both of these groups are characterized by having a temporal opening high up on the side of the

skull: just above the postorbital and squamosal bone (the **euryapsid** condition, Fig. 23.13*D*) in plesiosaurs; even higher in ichthyosaurs (**parapsid** condition).

Plesiosaurs could probably get onto the beaches to lay their eggs, but the extreme aquatic adaptation of the ichthyosaurs would preclude their doing so. How then did they reproduce, for cleidoic eggs cannot develop submerged in water? In an unusual fossil, several small ichthyosaurs are lodged in the posterior part of the mother's abdominal cavity, and one individual is part way out the cloaca. These must have been offspring about to be born, for the skeletons of individuals that had been eaten would not remain intact during a passage through the digestive tract. Apparently, these reptiles, like some modern lizards and snakes, were viviparous or ovoviviparous, the eggs being retained in the oviduct until embryonic development was complete.

These marine reptiles flourished during

Figure 23.14 *A,* Copulating loggerhead sea turtles, *Caretta caretta; B,* sea turtle laying eggs; *C,* diagram showing retraction of head into the shell by bending the neck in the vertical plane; *D,* the Australian side-necked turtle, *Chelodina longicollis.* (*A,* photograph by Frank Essapian, courtesy of Marine Studios; *B,* Life photo by Fritz Goro. © Time, Inc.; *C* from Gregory, William King: Evolution Emerging, Volume II, the Macmillan Co., 1951; *D* courtesy of the New York Zoological Society.)

Figure 23.15   Aquatic reptiles of the Mesozoic era. Plesiosaurs on the left; ichthyosaurs on the right. Plesiosaurs reached a length of 12 meters; ichthyosaurs, a length of about 3 meters. (Courtesy of the Chicago Museum of Natural History.)

the Mesozoic, competing with the more primitive kinds of fishes. Just why they became extinct near the close of this era is uncertain, but their extinction coincides with the evolution and increase of the teleosts. Possibly they could not compete successfully with these fishes.

Lizard-like Reptiles.   The most abundant of our present-day reptiles are the lizard-like ones of which lizards and snakes are the most familiar examples. The most primitive living member of this group is the tuatara (*Sphenodon*, Fig. 23.16) — the only surviving representative of the order **Rhynchocephalia.** Rhynchocephalians are lizard-like in general appearance, and are characterized by having a skull with two temporal openings (**diapsid** condition); one above and one below the squamosal-postorbital bar (Fig. 23.13*E*). At one time the group was very widespread, but now it is limited to a few small islands off the coast of New Zealand. *Sphenodon* is a surviving "fossil," for it has not changed greatly from species that were living 150 million years ago.

Lizards and snakes, though superficially different from each other, are similar enough in basic structure to be placed in the single order **Squamata.** Lizards (suborder **Lacertilia**) are the older and more primitive. They doubtless evolved from some rhynchocephalian-like ancestor early in the Mesozoic era, but have lost more of the temporal roof including the bar of bone just beneath the lower temporal opening. For the most part lizards are diurnal terrestrial quadrupeds but, like other successful groups, they have undergone an extensive adaptive radiation (Fig. 23.17).

Several groups have become arboreal and evolved interesting adaptations for climbing. The true chameleon of Africa (not to be confused with the circus chameleon of our Southeast) has a prehensile tail and an odd foot structure in which the toes of each foot are fused together into two groups that oppose each other like the jaws of a pair of pliers. Geckos, in contrast, cling to trees by means of expanded digital pads. Numerous fine ridges on the under surface of the pads increase the friction.

Many lizards, including the horned toads of our Southwest (*Phrynosoma*), burrow to some extent for protection, and some have taken to a burrowing mode of life. Appendages are lost in many burrowing lizards, though vestiges of girdles are present. The eyes may be reduced, and the body form becomes wormlike. The glass snake (*Ophisaurus*), although it burrows only part of the time, is a lizard of this type. The glass snake derives its name from its ability to break off its tail when seized. The tail, which constitutes about two-thirds of the animal's length, fragments into many pieces that writhe about, attracting attention while the lizard moves quietly away. Other lizards also have this ability, though developed to a less spectacular

Figure 23.16   The tuatara, *Sphenodon*, is one of the most primitive of living reptiles. (Courtesy of the New York Zoological Society.)

Figure 23.17   Adaptive radiation among lizards. *A*, The Old World chameleon has grasping feet and a prehensile tail with which to climb about the trees. *B*, The gecko climbs by means of digital pads. *C*, The horned-toad, *Phrynosoma*, is a ground-dwelling species that often burrows. *D*, The glass snake, *Ophisaurus*, also burrows. *E*, The Gila monster, *Heloderma*, and a related Mexican species are the only poisonous lizards in the world. (Courtesy of the New York Zoological Society.)

degree. Lost tails are regenerated, but the new tails are supported by a cartilaginous rod rather than by vertebrae.

The only poisonous lizards are the beaded lizards, such as the Gila monster (*Heloderma*) of the Southwestern United States. Modified glands in the floor of the mouth discharge a neurotoxic poison, which is injected into the victim by means of grooved teeth. This is a relatively inefficient method, so the bite is not so dangerous as the bite of most poisonous snakes. Charles Bogert of the American Museum of Natural History reports that eight of 34 bites that have come to his attention were fatal, and he believes that the majority of minor bites are never reported. It is probable that the poison is used for defense rather than for killing prey, for the Gila monster crushes its food with its powerful jaws.

Snakes (suborder **Ophidia**) differ from lizards most notably in being able to swallow animals several times their own diameter (Fig. 23.18). This is made possible by an unusually flexible jaw mechanism, which results in part from the further "erosion" of the temporal roof. Snakes have also lost the squamosal-postorbital bar of bone, and this permits the quadrate bone (the skull bone which in all reptiles and lower vertebrates articulates with the lower jaw) to participate in jaw movements. In a sense, snakes have five jaw joints (Fig. 23.19): (1) the usual one between quadrate and lower jaw, (2) one between quadrate and squamosal, (3) one between squamosal and brain case, (4) one about half-way along the lower jaw, and (5) one at the chin, for the two lower jaws are not united at this point. Other features which characterize snakes are the absence of movable eyelids, of a tympanic membrane and middle ear cavity, and of legs and girdles. The absence of the pectoral girdle is a necessary correlate of swallowing animals larger than the diameter of the body. There are exceptions to these generalizations, for geckos do not have movable eyelids, glass "snakes" lack legs, and some of the more primitive snakes, such as the python, have vestigial hind legs.

Snakes doubtless evolved from some primitive lizard group, and very probably from burrowing members of that group. The most primitive living snakes are burrowing species, and many details of ophidean anatomy suggest a fossorial ancestry. The absence of a muscular ciliary body and other features of their eyes, for example, indicates that the eyes redeveloped from eyes that had undergone marked retrogressive changes. Their forked tongue, which is often seen darting from the mouth (Fig. 23.20*A*), is an organ concerned with touch and smelling. Odorous particles adhere to it, the tongue is withdrawn into the mouth, and the tip is projected into a specialized part of the nasal cavity (Jacobson's organ). The great elaboration of such a device

Figure 23.18   A gopher snake eating a rat. (Courtesy of the New York Zoological Society.)

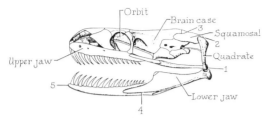

Figure 23.19 Lateral view of the skull of a python to show the five points at which motion can occur when the jaws are opened. (From Romer after M. Smith.)

would seem to be an adaptation to a burrowing mode of life in which other senses would be less useful.

In their subsequent evolution some snakes gave up the burrowing habit, adjusted to epigean life, and underwent an extensive adaptive radiation. A pattern of locomotion evolved that is dependent primarily upon undulatory movements of the long trunk. When a snake moves through grass, for example, loops of the trunk form behind the head and move posteriorly. When these loops meet protuberances from the ground, they push upon them and the resultants of these forces move the snake forward.

Of particular interest has been the evolution in several distinct groups of snakes of methods of prey immobilization. If a snake is to swallow an animal larger in diameter than itself, there is a distinct advantage in having the animal quiet, particularly if it is an animal

such as a rodent capable of inflicting a severe bite! Boa constrictors, pythons, and many harmless rodent-eating snakes, such as king snakes, entwine their prey in loops of the trunk and gradually suffocate the prey by stopping their respiratory movements. A number of other groups have evolved a poison mechanism consisting of specialized oral glands associated with grooved or hollow hypodermic-like teeth—the **fangs.** Old World vipers and New World pit vipers (rattlesnakes, copperheads, cottonmouths, water moccasins) have a pair of large hollow fangs at the front of the mouth that are articulated to bones of the upper jaw and palate in such a way that they are folded against the roof of the mouth when the mouth is closed and automatically brought forward when the mouth is opened (Fig. 23.20*B*). The poison of many of the snakes is hemolytic and causes a breakdown of the red blood cells in the animal bitten. Coral snakes belong to a group related to the Old World cobras. Their poison is neurotoxic, and their fangs are a pair of hollow, short, stationary teeth attached to the front of the upper jaw.

Pit vipers differ from other poisonous snakes in having a prominent **sensory pit** on each side of their heads between the nostril and eye. Experiments in which other sense organs have been rendered functionless show that the pit enables these snakes to seek out and strike accurately at objects warmer than their surroundings. The pits probably help

Figure 23.20 *A,* A coachwhip snake protruding its tongue; *B,* "milking" a rattlesnake to get poison for the production of antivenom. The tongue is a tactile and olfactory organ that is perfectly harmless; it should not be confused with fangs, which are specialized teeth. (*A* courtesy of the New York Zoological Society; *B* courtesy of Ross Allen's Reptile Institute.)

the snakes to feed upon small nocturnal mammals.

Dinosaurs and Their Allies. Lizards and snakes are the successful reptiles today, but during the Mesozoic era the land was dominated by another offshoot of primitive rhynchocephalian-like reptiles. These "ruling reptiles" were the **archosaurs**—an assemblage of several orders that shared many features, including a diapsid skull and a tendency to evolve a two-legged gait. Reduced pectoral appendages, enlarged pelvic appendages, and a heavy tail that could act as a counterbalance for the trunk were correlated with this method of locomotion.

Saurischian dinosaurs (order **Saurischia**) evolved from ancestors that were approximately 1 meter long, but later saurischians became giants of the land and swamps. *Tyrannosaurus* (Fig. 23.21*A*) was the largest terrestrial carnivore that the world has ever seen. It stood about 6 meters high and had large jaws

Figure 23.21   Representatives of the main groups of dinosaurs that flourished during the late Mesozoic era. *A, Tyrannosaurus*, a carnivorous saurischian; *B, Brontosaurus*, a herbivorous saurischian; *C, Stegosaurus*, an ornithischian; *D, Triceratops*, another ornithischian. *Brontosaurus* was the largest and reached a length of about 25 meters. (Courtesy of the Chicago Museum of Natural History.)

armed with dagger-like teeth 15 cm. long—a truly formidable creature! Other saurischian dinosaurs were herbivorous swamp-dwellers that reverted to a quadruped gait, but the bipedal gait of their ancestors was reflected in their long hind legs. The buoyancy of the water permitted some to grow to enormous size. *Brontosaurus* (Fig. 23.21*B*) and certain of its allies attained lengths of 25 meters and weights of 45 metric tons. Only certain modern whales have exceeded them in size.

Many dinosaurs in another group (order **Ornithischia**) became terrestrial rather than swamp herbivores. These also reverted to a quadruped gait and increased in size, though none was so large as the saurischians. These animals undoubtedly formed much of the diet of carnivores such as *Tyrannosaurus*, and many evolved protective devices such as spiked tails, bony plates on the body and horned skulls. *Stegosaurus* and *Triceratops* Fig. 23.21*C* and *D*) are examples of this group.

The reasons for the evolution of large size are not entirely clear. Within limits, large size has a protective value, but it may also have been a way of achieving a more nearly constant body temperature. Reptiles, being poikilothermic, derive a great deal of their body heat during warm weather from the external environment. As mass increases, the relative amount of body surface available for the absorption of heat decreases. An adaptation of this type may have been particularly important for animals that lived in a warm climate and were too big to shelter by burrowing or hiding beneath debris, for it would help to prevent body temperature from reaching a lethal point. As explained earlier, prolonged high temperature destroys most enzyme systems.

A bipedal gait naturally freed the front legs from use in terrestrial locomotion. The front legs became reduced in many dinosaurs, but in one group of archosaurs they evolved into wings. The wings of the flying reptiles (order **Pterosauria**) consisted of a membrane of skin supported by a greatly elongated fourth finger. (Fig. 23.22). The fifth finger was lost, and the others probably were used for clinging to cliffs. The hind legs were very feeble, and the animal must have been nearly helpless on the ground. Certain pterosaurs became very large, one having a wing spread of over 6 meters.

Most of the archosaurs became extinct

Figure 23.22 *Pteranodon*, the largest of the flying reptiles, or pterosaurs, that lived during the late Mesozoic era. (Courtesy of the American Museum of Natural History.)

toward the end of the Mesozoic, but the reason for this is not entirely clear. Perhaps the pterosaurs succumbed in competition with birds, which also evolved from primitive bipedal archosaurs. The extinction of the dinosaurs may have resulted from climatic changes. An inability of the specialized herbivores to adapt to the drying up of the large swamps and to changes in vegetation would have led to their death. Their disappearance, in turn, would deprive the huge carnivores of most of their food supply, so their days would be numbered too. The factors mentioned may not have wiped out a population but simply have reduced it to a size at which it became very difficult for the species to maintain itself.

Only one group of archosaurs survived

this wholesale extinction—the alligators and crocodiles (order **Crocodilia**). Crocodiles have reverted to a quadruped gait (though their hind legs are much longer than the front) and an amphibious mode of life. Only two species occur in the United States—the American alligator, which can be distinguished by its rounded snout, and the American crocodile, which has a much more pointed snout (Fig. 23.23).

Mammal-like Reptiles. Another line of evolution, which was destined to lead to mammals, diverged from the cotylosaurs millions of years before the advent of archosaurs. Early mammal-like reptiles (order **Pelycosauria**) were very similar to cotylosaurs, differing primarily in having a skull with a temporal opening ventral to the squamosal and postorbital bones (**synapsid** condition, Fig. 21.13C). They were medium-sized, somewhat clumsy, terrestrial quadrupeds with limbs sprawled out at right angles to the body. Their jaws contained numerous conical teeth and were composed of many dermal bones covering the mandibular arch. The jaw joint lay between the ossified posterior ends of the mandibular arch, i.e., between the **quadrate** bone of the upper jaw and the **articular** bone of the lower jaw. This is where the jaw joint is located in the frog (Fig. 21.4) and other lower vertebrates.

The **stapes** (a derivative of the hyoid arch of fishes) transmitted vibrations to the inner ear. It, in turn, may have received air-borne vibrations from the external environment by means of a tympanic membrane as it does in frogs (Fig. 21.19), or ground-borne vibrations may have been picked up by the lower jaw and transmitted via the articular and quadrate to the stapes. This point is uncertain, for a soft part such as a tympanic membrane would not be preserved in the fossils. It is known that a process of the stapes did connect with the quadrate.

Some pelycosaurs, such as *Dimetrodon* (Fig. 23.24A), were quite active and may have been warm-blooded. *Dimetrodon* had a peculiar sail along its back supported by long neural spines of the vertebrae. This sail may have been a device to radiate heat, for it considerably increased the body surface relative to mass. Active animals produce a large amount of heat as a by-product of their metabolic activity and need special means of dissipating it.

Later mammal-like reptiles (*Lycaenops*, order **Therapsida**, Fig. 23.24B) came to resemble mammals more closely. Their limbs were beneath the body where they could provide better support and move more rapidly back and forth. Their teeth were specialized, like those of mammals, into ones suited for cropping, stabbing, cutting and grinding.

Figure 23.23 The alligators and crocodiles are the only surviving members of the archosaurian reptiles, a group to which the dinosaurs belonged. *A,* The American alligator; *B,* the American crocodile. The southern part of the Florida Everglades is the only place in the United States where crocodiles can be found in the wild. (Courtesy of Ross Allen's Reptile Institute.)

Figure 23.24   Two mammal-like reptiles. *A, Dimetrodon,* an early member of the group; *B, Lycaenops,* a later mammal-like reptile similar to those that gave rise to mammals. (Courtesy American Museum of Natural History.)

The major osteologic character that separated them from mammals was the reptilian nature of the jaw joint and the sound-transmitting apparatus. The mammalian jaw joint is between two dermal bones (the **dentary** of the lower jaw and **squamosal** of the upper jaw) that lie just anterior to the quadrate and articular. The mammalian homologues of the quadrate and articular (the **incus** and **malleus,** respectively) are covered by a tympanic membrane and form, with the stapes, a chain of three delicate auditory ossicles that transmit air-borne vibrations from the tympanic membrane to the inner ear (Fig. 30.9). This character had not been achieved by the late therapsids, but the dentary and squamosal were very close together, and the quadrate and articular were small. The change to the mammalian condition was made by the middle of the Mesozoic; shortly afterward the mammal-like reptiles became extinct. Their mammalian descendants remained a rather inconspicuous part of the fauna until the disappearance of the dinosaurs.

SYNOPSIS OF AMPHIBIANS AND REPTILES

CLASS AMPHIBIA.   The amphibians. Cold-blooded vertebrates usually having an aquatic larval stage; adults typically terrestrial; skin moist and slimy; scales absent in most groups; microscopic vestiges of bony scales in one living group.

†**Subclass 1. Labyrinthodontia.**   Several orders of extinct and primitive amphibians collectively called labyrinthodonts; vertebral centra of the "arch" type, each usually consisting of two or three arches of bone encasing the notochord.

†**Subclass 2. Lepospondyli.**   Several orders of extinct amphibia with vertebral centra of the "spool" type; each centrum a single structure, spool-shaped, pierced by a longitudinal canal for persistent notochord.

Subclass 3. Lissamphibia.   Modern amphibians, probably evolved from lepospondyls. Skull usually flat and broad; pineal opening lost; brain case poorly ossified; pubis never ossified; carpals and tarsals largely cartilaginous.

†Extinct.

Superorder 1. Salientia.   Frogs and their allies. Trunk short; tail reduced or absent; ilia elongated; hind legs elongated.

†*Order 1. Proanura.*   Ancestral frogs of the Triassic. Tail still present; limbs not highly specialized. *Triadobatrachus.*

Order 2. Anura.   Modern frogs and toads. Caudal vertebrae form a urostyle; legs specialized for jumping. The leopard frog, *Rana;* tree frog, *Hyla;* American toad, *Bufo.*

Superorder 2. Caudata.   Tailed amphibians. Trunk long; tail present; legs, if present, not elongated.

Order 1. Urodela.   Salamanders. Tail long; legs usually present. The spotted salamander, *Ambystoma*; redbacked salamander, *Plethodon;* mudpuppy, *Necturus.*

Order 2. Apoda.   Caecilians. Wormlike trunk; limbs absent; tail very short; vestiges of dermal scales in the skin. Confined to the tropics.

CLASS REPTILIA.   The reptiles. Cold-blooded tetrapods that reproduce upon the land; body covered with horny scales or plates.

Subclass 1. Anapsida.   Primitive reptiles characterized by a solid roof in the temporal region of the skull.

†*Order 1. Cotylosauria.*   The cotylosaurs. Ancestral reptiles retaining a large number of primitive features.

Order 2. Chelonia.   The turtles. Anapsid reptiles with a short trunk encased in a bony shell which in turn is covered by horny plates; teeth absent. Red-eared turtle, *Pseudemys*; green sea turtle, *Chelonia*; side-necked turtle, *Chelodina.*

†**Subclass 2. Euryapsida.**   Ancient marine reptiles that propelled themselves with long paddle-shaped limbs; single temporal opening high on the skull.

†*Order 1. Sauropterygia.*   The plesiosaurs.

†**Subclass 3. Ichthyopterygia.**   Ancient, marine, fishlike reptiles; single temporal opening high on the skull.

†*Order 1. Ichthyosauria.*   The ichthyosaurs.

Subclass 4. Lepidosauria.   Primitive reptiles with two temporal openings in the skull (diapsid); pineal foramen usually retained; teeth on palate as well as jaw margins, usually not set in sockets; usually quadrupeds.

†*Order 1. Eosuchia.*   Ancestral lepidosaurians.

Order 2. Rhynchocephalia.   Primitive lizard-like reptiles. Temporal openings completely bounded by arches of bone; distinctive overhanging beak on upper jaw; now confined to certain islands off New Zealand. The tuatara, *Sphenodon.*

Order 3. Squamata.   Lizards and snakes. Advanced lepidosaurians in which there has been a loss of one or two arches of bone bordering the temporal openings.

SUBORDER 1. LACERTILIA.   Lizards. Only the lower arch of bone has been lost in the temporal region; most groups retain legs, eyelids and an auditory opening. The collared lizard, *Crotophytus*; horned toad, *Phrynosoma;* Gila monster, *Heloderma.*

SUBORDER 2. OPHIDIA.   Snakes. Both arches of bone bounding temporal openings have been lost; jaw mechanism extremely flexible so that food larger than head can be swallowed; pineal foramen, legs and auditory opening are lost; eyes covered by a transparent scale, the spectacle. The garter snake, *Thamnophis*; water snake, *Natrix*; rattlesnake, *Crotalus.*

Subclass 5. Archosauria.   Advanced diapsid reptiles. Pineal foramen usually absent; teeth usually restricted to jaw margin, set in sockets; an extra fenestra usually present in front of the eye or on the lower jaw; bipedal reptiles, or showing signs of bipedal ancestry.

†*Order 1. Thecodontia.*   Ancestral archosaurs. Show the beginning of archosaur tendencies but not the specializations of later archosaurs.

†*Order 2. Saurischia.*   Saurischian dinosaurs. Pelvis three-pronged with pubis located entirely anterior to ischium. *Tyrannosaurus, Brontosaurus.*

†*Order 3. Ornithischia.*   Ornithischian dinosaurs. Pelvis birdlike with part of pubis

growing posteriorly parallel to ischium; all herbivorous. *Stegasaurus, Triceratops.*

†*Order 4. Pterosauria.*   The flying reptiles. Wing a skin membrane supported by an elongated fourth finger. *Pteranodon.*

Order 5. Crocodilia.   Alligators and crocodiles. Quadrupeds but with hind legs noticeably larger than forelegs; adapted for an aquatic mode of life. The American alligator, *Alligator*; the American crocodile, *Crocodilus.*

Subclass 6. Synapsida.   Mammal-like reptiles characterized by a single temporal opening on the lateral surface of the skull.

Order 1. Pelycosauria.   Early mammal-like reptiles retaining many primitive features; limbs in primitive tetrapod position with humerus and femur moving in the horizontal plane. *Dimetrodon.*

Order 2. Therapsida.   Advanced mammal-like reptiles beginning to show many mammalian characteristics; limbs rotated beneath the body with humerus and femur moving in the vertical plane. *Lycaenops.*

QUESTIONS

1. List five differences in physical conditions between the aquatic and terrestrial environments to which terrestrial vertebrates had to adapt.
2. In what ways were crossopterygians preadapted to a terrestrial life? What other conditions favored crossopterygians in making the adaptive shift from water to land?
3. In what ways have amphibians successfully adapted to the terrestrial environment? In what ways are they poorly adapted for life on land?
4. List the distinguishing characters of the orders of living amphibians.
5. Which salamanders do not have lungs? How do these salamanders respire?
6. What features of toads enable them to live in drier environments than frogs?
7. In what ways are the embryos modified in frogs that have a direct development?
8. Under what environmental conditions have the larval stages of frogs been suppressed? Is it possible that similar conditions played a role in the evolution of terrestrial reproduction in the ancestors of reptiles?
9. In what ways are reptiles better adapted for terrestrial life than amphibians?
10. List the extraembryonic membranes of a reptile embryo and briefly state the function of each.
11. Define a cleidoic egg.
12. Which groups of vertebrates are amniotes; which are anamniotes?
13. What were the earliest reptiles?
14. Name two groups of Mesozoic reptiles that returned to the sea and became very well adapted to the marine environment.
15. How can one distinguish a legless lizard from a snake? How can one distinguish a lizard from a salamander?
16. Which group of living reptiles is most closely related to the dinosaurs?
17. Which group of reptiles gave rise to the mammals?

ANNOTATED REFERENCES

Many of the general references on vertebrates cited at the end of Chapter 22 contain considerable information on the biology of amphibians and reptiles.

Barbour, T.: Reptiles and Amphibians, Their Habits and Adaptations. Boston, Houghton Mifflin Co., 1926. Many of the fascinating adaptations of amphibians and reptiles are described.

Bishop, S. C.: Handbook of Salamanders of the United States, of Canada and of Lower California. Ithaca, N. Y., Comstock Publishing Co., 1943. A standard reference work on the taxonomy and natural history of salamanders.

Carr, A.: Handbook of Turtles of the United States, Canada and Baja California. Ithaca, N. Y., Comstock Publishing Co., 1952. A standard reference work on the taxonomy and natural history of turtles.

Cochran, D. M.: Living Amphibians of the World. New York, Doubleday & Co., 1961. A fascinating and superbly illustrated account of the groups of living amphibians.

Conant, R.: A Field Guide to Reptiles and Amphibians of Eastern North America. Boston, Houghton Mifflin Co., 1958. A very useful guide for the field identification of amphibians and reptiles; similar to the Peterson bird guides.

Gadow, H.: Amphibia and Reptilia. Weinheim, Germany, Engelmann, 1958. A recent reprint of a book originally published as a part of the "Cambridge Natural History" in 1901; it is still one of the best accounts of the anatomy and evolution of amphibians and reptiles.

Goin, C. J., and O. B. Goin: Introduction to Herpetology. San Francisco, W. H. Freeman & Co., 1962. Most aspects of the biology of amphibians and reptiles are considered briefly in this useful introduction to the field.

Moore, J. (Ed.): Physiology of the Amphibia. New York, Academic Press, 1964. Most aspects of amphibian physiology are covered in this very valuable source book.

Noble, G. K.: The Biology of the Amphibia. New York, Dover Publications, Inc., 1956. This is a recent reprint of an older but still very valuable reference work on the classification, anatomy, physiology and ecology of amphibians.

Peters, J. A.: Dictionary of Herpetology. New York, Hafner, 1964. A very valuable reference work for the serious student; includes many diagrams.

Schmidt, K. P., and R. F. Inger: Living Reptiles of the World. New York, Doubleday & Co., 1957. A beautifully illustrated account of the natural history of the families of living reptiles.

Smith, H. M.: Handbook of Lizards of the United States and Canada. Ithaca, N. Y., Comstock Publishing Co., 1946. A standard reference work on the taxonomy and natural history of lizards.

Wright A. H., and A. A. Wright: Handbook of Frogs of the United States and Canada. 3rd ed. Ithaca, N. Y., Comstock Publishing Co., 1949. A standard reference work on the taxonomy and natural history of frogs.

Wright, A. H., and A. A. Wright: Handbook of Snakes of the United States and Canada. Ithaca, N. Y., Comstock Publishing Co., 1957. A standard reference work on the taxonomy and natural history of snakes.

24 A HISTORY OF VERTEBRATES: BIRDS

Reptiles evolved two significant features that enabled them to occupy the terrestrial environment more successfully than amphibians: the cleidoic egg and ways of conserving body water. Birds (class **Aves**) and mammals (class **Mammalia**) evolved from reptiles, and both groups have further improved upon the adaptations of reptiles by developing mechanisms for the maintenance of fairly high and constant body temperatures. They are said to be **homoiothermic,** or warm-blooded, animals. Their metabolic processes can proceed at an optimal rate despite the wide range in external temperatures common in the terrestrial environment, and they are typically very active creatures.

Higher metabolic rates require higher rates of exchange of materials with the environment and rapid distribution of these materials within the body. Birds and mammals have met these requirements in somewhat similar ways; their adaptations for increased activity provide interesting examples of convergent evolution, although in other respects they are quite different. Birds evolved from early bipedal archosaurs (Fig. 23.4) and have undergone specializations for flight; mammals evolved from a stock of mammal-like reptiles and have become specialized for terrestrial life.

24.1
Principles of Flight

A group of extinct reptiles, the pterosaurs, and a group of mammals, the bats, have

evolved true flight, but neither group has been as successful fliers as have birds. Bird wings are modified pectoral appendages, and the flying surfaces are composed largely of feathers. A wing is shaped like an airfoil; thick in front and thin and tapering behind, and cambered so that it is slightly concave on the under surface and convex on the upper surface (Fig. 24.1). As the airstream flows across the wing, the stream moves faster along the upper surface than the lower surface. In accordance with Bernoulli's law in physics, which states that in a fluid stream

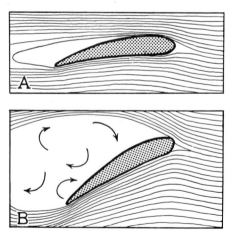

Figure 24.1 The effect of wings on the airstream. In *A*, the wing is held at such an angle that the airstream flows smoothly across it. The air flows more rapidly over the upper surface than across the under surface. This creates a low-pressure area above the wing that provides a lift force. In *B*, the wing is held at such an angle that lift-reducing turbulence and eddies form above it. (Modified after Young.)

the pressure is least where the velocity is greatest, this differential in air speed decreases the pressure above the wing relative to the underside, thereby providing a lift at least equal to the weight of the bird. The somewhat teardrop shape of the wing allows a smooth flow of air across the surface and keeps to a minimum lift-reducing eddies and drag.

Various factors can increase lift. Lift increases in direct proportion to the surface area of the wing. Wing areas differ among different species of bird, and can be varied in individual birds by the degree to which the wing is stretched out or unfolded. Lift increases greatly as the speed of airflow across the wing increases, for lift is proportional to the square of the speed. Fast flying birds, such as a swift, can and do have relatively smaller wings than slower flying species. When a bird is flying at low speeds, or during taking off and landing, other mechanisms are used to increase lift. The wing can be tilted so that its anterior edge is considerably higher, a procedure known as increasing the angle of attack (Fig. 24.1). This increases lift,

but also tends to create lift-reducing turbulence above the wing. Separating certain feathers, which produces slots through which the air moves very rapidly, can reduce this turbulence and make it possible for the wing to generate a very high lift (Fig. 24.2). A small group of feathers supported by the first digit and known as the **alula** can produce a slot at the front of the wing (Fig. 24.3). Additional slots are often formed along the trailing margin of the wing and at the wing tip. The latter slots reduce the turbulence known as tip vortex. Some birds obtain additional lift on landing by fanning out the tail feathers and bending them down. The tail, then, acts both as a brake and as a high-lift, low-speed airfoil.

There are many kinds of flight. The simplest is **gliding,** in which the wings provide some lift and the forward motion comes from falling through the air. Altitude is lost in a glide of this type, but altitude can be maintained or even increased if the bird also soars. Land birds, such as the turkey vulture or the osprey (Fig. 24.4), circle within a rising current of warm air, or above a bluff where

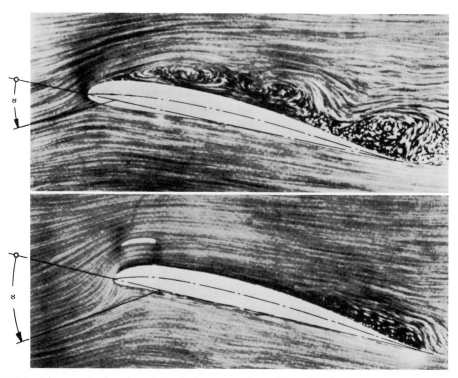

Figure 24.2 Diagrams to show how the turbulence over the surface of a wing (*top*) can be reduced (*bottom*) by a small extra wing forming a slot. Turbulence is reduced even though the angle of attack has been increased slightly. (From Hertel.)

Figure 24.3 Photograph of a red-shouldered hawk landing. Air speed is low and lift is increased by several slots: *1*, alulae; *2*, separation of primary wing feathers; *3*, separation of feathers on leading edge of wing; *4*, auxiliary feathers on upper surface of wing. (From Hertel.)

air is deflected upward. Birds that engage in **static soaring** of this type have relatively short, broad wings that enable them to maneuver easily in the capricious air currents, yet have enough surface area to provide lift. Flight is slow, and additional lift comes from considerable slotting of the wing,

particularly near the tip. Oceanic birds engage in **dynamic soaring,** which makes use of the increase in air speed with increasing elevation above the ocean surface. Friction with the ocean causes air speed to be slowest at the ocean surface (Fig. 24.5). Starting at a high elevation, these birds glide rapidly down-

Figure 24.4 Static soaring of an osprey. (Photograph by Allan D. Cruickshank, National Audubon Society.)

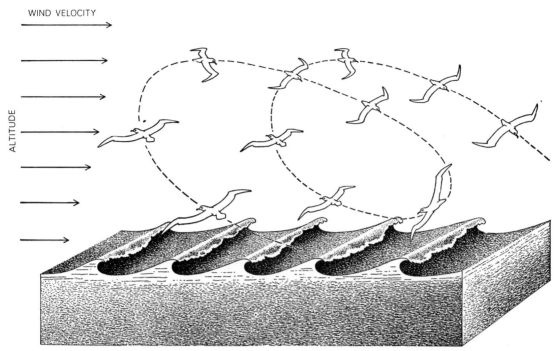

Figure 24.5   Dynamic soaring of an oceanic bird. (From The Soaring Flight of Birds by C. D. Cone, Jr. Copyright © by Scientific American, Inc. All rights reserved.)

ward with the wind. Just above the ocean they wheel into the wind and use the momentum gained in the glide to start to gain altitude. As they gain altitude, they encounter increasingly fast air speeds which in turn generate additional lift. In this way the birds regain their original altitude. Dynamic soarers have long narrow wings.

In the familiar **flapping flight** used by such birds as the pigeon (Fig. 24.6), the wings not only provide the lift, but they also serve as propellers. The up and down movement of the wings relative to the body of the bird is responsible for the forward movement, but the wings do not simply push back against the air as a swimmer would push back against the water. On the downstroke, they move down and forward; on the upstroke, up and back. As a wing moves down, the air pushes up against it and the more flexible posterior margin of the distal part of the wing is twisted up. The distal portion of the wing

Figure 24.6   Flapping flight as seen in pigeons leaving their loft. (U. S. Army photograph.)

twists the opposite way on the upstroke. The twisting of the distal portion of the wing gives it a pitch comparable to that of a propeller and this, together with the movements of this part of the wing, is responsible for the forward motion. In all types of flight, the tail helps to support and balance the body and is used as a rudder.

Most of the features of bird wings also apply to the wings of airplanes. But a bird's wings and tail have one great advantage over those of an airplane in that they can be varied considerably to adjust to different speeds and types of flight, for different angles of attack, and for many other variables. Even though recently designed planes have wings that can be varied to some extent, any bird is more versatile than any single type of airplane.

24.2
Structure of Birds

There are few features of the anatomy of birds that are not directly or indirectly related to flight. They are adapted structurally and functionally to provide a high energy output in a body of low weight.

Scales and Feathers. Birds have retained the horny scales of reptiles on parts of their legs, on their feet and, in modified form, as a covering for their beaks, but the scales that cover the rest of the reptilian body have been transformed into **feathers.** Feathers, like horny scales, are epidermal outgrowths whose cells have accumulated large amounts of keratin and are no longer living. Pigment deposited in these cells during the development of the feather, together with surface modifications that reflect certain light rays, is responsible for the brilliant colors of birds. Although feathers cover a bird, they fan out in most species from localized **feather tracts** rather than growing out uniformly from all of the body surface. Feathers, more than any other single feature, characterize birds, for they are found only in members of this class. They overlap, entrap air and form an insulating layer that reduces loss of body heat and helps to make a high body temperature possible. Those on the tail and wings form the primary flying surfaces.

The **contour feathers** that cover the body and provide the flying surface consist of a stiff, central **shaft** bearing numerous parallel side branches, the **barbs,** which collectively form the **vane** (Fig. 24.7). Each barb bears minute hooked branches, **barbules,** along its side, which interlock with the barbules of adjacent barbs to hold the barbs together (Fig. 24.8). If the barbs separate, the bird can preen the feather with its bill until they hook together again; thus, the vane is a strong and easily repaired surface ideal for flight. In birds that have lost the power of flight, such as the ostrich, hooklets are not present upon the barbules, and the feather is very fluffy. The proximal end of the shaft does not have barbs and is known as the **quill** or **calamus;** much of it is lodged within an epidermal follicle in the skin. The quill is hollow, and blood vessels enter it during the development of the feather. A small **aftershaft,** bearing a few barbs, may arise from the distal end of the quill.

Other types of feathers include the hair-like **filoplumes,** sometimes visible on plucked fowl, and **down feathers.** Down covers young birds and is found under the contour feathers in the adults of certain species, particularly aquatic ones. It is unusually good insulation, for it has a reduced shaft and long fluffy

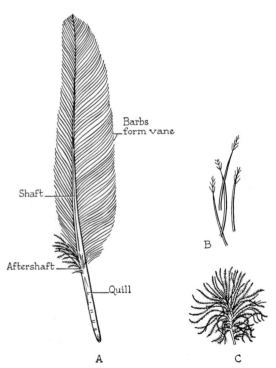

Figure 24.7 Types of feathers. *A,* Contour feather; *B,* filoplume; *C,* down feather. (*A* and *B* modified after Young; *C* after Thompson.)

Figure 24.8 Photomicrographs of barbs (the thickest structures) with their interlocking barbules. Notice the hooks and spines on the barbules. (From Welty.)

barbs arising directly from the distal end of the quill.

Most birds **molt** once a year, usually after the breeding season. Feathers are lost and replaced in a characteristic sequence for each species. The process is gradual in most cases, and the birds can move about normally during molting, but certain male ducks shed the large flight feathers on their wings so rapidly that they are unable to fly for a while.

Scales and feathers are the major derivatives of the skin in birds, but there is one conspicuous skin gland (the **uropygial gland**)

located on the back at the base of the tail. It produces an oily secretion that some birds spread over their feathers with their beak during preening. The gland is particularly well developed in water fowl and its secretions are important in waterproofing the feathers. Its secretions may also have other functions, including the maintenance of the horny covering of the beak.

Skeleton. Many adaptations for flight are apparent in the skeleton of birds (Fig. 24.9). The bones are very light in weight, for they are hollow and remarkably thin. Ex-

Figure 24.9 Skeleton of a pigeon. The distal part of the right wing has been omitted. (Modified after Heilmann.)

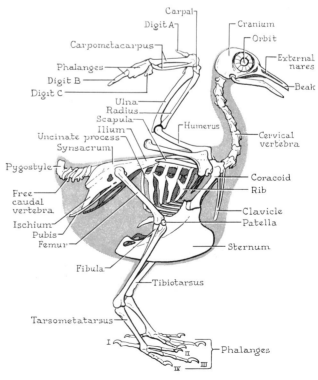

tensions from the air sacs enter the limb bones in many species. Robert Cushman Murphy of the American Museum of Natural History has reported that the skeleton of a frigate bird having a wingspread of over 2 meters weighed only 115 gm., which was less than the weight of its feathers! This is an extreme example, but the skeletons of all birds weigh less relative to their body weight than the skeletons of mammals. The bones are very strong because most of the bone substance is located at the periphery of the bone, where it gives better structural support. A bird bone may be compared to a metal tube, which is more resistant to certain types of stress than a metal rod of equal weight. The rod would be much narrower and could be bent more easily than the tube. Many bird bones are further strengthened by internal struts of bone arranged in a manner similar to the trusses inside the wing of an airplane (Fig. 24.10).

The **skull** is notable for the large size of the cranial region, the large orbits and the toothless beak. The neck region is very long, and the **cervical vertebrae** are articulated in such a way that the head and neck are very mobile. Since the bird's bill is used for feeding, preening, nest building, defense and the like, freedom of movement of the head is very important. The trunk region, in contrast, is shortened, and the **trunk vertebrae** are firmly united to form a strong fulcrum for the action of the wings and a strong point of attachment for the pelvic girdle and hind legs. The hind legs bear the entire weight of the body when the bird is on the ground. In the pigeon, 13 of the more posterior vertebrae (some of the trunk, all of the sacral and some of the caudal vertebrae) are fused together to form a **synsacrum** with which the pelvic girdle is fused. Several free **caudal vertebrae,** which permit movement of the

tail, follow the synsacrum. The terminal caudal vertebrae are fused together as a **pygostyle** and support the large tail feathers.

The last two cervical vertebrae of the pigeon and the thoracic vertebrae bear distinct **ribs.** The thoracic basket is firm yet flexible. Extra firmness is provided by the ossification of the ventral portions of the thoracic ribs (the parts articulating with the sternum and comparable to our costal cartilages) and by posteriorly projecting **uncinate processes** on the dorsal portions of the ribs, which overlap the next posterior ribs. Flexibility, needed in respiratory movements, is made possible by the joints between the dorsal and ventral portions of the ribs. The **sternum,** or breastbone, is greatly expanded and, in all but the flightless birds, has a large midventral **keel** which increases the area available for the attachment of the flight muscles.

The bones of the wing are homologous to those of the pectoral appendage of the frog and other tetrapods. A **humerus, radius** and **ulna** can be recognized easily, but the bones of the hand have been greatly modified. Two free **carpals** are present and a **carpometacarpus** (a safety-pin–shaped complex of bone representing the fused carpals and metacarpals of three fingers) lies distal to them. The end of the most anterior finger is represented by a spur-shaped **phalanx** articulated to the proximal end of the carpometacarpus. The main axis of the hand passes through the next finger, and it has two distinct phalanges articulated to the distal end of the carpometacarpus. Another small, spur-shaped phalanx at the distal end of the carpometacarpus represents the end of the last finger. There is some doubt whether the fingers are homologous to the first three or to the second, third and fourth fingers. The pectoral girdle, which supports the wing,

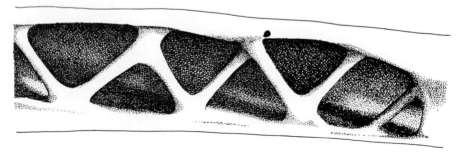

Figure 24.10 Longitudinal section of the metacarpal bone from a vulture's wing. Notice the internal trussing similar to that in an airplane's wing. (From D'Arcy Thompson.)

consists of a narrow dorsal **scapula,** a stout **coracoid** extending as a prop from the shoulder joint to the sternum, and a delicate **clavicle,** which unites distally with its mate of the opposite side to form the wishbone.

The legs of birds resemble the hind legs of bipedal archosaurs. The **femur** articulates distally with a reduced **fibula** and a large **tibiotarsus** (fusion of the tibia with certain tarsals). The remaining tarsals and the elongated metatarsals have fused to form a **tarso-metatarsus.** The fifth toe has been lost in all birds and the fourth in some species. The first toe is turned posteriorly in the pigeon and many other birds. It serves as a prop and increases the grasping action of the foot when the bird perches. The efficiency of the leg in running on the ground and jumping at take-off is increased by the elongation of the metatarsals, and by the elevation of the heel off the ground. The various fusions of the limb bones reduce the chance of dislocation and injury, for birds' legs must act as shock absorbers when they land. The pelvic girdle is equally sturdy; the **ilium, ischium** and **pubis** of each side are firmly united with each other and with the vertebral column. The pubes and ischia of the two sides do not unite to form a midventral pelvic symphysis as they do in other tetrapods. This permits a more posterior displacement of the viscera, which, together with the shortened trunk, shifts the center of gravity of the body nearer to the hind legs. The absence of a symphysis also makes possible the laying of large eggs with calcareous shells.

Muscles. The intricate movements of the neck and the support of the body by a single pair of legs entail numerous modifications of the muscular system, but the muscles concerned with flight are of particular interest. A large **pectoralis,** which originates on the sternum and inserts on the ventral surface of the humerus, is responsible for the powerful downstroke of the wings. One might expect that dorsally placed muscles would be responsible for the recovery stroke but, instead, another ventral muscle, the **supracoracoideus** (designated pectoralis minor by some authors), is responsible for the upstroke by virtue of a peculiar pulley-like arrangement of its tendon of insertion (Fig. 24.11). The origin of the supracoracoideus is on the sternum dorsal to the pectoralis. Its tendon passes through a canal in the pectoral girdle near the shoulder joint

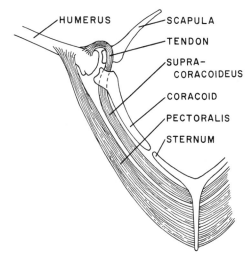

Figure 24.11 A diagrammatic cross section through the shoulder region and sternum showing the arrangement of major flight muscles. (From Welty after Storer.)

and inserts on the dorsal surface of the humerus. Muscles within the wing are responsible for its folding and unfolding and the regulation of its shape and angles during flight. Other muscles attach to the follicles of the large flight feathers of the wings and tail and control their positions.

As would be expected, flight muscles comprise a very large per cent of body weight in a bird that flies a great deal, and the per cent of body weight represented by leg muscles is reduced. In the pigeon, for example, flight muscles comprise about 0.45 of body weight and leg muscles about 0.05. These relationships are reversed in terrestrial and swimming birds; 0.22 of the body weight of a limpkin is represented by the leg muscles, and the flight muscles are only about 0.15 of body weight.

Major Features of the Visceral Organs. Less obvious but no less important adaptations for increased activity and flight are present in many of the internal organs (Fig. 24.12). Increased activity and a high metabolic rate necessitate a large intake of food. The digestive system is compact but it is so effective that, in some of the smaller birds, an amount of food equivalent to 30 per cent of the body weight can be processed each day! Moreover, most of the food that is selected has a high caloric value. Birds eat a variety of insects and other animals and such plant food as fruit and seeds. They do not attempt to eat such bulky, low caloric

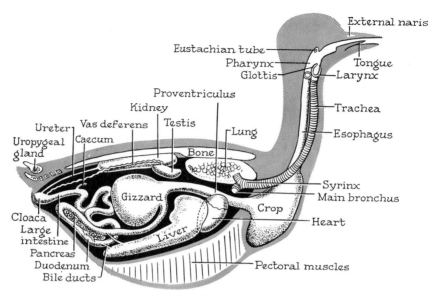

Figure 24.12   A lateral dissection of a pigeon to show the major visceral organs.

food as leaves and grass. Food taken into the **mouth** is mixed with a lubricating saliva and passes through the **pharynx** and down the **esophagus** without further treatment, for birds have no teeth. In grain-eating species, such as the pigeon, the lower end of the esophagus is modified to form a **crop** in which the seeds are temporarily stored and softened by the uptake of water. Food is mixed with peptic enzymes in the **proventriculus,** or first part of the stomach, and then passes into the **gizzard,** the highly modified posterior part of the stomach characterized by thick muscular walls and modified glands that secrete a horny lining. Small stones that have been swallowed are usually found in the gizzard and aid in grinding the food to a pulp and mixing it with the gastric juices. The **intestinal region** is relatively short compared to the intestine of mammals. As in mammals, it is lined with microscopic, finger-like projections, the **villi,** that greatly increase the surface area. Digestion is completed in this region with the aid of juices from the liver, pancreas and intestinal glands, and the digested food is absorbed.

The anterior parts of the respiratory system are similar to those of lower tetrapods, except that birds have a longer neck and, hence, a longer windpipe, or **trachea.** At the base of the neck, the trachea bifurcates into two **bronchi,** each of which leads to a lung. The **lungs** themselves are relatively small and compact organs with a very complex system of respiratory passages within them (Fig. 24.13). As each bronchus (now usually called a **mesobronchus**) passes through the lung it gives off a number of secondary bronchi (**dorsobronchi** and **ventrobronchi**) which extend through the lungs and are connected with each other by many small **parabronchi.** Minute branching and anastomosing **air capillaries** radiate from the parabronchi, and it is through their vascular walls that gas exchange with the blood occurs (Fig. 24.14). Much of the lung is composed of the parabronchi and their associated air capillaries, which together form hexagonal-shaped units. Other branches from the mesobronchus lead into a series of **air sacs** that extend into the abdomen, thorax, and even up into the neck and out into many of the bones. Most of the air sacs are connected through **recurrent bronchi** with the secondary bronchi. The course of airflow through this system is still in dispute, but it is clear that birds have a system in which the lungs can be rather thoroughly flushed out during breathing, so that the passages contain little stale air. A recent theory holds that air passes through the parabronchi during both inspiration and expiration and that its direction is reversed in each phase.

The flow of air through the lungs is brought about primarily by the contraction of muscles in the thoracic and abdominal walls. During inspiration the sternum is lowered,

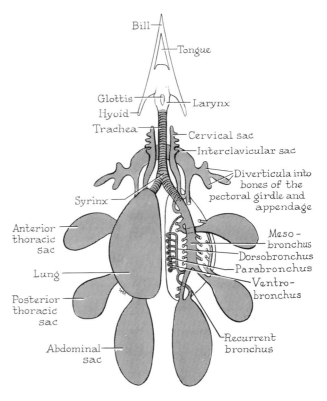

Figure 24.13 The respiratory organs of a bird as seen in a dorsal view. Only one ventrobronchus and one dorsobronchus and their interconnecting parabronchi are shown. (Partly after Welty.)

thereby increasing the vertical dimensions of the thorax and creating a slightly negative pressure within the lungs, air sacs and even the pneumatic bones; during expiration the sternum is raised. It is possible that these movements are enhanced by wing beats during flight.

A mechanism for the production of sounds is associated with the air passages. Membranes are set vibrating by the movement of air; however, the vibratory membranes are not in the larynx at the anterior end of the trachea but in a **syrinx** at its posterior end (Fig. 24.13). Muscles associated with the syrinx vary the pitch of the notes.

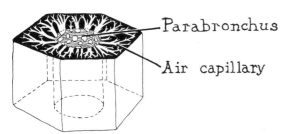

Figure 24.14 A diagram of a section of a parabronchus with its associated air capillaries. (From Welty after Hazellhoff.)

The bird **heart** is completely divided internally. Venous blood returning from the body and going to the lungs passes through a right atrium and right ventricle as it does in mammals, whereas the arterial blood returning from the lungs en route to the body flows through the left atrium and left ventricle (Fig. 24.12). The sinus venosus of primitive vertebrate hearts has been absorbed into the right atrium, and the conus arteriosus contributes to the arterial trunks leading to the lungs and body. An interesting feature of the vessels supplying the body is the unusually large size of those going to the powerful flight muscles. The complete separation of venous and arterial blood within the heart, the rapid heart beat (400 to 500 times per minute in a small bird such as a sparrow when it is at rest), and an increase in blood pressure make for a very rapid and efficient circulation. This is of the utmost importance in a homoiotherm, for the tissues need a large supply of food and oxygen, and waste products of metabolism must be removed quickly.

Nitrogenous wastes are removed from the blood by a pair of **kidneys,** which are drained by **ureters** and are basically similar to those of reptiles (Fig. 24.12). The high rate of metabo-

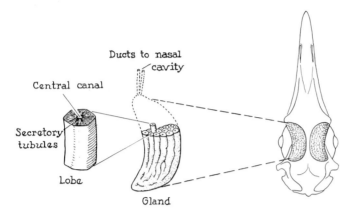

Figure 24.15 The salt-excreting glands of the herring gull. (Modified after Fänge, Schmidt-Nielsen and Osaki.)

lism of birds, however, requires a great increase in the number of kidney tubules. Indeed, most birds have relatively more of these functional units than do mammals; a cubic millimeter of tissue from the cortex of a bird's kidney contains 100 to 500 renal corpuscles (the proximal, filtration portion of the tubules, p. 506) in contrast to 15 or less in a comparable amount of mammal kidney. As in most vertebrates, a considerable amount of water leaves the blood in the renal corpuscles along with waste products, but most of the water is later reabsorbed from the kidney and cloaca, so that the urine is eliminated from the body along with fecal material as a whitish pastelike mass. As in reptiles, the great reduction in water content of the urine is possible because most of the nitrogen is eliminated as nontoxic uric acid. Birds have lost the urinary bladder, present in ground-dwelling vertebrates, possibly as one means of reducing body weight.

Birds lay cleidoic eggs, as do reptiles; hence their reproductive system is very similar to that of reptiles. Female birds have lost the right ovary and oviduct, probably as another means of reducing weight.

Body salts are generally conserved by terrestrial vertebrates, although any excess can be eliminated by the kidneys. Sea birds, however, have a large salt intake with their food and water and must eliminate more salts than can be disposed of by the kidneys. This is done by special **salt-excreting glands,** which in the herring gull, for example, are located above the eyes and discharge a concentrated salt solution into the nasal cavities. This solution leaves these cavities through the external nares and drips from the end of the beak (Fig. 24.15). Each gland consists of many lobes, each of which is composed of many vascularized secretory tubules radiating from a central canal.

The sense of smell is less important in vertebrates that spend a considerable part of their life off the ground than it is in terrestrial species, so it is not surprising to find that the olfactory organ and olfactory portions of the brain are reduced in birds. Sight, on the other hand, is very important, and the **eyes** and optic regions of the brain are unusually well developed. The eyes of birds occupy a large portion of the head, and both eyes together are often heavier than the brain. The visual acuity of birds, that is, their ability to distinguish objects as they become smaller and closer together, is several times as great as that of man. The ability to accommodate rapidly is also well developed in birds' eyes, for birds must change quickly from distant to near vision as they maneuver among the branches of a tree or swoop down to the ground from a considerable height. Muscular coordination is also very important in the bird way of life, and the **cerebellum** is correspondingly well developed. The **cerebral hemispheres** are large; however, their size is not a result of the expansion of the surface cortex, as it is in mammals, but rather the enlargement of a more deeply situated mass of gray matter, the **corpus striatum.**

24.3
The Origin and Evolution of Birds

One might infer simply from the structure of modern birds that they have evolved from archosaurian reptiles, but we need not stretch our inferences, for three specimens of a fossil bird are known that are clearly intermediate between archosaurs and modern birds. The fossils are preserved with remarkable detail in a fine-grained, lithographic limestone from Jurassic deposits in Bavaria.

Archaeopteryx lithographica (Fig. 24.16*A*) was about the size of a crow. Its skeleton is reptilian in having toothed jaws, no fusion of trunk or sacral vertebrae, a long tail, and a poorly developed sternum. Birdlike tendencies are evident in the enlarged orbits, some expansion of the brain case, and in the winglike structure of the hand. As in modern birds, the "hand" is elongated and only three "fingers" are present; however, there is little fusion of bones and each finger bears a claw. If the skeleton alone were known, the creature would probably have been regarded as a peculiar archosaur, but it is evident that this was a primitive bird and not a reptile, for there are clear impressions of feathers (Fig. 37.1). The feathers would suggest that *Archaeopteryx* was active and warm-blooded. The ratio of its wing surface to its body size, together with the poorly developed sternum, indicates that it was at best a weak flier. These most primitive birds are placed in the subclass **Archaeornithes.**

We, of course, do not know just how flight evolved in the ancestors of *Archaeopteryx*, but the early stages in the evolution of flight must have been adaptive in some way, even though the "proavis" would not at first have been able to fly. It is possible that the ancestors of birds were becoming more active, and possibly warm-blooded, and feathers may have first been of value in helping to conserve body heat. Given feathers, their enlargement along the posterior margin of the forelimb and tail may have conferred some stability in running rapidly along the ground, or even in rudimentary gliding from low branches. Thus structures originally of value in one way may have attained a certain threshold of size which enabled them to perform a different function. Complex organs such as feathers and wings could have evolved in this manner and could have been adaptive at all stages of their evolution.

The next group of fossil birds have been found in Cretaceous deposits. These birds had lost the long reptilian tail, had evolved a well-developed sternum and were modern in many other ways. A true pygostyle had not yet evolved, and teeth were present in at least certain species. There are clear indications of teeth in fossils of *Hesperornis* (Fig. 24.16*B*), a large diving species with powerful hind legs and vestigial wings. The nature of the jaws of *Ichthyornis*, which was a tern-sized flying species, is uncertain. Marsh, who described it

Figure 24.16 Extinct birds. *A*, A restoration of *Archaeopteryx*, the earliest known bird; *B*, a restoration of *Hesperornis*, a large diving bird of the Cretaceous. (*A* from Heilmann; *B* courtesy of the American Museum of Natural History.)

in 1880, considered that a toothed lower jaw, which was found in close association with the rest of the fossil, belonged to it. More recently, Gregory has identified the lower jaw as belonging to a small marine lizard. Although they are placed in the subclass **Neornithes** along with modern birds, the more primitive nature of these Cretaceous species is recognized by placing them in a distinct superorder—the **Odontognathae.**

All later birds have lost the reptilian teeth, but a few (superorder **Palaeognathae**) retain a somewhat reptilian palate, whereas others (superorder **Neognathae**) have a more specialized palatal structure. Living paleognathous birds are for the most part ground-dwelling, flightless species, such as the ostriches of Africa, the rheas of South America, the cassowaries of Australia and the peculiar kiwi of New Zealand (Fig. 24.17). The legs are well developed and powerful, the wings vestigial, and the feathers do not have hooklets. Presumably, these birds evolved from flying ancestors but readapted to a terrestrial mode of life in areas where there were an abundant food supply upon the ground and few competitors or enemies. The ancestry of certain of them can be traced back to the early Cenozoic era. A number of large ground-dwelling neognathous birds also lived then, which suggests that there might have been a competition at this time between birds and early mammals for the conquest of the land surface, which had recently, geologically speaking, been vacated by the large reptiles. Mammals won, and only a few ground-dwelling birds survived.

All other birds, including the vast majority of living species, are neognathous types. They have been very successful and have adapted to numerous habitats and modes of life (Fig. 24.18). Some, including the loons, ducks and gulls, are aquatic as well as good fliers. Other aquatic species, such as the penguins, have lost their ability to fly, and their wings are modified as paddles for swimming under water. The herons, cranes and coots have become specialized for a wading, marsh-dwelling mode of life. Hawks, eagles and owls are birds of prey. The grouse, pheasants and fowl are predominantly terrestrial forms, though they can fly short distances, and the perching and songbirds are well adapted for life in the trees. Twenty-three orders of neognathous birds are recognized (cf. synopsis at the end of this chapter). The songbirds are members of the order **Passeriformes.**

Figure 24.17 Representative paleognathous birds. *A*, Ostrich; *B*, a kiwi with its relatively huge egg. (*A* from Grzimek, B., in Natural History, Vol. LXX, No. 1; *B* courtesy of the American Museum of Natural History.)

Figure 24.18 A group of neognathous birds. *A*, Penguins use their modified wings as flippers; *B*, courtship of albatrosses; *C*, the young cormorant has to reach into the throat of its parent to get its food; *D*, an American egret, or heron, a wading bird; *E*, barn owl strikes; *F*, noddy terns on nest. (*A* courtesy of Smithsonian Institute; *B* courtesy of Lt. Col. N. Rankin; *C*, photo by L. W. Walker from National Audubon Society; *D* and *F* courtesy American Museum of Natural History; *E* from Payne, R. S., and Drury, W. H., Jr., in Natural History, Vol. LXVII, No. 6.)

24.4
The Bird Way of Life

Man has learned more about the habits of birds and their way of life than about most members of other classes, for he has long been fascinated by these colorful creatures that lead such intense and active lives. A few of their more interesting features are considered below.

Food Getting. Birds have a high rate of metabolism and must obtain large quantities of food to support it. During most of their waking hours they are on the lookout for seeds, insects, worms, or whatever makes up their diet. Crows and some other birds eat a variety of food, both plant and animal, but many birds have become specialists and have evolved adaptations for utilizing particular types of food. Their bills are modified accordingly, and one can often tell from this alone the nature of their food and how they get it (Fig. 40.1). Finches have short heavy bills well suited for picking up and breaking open seeds. The hooked beak of hawks s ideal for tearing apart small animals that they have seized with their powerful talons. Herons use their long sharp bills for spearing fish and frogs, which they deftly flip into their mouths. The length and shape of hummingbirds' bills are correlated with the structure of the flowers from which they extract nectar. Whippoorwills and swallows fly about in the evening catching insects with their gaping mouths. Bristle-like feathers at the base of the bill help them to catch their prey. When feeding, the skimmer flies just above the ocean with its elongated lower jaw skimming the surface. Any fish or other organisms that are hit are flicked into its open mouth. The woodcock's long and sensitive bill is adapted for probing for worms in the soft ground. The woodcock can open the tip of its bill slightly to grasp a worm without opening the rest of the mouth!

Support and Locomotion. Flight in its various forms is, of course, an important means of bird locomotion. When not flying, most birds support themselves and move about on their hind legs. The foot has under-

gone a variety of modifications as the bird has become adapted to special modes of life (Fig. 24.19). The foot and toes become particularly sturdy in ground-dwelling species, and the power of grasping is especially well developed in such perching specialists as our songbirds. In perching birds, the tendons of the foot are so arranged that the weight of the body automatically causes the toes to flex and grasp the perch when the bird alights upon a branch. The woodpeckers have sharp claws, and the fourth toe is turned backward with the first to form a foot ideally suited for clinging onto the sides of trees. Swimming birds have a web stretching between certain of their toes—the three anterior toes in loons, albatrosses, ducks, gulls and many others; all four toes in pelicans, cormorants and their relatives. The marsh-dwelling jacana of the tropics has a foot with exceedingly long toes and claws that enable it to scamper across lily pads and other floating vegetation. Swifts and hummingbirds have very small feet barely strong enough to grasp a perch. These birds spend most of their time on the wing and almost never alight on the ground.

Reproduction. Birds have developed elaborate behavioral patterns and structural modifications associated with reproduction,

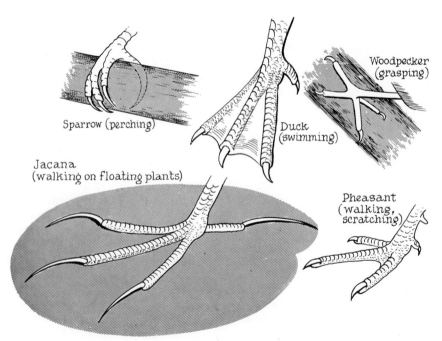

Figure 24.19 Adaptations of the feet of birds.

many of which have been carefully studied. For example, in most of the common species each male bird stakes out for himself a well-delineated nesting **territory** which he vigorously defends against all rivals and into which he hopes to attract a female. The distinctive song of the male during the breeding season advertises the territory to females of the appropriate species and warns rival males to stay away. The brilliant plumage of the male birds plays a similar role, serving both to warn rivals and to attract and stimulate females. Advantages of territorial organization of breeding birds are that it prevents overcrowding and ensures a reasonably uniform distribution of mating pairs in the inhabitable area. This helps to get and to keep the parent birds together and facilitates finding nesting materials and food without going far afield.

Once a female has been attracted to the territory, courtship begins. Sometimes it is accompanied by elaborate display rituals which apparently serve as a sexual stimulant leading to nest-building and copulation (Fig. 24.18*B*). A brief cloacal apposition is sufficient to transfer sperm to the female reproductive tract; only a few male birds, chiefly primitive species, retain the reptilian copulatory organ. Further courtship and copulation may occur after the eggs have been fertilized and laid. Presumably this aids in keeping the parents together for the tasks of incubating the eggs and caring for the young. Young chickens and some other birds are **precocial.** They are covered with down and can run about and feed for themselves when hatched. But most of our songbirds are **altricial** and are naked and helpless when they first emerge from the eggs. Such birds need close parental care to supply food and warmth during the critical period of their infancy. Either or both parents care for the young. As Professor Young, of University College, London, has so aptly put it, "In birds, as in man, the 'procreation of children' is not accomplished by a single act of fertilization."

Migration. The capture of sufficient food and the reproductive process are the motivations responsible for most of birds' activities. Some birds are able to fill all their needs in the general area in which they were hatched, but others have taken full advantage of their power of flight and go considerable distances in their search for favorable nesting sites and feeding areas. During much of the year the food supply in a given area is adequate to sustain a population of reasonable size. The food available may not suffice, however, during the breeding season when the increased activity of the birds increases their food requirements and when the population is more than doubling. Spreading out into new areas at this time has some advantage and permits a larger bird population. Although the reasons for the evolution of migration are uncertain, the search for food may have been a factor in the tendency for many birds to migrate north in the summer. There is a large land mass in the north and, during the summer at least, this area is rich in food. The tendency to return south as the weather becomes inclement in the autumn might be correlated with the reduction of the food supply; it apparently is in the case of certain insect-eating species, but others migrate before there is any food shortage. The glaciation of large parts of the Northern Hemisphere during the great Ice Ages may have been an additional factor in the evolution of the migratory habit. It has been proposed that seasonal movements appeared first as a conditioned response to environmental changes. This behavioral pattern and any genetic variation in this direction were favored by natural selection and gradually it became hereditary.

The pattern of migration is quite regular for each species, for it begins at very nearly the same time each year. Day length, weather conditions and food supply affect the onset of migration in various species. In most, day length is the major factor, and it appears to operate by affecting gonad size. As day length increases in the spring, the gonads enlarge, and many birds migrate north. Opposite changes occur in the autumn. Rowan, who first studied these phenomena in the 20's and 30's, attributed recrudescence of the gonads to the increased activity that resulted from longer days, but more recently Mewaldt and others have shown that, for certain species at least, increased activity without increased day length does not cause gonad enlargement.

Most birds migrate at night, stopping to feed and rest during the day. Some may fly several hundred miles during a single night, but then may rest for several days. The northward advance of these birds in the spring averages about 20 to 25 miles per day. Many species tend to follow the advance of certain temperature lines, or isotherms (Fig. 24.20). The length of migration and the

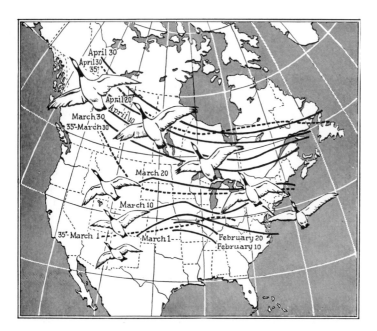

Figure 24.20 The northward migration of the Canada goose keeps pace with spring, following the isotherm of 35° F. (Modified after Lincoln.)

route taken are very consistent for each type of bird but vary with the species. The Canada goose winters in the United States from the Great Lakes south, breeds in Canada as far north as the arctic coast, and migrates along a broad front between the two areas. The scarlet tanager winters in parts of South America and breeds in the area from Nova Scotia, southern Quebec and southern Manitoba south to South Carolina, northern Georgia, northern Alabama and Kansas. In contrast to the Canada goose, it has a narrow migration route, which extends through southern Central America and then across the center of the Gulf of Mexico, passing between Yucatan and Cuba. The longest migration is that of the arctic tern; some of these birds travel 25,000 miles in a year. This species breeds in the Arctic, then follows the coast line of Europe and Africa to its winter quarters in the South Atlantic.

The season, speed and routes of migration have been carefully described for most species of birds, but how birds navigate and find their way during their migrations remains one of the intriguing, incompletely solved problems of animal behavior. Obviously, the birds must know where they are going; there must be some feature of the environment that is related to the goal of the bird; and the bird must have some way of perceiving this feature. Theories of navigation based on magnetic fields of the earth,

visual landmarks, celestial points of reference and other aspects of the environment have been proposed, but no single one explains all of the facts. The magnetic field theory is weakened by our inability to demonstrate that birds are sensitive to magnetic fields. Many migration routes parallel mountain ranges, coast lines and other major physiographic features, which suggests that visual landmarks are being used. Dr. Griffin of Harvard University, in a study of the related problem of homing, released sea birds (gannets) in unknown territory 100 miles or more inland from their nests and followed their return from an airplane. The birds did not head straight for home, but flew in widening circles over large areas, apparently in an exploratory fashion, until they came into familiar territory, and then they headed directly home. Dr. Matthews of Cambridge University believes that visual landmarks play a minor role and has suggested that birds use the position of the sun, a sense of time, and a knowledge of the position of the sun at different times at their destination to determine their position and find their way. This would be analogous to a mariner using a sextant, a chronometer and a knowledge of latitude and longitude. The fact that birds released in unfamiliar territory find their way home better on sunny days than on overcast days lends support to his hypothesis. Recent work by Sauer suggests that night flying migrants use the star pattern to navigate. Migrating birds caught in the spring and caged so they can see the sky become restless at night and tend to face in a northerly direction. In a planetarium, they orient themselves to the north of the artificial sky regardless of the direction of the true sky. We have learned a great deal about migration, but more observations and experiments will be necessary before the full story is known.

SYNOPSIS OF BIRDS

CLASS AVES. The birds. Warm-blooded, typically flying vertebrates covered with feathers.

†**Subclass 1. Archaeornithes.** Ancestral birds retaining many reptilian features including jaws with teeth, long tail, and three unfused fingers, each bearing a claw. *Archaeopteryx.*

Subclass 2. Neornithes. Birds with a reduced number of caudal vertebrae; wing composed of three highly modified fingers partly fused together.

†**Superorder 1. Odontognathae.** Cretaceous birds; some, at least, retaining teeth.

Superorder 2. Palaeognathae. Modern toothless birds with a primitive palate. Most are flightless.

Order 1. Tinamiformes. Tinamous. Largely a ground-dwelling group, but with weak powers of flight; sternum retains a keel. *Tinamus.*

Order 2. Struthioniformes. Ostriches. Huge flightless birds with small wings; unkeeled sternum; head and neck largely devoid of feathers; large powerful legs with only two toes. Africa and western Asia, *Struthio.*

Order 3. Rheiformes. Rheas. Large flightless birds with unkeeled sternum; head and neck feathered; heavy legs with three toes. South America, *Rhea.*

Order 4. Casuariformis. Cassowaries and emus. Large flightless birds with small wings and unkeeled sternum; long hairlike feathers with long aftershaft; heavy legs with three toes. New Guinea and Australia, *Casuarius.*

†*Order 5. Aepyornithiformes.* Elephant birds. Large flightless birds of Africa and Madagascar; became extinct in historic times; laid largest eggs known, 33 x 23 cm. *Aepyornis.*

†*Order 6. Dinornithiformes.* Moas. Largest of the flightless birds, attained a height of 3 meters. Became extinct about 700 years ago. New Zealand, *Dinornis.*

Order 7. Apterygiformes. Kiwis. Modest-sized flightless birds with unkeeled sternum and vestigial wings; four toes on feet; long bill with nostrils near the tip, used in probing soft ground for food. New Zealand, *Apteryx.*

Superorder 3. Neognathae. Modern birds with a less reptilian palate.

Order 1. Gaviformes. Loons. Legs located far back on the body; webbed feet; reduced tail; long, compressed and sharply pointed bill; very good divers. The common loon, *Gavia.*

Order 2. Podicipediformes. Grebes. Legs located far back on the body; lobate toes; reduced tail; very good divers. Eared grebe, *Colymbus.*

Order 3. Procellariiformes. Albatrosses, shearwaters, fulmars, petrels, tropic birds. Webbed feet; fourth toe vestigial; long narrow wings; tubular nostrils. The petrel, *Oceanodroma.*

Order 4. Sphenisciformes. Penguins. Flightless oceanic birds with four anteriorly directed toes with a web between three of them; wings modified as paddles; excellent divers. The group probably evolved from one of the groups of oceanic birds; confined to the southern hemisphere, chiefly Antarctica. The emperor penguin, *Aptenodytes.*

Order 5. Pelecaniformes. Pelicans, gannets, cormorants, water-turkey, man-o-war bird. Totipalmate swimmers with four toes included in the webbed foot; tendency for the development of a gular sac. The pelican, *Pelecanus.*

---

†Extinct.

Order 6. Ciconiiformes. Herons, bitterns, storks, ibises, flamingos. Long-legged and long-necked wading birds; feet broad, but usually not webbed; the portion of the head between the eye and nostril (the lores) usually devoid of feathers. Great blue heron, *Ardea.*

Order 7. Anseriformes. Ducks, geese, swans. Short-legged, web-footed swimming and diving birds; bill usually broad and flat with transverse horny ridges adapted for filtering mud. The mallard, *Anas;* white-fronted goose, *Anser.*

Order 8. Falconiformes. Vultures, kites, hawks, falcons, eagles. Diurnal birds of prey with strong, hooked bill; sharp, curved talons. Cooper's hawk, *Accipiter;* duck hawk, *Falco.*

Order 9. Galliformes. Grouse, quails, partridges, pheasants, turkeys, chickens. Seed- and plant-eating, largely ground-dwelling birds; short stout bill; heavy feet with short strong claws, adapted for running and scratching in the ground; wings relatively short. The chicken, *Gallus.*

Order 10. Ralliformes. Cranes, rails, gallinules, coots. Marsh birds; feet not webbed, but toes sometimes lobed; legs elongate in some groups; lores feathered. Virginia rail, *Rallus.*

†**Order 11. Diatrymiformes.** Large flightless birds of the early Cenozoic. *Diatryma.*

Order 12. Charadriiformes. Plovers, woodcock, snipe, sandpipers, stilts, phalaropes, gulls, terns, skimmers, auks, puffins. A diverse group of shore birds. The killdeer, *Charadrius.*

Order 13. Columbiformes. Pigeons, doves. Short slender bill with a fleshy cere at its base overhanging the slitlike nostrils; short legs. The domestic pigeon, *Columba.*

Order 14. Psittaciformes. Parrots. Feet adapted for grasping, with fourth toe capable of being turned back beside the first toe; bill heavy and hooked; often brilliantly colored plumage. Carolina parakeet, *Conurus.*

Order 15. Cuculiformes. Cuckoos, road-runners. Foot zygodactylous with fourth toe permanently reversed beside the first; tail long. The cuckoo, *Cuculus.*

Order 16. Strigiformes. Owls. Nocturnal birds of prey with strong hooked bills; sharp, curved talons; feathers arranged as a facial disc around the large, forwardly turned eyes. The barred owls, *Strix.*

Order 17. Caprimulgiformes. Nighthawks, whippoorwills. Twilight flying birds with small bills, but large mouths surrounded by bristle-like feathers that help net insects; legs and feet small. The whippoorwill, *Caprimulgus.*

Order 18. Apodiformes. Swifts and hummingbirds. Fast flying birds with long narrow wings; legs and feet very small. The chimney swift, *Chaetura.*

Order 19. Coliiformes. The colies of Africa. Small birds with long tails; first and fourth toes can be turned posteriorly.

Order 20. Trogoniformes. Trogons. Short stout bill; small feet; often green, iridescent plumage. The coppery-tailed trogon, *Trogon.*

Order 21. Coraciiformes. Kingfishers. Strong sharp bill; foot syndactylous with third and fourth toes fused at their bases; feathers often forming a crest on the head. The belted kingfisher, *Megaceryle.*

Order 22. Piciformes. Woodpeckers and toucans. Bill chisel-like (woodpeckers) or very large (toucans); zygodactylous foot with fourth toe permanently turned posteriorly. The flicker, *Colaptes.*

Order 23. Passeriformes. The perching birds and songbirds. The largest order of birds, it includes the flycatchers, larks, swallows, crows, jays, chickadees, nuthatches, creepers, wrens, dippers, thrashers, thrushes, robins, bluebirds, kinglets, pipets, waxwings, shrikes, starlings, vireos, wood warblers, weaver finches, blackbirds, orioles, tanagers, finches, sparrows, etc. Foot adapted for perching; three toes in front opposed by one well-developed toe behind. The English sparrow, *Passer.*

QUESTIONS

1. Contrast homoiothermic and poikilothermic vertebrates.
2. How do wings support and propel a bird?
3. Describe a typical feather. In what ways is it adapted for flight?
4. Compare the structure of the wings of a pterosaur, bird and bat.
5. In what ways are the internal organs of birds adapted for flight?
6. How does *Archaeopteryx* differ from modern birds?
7. List some modifications of birds' bills and feet. How are these correlated with methods of feeding and locomotion?
8. What are the advantages to birds of nesting territories?
9. What factors may have been involved in the evolution of the migratory habit?

ANNOTATED REFERENCES

Allen, A. A.: The Book of Bird Life. 2nd ed. Princeton, D. Van Nostrand Co., 1961. An excellent account of bird ecology with extensive discussions of methods for the field study and observation of birds.

George, J. C. and A. J. Berger: Avian Myology. New York, Academic Press, 1966. A thorough account of the biochemistry, physiology and anatomy of bird muscles.

Gilliard, E. T.: Living Birds of the World. New York, Doubleday & Co., 1958. The major groups of birds are summarized and superbly illustrated.

Hertel, H.: Structure, Form, Movement. New York, Reinhold Publishing Corp., 1966. One section of this important book on animal locomotion is devoted to various aspects of bird flight.

Howard, E.: Territory in Bird Life. New York, Atheneum, 1964. A reprint of a classic book on bird behavior.

Peterson, R. T.: A Field Guide to the Birds. 2nd ed. Boston, Houghton Mifflin Co., 1947. The standard and widely used guide for the field identification of birds from the Great Plains to the East Coast.

Peterson, R. T.: A Field Guide to Western Birds. Revised ed. Boston, Houghton Mifflin Co., 1961. A companion to the preceding volume, covers the birds from the Pacific Coast to the western parts of the Great Plains.

Pettingill, O. S., Jr.: A Laboratory and Field Manual of Ornithology. 3rd ed. Minneapolis, Burgess Publishing Co., 1956. A manual on the structure, habits and ecology of birds for the serious student of ornithology.

Storer, J. H.: The Flight of Birds, Bloomfield Hills, Mich., Cranbrook Institute of Science, 1948. A very good analysis of the principles of flight and the flight of birds.

Sturkie, P. D.: Avian Physiology. 2nd ed. Ithaca, N. Y., Comstock Publishing Co., 1965. A very important source book; covers most aspects of avian physiology.

Van Tyne, J., and A. J. Berger: Fundamentals of Ornithology. New York, John Wiley & Sons, Inc., 1959. An important text for the serious student; emphasizes the groups of birds.

Welty, J. C.: The Life of Birds. Philadelphia, W. B. Saunders Co., 1962. A comprehensive one-volume work on all aspects of the biology of birds.

Wolfson, A. (Ed.): Recent studies in Avian Biology. Urbana, University of Illinois Press, 1955. Thirteen contributors have written authoritative chapters on many aspects of bird anatomy, physiology and ecology.

25

A HISTORY OF VERTEBRATES: MAMMALS

Cats, mice, pigs, men and the other familiar haired creatures belong to the class **Mammalia.** Mammals are the group of organisms to which the term "animal" is often restricted by laymen, though zoologists object to such a usage. A jaw joint between the dentary and squamosal bones, and the presence of three auditory ossicles within the middle ear are convenient osteologic features for distinguishing between mammals and the extinct mammal-like reptiles from which they evolved. Osteologic criteria are necessary in dealing with fossil material, but contemporary reptiles and mammals can be distinguished in many other ways. The presence of hair and mammary glands is the most obvious diagnostic feature of mammals, but these are only two reflections of more fundamental changes—increased activity and greater care of the young.

25.1
Characteristics of Mammals

Temperature Regulation. Birds as a group are the most active of all vertebrates, but mammals are a close second, and they are certainly the most active of the primarily terrestrial vertebrates. An active life naturally requires a high and rather constant rate of metabolism. Most mammals are also **homoiothermic,** but temperature regulation is somewhat different from that of birds. **Hair,** rather than feathers, forms an insulating layer over the body surface of most mammals that en-

traps air and reduces heat loss. When the surrounding temperature drops, tiny muscles associated with the hairs contract, pull them more erect, and increase the effective thickness of the insulating layer. Heat production may also be increased by shivering. Heat is dissipated, when necessary, by an increased blood flow through the skin and by the evaporation of water. Many mammals lose water from the body surface in the form of sweat, secreted by **sweat glands,** but mammals such as dogs, that have few sweat glands, pant vigorously and lose water from the mouth and respiratory passages. Birds can cool themselves by the evaporation of water from the respiratory tract, but none has evolved sweat glands.

The temperature regulatory mechanism is situated in a part of the brain known as the hypothalamus (p. 540). It contains elements sensitive to changes in body temperature, and it also integrates reflexes initiated by thermal receptors in the skin.

Although mammals in general are homoiothermic, there are differences among them in their capacity to regulate body temperature. As might be expected this capacity is less developed among some of the more primitive groups such as the egg-laying monotremes and the pouched marsupials than among higher mammals. The Central American opossum (a marsupial), for example, can nearly stabilize its body temperature over an external temperature range of 10° to 30° C., but loses control of body temperature, and in effect becomes a poikilotherm, when external temperatures exceed 30° C. (Fig. 25.1). It can also better maintain a constant body temperature during its period of nocturnal activity than when it is sleeping during the day. Mammals of this type are sometimes described as **heterothermic.**

Many higher mammals also have better control over their body temperature during periods of activity than when sleeping, or when going into a state of dormancy. Bats can maintain their body temperature at a fairly high and constant level at night, but it drops to nearly that of their surroundings during the day when they are roosting. Many insectivores, bats and rodents go into a period of dormancy known as **hibernation** during the winter months. They lose considerable control over the regulatory mechanism of body temperature, and their temperature drops close to the ambient temperature. Metabolism is very low during hibernation, yet it is sufficient to sustain life and to keep the body from freezing. There are certain advantages to diurnal or seasonal dormancy accompanied by a fall of body temperature, especially for a small homoiotherm. Small mammals have a relatively higher rate of metabolism than large ones because they have more surface area in proportion to their mass. They lose a great deal of heat through their surface areas and must consume much food just to maintain body temperature. In many regions insects and certain types of plant food are not available in quantity during the winter. If an animal can permit its

body temperature to drop, it can get by on less food, or even on the food reserves within its body. Hibernation in mammals should not be confused with hibernation in certain poikilotherms (p. 386). Body temperature always fluctuates with ambient temperatures in poikilotherms, and when it is low enough the animals naturally are inactive. In a warm-blooded animal, a normally high and constant body temperature is permitted to drop; in a sense, the "thermostat" in the hypothalamus is turned down. Physiologic adjustments are more complex in this situation.

Many other features of mammals relate to their generally high rate of metabolism.

Metabolic Systems. The dentition of mammals enables them to obtain and handle a wide variety of foods. Their teeth are not all the same shape, as is generally the case in reptiles, but are differentiated into various types (Fig. 25.2). Chisel-shaped **incisors** are present at the front of each jaw and are used for nipping and cropping. Next is a single **canine** tooth, which is primitively a long, sharp tooth, useful in attacking and stabbing prey, or in defense. A series of **premolars** and **molars** follow the canine. These teeth tear, crush and grind up the food. In primitive mammals, the premolars are sharper than the molars and have more of a tearing function. A primitive placental mammal, such as an insectivore (Fig. 25.2), has three incisors, one canine, four premolars and three molars in each side of the upper and lower jaw. This can be expressed as a dental formula: $I\frac{3}{3}$, $C\frac{1}{1}$, $Pm\frac{4}{4}$, $M\frac{3}{3}$. No placental mammal has more teeth than this, but the number of teeth is reduced in many groups. Man, for example, has the dental formula of $I\frac{2}{2}$, $C\frac{1}{1}$, $Pm\frac{2}{2}$, $M\frac{3}{3}$. Considerable variation also occurs in the structure of particular teeth in the different groups, as we shall see.

Most mammals do not swallow their food whole but break it up mechanically with their teeth and mix it with saliva which, in addition to lubricating the food, usually contains an enzyme that begins the digestion of carbohydrates. Digestion is completed in the stomach and intestinal region. Numerous microscopic villi line the small intestine, as they do in birds, and increase the surface area available for absorption (Fig. 25.3).

A greater exchange of oxygen and carbon dioxide is made possible by a many-fold increase in the respiratory surface of the lungs and by improved methods of ventilation

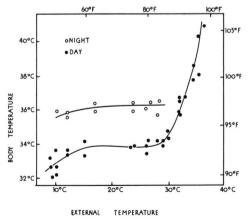

Figure 25.1 A graph showing relationship of body temperature to external temperature in a nocturnally active Central American opossum, *Metachirus*. (From Morrison.)

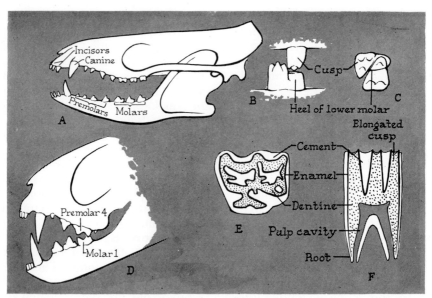

Figure 25.2 Teeth of mammals. *A*, The relatively unspecialized teeth of a primitive insectivore; *B* and *C*, lateral and crown views of the left upper and lower molars of an insectivore to show their occlusion; *D*, the stabbing and cutting teeth of a cat; *E* and *F*, a crown view and a vertical section through the left upper molar of a horse to show its adaptation for crushing and grinding.

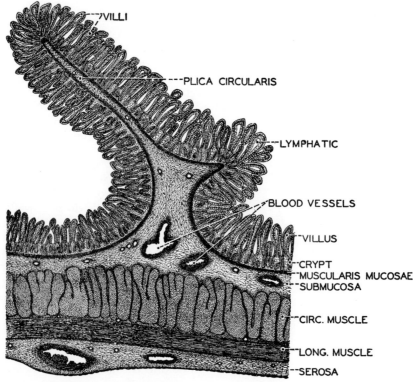

Figure 25.3 A longitudinal section of a portion of a mammalian small intestine. The internal surface area is greatly increased by numerous villi. (From Neal and Rand.)

(Fig. 27.10). The increase in surface is accomplished by a subdivision of the air passages within the lung so that all end in clusters of thin-walled sacs (**alveoli**) whose walls contain a dense capillary network. It has been estimated that the respiratory surface of the human lungs is between 50 and 100 square meters, or 25 to 50 times the surface area of the body. Birds also have a large respiratory surface, but their lungs are more compact organs and the respiratory surface may not be relatively so great as in mammals. Birds and mammals differ in the method of ventilation. Air must be moved in and out of blind sacs in mammalian lungs, whereas there can be a through draft in avian lungs. The lungs of birds are more efficient as gas exchangers, for the air in the air capillaries contains relatively more oxygen than the somewhat stale air in the alveoli, but the more thorough ventilation of avian lungs probably results in a greater loss of body water via this route.

The mechanics for the ventilation of mammalian lungs are more efficient than those of amphibians and reptiles. One important factor in improved ventilation has been the evolution of a muscular **diaphragm** whose contractions, together with a forward movement of the ribs, expand the chest cavity and draw air into the lungs. Another factor has been the evolution of a **secondary palate,** a horizontal partition of bone and flesh in the roof of the mouth that separates the air and food passages in this region (Fig. 25.4). In lower tetrapods the nasal cavities lead directly into the front of the mouth, but in mammals they open more posteriorly into the pharynx. The secondary palate permits nearly continuous breathing, which is certainly a desirable attribute for organisms with a high rate of metabolism. Mammals can manipulate food in their mouths, and breathing need be interrupted only momentarily when the food is swallowed, and in some species not even then (young of opossum, p. 435).

Mammals, like birds, have evolved an efficient system of internal transport of materials between sites of intake, utilization and excretion. Their heart is completely divided internally so there is no mixing of venous and arterial blood. Venous blood coming from the body and going to the lungs passes through the right atrium and right ventricle, while arterial blood coming from the lungs and going to the body passes through the left atrium and ventricle. Increased blood pressure also makes for a more rapid and efficient circulation.

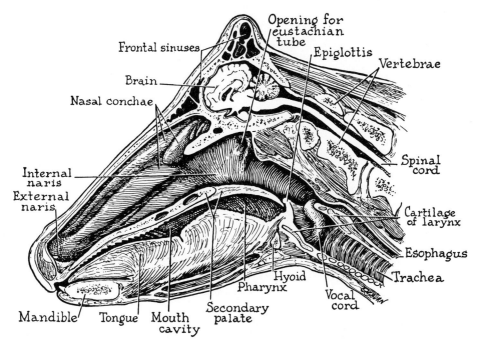

Figure 25.4   A sagittal section of the head of a cow showing the relationship between the digestive and respiratory systems. (Modified after Sisson and Grossman.)

Nitrogenous wastes from the breakdown of proteins and nucleic acids must be eliminated without an excessive loss of body water. In mammals most of the nitrogenous wastes are eliminated in the form of **urea,** which is more soluble and requires more water for its removal than does the uric acid excreted by some reptiles and birds. Approximately 99 per cent of the water that starts down the kidney tubules is later reabsorbed, so that the net loss of water in these animals is minimal. The generally high metabolic rate of mammals results in the formation of a large amount of wastes to be eliminated. An increase in blood pressure, and hence in blood flow through the kidney, and an increase in the number of kidney tubules have enabled mammals to increase the rate of excretion.

Locomotion and Coordination. Mammals also move about with greater agility than lower tetrapods. Their appendages ex-

tend directly down to the ground in the vertical plane, instead of out from the body in the horizontal plane as the proximal segment of the limb does in amphibians and most reptiles. This improves the effectiveness of the limbs in support and permits them to move rapidly. A firmer support is also provided for the pelvic girdle and hind limbs, because most mammals have three sacral vertebrae in contrast to the two of most reptiles. Arboreal species use the tail for balancing, and it plays a major role in the propulsion of aquatic mammals such as the whales, but in most mammals it has lost its primitive role in locomotion and is frequently reduced in size. Further details of the mammalian skeleton, and of other organ systems, will be emphasized in succeeding chapters but, in short, the whole skeleton reflects the increased activity and agility.

The increased speed of locomotion also en-

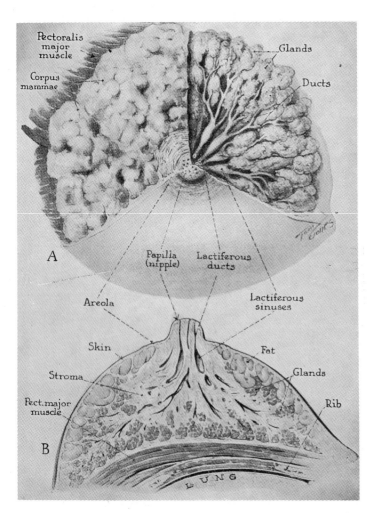

Figure 25.5 *A,* Successive stages of the dissection of the mammary gland of a lactating human being, are shown clockwise. *B,* Vertical section through the nipple of a mammary gland. (From King and Showers: Human Anatomy and Physiology, 5th ed.; courtesy of S. H. Camp Co.)

tailed changes in the neuromuscular apparatus. Shifts in many of the muscles concerned with support and locomotion are correlated with the new limb posture. Moreover, the muscular system of mammals is considerably more elaborate than that of reptiles, for many primitive muscles have been subdivided. This, together with a more highly developed nervous system, permits more varied responses and adjustments to environmental conditions.

Care of the Young. The evolution by reptiles of the cleidoic egg was a successful adjustment to terrestrial reproduction so long as vertebrates were cold-blooded. However, embryos that are to develop into homoiothermic adults must apparently have a warm, constant temperature to develop normally, so birds and mammals cannot lay eggs and then ignore them. Birds lay cleidoic eggs but incubate them by sitting on them, and one group of primitive mammals, which includes the duckbilled platypus of Australia, does the same. All other mammals are viviparous. The eggs are retained within a specialized region of the female reproductive tract, the **uterus,** and the young are born as miniature adults.

All of the extraembryonic membranes characteristic of reptiles are present in viviparous mammals, but albuminous materials are not ordinarily secreted about the egg. The allantois, or in a few species the yolk sac, unites with the chorion, thereby carrying the fetal blood vessels over to this outermost membrane. The vascularized chorion unites in varying degrees with the uterine lining to form a **placenta,** in which fetal and maternal blood streams come close together, though they remain separated by some layers of tissue (Fig. 29.10). The embryo derives its food and oxygen and eliminates its carbon dioxide and nitrogenous wastes across these membranes.

Different species of mammals are born at different stages of maturity. Certain mice, for example, are extremely **altricial,** being born naked and with closed eyes and plugged ears. Newborn deer and other large herbivores are quite **precocial** and can run about and largely care for themselves. But regardless of maturity at birth, all newborn mammals feed upon milk secreted by specialized **mammary glands** of the female (Fig. 25.5). In such primitive mammals as the platypus

(Fig. 25.6*A*), the milk is discharged onto the hairs and the young lap it up, but in other mammals, nipples or teats are associated with the glands and the young are suckled. When the young finally leave their mother, they are at a relatively advanced stage of development and are equipped to care for themselves.

25.2
Primitive Mammals

Monotremes. The most primitive mammals are the platypus (*Ornithorhynchus*) and its close relative, the spiny anteater (*Tachyglossus*) (Fig. 25.6*A* and *B*). In addition to the egg-laying habit, these mammals retain many other reptilian characteristics, including a cloaca. The ordinal name for the group, **Monotremata,** refers to the presence of a single opening for the discharge of feces, excretory and genital products. In other mammals the cloaca has become divided, and the opening of the intestine, the **anus,** is separate from that of the urogenital ducts.

Monotremes are curious animals that have survived to the present only because they have been isolated from serious competition in the Australian region. The platypus is a semiaquatic species with webbed feet, short hairs and a bill like a duck's used in grubbing in the mud for food. Spiny anteaters have large claws and a long beak adapted for feeding upon ants and termites. The animal can burrow very effectively with its claws, completely burying itself even in fairly hard ground in a few minutes. Many of its hairs are modified as quills.

When the first skins of the platypus were shipped to Europe in the late eighteenth century, many zoologists viewed them as skillful fakes such as the then current Chinese mermaids (the forepart of a monkey sewn onto the tail of a fish). After the authenticity of the platypus was established, a long controversy ensued as to whether to consider it a reptile or a mammal. Monotremes were finally regarded as mammals, but as such primitive and unusual ones that they are placed in a separate subclass—the **Prototheria.** Many investigators now believe that monotremes evolved from mammal-like reptiles earlier than, and independently of, the other mammals. If this be true, mammals have had a polyphyletic rather than a common evolu-

Figure 25.6 Monotremes and marsupials. *A*, The duckbilled platypus; *B*, the spiny anteater; *C*, opossum and young; *D*, koala bear; *E*, kangaroo. The platypus and anteater are monotremes; the others are marsupials. (*A* and *B* courtesy of the New York Zoological Society; *C* and *D* courtesy of American Museum of Natural History; *E* from Australian News and Information Bureau.)

tionary origin (Fig. 23.4). A corollary of such a view is that hair and mammary glands either evolved independently in monotremes and other mammals or were attributes of the mammal-like reptiles.

Marsupials. Other mammals living to-day are believed to have had a common origin and are placed in the subclass **Theria.** Therian mammals were present in the last half of the Mesozoic era, but they did not become abundant until the extinction of the ruling reptiles. During the Cenozoic, they increased rapidly, radiated widely, and became the dominant terrestrial vertebrates.

Contemporary therians fall into two infra-classes: (1) the **Metatheria,** which includes the opossum, kangaroo and other pouched mammals of the order **Marsupialia** (Fig.

25.6), and (2) the **Eutheria,** or true placental mammals. Both groups are viviparous, though the placental arrangements of marsupials is less effective than that of eutherians. In most marsupials the extraembryonic membranes, and chiefly the yolk sac, simply absorb a "uterine milk" secreted by the mother. There is no intimate union between the extraembryonic membranes and the uterine lining as there is in most eutherians.

Marsupials are born in what we would regard as a very premature stage. Their front legs, however, are well developed at birth, and the young pull themselves into a **marsupium,** or pouch, on the belly of the mother, attach to a nipple, and there complete their development. An opossum, for example, is born after only 13 days gestation, but it continues its development in the pouch until it is about 70 days old. It has long been believed that they are too immature to suck, and that milk is squirted from the mammary glands into their mouths. But in his fascinating book on "'Possums," Hartman relegates this notion to the limbo of false myths and cites careful experiments and observations proving that the young do indeed suck. A forward extension of the tubular epiglottis dorsal to the secondary palate completely separates the digestive and respiratory tracts, and breathing and feeding can take place concurrently.

Marsupials were world-wide during the early Cenozoic, but as eutherians began to spread out, marsupials became restricted. They have been most successful in those parts of the world where they have been isolated from competition with eutherians. They are the dominant type of mammal in Australia, have undergone an adaptive radiation and have become specialized for many modes of life. There are carnivorous marsupials such as the Tasmanian wolf, ant-eating types, molelike types, semiarboreal phalangers and koala bears (the original "Teddy-bear"), plains-dwelling kangaroos and rabbit-like bandicoots. In contrast, the only marsupial present in North America is the semiarboreal opossum.

25.3
Adaptive Radiation of Eutherians

The eutherians, or placental mammals as they are frequently called, are the most successful mammals in all the parts of the world

that they have reached. They have radiated widely and adapted to nearly every conceivable ecologic niche upon the land. Others have readapted successfully to an aquatic mode of life, and some have evolved true flight.

Insectivores. The most primitive eutherians, that is, the stem group from which the other lines of descent evolved, were rather generalized, insect-eating types of the order **Insectivora.** Among modern types are the shrews, moles and the European hedgehog (Fig. 25.7). All are small mammals with an unspecialized limb structure; five clawed toes are retained and the entire foot is placed flat upon the ground, a posture termed **plantigrade** (Fig. 25.12). They have a primitive dentition in which the molar teeth bear sharp cusps well adapted for feeding upon insects and other small invertebrates. The group includes the smallest of all known mammals—one species of shrew which as an adult weighs no more than 2 grams!

Flying Mammals. Bats, order **Chiroptera,** are closely related to this stem group and are sometimes characterized as flying insectivores. As in other flying vertebrates, the pectoral appendages have been transformed into wings. Bat wings are structurally closer to those of pterosaurs than to birds' wings, for the flying surface is a leathery membrane, but the wing of a bat is supported by four elongated fingers (the second to fifth) rather than by a single one as in the pterosaur. The wing membrane attaches onto the hind leg and, in some bats, the tail is included in the membrane. The first finger is free of the wing, bears a small claw and is used for grasping and clinging. The hind legs are small and are of little use upon the ground, but they, too, are effective grasping organs and are used for clinging to a perch from which the bats hang upside down when at rest.

Our familiar bats are insect eaters that fly about at dusk in search of their prey, but bats have diverged considerably in their feeding habits. Among the food that various groups are specialized to take are fruit, pollen and nectar, blood (vampire bats), small mammals and birds, and fish. Fish-eating bats catch their prey near the surface of the water by means of hooked claws on their rather powerful feet.

Fruit-eating bats find their food primarily by eyesight, but most of the others rely to a

Figure 25.7 *A,* A shrew eats more than its own weight every day; *B,* a mole in its burrow; *C,* a bat with its baby; *D,* the giant anteater. (*A* from Conoway, C. H., in Natural History, Vol. LXVIII, No. 10; *B, C* and *D* courtesy of the American Museum of Natural History.)

greater or lesser extent on a system of echo-location. As early as 1794, Spallanzani observed that a blinded bat could find its way about but that one in which the ears had been plugged was helpless. Using sensitive electronic apparatus, Griffin and other recent investigators have shown that our familiar bats of the family Vespertilionidae emit a steady stream of ultrasonic pulses as they fly about. These range from 25,000 to 120,000 cycles per second, well above our threshold of hearing. High frequency sounds of this type have small wave lengths, hence can produce sharp echoes from small objects. Each pulse lasts 1 to 4 milliseconds. During normal flight, pulses are emitted at a rate of about 10 per second, but as the bat gets close to an insect the rate increases to 100 per second. An interesting feature of the pulse is that it is frequency-modulated, and drops about one octave during its duration. This, of course, makes it possible for a bat at close range to an object to distinguish between the call still being emitted and the returning echo. There

is some uncertainty as to how the bat judges distance. One hypothesis is that it simply measures the time delay between the emitted sound and the returning echo, but this would require an extraordinarily sensitive measuring mechanism. Pye has recently pointed out that when two sounds of different high frequencies are generated at the same time they interact to produce a lower frequency beat note (Fig. 25.8). He proposes that the bat listens to the beat note, whose frequency would be directly proportional to the difference in frequency between the call and echo, and hence to the range of the target.

Bats are the only mammals to have evolved true flight, but some other mammals can stretch a loose skin fold between their front and hind legs and glide from tree to tree. The flying squirrel (Fig. 25.16*A*) of the order Rodentia is one. Another is the "flying lemur" of the East Indies. This animal is not a lemur, which is a primitive primate, but an insectivore.

Toothless Mammals. Since primitive

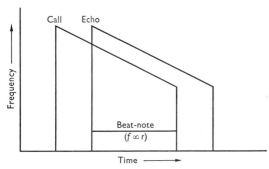

Figure 25.8 Diagram of the interaction between a bat's call and the echo returning from an object a certain distance away. At a different distance, the beat note would be at a different frequency. (From Pye.)

mammals were insectivorous, it is not surprising that certain ones became specialized to feed upon ants and termites, which are very abundant in certain regions. The South American anteater, order **Edentata** (Fig. 25.7D), is representative of this mode of life. Its large claws enable it to open ant hills, and then it laps up the insects with its long, sticky tongue. In contrast to a primitive insectivore, which crushes its insect food with its teeth, an anteater swallows whole the insects that it eats. Its teeth were not needed for survival and have been lost. The tree sloth and armadillo belong to this same order, though they retain vestiges of teeth.

The pangolins of Africa and Asia (order **Pholidota**) and the aardvark of South Africa (order **Tubulidentata**) are superficially similar to edentates, but this is a result of an in-dependent adaptation to a similar mode of life (Fig. 25.9). The acquisition by distantly related or unrelated groups of similar features as a result of adaptation to a common environment is known as **convergent evolution.** When more closely related groups evolve similarly the phenomenon is known as **parallel evolution.**

Primates. Members of the order **Primates,** the group to which monkeys and man belong, are also closely related to the primitive insectivorous stock. Indeed, one member of the order, the Oriental tree shrew (*Tupaia,* Fig. 25.10A), has at times been considered to be an insectivore. Primates evolved from primitive, semiarboreal insectivores and underwent further specializations for life in the trees. Even those that have secondarily reverted to a terrestrial life bear the stamp of this prior arboreal adaptation. Our flexible limbs and grasping hands are fundamentally adaptations for life in the trees. Claws were transformed into finger- and toenails when grasping hands and feet evolved. The reduction of the olfactory organ and olfactory portion of the brain and the development of stereoscopic, or binocular, vision represent other adaptations of our ancestors to arboreal life. Keen vision and the ability to appreciate depth are very important for animals moving through trees, whereas smell is less important for organisms living some distance from the ground than it is for terrestrial species. Muscular coordination is also very important, and the cerebel-

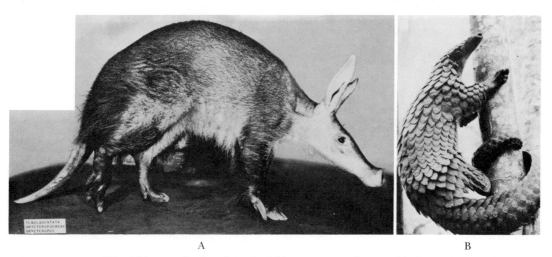

A   B

Figure 25.9 (*A*) The African aardvark and (*B*) the African tree pangolin resemble the South American anteater in their adaptations for insect eating, but these common features have evolved in these mammals independently. (*B* from Walker, E. P.: Mammals of the World. Baltimore, The Johns Hopkins Press, 1964, Vols. I and II, pp. 504 and 1317. Photograph by Jean-Luc Perret.)

Figure 25.10 A group of primates. *A*, Tree shrew; *B*, lemur; *C* and *D*, tarsier; *E*, chimpanzee; *F*, orangutan. (*A*, *C*, *D*, *E* and *F* courtesy of the American Museum of Natural History; *B* courtesy of the San Diego Zoo.)

lum of primates is unusually well developed. The evolution of stereoscopic vision, increased agility, and particularly the influx of a new sort of sensory information gained by the handling of objects with a grasping hand, was accompanied by an extraordinary development of the cerebral hemispheres. The cerebrum is the chief center for the integration of sensory information and the initiation of appropriate motor responses in all mammals, but it is particularly prominent in primates. It is believed that higher mental functions such as conceptual thought could only have evolved in organisms with a grasping hand. In a very real sense, we are a product of the trees.

Primates are often divided into four suborders. The first, suborder **Lemuroidea,** includes the tree shrew, lemurs, lorises, galagos and the peculiar aye-aye. Although fossils of lemurs are found in North America and Eurasia, lemur-like primates are now confined to the Old World tropics; Madagascar has a particularly rich fauna of lemurs. All are rather primitive creatures in which such primate specializations as grasping feet and toenails have begun to appear. However, most lemurs retain a rather long snout, for the nasal region has not been greatly reduced. The suborder **Tarsioidea** includes a single living genus, *Tarsius,* of the East Indies and Philippines. *Tarsius* is a rat-sized animal with large eyes suited for nocturnal vision, and elongated tarsals and digital pads that aid in hopping through the tree tops. It, and the known fossil tarsioids, are too specialized to be the ancestors of other primates, but its flattened face and forward turned eyes are the sort of advances over lemurs that we would expect to find in the ancestors of the higher primates, that is, the monkeys, great apes and man. These higher primates are often collectively called the **anthropoids.** All have a relatively flat face, stereoscopic vision, the capacity to sit on their haunches and examine objects with their hands, and an unusually large brain. However, Old World monkeys, apes and man differ from the New World monkeys in many particulars, including having only two premolar teeth instead of three. These two groups of anthropoids have probably had a long independent evolutionary history, which is reflected in the placing of the New World monkeys in the suborder **Platyrrhini** and the Old World species in the suborder **Catarrhini.** Primates will be considered more fully in connection with the evolution of man. (See Chapter 38.)

Carnivores. As mammals increased in number and diversity, the opportunity arose for them to feed upon one another. Certain ones became specialized for a flesh-eating mode of life, and these constitute the order **Carnivora.** Familiar living carnivores are the weasels, dogs, raccoons, bears and cats (Fig. 25.11). The shift from an insectivorous to a flesh-eating diet was not difficult. An improvement in the stabbing and shearing action of the teeth and the evolution of a foot structure that enabled them to run fast enough to catch their prey were about all that was necessary. Speed has been increased in most by the development of a longer foot and by standing upon their toes (though not their toe tips) with the rest of the foot raised off the ground in the manner of a sprinter. This **digitigrade** foot posture (Fig. 25.12) gives a longer stride than the primitive **plantigrade** posture, in which the entire foot is placed squarely upon the ground or tree branch.

Most carnivores are semiarboreal or terrestrial, but one branch of the order, which includes the seals, sea lions and walruses, early specialized for exploiting the resources of the sea. In addition to their adaptations as carnivores, which include the large canine tusks of the walrus used in gathering shellfish, these species evolved flippers and other aquatic modifications. When they swim, the large pelvic flippers are turned posteriorly and are moved from side to side like the tail of a fish.

Ungulates. Horses, cows and similar mammals have become highly specialized for a plant diet. This has entailed a considerable change in their dentition, for plant food must be thoroughly ground by the teeth before it can be acted upon by the digestive enzymes. The molars of plant-eating mammals (and those of omnivorous species such as man) have become square, as seen in a surface view. Those of the upper and lower jaws no longer slide vertically across each other to give some cutting action, as do the triangular molars of more primitive mammals, but meet and crush the food between them (Fig. 25.2). A simple squaring of the molars, and to some extent of the premolars, is sufficient for herbivorous mammals that browse upon soft vegetation. But those that feed upon grass and other hard and gritty

Figure 25.11 Representative carnivores and cetaceans. *A,* Raccoon; *B,* walrus; *C,* the birth of a porpoise; *D,* the whalebone plates of a toothless whale hang down from the roof of the mouth, *E,* weasels in summer pelage. The porpoise and whale are cetaceans; the others are carnivores. (*A, B, D* and *E,* courtesy of the American Museum of Natural History; *C,* courtesy of Marine Studios.)

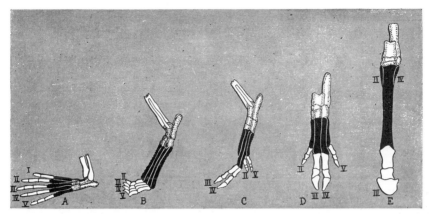

Figure 25.12 Lateral and anterior views of the skeleton of the left hind foot of representative mammals. *A,* The primitive plantigrade foot of a lemur; *B,* the digitigrade foot of a cat; *C* and *D,* the unguligrade foot of a pig, an even-toed ungulate; *E,* the unguligrade foot of a horse, an odd-toed ungulate. The digits are indicated by Roman numerals, the metatarsals are black and the tarsals are stippled.

fare, as do the grazing species, are confronted with the additional problem of the wearing away of the teeth. Two adaptations have occurred: the height of the cusps of the teeth has increased, and cement (a hard material previously found only on the roots of the teeth) has grown up over the surface of the tooth and into the "valleys" between the elongated cusps. More tooth is provided to wear away, and the tooth is more resistant to wear. Teeth of this type are referred to as high-crowned in contrast to the more primitive low-crowned type.

Herbivores constitute the primary food supply of carnivores and protect themselves primarily by the simple expedient of running away. Adaptations for speed have entailed a lengthening of the legs, especially their distal portions, and a relative shortening of the proximal parts of the limbs. The feet are very long, and the animals walk upon their toe tips, a gait termed **unguligrade** (Fig. 25.12). Those toes that no longer reached the ground became vestigial, or disappeared, and the primitive claws on the remaining ones were transformed into hoofs—a characteristic that gives the name ungulate to these mammals. The relatively shorter proximal segment of a limb places the retractor muscles closer to the fulcrum (Fig. 25.13); therefore a slight contraction of the muscle can induce a rather extensive movement of the distal end of a limb. As can be seen in Figure 25.13, the limb of an animal is basically a lever system in which the work arm is represented by the perpendicular distance from the fulcrum (the girdle joint) to the ground; the

power arm, by the perpendicular distance from the fulcrum to the line of action of the muscles in question. By varying limb proportions, the ratio of these lever arms can be changed to adapt for speed, as in the case of the horse, or to adapt for power, as in the case of an armadillo.

The numerous and varied contemporary ungulates (Fig. 25.14) are grouped into two orders that can be separated on the basis of the type of toe reduction. In the order **Perissodactyla,** the axis of the foot passes through the third toe, and this is always the largest. Ancestral perissodactyls, including the primitive forest-dwelling horses of the early Tertiary, had three well-developed toes (the second, third and fourth) and sometimes

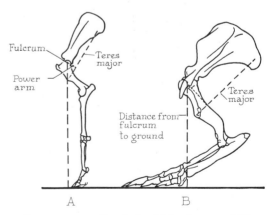

Figure 25.13 Forelimb of (*A*) a horse and (*B*) an armadillo, drawn to the same size to emphasize the difference in proportions. The horse's limb is adapted for speed, the armadillo's for power. (From Young after Smith.)

Figure 25.14 *A,* Tapir in Rangoon Zoo, Burma; *B,* expedition camel, Kalgan, China; *C,* cattle egret warns the weak-sighted rhinoceros of approaching danger; *D,* hippopotamus. (*A, B* and *D* courtesy Museum of Natural History; *C* from Natural History, Vol. LXVIII, No. 10, 1959.)

a trace of a fourth toe (the fifth). The tapir and rhinoceros, which still walk upon soft ground, retain the middle three toes as functional toes, but only the third is left in modern, plains-dwelling horses. Perissodactyls are characterized by having an odd number of toes.

In the order **Artiodactyla,** the axis of the foot passes between the third and fourth toes, which are equal in size and importance. Ancestral artiodactyls had four toes (the second, third, fourth and fifth). Pigs and their allies, which live in a soft ground habitat, retain these four toes, though the second and fifth are reduced in size. Vestiges of the second and fifth toes, the dew claws, are present in some deer, but camels, giraffes, antelope, sheep and cattle retain only the third and fourth toes. Artiodactyls, then, are even-toed ungulates. It is probable that these two orders have had a separate evolutionary origin and owe their points of similarity to parallel evolution.

Subungulates. Subungulates are a

group of plant eaters that have certain incipient ungulate tendencies. Elephants (order **Proboscidea,** Fig. 25.15*A*), for example, have five toes, each ending in a hoof-like nail. They also walk to some extent upon their toe tips, but a pad of elastic tissue posterior to the digits supports most of the body weight. Elephants are noted for their enormous size, which must approach the maximum for a completely terrestrial animal. Though large mammals have a relatively lower metabolic rate than small mammals, the huge mass of elephants necessitates their obtaining large quantities of food. The trunk, which represents the drawn out upper lip and nose, is an effective food-gathering organ. Elephants have a unique dentition in which all of the front teeth are lost except for one pair of incisors, which are modified as tusks. Their premolars, which have come to resemble molars, and their molars are very effective organs for grinding up large quantities of rather coarse plant food. They are high-crowned and so large that there is room for only one in each side of the upper and lower jaws at a time. When it is worn down, a new one replaces it. Mammals, unlike reptiles and other lower vertebrates in which there is a continuous replacement of worn-out teeth, have a limited replacement of teeth. Deciduous incisors, canines and premolars are present in young individuals and these are replaced later in life by permanent ones. The molars, which do not develop until after infancy, are not replaced. Elephants, by using up their premolars and molars one

at a time, have evolved an interesting way of prolonging total tooth life.

Living elephants are restricted to Africa and tropical Asia and are only a small remnant of a once worldwide and varied proboscidean population. During the Pleistocene Epoch, mastodons, mammoths and other proboscideans were abundant in North America.

The conies of the Middle East (order **Hyracoidea**), though superficially rabbit-like animals, show an affinity to the elephants in their foot structure and in certain features of their dentition.

A final group of contemporary subungulates are the sea cows or manatees (order **Sirenia**). These animals live in warm coastal waters and feed upon seaweed, grinding it up with molars that are replaced from behind in elephant-like fashion. Sea cows have a powerful, horizontally flattened tail and well-developed pectoral flippers. These features, together with a very mobile and expressive snout and a single pair of pectoral mammary glands, led mariners of long ago to regard them as mermaids.

Rodents and Lagomorphs. Other herbivorous mammals gnaw and, in addition to high-crowned, grinding molars, have an upper and lower pair of enlarged, chisel-like incisor teeth that grow out from the base as fast as they wear away at the tip. Gnawing has been a very successful mode of life; in fact, there are more species, and possibly more individuals, of gnawing mammals, or rodents (order **Rodentia**), than of all

Figure 25.15 Subungulates. The elephant (*A*) and the manatee (*B*) are believed to have had a common ancestry. (Courtesy of the American Museum of Natural History.)

Figure 25.16 Rodents and lagomorphs. *A,* A flying squirrel; *B,* the pika; *C,* a chipmunk shelling a nut; *D,* a group of beavers. (Courtesy of American Museum of Natural History.)

other mammals combined. Rodents have undergone their own adaptive radiation and have evolved specializations for a variety of ecologic niches. Rats, mice and chipmunks live on the ground, gophers and woodchucks burrow, squirrels and porcupines are adept at climbing trees, and muskrats and beavers are semiaquatic (Fig. 25.16).

Rabbits and the related pika of our Western mountains are superficially similar to rodents and were at one time placed in this order. True rodents, however, have only one pair of incisors in each jaw, whereas rabbits have a reduced second pair hidden behind the large pair of upper incisors. It is now believed that rabbits and the pika belong to a separate order, the **Lagomorpha,** and that their resemblance to rodents is a result of parallel evolution.

Whales. Whales, dolphins and porpoises, of the order **Cetacea,** are more highly specialized marine mammals that also may have evolved from primitive terrestrial carnivores. They have a fish-shaped body, pectoral flippers for steering and balancing, no pelvic flippers, and horizontal flukes on a powerful tail that is moved up and down to propel the animal through the water. Some species have even re-evolved a dorsal fin. Despite these fishlike attributes, cetaceans are air-breathing, viviparous and suckle their young (Fig. 25.11). Some hair is present in the fetus, but it is vestigial or lost in the adult stage in which its insulating function is performed by a thick layer of blubber. Certain species have evolved sonar-like systems that help them to avoid obstacles and find their prey even in muddy river waters that a few enter.

Most cetaceans have a good complement of conical teeth well-suited for feeding upon fish, but the largest whales have lost their teeth and feed upon plankton. With fringed, horny plates (the whalebone) that hang down from the palate, a toothless whale strains these small organisms from water passing through its mouth. The richness of the plankton together with the buoyancy of the water has enabled these whales to attain enormous size. The blue whale, which reaches a length of 30 meters and a weight of 135 metric tons, is the largest animal that has ever existed.

SYNOPSIS OF MAMMALS

CLASS MAMMALIA.   The mammals. Warm-blooded tetrapods, generally covered with hair; jaw joint between dentary and squamosal bones; three auditory ossicles.

Subclass 1. Prototheria.   One order of primitive mammals retaining many reptilian features including the egg-laying habit and cloaca; now confined to the Australian and New Zealand regions.

Order Monotremata.   The monotremes. The platypus, *Ornithorhynchus;* spiny anteater, *Tachyglossus.*

†**Subclass 2. Allotheria.**   One order of gnawing mammals from the Mesozoic and early Tertiary. The multituberculates.

Subclass 3. Theria.   Typical mammals. All living ones are viviparous.

†**Infraclass 1. Trituberculata.**   Two orders of Mesozoic mammals with a cusp pattern on their molar teeth which suggests that they were ancestral to higher mammals.

Infraclass 2. Metatheria.   Pouched mammals. Young are born at an early stage of development, and complete their development attached to teats which are located in a skin pouch; usually three premolar teeth and four molars in each jaw.

Order 1. Marsupialia.   Marsupials. The opossum, *Didelphis.*

Infraclass 3. Eutheria.   Placental mammals. Young develop to a relatively mature stage in the uterus; dental formula never exceeds $I\frac{3}{3}$, $C\frac{1}{1}$, $Pm\frac{4}{4}$, $M\frac{3}{3}$.

Order 1. Insectivora.   Insectivores including shrews, moles, hedgehog and flying lemur. Small mammals, usually with long pointed snouts; sharp cusps on molar teeth adapted for insect eating; feet retain five toes and claws. The common shrew, *Sorex.*

Order 2. Chiroptera.   The bats. Pectoral appendages modified as wings; hind legs small and included in wing membranes. The little brown bat, *Myotis.*

Order 3. Primates.   The primates. Rather generalized mammals retaining five digits on hands and feet; first digit usually opposable; claws usually replaced by finger- and toenails; eyes typically large and turned forward; often considerable reduction in length of snout.

SUBORDER 1. LEMUROIDEA.   The lemurs, lorises, galagos. Primitive primates; snout longer than in other groups; often one or two digits retain claws. The lemur, *Lemur.*

SUBORDER 2. TARSIOIDEA.   Short-faced primates; certain tarsal bones elongated. The tarsier, *Tarsius.*

SUBORDER 3. PLATYRRHINI.   New World monkeys. Nostrils far apart; three premolars retained; tail often prehensile. The capuchin, *Cebus.*

SUBORDER 4. CATARRHINI.   Old World monkeys, apes, man. Nostrils close together; two premolars; tail, if present, never prehensile. Macaque, *Macaca;* chimpanzee, *Pan;* man, *Homo.*

Order 4. Carnivora.   The carnivores. Flesh-eating mammals; large canine; certain premolars and molars modified as shearing teeth; claws well developed.

†SUBORDER 1. CREODONTIA.   Ancestral carnivores.

SUBORDER 2. FISSIPEDIA.   Modern terrestrial carnivores including the dogs, wolves, foxes, raccoons, pandas, bears, weasels, martens, wolverines, badgers, skunks, minks, otters, cats, lions, tigers, mongooses, hyenas. The domestic cat, *Felis.*

SUBORDER 3. PINNIPEDIA.   Marine carnivores including the seals, sea lions and walruses. Members of this group have many aquatic specializations such as paddle-like limbs and reduced tail. The harbor seal, *Phoca.*

†*Order 5. Condylarthra.*   Ancestral ungulates. Five toes were retained, but each bore a small hoof; except for loss of clavicle, limb skeleton little

---

†Extinct.

modified; dentition complete; molars slightly modified for plant eating.

Order 6. Proboscidea.   Elephants and related extinct mammoths and mastodons. Massive ungulates retaining five toes, each with a small hoof; two upper incisors elongated as tusks; nose and upper lip modified as a proboscis. African elephant, *Loxodonta;* Indian elephant, *Elephas.*

Order 7. Sirenia.   Sea cows. Marine herbivores; pectoral limbs paddle-like; pelvic limbs lost; large horizontally flattened tail used in propulsion. Florida manatee, *Trichechus.*

Order 8. Hydracoidea.   Coneys. Small, guinea pig-like herbivores of the Middle East; four toes on front foot, three on hind foot, each with a hoof. *Procavia.*

Order 9. Perissodactyla.   Odd-toed ungulates. Axis of support passes through third digit; lateral digits reduced or lost.

    SUBORDER 1. HIPPOMORPHA.   Horses and their allies. *Equus.*

    SUBORDER 2. CERATOMORPHA.   Tapirs and rhinoceroses.

Order 10. Artiodactyla.   Even-toed ungulates. Axis of support passes between third and fourth toes; first toe lost; second and fifth toes reduced or lost.

    SUBORDER 1. SUINA.   Pigs, peccaries, hippopotamuses. The pig, *Sus.*

    SUBORDER 2. RUMINANTIA.   The cud-chewing artiodactyls including camels. llamas, chevrotains, deer, giraffes, pronghorns, antelopes, cattle, sheep and goats. American buffalo, *Bison.*

Order 11. Edentata.   New World edentates including sloths, anteaters and armadillos. Teeth reduced or lost; large claws on toes. The armadillo, *Dasypus.*

Order 12. Pholidota.   The pangolin, *Manis,* of Africa and southeastern Asia. Teeth lost; long tongue used to feed on insects; body covered with overlapping horny plates.

Order 13. Tubulidentata.   The aardvark, *Orycteropus,* of South Africa. Teeth reduced; long tongue used to feed on insects.

Order 14. Cetacea.   The whales and their allies. Large marine mammals; pectoral limbs reduced to flippers; pelvic limbs lost; large tail bears horizontal flukes which are used in propulsion.

    SUBORDER 1. ODONTOCETI.   Toothed whales. The bottlenosed dolphin. *Tursiops.*

    SUBORDER 2. MYSTICETI.   Whalebone whales. Teeth lost; strain small animals from water with horny whalebone plates that hang down from upper jaws. The blue whale, *Balaenoptera.*

Order 15. Rodentia.   The rodents. Gnawing mammals with two pairs of chisellike incisor teeth. The largest order of mammals, it includes the squirrels, chipmunks, marmots, gophers, beavers, rats, mice, muskrats, lemmings, voles, porcupines, guinea pigs, capybaras and chinchillas. The woodchuck, *Marmota.*

Order 16. Lagomorpha.   Hares, rabbits, pikas. Gnawing mammals with two pairs of chisel-like incisors and an extra pair of small upper incisors that lie behind the enlarged first pair. The rabbit, *Lepus.*

QUESTIONS

1. Distinguish between mammals and reptiles.
2. What are the major anatomic features of mammals that are correlated with their increased activity?
3. Distinguish between poikilothermic, heterothermic and homoiothermic vertebrates.
4. What is the importance of a placenta? What structures form it?
5. List three ways in which monotremes are more primitive than other mammals.
6. Why are marsupials particularly abundant in Australia? Give an example of a North American marsupial.

7. What is the most primitive group of eutherian mammals?
8. How do bats find insects in the dark without the use of their eyes?
9. What features of man are a direct or indirect result of the arboreal adaptations of man's primate ancestors?
10. In what ways is the limb of an ungulate adapted for speed of movement?
11. How have the molar teeth of ungulates been adapted for the animals' herbivorous diet?
12. How do perissodactyls differ from artiodactyls?

ANNOTATED REFERENCES

Many of the general references on vertebrates cited at the end of Chapter 22 contain considerable information on the biology of mammals.

Bourlière, F.: The Natural History of Mammals. 2nd ed. New York, Alfred A. Knopf, Inc., 1956. A fascinating account of the natural history of mammals; originally published in French as Vie et Moeurs les Mammifères.

Burt, W. H., and R. P. Grossenheider: A Field Guide to the Mammals. Boston, Houghton Mifflin Co., 1952. A useful guide, in the style of the Peterson bird guides, for the field identification of mammals.

Davis, E. E., and F. B. Golley: Principles of Mammalogy. New York, Reinhold Publishing Corp., 1964. An excellent introductory text.

Griffin, D. R.: Listening in the Dark. New Haven, Yale University Press, 1958. A thorough account of the acoustic orientation of bats and its application to blind persons.

Hall, E. R., and K. R. Kelson: The Mammals of North America. New York, The Ronald Press Co., 1959. A two-volume monograph on mammals for the serious student.

Hartman, C. G.: 'Possums. Austin, University of Texas Press, 1952. Describes the habits, natural history and fascinating folklore of this unusual creature.

Sanderson, I. T.: Living Mammals of the World. Garden City, N.Y., Doubleday & Co., 1955. A superbly illustrated account of the major groups of mammals.

Schmidt-Nielsen, K.: Desert Animals. Oxford, Clarendon Press, 1964. The adaptations of camels, the kangaroo rat, man and other animals to desert life are thoroughly analyzed.

Scott, W. B.: A History of Land Mammals in the Western Hemisphere. 2nd ed. New York, Macmillan, 1937. An old but still very valuable source book on the evolution of horses, camels, mastodons and other groups that roamed the New World in ages past.

Slijper, E. J.: Whales. London, Hutchinson & Co., 1962. A valuable source book on the natural history and the specialized anatomy and physiology of cetaceans.

Walker, E. P., et al.: Mammals of the World. Baltimore, The Johns Hopkins Press, 1964. Each known genus of mammal is discussed and illustrated in the first two volumes of this treatise. A third volume is devoted to a classified bibliography of the literature regarding mammal groups and their anatomy, physiology, ecology, etc.

Young, J. Z.: The Life of Mammals. 2nd ed. Oxford, Clarendon Press, 1957. A very valuable source book emphasizing the anatomy and physiology of mammals.

26

PROTECTION, SUPPORT AND MOVEMENT

The preceding chapters traced the main currents of vertebrate evolution and discussed the major changes made by the various groups of vertebrates as they became adapted to the changing environment. With this as a background, the succeeding chapters will present the morphologic and physiologic aspects of each of the organ systems in turn. In these the major emphasis will be placed on the mammalian condition and on those transformations that have occurred in the line of evolution that leads to mammals.

26.1
The Integument

The skin, or **integument,** is the outermost layer of the body and separates the organism from its external environment. It helps to maintain a constant internal environment and protects the body against a variety of mechanical and chemical injuries. Yet the skin does not completely isolate the organism from its environment, since many sensory stimuli are received by the skin, and some exchange of gases, water and excretory products may occur through it. In addition, a variety of bony plates, scales, feathers, hair, pigment cells and glands develop from the skin and serve a variety of purposes. The skin is truly a "jack-of-all trades."

In general, it may be said that the greater the difference between the internal and external environments, the greater is the importance of this organ in protecting the underlying tissues, and the more elaborate is its structure. Lower chordates, for example, whose internal environment is very similar to the sea water in which they are living, have a very delicate skin consisting of a single layer of columnar epithelium supported by a few connective tissue fibers. In all vertebrates, the skin is more highly developed and is made up of an outer stratified epithelium (the **epidermis**) and a deeper, rather thick layer of dense connective tissue (the **dermis**).

The epidermis of fishes and amphibians contains relatively little horny material, but a large amount of horny **keratin** is deposited in the outer cells of the epidermis of the higher terrestrial vertebrates. These flattened, cornified cells are dead and in mammals form a thick, waterproofing **stratum corneum** that is clearly demarcated from the deeper, proliferating layers of the epidermis known as the **stratum germinativum** (Fig. 26.1). Well-defined, intermediate layers can also be recognized where the epidermis is especially thick, as on the palm of the hand and the sole of the foot. As new cells are produced and differentiate, the outer cells of the stratum corneum are lost. Groups of such cells are continually being shed in mammals; dandruff is a familiar example.

The dermis is composed of fibrous connective tissue; bone may develop in it in certain regions. The dermis is richly supplied with blood vessels, some of which lie close to the surface and enter papilla-like projections of the dermis that extend into

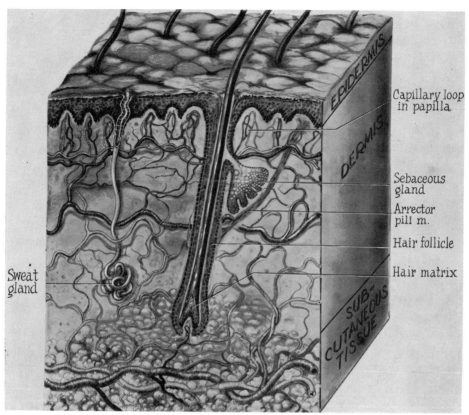

Figure 26.1   Diagrammatic vertical section through human skin. (Modified from Pillsbury, Shelley and Kligman; Manual of Cutaneous Medicine, 1961.)

the base of the epidermis. In addition to their nutritive function, these vessels in mammals play an important role in thermoregulation. Nerves and microscopic sense organs that receive stimuli of touch, pressure, temperature and pain are abundant in the dermis, but only a few naked nerve endings penetrate the epidermis. Fat may accumulate in the deeper parts of the dermis and in the subcutaneous tissue. The fat serves as a reserve supply of food, as a thermal insulator, and as a cushion against mechanical injury. The blubber of whales serves as a good insulation in the aquatic environment. Hair is not an efficient insulator in aquatic animals, for its thermal insulation depends on air trapped within it, and it has been lost on most of the body surface of adult whales.

Though the skin itself is relatively simple, its derivatives are numerous and complex. These may be grouped into bony structures, horny structures, glands and pigment. The bony structures develop within the dermis, though parts of them may become exposed if the overlying epidermis wears off. Thick

bony scales and plates were prominent in ancestral vertebrates and have been retained in reduced form in most groups of living fishes (Fig. 26.2*A*). Certain of the dermal plates in the head region early in evolution became associated with the skull and pectoral girdle, and these have been retained by later vertebrates as integral parts of the skeleton. Most of the primitive bony scales have been lost in tetrapods, but the dermis retains the ability to form bone and becomes heavily ossified in certain species. The shell of a turtle is composed of dermal plates covered by large horny laminae; a comparable condition is found in the skin of certain lizards and crocodiles and in the shell of the armadillo. The **antlers** of deer (Fig. 26.3) are also composed of dermal bone. During its development, the antler is covered by skin, the **velvet**, but this sloughs off when the antler is fully formed. Antlers branch, are shed annually and, with the exception of the reindeer and caribou, are found only on males. The **horns** of sheep and cattle, in contrast, do not branch, are not shed and occur in

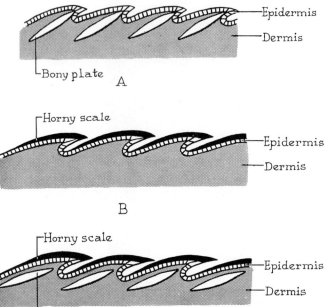

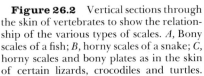

Figure 26.2 Vertical sections through the skin of vertebrates to show the relationship of the various types of scales. *A*, Bony scales of a fish; *B*, horny scales of a snake; *C*, horny scales and bony plates as in the skin of certain lizards, crocodiles and turtles.

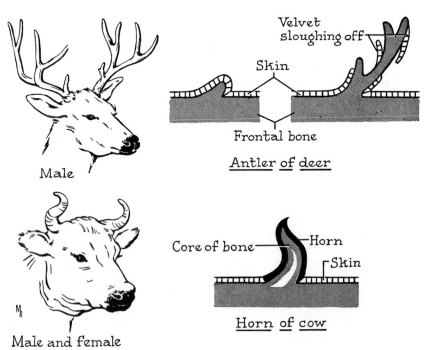

Figure 26.3 A diagram to show the differences between antlers (deer) and horns (cow). Antlers are annual growths that are shed in the winter; horns are permanent outgrowths.

both sexes. These horns have a core of bone covered by a highly cornified skin.

Horny skin derivatives develop by the accumulation of keratin in the cells of the epidermis. Reptiles have a covering of **horny scales** that reduce water loss through the skin. As the animal increases in size, the horny scales are periodically shed and newly formed ones are exposed beneath them. Bony scales, in contrast, are not shed but increase in size by the addition of new bone. Except for their retention in such regions as the feet of birds and the tails of certain mammals, horny scales are not present in most birds and mammals, though a prominent stratum corneum persists.

Feathers are believed to be modified horny scales, but the **hairs** of mammals are regarded as a different kind of horny skin derivative. A hair lies within a **hair follicle** (Fig. 26.1), which is composed of a tubular invagination of the epidermis supported by surrounding fibers of the dermis. A **hair papilla,** containing blood vessels and nerves, protrudes into the base of the follicle and nourishes the adjacent epithelial cells. These proliferate rapidly and add to the base of the hair, which extends up through the follicle as a column of keratinized cells. A small smooth muscle, the **arrector pili,** is associated with each follicle. These muscles contract when temperatures fall and pull the hair follicles and hairs into a more erect position, thereby increasing the depth of the hair layer and its effectiveness in insulation. They also depress the skin between the hairs, leaving little hillocks where the hairs emerge. We are familiar with this as "goose flesh." Hairs are effective mechanical amplifiers of the sense of touch; a slight movement of a hair can stimulate nerve ends wrapped around its base. This property is extremely well developed in the tactile whiskers seen in cats and many other mammals. Other specializations of hair include the quills of a porcupine and even the "horn" of a rhinoceros, which lacks a core of bone, appears to be a clump of specialized hairs.

Other horny derivatives of the integument include **claws,** which first appear in reptiles and may be modified as **nails** or **hoofs** in certain mammals, the **whalebone plates** of toothless whales, and the covering of the horns of sheep and cattle.

Individual mucus-secreting cells are common in the epidermis of fishes, and multicellular **mucous glands** are abundant in amphibian skin. Many fishes and amphibians also have a few cutaneous **poison glands.** Reptiles have lost the mucous and poison glands, and only a few glands, chiefly scent glands, are present in their dry, horny skin. This paucity persists in birds, but glands have again become abundant in mammalian skin. Alveolar-shaped **sebaceous glands,** epithelial outgrowths from the hair follicles (Fig. 26.1), discharge their oily secretions onto the hairs. Coiled, tubular **sweat glands** are also abundant in parts of the skin of most mammals. A little urea and some salts are eliminated in the sweat, but sweat glands are particularly important in secreting water whose evaporation cools the body surface. As explained in Chapter 25, the vascular supply to the skin, the hairs and their muscles and the sweat glands all play a role in regulating body temperature. Though the nature and function of their secretion is entirely different, **mammary glands** are regarded as modified sweat glands; the tubules of both sweat and mammary glands have a layer of myoepithelial cells peripheral to the glandular cells whose contractions aid in expelling the glandular contents. Musk and other **scent glands,** serving for sexual recognition, are also common in many mammals, although they do not occur in man.

In lower vertebrates, e.g., in the frog, pigments are contained within chromatophores located beneath the epidermis, and skin color can change by the concentration or dispersion of pigment within these stellate cells (Fig. 32.8). Chromatophores are rare in mammals, but the brownish pigment **melanin** is present within and between the cells of the epidermis. Some melanin is present in the skin of all men (except albinos, p. 634), but it is especially abundant in the skin of Negroes. Skin color is determined not only by the pigment present but by the vascularity of the dermis and by the presence of refractive substances such as guanine.

26.2

The Skeleton

Nature and Parts of the Vertebrate Skeleton. Organisms must remain small and slow moving unless they have a skeleton for support and to serve as levers on which muscles can act. All vertebrates have a skeleton that provides for this and that encloses and protects some of the more delicate internal organs. Certain of the central cavities of the bones of higher vertebrates contain red bone marrow and are the sites of the formation of red blood cells and certain of the white cells. The vertebrate skeleton is basically an internal skeleton, for it develops within the skin or in deeper body tissues. None of it is a secretion on the body surface, as is the exoskeleton of certain invertebrates, although such structures as horny scales, feathers and hair are sometimes classified as an exoskeleton.

The skeleton can be subdivided into a **dermal skeleton,** consisting of the bony scales and plates mentioned earlier in this chapter, and an **endoskeleton,** situated beneath the skin. During early embryonic development the endoskeleton is composed of the notochord and cartilage, but the notochord is ephemeral in most vertebrates and cartilage is replaced by bone in most adults. This bone is called **cartilage replacement bone** to distinguish it from the **dermal bone** that develops in more superficial parts of the body without any cartilaginous precursor. These types of bone differ only in their mode of development; they are the same histologically.

The endoskeleton and its associated dermal bones can be further subdivided into somatic and visceral skeletons:

Somatic skeleton (skeleton of the body wall)
 Axial skeleton (vertebral column, ribs, sternum and most of the skull)
 Appendicular skeleton (girdles and limb bones)
Visceral skeleton (skeleton of the pharyngeal wall, primitively associated with the gills)

The Fish Skeleton. The parts of the skeleton can be seen more clearly in a dogfish (Fig. 26.4) than in terrestrial vertebrates. The dogfish skeleton is typical of the skeleton of primitive vertebrates, except that the skeleton is entirely cartilaginous. It will be recalled that the failure of the dogfish's skeleton to ossify is believed to represent the retention of an embryonic condition rather than a primitive adult condition. The vertebral column is composed of vertebrae, each of which has a biconcave **centrum** that develops around and largely replaces the notochord. Dorsal to each centrum is a **neural arch** encasing the spinal cord; short **ribs** attach to the vertebrae; a sternum is absent; the individual vertebrae are rather loosely held together. A strong vertebral support is not necessary in the aquatic environment.

Most of the skull of the dogfish is an odd-shaped box of cartilage encasing the brain and major sense organs. This belongs to the axial skeleton and is known as the **chon-**

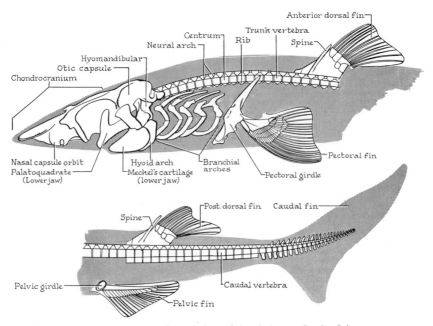

Figure 26.4 A lateral view of the skeleton of a dogfish.

drocranium. It forms the core of the skull of all vertebrates. Other basic components of a vertebrate skull include the anterior arches of the visceral skeleton and dermal bones that encase the chondrocranium and anterior visceral arches. These dermal bones have been lost during the evolution of cartilaginous fishes, but they were present in the fishes ancestral to tetrapods.

The visceral skeleton consists of seven pairs of >-shaped visceral arches. The arches are hinged at the apex of the >; they are interconnected ventrally, but are free dorsally. Each arch lies in the wall of the pharynx and supports gills in very primitive vertebrates. In jawed vertebrates the first or **mandibular arch** becomes enlarged and, together with associated dermal bones, forms the upper and lower jaws. It forms all of the jaws in the dogfish, for there are no surrounding dermal bones. The second or **hyoid arch** has moved forward in the dogfish and helps to support the jaws. Its dorsal portion extends as a prop from the **otic capsule** (the part of the chondrocranium housing the inner ear) to the angle of the jaw. The gill slit that in primitive fish lay between the mandibular and hyoid arches is reduced to a spiracle. The third to seventh visceral arches are known as **branchial arches;** they support the gills and complete gill slits lie between them.

The appendicular skeleton is very simple in the dogfish. A U-shaped bar of cartilage, the **pectoral girdle,** lies in the body wall posterior to the gill region and supports the **pectoral fins.** The **pelvic girdle** is a transverse bar of cartilage in the ventral body wall anterior to the cloaca. It supports the **pelvic fins** but is not connected with the vertebral column.

The Mammalian Skeleton. Many changes in the skeleton have taken place during evolution of the skeleton from primitive fishes to mammals (Fig. 26.5). The vertebral column must support the weight of the body in all tetrapods and it has become much stronger. It is thoroughly ossified, and the individual vertebrae are strongly united by overlapping articular processes **(zygapophyses)** borne on the neural arches (Fig. 23.2). Correlated with changes in the methods of locomotion and the independent movement of various parts of the body, we find that there is more regional differentiation of the vertebral column (Fig. 26.6). Man has

seven **cervical vertebrae,** 12 **thoracic vertebrae,** five **lumbar vertebrae,** five **sacral vertebrae** fused together to form a **sacrum** that articulates with the pelvic girdle, and three to five reduced **caudal vertebrae** generally fused into a single piece, the **coccyx.** Only the thoracic vertebrae bear distinct **ribs,** most of which connect, via the costal cartilages, with the ventral breast bone, or **sternum.** Rudimentary ribs, which are present in the other regions during embryonic development, fuse onto the transverse processes. The first two cervical vertebrae are modified, permitting a free movement of the head. The first, known as the **atlas,** has a pair of facets that articulate with the pair of **occipital condyles,** the rounded bumps on the base of the skull on each side of the foramen magnum. The head can rock back and forth at this point. Turning motion occurs at a unique joint between the atlas and the second cervical vertebra, the **axis.** All tetrapods have an atlas, but an axis does not appear in the evolutionary sequence until reptiles. The number of sacral vertebrae has increased as the tetrapods have evolved more effective terrestrial locomotion. Typically, amphibians have one, reptiles two and mammals three. The greater number in man is correlated with the additional problems of support inherent in a bipedal gait.

The mammalian skull has many of the features found in the frog's skull. The expanded portion housing the brain is the **cranium;** the jaws and the bones surrounding the eyes and supporting the nose constitute the **facial skeleton.** The eyes are lodged in **orbits,** the nasal cavities open on the surface through **external nares,** an **external auditory meatus** leads to the eardrum, the spinal cord emerges through the **foramen magnum,** and there are many smaller foramina for blood vessels and nerves. A **temporal fossa,** in which jaw muscles are lodged, lies posterior to the orbit. It is bounded laterally by a handle-like bar of bone, the **zygomatic arch.** A bony **hard palate** separates the mouth and nasal cavities, and the **internal nares** lie at the posterior end of this.

The skull is a hodgepodge of cartilage replacement and dermal bones that can be understood only when considered from an evolutionary point of view (Fig. 26.7). As the brain grew larger during the course of evolution, the cartilage replacement bones

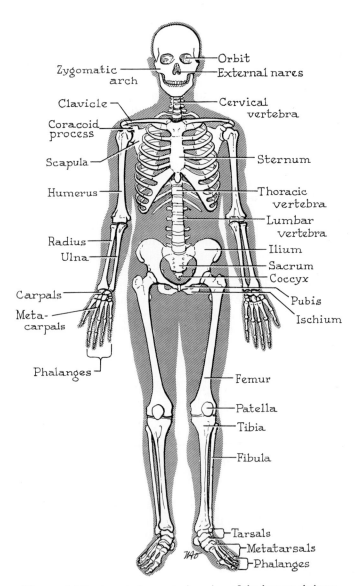

Figure 26.5   A ventral, or anterior, view of the human skeleton.

of the chondrocranium no longer completely encased it. They form a ring of bone around the foramen magnum (the **occipital bone**), encase the inner ear (part of the **temporal bone**), and form the floor of the cranium. The sides and roof of the cranium are completed by dermal bones such as the **frontal** and **parietals** and by a portion of the mandibular arch known as the **alisphenoid.** The last is a cartilage replacement bone.

Although the mandibular arch is associated with the jaws in most vertebrates, at least to the extent of forming the jaw joint, the jaws of mammals are formed entirely of certain of the dermal bones that usually encased the mandibular arch in primitive vertebrates. The mammalian jaw joint lies between two of these—the **dentary** and **squamosal** (part of the temporal). The posterior end of the mandibular arch, which forms the jaw joint in more primitive vertebrates, has become the **incus** and **malleus**—two of the three small auditory ossicles that transmit vibrations across the middle ear cavity. Our ancestral jaw joint is now part of our hearing mechanism, and earlier it was part of a gill arch and concerned with respiration! The third auditory ossicle, the **stapes,** evolved from the dorsal part of the hyoid arch. It is of interest to observe that the auditory ossicles have the same relationship to each other as their homologues in fish. The ventral part of the hyoid arch, together with the remains of the third visceral arch, form the **hyoid bone** (a sling for the support of the tongue) and the **styloid process** of the skull, to which the hyoid is connected by a ligament. With the loss of gills in tetrapods, the remaining visceral arches have become greatly reduced, but parts of them form the cartilages of the larynx.

Although the appendicular skeleton of the dogfish is quite different from that of terrestrial vertebrates, there is a close resemblance between the appendicular skeleton of crossopterygian fishes and tetrapods (Fig. 26.8). The **humerus** of our arm, or the **femur** of our leg, represents the single proximal bone of the crossopterygian fin; the **radius** and **ulna,** or **tibia** and **fibula,** the next two bones. The **carpals** or **tarsals, metatarsals** or **metacarpals,** and **phalanges** of the hand or foot are homologous with the more peripheral elements of the crossopterygian fin. We tetrapods have a single bone in the proximal part of the appendage followed by

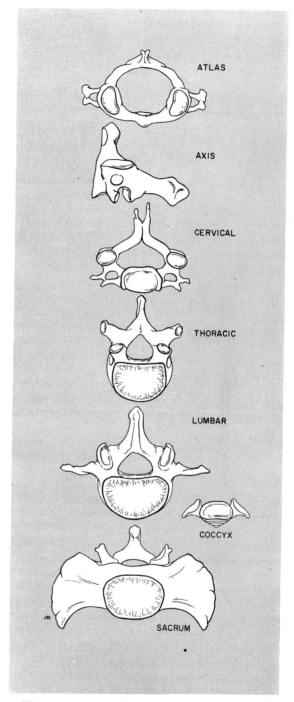

Figure 26.6 Types of mammalian vertebrae as represented by those of man. The atlas is seen in lateral view; the others are viewed from the anterior end. (From Villee: Biology, 5th ed.)

two bones in the second part because this pattern was established by our piscine ancestors.

The girdles of tetrapods are necessarily

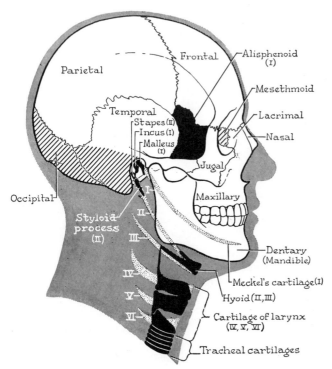

Figure 26.7 Components of the human skull, hyoid and larynx. Dermal bones have been left plain, chondrocranial derivatives are hatched, those parts of the embryonic visceral skeleton that disappear are stippled, parts of the visceral arches that persist are shown in black. Roman numerals refer to visceral arches and their derivatives. (Modified after Neal and Rand.)

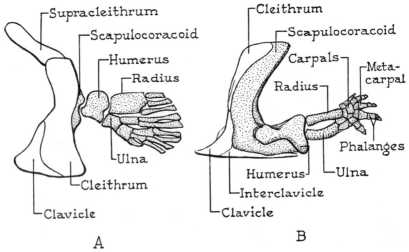

Figure 26.8 Lateral views of the appendicular skeleton of a crossopterygian (A) and labyrinthodont (B) to show the changes that occurred in the transition from water to land. Dermal bones have been left plain, cartilage replacement bones are stippled. (A modified after Gregory; B after Romer.)

stronger than those of fish. The pectoral girdle is bound onto the body by muscles, but the pelvic girdle extends dorsally and is firmly attached to the vertebral column. A **pubis, ischium** and **ilium** are present on each side of our pelvic girdle, though all have fused together in the adult. Our pectoral girdle includes a **scapula,** a **coracoid process,** which is a distinct bone in most lower tetrapods, and a **clavicle.** The clavicle is the only remnant of a series of dermal bones that are primitively associated with the girdle. All other girdle bones are cartilage replacement bones.

26.3

Joints

Where bones come together they do not simply abut one upon the other but are united by **joints** or **articulations** of varying complexity. Their nature is correlated with the functions the bones perform and the degree of movement between them. Three broad categories can be recognized: immovable joints, slightly movable joints and freely movable joints.

Bones of the cranium (e.g., parietal and frontal, Fig. 26.7) provide a solid protective housing for the brain and are united by immovable joints known as **sutures.** The connective tissue **periosteum,** which covers the surfaces of all bones, forms a septum that dips between the bones. The bones can grow at their periphery, but they remain firmly articulated with each other at all times.

The vertebrae must form a firm supporting beam, yet a beam that is capable of limited bending. Most vertebrae are united by slightly movable **symphyses.** An elastic pad of fibrocartilage separates them and they are held together by **ligaments** — tough bands of connective tissue that extend across the articulation.

Since the appendages are used as flexible struts in locomotion, a great deal of motion occurs between most of their bones. We find freely movable articulations of several kinds: ball and socket joints between the appendages and the girdles, a hinge joint at the knee, a combination of a hinge and pivot joint at the elbow, etc. All are often called synovial joints, for they contain a **synovial cavity** that permits the free movement. Structurally they are quite complex (Fig. 26.9). The adjacent bones

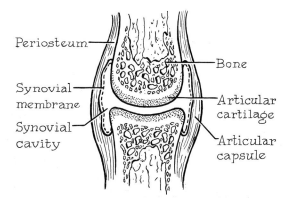

Figure 26.9 A diagrammatic section through a synovial joint. Ligaments, not shown, cross the joint peripheral to the articular capsule and provide additional strength to the joint in certain areas.

are usually shaped so that a protuberance of one fits into a depression in the other. This, of course, makes the bones less likely to disarticulate during movement. **Articular cartilages** cover the ends of the bones and provide a smooth, somewhat elastic surface. A **synovial membrane** lines the synovial cavity and produces, probably by filtration from blood vessels within it, a lymphlike synovial fluid which lubricates the articulation. Stiffness of joints in old age results in part from a reduction in the amount of this fluid. The periosteum covering the bones extends across the joint as an **articular capsule,** ligaments strengthen the joint, and it is also supported by the tonus of surrounding muscles.

26.4

Muscles

The movement of the vertebrate body and its parts depends upon the contraction of muscles, and muscles play an important role in supporting the body of terrestrial vertebrates. The nature of muscle contraction and the source of the energy required have been considered earlier. At this time we will be concerned with certain aspects of the evolution of the muscular system and the relation of these to changes in methods of locomotion.

Histologically, muscles may be classified as smooth, cardiac and skeletal (Fig. 3.15). In tracing their evolution it is more convenient to divide them into **somatic muscles,** associated with the body wall and appendages, and **visceral muscles,** associated with the pharynx and other parts of the gut tube. This

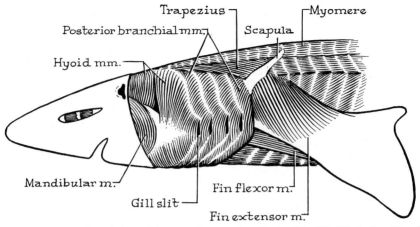

Figure 26.10   A lateral view of the anterior muscles of a dogfish. (Modified after Howell.)

grouping parallels the major subdivisions of the skeletal system. Somatic muscles are striated and under voluntary control. Most of the visceral muscles are smooth and involuntary; however, the visceral muscles associated with the visceral arches, called branchial muscles, are striated and under voluntary control.

Evolution of Somatic Muscles.   Most of the somatic musculature of fishes consists of segmented **myomeres** (Fig. 26.10). This is an effective arrangement for bringing about the lateral undulations of the trunk and tail that are responsible for locomotion. The muscles of the paired fins are very simple and consist of little more than a single dorsal **extensor,** or **abductor,** that pulls the fin up and caudally, and a ventral **flexor,** or **adductor,** that pulls the fin down and anteriorly.

The transition from water to land entailed

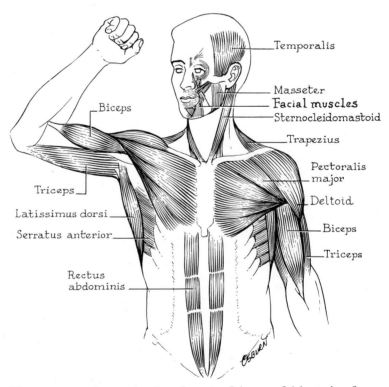

Figure 26.11   An anterior view of certain of the superficial muscles of man.

major changes in the somatic muscles. The appendages became increasingly important in locomotion, and movements of the trunk and tail less important. The primitive single fin extensor and flexor became divided into many components, and these became larger and more powerful. Despite the complexity of tetrapod appendicular muscles, it is possible to divide them into a dorsal group that evolved from the fish extensor and a ventral group derived from the flexor. Our **latissimus dorsi** and **triceps** (Fig. 26.11), for example, are dorsal appendicular muscles, whereas the **pectoralis** and **biceps** are ventral appendicular muscles. Segmentation is lost for the most part as one ascends the evolutionary scale, though traces of segmentation remain in the mammalian **rectus abdominis.** The muscle layers on the flank became relatively thin, and some trunk muscles, the **serratus anterior,** for example, became associated with the pectoral girdle.

Evolution of Branchial Muscles. Branchial muscles are well developed in fishes and are grouped according to the visceral arches with which they are associated (Fig. 26.10): **mandibular muscles** and certain of the **hyoid muscles** are concerned with jaw movements; most of the rest, with respiratory movements of the gill apparatus. Branchial muscles obviously become less important in tetrapods, for the gills are lost and the visceral arches are reduced. Nevertheless, certain ones are retained. Those of the mandibular arch remain as the **temporalis, masseter** and other jaw muscles (Fig. 26.11). Most of those of the hyoid arch move to a superficial position and become the **facial muscles** that are responsible for smiling and other facial expressions. Those of the remaining arches are associated with the pharynx and larynx and some, e.g., the **sternocleidomastoid** and **trapezius,** become important muscles associated with the pectoral girdle.

QUESTIONS

1. Of what value is the accumulation of keratin in the skin of tetrapods?
2. How would the structures in the skin that are concerned with thermoregulation interact to reduce the body temperature of a mammal?
3. Give an example of a bone in the human skull that is derived from each of the three basic components of the skull.
4. What changes are encountered in the visceral skeleton as one ascends the evolutionary scale from fish to mammal? With what are these changes correlated?
5. What changes in the muscular system are correlated with the changes in the method of locomotion encountered between fish and mammals?

ANNOTATED REFERENCES

General

The following references contain a great deal of information on the anatomy and physiology of vertebrate organ systems.

Bloom, W., and D. W. Fawcett: A Textbook of Histology. 8th ed. Philadelphia, W. B. Saunders Co., 1962. The microscopic and ultrastructure of the cells and tissues of mammalian organ systems are thoroughly described.

Cannon, W. B.: The Wisdom of the Body. New York, W. W. Norton & Co., 1939. A classic and very readable account of mammalian physiology.

Florey, E.: An Introduction to General and Comparative Animal Physiology. Philadelphia, W. B. Saunders Co., 1966. A very useful textbook on the physiology of invertebrates and vertebrates.

Guyton, A. C.: Textbook of Medical Physiology. 3rd ed. Philadelphia, W. B. Saunders Co., 1966. A detailed consideration of mammalian physiology is presented in this standard textbook.

Marshall, P. T., and G. M. Hughes: The Physiology of Mammals and Other Vertebrates. Cambridge, Cambridge University Press, 1965. An excellent account which gives the reader a good understanding of the structural and functional unity of the organ systems of vertebrates.

Prosser, C. L., and F. A. Brown, Jr.: Comparative Animal Physiology. 2nd ed. Philadelphia,

W. B. Saunders Co., 1961. A very valuable source book on the physiology of both invertebrates and vertebrates.

Romer, A. S.: The Shorter Version of the Vertebrate Body. 3rd ed. Philadelphia, W. B. Saunders Co., 1962. The morphological aspects of the evolution of vertebrates are thorroughly considered in this widely used textbook of comparative anatomy.

Ruch, T. C., and H. D. Patton: Physiology and Biophysics. 19th ed. Philadelphia, W. B. Saunders Co., 1965. An advanced text and source book on mammalian physiology.

Young, J. Z.: The Life of Mammals. New York, Oxford University Press, 1957. Structure and function are carefully considered in this thorough account of the gross and microscopic anatomy and the physiology of mammals.

Young, J. Z.: The Life of Vertebrates. 2nd ed. Oxford, Clarendon Press, 1963. One or more chapters are devoted to the anatomy, physiology and evolution of each of the classes of vertebrates in this excellent text.

Protection, Support and Movement

Gray, J.: How Animals Move. Cambridge, Cambridge University Press, 1953. An excellent analysis of the principles and types of animal locomotion.

Hill, A. V.: Muscular Movement in Man. New York, McGraw-Hill Book Co., 1927. A classic account by one of the pioneer investigators of muscle physiology.

Montagna, W.: The Structure and Function of Skin. New York, Academic Press, 1956. A thorough study of the skin and its regional variations is presented in this book.

Thompson, D'Arcy, W.: On Growth and Form. Revised ed. New York, Macmillan, 1942. Biomechanical principles are used to explain the form of skeletons and other structures.

27 DIGESTION AND RESPIRATION

A fundamental characteristic of living organisms is their ability to take in materials quite unlike themselves and to synthesize their own unique cellular constituents from them. Grass becomes beef and beef becomes human flesh by the alchemy of living organisms. Animals must take into their bodies a wide variety of substances to provide the raw materials and energy necessary for the synthesis and maintenance of the wide variety of substances present in cells, for reproduction and for the various activities of the body. These include energy-rich organic compounds, vitamins, oxygen, water and mineral salts. The carbohydrates, fats, proteins and vitamins are synthesized by plants and other animals.

In vertebrates oxygen enters through the respiratory system—gills or lungs—and through the skin in certain animals; the other materials enter through the digestive system. These are the intake systems of the body, but they also serve to some extent in the removal of waste products. Some toxins are removed by the digestive system, and most of the carbon dioxide produced in cellular respiration is eliminated by the respiratory system along with some water and, in fishes at least, some nitrogenous wastes from the metabolism of proteins and nucleic acids.

The vertebrate digestive tract is a tube passing through the body with openings at either end. Food is taken into this tract, where most of it is digested and absorbed. The undigested and unabsorbed residues are eliminated as **feces** from the posterior end of the tract. The process of elimination, known as **defecation,** should not be confused with excretion, which is the discharge of the by-products of metabolism. Excretion is primarily a function of the excretory and respiratory systems and the skin. Most of the material in the feces has, in fact, neither entered the tissues of the body nor taken part in metabolism.

27.1
The Mouth

The basic pattern of the vertebrate digestive system is similar in all vertebrates to that of the frog, described in Chapter 21. In very primitive vertebrates the mouth is unsupported by jaws, but most vertebrates have jaws and a good complement of teeth that aids in food-getting.

Teeth are similar in structure to the placoid scales of sharks and are believed to have evolved from bony scales. A representative mammalian tooth (Fig. 27.1) consists of a **crown** projecting above the gum, a **neck** surrounded by the gum, and one or more **roots** embedded in sockets in the jaws. The crown is covered by a layer of **enamel.** Enamel is the hardest substance in the body and consists almost entirely of crystals of calcium salts. Calcium, phosphate and fluoride are important constituents of enamel and all must be present in the diet in suitable amounts for proper tooth development and maintenance. The rest of the tooth is composed of **dentin,** a substance very similar to bone. In the center of the tooth is a **pulp cavity** containing blood vessels and nerves. A layer of **cement** covers much of the root and holds the tooth firmly in place in the jaw.

The teeth of most vertebrates are cone-shaped structures used primarily for seizing

461

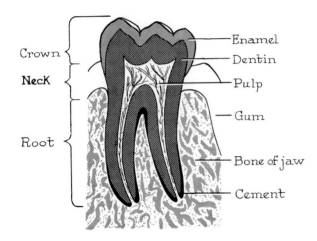

Crown

Neck

Root

Enamel

Dentin

Pulp

Gum

Bone of jaw

Cement

Figure 27.1 Diagram of a section through a human molar tooth. (Modified after Bloom and Fawcett.)

and holding the prey. In mammals, the teeth are differentiated into several types that are used not only for seizing food but often for its mechanical breakdown (p. 429). Mammalian teeth, unlike those of lower vertebrates, are not continuously replaced by new sets. Man, for example, first has a set of deciduous or **milk teeth**—two incisors, one canine and two premolars on each side of each side of each jaw. These are later replaced by **permanent teeth;** in addition, three molars develop on each side of each jaw behind the premolars. The molars last throughout life and are not replaced.

Once food is in the mouth, a fish easily manipulates and swallows it, for the flow of

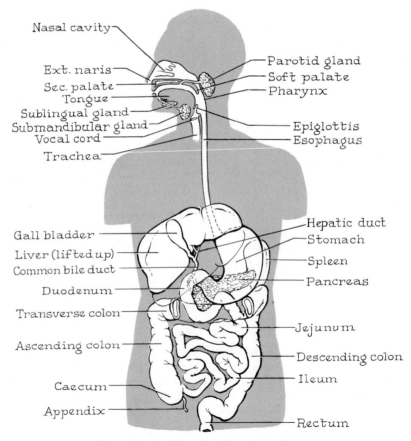

Nasal cavity

Ext. naris
Sec. palate
Tongue
Sublingual gland
Submandibular gland
Vocal cord
Trachea

Parotid gland
Soft palate
Pharynx

Epiglottis
Esophagus

Gall bladder
Liver (lifted up)
Common bile duct
Duodenum
Transverse colon
Ascending colon
Caecum
Appendix

Hepatic duct
Stomach
Spleen
Pancreas

Jejunum

Descending colon
Ileum

Rectum

Figure 27.2 The digestive system of man.

water aids in carrying it back into the pharynx. Oral glands and a tongue are poorly developed in fishes. The evolution of these structures accompanied the transition from water to land, and they became more elaborate in the higher tetrapods. In addition to a liberal sprinkling of simple glands in the lining of the mouth cavity, mammals have evolved several pairs of conspicuous **salivary glands** that are connected to the mouth by ducts. The location of the **parotid, submandibular** and **sublingual glands** of man is shown in Figure 27.2. Originally, oral glands simply secreted a mucous and watery fluid that lubricates the food, and this is still the major function of our saliva. The saliva of most mammals and of a few other tetrapods contains **salivary amylase** which hydrolyzes polysaccharides such as starch. The poison glands of reptiles and the glands of vampire bats that secrete an anticoagulant are other specialized oral glands.

The **tongue** of frogs and anteaters is specialized as a food gathering device, and that of snakes is part of the olfactory mechanism (p. 399), but its chief function in most vertebrates is to manipulate food in the mouth and to aid in swallowing. In many mammals, the tongue pushes the food between the teeth so that the food is thoroughly masticated and mixed with saliva. Then the food is shaped into a ball, a **bolus,** and moved by raising the tongue into the pharynx. The tongue bears numerous microscopic taste buds, and the human tongue is of great importance in speech.

27.2
The Pharynx and Esophagus

Part of the **pharynx** of man lies above the **soft palate** (Fig. 27.3) and receives the internal nares and the openings of the pair of **eustachian tubes** from the middle ear cavities. Another part lies beneath the soft palate just posterior to the mouth cavity. The rest of the pharynx lies posterior to these parts and leads to the esophagus and larynx. Passage of the food into the pharynx initiates a series of reflexes: The muscular soft palate rises and prevents food from entering the nasal cavities, breathing momentarily stops, the larynx is elevated and the epiglottis swings over the glottis, preventing food from entering the larynx; the tongue prevents food from returning to the mouth, and muscular contractions of the pharynx move the bolus into the esophagus.

The pharynx of tetrapods is a rather short region in which the food and air passages cross, but in fishes it is a more extensive area associated with the gill slits. Gill pouches are present in the embryos of mammals, and some of them give rise to glandular structures such as the **thymus** and **parathyroids,** but only parts of the first two remain in adults. The middle ear cavity and the eustachian tube develop from the first pouch (the spiracle of fishes), and part of the second forms the fossa in which the palatine tonsil lies. The **thyroid gland** and the lungs are outgrowths from the floor of the pharynx. Glands de-

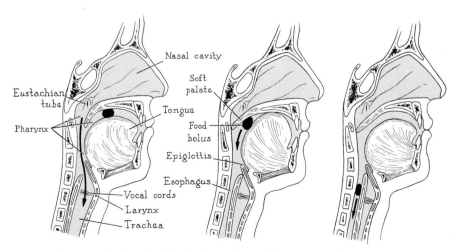

Figure 27.3 Diagrams showing the shifts in the position of the tongue, soft palate and epiglottis when a bolus of food is swallowed. (Slightly modified after Villee: Biology, 5th ed.)

rived from the pharynx are endocrine in nature and will be considered in Chapter 32.

Successive waves of contraction and relaxation of the muscles, known as **peristalsis,** propel the bolus down the esophagus to the stomach. The muscles relax in front of the food and contract behind it. When the food reaches the end of the esophagus the cardiac sphincter, which closes off the entrance to the stomach, relaxes and allows it to enter. The esophagus is generally a simple conducting tube, but in some animals its structure has been modified for storage. The crop of the pigeon, for example, is a modified part of the esophagus.

27.3
The Stomach

The **stomach** is usually a J-shaped pouch (Fig. 27.2) whose chief functions are the storage and mechanical churning of food and the initiation of the chemical breakdown of proteins. Lampreys, lungfishes and some other primitive fishes do not have a stomach, and the absence of this organ is thought to have been a characteristic of the ancestral vertebrates. The early vertebrates, like the lower chordates, were probably filter-feeders that fed more or less continuously on minute food particles that could be digested by the intestine alone. Presumably, the evolution of jaws and the habit of feeding less frequently and on larger pieces of food required an organ for the storage and initial conversion of this food into a state in which it could be digested further in the intestine. In most vertebrates both mechanical and chemical breakdown of food begins in the stomach.

After food enters a typical stomach, the **cardiac sphincter** at its anterior end and the pyloric sphincter at the posterior end close. Muscular contractions of the stomach churn the food, breaking it up mechanically and mixing it with the gastric juice secreted by tubular-shaped **gastric glands.** The gastric juice contains **hydrochloric acid** and the proteolytic enzyme **pepsin.** In addition, **rennin** is particularly abundant in the stomach of young mammals and causes the milk protein casein to coagulate and remain in the stomach long enough to be acted on by pepsin. Rennin has been extracted for centuries from the stomachs of calves and used to curdle milk;

this is an important step in the manufacture of cheese.

In view of the strong proteolytic action of pepsin, one might wonder why it does not digest the wall of the stomach. A major factor preventing such autodigestion is the secretion of copious amounts of mucus by other multicellular glands in the stomach and by scattered cells throughout the stomach lining. The mucus forms a coating which protects the stomach walls from the action of pepsin. Furthermore, the amounts of pepsin and acid in the stomach are very small except when food is present to be digested. Sometimes, however, these safeguards break down, pepsin digests away part of the stomach lining, and a **peptic ulcer** results.

When the food has been reduced to a creamy material known as **chyme,** and most of the microorganisms that entered the stomach with it have been killed by the action of the gastric juices, the pyloric sphincter opens and the food passes into the small intestine. The most fluid food passes first. Indeed, upon entering the stomach, water passes almost immediately into the intestine. The food enters the intestine in spurts and is quickly brought close to a pH of neutrality by the alkalinity of secretions flowing into the intestine from the liver and pancreas.

One striking modification of the stomach is seen in the cow and other ruminants. A cow's stomach consists of a series of four chambers (Fig. 27.4). Food passes first into the **rumen,** where it is temporarily stored and from which it is regurgitated from time to time as the animal ruminates, or chews its cud. The rumen, which has a capacity up to about 200 liters, contains a large colony of bacteria and other microorganisms which play a twofold role in the animal's nutrition. They produce **cellulases,** which split the β-glucosidic bonds of cellulose, and other enzymes that convert the glucose to smaller units, chiefly acetic acid, that are absorbed directly from the rumen. No vertebrate can synthesize cellulases, so herbivores cannot digest cellulose without the aid of microorganisms contained in some part of their digestive tract. Secondly, as the microorganisms multiply, they synthesize amino acids and proteins which are "harvested" and digested by the cow. Eventually, material from the rumen passes through the reticulum and omasum, where much of the water is pressed out of the food mass, and into the

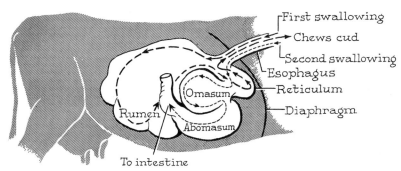

Figure 27.4   Course of food through the stomach of a cow.

abomasum. The abomasum alone contains the gastric glands.

27.4
The Liver and Pancreas

The liver and pancreas are large glandular outgrowths from the anterior part of the intestine. The **liver,** in fact, is the largest organ of the body. Its cells continually secrete **bile,** which passes through hepatic ducts into the **common bile duct** and then up the cystic duct into the **gallbladder.** Bile does not enter the intestine immediately, for a sphincter at the intestinal end of the bile duct is closed until food enters the intestine. Contraction of the wall of the gallbladder forces bile out. The bile that is finally poured into the intestine is concentrated, for a considerable amount of water and some salts are absorbed from the bile in the gallbladder.

Although bile contains no digestive enzymes, it nevertheless has a twofold digestive role. Its alkalinity, along with that of the pancreatic secretions, neutralizes the acid food entering the intestine and creates a pH favorable for the action of pancreatic and intestinal enzymes. Its **bile salts** emulsify fats, breaking them up into smaller globules and thereby providing more surfaces on which fat-splitting enzymes can act. These salts are also essential for the absorption of fats and fat-soluble vitamins (A, D, K). Most of the bile salts are not eliminated with the feces but are absorbed in the intestine along with the fats and are carried back to the liver by the blood stream to be used again.

The color of bile (green, yellow, orange or red in different species) results from the presence of **bile pigments,** excretory products derived from the breakdown of hemoglobin in the liver. The bile pigments undergo further chemical reactions by the intestinal bacteria and are converted to the brown pigments responsible for the color of the feces. If their excretion is prevented by a gallstone or some other obstruction of the bile duct, they are reabsorbed by the liver and gallbladder, the feces are pale, and the skin assumes the yellowish tinge characteristic of jaundice.

All of the blood returning from the intestine, where it has absorbed a variety of materials, passes through the liver before entering the general circulation of the body. In the minute capillary-like spaces of the liver the blood comes into intimate contact with the hepatic cells, which take up, store, interconvert, and alter in many ways the absorbed food molecules. The liver cells also detoxify certain poisonous substances and excrete some of them in the bile.

The **pancreas** is an important digestive gland, producing quantities of enzymes that act upon carbohydrates, proteins, fats and nucleic acids. These enzymes enter the intestine by way of a pancreatic duct that joins the common bile duct. An accessory pancreatic duct may be present and empty directly into the intestine. The pancreas contains patches of endocrine tissue, the **islets of Langerhans,** which will be considered in Chapter 32.

27.5
The Intestine

Most digestion, and virtually all of the absorption of the end products of digestion, occurs in the intestine. Most of the digestive enzymes found in the intestines of vertebrates come from the pancreas, but distinct **intestinal glands** are also present in the wall of the intestines of birds and mammals. Adequate surface area for absorption is made available by the length of the intestine and by outgrowths and internal foldings of various sorts.

The structural details of the intestine vary considerably among vertebrates. Primitive fishes have a short, straight **valvular intestine** extending from the stomach to the cloaca (Fig. 22.11). Its internal surface is increased by a helical fold known as the spiral valve. Tetrapods have lost the spiral valve and make up for this by an increase in the length of the intestine, which becomes more or less coiled. The tetrapod intestine has become further differentiated into an anterior **small intestine** and a posterior **large intestine.** The first part of the small intestine is known as the **duodenum** and, in mammals, the two succeeding parts are the **jejunum** and **ileum** (Fig. 27.2). Most of the large intestine is known as the **colon,** but in mammals the caudal end, which has evolved from part of the cloaca of more primitive vertebrates, constitutes the **rectum.** The rec-

tum opens on the body surface through the **anus.** A blind pouch called the **caecum** is present at the junction of small and large intestines. This is very long in such herbivores as the rabbit and horse and contains a colony of bacteria that digest cellulose. Man has a small caecum with a vestigial **vermiform appendix** on its end. An **ileocaecal** valve is located between the small and large intestine and prevents bacteria in the colon from backing up into this region.

A transverse section of the small intestine of a mammal illustrates the microscopic structure of the digestive tract (Fig. 27.5). As in the frog's stomach (section 21.7), there is an outer covering of **visceral peritoneum** (the serous coat), a layer of **smooth muscle,** a layer of vascular connective tissue, the **submucosa** and, finally, the innermost layer, the **mucosa** or mucous membrane. The stomach and intestine lie in the **peritoneal cavity** — the largest division of the coelom — and are covered by the visceral peritoneum. **Mesenteries,** which support the internal organs and provide a route for blood vessels and nerves, extend from the viscera to the body wall. The outer fibers of the muscular coat are usually described as longitudinal; the inner, as circu-

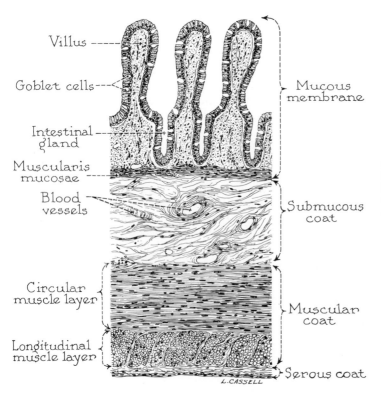

Villus

Goblet cells

Intestinal gland

Muscularis mucosae

Blood vessels

Circular muscle layer

Longitudinal muscle layer

Mucous membrane

Submucous coat

Muscular coat

Serous coat

L. CASSELL

Figure 27.5 Diagrammatic cross section of a portion of the small intestine. Numerous capillaries and a lymphatic vessel enter each villus. (From King and Showers: Human Anatomy and Physiology, 5th ed.)

lar. Actually, both layers are spiral; the outer is an open spiral and the inner, a tight spiral. The relaxations and contractions of these layers are responsible for the peristaltic and churning movements. The mucosa consists of a layer of smooth muscle, connective tissue and, finally, the simple columnar epithelium next to the lumen. In the small intestine of mammals and birds, the mucosa bears. numerous minute, finger-shaped **villi** containing blood capillaries and small lymphatic vessels. The villi protrude into the lumen and increase the intestinal surface manyfold. They are moved about by the muscle layer in the mucosa, the **muscularis mucosae,** and by strands of smooth muscle that extend into them. **Intestinal glands,** which secrete a variety of enzymes, lie at their base. Many mucus-producing **goblet cells** are present in the lining epithelium and their secretion helps to lubricate the food and to protect the lining of the intestine.

The material left in the small intestine, which is still very fluid, passes into the large intestine. Water and many of the salts are absorbed as the residue passes through the colon. If the residue passes through very slowly so that too much water is absorbed, the feces become very dry and hard and **constipation** may result; if it goes through very rapidly and little water is absorbed, **diarrhea** results. Many bacteria reside in the colon and synthesize a variety of vitamins which are absorbed from the colon. The bacteria reproduce very rapidly, and many are eliminated. As much as 25 per cent of the feces may consist of bacteria.

27.6
Digestion of Foods

As we explained in section 2.4, carbohydrates, proteins and fats are all composed of smaller molecules that are held together by **anhydro bonds,** i.e., bonds formed essentially by the removal of a molecule of water. The chemical breakdown, or **digestion,** of these foods is a process of **hydrolytic cleavage,** in which the anhydro bond is split by the addition of water. It requires, however, a great many different enzymes to effect the splitting because the various foodstuffs contain a great variety of molecular species, and enzymes are very specific with respect to the types of molecules they can cleave. Although

digestion is a continuous process involving the simultaneous breakdown of a variety of materials by a host of enzymes, it is convenient to discuss it by considering each major food category in turn.

The building units of most carbohydrates are six carbon sugars (single sugars or **monosaccharides**) including **glucose, galactose** and **fructose.** These are united by pairs into larger double sugars (**disaccharides**) and these in turn into complex **polysaccharides** such as **starch, glycogen** and **cellulose.** Enzymes known as amylases first attack the polysaccharides and split them into disaccharides. Vertebrates do not synthesize an enzyme that can attack the bonds in cellulose (herbivores have a bacterial colony that produces such enzymes), but starch and glycogen are first acted on by **salivary amylase** produced in the salivary glands and split into a double sugar known as **maltose.** Chloride ions present in the saliva are necessary to activate amylase. Its pH optimum is close to neutrality, so its action is eventually stopped by the acidic gastric juice of the stomach. But, since it takes one-half hour or longer for the food and gastric juice to become thoroughly mixed, 40 per cent or more of the starches are split before the amylase is inactivated. Those not broken down in the stomach are soon converted to maltose in the neutral environment of the small intestine by **pancreatic amylase.** There may also be traces of amylase in the intestinal juice. Maltose and the double sugars sucrose and lactose in the food are acted on by specific enzymes (maltase, sucrase and lactase, Table 27.1) produced by the intestinal glands. All yield glucose, and the last two yield fructose and galactose as well. Hydrochloric acid in the stomach also hydrolyzes a certain amount of sucrose. It is in the form of these single sugars that most carbohydrates are absorbed.

You will recall that proteins are composed of **amino acids** linked together by a type of anhydro bond known as a peptide bond. Proteolytic enzymes are either **endopeptidases,** capable of attacking protein molecules at many points along their amino acid chains, except for the terminal groups, or **exopeptidases,** which strip off terminal amino acids from chain fragments. The first of the endopeptidases is **pepsin.** Pepsin is secreted as the enzyme precursor, **pepsinogen,** by the **chief cells** of the gastric glands. The conversion of pepsinogen to pepsin is ini-

Table 27.1 Major Digestive Enzymes

PRODUCED BY	ENZYME	SUBSTRATE ACTED UPON	PRODUCT
Salivary glands	Amylase	Starch	Maltose (double sugar)
Gastric glands	Pepsinogen, converted to pepsin	Proteins	Peptides
	Rennin	Casein	Coagulated casein
Pancreas	Amylase	Starch	Maltose
	Trypsinogen, converted to trypsin	Proteins	Peptides
	Chymotrypsinogen, converted to chymotrypsin	Chymotrypsinogen Proteins	Chymyotrypsin Peptides
	Exopeptidases	Peptides	Amino acids
	Lipase	Emulsified fat	Fatty acids and glycerol
	Nucleases	Nucleic acids	Nucleotides
Intestinal glands	Amylase	Starch	Maltose
	Maltase	Maltose	Glucose (single sugar)
	Sucrase	Sucrose (double sugar)	Glucose and fructose
	Lactase	Lactose (double sugar)	Glucose and galactose
	Enterokinase	Trypsinogen	Trypsin
	Exopeptidases	Peptides	Amino acids
	Lipase	Emulsified fats	Fatty acids and glycerol
	Nucleases	Nucleic acids	Nucleotides

tiated by hydrochloric acid produced by the **parietal cells** of these glands but, once formed, pepsin helps to continue the activation of additional pepsinogen. The acid also brings the stomach contents close to pH 2.0, the optimum for pepsin action. Pepsin action stops when the chyme enters the duodenum, but other endopeptidases, **trypsin** and **chymotrypsin,** then go to work. Both of these are secreted by the pancreas as inactive precursors, **trypsinogen** and **chymotrypsinogen.** Their activation is initiated by **enterokinase,** an intestinal enzyme that converts trypsinogen to trypsin. Once formed, trypsin helps to continue the activation of trypsinogen, and it alone activates chymotrypsinogen. Since the various endopeptidases split bonds adjacent to specific amino acids (e.g., pepsin splits bonds next to tyrosine or phenylalanine), their concerted action is necessary for the fragmentation of protein molecules. Exopeptidases secreted by the pancreas and intestinal glands work on the ends of amino acid chains, stripping off one amino acid after another. Exopeptidases known as **carboxypeptidase** split off the terminal amino acid with the free carboxyl group (COOH, Fig. 2.7); others known as **aminopeptidases** separate the terminal amino acid with the free amino group (NH_2). The free amino

acids resulting from the digestion of proteins are then absorbed into the blood stream.

Fats emulsified by bile salts are attacked by **lipase,** most of which is produced by the pancreas, although some comes from intestinal glands. Fatty acids are disengaged one at a time from glycerol. The mixture of bile salts, fatty acids and partly digested fats collectively emulsifies fats further into particles, many of which are small enough to be absorbed directly.

Carbohydrates, proteins and fats constitute the bulk of the food digested, but many other complex materials are degraded by less familiar enzymes. For example, nucleic acids are hydrolyzed by pancreatic and intestinal enzymes. **Nucleases** break nucleic acids into their constituent nucleotides, and other enzymes separate each of these into their constituent pentoses, phosphoric acid and nitrogenous bases.

27.7
The Control of Digestive Secretions

Each of the various enzymes is secreted at an appropriate time: We salivate when we eat, and gastric juice is produced when food reaches the stomach. The control of these digestive secretions is partly nervous and partly endocrine. The smell of food or its presence in the mouth stimulates sensory nerves that carry impulses to a salivating center in the medulla of the brain. From there the impulses are relayed along motor nerves to the salivary glands, which then secrete.

The control of gastric secretion is more complex. Years ago the famous Russian physiologist Pavlov performed an experiment in which he brought the esophagus of a dog to the surface of the neck and severed it. When the dog ate, the food did not reach the stomach, yet some gastric juice was secreted provided that the **vagus nerve,** which carries motor fibers to the stomach and other internal organs, was left intact. If the vagus nerve was cut, this secretion did not occur. This experiment proved that the control of gastric secretion was at least partly nervous. Subsequently, it was discovered that if the vagus was cut but food was permitted to reach the stomach, a considerable flow of gastric juice was produced. Obviously, the vagus nerve is not the only means of stimulating the gastric glands. Further investigation revealed that, when partly digested food reaches the pyloric region of the stomach, certain of the mucosal cells produce the hormone **gastrin,** which is absorbed into the blood through the stomach wall and ultimately reaches the gastric glands, stimulating them to secrete. When food, especially fats, enters the duodenum, the duodenal mucosa produces the hormone **enterogastrone** which, on reaching the stomach, inhibits the secretion of the gastric glands and slows down the churning action of the stomach. The rate of digestion in the stomach is reduced or stopped. This not only helps to prevent the stomach from digesting its own lining but also enables fatty foods to stay for a longer period in the duodenum where they can be acted on by bile salts and lipase.

One of the first hormones to be discovered was **secretin,** which initiates pancreatic secretion. In 1902 Bayliss and Starling were investigating the current belief that the secretion of pancreatic juice was under nervous control. They found that the pancreas secreted its juice when acid food entered the small intestine even though the nerves to and from the intestine were cut. A stimulant of some sort apparently traveled in the blood.

The injection of acids into the blood stream had no effect, so they reasoned that some stimulating principle must be produced by the intestinal mucosa upon exposure to acid foods. When they injected extracts of such a mucosa into the circulatory system the pancreas secreted.

Secretin has a side effect on the liver, for it increases slightly the rate of bile secretion. However, another hormone, **cholecystokinin,** which is also produced by the duodenal mucosa when acid food is in the duodenum, is largely responsible for causing the gallbladder to contract and release the bile. Vagal stimulation also plays a role in the release of bile.

27.8
Absorption and Utilization of Materials

The large surface area for absorption provided by the intestinal villi is further increased by countless closely packed **microvilli** that protrude from the surface of most of the epithelial cells (Fig. 27.6). These are very small structures that can be resolved only by the electron microscope; in a light microscope they appear as a delicate striation on the border of the cell. Absorption of the end products of digestion and of other simple compounds partly involves simple diffusion of molecules from the intestinal lumen through the mucosa and into the blood and lymphatic capillaries, and partly the active uptake of molecules by the mucosal cells. That the mucosal cells play an active role is indicated by the fact that poisons which interfere with their metabolism greatly reduce the rate and amount of absorption. Among the single sugars, glucose in particular is absorbed much more rapidly than can be accounted for by simple diffusion, and it is also absorbed against a concentration gradient.

The absorption of fats and fatty acids presents a special problem for, unlike the other end products of digestion, they are not water soluble. Apparently, their uptake is facilitated by their combining with bile salts, for this makes a soluble complex. Bile salts are freed within the mucosal cells, and the fatty acids and glycerol are combined with phosphate to form water soluble **phospholipids.** Unhydrolyzed fat and most of

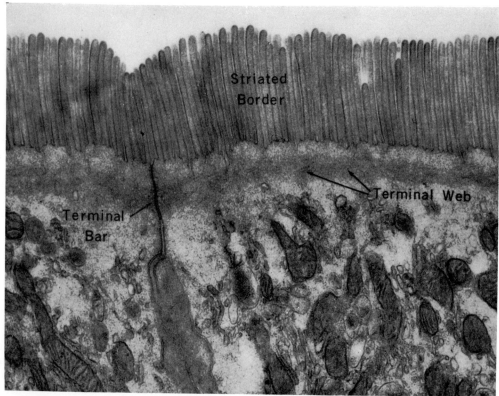

Figure 27.6   Electron micrograph of part of the surface of two epithelial cells from a villus to show the striated border composed of numerous microvilli. The terminal bar is a specialization of the plasma membrane of adjacent cells that unites them tightly and closes the intercellular space. Original photograph, ×30,000. (From Bloom and Fawcett: A Textbook of Histology, 8th ed.)

the phospholipids enter the lymphatic capillaries, but the other absorbed materials enter the capillaries of the blood vessels.

Energy Requirements.   The absorbed products may be used as raw materials for the synthesis of cellular components, as a source of energy, or they may be stored for later use. The minimum energy requirements for a young man are about 1600 Calories per day; they are slightly less for a young woman. This is known as the **basal metabolic rate,** for it represents the amount of energy needed to keep alive when no muscular work is being done and no food is being digested. With heavy physical work, energy requirements may go as high as 6000 Calories per day. A person leading a rather sedentary life requires 2500 to 3000 Calories a day. Most of us establish a balance between the amount of energy expended and the amount taken in with our food. If we consume more food than is required to balance our expenditure of energy, we of course gain weight.

All kinds of food yield energy when me-

tabolized, but not to the same extent. When burned completely in a calorimeter, 1 gm. of carbohydrate or protein yields about 4 Calories, and 1 gm. of fat 9.5 Calories. Though carbohydrates do not contain so many Calories per gram as fats, they constitute the major body fuel for most people. Normally, our diet contains more carbohydrates than fats or proteins.

Carbohydrate Metabolism.   The various kinds of single sugars that are absorbed are carried to the liver, where most are first converted to glucose-6-phosphate and then to glycogen (animal starch) for storage. When energy is needed by body cells, liver glycogen is reconverted to glucose-6-phosphate, and this is transformed to glucose, which is released into the blood stream. Muscle cells can also store glucose as glycogen, but they lack the enzyme (glucose-6-phosphatase) to hydrolyze glucose-6-phosphate to glucose, so muscle glycogen can serve as a fuel for the muscle cells but not as a general reserve for the other cells of the body.

The role of the liver in maintaining a constant level of glucose in the blood was discussed in section 5.2. The glucose molecules are carried to all the cells of the body, where they are oxidized via the Krebs citric acid cycle to carbon dioxide and water and their energy is released. If sugars are absorbed in great excess, not all are converted to glycogen and released as glucose. Some are converted by the liver and other cells to fat and then transported to fat depots for storage. It is a common observation that an excessive intake of carbohydrates or proteins is just as fattening as an excessive intake of fats.

Protein Metabolism. Studies on nitrogen intake and output in animals show that body proteins are continually being broken down and resynthesized. Most of the amino acids in the diet, therefore, are used as raw material for the synthesis of protein needed in the growth, repair and maintenance of tissue; to maintain an adequate supply of enzymes; and for the production of certain hormones including adrenalin, insulin and thyroxin. Many amino acids can be synthesized from other substances, but certain **essential amino acids** can be obtained only from the diet. Most plant proteins lack certain of our essential amino acids, but all are present in a diet that includes meat, eggs and dairy products.

Amino acids are not stored in any appreciable quantity. Excess acids are **deaminated,** the amino group being stripped off; the rest of the molecules can then enter the citric acid cycle to be used immediately as a source of energy or can be converted to glycogen or fat. Carnivores obtain most of their glycogen from amino acids. Deamination occurs principally in the cells of the liver, but it can take place in any of the cells of the body. After deamination, the amino group is converted to ammonia, a toxic substance that would be injurious if it accumulated in the cells. In mammals, ammonia is combined with carbon dioxide to form the less toxic **urea,** which is excreted by the kidney. Urea synthesis takes place in the liver and kidney cells and involves a number of intermediate steps, including ornithine, citrulline and arginine, in a series of reactions known as the **urea cycle.**

Fat Metabolism. As we have pointed out, most fatty acids and glycerol are resynthesized into fat during absorption and the fat is transported as small globules, the chylomicrons, by the lymphatic system to the blood vessels. Within two or three hours after absorbing a fatty meal, the chylomicrons disappear from the blood; some are taken up by liver cells; others are digested within the blood stream by **lipoprotein lipase.** Lipoprotein lipase is produced in great quantities by the fat depots of the body (mesenteries, subcutaneous connective tissue, intermuscular connective tissue), and it is believed that most of the hydrolyzed fat is quickly absorbed and resynthesized by these tissues. In addition to being stored for future use, the fat in certain of these tissues helps to insulate the body against heat loss. Fat absorbed by the liver may be stored or undergo various conversions to other lipid materials. As the need arises for lipid material or more energy, fatty acids and glycerol are mobilized from the adipose tissue and liver and transported chiefly in combination with protein or as phospholipids to the various tissues.

Lipids are found in the plasma membrane and in the membranes of many cell organelles. Fats are also a very important fuel reserve, for they can be metabolized in the citric acid cycle. They yield about twice as much metabolic water as other foodstuffs. Camels, for example, derive a great deal of their water from the metabolism of fat stored in their humps, and much of the water required by the embryos of egg-laying terrestrial vertebrates is derived from fat metabolism.

Vitamins. Other absorbed materials include minerals, steroids, the various building blocks of nucleotides, water and vitamins. By definition, the vitamins are organic substances that an animal needs in minute amounts and must obtain from its environment, for they cannot be synthesized in adequate amounts by the animal in question. Insofar as their specific role in metabolism is understood, they are constituents of coenzymes. If they are lacking in the diet, the reservoir of vitamins that can be stored in the body cells (chiefly liver cells) is used up, metabolic processes dependent on these coenzymes are impaired, and deficiency diseases result. A list of the more common vitamins needed by man and their characteristics is presented in Table 27.2.

Certain vitamin deficiencies are the cause of diseases that have long plagued man. **Beriberi** has been common for centuries among Orientals and other peoples who

Table 27.2   Common Vitamins

VITAMINS	COMMON SOURCES	IMPORTANCE	DISEASE AND SYMPTOMS IF DEFICIENT IN DIET
A	Butter, eggs, fish liver oils. Carotene in plants can be converted to A	Maintenance of epithelial cells, chemistry of vision	Scaly skin, easy infection, night-blindness, xerophthalmia
B Complex:			
B₁, Thiamine	Yeast, meat, whole grain, eggs, milk, green vegetables	Carbohydrate metabolism	Beriberi: nerve and muscle degeneration
B₂, Riboflavin	Same as B₁	Cellular oxidations	Stunted growth, cracked skin
Niacin	Same as B₁	Cellular oxidations	Pellagra: inflammation of the skin, nervous disorders
Folic acid and B₁₂	Same as B₁	Formation of blood cells	Anemia
C, Ascorbic Acid	Citrus fruits, fresh vegetables. Destroyed on cooking	Maintenance of connective tissue and capillary walls	Scurvy: bleeding gums, swollen joints, general weakness
D, Calciferol	Eggs, milk, liver oils. 7-Dehydrocholesterol in skin converted to D on exposure to sunlight	Absorption and utilization of calcium and phosphorus	Rickets: weak bones, defective teeth
E, Alpha-tocopherol	Green vegetables, wheat germ, vegetable oils	Maintenance of reproductive cells	Sterility in poultry, rats and possibly man
K	Green vegetables, colon bacteria. Bile salts necessary for its absorption	Synthesis of prothrombin in liver, hence normal clotting of blood	Bleeding

Figure 27.7 Illustration of hypophosphatemic vitamin D-refractory rickets of simple type. Mother and four year old daughter show typical deformities. (Courtesy of D. Fraser, J.A.M.A., *176*:281, 1961.)

subsist largely on polished rice. Rice hulls, which contain thiamine, prevent the disease when added to the diet. **Pellagra** used to be common in our southern states, for cornmeal, which formerly made up a large part of the diet, contains very little niacin. **Scurvy** was long the scourge of sailors, explorers and others who could not get fresh fruits and vegetables and the ascorbic acid they contain. Many Civil War prisoners such as the ones in Andersonville prison were victims of this disease. Captain James Cook was among the first to notice that feeding his crew such unusual foods (to sailors at least) as sauerkraut reduced the incidence of scurvy. He reported his findings to the Royal Society in 1776, and about two decades later, when more was known about the disease, the British Navy periodically enforced a ration of lime juice on members of all crews. British sailors have been called "limeys" ever since. **Rickets** is a disease of children who have not received sufficient vitamin D; it is characterized by marked malformation of the skeleton (Fig. 27.7).

27.9
Respiratory Membranes

Cellular respiration is an oxidative process in which the energy in the absorbed food molecules is released and made available for the various cellular activities. To maintain it, oxygen must be continuously supplied and the by-products, carbon dioxide and water, must be continuously removed. In vertebrates this involves the uptake of oxygen and the release of carbon dioxide in the respiratory organ, the transportation of these gases by the blood and their exchange between the blood and cells. Gas transportation by the blood, together with exchanges between the blood and cells, were considered in Chapter 5. Here we are concerned with the structure and function of the vertebrate respiratory organs, in which gas exchange with the environment occurs.

All respiratory surfaces, whether in a worm, a fish or a man, consist of a moist, semipermeable, vascular membrane exposed to the external environment so that gas exchange by diffusion can take place between the blood and the environment. The entire body surface of primitive organisms may serve as a respiratory membrane, but the respiratory surface in the higher animals is

generally confined to a limited region and protected in various ways. This reduces the chance of mechanical injury and the amount of body water lost or gained by osmosis via this route, but restricting the size of this membrane poses the problem of providing adequate surface for gas exchange. Each kind of vertebrate has had to solve the dilemma of how to expose these delicate membranes to the environment while protecting them from it to some extent.

27.10
The Respiratory System of Fishes

The respiratory organs of fish are **gills** located in the gill slits and attached to the visceral arches. Since water contains only about 1 per cent dissolved oxygen in contrast to 21 per cent in air, fish must move a large volume of water across their gills. The mechanics of this in a typical bony fish has recently been worked out by Dr. Hughes and his associates at the University of Cambridge. During inspiration both the pharynx and **opercular chambers** expand (Fig. 27.8), causing a decrease in pressure within them relative to the surrounding water. Water is drawn in only through the mouth, for a thin membrane on the free edge of the operculum acts as a valve, preventing entry in this direction. Once in the pharynx, the water passes across the gills into the opercular chamber as a result of the lower pressure there. The opercular chamber acts as a suction pump. Expiration begins with a closure of the mouth, or of **oral valves,** and a contraction of the pharynx and opercular chambers so that the pressure in them exceeds that of the surrounding water. During both inspiration and expiration there is a pressure gradient moving water across the gills. Water does not go down the esophagus, for this is collapsed except when swallowing. Food and other particles are prevented from clogging the gills by **gill rakers,** which act as a strainer.

The gills themselves consist of numerous filaments bearing secondary folds perpendicular to them. Capillary beds are located in the latter, and it is here that gas exchange with the water occurs. This exchange is particularly efficient because the direction of the blood flow in the capillary beds is counter to that of the water current. This

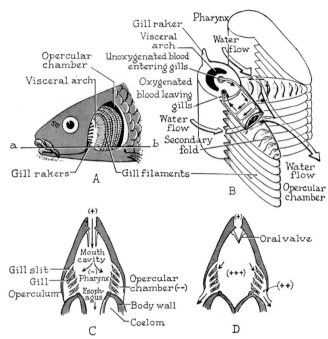

Figure 27.8 External respiration in fishes. *A,* The operculum has been cut away to show the gills in the gill chamber. *C* and *D,* Frontal sections through the mouth and pharynx in the plane of line *a–b* in *A.* Inspiration occurs in *C* and expiration in *D.* Relative water pressures in the various parts of the system are shown by + and −. *B,* An enlargement of several gill filaments. (*B* modified after Hughes.)

ensures that for the duration of the contact there is a greater oxygen tension in the water than in the adjacent capillary bed (Fig. 27.9). The blood can continue to pick up oxygen from the water as long as it is not fully saturated and any oxygen remains in the water. If blood and water were flowing in the same direction, some point of equilibrium would soon be reached at which the blood was not fully saturated, yet considerable oxygen remained in the water.

In addition to gas exchange, the body gains or loses water through the gills and, except for cartilaginous fishes, some nitrogenous wastes are excreted here. The salt-water teleosts also excrete salts through the gills (p. 509).

A number of fishes live in water which has a low oxygen content and they supplement gill respiration by occasionally gulping air. The oxygen in the air can be extracted by gills so long as they remain moist

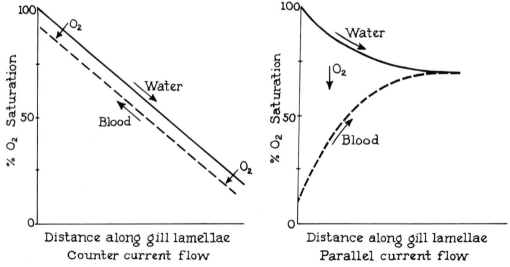

Figure 27.9 Theoretical diagrams to illustrate the effects of counter current or parallel flow on the exchange of oxygen between water and blood. The equilibrium attained in parallel flow would be somewhere about 50 per cent saturation of the blood because of the presence of hemoglobin, yet the blood becomes less fully saturated than it would during counter current flow. (Modified after Hughes.)

and are not collapsed. Closing the opercular chamber enables the mudskipper to keep its gills moist for a while, and even to come out onto the land. The European loach swallows air and extracts the oxygen in a special chamber of its intestine! Other fishes have vascular outgrowths from various parts of the pharynx or opercular chamber that serve as accessory respiratory organs. Seemingly, the development of lungs, which are ventral outgrowths from the pharynx, by early bony fishes was just one of many adaptations which have evolved to supplement aquatic respiration.

Extracting oxygen from swamp water, which is probably the environment in which lungs evolved, poses the problem of saturating the blood with oxygen in an environment with a low oxygen and high carbon dioxide content. As we explained in Chapter 5, the presence of carbon dioxide reduces the oxygen-carrying capacity of respiratory pigments such as hemoglobin. The chemical properties of the hemoglobin of contemporary swamp fish have changed in such a way that it can take up more oxygen in the presence of a given amount of carbon dioxide. This change must also have occurred during the evolution of terrestrial vertebrates, for the carbon dioxide content of the lungs is always higher than that of the external environment, though, of course, not so high as that in the tissues.

27.11
The Respiratory System of Terrestrial Vertebrates

The lungs of early bony fishes evolved into hydrostatic swim bladders in most of their descendants, but they were retained in some that remained in fresh water, and it is from certain of these fishes that tetrapods evolved. Gills, which dry out on exposure to the air, have been lost by adult amphibians but are retained by their aquatic larvae. Many larval amphibians, however, have external gills protruding from the surface of the neck rather than ones within the gill slits. Adult amphibians breathe by simple, saccular lungs, supplemented by a moist skin and other mucous membranes (p. 341). The somewhat awkward mouth pump for moving air in and out of the lungs, and the need for auxiliary respiratory membranes, are among the factors that prevent amphibians from fully exploiting the terrestrial environment. The internal surfaces of the lungs of higher tetrapods have become greatly subdivided and have increased in area enough to dispense with respiration in the skin. These organisms have also developed more efficient means of ventilating the lungs.

In mammals (Fig. 27.10), air is drawn into the paired **nasal cavities** through the **external nares**. These cavities are separated

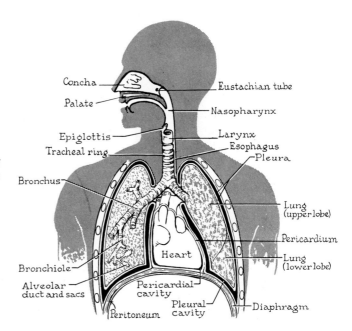

Figure 27.10 Respiratory system of man. Details of the alveolar sacs, here drawn enlarged, are shown in Fig. 27.12.

Concha — Palate — Epiglottis — Tracheal ring — Bronchus — Bronchiole — Alveolar duct and sacs — Peritoneum — Pericardial cavity — Pleural cavity — Heart — Eustachian tube — Nasopharynx — Larynx — Esophagus — Pleura — Lung (upper lobe) — Pericardium — Lung (lower lobe) — Diaphragm from the mouth cavity by a bony palate, and the animal can breathe while food is in its mouth. The surface area of the cavities is increased by a series of ridges known as **conchae,** and the nasal mucosa (in addition to having receptors for smell) is vascular and ciliated and contains many mucous glands. In the nasal cavities the air is warmed and moistened and minute foreign particles are entrapped in a sheet of mucus, which is carried by ciliary action into the pharynx where it is swallowed or expectorated. Inspired air is moistened in primitive tetrapods such as the frog, but cold-blooded tetrapods, in general, do not need so much conditioning of the air as birds and mammals.

Air continues through the **internal nares,** passes through the **pharynx** and enters the **larynx,** which is open except when food is swallowed. The raising of the larynx during swallowing can be demonstrated by placing your hand on the Adam's apple, the external protrusion of the larynx. The **epiglottis** flips back over the entrance of the larynx when it is raised.

The larynx is composed of cartilages derived from certain of the visceral arches and serves both to guard the entrance to the windpipe, or **trachea,** and to house the **vocal cords** (Fig. 27.11). The vocal cords are a pair of folds in the lateral walls of the larynx. They can be brought close together, or be moved apart, by the pivoting of laryngeal

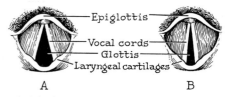

Figure 27.11 A laryngoscopic view of the vocal cords, looking into the larynx from above. *A,* Normal position of vocal cords; *B,* position of cords during speech.

cartilages connected to their dorsal ends. When we speak, they are moved toward each other and the current of air expelled from the lungs sets them vibrating. They, in turn, vibrate the column of air in the larynx, pharynx and mouth, just as the reed in an organ pipe vibrates the column of air in the pipe. Muscle fibers extending between the various cartilages of the larynx control the tension of the cords and the pitch of the sound. The shape of the pharynx, mouth, tongue and lips affects the final quality of the sound. The **glottis** is the opening into the larynx between the vocal cords.

The **trachea** extends down the neck and finally divides into **bronchi** that lead to the pair of **lungs.** Unlike the esophagus, which is collapsed except when a ball of food is passing through, the trachea is held open by C-shaped cartilaginous rings, and air can move freely back and forth. Its mucosa continues to condition the air.

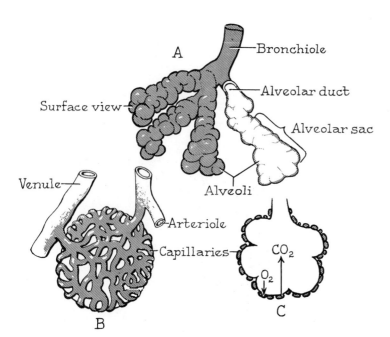

Figure 27.12 *A,* Termination of the respiratory passages in the mammalian lung; *B,* a further enlargement to show the dense capillary network covering a single alveolus; *C,* an alveolus in section. Alveoli have a diameter of 0.2 to 0.3 mm.

The lungs of amphibians lie in the anterodorsal part of the pleuroperitoneal cavity, which is the larger part of the coelom. (The pericardial cavity is the other part.) In most higher vertebrates, the pleuroperitoneal cavity is subdivided into a **pleural cavity** around each lung and a **peritoneal cavity** housing the abdominal viscera. The pleural cavities of mammals lie within the chest, or **thorax,** and are separated from the peritoneal cavity by a muscular diaphragm. A coelomic epithelium, the **pleura,** lines the pleural cavities and covers the lungs. Each bronchus enters a lung, accompanied by blood vessels and nerves, in a mesentery-like fold of pleura (Fig. 27.10).

The bronchi branch profusely within the lungs, and the walls of the respiratory passages become progressively thinner (Fig. 27.10). Each passage eventually terminates in an **alveolar sac** whose walls are so puckered by pocket-shaped **alveoli** that it resembles a cluster of miniature grapes (Fig. 27.12). The alveolar walls are extremely thin and could not be detected with certainty until they were studied with the electron microscope. A network of capillaries, which is so dense that there is little space left between the individual vessels, covers the alveoli. All this provides a huge protected surface for the exchange of gases. A large surface is, of course, necessary in a homoiothermic animal. A frog's lung is a hollow sac with pockets in its walls, but the mammalian lung is so greatly subdivided internally that it resembles a fine-grained sponge.

27.12

The Mechanics and Control of Breathing

Mammalian lungs are ventilated by changing the size of the thoracic cavity and, consequently, the pressure within the lungs. The lungs follow the movements of the chest wall, for they are at once separated from it and united to it by the adhesive force of a thin layer of fluid that lies within the pleural cavities. During normal, quiet inspiration, the size of the thorax is increased slightly, intrapulmonary pressure falls to about 3 mm. Hg below atmospheric pressure, and air passes into the lungs until intrapulmonary and atmospheric pressures are the same.

During normal **expiration,** the size of the thorax is decreased, intrapulmonary pressure is raised to about 3 mm. Hg above atmospheric pressure, and air is driven out of the lungs until equilibrium is again reached. During inspiration, the thorax is enlarged by the contraction of the dome-shaped **diaphragm** and the **external intercostal muscles.** The diaphragm pushes the abdominal viscera posteriorly and increases the length of the chest cavity (Fig. 27.13*A*); the external intercostals raise the sternal ends of the ribs and expand the dorsoventral diameter of the chest. Expiration results primarily from the relaxation of the inspiratory muscles and the elastic recoil of the lungs and chest wall, which are stretched during inspiration. But during heavy breathing, antagonistic expiratory muscles can decrease the size of the thoracic cavity. Contraction of **abdominal muscles** forces the abdominal viscera against the diaphragm and pushes them anteriorly; **internal intercostals** pull the sternal ends of the ribs posteriorly.

The lungs of an adult man can hold about 6 liters of air, but in quiet breathing they contain only about half this amount, of which 0.5 liter is exchanged in any one cycle of inspiration and expiration. This half liter of **tidal air** is mixed with the 2.5 liters of air already in the lungs. Vigorous respiratory movements can lower and raise the intrapulmonary pressure 60 mm. Hg below and above atmospheric pressure, and under these conditions 4 to 5 liters of air can be exchanged. This maximum is known as the **vital capacity.** There is always, however, at least a liter of **residual air** left in the lungs to mix with the tidal air, for the strongest respiratory movements cannot collapse all the alveoli and respiratory passages. Since the inspired air always mixes with a certain amount of stale air already in the lungs, alveolar air always has a lower oxygen content and a higher content of carbon dioxide than atmospheric air. Alveolar air is also saturated with water vapor.

Respiratory movements are cyclic and are controlled by inspiratory and expiratory centers (collectively called the **respiratory center**) in the medulla of the brain. The inspiratory center sends out impulses along the nerves to the inspiratory muscles (neuron #1, Fig. 27.13*B*), and we breathe in. The alveoli fill with air, become stretched, and the resultant sensory impulses traveling to the

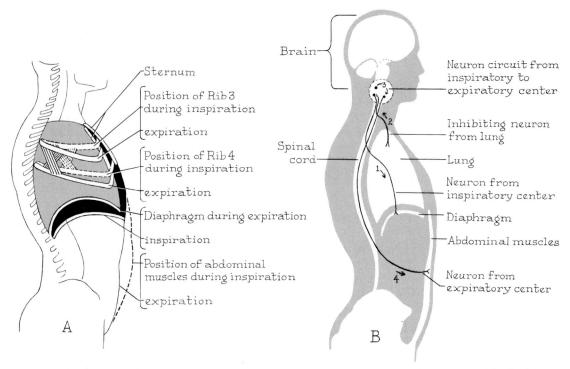

Figure 27.13   Mechanics and control of breathing. *A,* The elevation of the ribs and depression of the diaphragm during inspiration increases the size of the chest cavity, indicated by the black area. *B,* A diagram of the nervous mechanism for controlling the rhythm of breathing. See text for explanation.

respiratory center inhibit inspiration (#2). At the same time, impulses that were initiated in the inspiratory center and took a rather circuitous route within the brain reach the expiratory center (#3) and stimulate it to send impulses out to the expiratory muscles (#4). We breathe out, another volley of impulses leaves the inspiratory center, and the breathing cycle begins again. The inspiratory center tends to be active all the time, ceasing to send out impulses only when it is momentarily inhibited.

This, in brief, is the basis for our regular breathing, but many other factors can affect the rate and depth of respiration. Increased metabolism during exercise, for example, results in an increased carbon dioxide content of the blood. This, in turn, increases the excitability of the respiratory center and we breathe more rapidly and deeply. The same thing happens when we voluntarily hold our breath. Since the lungs are not being ventilated, carbon dioxide accumulates in the alveolar air and blood and eventually reaches a level that activates the respiratory center, and we breathe again involuntarily. One cannot suffocate by holding one's breath.

By expiring vigorously and frequently, we can reduce the carbon dioxide content of the alveolar air and blood below normal limits, and breathing stops until carbon dioxide accumulates again. This is what distance underwater swimmers do, for it increases the time needed for the carbon dioxide content of the blood to reach the threshold and initiate breathing. Hyperventilation, however, can be a dangerous procedure, for the carbon dioxide level may become so low that the oxygen content of the blood is exhausted and one becomes unconscious before carbon dioxide has been restored to levels high enough to activate the respiratory center. The accumulation of carbon dioxide in the blood is responsible for initiating breathing in a newborn baby.

Receptors in the larynx and trachea can also affect respiration. If food inadvertently enters these passages, these receptors are stimulated and a very vigorous expiration, i.e., a cough, results. The cough reflex is one of many safeguards in the body that are activated if something goes wrong with the primary control mechanism, in this case the swallowing reflex.

QUESTIONS

1. How do the teeth of mammals differ from those of lower vertebrates?
2. What normally prevents food from going down "the wrong way" when we swallow? What happens if it does start down the larynx?
3. What reasons can you give for the absence of a stomach in ancestral vertebrates?
4. Would you expect rennin to be present in the stomach of the young of nonmammalian vertebrates?
5. What prevents the wall of the digestive tract from being digested?
6. How is it possible for herbivorous vertebrates to digest cellulose?
7. If one were to eat a ham sandwich, where and by what would its various components be digested? What controls the secretion of the digestive enzymes required? What would happen to the products of digestion?
8. What are the functions of the large intestine?
9. How does defecation differ from excretion? What excretory products may be present in the feces?
10. List the functions of the liver.
11. How do the gills of fishes fulfill the requirements of respiratory membranes? How is water circulated across them?
12. What exchanges between the body and the environment occur in the gills of fishes?
13. In what group of vertebrates, and under what environmental conditions, did lungs first evolve?
14. In what respects is the external respiration of amphibians poorly adapted to the terrestrial environment? How has this been improved in higher tetrapods?
15. How is inspired air conditioned in mammals? Why is this more important in a mammal than in a frog?
16. Why is it that alveolar air differs in composition from atmospheric air? Of what significance is this?
17. What causes the increase in the rate and depth of breathing during exercise? Why is such an increase necessary?

ANNOTATED REFERENCES

Additional information on digestion and respiration can be found in the general references on vertebrate organ systems cited at the end of Chapter 26.

Baldwin, E. B.: Dynamic Aspects of Biochemistry. 3rd ed. Cambridge, Cambridge University Press, 1957. The chemistry of digestion and many aspects of metabolism are lucidly described.

Comroe, J. H., Jr.: The lung. Scientific American *214*:57, (Feb.) 1966. A fascinating summary of pulmonary anatomy and physiology.

Conference for National Cooperation in Aquatics: The New Science of Skin and Scuba Diving. New York, Association Press, 1962. This standard and widely used manual includes excellent discussions on the physiology of diving.

Dill, D. B.: Life, Heat and Altitude. Physiological Effects of Hot Climates and Great Heights. Cambridge, Harvard University Press, 1938. Respiratory adaptations to deserts and mountains are included in this old but still reliable little book.

Fulton, J. F.: Selected Readings in the History of Physiology. Springfield, Ill., Charles C Thomas, 1930. Interesting accounts of the discovery of digestive and respiratory processes are included in this very readable book.

28 BLOOD AND CIRCULATION

All animals, from the simplest protozoan to the most complex vertebrate, must have some arrangement for transporting a wide variety of materials throughout their bodies. As we pointed out in Chapter 5, the simple diffusion of molecules always plays an important part in transportation and this is adequate in itself in the smaller and less active organisms. But the vertebrates and many of the higher invertebrates are so large and active that diffusion alone cannot suffice. Complex circulatory systems are necessary for the rapid transport of digested food from the alimentary tract, and of oxygen from the lungs, to all the tissues, and for carrying carbon dioxide and other metabolic wastes to the sites where they are discharged from the body.

28.1
The Vertebrate Circulatory System

The vertebrate circulatory system not only transports gases, foods and waste products but has other important functions as well. By conveying hormones it supplements the nervous system in integrating body activities. It plays an important role in maintaining **homeostasis,** i.e., the constancy of the internal environment. The blood carries away excess water from the tissues and supplies water when necessary. It helps to regulate the pH of the body fluids. The rate of its circulation through the skin is a factor in the control of body temperature in birds and mammals. Special cells in the blood function

in wound healing and in protecting the body from the invasion of viruses and bacteria.

The circulatory system includes not only the complex system of vessels but also the fluids within them. There are about 15 liters of extracellular fluid in the body of an adult man, and about one-third of this is **blood.** The remainder includes the **tissue fluid** that lies between and bathes the cells of the body, the **lymph** that moves slowly in the lymph vessels, the **cerebrospinal fluid** in the cavities of the central nervous system, the aqueous and vitreous humors of the eye, and the fluids in the coelom. The chief difference between blood and tissue fluid or lymph is the presence in the blood of red blood cells and abundant soluble proteins.

The fundamental pattern of the vessels in a mammal is shown in Figure 28.1. A muscular **heart** propels blood through **arteries** to **capillaries** in the tissues. Exchanges between the circulatory system and the cells of the body can occur only through the walls of the capillaries. Molecules of nutrients, wastes, oxygen, carbon dioxide and water, but not the large protein molecules or the red blood cells, pass readily through the capillary walls. The tissues are drained by the veins, which return blood to the heart, and by a separate system of **lymph capillaries.** Lymph capillaries lead to **lymph vessels,** which pass through **lymph nodes,** and finally empty into the veins where the venous pressure is lowest, a short distance from the heart. The lymph nodes are an important link in the body's system of defense mechanisms. They produce one kind

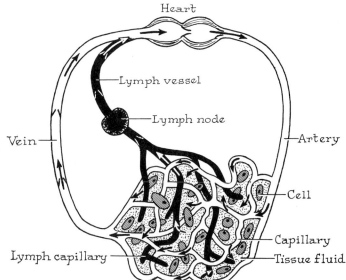

Figure 28.1 The fundamental structure of the mammalian circulatory system. Arrows indicate the direction of the flow of blood and tissue fluid.

of white blood cell (**lymphocytes**) and contain cells that engulf foreign particles.

28.2
Blood Plasma

Blood is one of the tissues of the body. It consists of a liquid component, the **plasma,** and several types of formed elements—red blood cells, white blood cells and platelets

(Fig. 28.2)—which flow along in it. The plasma is a complex liquid that is in dynamic equilibrium with the tissue fluid and the fluid within the cells. It is constantly gaining and losing substances, yet its composition remains remarkably constant. We have seen, for example, how the liver maintains a constant concentration of glucose in the blood despite the heavy intake of glucose from the digestive tract after a meal, and the constant release of glucose to the tissue fluid and cells. Plasma

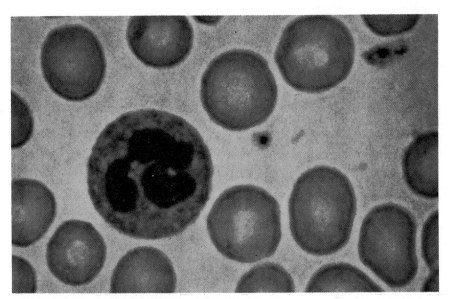

Figure 28.2 Photomicrograph of human blood cells. Many erythrocytes and one large leukocyte (a neutrophil) can be seen. The single dark dot and the clump of several dots are platelets. (From Zucker, Scientific American, Vol. 204, No. 2.)

is about 90 per cent water, 7 to 8 per cent soluble proteins, 1 percent salts, and the remaining 1 to 2 per cent is made up of a variety of small organic molecules—urea, amino acids, glucose, lipids and hormones.

The chief plasma proteins are albumins, globulins and fibrinogen. Other components of the plasma can easily pass through the semipermeable capillary walls, but the proteins are rather large molecules and most remain in the blood in the capillary bed. They exert an osmotic pressure that is responsible for the return of water from the tissue fluids. Hydrostatic pressure, i.e., blood pressure, forces the water out of the capillaries into the tissue fluid. These two forces normally just balance and keep the blood volume constant. Many of the proteins have additional functions. Fibrinogen is essential for blood clotting, and certain of the globulins, particularly the gamma globulins, are antibodies which provide immunity to certain infectious diseases.

The plasma proteins, hemoglobin in the red blood cells and certain of the inorganic salts in the blood are also important buffers. A **buffer** is a mixture of a weak acid and its salt, or of a weak base and its salt. A buffer tends to prevent a change in the pH of a solution when an acid or base is added. Complex animals such as mammals cannot tolerate wide fluctuations in pH, and the pH of the blood is held remarkably constant, at about 7.4. Buffers combine reversibly with the hydrogen ions (H^+) released by the dissociation of acids into their constituent ions. Acidic substances are constantly produced as by-products of cell metabolism and enter the blood. Carbon dioxide, for example, is produced in cellular respiration and tends to increase the acidity of the blood for it combines with water to form carbonic acid, H_2CO_3. Basic substances, which release hydroxyl ions (OH^-), are much less common by-products of metabolism. Buffers neutralize their effects by releasing hydrogen ions, which combine with the hydroxyl ions to form water (H_2O). Eventually, the acidic or basic substances are removed from the body, carbon dioxide by the lungs and the others by the kidneys.

28.3
Red Blood Cells

The red blood cells, or **erythrocytes,** are the most numerous of the formed elements

of the blood, there being about 5,000,000 of them in each cubic millimeter of blood in an adult human. Those of mammals lose their nuclei as they develop, and mature mammalian red cells are biconcave discs. Such a shape provides more surface area than a sphere of equal volume, and the increased surface area, in turn, facilitates the passage of materials through the plasma membrane.

Erythrocytes contain the respiratory pigment **hemoglobin,** which acts as a buffer and is essential for the transport of oxygen and carbon dioxide. As we explained in section 5.4, hemoglobin (Hb) combines with oxygen in the capillaries of the lungs, where the oxygen tension is high, to form **oxyhemoglobin** (HbO_2), and oxyhemoglobin releases oxygen in the tissue capillaries, where the oxygen tension is low. It has been estimated that we would need a volume of blood 75 times as great or the blood would have to circulate very much faster than it does if all of the oxygen were carried in physical solution instead of in combination with hemoglobin.

The uptake and release of oxygen by hemoglobin is intimately related to the transport of carbon dioxide. Carbon dioxide, which has a high tension in the tissues, diffuses into the blood. Only a little bit is carried in physical solution. Up to 20 per cent combines directly with oxyhemoglobin to form **carbaminohemoglobin** ($HbCO_2$), and in so doing tends to drive off the oxygen as shown at top of opposite page.

This reaction does not have any marked effect upon the pH of the blood. The rest of the carbon dioxide unites with water to form carbonic acid. This reaction occurs much more rapidly in the erythrocytes than in the plasma because they contain the enzyme **carbonic anhydrase,** which speeds up the reaction some 1500 times. Most of the carbonic acid, in turn, dissociates into its constituent hydrogen and bicarbonate ions. The hydrogen ions produced combine with oxyhemoglobin, and this facilitates the dissociation of oxyhemoglobin and the release of oxygen to the tissues. Potassium ions (K^+), which are loosely associated with oxyhemoglobin, are also released as oxyhemoglobin takes up hydrogen ions to become reduced hemoglobin. Many of the bicarbonate ions diffuse out of the cell into the plasma, where they combine with sodium to form sodium bicarbonate. As the cell loses

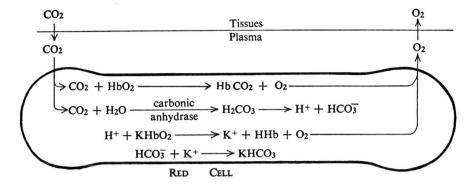

these negative ions, chloride ions (Cl^-) diffuse in, so the electrochemical balance of the cell is maintained. Most of the bicarbonate remaining in the cell unites with the potassium ions to form potassium bicarbonate. Thus most of the carbon dioxide is carried as carbonic acid, bicarbonate ions and potassium and sodium bicarbonate.

These reactions associated with the transport of carbon dioxide also maintain the pH of the cell close to neutrality. Oxyhemoglobin is a stronger acid than hemoglobin, and the conversion of oxyhemoglobin (HbO_2) to hemoglobin (Hb) would tend to raise the pH within the red cell (make it more alkaline). The formation and dissociation of carbonic acid would tend to lower the pH within the red cell (make it more acid). These two opposing phenomena tend to balance each other and the pH of the erythrocyte is maintained essentially unchanged.

All these reactions are reversible, and their direction is determined by the relative levels of carbon dioxide and oxygen. In the tissues, carbon dioxide is continually produced, oxygen continually consumed. There is a relatively high level of carbon dioxide, so the reactions move in the direction of binding carbon dioxide and releasing oxygen. Oxygen is diffusing into the capillaries of the lungs and carbon dioxide out. There is a

relatively high level of oxygen, so the reactions move in the direction of binding oxygen and releasing carbon dioxide as shown in the diagram below.

These reactions enable the blood to carry a great deal more oxygen and carbon dioxide than it could in simple physical solution; they prevent the pH of the blood from changing greatly; and they facilitate the release of oxygen in the tissues of the body and the release of carbon dioxide in the lungs. The amount of oxygen that can be delivered to the tissues is shown in the oxygen dissociation curve for hemoglobin in Figure 28.3. (Review pp. 82 to 84 for an interpretation of such a curve.)

The oxygen-carrying capacity of hemoglobin is determined by its structure. Each molecule of hemoglobin is composed of a protein (a **globulin**) which in turn is made up of four polypeptide chains. One prosthetic group (a **heme**), containing an atom of iron, is associated with each chain, hence there are four iron atoms in each molecule of hemoglobin. During the formation of oxyhemoglobin, one molecule of molecular oxygen (O_2) forms a very loose bond with each iron atom. Since a single erythrocyte contains as many as 265,000,000 molecules of hemoglobin, a tremendous amount of oxygen can be carried.

O₂ Lungs CO₂
Plasma

$O_2 + Hb\,CO_2 \longrightarrow HbO_2 + CO_2$

$KHCO_3 \longrightarrow K^+ + HCO_3^-$

$O_2 + HHb + K^+ \longrightarrow KHbO_2 + H^+$

$H^+ + HCO_3^- \xrightarrow{\text{carbonic anhydrase}} H_2CO_3 \longrightarrow H_2O + CO_2$

RED CELL

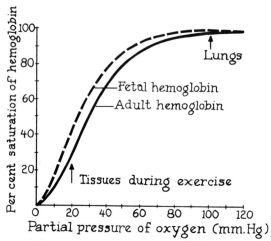

Figure 28.3 Oxygen dissociation curves for fetal and adult hemoglobin. At a partial pressure of 100 mm. Hg in the lungs, adult hemoglobin becomes about 98 per cent saturated. It can give up nearly 70 per cent of its oxygen when it reaches the tissues, where the partial pressure of oxygen may be as low as 20 mm. Hg.

The composition of the polypeptide chains influences the facility with which hemoglobin takes up and gives off oxygen. Not all hemoglobins are alike. Fetal hemoglobin, for example, has a greater affinity for oxygen than adult hemoglobin. At any given partial pressure of oxygen it has a higher per cent saturation than maternal hemoglobin (Fig. 28.3), which, of course, enables it to take oxygen away from the mother's blood. By 20 weeks after birth, fetal hemoglobin has been replaced by the adult type.

Mature mammalian erythrocytes do mot survive indefinitely. Experiments which involve tagging them with radioactive iron show that they have a life span of about 120 days. Cells lining the blood spaces of the spleen and liver eventually engulf or **phago-cytize** the red cells and digest them. The iron of the heme is salvaged by the liver and is reused, but the rest of the molecule is excreted as bile pigment. Under normal circumstances, new erythrocytes and hemoglobin are synthesized as rapidly as the old are destroyed. But if delivery of oxygen to the tissues is reduced, as during prolonged exercise or when ascending to a high altitude, more cells are made available so that delivery of oxygen to the tissues is restored to normal levels. Many additional erythrocytes can be released immediately into the circulatory blood from reserves stored in the spleen,

but the reduction in the level of oxygen also triggers a set of incompletely understood reactions that leads to an increased rate of synthesis of erythrocytes. In lower vertebrates, red cells are produced in vascularized connective tissues of the kidney, liver and spleen. These sites are important during the embryonic development of mammals, but the red bone marrow is the primary source of erythrocytes in the adult.

Erythrocyte destruction and production are surprisingly rapid. From the total number of red cells in the body and their average life span, one can calculate that about 2,500,000 are made and destroyed each second of the day and night. If the rate of production of cells or of hemoglobin decreases, some type of **anemia** results. Anemia is characterized by a decrease in the number of red cells per cubic millimeter of blood, by a decrease in the amount of hemoglobin per red cell, or both. In pernicious anemia the number of erythrocytes steadily decreases. Eating large quantities of liver increases the rate of red cell formation, for liver is rich in vitamin B_{12}, which is necessary for normal erythrocyte development. A person with pernicious anemia cannot absorb enough B_{12}, even though the requisite amount may be present in the diet, because the lining of his stomach does not secrete enough "intrinsic factor," necessary for the absorption of B_{12}. If an excess is made available by giving foods especially rich in B_{12}, enough can be absorbed.

28.4
Platelets and Blood Clotting

Platelets are non-nucleated blobs of cytoplasm that continually bud off from giant cells in the bone marrow. They number about 250,000 per cubic millimeter of blood in man and live for eight to 10 days. They, and the thrombocytes of lower vertebrates, play an important role in stopping blood flow after an injury. First, they tend to collect at the injured surface of small, cut vessels, forming a mechanical plug. Second, they break down at the site of an injury, releasing phospholipids that interact in a complex and incompletely understood way with tissue factors and certain plasma globulins to form **thromboplastin.** Thromboplastin acts as an enzyme, quickly converting another plasma globulin, **prothrombin,** into **thrombin.** This reaction requires the presence of calcium ions and other plasma factors. (A common way to preserve whole blood and prevent clotting is to add substances, such as sodium citrate, that bind calcium.) Thrombin, in turn, acts as an enzyme and mediates the change of the soluble protein **fibrinogen** into an insoluble one known as **fibrin.** This involves the removal of two peptides from the fibrinogen molecule to form activated fibrin. These activated molecules polymerize rapidly into long fibrin threads which form a delicate network within which the formed elements of the blood and plasma are trapped. A **clot** has formed. As time goes on the clot contracts, and within an hour it has squeezed out most of the plasma. This expressed plasma, which is similar to normal plasma except for the absence of fibrinogen, is a yellowish liquid known as **serum.** Serum, of course, cannot clot. Vitamin K, which is necessary for clotting, does not enter into this series of reactions directly, but is essential for the production of prothrombin in the liver. The essentials of this complex series of reactions are below.

Clotting rarely occurs within blood vessels because the process must be triggered by the breakdown of a sufficient number of platelets to overcome the effects of a strong anticoagulant, **heparin,** which is also present in circulating blood. Heparin normally prevents the conversion of prothrombin to thrombin but occasionally a clot, known as a **thrombus,** will form in a vessel, and it can be very serious if it plugs a vessel that supplies a vital area. In the hereditary disease **hemophilia** there is a deficiency of one of the substances required for the formation of thromboplastin, clots do not form and the slightest scratch may lead to fatal bleeding. This disease attracted special attention because it appeared in several different European royal families and was apparently inherited from Queen Victoria of England.

28.5
White Blood Cells

Five types of white blood cells, or **leukocytes,** can be recognized—**lymphocytes, monocytes, neutrophils, eosinophils** and **basophils** (Fig. 3.16). They differ in the size and shape of the nucleus, and in the amount and granulation of the cytoplasm. Collectively, there are only about 7000 per cubic millimeter in human blood. They are produced in the lymph nodes, the spleen and red bone marrow, and live from one to four days. Although they are passively carried by the blood, most leukocytes can also creep about by sending out cytoplasmic processes in ameboid fashion. This enables them to squeeze between the cells of the capillary walls, and many are lost from the body by escaping through the capillaries in the lungs, digestive tract and kidneys.

These cells play important roles in protecting the body against disease organisms. Bacteria penetrating through a wound produce toxins which, together with factors in injured tissue, cause blood vessels in the infected area to dilate and also to become more permeable to liquids and to white blood cells. The area becomes **inflamed** and **swollen;** vast numbers of leukocytes migrate into the region and begin to engulf and digest bacteria and destroyed tissue. Neutrophils are among the first cells to become active, but if the infection

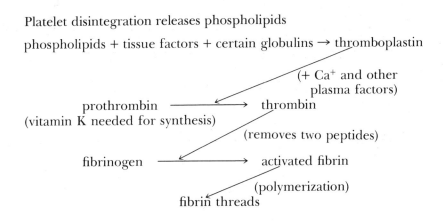

Platelet disintegration releases phospholipids

phospholipids + tissue factors + certain globulins → thromboplastin

(+ Ca$^+$ and other plasma factors)

prothrombin ———→ thrombin
(vitamin K needed for synthesis)

(removes two peptides)

fibrinogen ———→ activated fibrin

(polymerization)

fibrin threads

is severe they break down and contribute, along with the bacteria and tissue debris, to the **pus** that forms. As time goes on, monocytes and lymphocytes transform into large phagocytic cells known as **macrophages,** and they clean up the area. Other lymphocytes transform into fibroblasts which, along with fibroblasts in the connective tissue, repair the injury by producing fibers and forming **scar tissue.**

28.6
Immunity

The **plasma cells** in the tissues are an additional line of defense against invading bacteria or other foreign protein **(antigens),** for they respond by producing **antibodies** that help to destroy the antigen. Plasma cells develop primarily from the delicate connective tissue reticular cells in lymph nodes and other lymphoid tissues and migrate into the tissues. An extensively developed endoplasmic reticulum makes it possible for them to produce large amounts of antibody (Fig. 28.4). Al-

though any foreign protein and certain polysaccharides may act as an antigen and activate the plasma cells, the antigens with which we are most familiar are certain proteins of the bacteria and viruses that cause infectious diseases. Antibodies combat the antigens in one of several ways. They may combine with the antigens and neutralize them; they may cause the invading microorganisms to clump, or **agglutinate,** thereby effectively preventing a further penetration of the body; they may cause the invading microorganisms to break up and dissolve (a phenomenon known as **lysis**); or they may make the invaders more susceptible to phagocytosis.

The antigen-antibody reaction is generally very specific. Antibodies that have developed in response to mumps viruses, for example, will not combine with other antigens. It is believed that the specific configuration of the antigen and antibody molecules resembles a lock and key. Only antibodies that have developed in response to a given antigen can fit on the surface of the antigen and react with it.

The production of antibodies by plasma cells continues, perhaps for many years, after

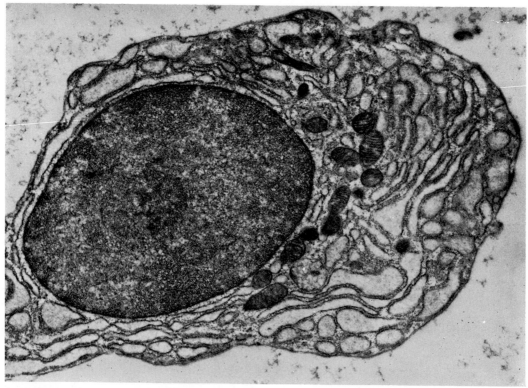

Figure 28.4 Electron micrograph of a human plasma cell showing the hypertrophied endoplasmic reticulum. (From Bloom and Fawcett after Van Breeman.)

the patient has recovered. The gamma globulin fraction of the plasma is largely composed of antibodies. If a subsequent invasion of the same type of antigen occurs during this period, antibodies specific for it will already be present and more can be made quickly from sensitized plasma cells. The infected person does not contract the disease and is said to be **immune.** The immunity that is acquired as a result of having once had mumps, smallpox and certain other infectious diseases lasts a very long time, generally for life. The immunity to certain other diseases lasts for a much shorter time and, after it is lost, one can get the disease again.

However, one need no longer become ill in order to develop an immunity to many diseases. During the late eighteenth century, Edward Jenner observed that milkmaids and others who handled the udders of cows infected with cowpox never got smallpox. In 1796, he took a bit of the material from the pustules of an infected cow and scratched it into the skin of a person. Individuals so treated acquired a mild disease but thereafter were immune to smallpox. Cowpox is caused by a virus known as the **vaccinia** virus; smallpox, by a different but related **variola** virus. Vaccinia does not cause serious disease in man, but is similar enough to variola so that antibodies that develop in response to it are effective in combating variola. Jenner's experiments were the beginning of the **vaccination technique.** Since then, many kinds of vaccines have been developed. Usually a related and less virulent microorganism, which could serve as the basis of a vaccine, is not available, but vaccines can be produced by taking the actual disease organisms, rendering them harmless by appropriate treatment, and injecting them. Although the organisms are incapable of causing the disease, they are still capable of inducing antibody formation. One of man's recent triumphs over disease has been the development by this method of a vaccine for poliomyelitis.

Immunities may be natural, be actively acquired, or be passively acquired. All of us have a **natural immunity** to certain infectious diseases that affect other organisms. Thus, the virus for distemper, which is often fatal to dogs, has no effect on man. It is probable that some of our naturally occurring gamma globulins react with these invading antigens before they can cause any trouble. Immunity that is acquired by exposure to the antigen, either by contracting the disease or by vaccination, is said to be **active immunity,** for the person exposed actively produces the antibodies. A **passive immunity** can be acquired by injecting serum or the gamma globulin fraction which contains antibodies that have been produced by another individual or organism **(antisera).** A passive immunity lasts for only a few weeks, so injections of antisera are used to help combat antigens that have already invaded a patient rather than as a long-term preventive measure.

28.7
Blood Groups

When the practice of transfusing blood from one person to another was begun, it was found that the transfusions were sometimes successful, but more often they were not and erythrocytes in the blood of the recipient would clump (agglutinate), with fatal results. Careful analysis by Landsteiner at the beginning of this century showed that specific antigenic proteins, called A and B, might be present within the erythrocytes. These antigens are called **agglutinogens,** since they may cause agglutination of the red cells. Some individuals have protein A, some B, some both A and B, and some neither. Antibodies **(agglutinins)** specific for these agglutinogens, and designated *a* and *b*, may be present in the plasma. If an individual whose plasma contains agglutinin *a* should receive blood from another whose erythrocytes contain agglutinogen A, an antigen-antibody reaction occurs, and the donor's erythrocytes agglutinate in the recipient's plasma.

Four main groups of persons can be recognized, according to the presence or absence of these agglutinogens and agglutinins (Table 28.1). Blood containing a certain agglutinogen does not, of course, contain the agglutinin specific for it. If it did, it would agglutinate itself. Transfusions between members of the same group are perfectly safe, and transfusions between different groups are also safe provided that the donor's erythrocytes do not contain an agglutinogen that will react with the recipient's agglutinins. The agglutinins in the donor's plasma become so diluted in the recipient that they have no effect and they may be disregarded unless an unusually large transfusion is

Table 28.1   Human Blood Groups

BLOOD GROUP	AGGLUTINOGEN IN ERYTHROCYTES	AGGLUTININS IN PLASMA
O (Universal donor)	None	*a* and *b*
A	A	*b*
B	B	*a*
AB (Universal recipient)	A and B	None

given. Members of Group O, who have neither of the agglutinogens, can give blood to members of any group and are "universal donors." But since their plasma contains both of the agglutinins, they can receive blood only from members of their own group. Members of Group AB, in contrast, have neither agglutinin, and can receive blood from members of any group. Since they have both agglutinogens, they can give blood only to members of their own group. They are "universal recipients." Members of Groups A and B can give blood to members of Group AB and receive from members of Group O. The inheritance of these blood groups is considered in section 34.17.

28.8
The Rh Factor

A number of other inherited antigenic proteins may be present in the blood. Most are rare and not apt to be involved in transfusions, but one that is common is the **Rh factor,** so called because it was first discovered in the rhesus monkey. About 87 per cent of North American whites have this factor in their red cells and are said to be Rh positive. The remaining 13 per cent do not have it, hence are Rh negative. If a mother is Rh negative and the father Rh positive, the fetus may inherit the factor from the father. In theory, none of the fetal blood crosses the placenta to enter the mother's blood, but there are usually small breaks in the placenta that permit some mixing. Rh positive blood of the fetus, on entering the mother, induces the formation of antibodies. This is a slow process and not enough are likely to be formed to cause trouble in the first pregnancy. If a second fetus is also Rh positive, more Rh positive blood enters the mother and the build-up of antibodies in the mother's blood is quite fast. Some of these get back into the Rh positive blood of the fetus and cause agglutination and hemolysis of the red blood cells. This condition, **erythroblastosis fetalis,** may be fatal, or may result in injury to the brain from the bile pigment (bilirubin) formed from the breakdown of hemoglobin released by the hemolysis of the red cells. A newborn infant showing symptoms of it can be saved by extensive transfusions. Ordinarily, not enough Rh positive blood enters the mother to cause any harm, but her blood contains the antibodies, and if she subsequently needs a transfusion for any reason, Rh negative blood must be used.

28.9
Patterns of Circulation

Heart, arteries, capillaries and veins constitute the **cardiovascular system;** the lymphatic vessels and nodes comprise the **lymphatic system.** Most vertebrates have both, but primitive vertebrates such as cyclostomes and cartilaginous fishes have no lymphatic system.

Primitive Fishes. The cardiovascular system has undergone some striking changes during the evolution of vertebrates. Most of these are correlated with the shift from gills to lungs as the site of external respiration that occurred during the transition from water to land and with the development of the efficient, high pressure circulatory system necessary for an active terrestrial vertebrate.

In a primitive lungless fish (Fig. 28.5), all of the blood entering the heart from the veins has a low oxygen and a high carbon dioxide content; i.e., it is venous blood. The heart consists of a series of chambers (a **sinus venosus,** a single **atrium,** a single **ventricle** and a **conus arteriosus**) arranged in linear sequence. The heart increases the blood pressure, which is very low in the veins, and sends the blood out through an artery, the **ventral aorta,** to five or six pairs of **aortic arches** that extend dorsally through capillaries in the gills to the **dorsal aorta.** Carbon

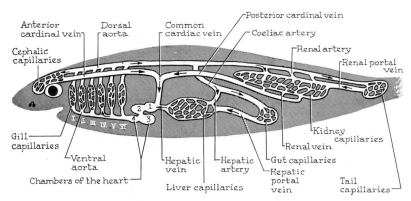

Figure 28.5 The major parts of the cardiovascular system of a primitive fish. *1,* Sinus venosus; *2,* atrium; *3,* ventricle; *4,* conus arteriosus of the heart. The aortic arches are numbered with Roman numerals. Only traces of the first aortic arch remain in the adults of most fishes.

dioxide is removed and oxygen is added as the blood flows through the gills; i.e., it changes to arterial blood. The dorsal aorta distributes this through its various branches to all parts of the body.

Blood pressure decreases as blood flows along because of the friction between the blood and the lining of the vessels. Blood pressure is reduced considerably as the blood passes through the capillaries of the gills, for friction is greatest in vessels of small diameter. Blood pressure in the ventral aorta of a dogfish during heart contraction, for example, is 32 mm. Hg; that in the dorsal aorta is 16 mm. Hg. Thus the blood distributed by the dorsal aorta is under relatively low pressure, and this will be even lower by the time it reaches the capillaries in the tissues. Circulation in primitive fishes is rather sluggish and not conducive to great activity.

Veins drain the capillaries of the body (where blood pressure is further reduced) and lead to the heart, but not all veins go directly to the heart. In primitive fish, blood returning from the tail first passes through capillaries in the kidneys before entering veins leading to the heart. Veins that drain one capillary bed and lead to another are called portal veins, and these particular veins are known as the **renal portal system.** Another group, known as the **hepatic portal system,** drains the digestive tract and leads to capillary-like passages in the liver. Since much of the blood returning to the heart has passed through one or the other of these portal systems in addition to the capillaries in the gills and tissues, its pressure is very low.

It is not difficult to appreciate the significance of a hepatic portal system, since the liver plays such an important role in the metabolism of foods, but the adaptive significance of a renal portal system in primitive vertebrates is less clear.

Amphibians. Correlated with the shift from gills to lungs, many changes occurred in the heart and aortic arches (Fig. 28.6). The aortic arches were reduced in number, the first two and the fifth being lost. Those that remain are no longer interrupted by gill capillaries. In a primitive tetrapod, such as the frog, the third pair of aortic arches forms part of the **internal carotid** arteries supplying the head; the fourth, the **systemic arches** leading to the dorsal aorta; and the sixth, the **pulmocutaneous arches** leading to the lungs and skin. New veins, the **pulmonary veins,** return aerated blood from the lungs to the heart. The heart now receives blood from both the body and lungs. Though blood streams from the body and lungs are separated in the frog by a divided atrium, they can, and probably do, mix to some extent in the single ventricle. This mixing is not detrimental to amphibians, for some of the blood from the body is returning from the skin, where aeration also occurs. When the frog is under water the lungs are not used, and the lack of a divided ventricle is probably an advantage because it allows aerated blood returning to the right atrium from the skin to be distributed directly to the body.

These changes result in a much higher blood pressure in the arteries of a primitive tetrapod than in a fish. Blood in the dorsal aorta of a frog has a pressure of 27 mm. Hg, about twice that of the dogfish. This

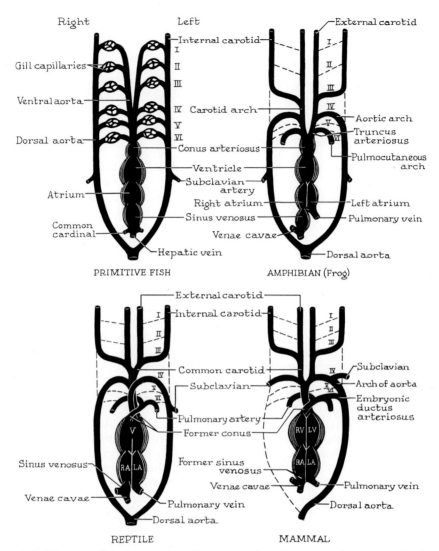

Figure 28.6 Diagrams of the heart and aortic arches to show the changes that occurred in the evolution from primitive fishes to mammals. All are ventral views. The heart tube has been straightened so that the atrium lies posterior to the ventricle.

increases the circulatory rate, but this benefit is somewhat offset by the fact that the blood delivered to the tissues is mixed to some extent and does not contain so much oxygen, relatively, as it did in a fish.

Reptiles and Birds. Higher tetrapods depend upon their lungs for external respiration. Since no respiration occurs in the skin, there is no mixing of aerated blood from the skin with blood from the body. The mixing in the heart of arterial blood from the lungs with venous blood from the body is lessened in reptiles by a partial division of the ventricle and by a complex, tripartite division of the conus (Fig. 28.6). In a lizard, for ex-

ample, oxygen-rich blood is sent from the left side of the ventricle to the head and also toward the trunk via the right fourth aortic arch; oxygen-poor blood, from the right side of the ventricle to the lungs; a blood intermediate in oxygen content, toward the trunk via the left fourth aortic arch. Blood in the dorsal aorta is a combination of rich and mixed bloods entering from the fourth aortic arches of opposite sides of the body. Birds have no mixing of blood at all, for their ventricle is completely divided and they have lost the left fourth aortic arch of their reptilian ancestors.

Mammals. Mammals too have a completely divided ventricle, so there is no mixing of oxygen-rich and oxygen-depleted bloods (Fig. 28.6). Venous blood from the body enters the **right atrium,** into which the primitive sinus venosus has become incorporated. Arterial blood from the lungs enters the **left atrium.** The atria pass the blood on to the **right** and **left ventricles,** respectively. The ventricles have more muscular walls than in lower vertebrates and so can increase the blood pressure considerably. The primitive conus arteriosus has become completely divided, part contributing to the pulmonary artery leading from the right ventricle to the lungs and the rest to the arch of the aorta leading from the left ventricle to the body.

The sixth pair of aortic arches form the major part of the mammalian **pulmonary arteries,** and the third pair contribute to the **internal carotid arteries.** But it will be observed in Figure 28.6 that only the left side of the fourth arch, known as the **arch of the aorta,** leads to the dorsal aorta. The right fourth arch contributes to the right **subclavian artery** to the shoulder and arm but does not connect with the aorta.

The major change in the veins is the complete loss of a renal portal system. Blood from the tail and posterior appendages enters a **posterior vena cava,** which continues forward to the heart. It receives blood from the kidneys but does not carry blood to them. An **anterior vena cava** drains the head and arms. The hepatic portal system is still present. The

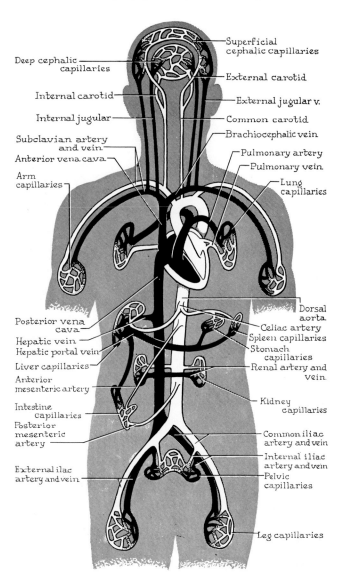

Figure 28.7 The major parts of the cardiovascular system of man as seen in an anterior view.

pattern of the major arteries and veins of man is shown in Figure 28.7.

These evolutionary changes have resulted in a very efficient cardiovascular system. Mammals have relatively more blood than lower vertebrates, it is distributed under greater pressure, and there is no mixing of arterial and venous blood. Man, for example, has 7.6 ml. of blood per 100 gm. of body weight compared with 2 ml. per 100 gm. in a fish. The mean pressure in the dorsal aorta of man is about 100 mm. Hg.

As blood pressures have increased during the evolution of the cardiovascular system, more liquids and plasma proteins have escaped from the capillaries into the tissue fluid than have been returned by the veins. A separate **lymphatic system** evolved. Lym-

phatic vessels arise as outgrowths from the veins and, in general, tend to parallel the veins and ultimately empty into them.

The system reaches its greatest development in mammals (Fig. 28.8). **Lymphatic capillaries** occur in most of the tissues of the body. They are more permeable than cardiovascular capillaries, and pressures within them are exceedingly low. Residual tissue fluid and large molecules, such as plasma proteins and fat being absorbed from the intestine, can easily enter them. Their high permeability also makes them the most likely route for the spread of microorganisms, or cancer cells, within the body. **Lymph nodes** lie at many points where small lymphatic vessels converge. Since they are major sites for the production of lymphocytes and retic-

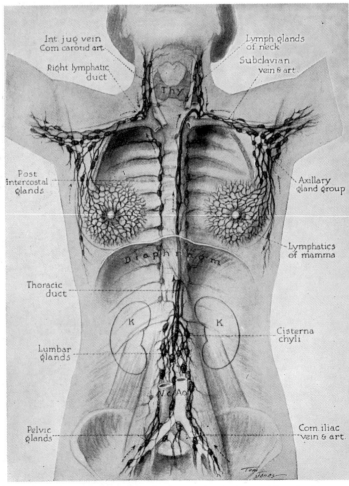

Figure 28.8   Major lymphatic vessels and nodes in the trunk of a human female. (Courtesy of S. H. Camp Co.)

ular cells, cells within them can phagocytize invading bacteria or respond to them by producing antibodies. Lymphatic vessels draining the hind limbs and the pelvic and abdominal regions finally converge upon a lymph sac, the **cisterna chyli,** located posterior to the diaphragm and dorsal to the aorta. The largest lymphatic vessel of the body, the thoracic duct, extends anteriorly from this point, receives the drainage from the left side of the anterior parts of the body, and finally enters the left brachiocephalic vein. A smaller **right lymphatic duct** drains the right anterior parts of the body and enters the right brachiocephalic vein.

28.10

The Fetal Circulation

The placenta of the mammalian fetus, rather than the digestive tract, lungs and kidneys, is the site for exchange of materials. This, together with the fact that the vessels in the lungs of the fetus are not developed

enough to handle the total volume of blood that is circulating through the body, requires certain differences in the fetal circulation (Fig. 28.9). Blood rich in oxygen returns from the placenta in an **umbilical vein,** passes rather directly through the liver via the **ductus venosus,** and enters the posterior vena cava, where it is mixed with blood returning from the posterior half of the fetus. The posterior vena cava empties into the right atrium, which also receives venous blood from the head by way of the anterior vena cava.

The lungs cannot accommodate all of this blood early in development, yet a large volume of blood must pass through all chambers of the heart to ensure their normal development. The entrance of the posterior vena cava is directed toward an opening, the **foramen ovale,** in the partition separating the two atria. Most of the blood from the posterior vena cava tends to go through this into the left atrium, thence to the left ventricle and out to the body through the arch of the aorta. This blood by-passes the lungs yet permits the left side of the heart, which other-

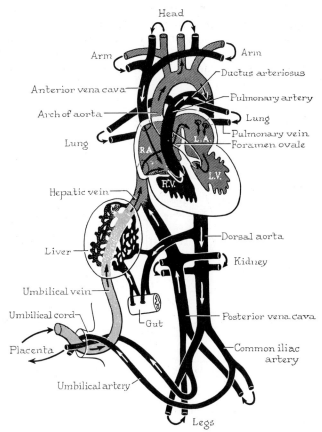

Figure 28.9 Circulation in a fetal mammal. The shading gives some indication of the mixing of the blood, though there is more mixing than can be indicated diagrammatically. The lightest shading represents blood with the highest oxygen content; the darkest shading, blood with the lowest oxygen content. (Modified after Patten.)

wise would receive little blood from the collapsed lungs, to function and develop normally. The rest of the blood from the posterior vena cava enters the right ventricle along with the blood from the anterior vena cava and starts out the pulmonary artery toward the lungs. However, only a fraction of this blood passes through the lungs to return to the left atrium and mix with blood from the posterior vena cava. Most of the blood in the pulmonary artery goes through another by-pass, the **ductus arteriosus,** to the dorsal aorta. The ductus arteriosus represents the dorsal part of the left sixth aortic arch (Fig. 28.6). Since the ductus arteriosus enters the aorta after the arteries to the head have been given off, the head receives the blood with the highest oxygen content. After the entrance of the ductus arteriosus, the blood in the aorta is highly mixed. This is the blood that is distributed to the rest of the body and, by way of umbilical arteries, to the placenta.

As the lungs develop during fetal life, more and more blood is sent through their capillary bed, because the foramen ovale becomes relatively smaller and less blood by-passes the lungs via this route. The return of blood from the lungs to the left atrium is consequently gradually increased, which increases the blood pressure in the left atrium. The increased pressure in the left atrium keeps the flap guarding the foramen ovale

closed a greater fraction of the time and decreases the amount of blood entering from the right atrium. These changes insure a normal development of the pulmonary circulation and chambers of the heart, so the transition from the fetal to the adult pattern is less abrupt.

28.11
Changes at Birth

Throughout fetal life the lungs and most of the vessels within them are collapsed. The resistance to blood flow through the lungs (pulmonary resistance) is greater than the resistance to flow through the body and placenta (systemic resistance). As a consequence there is a large flow of blood through the placenta and a small flow through the lungs. The volume of blood returning to the left atrium is less than the volume entering the right atrium. This facilitates the opening of the valve in the foramen ovale and the continued by-passing of the lungs (Fig. 28.10A).

These conditions are immediately reversed at birth. The placenta is expelled and blood volume in the systemic circuit is reduced. Carbon dioxide accumulates in the fetal blood, activating the respiratory system; the lungs fill with air and the pulmonary vessels that were collapsed open up. Resistance to

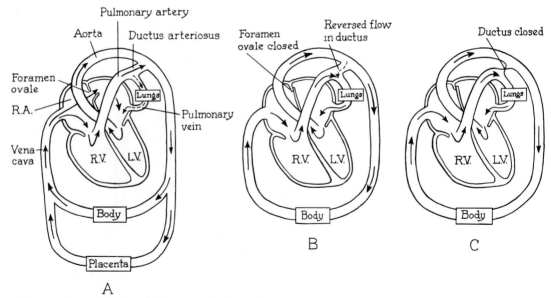

Figure 28.10 Circulatory changes at birth: *A,* fetal; *B,* neonatal. *C,* Adult circulation. Solid arrows represent major blood circuits; broken arrows, lesser circuits.

blood flow in the pulmonary circulation is now less than that in the systemic circulation. More blood flows through the lungs and returns to the left atrium than during fetal life. The valve in the foramen ovale is pushed against the interatrial septum and soon adheres to it by the growth of tissue. This bypass of the lungs is cut off.

The circulatory pattern is now very close to the adult condition except that the ductus arteriosus remains open (Fig. 28.10B). Since pulmonary resistance is less than systemic resistance, the direction of flow in the ductus arteriosus is reversed. Some of the blood which has already been through the lungs and is leaving the heart in the arch of the aorta flows back to the lungs through the ductus arteriosus. This pattern of circulation, which lasts from several hours to a day or two in the human infant, is known as the **neonatal circulation.** Experiments on newborn lambs show that this reversal of flow, and the consequent double aeration of some of the blood at a time when the lungs are not functioning at maximal efficiency, is of great significance. If the ductus arteriosus is experimentally tied off during this period, the hemoglobin is 10 to 20 per cent less saturated with oxygen than it normally is.

Muscles in the wall of the ductus arteriosus eventually contract and stop all blood flow through it, and the adult pattern is established (Fig. 28.10C). As time goes on the duct becomes permanently occluded by the growth of fibrous tissue into its lumen. The stimulus for these changes is unknown, but if the duct remains open, an undue strain is placed upon the heart, for it must pump this extra amount of blood that is recirculating through the lungs in addition to the normal amount of blood to the tissues.

28.12
Flow of Blood and Lymph

The Heart. The heart (Fig. 28.11) is the pump that provides the pressure gradient necessary for the blood and lymph to flow. It lies within a division of the coelom, the **pericardial cavity,** which contains some lymph-like fluid that lubricates it and facilitates its movements. It is covered with a smooth coelomic epithelium, the **visceral pericardium,** and is lined by the simple squamous epithelium, the **endothelium,** which lines all parts

of the circulatory system. The rest of its wall is composed of **cardiac muscle,** which is unique in that its fibers branch and anastomose profusely (see Fig. 3.15). Prominent cross bands occur periodically. For a long time their nature was a puzzle, but electron micrographs (Fig. 28.12) reveal that cells uniting end-to-end interdigitate complexly with each other in this region. This specialization presumably joins the cellular units more tightly and enables them better to withstand the tensions that are continually developed as the heart beats. The musculature of the atria is separated from that of the ventricles, but the individual muscle cells or fibers in each are more intimately united than in other types of muscle. Atria or ventricles respond as a unit. Any stimulus that is strong enough to elicit a response will elicit a total response. Thus, the atria and ventricles follow the "all-or-none" law that applies to individual motor units of skeletal muscle.

During a heart cycle, the atria and ventricles contract and relax in succession. Contraction of these chambers is known as **systole;** relaxation, as **diastole.** Ventricular systole is very powerful and drives the blood out into the pulmonary artery and arch of the aorta under high pressure. Since the muscle fibers of the ventricles are arranged in a spiral, the blood is not just pushed out but is virtually wrung out of them. When the ventricles relax, their elastic recoil reduces the pressure within them, and blood enters from the atria. Atrial contraction does not occur until the ventricles are nearly filled with blood. The atria are primarily antechambers that accumulate blood during ventricular systole.

Blood being pumped by the heart is prevented from moving backward by the closure of a system of valves (Fig. 28.11). One with three cusps, known as the **tricuspid valve,** lies between the right atrium and ventricle; one with two cusps, the **bicuspid valve,** between the left chambers. These valves operate automatically as pressures change, opening when atrial pressure is greater than ventricular, closing when ventricular pressure is greater. **Tendinous cords** extend from the free margins of the cusps to the ventricular wall and prevent them from turning into the atria during the powerful ventricular contractions. When the ventricles relax, blood in the pulmonary artery and aorta, which is under pressure, tends to back up into them. This closes the pocket-shaped **semilunar**

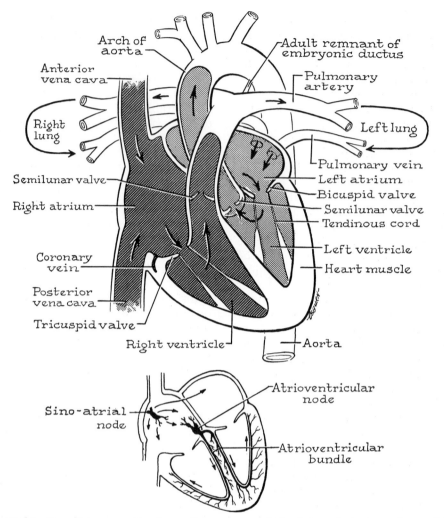

Figure 28.11   The adult mammalian heart. Upper, course of blood through the heart; lower, distribution of the specialized cardiac muscle that forms the conducting system of the heart.

valves at the base of these vessels that prevent blood from returning to the ventricles. Abnormalities in the structure of the valves occurring congenitally or produced by disease organisms may prevent their closing properly. Blood then leaks back during diastole; the leaking blood is heard as a "heart murmur."

Cardiac muscle has an inherent capacity for beating, and the hearts of vertebrates, if properly cultured, will continue to beat rhythmically when excised from the body. Each contraction is initiated in the **sino-atrial node,** or "pacemaker"—a node of specialized cardiac muscle (**Purkinje fibers**) located in that part of the wall of the right atrium into which the primitive sinus venosus is incorporated (Fig. 28.11). The impulse spreads to

all parts of the atria and to another node of Purkinje fibers, the **atrioventricular node,** from which it continues along pathways of Purkinje fibers to all parts of the ventricles. Since there is no muscular connection between atria and ventricles, an impulse can reach the ventricular muscles only through the Purkinje fibers. It does so very rapidly, so that ventricular contraction begins at the apex of the heart and spreads quickly toward the origin of the great arteries leaving the heart.

The rhythmicity of the sino-atrial node results from the leakage of positively charged sodium ions, which are abundant outside all cells, through the plasma membranes of the cells of the node. The electrical potential of

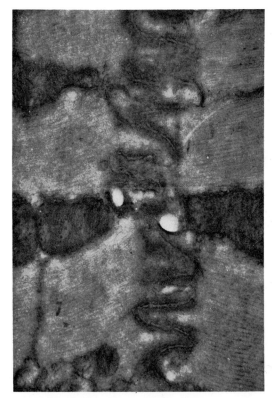

Figure 28.12 Electron micrograph of a portion of the end-to-end union (intercalated disc) of two cardiac muscle cells or fibers to show the interdigitation of their plasma membranes. Parts of three myofibrils can be seen in each muscle fiber. (From Bloom and Fawcett.)

the membrane is reversed and the cells become active. A similar phenomenon occurs in nerve cells and in the activation of other muscle fibers; the unique feature of the cells of the sino-atrial node is the leakage after the membrane potential has been re-established that leads to their rhythmic self-activation.

Control of Heart Output. Though the heart has an inherent rhythm, its rate of contraction and the volume of blood pumped per stroke can be regulated by a number of extrinsic factors so as to adjust the heart output to body requirements. Nervous pathways are present for many cardiac reflexes. Motor nerves that increase or decrease the heart rate go to the heart from the vasomotor center in the medulla of the brain, and sensory impulses from many parts of the body reach this center. For example, receptors in the right atrium are stimulated by the increase in the pressure of the venous blood returning to the heart which occurs during exercise. They travel to the vaso-

motor center (*1,* Fig. 28.13) and, by inhibiting the depressor nerve fibers and activating accelerator fibers, cause an increased number of nerve impulses to go out on the accelerator nerve (*2*). The rate of heart beat and strength of contraction increases to accommodate the greater return of venous blood. Blood pressure also rises and, if it exceeds a certain threshold, pressure receptors in the aortic arch and other vessels near the heart are activated. Impulses travel to the vasomotor center (*3*) and, again by an appropriate combination of inhibition and excitation, the rate of impulses traveling down the accelerator nerve is decreased and an increased number go out on the depressor nerve (*4*). Heart rate and force of contraction are reduced to appropriate levels. Other reflexes are initiated by chemoreceptors. A reduction in the level of oxygen in the arterial blood is detected by receptors in the carotid body (*5*), and this can lead to an increase in heart rate (*6*). Yet other extrinsic factors such as temperature, carbon dioxide content of the blood, and one's emotional state can influence heart rate by acting on the vasomotor center.

In addition to these extrinsic factors, heart muscle itself can make certain adjustments. For example, the increased pressure and more rapid return of venous blood during exercise stretches the heart musculature. This causes it to contract with greater force and to send out the greater volume of blood received during each period of atrial diastole. Within physiologic limits, the greater the tension on cardiac (or any other) muscle, the more powerful will be its contraction. This capacity of the heart to adjust its output per stroke to the volume of blood delivered to it is known as Starling's **law of the heart.**

The heart of a normal adult man who is not exercising sends about 70 ml. of blood per beat out into the aorta. At the normal rate of 72 beats per minute, this is a total output of 5 liters per minute, which is approximately equivalent to the total amount of blood in the body. A similar observation made in 1628 by William Harvey helped to lead him to the conclusion that the blood recirculates. Until that time it was believed that blood was continually produced in the liver, pumped to the tissues and consumed. Harvey's calculations showed that the amount of blood pumped by the heart each hour was much more than could possibly be produced and consumed. He made the correct inference

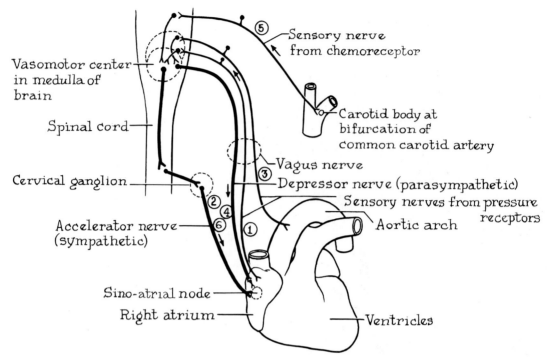

Figure 28.13 Diagram of major nerve reflexes controlling heart output and blood pressure. Motor nerve fibers have been drawn more heavily than sensory fibers. The motor nerves to the heart are parts of the autonomic nervous system, which is discussed more fully in Chapter 31.

that the blood must recirculate, even though he could not see the microscopic capillaries that connect arteries and veins.

Although a large volume of blood flows through the cavities of the heart, this blood does not provide for the metabolic needs of the heart musculature. A pair of **coronary arteries** arise from the base of the arch of the aorta and supply capillaries in the heart wall. This capillary bed is drained ultimately by a **coronary vein** that empties into the right atrium. Obviously, any damage to the coronary vessels, the plugging of one of the larger arteries by a thrombus, for example, could have serious consequences, for the heart muscles cannot function without a continuing supply of oxygen and food.

The Arteries. Arteries are lined with endothelium and have a relatively thick wall containing elastic connective tissue and smooth muscles. The walls of the larger arteries are richly supplied with elastic tissue. The force of each ventricular systole forces blood into the arteries and stretches them to accommodate it. During diastole, the elastic recoil of the first part of the artery to expand helps to push the blood into the adjacent

part of the artery, which in turn expands. If the arteries were rigid pipes, they would deliver blood to the tissues in spurts that coincided with ventricular systole. The blood would pound like steam rushing into empty radiator pipes. The elasticity of the large arteries transforms what would otherwise be an intermittent flow into a steady flow. The alternate stretching and contracting of the arteries travels peripherally very rapidly (7.5 meters per second) and constitutes the **pulse,** but the blood itself does not move as fast.

The smaller arteries (Fig. 28.14), and especially the **arterioles** preceding the capillaries, contain a relatively large amount of smooth muscle, and they are concerned with regulating the supply of blood to the various organs. **Vasodilator** and **vasoconstrictor nerves** supply these muscles, causing them to relax or contract. If a region of the body becomes very active, its small arteries enlarge, and the blood flow through them is increased. If an area is not particularly active, its small arteries constrict, and blood flow is reduced. In this way, maximum use is made of the volume of blood available. The body does not

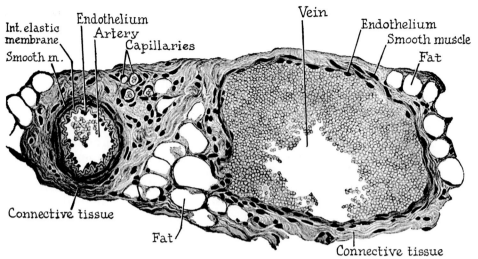

Figure 28.14 A drawing of a cross section through a small artery and its accompanying vein. Several capillaries lie between them. (Modified from Bloom and Fawcett.)

contain enough blood to supply fully all tissues and organs at the same time.

As the arteries extend to the tissues, they branch and rebranch. Each time the lumen becomes smaller, but the total cross sectional area of all these branches increases greatly. The velocity of blood flow, therefore, decreases, for the blood, like a river widening out and flowing into a lake, is moving into an area that grows larger and larger. The mean

blood pressure is also decreased continually because of the friction of the blood moving in the vessels (Fig. 28.15). Blood pressure continues to decrease as the blood flows through the capillaries and veins. The rate of flow, however, increases as the blood passes from the capillaries to the venules, and as these smaller veins lead into fewer larger ones. The blood is now moving into a smaller and smaller area and, like water flowing out

Figure 28.15 Variation in blood velocity and pressure in different parts of the cardiovascular system. The velocity does not return to its original value, for the cross sectional area of the veins is greater than the cross sectional area of the arteries. The blood pressure in the veins near the heart is less than atmospheric pressure because of the negative pressure within the thorax.

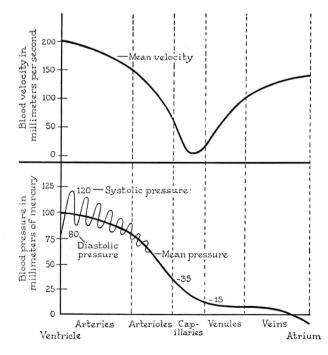

of a lake into a narrowing river, moves faster and faster.

Capillary Exchange. Capillaries are small and exceedingly thin-walled vessels. Their diameter is about that of the blood cells, and their walls consist of little more than an endothelial lining, which is continuous with that of the larger vessels. The capillary wall is a semipermeable membrane, and molecules that are small enough can easily pass back and forth between the blood and the surrounding tissue fluid (Fig. 28.16). Some large molecules, including a fraction of the plasma proteins, also leak out. Most substances are exchanged by simple diffusion following concentration gradients. There is more glucose and oxygen in the blood than in the tissue fluid, so their net movement is out of the capillaries. There are more wastes and carbon dioxide in the tissue fluid, so their net movement is into the capillaries.

The exchange of water is more complicated than the exchange of solutes, for its movement depends upon two opposing forces. The blood pressure tends to force water out of the capillaries, whereas the osmotic pressure exerted by the plasma protein molecules tends to draw water back in. The osmotic pressure of the blood, which depends to a large extent on the plasma proteins, drops only slightly from the arterial to the venous ends of the capillary bed, but blood pressure decreases sharply. At the arterial end of the capillary bed, blood pressure is greater than osmotic pressure and

some water is driven out of the capillaries. At the venous end, osmotic pressure is greater than blood pressure, and water is drawn back into the capillaries. Excess residual liquid and the few proteins that leak out are drained by the lymphatics.

Not all capillaries function concurrently. Within a capillary bed there are certain thoroughfare channels through which some blood flows from arterioles to venules all of the time. But tiny muscular **precapillary sphincters** are situated at the beginning of the capillaries leading from these channels, so other parts of the bed may be open or closed according to the needs of the tissues. Total blood flow through a capillary bed is regulated both by the arterioles and precapillary sphincters.

Venous and Lymphatic Return. The structure of the veins is fundamentally similar to that of arteries, though a vein is larger and has a much thinner and more flaccid wall than its companion artery (Fig. 28.14). Since they are larger, the veins hold more blood than the arteries and are an important reservoir for blood. Lymphatic vessels have even thinner walls. Valves present in both veins and lymphatics permit the blood and lymph to flow only toward the heart. It is sometimes easy to demonstrate the valves in the veins on the back of your hand. Push your finger on a vein at the point where several join on the back of your wrist and move your finger distally along the vessel. This will force the blood out of the vein, and you will notice

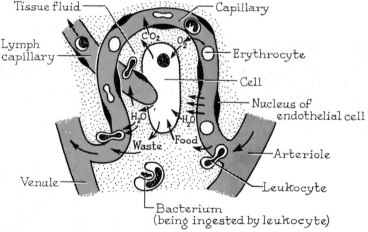

Figure 28.16 Exchange of materials in a capillary bed. Solutes enter and leave all parts of a capillary. Most of the water leaves at the arterial end and re-enters at the venous end. Less than 1 per cent of the water that leaves the capillaries is returned by the lymphatic system.

that blood does not re-enter this vein from the others at the wrist, for valves prevent it from doing so. Remove your finger from the vein and it immediately fills with blood from the periphery. William Harvey in the seventeenth century demonstrated the presence of valves in the veins in a similar way (see Fig. 1.5).

Though blood pressure is low in the veins (Fig. 28.15), and lowest in the large veins near the heart, it is still the major factor in the return of blood. Two other factors assist it. One is the fact that the elastic lungs are always stretched to some extent and tend to contract and pull away from the walls of the pleural cavities. This creates a slight subatmospheric or negative pressure within the thoracic cavity, which is greatest during inspiration. The larger veins, of course, pass through the thorax, and the reduction of pressure around them decreases the pressure within them and increases the pressure gradient. The other factor is that the contraction and relaxation of body muscles exert a "milking" action on the veins. When the muscles contract, their bulging squeezes the veins and forces the blood toward the heart, for the valves in the veins prevent the blood from moving in any other direction. All these factors increase during exercise, which makes for a more rapid return of blood and an increased cardiac output.

The return of lymph is dependent upon similar forces. The tissue fluid itself has a certain pressure derived from the flow of liquid out of the capillaries. This establishes a pressure gradient in the lymphatics that is made steeper by the negative intrathoracic pressure. The "milking" action of surrounding muscles and, for lymphatics returning from the intestine, the movement of the villi, help considerably. Some lower vertebrates have lymph "hearts" — specialized pulsating segments of lymphatic vessels.

QUESTIONS

1. How does the blood maintain a relatively constant pH despite its uptake of acid substances in the tissues?
2. How is oxygen carried by the blood? Name two ways by which the oxygen-carrying capacity can be increased.
3. Describe the current theory of the mechanism of blood clotting.
4. Describe the ways that leukocytes protect the body from microorganisms.
5. Distinguish between active and passive immunity. Which body cells are the major source of antibodies?
6. What factors would have to be taken into consideration in giving a blood transfusion to an Rh negative woman who has had several Rh positive children?
7. How did the transition from water to land affect the pattern of the blood vessels and the structure of the heart? What further changes have occurred during the evolution to mammals?
8. Define and give an example of a portal system.
9. In what respects is the pattern of circulation in a fetus adapted to intrauterine life? Describe the sequence of changes that occurs at birth, indicating the functional significance of each.
10. What prevents blood from flowing the wrong way in the heart?
11. How does the heart adjust its rate and output per beat to the increased venous return that occurs during increased body activity?
12. Describe two functions of arteries in addition to their function of transportation.
13. What forces are involved in the exchange of water and solutes between the capillaries and tissue fluid?
14. What factors supplement blood pressure in the return of venous blood?
15. List the functions of the lymphatic system. Do all vertebrates have this system?

ANNOTATED REFERENCES

Attention is again directed to the general references on vertebrate organ systems cited at the end of Chapter 26.

Burnet, F. M.: The mechanism of immunity. Scientific American 204:58, (Jan.) 1961.

Theories of immunity are discussed by this investigator, who shares a Nobel prize in medicine for his work in this field.

Harvey, W.: Anatomical Studies on the Motion of the Heart and Blood. Springfield, Ill., Charles C Thomas, 1931. This is one of a number of available translations of Harvey's important studies in 1628 which established the circulation of the blood and introduced the experimental method into biology.

Krogh, A.: The Anatomy and Physiology of Capillaries. New Haven, Yale University Press, 1922. The classic study on this subject written by one of the pioneer investigators of capillary circulation.

Mayerson, H. S.: The lymphatic system. Scientific American *208*:80, (June) 1963. The importance of this second drainage system of the tissues is thoroughly discussed.

Wiener, A. S.: Blood Groups and Blood Transfusions. 3rd ed. Springfield, Ill., Charles C Thomas, 1943. An old but classic treatise which traces the history of the discovery of blood groups and their applications to problems of transfusion, anthropology, disputed paternity and forensic medicine.

Wiggers, C. J.: The heart. Scientific American *196*:87, (May) 1957. A fine discussion of the activities of the heart and the safety factors that enable it to continue operating even though partially impaired by coronary disease.

Zuckerkandle, D.: The evolution of hemoglobin. Scientific American *212*:110, (May) 1965. An analysis of the various types of mammalian hemoglobin and the evolutionary information which they can provide.

Zweifach, B. W.: The microcirculation of the blood. Scientific American *200*:54, (Jan.) 1959. A discussion of the factors that control circulation in capillary beds.

29

THE UROGENITAL SYSTEM— EXCRETION AND REPRODUCTION

Functionally, the kidneys have nothing in common with the reproductive organs. They are concerned with excretion of wastes and regulation of body fluids; the reproductive organs, with the perpetuation of the species. But the two systems are morphologically interrelated in vertebrates because certain excretory ducts are used for discharging gametes, and it is convenient to treat them together as the **urogenital system.** First, we shall consider the excretory portion of the system, and then relate the reproductive organs to it.

Although the kidneys come to mind when one thinks of excretion in vertebrates, they do not have a monopoly on the removal of the waste products of metabolism. Special salt-secreting glands are present in many marine vertebrates, and the gills and lungs, the skin and, to some extent, the digestive tract play a role in excretion. Gills eliminate carbon dioxide and some nitrogenous wastes; lungs, carbon dioxide; the skin (especially in amphibians), a certain amount of carbon dioxide and traces of salts and nitrogenous wastes; the digestive tract, bile pigments and certain metal ions. The kidneys remove most of the nitrogenous wastes in the higher vertebrates, but this is not their only function. By removing, or conserving, water, salts, acids, bases and various organic substances as the situation requires, they play a vital role in regulating the composition of the blood and the internal environment of the body.

29.1
Evolution of the Kidneys and Their Ducts

The **kidneys** of vertebrates are paired organs that lie dorsal to the coelom on each side of the dorsal aorta. All vertebrate kidneys are composed of units called kidney tubules, or **nephrons,** which remove materials from the blood, but the number and arrangement of the nephrons differ in the various groups of vertebrates. Comparative studies have led to the conclusion that each kidney in ancestral vertebrates contained one nephron for each of those body segments that lay between the anterior and posterior ends of the coelom (Fig. 29.1A). These nephrons drained into a **wolffian,** or **archinephric, duct** which continued posteriorly to the cloaca. Such a kidney may be regarded as a complete kidney, or **holonephros,** for it extends the entire length of the coelom. A holonephros is found today in the larvae of certain cyclostomes but not in any adult vertebrate.

In the kidney of adult fishes and amphibians (see Fig. 29.1B), the most anterior tubules have been lost, some of the middle tubules are associated with the testis, and

503

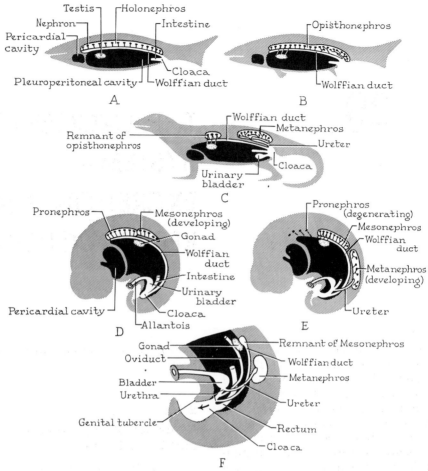

Figure 29.1   A comparison of the evolution and embryonic development of the kidney and its ducts. *A, B* and *C:* The evolutionary sequence of kidneys. *A,* Hypothetical ancestral vertebrate with a holonephros; *B,* a fish with an opisthonephros; *C,* a reptile with a metanephros. *D* and *E,* The developmental sequence of kidneys in a reptile. *F,* A mammalian embryo in which the cloaca is becoming divided by the growth of the fold indicated by the arrow. The ventral part of the cloaca contributes to the urethra in the male. It becomes further subdivided in the female and contributes to both urethra and vagina. In both sexes, the dorsal part of the cloaca forms the rectum.

there is a concentration and multiplication of tubules posteriorly. Such a kidney is known as a posterior kidney or **opisthonephros.**

Reptiles, birds and mammals (Fig. 29.1*C*) have lost all the middle tubules not associated with the testis and have an even greater multiplication and posterior concentration of tubules. The number of nephrons is particularly large in birds and mammals; their high rate of metabolism yields a large amount of wastes to be removed. It is estimated that man has 1,000,000 or more nephrons per kidney, whereas certain salamanders have less than 100. The tubules concerned with urine production drain into a **ureter,** which evolved as an outgrowth from the wolffian duct. The wolffian duct itself has been taken over com-

pletely by the male genital sytem. The kidney of the higher vertebrates is known as a **metanephros.**

The evolutionary sequence of kidneys is holonephros, opisthonephros and metanephros. In the embryonic development of vertebrates, we find a slightly different sequence, but one that also involves a posterior concentration of kidney functions (Fig. 29.1*D* and *E*). In an early embryo of a reptile, for example, segmentally arranged tubules appear dorsal to the anterior end of the coelom, form the wolffian duct, and disappear. These transitory tubules constitute a **pronephros.** Then a middle group of tubules, known as the **mesonephros,** appear and connect with the wolffian duct (see Fig. 29.9). These func-

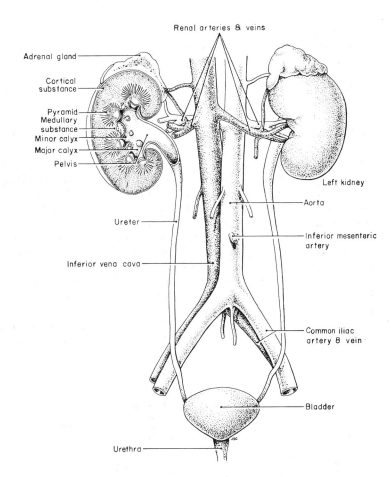

Figure 29.2 The human excretory system as seen in a ventral view. The right kidney has been sectioned to show the internal structures. (From Villee: Biology, 5th ed.)

tion during much of embryonic life, but when the metanephric tubules develop, all the mesonephric tubules are lost except for those associated with the testes. The embryonic sequence of kidneys in the development of a higher vertebrate is pronephros, mesonephros and metanephros.

A **urinary bladder,** for the temporary accumulation of urine, is associated with the excretory ducts of many vertebrates. Most tetrapods have a bladder, which develops as a ventral outgrowth from the cloaca. Generally, the excretory ducts from the kidneys lead to the dorsal part of the cloaca, and urine must flow across it to enter the bladder; however, in mammals (Figs. 29.1F and 29.2) the ureters lead directly to the bladder, and the bladder opens to the body surface through a short tube, the **urethra.** The cloaca becomes divided and disappears as such in all but the most primitive mammals. The dorsal part of the cloaca forms the rectum and the ventral part contributes to the urethra of higher mammals (Fig. 29.1F).

Urine is produced continually by the kidneys and is carried down the ureters by peristaltic contractions. It accumulates in the bladder, for a smooth muscle sphincter at the entrance of the urethra and a striated muscle sphincter located more distally along the urethra are closed. Urine is prevented from backing up into the ureters by valvelike folds of mucous membrane within the bladder. When the bladder becomes filled, stretch receptors are stimulated and a reflex is initiated which leads to the contraction of the smooth muscles in the bladder wall and the relaxation of the smooth muscle sphincter. Relaxation of the striated muscle sphincter is a voluntary act.

29.2

The Nephron and Its Function

Nephron Structure. The excretory ducts and the urinary bladder are important adjuncts to the kidneys, but the essential work of the system, the selective removal of materials from the blood, is performed by the individual kidney tubules. The general nature and function of these tubules was described in Chapter 5. The mammalian nephron may be taken as an example. The proximal end of each nephron (Fig. 29.3) is known as **Bowman's capsule.** It is a hollow ball of squamous epithelial cells, one end of which has been pushed in by a knot of capillaries called a **glomerulus.** Bowman's capsule and the glomerulus constitute a **renal corpuscle.** The rest of the nephron is a tubule largely composed of cuboidal epithelial cells and subdivided in mammals into a **proximal convoluted tubule,** a **loop of Henle** and a **distal convoluted tubule.** A **collecting tubule** receives the drainage of several nephrons and leads to the **renal pelvis,** an expansion within the kidney of the proximal end of the ureter (Fig. 29.2). The location of the different parts of a nephron within the kidney and

their relationship to blood vessels have important functional consequences. As shown in Figure 29.3, the renal corpuscles and convoluted tubules lie in the outer part, or **cortex,** of the kidney and a dense capillary network surrounds the convoluted tubules; the loops of Henle extend toward the center, or **medulla,** of the kidney. Most of the human nephrons extend only a short distance into the medulla, but about one-fifth of them (the **juxtamedullary nephrons**) have long loops of Henle that extend, along with the collecting tubules and capillary loops, far into the medulla. It is the convergence of these structures into subdivisions of the renal pelvis (the **calyces**) that forms the renal **pyramids** (Fig. 29.2).

Glomerular Filtration.   The wall of Bowman's capsule is a semipermeable membrane, and small molecules in the glomerular capillaries should pass through it readily. By carefully inserting a micropipette into a Bow-

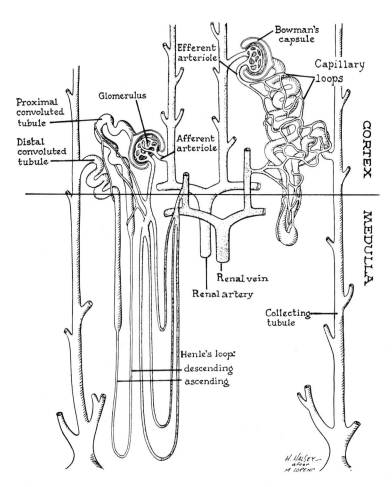

Figure 29.3 A diagram of mammalian nephrons and associated blood vessels. A juxtamedullary nephron is shown on the left; a cortical nephron on the right. (After Smith.)

man's capsule in a frog's kidney and drawing off and analyzing a sample of the contents (the **glomerular filtrate**), Dr. A. N. Richards of the University of Pennsylvania demonstrated in 1921 that this is indeed the case. Only the blood cells, fats and plasma proteins are held back in the capillaries. The other plasma components are found in the glomerular filtrate in nearly the same proportion as in the plasma. Other experiments have shown that this is true for glomerular filtration in mammalian nephrons too.

Materials leave the blood in the glomeruli as they do in other capillary beds, but the arrangement of the blood vessels is such that a larger volume of material is forced out. An **afferent arteriole** leads from a branch of the renal artery to each glomerulus, and an **efferent arteriole** from the glomerular capillaries to a second capillary network distributed over the rest of the tubule. These capillaries are drained by branches of the renal vein. A glomerulus thus lies between two arterioles. The efferent arteriole is smaller than the afferent one; this ensures a high blood pressure in the glomerular capillaries and, hence, **a high filtration pressure** that drives liquids and many solutes from the blood. The filtration pressure in a glomerulus is normally about twice as great as that at the arterial end of an ordinary capillary bed. It has been estimated that some 180 liters of glomerular filtrate are normally produced by a man in one day!

Tubular Reabsorption and Augmentation. Glomerular filtration is not a selective process. Glucose, amino acids, inorganic ions and many other useful materials leave the blood along with urea, other wastes, and enough water to dehydrate a terrestrial vertebrate in a few hours. Fortunately, the glomerular filtrate undergoes further treatment as it passes down the tubule. Whether substances are reabsorbed from the filtrate or secreted into it by tubular cells can be determined by comparing their rate of excretion with that of a substance such as inulin, which can be added to the blood. Inulin is known to be filtered freely and not to be reabsorbed or secreted. From these studies it is concluded that virtually all of the glucose and amino acids, most of the inorganic ions, about 99 per cent of the water, as well as some of the urea in the filtrate are reabsorbed into the intercellular fluid and capillaries around the tubules. Creatinine, ammonia, hydrogen and potassium ions and various drugs (penicillin) are among the few substances added to the filtrate by tubular secretion, or **augmentation,** in mammals. But in certain teleosts, which have lost their renal corpuscles, this is an essential way of eliminating waste products.

A large volume of water and solutes of value to the organism are reabsorbed, but most of the urea and other waste products are not taken back. The fluid that reaches the end of the collecting tubules is known as **urine.** In man, the volume of urine is only about 1 per cent of the volume of the glomerular filtrate, and its composition is quite different from that of the filtrate, for a great many substances have been reabsorbed and others have been added. As a result of these processes, the waste products are concentrated in the urine. The most important nitrogenous waste in human urine is urea, but lesser amounts of ammonia, uric acid and creatinine are present. The yellowish color of the urine is due to the presence of **urochrome,** a pigment derived from the breakdown of hemoglobin and, hence, related to the bile pigments.

Reabsorption, which plays such an important role in urine formation, involves both the passive diffusion of materials back into the capillaries surrounding the tubules and the active uptake of materials by the tubular cells and their secretion into the blood against a concentration gradient. This, of course, requires the expenditure of energy by the tubular cells. Most of the reabsorption of solutes takes place in the proximal convoluted tubule, and this is an active process because the concentration of these substances in the filtrate in this region is the same as their concentration in the blood. Nearly all the glucose, the amino acids and the few plasma proteins that escape into the filtrate are reabsorbed in the proximal tubule. Those materials that can be actively reabsorbed are taken back in varying amounts, depending upon their concentration in the blood. If the concentration of one of these materials in the blood and glomerular filtrate rises above a certain level, known as the **renal threshold,** not all of it will be reabsorbed into the blood from the tubule, and the amount present in excess of the renal threshold is excreted. The quantitative value of the renal threshold differs for different substances. In **diabetes mellitus,** for example, in which impaired cellular utilization of glucose leads to a high concentration of glucose in the blood, the renal threshold for glucose (about 150 mg. of glucose per 100 ml. blood) is exceeded and the sugar appears in the urine in large amounts. The osmotic pressure of the body fluids is controlled by the amount of salts and the pH by the amount of hydrogen ions that are taken back into the blood from the glomerular filtrate.

Water is reabsorbed passively. As solutes are actively taken out of the filtrate in the proximal tubule, the water in the filtrate would tend to become more concentrated than it is in the blood. However, water molecules passively diffuse out as fast as solutes are pumped out; hence the concentration of the filtrate remains the same as that of the blood. About 80 per cent of all the water taken back is reabsorbed in this way in the proximal tubule, but the tubular filtrate cannot be made more concentrated (i.e., to contain less water) than the blood by this mechanism.

In most of the lower vertebrates the urine is not more concentrated than the blood; however, the higher vertebrates, and especially mammals, do produce a hypertonic urine. The unique feature of the mammalian nephron is the loop of Henle, and for a long time it has been implicated in the ability of these vertebrates to produce a very concentrated urine, but the mechanism of its operation has only recently been discovered. One important factor is that the descending and ascending limbs of the loop of Henle lie parallel to each other so that the direction of flow of fluid in one is opposite to that in the other (Fig. 29.4). Another factor is the active transport of sodium ions out of the ascending limb into the interstitial fluid, and the passive diffusion of these ions back into the descending limb. Together these factors result in a countercurrent multiplying mechanism. Sodium pumped out of the ascending limb goes right back into the descending limb. The recycling of sodium in the loop of Henle, together with additional sodium being continually brought to the loop in the glomerular filtrate, results in an accumulation of sodium in the loop of Henle and the surrounding interstitial fluid of the medulla. A concentration gradient is established as shown in Figure 29.4. The degree of accumulation depends upon the length of the loop; there is more opportunity to pump out sodium in a long loop. The importance of the capillary loops associated with the juxtamedullary nephrons is that here too we have a countercurrent mechanism that permits most of the

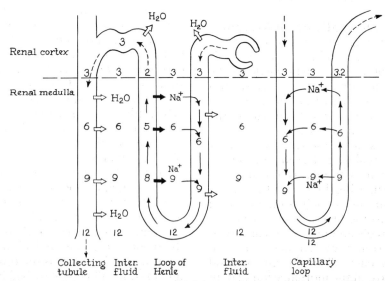

Figure 29.4　Diagram of the countercurrent multiplying mechanism of the mammalian kidney. The general direction of fluid movement is shown by broken arrows; active sodium transport, by heavy black arrows; passive sodium transport, by small black arrows; water movements, by white arrows. Numerals show the relative concentration of osmotically active solutes. In hundreds (add 00), they express the concentrations in milliosmols per liter.

sodium that starts out of the medulla in the blood to diffuse back into the blood entering the medulla. This, combined with the rather sluggish rate of blood flow through these vascular loops, means that little sodium is carried away from the medulla by this route.

The osmotic gradient established by these mechanisms makes it possible for additional water to be passively reabsorbed and for a hypertonic urine to be produced. Water simply follows the osmotic gradient, moving from an area of low osmotic pressure (high concentration of water) to one of high osmotic pressure (low concentration of water). The glomerular filtrate, which was isotonic to the blood in the proximal tubule, loses water as it passes down into the loop of Henle. It does not regain this water as it ascends the loop of Henle, for the cells of the ascending limb of the loop have a low permeability to water. However, the filtrate becomes more dilute because of the large amount of sodium pumped out. By the time the filtrate reaches the distal tubule it is again isotonic, or in some cases hypotonic, to the blood. The filtrate now descends through the medulla again, this time in the collecting tubule, loses additional water, and becomes very hypertonic.

Kidney Regulation of Body Fluids. Antidiuretic hormone, which is released by the neural lobe of the pituitary gland (p. 563), increases the permeability of the cells of the collecting tubule to water. Variations in the blood level of this hormone, together with variations in the amount of filtrate, make it possible for the kidney to regulate the volume of body fluids. If an excess of water is present in the body fluids, the blood volume and pressure increase. This raises the glomerular filtration pressure, and more filtrate is produced. An increase in the amount of water in the tissue fluid inhibits the release of the antidiuretic hormone, the permeability of collecting tubule cells is lowered, and less water is reabsorbed. Increased production of filtrate and decreased reabsorption of water rapidly bring the volume of body fluids down to normal. If the volume of body fluids falls below normal, as in a severe hemorrhage, these factors work in the opposite direction: Less glomerular filtrate is produced, more water is reabsorbed, and the volume of body fluid is soon raised to normal. The osmotic pressue of the tubular contents also affects

the amount of water removed. If a large amount of salts or sugars is being eliminated, the osmotic pressure of the tubular contents is increased and less water can be reabsorbed. The urine volume is greater when there is a large amount of osmotically active substances in the urine, as after a large intake of salt or in diabetes mellitus.

Water and Salt Balance. The nephrons of other vertebrates are essentially similar in structure and function to these mammalian nephrons, although there are differences in detail. In addition to being associated with the glomerulus, some of the nephrons of primitive vertebrates are connected with the coelom via a **nephrostome** and can remove materials from the coelomic fluid. This is analogous to the nephridia of the earthworm (p. 235). It may have been the primitive condition in vertebrates, for in the tubules of still more primitive vertebrates the glomerulus protrudes into the coelom, instead of into the beginning of the tubule, and the glomerular filtrate is discharged into the coelom.

The size of the renal corpuscles and other details of the nephron vary with the environment in which the animal lives. Primitive fresh-water fishes have large renal corpuscles that produce copious amounts of filtrate and do not have special water-reabsorbing mechanisms (Figure 29.5). The concentration of salts within their bodies is greater than that in the surrounding medium, and water moves by osmosis into their bodies. Their problem is to pump out the excess water, yet retain the needed salts. The type of tubule found in these fishes is well adapted for this. The primary function of this primitive tubule type may have been water regulation, for much of the nitrogenous waste is eliminated by diffusion through the gills.

Most salt-water fishes have the opposite problem, for the concentration of salt in the sea is greater than in their bodies; they lose water by osmosis. Small glomeruli, or even aglomerular tubules in some species, reduce the loss, and the deficit is made up by drinking salt water. Excess salt is then excreted by specialized cells in the gills. Marine cartilaginous fishes are an exception. A considerable amount of urea is retained in their tissues since not so much urea is eliminated by the tubules and, unlike other fishes, little is lost through the gills. The retained urea

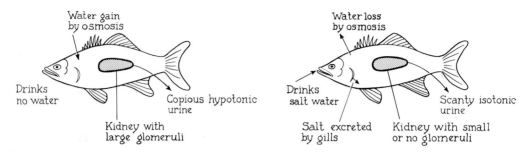

FRESH-WATER FISH IN HYPOTONIC MEDIUM   SALT-WATER FISH IN HYPERTONIC MEDIUM

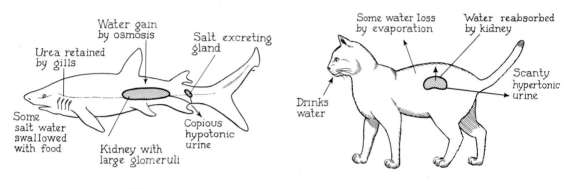

SHARK IN HYPOTONIC MEDIUM   TERRESTRIAL MAMMAL

Figure 29.5   Water and salt balance in representative vertebrates.

raises their internal osmotic pressure sufficiently for water to diffuse in. Their nephrons resemble those of fresh-water fishes. Excess salt taken in with their food is eliminated by the rectal gland (p. 366).

Amphibians retain the primitive fresh-water type of tubule and have little control over the loss of water. Frogs can lose through their skin and urine an amount of water equivalent to one-third of their body weight each day. The need to soak up water and to keep the skin moist for gas exchange is a factor that compels frogs to stay near water. Water is conserved in reptiles by their horny skin and by the small size of their glomeruli. Less water is removed from the blood by these glomeruli than by the large ones of primitive fresh-water fishes and amphibians. Birds and mammals have glomeruli of moderate size but have evolved loops of Henle that make it possible for a hypertonic urine to be produced. Mammals that live in deserts have exceptionally long loops of Henle and can remove more water from the urine than other mammals. Some terrestrial vertebrates (toads and many reptiles) also reabsorb water from the urinary bladder, although ordinarily

urine is not changed after it leaves the collecting tubules.

Some terrestrial vertebrates have secondarily adapted to a marine environment and many of these resemble typical marine fishes in that they drink sea water and excrete excess salt by way of specialized head glands. These glands open beside the eyes in sea turtles and into the nasal cavities in most marine birds (Fig. 24.15, p. 418). Marine mammals apparently eliminate excess salt through their kidneys.

As we pointed out in Chapter 5, animals can also save water by converting ammonia into nitrogenous wastes that require less water for their removal. Ammonia, which is produced by the deamination of amino acids, is a very toxic compound, but it is highly soluble in water and can be excreted rapidly if ample water is available to carry it away. If an animal converts its ammonia to urea, some water can be conserved, for each molecule of urea is formed from two molecules of ammonia. If ammonia is converted to uric acid, more water can be saved, for uric acid has a low toxicity, is relatively insoluble and can be excreted as an insoluble paste. Ammonia is the primary nitrogenous waste of fresh-water fishes, whereas urea and uric acid are excreted by terrestrial vertebrates.

29.3
The Gonads

From a biologic point of view, all the structures and processes that permit a species to survive are of no avail unless the species can reproduce its kind. The general aspects of reproduction, including the production of gametes in the gonads, fertilization, and the early development of the embryo, were considered in Chapter 6. At this time we shall be concerned more specifically with the reproductive organs of vertebrates and their role in reproduction.

Reproduction is sexual in vertebrates, and the sexes are separate in all but a few teleosts. The **testes** are paired organs of modest size, each consisting of numerous, highly coiled **seminiferous tubules** (Fig. 29.6), whose total length in man has been estimated at 250 meters! This provides an area large enough for the production of billions of sperm. As the sperm mature, they enter the lumen of the tubule and move toward the genital ducts. The **ovaries** are more variable in size. They fill much of the body cavity in primitive vertebrates that produce millions of eggs but are much smaller in higher vertebrates that produce fewer eggs and give more care to those produced. The human ovary is little more than 2.5 cm. long (Fig. 29.7). The eggs are not free within the ovary, for each one is surrounded by a **follicle** of epithelial and connective tissue cells. When the egg is ripe, the follicle bursts and the egg is discharged into the coelom, a process known as **ovulation** (Fig. 29.8). The accumulation of fluid within the follicle is an important factor in causing it to burst in mammals, although, as we have seen, muscular contraction produces ovulation in frogs.

In the frog and most other vertebrates, the gonads are suspended by mesenteries in the abdominal cavity, and they remain there throughout life. But in the males of most mammals the testes undergo a posterior migration, or descent, and move out of the main part of the abdominal cavity into a sac of skin known as the **scrotum** (Fig. 29.6). As they move into the scrotum, they carry a coelomic sac, the **tunica vaginalis,** down with them so that, despite their superficial position, they lie within a portion of the coelom.

In most mammals spermatogenesis does not occur unless the testes are descended. They remain descended in the majority of species, but in rabbits and rodents they are migratory—descending into the scrotum during the breeding season, withdrawing into

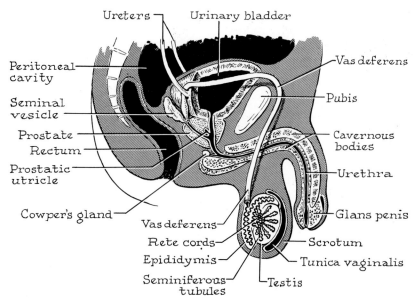

Figure 29.6 A diagrammatic sagittal section through the pelvic region of a man to show the genital organs. The prostatic utricle is a vestige of the oviduct that is present in the sexually indifferent stage of the embryo. (Modified after Turner.)

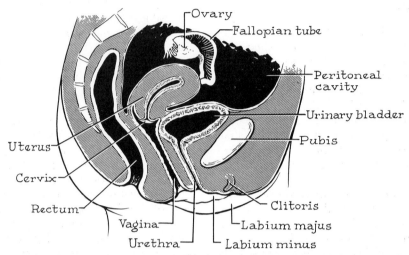

Figure 29.7 A diagrammatic sagittal section through the pelvic region of a woman to show the genital organs. (Modified after Turner.)

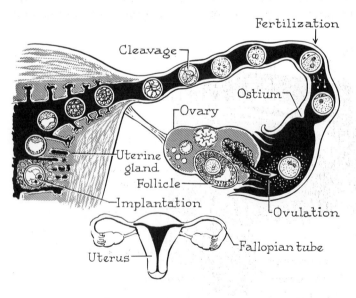

Figure 29.8 A diagram to show the path of an egg from the ovary to the uterus and the changes that occur en route. The last stage is about a week and one-half old. (Modified after Dickinson.)

the abdominal cavity at other times. Spermatogenesis, like other vital processes, can only occur within a limited temperature range. Apparently, this range is exceeded by the temperature in the abdominal cavity but not by the temperature in the scrotum, which is approximately 4° C. lower. In order to test this hypothesis, Dr. Carl R. Moore of the University of Chicago confined the testes of rats to the abdominal cavity and found that spermatogenesis did not occur. Indeed, the seminiferous tubules underwent regression. He also insulated the scrotum of a ram in which the testes were descended. This raised the temperature, and again spermatogenesis did not occur. Apparently, during the evolution of homoiothermism in mammals, spermatogenesis did not become adapted to the higher body temperatures.

29.4

Reproductive Passages

Once the sperm and eggs have been produced, they must be removed from the body and be brought together to form a zygote. This is a simple procedure in primitive vertebrates such as cyclostomes. No reproductive ducts are present, and both eggs and sperm simply break out of the gonad into the coelom. Ciliary currents carry them to the posterior end of the coelom, where they are discharged through a pore into the cloaca. Fertilization and development are external.

Embryonic Formation of Reproductive Ducts. Other vertebrates have a system of ducts for the removal of the gametes, and some of them are intimately related to the excretory system. In order to understand this relationship, it is necessary to go back to a period in embryonic development when the embryo is **sexually indifferent** (Fig. 29.9). Its sex is determined genetically at the time of fertilization (p. 597), but early in development the embryo has the morphologic potentiality of differentiating into either a male or a female, for the primordia of both male and female duct systems are present. A pair of **oviducts** are present, each one opening anteriorly into the coelom through a funnel-shaped ostium and connecting posteriorly with the cloaca. The developing gonad, which is not recognizable as an ovary or a testis at first, is adjacent to each mesonephros, and **rete**

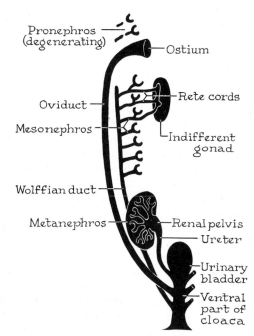

Figure 29.9 A ventral view of the urogenital organs of the sexually indifferent stage of the embryo.

cords develop and connect the gonad with some of the mesonephric tubules. Gametes could thus pass through the rete cords, the mesonephric tubules and the wolffian duct. If the embryo differentiates into a male, the route through the mesonephros materializes, and the embryonic oviduct disappears, leaving at most a few traces. If the embryo differentiates into a female, the route through the coelom and oviducts is used, the oviducts develop further, and those parts of the male system not concerned with excretion largely disappear.

Male Vertebrates. In male frogs (Fig. 21.17) and other lower vertebrates the rete cords become the **vasa efferentia,** which carry sperm from the seminiferous tubules in the testis to the anterior part of the kidney. The frog's kidney is an opisthonephros, but its anterior portion develops from the embryonic mesonephros. Sperm pass through kidney tubules into the wolffian duct, which carries both sperm and urine to the cloaca, though not at the same time.

Higher vertebrates, such as man (Fig. 29.6), have metanephric kidneys, and sperm pass from each testis to an **epididymis,** thence out a **vas deferens** to the urethra. This, seemingly, is a different pattern, but it is not so different as it first appears. Rete cords connect the seminiferous tubules with the epididymis, and the epididymis represents that part of the mesonephros that was associated embryonically with the testis, together with a highly convoluted portion of the wolffian duct. The vas deferens represents the rest of the wolffian duct, and most of the urethra represents the ventral part of a divided cloaca. Man thus utilizes passages homologous to those of a frog.

Other differences between the male reproductive organs of lower and higher vertebrates are correlated with differences in mode of reproduction. Frogs mate in the water and spray the sperm over the eggs as they are discharged. Fertilization is external. This mating procedure is perfectly satisfactory for species that mate in water, but the gametes are too delicate for external fertilization in the terrestrial environment. To accomplish internal fertilization, male mammals have a **penis** with which sperm is deposited in the female reproductive tract, and a series of **accessory sex glands** that secrete a fluid in which the sperm are carried. The penis develops around the urethra and contains three **cavernous bodies** composed of spongy **erectile tissue.** Arterial dilatation coupled with a restriction of venous return causes the vascular spaces within the erectile tissue to become filled with blood during sexual excitement, making the penis turgid and effective as a copulatory organ. The accessory sex glands are a pair of **seminal vesicles,** which connect with the distal end of the vasa deferentia; a **prostate gland** surrounding the urethra at the point of entrance of the vasa deferentia; and a pair of **Cowper's glands** located more distally along the urethra.

Female Vertebrates. Eggs are removed from the coelom in most female vertebrates by a pair of oviducts, but the oviducts are modified for various modes of reproduction. Lower vertebrates reproduce in the water. Most are oviparous, fertilization is external, and the eggs develop into larvae that can care for themselves. In the frog (Fig. 21.16), each oviduct is a simple tube that extends from the anterior end of the coelom to the cloaca. The oviducts contain glandular cells that secrete layers of jelly about the eggs, and their lower ends are expanded for temporary storage of the eggs, but they are not otherwise specialized.

Fertilization is internal in vertebrates that reproduce on the land, and the free larval stage has been replaced by the evolution of a cleidoic egg (p. 394). Most reptiles and all birds are oviparous and the eggs develop externally. The oviducal glands, which secrete the albumin and a shell around the egg, are more complex in the oviducts of reptiles than in those of amphibians and most fishes, but in other respects the oviducts of reptiles have not changed greatly. Birds have lost the right oviduct along with the right ovary, but the remaining left oviduct is essentially similar to the reptilian oviduct.

Most mammals and a few fishes and reptiles have become viviparous; they retain the fertilized egg within the reproductive tract until embryonic development is complete and the embryo receives its nutrients from the mother. The oviducts are modified accordingly. In the human female (Figs. 29.7 and 29.8), the **ostium** lies adjacent to the ovary and may even partially surround it. When ovulation occurs, the discharged eggs are close enough to the ostium to be easily carried into it by ciliary currents. The anterior portion of each oviduct is a narrow tube known as the **fallopian tube,** and eggs are carried down it by ciliary action and muscular contractions. The remainder of the primitive oviducts have fused with each other to form a thick-walled, muscular **uterus** and part of the **vagina.** The terminal portions of the vagina and urethra develop from a further subdivision of the ventral part of the cloaca. The vagina is a tube specialized for the reception of the penis, and it is lined with stratified squamous epithelium. It is separated from the main body of the uterus, in which the embryo develops, by a sphincter-like neck of the uterus known as the **cervix.** The orifices of the vagina and urethra are flanked by paired folds of skin, the **labia minora** and **labia majora.** A small bundle of sensitive erectile tissue, the **clitoris,** lies just in front of the labia minora. Structures comparable to these are present in the sexually indifferent stage of the embryo and develop into more conspicuous organs in the male. The labia majora are comparable to the scrotum; the labia minora and clitoris, to the penis. A pair of glands, homologous to Cowper's glands in the male, discharge a mucous secretion near the orifice of the vagina. A fold of skin, the **hymen,** partially occludes the opening of the vagina but is ruptured during the first intercourse.

29.5
Mammalian Reproduction

Fertilization. During copulation, the sperm that have been stored in the epididymis and vas deferens are ejaculated by the sudden contraction of muscles in and around the male ducts, and the accessory sex glands concurrently discharge their secretions. The seminal fluid that is deposited in the upper part of the vagina may contain as many as 400,000,000 sperm. Other important constituents include fructose from which the sperm derive energy, mucus that serves as a conveyance, and alkaline materials that neutralize the acids produced by sperm metabolism and those normally present in the vagina. Sperm are quickly killed in an acid environment.

Sperm move from the vagina through the uterus and up the fallopian tube in a little over one hour. How they do this is not entirely understood. They can swim, tadpole fashion, by the beating of the tail, but muscular contractions of the uterus and fallopian tubes, which are particularly pronounced if the female attains a sexual climax (orgasm), and ciliary currents in the tubes must help considerably. Fertilization occurs in the upper part of the fallopian tube (Fig. 29.8), but the arrival of an egg and the sperm in this region need not coincide exactly. Sperm retain their fertilizing powers for a day or two, and the egg moves slowly down the oviduct, retaining its ability to be fertilized for about a day. The chance of fertilization is further increased in many species of mammals (but not in human beings) by the female coming into "heat" and receiving the male only near the time of ovulation. Ovulation, "heat," and changes in the uterine lining in preparation for the reception of a fertilized egg are controlled by an intricate endocrine mechanism that will be considered in Chapter 32.

Only one sperm fertilizes each egg, yet unless millions are discharged, fertilization does not occur. One reason for this is that only a fraction of the sperm deposited in the vagina reach the upper part of the fallopian tube. The others are lost or destroyed along the way. Another reason is that when the egg enters the fallopian tube, it is still surrounded by a few of the follicle cells that encased the egg within the ovary (Fig. 3.18),

and a sperm cannot penetrate the egg until these are dispersed. This requires an enzyme, **hyaluronidase,** which can break down **hyaluronic acid,** a component of the intercellular cement. Hyaluronidase is believed to be produced by the sperm themselves, and large numbers are apparently necessary to produce enough of it. After the follicle cells are dispersed and one sperm has fertilized the egg, a **fertilization membrane** is raised from the surface of the egg and additional sperm penetration is not possible.

Establishment of the Embryo in the Uterine Lining. The fertilized egg passes down the fallopian tube into the uterus, undergoing cleavage along the way. Energy for early development is supplied by the small amount of food within the egg (mammalian eggs are isolecithal) and by secretions from glands in the uterine lining. About a week after fertilization the embryo of most mammals penetrates the uterine lining, apparently by secreting digestive enzymes, and the lining folds over it. As explained earlier (p. 117), a placenta, which provides the metabolic requirements of the embryo, is formed by the union of the chorioallantoic membrane of the embryo with the uterine lining. The degree of union of fetal and maternal tissues differs among the various groups of mammals. In some, including the pig, the fetal chorion simply rests against the uterine lining. There is no breakdown of fetal or maternal tissue. In human beings the union is more intimate, for microscopic **chorionic villi,** which contain the fetal capillaries, penetrate the uterine lining, break down maternal tissue, and become bathed in maternal blood (Fig. 29.10). Since maternal blood and fetal chorion are in contact, this type of union is called a **hemo-chorial placenta.** It should be emphasized that, except for occasional breaks in the placental membrane, no blood is exchanged between fetus and mother. Most gases, nutrients and waste products simply diffuse across the membrane. However, there is some evidence that active transport may play a role for certain substances; the fetal blood contains more amino acids, calcium and ascorbic acid than the maternal blood.

Birth. As the embryo develops, the uterus enlarges considerably to accommodate it. At the time of conception, the human uterus does not protrude far above the pubic symphysis (Fig. 29.7), but nine months later,

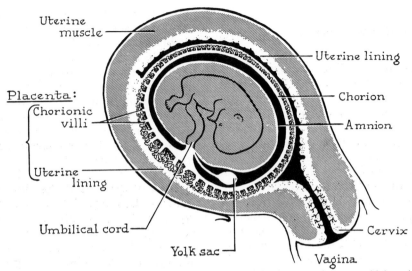

Figure 29.10 A young human embryo surrounded by its extraembryonic membranes and lying within the uterus. Notice that the whole complex of embryo and membranes is embedded in the uterine lining. Villi are present all over the surface of the chorion at this stage, but only those on the side toward the uterine wall enlarge and contribute to the definitive placenta. (Modified after Patten.)

when embryonic development has been completed, it extends up in the abdominal cavity nearly to the level of the breasts. During this enlargement, the individual muscle fibers in its wall increase in size, and additional muscle develops from undifferentiated cells in the uterine wall. The uterus becomes a powerful muscular organ ready to assume its role in childbirth, or **parturition.**

The factors that initiate birth are uncertain, but hormones produced by the pituitary, ovary and the placenta itself have prepared the mother's body for the birth. The mammary glands have enlarged and are ready for milk production, the uterine musculature has increased, and the pubic and other pelvic ligaments have relaxed so that the pelvic canal can enlarge slightly. Birth begins by a series of involuntary uterine contractions, "labor," that gradually increase in intensity and push the fetus, generally head first, against the cervix (Fig. 29.11). The cervix gradually dilates, but in human beings as much as 18 hours or more may be required to open the cervical canal completely at the

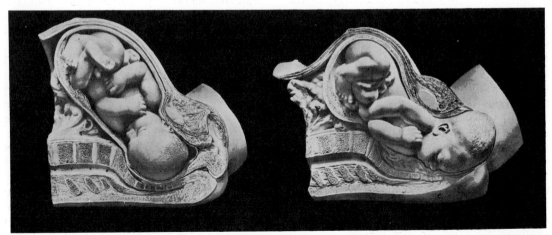

Figure 29.11 Photographs of two models from the Dickinson-Belski series on human birth. (From the *Birth Atlas,* published by Maternity Center Association, New York.)

first birth. The sac of amniotic fluid that surrounds the fetus acts as a wedge and also helps to open the cervix. The amnion normally ruptures during this process, and the amniotic fluid is discharged. When the head begins to move down the vagina, particularly strong uterine contractions set in, and the baby is born within a few minutes. A few more contractions of the uterus force most of the fetal blood from the placenta to the baby, and the umbilical cord can be cut and tied, although tying is unnecessary since contraction of the umbilical arteries would prevent excessive bleeding of the infant. Other mammals simply bite through the cord. Within a week, the stump of the cord shrivels, drops off, and leaves a scar known as the **navel.**

Uterine contractions continue for a while after birth, and the placenta and remaining extraembryonic membranes are expelled as the "after-birth." Much of the uterine lining is lost at birth, for the human placenta is an intimate union of fetal membranes and maternal tissue. Uterine contractions prevent excessive bleeding at this time. Following the birth, the uterine lining is gradually reconstituted and the uterus decreases in size, though it does not become as small as it was originally.

QUESTIONS

1. Describe the evolutionary sequence of kidneys. Compare this with the embryonic sequence.
2. Describe a mammalian nephron and its blood supply.
3. Define renal threshold. Of what significance is this in maintaining the constancy of the internal environment?
4. To what extent is water reabsorbed by the kidneys of a fresh-water fish? A salt-water fish? A mammal?
5. Explain the mechanism that makes it possible for the mammalian kidney to produce a hypertonic urine.
6. What changes have occurred in the products of excretion during the evolution of terrestrial vertebrates?
7. With what is the descent of the mammalian testes correlated?
8. How are the male genital ducts related to the kidney and excretory ducts?
9. How are the reproductive organs of male and female mammals adapted for reproduction in a terrestrial environment?
10. Why are millions of sperm necessary to ensure fertilization in mammals?
11. What relationship exists between fetal and maternal tissues in the human placenta? How do exchanges between fetus and mother occur in the placenta?
12. Describe the birth process in man.

ANNOTATED REFERENCES

Attention is again called to the general references on vertebrate
organ systems cited at the end of Chapter 26.

Asdell, S. A.: Patterns of Mammalian Reproduction. 2nd ed. Ithaca, N.Y., Comstock Publishing Co., 1964. An important source book on differences in reproduction and reproductive cycles that occur in the various kinds of mammals, from the aardvark to the zebu.

Baldwin, E. B.: An Introduction to Comparative Biochemistry. 4th ed. Cambridge, Cambridge University Press, 1964. Contains an interesting account of the osmotic and excretory problems of vertebrates living in different environments.

Masters, W. H. and V. F. Johnson: Human Sexual Response. Boston, Little, Brown and Co., 1966. A careful analysis of the physiological aspects of human mating.

Schmidt-Nielsen, K.: Desert Animals. Oxford, Clarendon Press, 1964. The ways vertebrates meet the problems of water conservation in arid environments are thoroughly discussed.

Smith, H. W.: From Fish to Philosopher. Boston, Little, Brown and Co., 1953. A very entertaining and readable account of vertebrate evolution with emphasis on kidney structure and function.

Smith, H. W.: The kidney. Scientific American *188*:40, (Jan.) 1953. An excellent summary of the evolution of the kidney and its relation to the environment of vertebrates.

Smith, H. W.: Principles of Renal Physiology. New York, Oxford University Press, 1956. Smith's definitive account of his lifelong study of kidney function.

Turner, C. D.: General Endocrinology. 4th ed. Philadelphia, W. B. Saunders Co., 1966. Contains an excellent chapter on the biology of sex and reproduction.

Villee, C. A. (Ed.): The Control of Ovulation. London, Pergamon Press, 1961. Summarizes recent studies on the process of ovulation and its control in a series of papers prepared by leading students of the subject.

30   SENSE ORGANS

If an organism is to be successful and survive in the complex world in which it lives, the activities of all its organs must be integrated so that the organism will function and will make appropriate responses to its external and internal environment. In the higher animals, integration is accomplished by special **receptors,** or sense organs, which detect changes in the environment, and by the **nervous system,** which receives and integrates information from all the sense organs and sends impulses to appropriate **effectors** (muscles, glands), whose activity brings about the appropriate response. Many vertebrate and invertebrate effectors are regulated, in part, by hormones that are secreted by endocrine glands and transported in the blood stream. It will be shown in a later chapter that a great deal of endocrine integration tends to be general rather than specific in its action; that is to say, one hormone may affect more than one organ. Endocrine integration is generally slower but longer lasting than nervous integration; it is especially effective in controlling continuing processes such as metabolism and growth. In a few instances, e.g., in the control of pancreatic secretion, endocrine integration is specific and rapid, but most of the specific and rapid adjustments are achieved by the sense organs and the nervous system. Nervous integration is highly specific; the neurons carry impulses from specific receptors to the spinal cord or brain, from which impulses go out through other neurons to specific effectors. It is rapid because the nerve impulse can travel very fast—as fast as 140 meters per second in the larger, myelinated mammalian neurons—and a second impulse can follow after a brief recovery period that lasts at most only several milliseconds.

It will be recalled from Chapter 5 that our ability to perceive different kinds of stimuli (touch, light, sound, etc.) is a function of the specificity of the receptors, which are attuned to specific stimuli, and of their specific connections within the nervous system. The nerve impulse that is initiated is not specific and is fundamentally the same regardless of where it comes from. Differences in intensity are coded in the number of nerve fibers activated and in the number of impulses passing along a given fiber. Awareness of the sensation depends on the precise part of the brain the impulse reaches. This can be demonstrated by by-passing the receptor and stimulating its neurons directly. The subject then feels the same sort of sensation as if the receptors themselves had been stimulated.

30.1
Receptor Mechanisms

Vertebrates have evolved the capability of sensing those changes in the external and internal environments that are of survival value to the organism. We, in common with other vertebrates, are able to detect changes in many features of the environment, but we must be aware that our knowledge of the world is not complete. There are parameters, such as cosmic and radio waves, that we cannot detect without instruments, and there may be yet other parameters of which we are completely unaware. Receptors can be grouped into four broad categories according to the nature of the environmental change that activates them: **Chemoreceptors** in the mouth and nose detect chemical changes in the environment; various kinds of **mechanoreceptors** in many parts of the body are

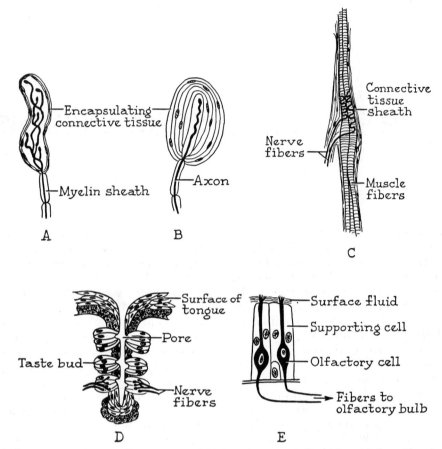

Figure 30.1 A group of mammalian receptors. *A,* Meissner's corpuscle found beneath the epidermis, assumed to be sensitive to touch; *B,* Pacinian corpuscle found in the dermis and many internal organs, sensitive to pressure; *C,* neuromuscle spindle, sensitive to muscle tension (proprioception); *D,* taste buds between papillae on the surface of the tongue; *E,* olfactory cells in the nasal mucosa. (*A* modified after Ranson; *B* and *E* after Gardner; *C* after Maximow and Bloom.)

affected by touch, pressure, muscle stretch, vibrations and balance; **photoreceptors** respond to changes in light; and **thermoreceptors** in the skin and mouth to changes in temperature (Fig. 30.1).

All of these receptors consist of one or more specialized cells or of free nerve endings that may or may not be encapsulated in surrounding connective tissues. Physically, they respond as miniature transducers for, like the piezoelectric crystal in a phonograph pickup, they convert one form of energy into another. Each receptor is easily affected by the type of energy to which it is attuned and converts this to an electric current, **the generator potential,** which, in turn, initiates a nerve impulse. The generator potential has been studied particularly in certain mechanoreceptors. It depends, as does the action

potential of muscle and nerve, on changes in cell membrane permeability and the flow of ions. But unlike muscle and nerve, the activity of a receptor cell is not an all-or-none phenomenon; it varies directly with the strength of the stimulus. The generator potential must attain a certain threshold to initiate a nerve impulse. If the intensity of the potential exceeds the threshold, it initiates additional impulses.

30.2
Some Microscopic Receptors

All receptor cells are microscopic, and most are widely scattered throughout the body. After briefly examining certain of these, we will consider more thoroughly the eye and the ear, two sense organs which are aggregations of receptive cells along with tissues that help to gather and amplify the stimuli.

The chemoreceptors of taste are small groups of receptive cells, the **taste buds,** found in mammals in association with certain of the tongue papillae. In lower vertebrates, they are found in many parts of the mouth and pharynx and, in some fishes, even on the skin of the head. Most investigators recognize four pure taste qualities localized to some extent on different parts of the tongue. Thus the tip of the tongue is particularly sensitive to sweet and salty stimuli; the sides, to sour or acid stimuli; the back of the tongue, to bitter stimuli. However, taste is far more complex than this classification implies. Although a given taste bud is particularly sensitive to one modality, there is evidence that it can be easily activated by others. Considerable comparison of the modalities and intensities of stimuli from different parts of the tongue must occur centrally, i.e., in the brain, to give us our final sensation of taste.

The olfactory epithelium within the nose contains **olfactory cells,** the chemoreceptors of smell. Unlike other receptors, processes of these cells lead directly to the brain, hence they are considered to be **neurosensory cells.** They are activated by water- or oil-soluble molecules of an odorous substance. Less is known about the kinds of qualities of odor, but there are doubtless many. It has recently been proposed that man can distinguish seven primary odors (camphoraceous, musky, floral, pepperminty, ethereal, pungent and putrid). Substances having these odors have molecules of different size and shape, and there is evidence that these fit into sites of specific size and shape on different receptor cells. Our final sensation of a substance is usually a complex mixture of taste, odor, texture and sight, and it is sometimes difficult to resolve the specific contribution of each particular sensation.

Man's chemical senses, especially olfaction, are somewhat rudimentary. In most vertebrate groups, apart from birds, they provide vital sensory clues to the external world: clues to food, predators, mates, and even the way home. It has been demonstrated that salmon with plugged nasal sacs are unable to find their home tributary in which to spawn, but normal salmon readily recognize their own river, apparently by recalling its distinctive odor!

Particularly important mechanoreceptors are the **neuromuscle spindles** (Fig. 30.1C) that occur in most muscles and tendons. They mediate our sense of **proprioception,** or **kinesthesis,** by detecting changes in the tensions that are developed in the muscles. You can, for example, put your hands behind your back and without touching anything detect their movements by tensions developed in the muscles. It is this sort of feedback from the muscles that is essential for coordinated muscle activity, for example, for the appropriate amount of relaxation of one group of muscles as another group contracts.

Stimuli of touch, pressure, cold, warmth and pain are received by specialized, microscopic receptors and free nerve endings in the skin (Fig. 30.1A and B). There is no doubt that there is a physiologic specificity to the reception and transmission of these stimuli; that is, the excitation of certain neurons results in sensations of cold, of touch, and so forth. This principle was clearly set forth by the famous German physiologist Johannes Müller near the middle of the last century and is known as the doctrine of specific nerve energies. At one time, it was assumed that this physiologic specificity was mirrored by a morphologic specificity in the end organ. To some extent this is true, but there are not enough specialized endings in most parts of the skin to account for all of the physiologic specificity. Considerable sorting out and interpretation of stimuli must occur in the brain.

30.3
The Eye

Ancestral vertebrates had eyes of two types —a median eye on the top of the head, which probably distinguished only between light and dark, and a pair of image-forming eyes on the sides of the head. Cyclostomes and a few reptiles retain a functional median eye but, in most groups it has become a small organ, the **pineal body,** attached to the top of the brain. The mammalian pineal body is a small glandlike organ that probably has an endocrine role (p. 572).

Structure of the Mammalian Eye. Although the lateral, image-forming eyes of different groups of vertebrates vary in their adaptation for seeing beneath water, in the air and under varying light intensities, all are alike in their major features. Those of mammals may be taken as an example. Each eyeball is an oval-shaped organ constructed on the principles of a simple camera (Fig. 30.2). It has a small opening at the front, the **pupil,** through which light enters; a **lens,** which brings the images of objects into sharp focus; and a light-sensitive **retina,** which is analogous to the film.

The wall of the eyeball is composed of three layers of tissue. The outermost one is a dense, fibrous connective tissue that gives strength to the wall. Most of this layer is opaque and is known as the **sclera,** but its anterior portion, through which light passes, is clear and is called the **cornea.** The surface of the cornea is covered with a layer of stratified epithelium, the **conjunctiva,** which is continuous with the epidermis.

The next layer of the eyeball wall is a darkly pigmented and very vascular **choroid coat.** Its pigmentation absorbs light rays, thereby reducing internal reflections that might blur the image, and its vessels nourish the retina. The anterior portion of the choroid coat, together with a nonsensitive portion of the retina, extends in front of the lens and forms the **iris**—an opaque disc with the pupil in its center. The iris prevents the light from entering the eye except through the center of the lens, which is optically the most efficient part. The amount of light entering the eye is controlled by circularly and radially arranged smooth muscles in the iris that constrict or dilate the pupil. In this respect, the iris is analogous to the iris diaphragm of a camera

or microscope. The thickened portion of the choroid around the base of the iris is the **ciliary body.** A number of **zonule fibers** extend from it to the lens and help to hold it in place. Muscles within the ciliary body are concerned with focusing the eye.

The retina is the innermost layer of the eyeball. It consists of a **pigmented layer,** intimately associated with the choroid, and a **nervous layer,** which contains millions of receptor cells, the **rods** and **cones,** and neurons that initiate the processing of light signals and relay the information to the brain by way of the **optic nerve.** The rods and cones lie in the surface of the nervous layer that faces the choroid, and light must pass through most of the retina before it can stimulate them. This apparently illogical arrangement is explained by the mode of development of the eye. The retina develops from an outgrowth of the brain which, in turn, develops from an infolding of the surface ectoderm (Fig. 30.3). What was the outer surface of the ectodermal cells becomes the inner surface of the nervous layer of the retina. The polarity of the cells is retained during their various developmental gymnastics. The fact that the retina and optic nerves are developmentally parts of the brain also explains why at least two afferent neurons (**bipolar** and **ganglion cells**) are involved in transmitting impulses from the rods and cones. Chains of neurons are common in brain tracts, but in most nerves only one neuron extends from a receptor cell to the brain or spinal cord.

The cavities within the eye are filled with liquid. A gelatinous **vitreous humor** occupies the large chamber that lies between the lens and the retina and helps to hold the lens in place. A watery **aqueous humor** fills the **posterior chamber** between the iris and the lens and the **anterior chamber** between the iris and the cornea. The aqueous humor is secreted continually by the ciliary body and drained through the **canal of Schlemm** at the base of the cornea. This humor performs a twofold function. Firstly, it helps to nourish the cornea and lens, which are devoid of blood vessels; secondly, by maintaining the intraocular pressure, it helps to maintain the turgidity and shape of the eyeball. Blockage of the canal of Schlemm leads to increased intraocular pressure and the disease **glaucoma,** in which the pressure flattens and eventually injures the retina.

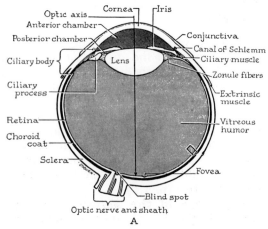

Figure 30.2   Diagram of a section through a mammalian eye.

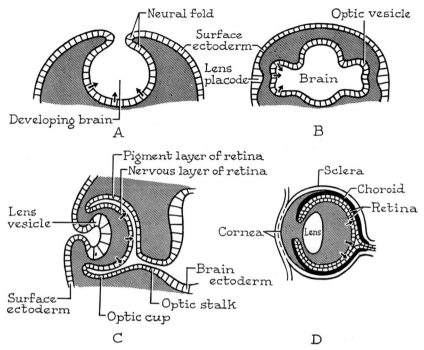

Figure 30.3 The development of the eye. *A*, Cross section through an embryo in which the anterior portions of the neural folds are closing to form the brain; *B*, the optic vesicles evaginate from the sides of the forebrain; *C*, an optic cup develops from each optic vesicle and the lens forms from adjacent surface ectoderm; *D*, the choroid, sclera and part of the cornea develop from surrounding mesoderm. Arrows indicate the original polarity of the ectoderm cells. (*D* from Romer.)

The eyeball lies in the orbit of the skull, and six **extrinsic ocular muscles,** which move the entire eyeball, extend from it to the walls of the orbit. A pair of movable **eyelids** cover the eyeball, and the cornea is kept moist, cleansed, and possibly nourished, by the secretion of tears from several **tear glands.** Tears are drained from the median corner of the eye by a **lacrimal duct,** which leads into the nasal cavity. Pigs, cats and many other mammals have a third lid, known as the **nictitating membrane,** located in the median corner of the eye. It is moved passively over the cornea when the eyeball is retracted slightly, and aids in cleaning and protecting the eye. This membrane is reduced to a vestigial **semilunar fold** in man.

Refraction of Light. Light that enters the eye is bent toward the optic axis in such a way that it forms a sharp, though inverted, image upon the retina (Fig. 30.4*A*). The lens is important in bending the light rays but the cornea, humors and the retina itself are also involved. The cornea is the major refractive agent in terrestrial vertebrates, for the dif-ference between the refractive index of air and the cornea is greater than that between any of the other refractive media. The action of the cornea places the image approximately on the retina; the lens brings it into sharp focus.

When the eye is at rest, distant objects are in focus. The refractive power of the eye must be increased in viewing a near object or its image would be blurred, for the image would come into sharp focus theoretically at a point behind the retina. Accommodation for near vision is accomplished by the contraction of muscles within the ciliary body. This brings the point of origin of the zonule fibers a bit closer to the lens and releases the tension of these fibers. The front of the elastic lens bulges out slightly, and its refractive powers are increased accordingly. When the ciliary muscles are relaxed, intraocular pressure pushes the wall of the eyeball outward, increases the tension of the zonule fibers, and the lens is flattened a bit. The lens becomes less elastic with age, and our ability to focus on near objects decreases.

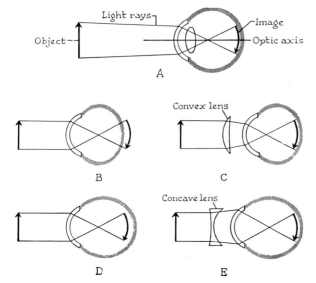

Figure 30.4 Image formation by the eye. *A*, Normal eye; *B*, far-sighted eye; *C*, far-sighted eye corrected by a convex lens; *D*, near-sighted eye; *E*, near-sighted eye corrected by a concave lens.

The refractive parts of the eye form a sharp image of an object on the retina only in an eyeball of appropriate length. If the eyeball is shorter than normal, as it is in far-sighted people, the image of an object in theory falls behind the retina. Accommodation is necessary to bring the image into focus, and the power of accommodation may not be great enough to focus on a near object. This can be corrected by placing a convex lens in front of the eye (Fig. 30.4*B* and *C*). Near-sighted people have eyeballs that are longer than normal and the image falls short of the retina. This can be corrected by a concave lens (Fig. 30.4*D* and *E*).

Chemistry of Vision. Light that strikes the rods and cones activates them and they, in turn, initiate nerve impulses. Recent studies have given us an indication of some of the steps in this process in the rods. The outer segment of each rod contains a great elaboration of the membrane system of the cell, and a great deal of the pigment visual purple, or **rhodopsin,** is associated with these membranes. Rhodopsin consists of **retinene,** which is an aldehyde of vitamin A, conbined with the protein **opsin.** Retinene can exist as two isomers, that is, as identical molecules except for slightly different geometrical configurations. It is in the form of the isomer ***cis*-retinene** when combined with opsin. Upon absorbing light energy, it changes (by photoisomerization) to ***trans*-retinene.** When retinene is in the *trans* configuration, the rhodopsin (now called **lumi-**

rhodopsin) is unstable, presumably because *trans*-retinene no longer fits its site on the opsin molecule, and opsin and *trans*-retinene separate. These changes apparently affect, in some way not yet understood, the membrane system of the cell, and the rod becomes electrically active. Recovery involves the conversion of *trans*-retinene to *trans*-vitamin A, the isomerization of this to *cis*-vitamin A, and the conversion of this to *cis*-retinene. Each of these steps requires the expenditure of energy on the part of the cell. *Cis*-retinene now recombines with opsin to reconstitute rhodopsin. A cycle of breakdown and reconstitution of rhodopsin goes on continually if the eyes are exposed to any light. The cycle, however, is influenced by the amount of light, for rhodopsin breaks down faster in bright light and is reconstituted faster in the dark. To see well in dim light one should stay in a dark room for a while so that a maximum amount of rhodopsin is reconstituted.

The series of reactions described have been demonstrated in extracts of rhodopsin. That rhodopsin is the pigment responsible for black and white vision in dim light is suggested by the fact that the wave length of maximal absorption of light by rhodopsin corresponds to the wave length of maximal sensitivity of the eye, i.e., to the wave length at which one can best distinguish a dim flash of light. Other points of the rhodopsin absorption spectrum and the human dark-adapted visual sensitivity curve also coincide

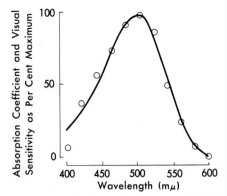

Figure 30.5 The absorption spectrum of rhodopsin (solid line) and the spectral sensitivity of the human dark-adapted eye (circles). The coincidence of these curves shows that rhodopsin can be the pigment used in viewing in dim light. (From F. G. Crescitelli and H. J. A. Dartnall. Nature, *172*:195, 1953.)

(Fig. 30.5). Moreover, it has been shown that a deficiency of vitamin A, a precursor of retinene, leads to a reduction in ability to see in dim light. Rhodopsin is extremely sensitive to light, and it has been calculated that a single photon of light can activate one molecule of rhodopsin and that this, in turn, can activate an entire rod. But it does not follow, as we shall see, that a single active rod can initiate an impulse in a neuron to the brain.

Cones are activated only by light of greater intensity, and they are also believed to be responsible for color vision. It has long been assumed that there are probably three types of cones (blue, green and red) whose interactions are responsible for our range of color vision. This hypothesis is consistent with the three known types of color blindness, but only recently has it been possible to get more direct evidence for this trichromatic theory. By exploring isolated retinas from individuals who have just died with a very small beam of light, it has been possible to find three types of cones with absorption spectra maxima in the blue, green or red parts of the spectrum. However, extracts of all three of the different pigments which presumably are involved have not yet been made.

Organization of the Retina. As we have seen, the retina develops embryonically as an outgrowth of the brain, so it is not surprising that its organization is very complex, nor that the retina itself plays a role in the processing of visual information. There are about seven million cones in the retina of each human eye. These are particularly dense in a small part of the retina opposite the optic axis which is known as the **fovea** (Fig. 30.2). Only cones are formed in this region, and they become less dense toward the periphery of the retina, where they finally disappear. Each retina contains about 120 million rods, and they are most dense near the periphery of the eye. Rods and cones synapse with **bipolar cells** (Fig. 30.6) which in turn synapse with **ganglion cells** whose axons cross the retina, congregate at the blind spot, and go to the brain as the **optic nerve.** However, the synaptic relationships of rods and cones vary in an important way. Many rods, sometimes as many as 200 of them in the peripheral part of the retina, converge on a single bipolar cell, and a number of bipolar cells may converge on one ganglion cell. Far fewer cones converge on a single bipolar cell, and in the fovea many of the cones synapse with a single bipolar and ganglion cell. This difference in neuron pathways, together with a difference in threshold of illumination, explains why rods are more efficient than cones in light of low intensity. Stimuli from a number of rods, each of which is below the threshold of a bipolar cell, converge upon a single cell, have an additive effect upon it, and may activate it. Less summation, or none, of this type occurs in the more "private line" system of the cones. Since the greatest density of rods and the greatest degree of convergence occur in the periphery of the retina, one can see best in dim light by looking out of the side of the eye so that the image falls on the periphery of the retina. Rods are particularly abundant in the eyes of nocturnal vertebrates. Although rod vision is more sensitive than cone vision, it also follows from their different pathways that rod vision is less acute. The eye cannot distinguish which rods are receiving light among a number of rods that converge on a single bipolar cell. Cone vision in the fovea is extremely acute, because most of the cones here have a "private line" to the brain. Rod vision is analogous to a high-speed, coarse-grained, black and white photographic film; cone vision, to a slower, fine-grained color film.

Other complexities occur within the retina (Fig. 30.6). A network of **horizontal cells** interconnects the rods and cones and the

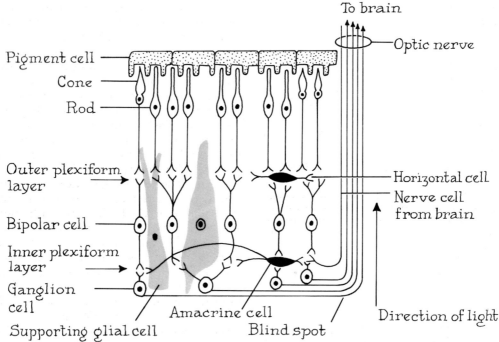

Figure 30.6 A diagrammatic vertical section through the retina to illustrate major types of interconnections among the component cells.

bipolar cells at the level of the synapses between receptors and bipolar cells, and a second network of **amacrine cells** interconnects the bipolar cells at the level of their synapses with the ganglion cells. These interconnections, of which some are inhibitory and others facilitory, appear to be the morphological basis for phenomena one can identify in ganglion cells. By recording from individual ganglion cells with fine electrodes, it has been found that some ganglion cells discharge impulses only when a light stimulus is impinging on the retina **(on system),** some are activated only when the light is turned off **(off system),** others are activated only at the beginning and termination of illumination **(on-off system),** and still others exhibit a spontaneous activity when no light is on **(steady-background system).** The interplay among these various systems probably enhances the retina's ability to respond to contrasts in illumination. Although most cells in the retina carry impulses to the brain, there are a few nerve cells that carry impulses from the brain to the retina. These fibers probably enhance or suppress retinal activity, but we know little about them.

Eyes of Other Vertebrates. The eyes

of all vertebrates are essentially alike, but those of primitive vertebrates differ from mammalian eyes in several important respects, for the problems associated with sight beneath water are not identical with those in the air. For one thing, the water itself cleans and moistens the eye, and fishes have not evolved movable eyelids or tear glands. Secondly, the refractive index of water is nearly the same as that of the cornea, so the cornea of a fish's eye does not bend light rays. Most refraction is accomplished by the lens, which is nearly spherical and, hence, has a greater refractive power than the oval lens of tetrapods. It is interesting in this connection that the lens of a frog's eye flattens a bit during metamorphosis, when a change in environment occurs. Finally, the method of accommodation differs, for the lens is moved back and forth in camera fashion in fishes and amphibians and does not change shape.

30.4
The Lateral Line and The Ear

Equilibrium. All vertebrates have the ability to perceive differences in the orientation of their bodies with respect to their surroundings and to maintain their equilibrium. Although vision and proprioceptive impulses from the muscles play a part, this ability is primarily a function of the inner ear. The inner ear is embedded within the otic capsule of the skull and consists of a complex of membranous walled sacs and canals, the **membranous labyrinth,** which are filled with a liquid **endolymph** and surrounded by a protective liquid cushion, the **perilymph** (Fig. 30.7). The dorsal part of the membranous labyrinth consists of three **semicircular canals,** each of which is perpendicular to the other two. Two lie in the vertical plane, but at right angles to each other, and one is in the horizontal plane at right angles to the other two. Each has a round swelling, an **ampulla,** at one of its ends in which there is a patch of **hair cells**—receptor cells bearing hairlike processes. The three semicircular canals connect with a chamber known as a **utriculus** and this, in turn, connects with a more ventral chamber known as a **sacculus.** Both of these chambers contain patches of hair cells. Calcareous **otoliths** are in contact with these cells. Different parts of the membranous labyrinth are concerned with different aspects of equilibrium—static equilibrium, linear acceleration and angular acceleration. Differences in the position of the head and body **(static equilibrium)** affect the way in which gravity pulls the otoliths upon the underlying hair cells. Rapid forward movement **(linear acceleration)** causes

the otoliths, which have more inertia than the surrounding endolymph and hence lag, to push back upon certain hair cells. During sudden turns of the head in various planes **(angular acceleration),** the endolymph in the semicircular canals, because of its inertia, does not move as fast as the head and the hair cells in the ampullae. This differential in rate of movement stimulates the hair cells.

Phonoreception in Fishes. The part of the ear concerned with equilibrium is essentially the same in all vertebrates, but the part concerned with phonoreception or hearing differs considerably among vertebrates. By hearing we mean the detection of pressure waves resulting from a mechanical disturbance some distance away. The human ear can detect waves with frequencies of 20 to about 20,000 cycles per second, and some animals, e.g., bats, can detect frequencies of over 100,000 cycles per second. Frequencies lower than 20 cycles per second are usually perceived as vibrations and not as sound.

Mammals, birds and some reptiles have a **cochlear duct,** an elongated cul-de-sac extending from the sacculus that is clearly concerned with phonoreception. Fishes have a homologous but very small diverticulum known as the **lagena.** The rudimentary nature of this structure, together with early experiments in which fishes were shown to be unresponsive to sounds made in the air, led to the conclusion that they could not hear. Later this conclusion was shown to be wrong,

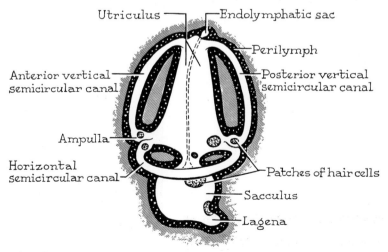

Figure 30.7 The left ear of a fish seen in a lateral view. Only an inner ear is present, embedded within spaces in the otic capsule of the skull. (Modified after Kingsley.)

for it was realized that most air-borne sound waves are reflected by the air-water surface, but sounds generated in the water travel rapidly and far. By using underwater listening and sound-generating devices, investigators have discovered that aquatic organisms produce and respond to a great many sounds. But a fish must overcome one problem. Since their ears and tissues are mostly water, they are essentially transparent to a sound generated in the water; the sound waves pass right through the fish without interruption. For a fish to detect the waves, there must be some tissue that will respond to the waves differently than the body as a whole. In most fishes this is simply a large calcareous **otolith** in the sacculus. Catfish, suckers and minnows also utilize the air-filled swim bladder as a hydrophone. This interrupts waves passing through a large part of the body, and transmits them via a chain of small bones derived from the vertebrae (**weberian ossicles,** Fig. 22.21) to the sacculus. This mechanism is particularly effective, for members of this group of fishes can respond to a wider range of frequencies (60 to 6000 cycles per second) than other fishes, and they can also discriminate better between frequencies.

Clearly, fishes can detect underwater sounds by means of a part of the membranous labyrinth. In addition, fishes have a **lateral line system** that is sensitive to currents, to changes in pressure and to vibrations of low frequency. It consists of groups of hair cells similar to those in the ear. Most of these are arranged in a longitudinal canal extending the length of the trunk and tail and in a series of canals that ramify over the head, but often other groups of hair cells are scattered over the surface (Fig. 30.8A). The canals are embedded in the skin, but connect with the surface through a series of pores. The system is sometimes described as one of "distant touch," because the fish can detect its approach to an object, or an objects' approach to it (Fig. 30.8B), by the resulting deflection of certain of the groups of hair cells. Neurons from these receptors enter an **acoustico-lateralis area** of the brain along with neurons from the ear, which suggests that there is a close relationship between the ear and lateral line. The inner ear develops embryonically in close association with certain lateral line canals, and it may have evolved in the same way. Larval amphibians have a lateral line system, but it is lost during metamorphosis. Higher vertebrates never have this system at all.

Phonoreception in Tetrapods. In all tetrapods, a part of the membranous labyrinth, generally the lagena or cochlear duct, is specialized for phonoreception, and various devices have evolved which transmit either ground- or air-borne vibrations to it. Frogs have an external tympanic membrane (Fig. 21.19), which responds to vibrations in the air, and a stapes, which transmits the vibrations across the middle ear cavity to a **fenestra ovalis** in the otic capsule. The fenestra ovalis communicates with the inner ear.

The hearing apparatus of mammals is basically similar but much more elaborate (Fig. 30.9A). Most mammals have a well-developed external ear consisting of a canal,

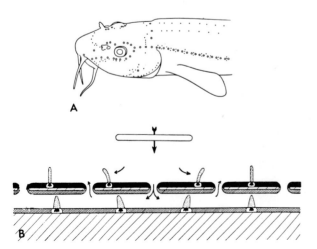

A

B

Figure 30.8 Lateral line organs of a fish. *A,* Surface view of the anterior end of the catfish, *Nemachilus.* Circles indicate the position of the lateral line; small dots, isolated groups of hair cells. *B,* Diagrammatic vertical section through a lateral line canal and several isolated groups of hair cells. Water currents (small arrows) and the deflection of groups of hair cells caused by an approaching object are shown. (From Dijkgraaf, S.: Bau und Funktionen der Seitenorgane und des Ohrlabyrinths bei Fischen. Experientia *8:*205-216, 1952.)

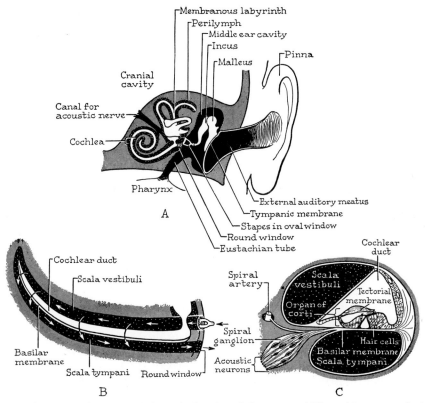

Figure 30.9 The mammalian ear. *A*, Schematic drawing of the outer, middle and inner ear of a human being. *B*, Diagram of the cochlea as though it were uncoiled. *C*, An enlarged cross section through the cochlea. The cochlear duct and other parts of the membranous labyrinth are filled with endolymph and are shown in white; perilymph is black with white stipples.

the **external auditory meatus,** and an external flap, the **pinna.** Together they act as an ear trumpet, concentrating and increasing slightly the pressure of the sound waves by the time they reach the delicate **tympanic membrane,** which is situated in a protected site at the internal end of the meatus. Acoustic pressure variations cause slight movements of the tympanic membrane. Three auditory ossicles (the hammer-shaped **malleus,** the anvil-shaped **incus** and the stirrup-shaped **stapes,** arranged in sequence) transmit these vibrations across the middle ear cavity to the **fenestra ovalis,** or oval window. The stapes evolved from a part of the hyoid arch of fishes, and the malleus and incus were derived from the posterior part of the mandibular arch when a new jaw joint evolved in mammals anterior to the former one. These three ossicles form a system of levers that reduces the displacement amplitude but increases the pressure amplitude of the sound waves. The movement of the foot plate of

the stapes against the membrane within the oval window is only about one-half as extensive as the movement of the tympanic membrane, but the force of the movement is several times as great. Two small muscles, derived from visceral arch muscles, attach onto the ossicles and reflexly dampen their oscillation to sounds of very high intensity. They form a protective mechanism somewhat analogous to the iris of the eye. Additional pressure amplification results from the fact that the tympanic membrane has nearly 20 times the surface area of the membrane in the oval window. Virtually all of the force that impinges on the tympanic membrane reaches the membrane in the oval window and, since this membrane is smaller, the force per unit area is increased. Pressure amplification is essential for an efficient transfer of energy from the light, compressible external air to the dense, incompressible liquid of the inner ear.

The **middle ear cavity,** in which the ossicles lie, evolved from the first gill slit, homologous to the spiracle of many fishes. It connects with the pharynx via the **eustachian tube** and, hence, indirectly with the outside of the body. The pharyngeal opening of the eustachian tube is normally closed, but if pressures become unequal on the two sides of the tympanic membrane, the eustachian tubes usually reflexly open and the pressures are equalized. If pressure differences on the two sides of the membrane are great, a situation that often occurs during SCUBA diving, it is sometimes necessary to swallow in order to open the tubes.

A long **cochlear duct** has evolved from the lagena of fishes, and it contains the actual receptive structure, the **organ of Corti** (Fig. 30.9, B and C). The cochlear duct is filled with endolymph and is a part of the membranous labyrinth. Pressure waves reach the cochlear duct via specialized perilymphatic channels. A **scala vestibuli** begins at the oval window, extends along the cochlear duct, curves around its apex and returns as the **scala tympani** to a **fenestra rotunda,** or round window, that is separated by a delicate membrane from the middle ear cavity. The scala vestibuli and scala tympani have a different origin from the cochlear duct, but all three are in intimate association and collectively form the spiral-shaped **cochlea.**

Pressure waves induced by the stapes at the oval window pass through the scala vestibuli, cross the cochlear duct, travel back through the scala tympani, and escape at the round window. The **basilar membrane,** which supports the organ of Corti, is set in vibration. Since the basilar membrane and the **tectorial membrane** of the organ of Corti are hinged at different places, a pressure wave causes a slight differential movement between them and develops a shearing force that stimulates the intervening hair cells. The ear is extremely sensitive for, at certain frequencies, it can detect any displacement of these membranes considerably less than the diameter of a hydrogen atom! Sensory neurons of the acoustic nerve extend from the hair cells to the brain.

Sound analysis by the cochlea is very complex and not completely understood. It is well established that pitches or tones of different frequencies are detected in different regions of the cochlea. According to the current traveling wave hypothesis, pressure waves traveling through the cochlea set the basilar membrane in motion in a way somewhat similar to the way a jerk sends waves along a slack rope (Fig. 30.10). The whole membrane is set in motion, but waves of different frequency reach maximal amplitude at different points. Long wave length (low notes) cause a maximal displacement near the apex of the cochlea; short wave lengths (high notes), a maximal displacement at the proximal end of the basilar membrane. Von Békésy has demonstrated the essential truth of this view by direct observations on the ears of fresh cadavers. More intense sounds, in addition to stimulating hair cells to move vigorously, cause a longer length of basilar membrane to vibrate, but the displacement peak remains the same for any given frequency. Two different musical instruments playing the same note have different qualities because of differences in the number and kinds of overtones or harmonics also present. Both instruments will maximally stimulate the same part of the basilar membrane, but they will differ with respect to the other parts of the membrane also stimulated.

In an organ as elaborate as the ear, many things can go wrong. Infections may enter the middle ear via the eustachian tube and affect the auditory ossicles. The stapes may become locked in the oval window by an abnormal growth of bone, or the individual ossicles may fuse together. Conduction deafness of these types can be corrected by a hearing aid that amplifies vibrations enough to be transmitted directly through the skull bones to the cochlea. More rarely, the acoustic nerve or the cochlea may be damaged. Deaf-

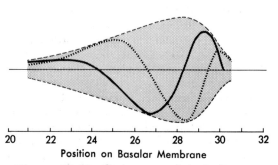

20   22   24   26   28   30   32
Position on Basalar Membrane

Figure 30.10 Displacement of the basilar membrane resulting from a traveling wave of a specific frequency. The shape of the wave at two instances in time is shown. Maximum displacement of the membrane occurs only at one point. (From Case after Von Békésy.) (From G. Von Békésy; J. Acoust, Soc. Amer., *19*:452, 1947.)

ness of this sort cannot be corrected. If only a part of the cochlea is injured, one may become deaf only to sounds of certain frequencies. The continuing, loud, high-pitched noises to which boilermakers are subjected sometimes destroy a part of the cochlea, and the men become deaf to sounds of this frequency.

QUESTIONS

1. In what ways is a receptor cell like a transducer?
2. Name the major categories of receptors, and cite an example of each.
3. Describe what happens to a ray of dim light that enters the eye from a point near the observer. Through what structures does it pass? What, if any, adjustments are necessary to make it fall upon the retina? And how does it activate a receptor cell?
4. What morphological arrangements within the retina cause rod vision to be more sensitive but less acute than cone vision?
5. What effect did the transition from water to land during the course of vertebrate evolution have upon the eyeball and surrounding structures?
6. What problem must be overcome by fish in order to hear? How is this done?
7. Describe how we become aware of a loud sound of low frequency.
8. How has the ear changed during evolution from fish to mammal? What part of the ear has changed very little?

ANNOTATED REFERENCES

Attention is again called to the general references on vertebrate organ systems cited at the end of Chapter 26.

Amoore, J. E., J. W. Johnson, Jr., and M. Rubin: The stereochemical theory of odor. Scientific American 205:74, (Feb.) 1964. An analysis of the theory that smell is based on the shapes of odoriferous molecules and receptor cells.

Case, J.: Sensory Mechanisms. New York, Macmillan, 1966. Prepared for Macmillan's Current Concepts in Biology series, this is a thorough account of the sense organs of invertebrates and vertebrates. Much recent work is included.

Davson, H. (Ed.): The Eye. New York, Academic Press, 1962. A four-volume reference book on the eye.

Geldard, F.: The Human Senses. New York, John Wiley & Sons, Inc., 1953. A valuable and detailed account of the human senses.

Lowenstein, W. R.: Biological transducers. Scientific American 203:98, (Aug.) 1960. A discussion of the way receptor cells convert the energy they receive into electric pulses.

MacNichol, E. F., Jr.: Three-pigment color vision. Scientific American 211:48, (Dec.) 1964. A discussion of the evidence for the existence of three cones that distinguish blue, green and red light.

Miller, W. H., F. Ratliff, and H. K. Hartline: How cells receive stimuli. Scientific American 205:222, (Sept.) 1961. A general analysis of the problem of reception.

Polyak, S.: The Vertebrate Visual System. Chicago, University of Chicago Press, 1957. A very valuable source book.

Van Bergeijk, W. A., J. R. Pierce, and E. E. David, Jr.: Waves and the Ear. Garden City, Doubleday & Co., 1960. An excellent and authoritative account of all aspects of hearing.

Von Békésy, G.: The ear. Scientific American 197:66, (Aug.) 1957. An excellent account of the ear by the man who made many of the basic discoveries in the physiology of hearing.

Von Buddenbrock, W.: The Senses. Ann Arbor, University of Michigan Press, 1958. An authoritative and entertainingly written account of the sense organs of invertebrates and vertebrates.

Walls, G. L.: The Vertebrate Eye and Its Adaptive Radiation. Bloomfield Hills, Mich., Cranbrook Institute of Science, 1942. An old but still very valuable source book on the evolution of the eye and its adaptations to different environments.

31 _____ NERVOUS COORDINATION

The nervous system provides for the coordination and integration of the body's many activities by conducting impulses from the receptors to the appropriate effectors. It is composed of nerve cells or **neurons,** which conduct the impulses, and of supporting cells known as **neuroglia.** We previously considered the morphology and many aspects of the physiology of these cells (pp. 93–97).

31.1
Organization of the Nervous System

The neurons in the body are so arranged that it is possible to divide the nervous system grossly into a **central nervous system,** consisting of the brain and spinal cord, and a **peripheral nervous system,** which includes the nerves that extend between the central nervous system and the receptors and effectors. The neurons themselves can be grouped into three broad categories: (1) sensory or **afferent neurons,** which carry impulses from the sense organs through the nerves to the brain or cord; (2) motor or **efferent neurons,** which carry impulses from the brain or cord through the nerves to the muscles and other effectors of the body; and (3) connector or **internuncial neurons,** which lie entirely within the central nervous system and are interposed between the other two. The efferent neurons are often referred to as the **final common pathway** of the nervous system, for they receive excitatory and inhibitory impulses from many different afferent and internuncial neurons,

and all impulses to the effector organs ultimately converge upon them.

The interrelations of the various kinds of neurons can be seen by considering a specific example When you touch a hot stove, for example (Fig. 31.1), a receptor in the skin is stimulated and it initiates an impulse in an afferent neuron. This neuron is part of a spinal nerve and extends into the spinal cord, where it ends in a synapse with one or more internuncial neurons. An internuncial neuron, in turn, carries the impulse to an appropriate efferent neuron, which extends from the cord and carries the impulse back through the spinal nerve to a group of extensor muscle fibers of the hand. Their contraction withdraws your hand from the stove. For the movement to be effective, however, the antagonistic flexor muscles should relax, and this relaxation would involve the inhibition of impulses going to these muscles. Normally, some impulses go out to all of the muscles of the body continually and cause a partial contraction, a condition called muscle **tonus.** There is now evidence for the existence of inhibitory neurons in the spinal cord which, upon activation, probably release an inhibitory transmitter substance at their synapses with the motor neurons. According to the chemical theory of synaptic transmission, inhibitory substances act by making the cell membrane of the postsynaptic neuron more permeable to certain ions. Chlorine (Cl^-) flows into the postsynaptic cell and potassium (K^+) flows out; the cell membrane becomes hyperpolarized and hence less subject to stimulation by excitatory transmitter substances. Excitatory

532

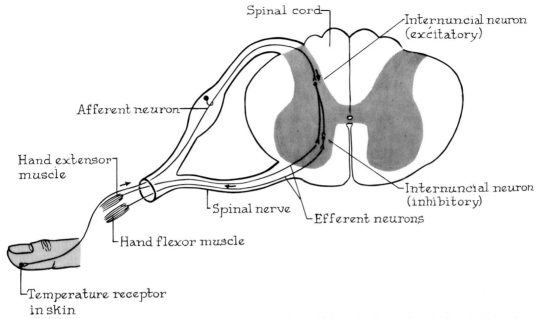

Figure 31.11 Diagram of the types of neurons involved in a withdrawal reflex in the spinal cord. The pathways shown here are superimposed upon neural mechanisms (not shown) that maintain muscle tone.

substances depolarize the membrane and thereby initiate a nerve impulse.

The stimulus and response just described is a simple **spinal reflex,** and the neuronal pathway along which the impulse travels is called a **reflex arc.** Reflexes are fixed patterns of response to stimuli and they need not involve an awareness of the stimulus. The impulse need not pass through any of the higher centers in the brain in order that the response occur. An impulse may be carried to the cerebral cortex of the brain by other connector neurons, **afferent internuncial neurons** (Fig. 31.2). You then become aware of the stimulus and may voluntarily decide to do something about it, perhaps withdraw your whole arm or turn off the stove. If so, impulses will pass out from the brain along **efferent internuncial neurons** to the appropriate efferent neurons.

The **withdrawal reflex** described above requires at least two internuncial neurons. Many other kinds of reflexes occur in the spinal cord and brain. A **stretch reflex,** which is the automatic contraction of a muscle when it or its tendon is unduly stretched, involves fewer neurons. In the familiar knee jerk, for example, afferent neurons coming from neuromuscular spindles in the tendon of the large muscle in the front of the thigh synapse directly with motor neurons going to the same muscle; as the tendon is stretched, the muscle contracts. But even here, inhibitory neurons go to the antagonistic muscles. More complex reflexes can involve several regions of the body. If a drop of acid is placed on the flank skin of a frog, both hind legs will converge on this spot and alternately flex and extend in an attempt to scrape off the acid. This will happen even if the entire brain has been destroyed. Complex, coordinated reflexes of this type are possible because internuncial neurons extend from the afferent neurons through the cord to many different efferent neurons.

Reflexes of the types described are present in all individuals as soon as the neuronal pathways have developed. These are inherited or **inborn reflexes,** and they are not dependent upon the training that the individual receives. Other reflexes, known as **conditioned reflexes,** develop as a result of specific training. Conditioned reflexes were first demonstrated in the early part of the twentieth century by Pavlov, the Russian physiologist who also performed experiments on the control of gastric secretion. In a classic experiment, Pavlov fed a dog and simultaneously rang a bell. The bell, of course, had nothing to do with salivation, and at the beginning of the experiment would not induce salivation by itself. Saliva-

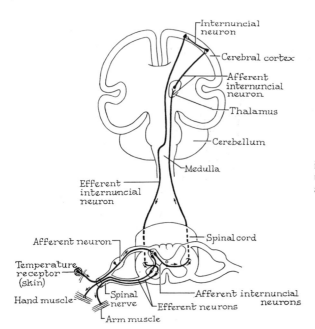

Figure 31.2 Diagram of the neurons involved in the passage of impulses to and from the brain, and the relationship of these to the neurons in a reflex arc (shown simplified).

tion was reflexly stimulated by the sight or smell of food. The bell was rung each time the dog was fed, and the dog gradually learned to associate the bell with food. Eventually, ringing the bell without presenting food would initiate salivation. A classic conditioned reflex is established when a new sensory clue (the bell) becomes associated with an inborn reflex (salivation). The neuronal mechanism involved is not known. More complex conditioned reflexes can be developed. Once the dog has been conditioned to the bell, it can be secondarily conditioned to a flash of light preceding the bell. Elaborate reflex responses can be built up in this way as a result of specific training.

Reflexes in the spinal cord and brain form the basis of a great many of our responses,

but there are other neuronal interrelations that are important for an understanding of the activities of the nervous system. Most pathways within the nervous system involve many neurons, not just two or three as in the simpler reflexes, and this permits a variety of complex interrelations. A great many pathways are **divergent** (Fig. 31.3*A*). The axon of a neuron may branch many times, synapse with a number of different neurons, and these, in turn, may branch further. Such an arrangement permits a single impulse to exert an effect over a wide area; a single impulse may ultimately activate a thousand or more neurons. Many other pathways are **convergent** (Fig. 31.3*B*); neurons coming from many different areas converge upon a single neuron or group

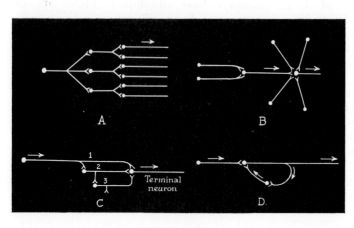

Figure 31.3 Diagrams of important types of neuronal interrelationships. *A,* A divergent pathway; *B,* a convergent pathway; *C,* a multiple chain circuit; *D,* a closed chain circuit. A given neuron may be involved in more than one of these pathways.

of neurons. The convergence of neurons upon centers in the brain and upon the cell bodies of efferent neurons are examples of this type of pathway. It has been estimated that the efferent neurons receive impulses that originate from 15 or 20 different sources. The response of the last neuron in a convergent pathway is the result of the interaction of a variety of excitatory and inhibitory influences. Convergent pathways are important in forming the structural basis for the integrative activity of the nervous system.

Many neuronal circuits, including those diagrammed in Figure 31.3*A* and *B*, involve the passage of impulses only as long as the first neuron continues to be stimulated. When the stimulation stops, the passage of impulses stops. There are other arrangements in the nervous system that ensure the continuation of the impulse for a period of time after the stimulus has stopped. One of these is the **multiple chain circuit** (Fig. 31.3*C*). The first neuron is stimulated momentarily, an impulse travels rapidly to the terminal neuron and also, via a branch, to a second neuron. The second neuron is stimulated and a moment later sends a second impulse to the same terminal neuron and also, via a branch, to a third neuron, which is stimulated and sends yet a third impulse to the same terminal neuron. If a great many neurons are involved, the terminal neuron will receive a whole series of impulses, and receive them for some time after the initial stimulus has stopped. In another arrangement, the **closed chain circuit** (Fig. 31.3*D*), one or more branches of the neurons in the circuit feed back to a point near the beginning of the circuit. Once such a circuit is activated, impulses could continue indefinitely unless the neurons became fatigued or were inhibited. Possibly, such circuits form the basis for the spontaneous activity of the inspiratory center and similar centers in the brain.

31.2

Peripheral Nervous System

Spinal Nerves. The vertebrate body is segmented (although segmentation is obscure in the head region), and there is a pair of peripheral nerves for each body segment: those arising from the spinal cord are known as **spinal nerves;** those from the brain, as **cranial nerves.** Afferent and efferent neurons lie together in most of a spinal nerve, but near the cord the nerve splits into a dorsal and a ventral root, and the neurons are segregated (Fig. 31.4). The **dorsal root** contains the afferent neurons and bears an enlargement, the dorsal root ganglion, which contains their cell bodies. The cell bodies of afferent neurons are nearly always located in ganglia on both spinal and cranial nerves. The afferent neurons enter the spinal cord and generally terminate in synapses with the dendrites or cell bodies of internuncial neurons. Most of these cell bodies are located in the dorsal portion of the gray matter of the cord. The **ventral root** contains the efferent neurons, and their cell bodies nearly always lie in the ventral portion of the gray matter of the cord.

The spinal nerves of all vertebrates are essentially alike, although in the most primitive vertebrates the roots do not unite peripherally, and the segregation of afferent and efferent neurons within the roots is not so clear-cut. In most vertebrates, the roots unite to form a spinal nerve that divides into a dorsal branch, or **dorsal ramus,** which supplies the skin and muscles in the dorsal part of the body, a **ventral ramus,** which innervates the lateroventral parts of the body, and frequently one or more **communicating rami** to the visceral organs. Afferent and efferent neurons occur in each ramus. Man has 31 pairs of spinal nerves. Those supplying the receptors and effectors of the limbs are larger than the others, and their ventral rami are interlaced to form a complex network, or **plexus,** from which nerves extend to the limbs (Fig. 21.21).

Cranial Nerves. The nerves from the nose, the eye and the ear have evolved along with the organs of special sense. They are composed entirely of afferent fibers, except for a few efferent neurons in the optic and vestibulocochlear nerve that feed back to the sense organs and may modulate their activity. The other cranial nerves contain large numbers of both afferent and efferent fibers, and they are considered to be serially homologous with the separate roots of the spinal nerves of primitive vertebrates. Some of them are essentially the cephalic counterparts of dorsal roots; others, the counterparts of ventral roots. The location of the cell bodies of the neurons of cranial nerves, and

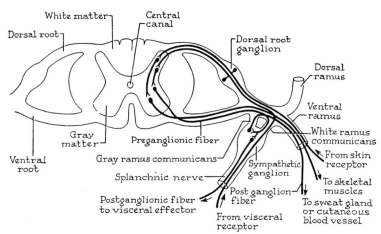

Figure 31.4 A diagrammatic cross section through the spinal cord and a spinal nerve. Each spinal nerve is formed by the union of dorsal and ventral roots and divides laterally into several branches (rami) going to different parts of the body. The dorsal ramus contains the same types of neurons as the ventral ramus.

of their endings within the brain, follows the pattern described for spinal neurons.

Reptiles, birds and mammals have 12 pairs of cranial nerves, if we omit the minute and poorly understood nervus terminalis. Though distributed to the nasal mucosa, this nerve is not olfactory. The other cranial nerves and their distribution are shown in Table 31.1, and their stumps can be seen in a figure of the brain (Fig. 31.5).

Fishes and amphibians lack discrete spinal accessory and hypoglossal nerves. The homo-

logues of neurons that are segregated in the spinal accessory of higher vertebrates are included in the vagus of fishes and amphibians, and the homologues of neurons in the hypoglossal are included in several minute nerves emerging from the occipital region of the skull. The trigeminal, facial, glossopharyngeal and vagus nerves of fishes are primarily associated with the muscles of the visceral arches and, as shown in Table 31.1, they supply the derivatives of this musculature in the higher vertebrates.

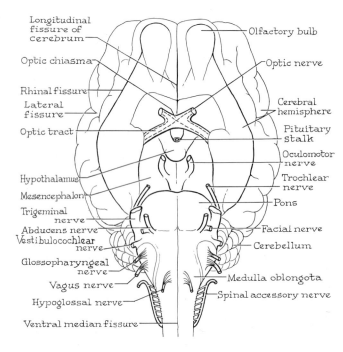

Figure 31.5 A ventral view of the brain of a sheep. The stumps of all but the first pair of cranial nerves are visible. The olfactory nerves consist of the processes of olfactory cells (cf. Fig. 30.1*E*), which enter the olfactory bulbs in many small groups that cannot be seen with the unaided eye. The rhinal fissure separates the ventral, olfactory portion of each cerebral hemisphere from the rest of the hemisphere. The paths of the optic fibers in the optic chiasma have been indicated by broken lines.

Table 31.1 Cranial Nerves of Man

Nerve	Origin of Afferent Neurons	Distribution of Efferent Neurons
I, Olfactory	Olfactory portion of nasal mucosa (smell)	
II, Optic	Retina (sight)	A few to retina
III, Oculomotor	A few fibers from proprioceptors in extrinsic muscles of eyeball (muscle sense)	Most fibers to four of the six extrinsic muscles of eyeball, a few to muscles in ciliary body and pupil
IV, Trochlear	Proprioceptors in extrinsic muscles of eyeball	Another extrinsic muscle of eyeball
V, Trigeminal	Teeth, and skin receptors of the head (touch, pressure, temperature, pain); proprioceptors in jaw muscles	Muscles derived from musculature of first visceral arch, i.e., jaw muscles
VI, Abducens	Proprioceptors in extrinsic muscles of eyeball	One other extrinsic muscle of eyeball
VII, Facial	Taste buds of anterior two-thirds of tongue (taste)	Muscles derived from musculature of second visceral arch, i.e., facial muscles; salivary glands; tear glands
VIII, Vestibulocochlear	Semicircular canals, utriculus, sacculus (sense of balance); cochlea (hearing)	A few to cochlea
IX, Glossopharyngeal	Taste buds of posterior third of tongue; lining of pharynx	Muscles derived from musculature of third visceral arch, i.e., pharyngeal muscles concerned in swallowing; salivary glands
X, Vagus	Receptors in many internal organs: larynx, lungs, heart, aorta, stomach	Musculature derived from musculature of remaining visceral arches (excepting those of pectoral girdle), i.e., muscles of pharynx (swallowing) and larynx (speech); muscles of gut, heart; gastric glands
XI, Spinal Accessory	Proprioceptors in certain shoulder muscles	Visceral arch muscles associated with pectoral girdle, i.e., sternocleidomastoid and trapezius
XII, Hypoglossal	Proprioceptors in tongue	Muscles of tongue

Muscles change in shape and function during the course of evolution, but their innervation remains remarkably constant.

Autonomic Nervous System. Most of the efferent fibers in the spinal and cranial nerves supply somatic muscles of the body and visceral muscles associated with the gill region. But in addition to these, certain of the cranial and spinal nerves contain other efferent fibers going to muscles in the walls of the gut, heart, blood vessels and other internal organs; to the small muscles associated with the hairs; to the ciliary and iris muscles in the eye; and to many of the glands of the body (Fig. 31.6). These efferent fibers constitute the **autonomic nervous system.** The organs supplied by these fibers function automatically, requiring no thought on our part. Indeed, they cannot be controlled voluntarily. It should be emphasized that the autonomic nervous system is usually defined as a motor system, and the afferent fibers that return from internal organs are not a part of this system, even though they may be in nerves composed largely of autonomic fibers.

The autonomic nervous system is morphologically unique in that the autonomic neurons that emerge from the central nervous system do not extend all the way to the

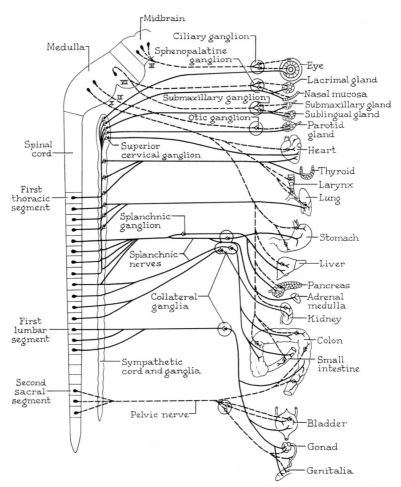

Figure 31.6 The human autonomic nervous system. Sympathetic fibers are drawn in solid lines; parasympathetic fibers in broken lines. The sympathetic fibers that go to the skin are not shown. (After Howell.)

effectors, as do other efferent neurons. They go only to a **peripheral ganglion** in which there is a relay, and a second set of autonomic fibers continues from the ganglion to the organ. Autonomic fibers having their cell bodies in the central nervous system and extending to a peripheral ganglion are known as **preganglionic fibers;** those having their cell bodies in the ganglia and extending to the organs are the **postganglionic fibers.**

The autonomic nervous system is subdivided into **sympathetic** and **parasympathetic systems.** Most organs innervated by the autonomic nervous system receive fibers of both types. The preganglionic sympathetic fibers leave the central nervous system through the ventral roots of spinal nerves in the thoracic and anterior lumbar regions (Figs. 31.4 and 31.6), and pass through the ramus communicans to a **sympathetic cord,** one of which lies on each side of the vertebral column. These fibers may synapse with the postganglionic fibers in the **sympathetic ganglia** along the sympathetic cord, or they may continue from the sympathetic cord through **splanchnic nerves** to **collateral ganglia** located at the base of the coeliac and mesenteric arteries. Postganglionic sympathetic fibers continue from the ganglia to the organs they supply. Those to the skin re-enter the spinal nerves (Fig. 31.4), but the others tend to follow along the arteries to the organs (Fig. 31.6). Preganglionic parasympathetic fibers are distributed to the organs through the oculomotor, facial, glossopharyngeal and vagus nerves and through a pelvic nerve derived from certain spinal nerves in the sacral region. Preganglionic parasympathetic fibers are longer than those of the sympathetic system, for they end in ganglia that are very near the organs they supply or are in the walls of the organs. Relatively short postganglionic parasympathetic fibers continue to the muscle and gland cells.

Sympathetic and parasympathetic systems usually have opposite effects upon the organs innervated. Sympathetic stimulation speeds up the rate and increases the force of the heart beat (Fig. 28.13), causes arteries to constrict, thereby increasing the blood pressure; increases the glucose content of the blood; and, in general, has effects that enable the body to adjust to conditions of stress. It inhibits the activity of the digestive tract generally. Parasympathetic stimulation, on the other hand, speeds peristalsis of the digestive tract and similar vegetative processes, but it slows down the heart and decreases blood pressure. Sometimes the effects of the two systems complement each other. The salivary glands are activated primarily by the parasympathetic fibers, but sympathetic stimulation does increase their

activity. A summary of the major effects of the two systems is presented in Table 31.2.

Ingenious experiments performed by Loewi in 1921 demonstrated the cause of the different effects of sympathetic and parasympathetic fibers. He removed the heart of a frog, leaving only its nerve supply intact, then perfused a salt solution through it and into another completely isolated heart. Both hearts continued to beat. When the vagus nerve (parasympathetic fibers) going to the first heart was stimulated, the rates of both hearts slowed down; when the sympathetic fibers were stimulated, the rates of both hearts increased. Apparently, some substance secreted by the nerves going to the first heart entered the salt solution and reached the second heart. Further work revealed that two **neurohumors** are produced. **Acetylcholine** is secreted by the parasympathetic and **sympathin** by the sympathetic fibers. Acetylcholine may also be involved in the transmission of the nerve impulse across the synapses in other parts of the nervous

Table 31.2 Selected Effects of Autonomic Stimulation*

Organ	Sympathetic Stimulation	Parasympathetic Stimulation
Skin		
Hair muscles	Contraction	....
Sweat glands	Secretion	....
Blood vessels	Constriction	....
Eye		
Iris sphincter	....	Contraction
Iris dilator	Contraction	....
Ciliary muscles	Relaxation	Contraction
Circulatory system		
Heart (rate and force)	Increased	Decreased
Coronary vessels	Dilation	Constriction
Most other vessels	Constriction	Dilated
Lung bronchi	Dilation	Constriction
Digestive organs		
Muscles of stomach and intestine	Decreased peristalsis	Increased peristalsis
Major sphincters	Contraction	Relaxation
Salivary glands	Some mucus secretion	Secretion
Gastric and intestinal glands	....	Secretion
Pancreas	....	Secretion
Liver	Bile flow inhibited Glucose released	Bile flow stimulated
Urogenital organs		
Urinary bladder muscles	Relaxation	Contraction
Bladder sphincter	Contraction	Relaxation
Penis	Ejaculation	Erection
Adrenal medulla	Secretion	....

*Dotted line indicates the absence of innervation.

system and across the junction between neuron and muscle. It may also play a role in the transmission of the nerve impulse along the neuron. Sympathin has been found only in connection with postganglionic sympathetic fibers, but it is closely related to the hormones secreted by the medullary cells of the adrenal glands, and especially to norepinephrine (p. 559). There is fairly clear evidence that these cells are themselves modified postganglionic sympathetic fibers.

31.3
Central Nervous System

Spinal Cord. A small **central canal** (Fig. 31.4) extends through the center of the spinal cord, gray matter surrounds the central canal, and white matter lies peripheral to the gray. The **gray matter** is dark in color, for it is composed of the cell bodies of neurons and of unmyelinated fibers; the **white matter** is light because it is composed of fibers surrounded by fatty myelin sheaths. The gray matter forms continuous longitudinal columns, which are H-shaped in cross section. There are a pair of **dorsal columns,** a pair of **ventral columns** and a **gray commissure** connecting the columns of opposite sides. The dorsal column contains the dendrites and cell bodies of afferent internuncial neurons, with which many afferent neurons synapse. The ventral column contains the dendrites and cell bodies of the efferent neurons, and also the cell bodies of some of the inhibitory neurons (Fig. 31.1). The gray commissure is composed of fibers crossing from one side of the spinal cord to the other. The gray matter lying dorsal to the central canal is concerned with relaying sensory impulses that enter the cord, and the part lateral and ventral to the central canal relays motor impulses that leave the cord in the efferent neurons.

Much of the white matter consists of the fibers of afferent neurons, some of which extend some distance in the central nervous system before entering the gray matter, and of afferent internuncial neurons, which end in the brain. The rest of the white matter consists of the processes of efferent internuncial neurons coming from the brain to the efferent neurons. Most afferent impulses that enter the spinal cord cross to the opposite side before they reach the brain, and efferent impulses coming from the brain cross within the brain. Thus, afferent impulses initiated on the left side of the body reach the right side of the brain, and efferent impulses initiated in the right side of the brain reach the left side of the body.

Though all of the white matter looks the same, careful experimentation has enabled neuroanatomists to localize the various groups of fibers that comprise it. Impulses initiated by temperature receptors on the left side of the body, for example, are carried to the brain by fibers located in the lateral portion of the white matter on the right side of the cord (Fig. 31.2). A lesion in this part of the cord would prevent one from being conscious of temperature changes on the opposite side of the body posterior to the lesion, though one would still respond reflexly to such changes.

The Brain.   *Major Parts of the Brain.*   A brief consideration of the embryonic development of the brain makes it easier to understand its major divisions and parts. The brain develops as a series of enlargements of the anterior portion of the embryonic neural tube (Fig. 31.7). In an early embryo there are only three swellings (forebrain, midbrain and hindbrain), but the forebrain and hindbrain are later subdivided, so that five regions are present in an adult. The forebrain divides into a **telencephalon** and a **diencephalon.** The telencephalon differentiates into a pair of **olfactory bulbs,** which receive the endings of olfactory cells, and a pair of **cerebral hemispheres,** which become the major brain center in the higher vertebrates. The lateral walls of the diencephalon become the **thalamus,** its roof the **epithalamus,** and its floor the **hypothalamus.** Fibers in the optic nerves cross below the hypothalamus and form an **optic chiasma** (Fig. 31.5). All the optic fibers cross and go to the opposite side of the brain in most vertebrates, but only half of them cross in mammals. The pituitary gland is attached to the hypothalamus just posterior to the chiasma, and the pineal body is attached to the epithalamus. No further division occurs in the midbrain, or **mesencephalon,** but its roof differentiates into a pair of optic lobes in all vertebrates. In addition to the optic lobes, or **superior colliculi,** the mesencephalic roof of mammals bears a pair of **inferior colliculi.** The hindbrain divides into

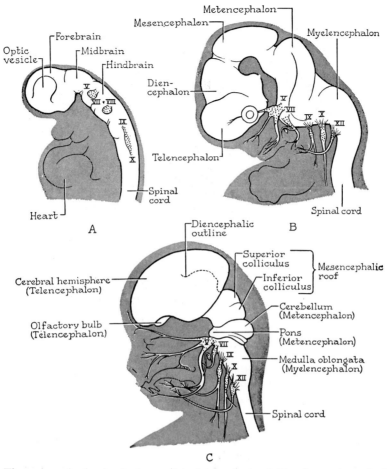

Figure 31.7 Three stages in the development of the human brain. *A,* The three primary brain regions can be recognized in an embryo that is about three and one-half weeks old. *B,* All five brain regions are evident in an embryo seven weeks old. *C,* The various structures found in a fully developed brain are beginning to differentiate in an embryo eleven weeks old. (After Patten.)

a **metencephalon,** the dorsal portion of which forms the **cerebellum,** and a **myelencephalon,** which becomes the **medulla oblongata.**

The central canal of the spinal cord extends into the brain and is continuous with several large, interconnected chambers known as **ventricles** (Fig. 31.8). A lateral ventricle lies in each cerebral hemisphere and each is connected with the third ventricle in the diencephalon by a **foramen of Monro.** The **cerebral aqueduct of Sylvius** extends from the third ventricle through the mesencephalon to a fourth ventricle in the metencephalon and medulla oblongata. All of these passages are filled with a lymphlike **cerebrospinal fluid,** which is produced by vascular **choroid plexuses.** Choroid plexuses develop in the thin roof of the diencephalon and

medulla and are also present in the lateral ventricles of mammals. Cerebrospinal fluid escapes from the brain through foramina in the roof of the medulla and slowly circulates in the spaces between the layers of connective tissue, the **meninges,** that encase the brain and spinal cord. The innermost meninx, the **pia mater,** is a very vascular membrane that is closely applied to the surface of the brain and spinal cord. Certain parts of it help to form the choroid plexuses. A delicate **arachnoid membrane** lies peripheral to the pia, and a very tough **dura mater** forms a protective envelope around the entire central nervous system. The cerebrospinal fluid lies in the space between the arachnoid and pia. It is produced continuously and re-enters the circulatory system by filtering into certain

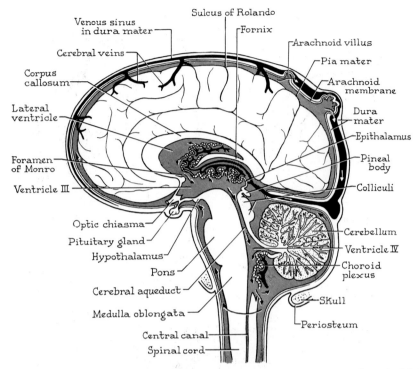

Figure 31.8 A sagittal section of the human brain and its surrounding meninges. Cerebrospinal fluid is produced by the choroid plexuses, circulates as indicated by the arrows, and finally enters a venous sinus in the dura mater. (Modified after Rasmussen.)

venous sinuses located in the dura mater covering the brain. The cerebrospinal fluid forms a protective liquid cushion about the brain and spinal cord and also helps to nourish the tissue of the central nervous system.

Medulla Oblongata. Brain functions are exceedingly complex and far from completely understood. The medulla oblongata (Fig. 31.9) lies between the spinal cord and the rest of the brain and is fundamentally the same in all vertebrates. The gray columns of the spinal cord extend into the medulla, but within the brain they become discontinuous, breaking up into discrete islands of cell bodies known as **nuclei.** The dorsal nuclei receive the afferent neurons from cranial nerves that are attached to this region and contain the cell bodies of afferent internuncial neurons. These are sensory nuclei, just as the dorsal columns of the cord are sensory columns. The ventral nuclei contain the cell bodies of the efferent neurons of the cranial nerves and, hence, are motor nuclei. In mammals, reflexes that regulate the rate of heart beat, the diameter of arterioles, respiratory movements, salivary secretion, swallowing and

many other processes are mediated by these nuclei. Afferent impulses come into the sensory nuclei, are relayed by the internuncial neurons to the motor nuclei, and efferent impulses go out to the effectors. Motor and sensory nuclei associated with other cranial nerves are also found in the metencephalon and mesencephalon.

Reticular Formation. Between the motor and sensory nuclei throughout the brain stem there is a network of thousands of cell bodies and their processes that is known as the **reticular formation.** Dendrites and axons of these neurons branch profusely and have numerous connections with each other and with many sensory and motor pathways passing to and from the brain (Fig. 31.9). Certain of these neurons receive an input from as many as 4000 other neurons and feed out to 25,000 other neurons! The reticular formation is considered to be a very primitive part of the brain from which the long ascending and descending fiber tracts and the various centers evolved. Certain of its specific functions in mammals are now being clarified. A convergence and interaction of neurons from many of the sense organs, the cerebellum, the

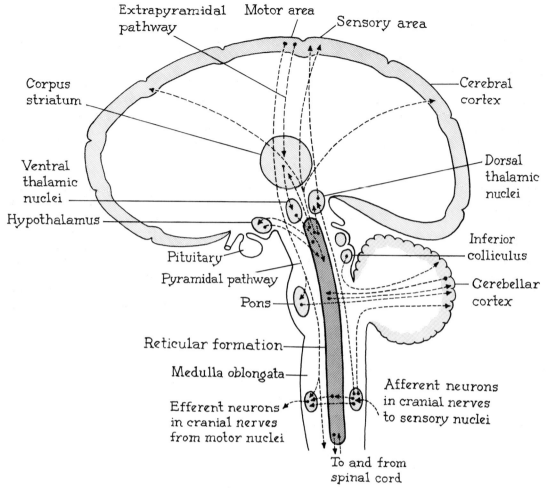

Figure 31.9 Diagrammatic lateral view of the human brain on which some of the major masses of gray matter, the reticular formation and certain important pathways have been projected.

cerebrum, the thalamus, the hypothalamus and other areas occurs here, and the region appears to be able to suppress, enhance, or otherwise modify impulses passing through it. For example, branches from cells in the sensory nuclei, in addition to synapsing with motor cells and ascending to higher centers, feed into this system. If the sensory input is the type the individual has learned is important (an unusual noise, the cry of a baby at night, etc.), the reticular formation, in turn, sends nonspecific impulses to the cerebral cortex. These fan out widely in the cortex and rouse the animal if it is asleep, or help to keep it alert if it is awake. Without this source of stimulation, the cortex does not function and cannot interpret the specific sensory information brought to it. Descending fibers in the reticular formation form a

part of a motor pathway from the cerebrum known as the **extrapyramidal pathway,** and impulses passing down to motor neurons of cranial and spinal nerves may also be facilitated or inhibited.

Cerebellum and Pons. All vertebrates have a **cerebellum,** which develops in the dorsal part of the metencephalon, and is a center for balance and motor coordination. It is small in many of the lower vertebrates such as the frog (Fig. 21.20), in which muscular movements are not complex, but it is very large in birds and mammals. Impulses enter it from most of the sense organs, but those from the proprioceptive organs in the muscles and the parts of the ear concerned with equilibrium play a particularly prominent role (Fig. 31.9). The cerebellum keeps track of the orientation of the body in space and the degree of contraction of the skeletal muscles. In mammals, this information is sent, by way of part of the reticular formation and thalamus, to the cerebrum, where voluntary movements are initiated. Copies, so to speak, of the motor directives sent out by the cerebrum to the muscles are also sent to the cerebellum. It monitors the responses of the body and returns corrective signals to the cerebrum or, in some cases, directly to the muscles. Much of the gray matter of the mammalian cerebellum lies on the surface, where there is more room for the increased number of cell bodies. The surface is also complexly folded, which further increases the surface area available for cell bodies.

The floor of the metencephalon is unspecialized in lower vertebrates and simply contributes to the medulla oblongata, but this region differentiates into a **pons** in mammals (Figs. 31.5 and 31.9). Evolution of the pons is correlated with the elaboration of the cerebellum. It contains nuclei that relay cerebral impulses into the cerebellum, and transverse fibers that interconnect the two sides of the cerebellum.

Optic Lobes. In fishes and amphibians, the optic lobes (Figs. 21.20 and 31.10) receive the termination of all the fibers in the optic nerve, and they also receive projections from most of the other sense organs. This sensory information is integrated, and motor impulses are sent to the appropriate efferent neurons. The optic lobes are the master integrating center of the brain, insofar as these vertebrates have such a center. The cerebral hemispheres of the lower vertebrates are rather small and are concerned almost exclusively with integrating olfactory impulses. In reptiles, some of the optic and other types of sensory data are sent to the cerebral hemispheres, and the cerebrum begins to assume

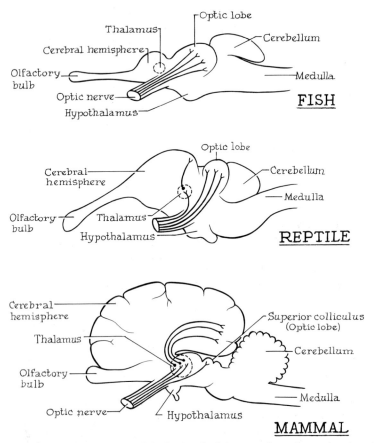

Figure 31.10 Diagrammatic lateral views of the brain of a fish, a reptile and a mammal to show the increasing importance of the cerebral hemispheres, and the decreasing importance of the optic lobes, as integration centers. The shift in optic pathways is shown; a similar shift occurs for other sensory modalities.

certain of the functions of the optic lobes (Fig. 31.10). Still more sensory information is sent to the cerebral hemispheres of birds and mammals, and the hemispheres of mammals have taken over most of the functions of the optic lobes. The optic lobes (**superior colliculi**) of mammals remain as relatively small centers that regulate the movements of the eyeballs and pupillary and accommodation reflexes. A pair of **inferior colliculi** are present posterior to them, and they are a center for certain auditory reflexes.

Thalamus and Hypothalamus. Much of the thalamus is a relay center to and from the cerebral hemispheres, and it has become enlarged during the course of evolution as the cerebral hemispheres have assumed a dominant role in integrating the activities of the body. All the sensory impulses that go to the cerebrum, except those from the olfactory organ, are relayed in nuclei in the dorsal part of the thalamus (Figs. 31.2 and 31.9). Many motor impulses descending from the cerebrum go directly to the motor nuclei and columns, but some of these are relayed in nuclei in the ventral part of the thalamus.

The thalamus is, however, more than just a relay station in the higher vertebrates. Considerable processing of the sensory input occurs here, for the thalamic nuclei have many interconnections with each other, with the hypothalamus, with the reticular formation and with many parts of the cerebral hemispheres. Pain, temperature and certain other sensory modalities reach the level of conscious awareness in the thalamus. Other sensations are to some extent sorted out in this region, and a determination is made as to which of these we will concentrate on among the hundreds of stimuli continually impinging upon us. The thalamus also influences the manner in which we view many stimuli, that is, the different degree of agreeableness or disagreeableness that we may place upon the same type and intensity of stimuli at different times. Many of our emotions, such as pleasure and fear of punishment, are influenced by the thalamus. Experimental rats with an electrode implanted in a "pleasure center" will push a lever that stimulates the center thousands of times per hour. Other areas appear to be "punishing centers," and experimental animals will avoid activity that activates an electrode implanted in one of them.

The rest of the diencephalon has not changed very much during vertebrate evolution. The hypothalamus is an important center for the control of many autonomic functions. Body temperature, water balance, appetite, carbohydrate and fat metabolism and sleep are among the processes regulated by the hypothalamus in mammals. The hypothalamus exerts its control by neuronal connections with the motor nuclei and columns and by the production of hormones that travel along axon tracts to the posterior lobe of the pituitary gland, where they are stored and released (p. 563). Damage to it is often fatal, for so many vital processes are disturbed.

Cerebral Hemispheres. As the cerebral hemispheres assumed the dominant role in nervous integration during the course of evolution, they enlarged and grew posteriorly over the diencephalon and mesencaphalon (Fig. 31.10). A layer of gray matter has developed on the surface of the cerebrum and has formed a **gray cortex** which provides more area for the increased number of cell bodies. The cortex is also complexly folded, forming numerous ridges (**gyri**) with furrows (**sulci**) between them, and this further increases the surface area. Over 12 billion neurons, and even more neuroglial cells, are present.

Parts of the cerebral hemispheres are still concerned with their primitive function of olfactory integration, but their great enlargement is correlated with the evolution of other integration centers (Fig. 31.11). Afferent impulses from the eyes, ears, skin and many other parts of the body are carried to the cerebral cortex by afferent internuncial neurons after being relayed in the thalamus. The impulses terminate in specific parts of the cerebral cortex; their locations have been determined by correlating brain injuries with loss of sensation and also by electrical stimulation during brain operations. Many human brain operations are performed under local anesthesia, and the patient can describe the sensations that are felt when particular regions are stimulated. Impulses from the skin terminate in the gyrus that is located just posterior to the **central sulcus of Rolando,** a prominent sulcus extending down the side of each hemisphere and dividing the hemisphere into an anterior **frontal** and a posterior **parietal lobe.** The sensory areas of the skin are projected upside down. Impulses from the head are conducted to the lower

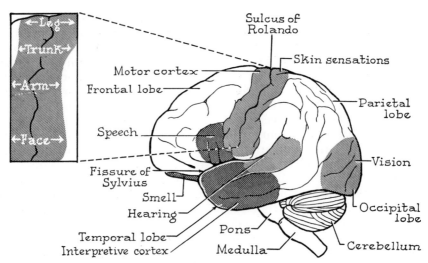

Figure 31.11 Important cortical areas of the human brain as seen in a lateral view. Most association areas of the cortex have not been hatched.

part of the gyrus, whereas those from the feet reach the upper part. The extent of the area receiving impulses from any part of the body is proportional to the number of sense organs in that part of the body. Thus, the area receiving impulses from the fingers is more extensive than that receiving impulses from the trunk.

Impulses from the ear are carried to part of the **temporal lobe,** which is separated from the frontal and parietal lobes by the **lateral fissure of Sylvius.** Impulses from the eye are received in the **occipital lobe,** which lies just posterior to the parietal lobe. The path of the optic fibers of mammals is an exception to the generalization that most afferent impulses cross at some point during their ascent to the brain. Half of the fibers in each optic nerve cross in the optic chiasma and end up on the opposite side of the brain, but the other half do not. Thus, destruction of one occipital lobe results in inability to perceive images that fall on half of each retina rather than complete loss of vision in one eye (Fig. 31.5).

Appropriate motor impulses to the striated muscles are initiated in response to all the sensory data that enters the cerebrum. The cell bodies of the efferent internuncial neurons are contained in the motor cortex, which lies just anterior to the sulcus of Rolando. The motor cortex is subdivided, in the manner of the adjacent sensory cortex, into areas associated with the different parts of the body. Fibers to the hand occupy a large portion of

it, for the muscles that control finger movements contain more motor units than do most muscles. This is correlated with the intricacy of our finger movements. Many efferent internuncial neurons pass directly to the motor nuclei of the brain and to the motor columns of the spinal cord, crossing to the opposite side along the way (Fig. 31.9). This direct pathway to the lower motor neurons is called the **pyramidal pathway.** It is phylogenetically a new pathway, being present only in mammals and reaching its greatest development in primates. Skilled and learned movements, are for the most part mediated by this pathway. Many other motor impulses leave the cortex by way of the **extrapyramidal pathway,** which involves the relay of motor impulses in a mass of gray matter (the **corpus striatum**) situated deep within each cerebral hemisphere, and additional relays in the thalamus and reticular formation of the brain stem. This is phylogenetically an older system, and it is associated with grosser movements, automatic postural adjustments and stereotyped responses.

Billions of **association neurons** lie between the areas where sensory impulses terminate and motor pathways begin. In most parts of the cortex, the neurons are arranged in six vertical layers with numerous interconnections between them and with the afferent neurons bringing impulses into the cortex and efferent ones carrying impulses out. Such an organization makes possible exceedingly complex functional interrelationships between different parts of the cortex and between the cortex and subcortical regions. Information in one hemisphere can also affect the other by crossing on **commissural fibers** that extend between them. A particularly large commissure, known as the **corpus callosum** and found only in placental mammals, can be seen in a sagittal section of the brain (Fig. 31.8). All these interconnections permit the integration of many different sensory modalities, the comparison of current sensory input with information stored in the brain, and the composition of a motor response appropriate to the present requirements of the organism.

In man and other higher mammals, large parts of the cortex, which are known as association areas, are composed primarily of association neurons and their interconnections (Fig. 31.11). Presumably such complex mental processes as thought, learning and memory occur here. **Learning** may be defined as the modification of behavior by experience. Basic to learning is memory, that is, the ability to store information concerning past experience. Learning, therefore, entails the transmission of sensory impression to the cortex, the retention of this as some sort of memory trace, or **engram,** the ability to recall the engram subsequently and compare it with a new situation, and the ability to act in an appropriate way.

There are probably at least two types of memory, short term and long term, which have different mechanisms. **Short-term memory,** i.e., the ability to recall events a few minutes to a few hours after their occurrence, may entail some type of reverberating electric impulses on a closed chain circuit (Fig. 31.3D). It is known that certain electrical stimuli applied to the cortex can produce a prolonged after-discharge. But electrical phenomena of this type cannot be the basis for **long-term memory,** because even when electrical activity in the brain is stopped, as during hibernation in certain mammals, this does not interfere with long-term memory. The engram of long-term memory must require more profound and lasting changes that facilitate the passage of impulses along a definite and probably very complex pattern of pathways. We do not know just what happens. More synapses may be established between neurons in the pathway, or the capacity of the presynaptic terminals to release transmitter substance may be enhanced, or changes in neuroglial cells around synapses may affect synaptic transmission. That profound changes do occur is suggested by experiments in which it has been shown that the cerebral cortex increases significantly in thickness and weight and that acetylcholinase activity increases in the cortex and other parts of the brain in rats exposed to an enriched learning experience. Other experiments have shown that there are also increases in RNA, and possibly changes in its base sequence. This has led to the suggestion that RNA is the molecule of memory, but the alterations in RNA metabolism may simply reflect changes in protein synthesis occurring in the synaptic region.

Memory appears to involve the interaction of many cortical areas, and probably subcortical areas as well. Injury to the association areas is manifested in many ways. Sometimes there is a loss of ability to recognize the significance of familiar objects, a condition known as **agnosia.** One may see and feel a pencil but not be able to recall what it is for. In **aphasia,** there is an interference with the ability to understand or use symbolic ideas such as language. In one type of aphasia, words may be heard, but they might as well be in an unknown language for they cannot be recognized. In another type, one may be unable to formulate words even though there is no interference with the motor pathways or muscles concerned. Some of these higher functions can be partially localized; for example, a part of the frontal lobe is concerned with articulated speech (Fig. 31.11), but other functions appear to depend upon the integrity of extensive areas of the cortex.

Regardless of what memory is, or of how or where information is stored, one part of the cortex does appear to be involved in recall and in relating present experience with relevant past events. This has been called the **interpretive** or **psychical cortex,** and it occupies a large part of each temporal lobe. Electrical stimulation of the various sensory areas produces somewhat vague sensations of light, sound, or touch, but stimulation of the interpretive cortex sometimes causes a vivid and detailed recall of past events—of sights and sounds and feelings long forgotten. At other times, its stimulation alters the interpretation one places on present events. Objects may seem suddenly strange, distant or near. Dr. Penfield of the Montreal Neurological Institute considers that the interpretive cortex makes some contribution to the reflex comparison of the present with the past and thus contributes to the interpretation of the present.

A primary function of certain of the commissures, such as the corpus callosum, appears to be to make memory traces imprinted on one side of the brain available to the other side. In early experiments on "split-brained" animals, in which the corpus callosum, optic chiasma and all other cross connections in the cerebrum were cut, little behavorial disturbance was evident. This result was unexpected, since the corpus callosum contains several hundred million fibers and seemingly should have an important function. Further work with split-brained monkeys showed that a monkey could be trained to respond in a certain way to a visual stimulus entering the left eye, but that it could not respond in this way to the same stimulus entering the right eye and the untrained side of the brain. However, if a monkey with a split optic chiasma and an intact corpus callosum is trained to respond to a stimulus entering the left eye, the same response can later be elicited by a stimulus entering the right eye. Clearly, whatever an engram is, it is available to both sides of the brain if the corpus callosum is intact.

Brain research is a challenging field. Many of the brain's functions are beyond our present comprehension, but we are beginning to understand this complex organ.

QUESTIONS

1. List the major categories of neurons that comprise the nervous system. In which parts of the nervous system are each located?
2. Describe the mechanism for a withdrawal reflex.
3. Distinguish between the roots and rami of a spinal nerve.
4. What are the major differences between the cranial nerves of mammals and fishes?
5. Define the autonomic nervous system. How does autonomic innervation differ from the innervation of other organs?
6. What is the effect on the body of sympathetic stimulation?
7. How do the dorsal and ventral columns of the spinal cord differ?
8. List the five divisions of the brain and the major brain structures that develop in each.
9. In what ways has the structure and function of the cerebral hemispheres changed in the evolution from fish to mammals?
10. Briefly state the function of each of the following: medulla, cerebellum, thalamus, hypothalamus.
11. What do we know about memory, its storage and subsequent recall?

ANNOTATED REFERENCES

Attention is again called to the general references on vertebrate organ systems cited at the end of Chapter 26

Bitterman, M. E.: The evolution of intelligence. Scientific American *212*:92 (Jan.) 1965. An interesting report on the qualitatively different sorts of intelligence found in different classes of vertebrates.

Gardner, E.: Fundamentals of Neurology. 4th ed. Philadelphia, W. B. Saunders Co., 1963. A good and concise account of the morphology and physiology of the human nervous system.

Hydén, H.: Satellite cells in the nervous system. Scientific American *205*:62 (Dec.) 1961. A discussion of the author's theory that changes in RNA metabolism in neurons and neuroglia are associated with learning.

Katz, B.: Nerve, Muscle, and Synapse. New York, McGraw-Hill Book Co., 1966. An excellent review of neuron physiology and synaptic transmission written for the McGraw-Hill series in the New Biology.

Noback, C. R.: The Human Nervous System. New York, McGraw-Hill Book Co., 1967. An excellent and superbly illustrated discussion of the nervous system and sense organs. Structural and functional aspects of the subject are closely integrated.

Ranson, S. W., and S. L. Clark: The Anatomy of the Nervous System. 10th ed. Philadelphia, W. B. Saunders Co., 1959. An excellent advanced text and reference work in neuroanatomy.

Sherrington, C. S.: Integrative Action of the Nervous System. New Haven, Yale University
Press, 1948. A classic on the subject, written by one of the pioneers in neurophysiology.
Walter, W. G.: The Living Brain. New York, W. W. Norton & Co., 1953. An authoritative
and nontechnical account of the evolution of the brain and its great elaboration in man.
Wilson, V. J.: Inhibition in the central nervous system. Scientific American *214*:102 (May)
1966. A careful discussion of the evidence for inhibition in spinal reflexes.

32 _____ HORMONAL INTEGRATION

The integration of the activities of the several parts of the higher, more complex animals has been achieved by the evolution of two major coordinating systems: the nervous system, discussed in the previous chapter, and the endocrine system. The nerves and sense organs enable an animal to adapt very rapidly—with responses measured in milliseconds—to changes in the environment. The swift responses of muscles and glands are typically under nervous control. The glands of the endocrine system secrete substances called **hormones,** which diffuse or are transported by the blood stream to other parts of the body and coordinate their activities. The responses under endocrine control are generally somewhat slower—measured in minutes, hours or weeks—but longer lasting than those under nervous control. The long-range adjustments of metabolism, growth and reproduction are typically under endocrine control. The endocrine control of physiologic processes in insects and crustacea was discussed previously (p. 277).

32.1
Endocrine Glands

Endocrine glands secrete their products into the blood stream rather than into a duct leading to the exterior of the body or to one of the internal organs as do exocrine glands and, hence, are called ductless glands or glands of internal secretion. The pancreas is an example of a gland with both endocrine and exocrine functions, for it secretes enzymes which pass via the pancreatic duct to the duo-

denum and it also secretes hormones which are transported to other parts of the body in the blood stream. In the toadfish the two parts of the pancreas are anatomically separate.

The term "hormone" was originated in 1905 by the British physiologist E. H. Starling, who was studying the control of the exocrine function of the pancreas by **secretin,** a substance produced in the duodenal mucosa. Starling defined a hormone as "any substance normally produced in the cells in some part of the body and carried by the blood stream to distant parts, which it affects for the good of the body as a whole." Our rapidly increasing knowledge of the many different hormones produced by both vertebrate and invertebrate animals and by plants has led to the generalization that these are special chemical substances, produced by some restricted region of an organism, which diffuse, or are transported by the blood stream, to another region of the organism, where they are effective in very low concentrations in regulating and coordinating the activities of the cells.

The hormones isolated and characterized to date have proved to be proteins, amino acids or steroids; thus, we cannot define a hormone as a member of some particular class of organic compound. All the hormones are required for normal body function and they must be present in certain optimal amounts. Either a hyposecretion (deficiency) or hypersecretion (excess) of any one may result in a characteristic pathologic condition.

Some practical knowledge of endocrinology, such as the results of the castration of men and animals, has existed for several thousand years. However, it was not until 1849 that Berthold, from clear-cut experiments in which testes were transplanted from one bird to another, postulated that these male sex glands secrete some blood-borne substance which is essential for the differentiation of the male secondary sex characters. In 1855 the British physician Thomas Addison described the signs and symptoms of the human disease which now bears his name; he realized that this was associated with the deterioration of the cortex of the adrenal. The first attempt at endocrine therapy was made in 1889, when the French physiologist Brown-Séquard injected himself with testicular extracts and claimed that they had a rejuvenating effect. Epinephrine was the first hormone to be isolated and chemically identified (1902). Many of our theoretical concepts regarding endocrines stem from the classic work of Starling and of Bayliss with secretin during the first two decades of this century.

The basic problem of just how a hormone may act upon a tissue to regulate its activities remains to be solved. It would appear that hormones are not essential for the survival of individual cells, for many kinds of cells can be grown in tissue culture indefinitely without added hormones. It has been postulated that hormones produce their effects by directly stimulating or inhibiting one or more of the intracellular enzyme systems, by modifying in some way the permeability of the cell membrane so that substances can enter more readily, or by regulating the transcription of a particular segment of genetic information (DNA) in the nucleus of the target cell. The tissues in various parts of the body differ greatly in their sensitivity to particular hormones, but the explanation for this phenomenon is lacking. It is not clear at present whether a hormone is used up in the process of regulating metabolism in a target cell. There is evidence that estradiol, one of the female sex hormones, is not changed chemically and is not used up in the course of stimulating the growth of the uterus. Hormones are fairly rapidly inactivated and eliminated from the blood stream and, hence, must be continually replaced by the appropriate endocrine gland. Both the synthesis and the inactivation and degradation of hormone molecules are enzymic processes.

32.2
Methods of Investigating the Endocrine Glands

The complete understanding of the role of an endocrine gland requires information about (1) the number and kinds of hormones it secretes, (2) what chemical and physical properties each of these hormones has, (3) where and how they are made within the endocrine organ, (4) what factors control their production, (5) what stimulates their secretion by the gland, (6) how they are transported to the target organ, (7) how they act to alter the metabolism of the target organ, (8) how they are broken down and eliminated from the body, (9) how they may be produced synthetically and (10) what use they may have in the treatment of disease.

The fact that a certain gland has endocrine function is frequently first learned as a result of its accidental or deliberate removal. When an organism is deprived of its normal source of the hormone some readily observable abnormalities usually result. As we shall see, the normal functioning of any given organ is usually the result of the effects of a number of different hormones, some of which work together (act synergistically) while others oppose the action of the first (act antagonistically). It may be incorrect to attribute the effects of the surgical removal of one gland to the simple lack of its hormone; they may result from the unopposed action of hormones secreted by other glands. It may require a complex experimental design, including the removal of several endocrine glands and the replacement of their secretions by injecting pure hormones, to elucidate the role of each.

Further information about endocrine function is obtained by replacing the surgically extirpated gland with a gland transplanted from another animal, by feeding dried glands, or by injecting an extract or a purified compound obtained from the gland. The administration of one hormone may suppress or stimulate the secretion of hormones by other glands. By proper experimental design, one can distinguish between the primary effect of the injected hormone and its possible secondary effects via the stimulation or inhibition of other endocrines.

Another experimental approach to the endocrine problem is the extraction and purification of the hormone by chemical and physical procedures from the gland itself or from the blood or urine of the organism. Only an extremely small amount of hormone is required to produce its normal effects, and the amount present in the endocrine gland, or in the blood and urine, is usually quite small. The isolation of a pure hormone is a difficult procedure; more than two tons of pig ovaries had to be extracted to yield a few milligrams of estradiol, and to obtain 15 mg. of androsterone, a male sex hormone, it was necessary to extract over 5000 gallons of urine!

Much has been learned about endocrine function by careful observation of the symptoms of human diseases resulting from the hypo- or hypersecretion of hormones. Further information has been derived from the careful study of strains of rats, mice and other animals with particular endocrine abnormalities—dwarf mice, obese mice, diabetic mice, and so on.

The location of the human endocrine glands is shown in Figure 32.1. Their relative position in the body is much the same in all the vertebrates. The source and physiologic effects of the principal mammalian hormones

Table 32.1   Hormones and Their Effects

Hormone	Source	Physiologic Effect
Thyroxin	Thyroid gland	Increases basal metabolic rate
Thyrocalcitonin	Thyroid gland	Regulates calcium and phosphorus metabolism
Parathormone	Parathyroid glands	Regulates calcium and phosphorus metabolism
Insulin	Beta cells of islets in pancreas	Decreases blood sugar concentration, increases glycogen storage and metabolism of glucose
Glucagon	Alpha cells of islets in pancreas	Stimulates conversion of liver glycogen to blood glucose
Epinephrine	Adrenal medulla	Reinforces action of sympathetic nerves; stimulates breakdown of liver and muscle glycogen
Norepinephrine	Adrenal medulla	Constricts blood vessels
Cortisol	Adrenal cortex	Stimulates conversion of proteins to carbohydrates
Aldosterone	Adrenal cortex	Regulates metabolism of sodium and potassium
Dehydroepiandrosterone	Adrenal cortex	Androgen, stimulates development of male characters
Growth hormone	Anterior lobe of pituitary	Controls bone growth and general body growth; affects protein, fat and carbohydrate metabolism
Thyrotropin	Anterior pituitary	Stimulates growth and functional activity of the thyroid
Adrenocorticotropin (ACTH)	Anterior pituitary	Stimulates adrenal cortex to grow and to produce cortical hormones
Follicle-stimulating hormone (FSH)	Anterior pituitary	Stimulates growth of graafian follicles in ovary and of seminiferous tubules in testis
Luteinizing hormone (LH)	Anterior pituitary	Controls production and release of estrogens and progesterone by ovary and of testosterone by testis
Prolactin	Anterior pituitary	Maintains secretion of estrogens and progesterone by ovary; stimulates secretion of milk by breast; controls maternal instinct
Oxytocin	Hypothalamus, via posterior pituitary	Stimulates contraction of uterine muscles and secretion of milk by mammary glands
Vasopressin	Hypothalamus, via posterior pituitary	Stimulates contraction of smooth muscles; has antidiuretic action on kidney tubules
Intermedin	Intermediate lobe of pituitary	Stimulates dispersal of pigment in chromatophores
Testosterone	Interstitial cells of testis	Androgen; stimulates development and maintenance of male sex characters
Estradiol	Follicle of ovary	Estrogen; stimulates development and maintenance of female sex characters
Progesterone	Corpus luteum of ovary	Acts with estradiol to regulate the estrous and menstrual cycles
Chorionic gonadotropin	Placenta	Acts, along with other hormones, in the maintenance of pregnancy
Relaxin	Ovary and placenta	Relaxes pelvic ligaments

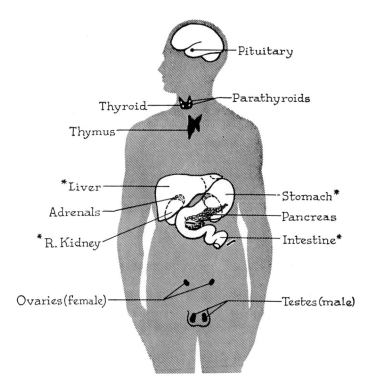

Figure 32.1 The human body, showing the location of the endocrine glands. The starred organs, though not primarily endocrine glands, do secrete one or more hormones.

are listed in Table 32.1. It must be kept in mind that hormones are not found solely in vertebrates but occur as well in such invertebrates as insects, crustaceans, annelids and mollusks.

32.3
The Thyroid Gland

All vertebrates have a bilobed thyroid gland located in the neck. In mammals the two lobes are located on either side of the larynx and are joined by a narrow isthmus of tissue which passes across the ventral surface of the trachea near its junction with the larynx. The thyroid has an exceptionally rich blood supply, which reflects its function as an endocrine gland. The thyroid develops as a ventral outgrowth of the floor of the pharynx, but the connection with the pharynx is usually lost early in development. In a microscopic section the thyroid is seen to consist of many hollow spheres, called **follicles.** Each follicle is composed of a single layer of cuboidal epithelial cells surrounding a cavity filled with a gelatinous material called **colloid,** secreted by the follicle cells (Fig. 32.2).

The follicle cells have a remarkable ability to accumulate iodide from the blood. This is used in the synthesis of the protein thyroglobulin, which is secreted into the colloid and stored. Thyroglobulin is a large molecule and not readily diffusible into the blood stream, but proteolytic enzymes in the colloid hydrolyze thyroglobulin to its constituent amino acids, one of which is **thyroxin,** a derivative of the amino acid tyrosine containing 65 per cent iodine. Thyroxin passes into the blood stream, where it is transported loosely bound to certain plasma proteins. In tissues, thyroxin, which contains four atoms of iodine, may be converted to triiodothyronine, which contains one less atom of iodine and is several times more active than thyroxin. It is not yet clear whether the hormone active at the cellular level is thyroxin itself, triiodothyronine, or some closely related derivative.

The first clue to thyroid function came from observations on human disease in 1874 by the British physician Sir William Gull, who noted the association of spontaneous decreased function of the thyroid and puffy dry skin, dry brittle hair, and mental and physical lassitude. The Swiss surgeon Kocher removed the thyroid from a series of patients

SECRETORY EPITHELIUM   BLOOD VESSEL   INTERFOLLICULAR CONNECTIVE TISSUE

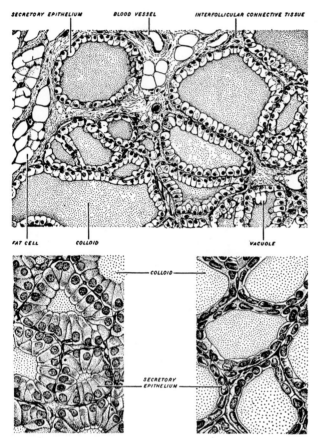

FAT CELL   COLLOID   VACUOLE

COLLOID

SECRETORY
EPITHELIUM

Figure 32.2 Upper, Cells of the normal thyroid gland of the rat. Lower left, Thyroid from a normal rat which had received ten daily injections of thyrotropin. Lower right, Thyroid from a rat six months after complete removal of the pituitary gland. (Turner: General Endocrinology, 2nd ed.)

and then noted that they developed the same symptoms as Gull's patients. In 1895, using a newly devised calorimeter to measure the rate of metabolism in patients by the amount of heat they produced, Magnus-Levy found that persons with **myxedema** (Gull's disease) had notably lower than normal metabolic rates. When these patients were fed thyroid tissue, their metabolic rate was raised toward normal. This led to the idea that the thyroid secretes a hormone which regulates the metabolic rate of all body cells. It was found in 1896 that the thyroid hormone contains iodine. Thyroglobulin was first isolated in 1897 and thyroxin in 1914. Its chemical formula was determined in 1926 and it was first synthesized in 1927.

The role of thyroid hormone in all vertebrates is to increase the rate of the oxidative, energy-releasing processes in all body cells by uncoupling the phosphorylation process from the electron transmitter system (p. 61). The amount of energy released by an organism under standard conditions at rest,

measured in a calorimeter by the amount of heat given off, or calculated from the amount of oxygen consumed, is decreased in thyroid deficiency and increased when thyroid is administered or when the gland is overactive. Thyroxin added to a suspension of mitochondria alters the permeability of the mitochondrial membrane, causes the mitochondria to swell, and perhaps in this way uncouples oxidative phosphorylation from electron transport. Whether thyroxin has a similar effect on mitochondria within an intact cell is not yet clear. Complete removal of the thyroid gland from a mammal reduces its metabolic rate to half of the normal value, and the body temperature decreases slightly. Since foods are metabolized at a lower rate, they tend to be stored and the animal becomes obese. Not only is the metabolic rate of the intact animal decreased by thyroid deficiency, but individual bits of tissue removed from the animal and incubated in vitro show a decreased metabolic rate—decreased oxygen consumption and decreased utilization of substrate molecules. The metabolism of carbohydrates, fats, proteins, water and salts is affected, probably secondarily, by the amount of thyroid hormone present.

Thyroid hormone, by its action on metabolic processes, has a marked influence on growth and differentiation. Extirpating the thyroid of young animals causes decreased body growth, retarded mental development, and delayed or decreased differentiation of gonads and external genitalia. All of these changes are reversed by the administration of thyroxin. The metamorphosis of frog and salamander tadpoles into adults is controlled by the thyroid. Removal of the larval thyroid completely prevents metamorphosis, and administering thyroxin to tadpoles causes them to metamorphose prematurely into miniature adults (Fig. 32.3). The effect of thyroxin on amphibian metamorphosis appears not to be simply a secondary result of its effect on metabolism, for tadpole metabolism can be increased by dinitrophenol but premature metamorphosis does not occur. Some specific effect of thyroxin on metamorphosis appears to be involved.

The production and discharge of thyroxin is not regulated by the nervous system but by the hormone **thyrotropin** secreted by the anterior lobe of the pituitary gland. In 1916, P. E. Smith found that the removal of the pituitary of frog tadpoles produced deterioration of the thyroid and prevented metamorphosis. The same pituitary control of thyroid function has been found in rats, man and other mammals. The secretion of thyrotropin by the pituitary is regulated in part by the amount of thyroxin in the blood. Thus, a decreased production of thyroxin by the thyroid leads to less thyroxin in the blood stream and this stimulates the pituitary to release thyrotropin, which passes to the thyroid gland and raises its output of thyroxin. When the blood level of thyroxin is brought back to normal, the release of thyrotropin is decreased. By this "feedback" mechanism the output of thyroxin is kept relatively constant, and the basal metabolic rate is kept within the normal range. Since iodine is an essential atom in thyroxin, a deficiency of this element leads to decreased synthesis of thyroxin. Iodine deficiency stimulates the thyroid follicle cells to enlarge and to increase in number. Enlargement of the thyroid is known as **goiter.** Thiouracil and related compounds are goitrogenic. They inhibit the production of thyroid hormone by blocking the reactions by which iodide is oxidized and fixed onto the tyrosine molecule. The deficiency of thyroid hormone stimulates the pituitary to release more thyrotropin which, in turn, stimulates the

Figure 32.3 The effect of thyroid feeding upon the tadpoles of *Rana catesbiana. A,* The untreated control, which was killed at the end of the experiment. The metamorphosed animal at the lower right (*G*) was killed two weeks after starting the feeding of thyroid gland. The remaining animals (*B* to *F*) were removed from the experiment at intervals during this period. Note the effect of thyroid substances on the metamorphosis of the mouth, tail and paired appendages. (Turner: General Endocrinology, 3rd ed.)

thyroid cells to enlarge, producing a goiter. Thiouracil is used clinically to decrease thyroxin production by hyperactive thyroids.

The chief human diseases resulting from malfunction of the thyroid are cretinism, myxedema, simple goiter and exophthalmic goiter. Thyroid deficiency in infancy produces a dwarfed, mentally retarded child known as a **cretin** (Fig. 32.4A). A cretin has an enlarged tongue, coarse features, malformed bones, distended belly and wrinkled, cold skin. If thyroid therapy is begun early enough, normal development of the brain and body can be induced. Thyroid deficiency in adults results in myxedema, characterized by decreased metabolic rate, mental deterioration, obesity, loss of hair and cold rough skin. Simple goiter, or enlarged thyroid, results usually from a deficiency of iodine, with a secondary increase in the size of the thyroid due to its stimulation by thyrotropin (Fig. 32.4B). Iodine is deficient in the soil and water of certain parts of the world and, hence, deficient in plants grown there and in the animals eating these plants. The prevalence of human goiter has been greatly decreased by the practice of adding iodide to table salt and by better distribution of food.

The overproduction of thyroid hormone produces a condition known as Graves' disease, or **exophthalmic goiter** (Fig. 32.4C). The thyroid may be enlarged, or may be of

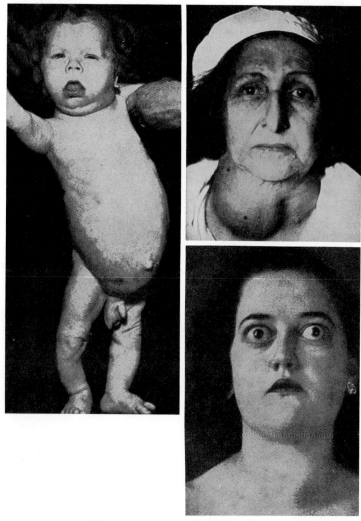

Figure 32.4 *A*, A cretin. *B*, Simple goiter. *C*, Exophthalmic goiter. (*A* and *B* from Selye: Textbook of Endocrinology, published by Acta Endocrinologia, Inc.; *C* from Houssay: Human Physiology, published by McGraw-Hill Book Company, Inc.)

nearly normal size, but it produces excessive amounts of hormone, with a resulting increased basal metabolic rate, increased production of heat, loss of weight, increased heart rate and blood pressure, nervousness, and exophthalmos, or protrusion of the eyeballs. Hyperthyroidism can be treated by surgical removal of part of the thyroid or by its destruction with x-rays or with radioactive iodine.

In recent years another hormone, termed **thyrocalcitonin,** has been shown to be secreted by the thyroid gland. Thyrocalcitonin is a peptide hormone with a molecular weight of about 4000. It plays a role, together with parathyroid hormone, in regulating the metabolism of calcium and phosphorus. It inhibits bone resorption and inhibits the effects of parathormone on bone. Thyrocalcitonin decreases the concentration of calcium in the blood and decreases the excretion of calcium in the urine.

32.4

The Parathyroid Glands

Embedded in the thyroid glands of terrestrial vertebrates are small masses of tissue called **parathyroid glands.** There are usually two pairs of parathyroids, which develop embryologically as outgrowths of the third and fourth pairs of pharyngeal pouches. Each gland consists of solid masses and cords of epithelial cells, rather than of spherical follicles as in the thyroid. The hormone secreted by the parathyroids, called **parathormone,** was first extracted from parathyroid glands by Collip in 1925. It regulates, by mechanisms which are not yet clear, the levels of calcium and phosphorus in the blood and body fluids. It is essential for life; the complete removal of the parathyroids results in death in a few days. Parathormone is a single peptide chain containing 77 amino acids; its molecular weight is 8500. It is inactivated by proteolytic enzymes and cannot be administered orally. It appears to affect two different processes—the excretion of phosphorus by the kidney and the deposition of calcium in bone and other tissues. Parathyroidectomy produces a decreased concentration of calcium in the serum, a decreased excretion of phosphorus, and a resulting increase in the amount of phosphorus in the serum. The animal is subject to muscular tremors, cramps

and convulsions, a condition known as **tetany,** which results from the low level of calcium in the body fluids. An injection of a solution of calcium stops the tetanic convulsions, and further convulsions can be prevented by repeated administration of calcium.

Parathyroid deficiencies are rare, occurring occasionally when the glands are removed inadvertently during an operation on the thyroid, or when degeneration results from an infection. The administration of parathormone cannot be used for the long-term treatment of parathyroid deficiencies, for the patient becomes refractory to repeated injections of the extract. The deficiency can be treated successfully by a diet rich in calcium and vitamin D and low in phosphorus.

Hyperfunction of the parathyroid, induced by a tumor of the gland, is characterized by high calcium and low phosphorus content of the blood and by increased urinary excretion of both calcium and phosphorus. The calcium comes, at least in part, from the bones and, as a result, the bones become soft and are easily broken. The increased level of calcium in the body fluids eventually leads to deposits of calcium in abnormal places—the kidneys, intestinal wall, heart and lungs.

32.5

The Islet Cells of the Pancreas

The pancreas is known to secrete two hormones, insulin and glucagon, in addition to a number of digestive enzymes. Scattered among the acinar cells which secrete the digestive enzymes are clusters of hormone-secreting cells, called **islets of Langerhans,** which are quite different in appearance and staining properties. They have a richer supply of blood vessels than the acinar cells and have no associated ducts. The islet cells can be differentiated into two or more types by the staining reactions of their cytoplasmic granules. The pancreas develops as two outgrowths from the duodenum which grow together and fuse in most vertebrates. The islet cells develop as buds from the pancreatic ducts and eventually lose all connection with the ducts. In some bony fishes the acinar and islet tissues form spatially separate organs. The pancreas of the cyclostomes is ductless and located in the wall of the duodenum or in the liver.

The human disease **diabetes** had been recognized for many centuries but its cause and cure were equally unknown. A similar condition was produced experimentally in dogs by von Mering and Minkowski in 1889 when they surgically removed the pancreas while studying its role in digestion. Many attempts were subsequently made to feed pancreas or to prepare an extract for injection into diabetics, but all were unsuccessful because the proteolytic enzymes made by the pancreas destroyed the protein hormone before it could be extracted. Finally, in 1922, Banting and Best prepared an extract of fetal pancreas which had antidiabetic potency. The endocrine cells of the pancreas become active before the exocrine ones do. The first preparation of pure crystalline **insulin** was made in 1927 by Abel. The present commercial insulin is extracted from beef, sheep or hog pancreas by an acid alcohol method which rapidly inactivates the proteolytic enzymes. Insulin is a protein with a molecular weight of 12,000. From the brilliant work of F. Sanger in England the exact sequence of the amino acids in each of the two peptide chains making up the insulin molecule is now known. One chain contains 21 amino acids and the other contains 30.

Most commercial preparations of insulin were found to contain a second hormone, which increases blood sugar concentration instead of decreasing it as insulin does. This hormone, now christened **glucagon,** has been separated from insulin, crystallized, and found to be a single peptide chain composed of 29 amino acids. Glucagon is secreted by the alpha cells of the islets, and insulin by the beta cells.

Insulin and glucagon both take part in the regulation of carbohydrate metabolism, along with certain hormones secreted by the pituitary, adrenal medulla and adrenal cortex. Glucagon activates the enzyme **phosphorylase,** which is involved in the conversion of liver glycogen to blood glucose, and thus raises the concentration of glucose in the blood. Insulin increases the rate of conversion of blood glucose to intracellular glucose-phosphate, thereby decreasing the blood glucose level, increasing the storage of glycogen in skeletal muscle, and increasing the metabolism of glucose to carbon dioxide and water. A deficiency of insulin decreases the utilization of sugar, and the alterations in carbohydrate metabolism which result secondarily produce many other changes in the metabolism of proteins, fats and other substances.

The surgical removal of the pancreas, or its hypofunction in diabetes mellitus, produces impaired glucose utilization, which results in high concentration of glucose in the blood (**hyperglycemia**) and the excretion of large amounts of glucose in the urine (**glycosuria**) because the concentration of sugar in the blood exceeds the renal threshold (p. 507). Extra water is required to excrete this sugar, the urine volume increases, and the patient tends to become dehydrated and thirsty. Because the tissues are unable to get enough glucose from the blood, they break down protein and convert the carbon chains of the amino acids into glucose. Much of this is excreted and there is a steady loss of weight. The fat deposits are also mobilized and broken down, and the concentration of fat in the blood may increase to the point where the blood has a milky appearance. The fatty acids are not metabolized completely but tend to accumulate as partially oxidized **ketone bodies** such as acetoacetic acid. These acidic substances accumulate in the blood and are excreted in the urine, causing an acidosis (loss of base) which finally results in coma and death. The injection of insulin alleviates all of these symptoms; with the utilization of glucose made normal by insulin, all the other metabolic conditions return to normal.

The effect of an injection of insulin lasts for only a short time, a day at most, for the insulin is gradually destroyed in the tissues. A person with diabetes must receive daily injections of insulin to maintain good health. Long-lasting insulins, such as protamine zinc insulin and globin insulin, have been developed, and they reduce the number of injections needed to one a day for most diabetics.

The administration of a large dose of insulin to a normal or a diabetic person causes a marked decrease in the blood sugar level. The nerve cells, which require a certain amount of glucose for normal function, become hyperirritable and then fail to respond as the glucose level decreases. The patient becomes bewildered, incoherent, and comatose and may die unless some glucose is administered. There are rare cases of pancreatic tumors that, by hypersecretion of insulin, cause recurring attacks of convulsions and unconsciousness by reducing the blood glucose level.

The secretion of insulin is controlled by the level of glucose in the blood. When the blood glucose level rises, e.g., after a meal, the secretion of insulin is stimulated and it acts to restore the glucose level to normal. When the glucose concentration has been lowered, the stimulus for insulin secretion is removed, and it decreases or stops. The long-continued injection of insulin into a nondiabetic animal or person may render it diabetic.

32.6

The Adrenal Glands

The small, paired **adrenal glands** of mammals are located at the anterior end of each kidney. The two human glands weigh only about 12 gm. but have a richer supply of blood vessels per mass of tissue than any other organ of the body. Each adrenal consists of two parts, an outer, pale, yellowish pink **cortex** and a dark, reddish brown inner **medulla.** In cyclostomes and fishes the two parts are spatially separate; in amphibians, reptiles and birds their anatomic relations are quite variable and the two parts are interspersed. Cortical tissue develops from coelomic mesoderm near the mesonephric kidneys, whereas the medullary tissue is ectodermal, derived from the neural crest cells which also form the sympathetic ganglia.

The cells of the medulla are arranged in irregular cords and masses around the blood vessels (Fig. 32.5). The medulla secretes two closely related hormones, **epinephrine** (also called adrenin and adrenalin) and **norepinephrine.** These are comparatively simple chemicals derived from the amino acid tyrosine. Epinephrine produces an increase in heart rate, a rise in blood pressure, a decrease in the glycogen content of liver and muscle, an increase in blood glucose, and an increase in the rate at which blood coagulates. It causes dilation of the pupils of the eye, goose flesh, and dilation of most blood vessels but constriction of those of the skin, so that the skin becomes pale. Norepinephrine

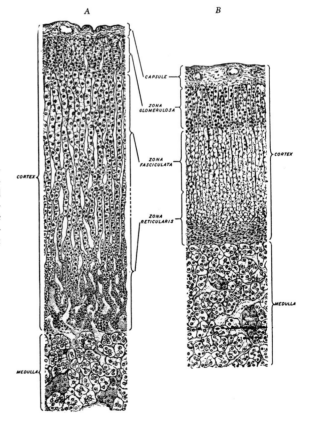

Figure 32.5 Sections through the adrenal cortex and medulla of (*A*) normal and (*B*) hypophysectomized rats. Since the functional capacity of the adrenal cortex is conditioned by the release of ACTH, hypophysectomy results in tremendous shrinkage of the cortex. The medulla is not influenced by hypophysectomy. Both sections are drawn to scale. (Turner: General Endocrinology, 3rd ed.)

has much weaker effects on blood sugar and heart rate but is a more powerful vasoconstrictor.

The adrenal medulla, in contrast to most other endocrine glands, is not essential for life; its removal does not cause a deficiency disease. This gland is believed to secrete a small amount of epinephrine and norepinephrine continuously; the rate of secretion is under nervous control.

It is widely believed that the secretion of the adrenal medulla functions during emergencies to reinforce and prolong the action of the sympathetic nervous system. There is good evidence that epinephrine secretion is greatly increased by stresses such as cold, pain, trauma, emotional states and certain drugs. The changes resulting from the action of the sympathetic nerves and epinephrine would prepare an animal to attack its prey, defend itself against enemies or run away. These changes include the following: (1) The efficiency of the circulatory system is increased by increased blood pressure and heart rate and the dilation of the large blood vessels. (2) The increase in the ability of blood to coagulate and the constriction of the vessels in the skin tend to minimize the loss of blood if the animal is wounded. (3) The intake of oxygen is increased by the increased rate of breathing and dilation of the respiratory passages. (4) The mobilization of the glycogen stores of the liver and muscle makes glucose available for energy. (5) The release of ACTH from the pituitary is stimulated (p. 567). The ACTH, in turn, stimulates the release from the adrenal cortex of glucocorticoids which increase the breakdown of protein and make further carbohydrate available.

Epinephrine is widely used clinically in treating asthma (it dilates respiratory passages), in increasing blood pressure and in stimulating a heart that has stopped beating.

The adrenal cortex is more complex than the medulla both structurally (for it is composed of three layers of cells) and functionally (for it secretes a number of hormones with different types of activity). The cortex is composed of three zones: an outer glomerulosa, a middle fasciculata and an inner reticularis (Fig. 32.5). Cells are formed by mitosis in the outer layer and are pushed inward to the reticularis, where they degenerate and disappear. The cells of the fasciculata

are believed to be most active in hormone production. The embryos of man and other primates have very large adrenals—as large as the kidneys—which result from the presence of a large mass of cells, the **fetal zone,** interposed between the cortex and medulla. The fetal zone regresses and disappears after birth.

Some 30 different hormones have been extracted from the adrenal cortex of various species; all belong to the class of chemicals called steroids, to which the male and female sex hormones also belong. No single one of these hormones is the physiologic equivalent of whole adrenal extract. The cortical hormones have been grouped into three categories with different physiologic effects and different chemical structures. These are (1) **glucocorticoids,** which stimulate the conversion of proteins to carbohydrates, (2) **mineralocorticoids,** which regulate sodium and potassium metabolism, and (3) **androgens,** which have male sex hormone activity. The most potent glucocorticoid is **cortisol** (Compound F). The most potent mineralocorticoid is **aldosterone,** discovered in 1953; **deoxycorticosterone** is an effective regulator of salt and water metabolism and is widely used clinically.

The adrenal cortex of both males and females produces dehydroepiandrosterone and adrenosterone, steroids with slight male sex hormone activity. In addition the cortex produces small amounts of the much more potent male sex hormone, testosterone, the principal hormone secreted by the testis. Hyperfunction of the adrenal cortex in male children may increase the production of androgens and cause precocious sexual maturity. The child has the muscular development, hair distribution and voice of a man. Cortical hyperfunction in females may cause masculinization—growth of a beard, deep voice, regression of the ovaries, uterus and vagina, and development of the clitoris to resemble a penis.

Experiments on the biosynthesis of steroids have shown that they are made by the union of two-carbon acetyl coenzyme A units to form cholesterol. The cholesterol content of the adrenal cortex exceeds that of any other organ; as much as 5 per cent of the wet weight of the gland may be cholesterol. Steroids are synthesized from cholesterol not only in the adrenal cortex but in the testis, ovary and placenta as well. The synthetic pathways of these compounds are interrelated; progesterone, for example, appears to be the precursor of both aldosterone and cortisol in the adrenal cortex and of testosterone and estradiol as well. The hormones produced by each of these organs are summarized in Table 32.2.

The complete removal of the adrenal cortex, or its hypofunction in **Addison's disease,** results in an increased excretion of sodium in the urine and a corresponding excretion of chloride, bicarbonate and water. The loss of sodium produces an acidosis, and the loss of body fluid leads to lowered blood pressure and a decreased rate of blood flow. The concentration of potassium in the blood increases. There is a marked decline in blood sugar concentration and in the glycogen content of liver, muscle and other tissues. It is clear from experimental evidence that the animal's ability to produce carbohydrates from proteins is greatly impaired.

The appetite for food and water decreases, and there is loss of weight. There are marked upsets in the digestive tract, with diarrhea, vomiting and pain. Muscles are more readily fatigued and less able to do work. The basal metabolic rate decreases, and the animal is less able to withstand exposure to cold and other stresses. Death ensues within a few days after complete adrenalectomy. The skin of a patient with Addison's disease develops a peculiar bronzing in patches, owing to the deposition of melanin.

Cortisol and cortisone have marked effects in inhibiting hypersensitivity, allergies and inflammation in tissues, presumably by modifying the reactivity of mesenchymal tissue. They also inhibit the proliferation of tissues in the joints of persons suffering from rheumatoid arthritis. The two hormones are widely used clinically in the treatment of these conditions.

The development and function of the adrenal cortex is regulated by adrenocorticotropic hormone, ACTH, secreted by the anterior lobe of the pituitary. The secretion of ACTH is stimulated when the concentration of adrenal cortical steroids, especially cortisol, in the blood decreases. ACTH stimulates the adrenal cortex to secrete more cortisol and the concentration of cortisol in the blood is returned to normal. An excess of cortisol in the blood inhibits the secretion of ACTH by the pituitary.

Enlargement of the adrenal cortex and hypersecretion of adrenal hormones is known as **Cushing's syndrome.** All three types of corticoids are produced in excess, and salt, water and carbohydrate metabolism is deranged. Females with this disease may develop a pattern of body hair like the male and have an enlarged clitoris. Fat is deposited in the trunk but not the legs; muscles are weak and tend to waste away; bones are weakened and fracture easily; and the excess of glucocorticoids produces a metabolic condition very similar to diabetes mellitus. This can be cured by surgical removal of the adrenal. A different disease, called **adrenogenital syndrome,** results from the genetic deficiency of one or another of the enzymes involved in the synthesis of cortisol. The deficiency of cortisol in the blood leads to an increased secretion of ACTH by the pituitary, and the ACTH stimulates the over-all production of adrenal steroids. The genetic deficiency of the enzyme prevents the synthesis of cortisol and the adrenal steroids are converted to other products, including androgens. The androgens produce precocious sexual maturity in males and masculinization in females.

We can summarize the major roles of the several adrenal hormones as follows: they regulate the concentration of sodium, potassium and water in the body fluids and tissues; they participate in the control of carbohydrate metabolism, accelerating the

Table 32.2 Steroid Hormones

Adrenal Cortex	Ovary	Testis	Placenta
Cortisol	Estradiol	Testosterone	Progesterone
Deoxycorticosterone	Progesterone	Androstenedione	Estradiol
Aldosterone	Androgens	Estradiol	Corticoids
Androsterone		Estrone	
Dehydroepiandrosterone		Corticoids	
Estradiol			

conversion of proteins to carbohydrates; and they supplement the actions of the sex hormones.

32.7
The Pituitary Gland

The pituitary gland, or hypophysis cerebri, is an unpaired endocrine gland which lies in a small depression on the floor of the skull, just below the hypothalamus of the brain, to which it is attached by a narrow stalk. Its only known function is the secretion of hormones. The pituitary has a double origin: a dorsal outgrowth (**Rathke's pouch**) from the roof of the mouth grows up and surrounds a ventral evagination (the **infundibulum**) from the hypothalamus (Fig. 32.6). Both parts are of ectodermal origin. Rathke's pouch soon loses its connection to the mouth, but the connection to the brain, the infundibular stalk, remains. The hypophysis has three lobes: anterior and intermediate lobes derived from Rathke's pouch and a posterior

lobe from the infundibulum. The pituitary, like the adrenal, is a double gland whose parts have quite different functions. The anterior lobe has no nerve fibers and is stimulated to release its hormones by hormonal factors reaching it through its blood vessels. The anterior lobe receives a double blood supply, arterial and portal. Some branches of the internal carotid artery pass directly to the pituitary, others serve a capillary bed around the infundibular stalk and the median eminence of the hypothalamus (Fig. 32.7). Portal veins from these capillaries then pass down the infundibular stalk and empty into the capillaries surrounding the secretory cells of the anterior lobe. The posterior lobe has a separate blood supply, via the inferior hypophysial arteries. There is, thus, a direct route for substances to pass from the hypothalamus to the anterior lobe by way of these portal vessels. Axons are known to release active neurohumors (e.g., acetylcholine or sympathin) at their tips, and this portal system provides a means by which substances released by the tips of axons

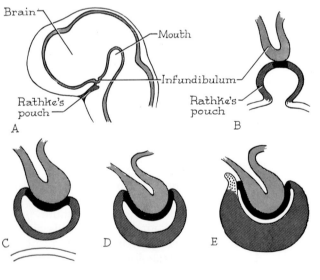

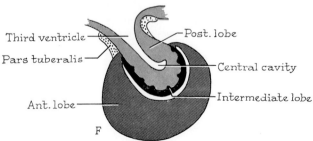

Figure 32.6 The development of the pituitary gland. *A*, Sagittal section through head of young embryo. *B–F*, Sagittal sections of successive stages of developing pituitary gland.

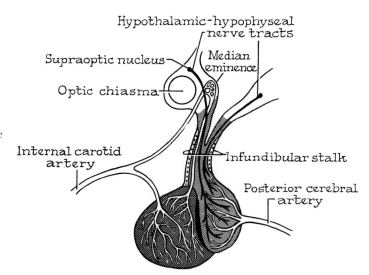

Hypothalamic-hypophyseal nerve tracts

Supraoptic nucleus

Median eminence

Optic chiasma

Figure 32.7 Blood supply of the pituitary gland.

Internal carotid artery

Infundibular stalk

Posterior cerebral artery

ending in the median eminence may be carried to the anterior lobe and influence its secretory rate.

The anterior lobe is composed of irregular cords and masses of epithelial cells surrounding blood vessels. Three kinds of cells can be distinguished by the shape and staining properties of their granules: acidophils, basophils and chromophobes. The intermediate lobe contains basophil cells smaller than those of the anterior lobe, some with and some without granules. The posterior lobe is composed of many nonmyelinated nerve fibers and branching cells (pituicytes) which contain brownish cytoplasmic granules.

The posterior lobe contains two hormones, **oxytocin** and **vasopressin.** The latter is also known as **antidiuretic hormone,** or ADH. The brilliant work of Vincent du Vigneaud, for which he was awarded the Nobel Prize in 1955, led to the isolation of these two hormones, the determination of their molecular structure, and their synthesis. Each is a peptide containing nine amino acids, seven of which are identical in the two. It is of considerable interest that these two substances, with quite different physiologic properties, differ in only two amino acids. Oxytocin stimulates the contraction of the uterine muscles and is sometimes injected after childbirth to contract the uterus. Vasopressin causes a contraction of smooth muscles; its contraction of the muscles in the wall of arterioles causes a general increase in blood pressure. It also regulates the reabsorption of water by the

cells of the distal convoluted tubules and Henle's loop in the kidney (p. 507).

These two hormones are not produced in the posterior lobe but are secreted by neurosecretory cells in the supraoptic and paraventricular nuclei of the brain. They then pass along the axons of the hypothalamic-hypophyseal tract and are stored and released by the posterior lobe. An injury of these brain nuclei, of the posterior lobe or of the connecting nerve tracts, may lead to a deficiency of ADH and the condition known as **diabetes insipidus.** In this disease the patient's kidneys have a lessened ability to reabsorb water and his urine volume increases from the normal 1 or 2 liters to 10 to 25 liters per day. He suffers from excessive thirst and drinks copiously. Injection of ADH relieves all the symptoms, but the injections must be repeated every few days. A comparable condition can be produced in experimental animals by severing the hypothalamic-hypophyseal tract by electrolytic lesions accurately placed with a microelectrode.

The intermediate lobe of the pituitary secretes a hormone, **intermedin,** which darkens the skin of fishes, amphibians and reptiles by dispersing the pigment granules in the chromatophores. The skin of a frog becomes darkened in a cool, dark environment and light-colored in a warm, light place (Fig. 32.8). Hypophysectomy produces a permanent blanching of the skin, and injection of intermedin causes darkening. The location of the pigment in the chromato-

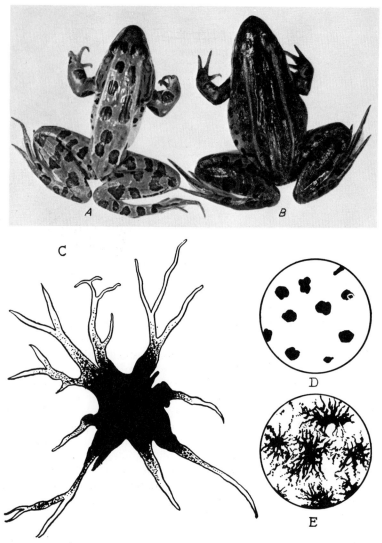

Figure 32.8 Integumentary adaptations in normal frogs (*Rana pipiens*). *A*, Light-adapted animal; *B*, dark-adapted animal. (Turner: General Endocrinology, 2nd ed.) *C*, A chromatophore, greatly magnified, showing the pigment. *D*, A section of skin of frog adapted to a warm, light environment. *E*, Skin adapted to a cool, dark environment.

phore is controlled directly by the amount of intermedin present, not by nerves. The pituitaries of birds and mammals are rich in intermedin, but there is no known function for this hormone in these animals; it does not affect their pigmentation.

The anterior lobe of the pituitary secretes the following hormones, all of which are proteins: growth hormone (somatotropin), thyrotropin, adrenocorticotropin (ACTH), follicle-stimulating hormone (FSH), luteinizing hormone (LH) and prolactin (lactogenic hormone). A number of other hormones have been postulated to be products of the

anterior lobe but their existence has not generally been confirmed. The importance of these hormones is demonstrated by the marked abnormalities which follow hypophysectomy: cessation of growth in young animals, regression of gonads and reproductive organs, and atrophy of the thyroid and adrenal cortex (Fig. 32.9).

Growth hormone was the first pituitary hormone to be described. As early as 1860 it was recognized that gigantism was correlated with an enlargement of the pituitary. A growth-promoting extract of beef pituitaries was prepared by Evans and Long in

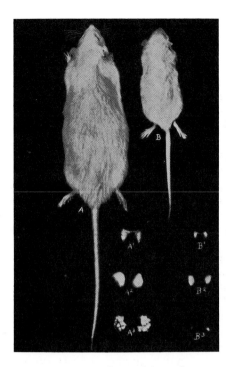

Figure 32.9 The effects of hypophysectomy in the rat. *A,* Normal littermate control; *B,* littermate hypophysectomized when 36 days of age. These photographs were made at 144 days of age, when the control animal weighed 264 gm. and the hypophysectomized rat weighed 80 gm. A¹, A² and A³ are thyroids, adrenals and ovaries from normal animal; B¹, B² and B³ are thyroids, adrenals and ovaries from hypophysectomized animal. Note marked differences in size. (Turner: General Endocrinology, 2nd ed.)

1921 and pure growth hormone was isolated in 1944. This controls general body growth and bone growth and leads to an increase in the amount of cellular protein (Fig. 32.10). Overactivity of the pituitary during the growth period leads to very tall, but well-proportioned persons, and underactivity leads to small persons of normal body proportions, called midgets. After normal growth has been completed, hypersecretion of growth hormone produces **acromegaly,** characterized by the thickening of the skin, tongue, lips, nose and ears and by growth of the bones of the hands, feet, jaw and skull. Other bones have lost their ability to respond to growth hormone. A race of hereditary dwarf mice is known whose pituitaries apparently lack the type of cell which secretes growth hormone. These animals can be induced to grow to normal size by implanting a pituitary from a normal mouse. Growth hormones from different species have been found to differ slightly in their amino acid composition and in their effectiveness. Thus, beef growth hormone will cause growth in rats but not in man or monkeys. Growth hormone prepared from human or monkey pituitaries will stimulate growth in man and monkeys. In addition to its general effects on growth, this hormone affects protein, lipid and carbohydrate metabolism, leading to increased protein syn-

Figure 32.10 The effect of growth hormone on the dachshund. Top, normal dog. Bottom, dog injected with growth extract for a period of six months. (From Evans, Simpson, Meyer and Reichert.)

thesis, a mobilization of lipid from tissues and an increased lipid concentration in the blood, and an increased deposition of glycogen in liver and muscle but an increased concentration of glucose in the blood.

Chemical analysis of the **adrenocorticotropic hormone, ACTH,** has shown that the active fraction is a peptide containing 39 amino acids. The sequence of these amino acids is now known and in 1961 a peptide containing 24 amino acids was synthesized by Hofmann at the University of Pittsburgh and found to have ACTH-like activity. In recent years ACTH has become famous because of the remarkable results it sometimes gives in the treatment of allergies and arthritis. However, the prime, and perhaps the only, physiologic function of ACTH is to stimulate the adrenal cortex to grow and to release cortical steroids. The injection of ACTH reduces the amount of cholesterol and ascorbic acid in the adrenal cortex, presumably because they are used in the synthesis of steroids. The injection of ACTH stimulates, within a few minutes, a marked increase in the amount of cortisol in the blood. The adrenal cortex undergoes a prompt atrophy after the removal of the pituitary and can be returned to normal by the injection of ACTH.

The extirpation of the pituitary also causes atrophy of the thyroid. The gland decreases in size and the follicle cells become flattened. The thyroid is returned to normal by the implantation of a pituitary gland or by the administration of an extract containing **thyrotropin.** The injection of thyrotropin in a normal animal causes growth of the thyroid and thickening of the follicle cells so that they become columnar rather than cuboidal epithelium (Fig. 32.2).

The ovaries or testes of a hypophysectomized young animal never become mature; they neither produce gametes nor secrete enough sex hormones to develop the secondary sex characters. Hypophysectomy of an adult results in involution and atrophy of the gonads. It is now clear that there are two gonadotropins, called **follicle-stimulating hormone (FSH)** and **luteinizing hormone (LH)** and that both are necessary for achieving sexual maturity and for the regulation of the estrous cycle. The effect of follicle-stimulating hormone is primarily on the development of graafian follicles in the ovaries: it does not produce any significant release of estrogen. Luteinizing hormone controls the release of ripe eggs from the follicle, the formation of corpora lutea, and the production and release of estrogens and progesterone. **Prolactin,** or lactogenic hormone, maintains the secretion of estrogens and progesterone and stimulates the secretion of milk by the breast. It is effective, however, only after the breast has been stimulated by the proper amounts of estrogen and progesterone. Prolactin induces behavior patterns leading to the care of the young (the "maternal instinct") in mammals and in other vertebrates as well. Roosters treated with prolactin will take care of chicks, taking them to food and water, sheltering them under their wings, and protecting them from predators. The cyclic release of FSH and LH is involved in the control of the estrous cycles of lower mammals and the menstrual cycles of primates. The simultaneous administration of FSH and LH produces much greater effects on ovarian growth than either one alone; similar instances of hormonal synergism have been observed with certain other pairs of hormones.

The development and functioning of the testis is also controlled by FSH and LH. FSH increases the size of the seminiferous tubules, and both FSH and LH are needed for normal spermatogenesis. LH, but not FSH, stimulates the interstitial cells of the testis to produce male sex hormone.

Extracts of the pituitary have been prepared which have other effects when injected, and it has been postulated that the gland secretes other hormones in addition to these six. Despite repeated attempts, it has not been possible to separate and purify the agents of these other activities and many investigators now regard them as side effects of one of the known hormones. The insulin-antagonist effect of the pituitary, the "diabetogenic hormone," is now believed to be a property of the growth hormone.

The control of pituitary function, which ensures that the proper amount of each of these hormones will be released at the proper moment in response to the demands of the organism, is indeed complex. Recent research has revealed that the release of each tropic hormone is controlled in part by the level of the target hormone in the circulating blood. The release of ACTH is inhibited by cortisol, the release of thyrotropin is inhibited by thyroxin, estrogens decrease the output of FSH, and progesterone decreases the secretion of LH. This provides for a cutoff mechanism so that in a normal animal the secretions of the pituitary and its target organs are kept in balance.

The release of ACTH is also stimulated by epinephrine. This is apparently a direct effect, for it is observed when the pituitary is removed from its normal site and transplanted to the eye. Epinephrine is not indispensable for ACTH release; the latter can occur normally after removal of the adrenal medulla.

The hypothalamus provides a third, and very important, control of pituitary function. It is currently believed that axons from certain centers in the hypothalamus end in the median eminence (Fig. 32.7). The tips of these axons secrete some neurohumor which is carried by the portal veins to the hypophysis, where it stimulates the release of ACTH. Evidence of ACTH secretion is obtained when the median eminence is stimulated electrically but not when the stimulus is applied to the supraoptic nuclei whose axons pass to the posterior lobe of the pituitary. The electrical stimulus is ineffective if the blood vessels between the hypothalamus and pituitary are cut. If the nerve fibers to the median eminence are destroyed, ACTH is no longer released in response to stresses. There is evidence that the release of other pituitary hormones—growth hormone, thyrotropin and the gonadotropins—is also under hypothalamic control.

All the living vertebrates have pituitaries which are basically similar, and they all appear to secrete the same battery of hormones. The intermediate lobes of birds and mammals secrete intermedin, although these forms have no chromatophores; birds secrete luteinizing hormone but have no corpora lutea; and all vertebrates secrete prolactin, but only mammals have its target organ, the mammary glands.

32.8

The Testis

In between the seminiferous tubules of the testes are hormone-secreting cells, the interstitial cells of Leydig. Although Berthold concluded in 1849 that the testis produces a blood-borne substance needed for the development of male sex characters, no effective testicular extract was prepared until 1927. Extracts of human urine with androgenic activity were made in 1929, and by 1934 two hormones, **androsterone** and **dehydroepiandrosterone,** had been isolated from urine and identified. A new androgen, **testosterone,** six times more potent than androsterone, was extracted from testicular tissue in 1935. All these androgens are steroids. The testis will synthesize carbon[14]-labeled testosterone if provided with C^{14}-labeled acetate.

Testosterone has a general effect on metabolism, inducing growth by stimulating the formation of cell proteins. The administration of androgens leads to an increase in body weight owing to the synthesis of protein in muscle and to a lesser extent in the liver and kidney.

Testosterone and other androgens stimulate the development and maintenance of the **secondary male characters:** the enlargement of the external genitals, the growth of the accessory glands such as the prostate and seminal vesicles, the growth of the beard and body hair, and the deepening of the voice. The secondary sex characters of other animals, the antlers of deer and the combs, wattles and plumage of birds, are controlled by androgens. Male sex hormones are responsible, in part, for the development of mating behavior.

The removal of the testis (castration) of an immature male prevents the development of the secondary sex characters. A castrated man, a **eunuch,** has a high-pitched voice, beardless face, and small genitals and accessory glands. Castration was practiced in the past to provide guardians for harems and sopranos for choirs. Many kinds of domestic animals are castrated to make them more placid. The injection of testosterone into a castrated animal restores all the sex characters to normal. The anal fin of the male mosquito fish, *Gambusia,* is differentiated into a penis-like organ used to transfer sperm to the female. This fails to develop if the fish is castrated but appears if the castrate male or the female is treated with testosterone.

It should be emphasized that males produce female sex hormones (estrogens) and that females produce androgens in considerable amounts. One of the richest sources of female sex hormones is the urine of stallions. The normal differentiation of the sex characters is a function of a balance between the two.

The failure of the testes to descend normally from the body cavity to the scrotal sac, called **cryptorchidism,** produces sterility but has little or no effect on the production of testosterone. Microscopic examination of an undescended testis shows that the cells in the seminiferous tubules regress, but the interstitial cells are normal. The cells of the seminiferous tubules are particularly susceptible to heat, and the temperature of the body cavity, 3 or 4 degrees higher than that of the scrotal sac, destroys them. It is probable that the elevated temperature during a prolonged fever makes a man sterile for some time. In many wild animals the testes remain in the body cavity except during the breeding season, when they descend into the scrotal sac.

The removal of the pituitary causes regression of both the interstitial cells and the seminiferous tubules of the testis. Androgen secretion is decreased, and the secondary sex characters regress. Normal development and spermatogenesis of the cells of the seminiferous tubules apparently require the combined action of FSH, LH and testosterone. The administration of excessive amounts of testosterone or estrogen may produce regression of the testes, presumably by inhibiting the release of FSH and LH from the pituitary.

The cyclic growth and regression of the testes in animals with periodic breeding seasons appears to be mediated via the pituitary. Such animals have very low amounts of gonadotropin in the nonbreeding season. Changes in the temperature or in the amount of daily illumination produce stimuli which are mediated by the brain and hypothalamus to induce gonadotropin secretion by the pituitary and consequent growth and functional state of the testes and secondary sex characters.

32.9
The Ovaries

The ovaries of vertebrates are endocrine organs as well as the source of eggs; they produce the steroid hormones **estradiol** and **progesterone.** Some mammalian ovaries produce a third hormone, the protein **relaxin.**

Both ovaries and testes develop from mesoderm, from the **genital ridge** on the ventral side of the mesonephros (Fig. 32.11). Each ovary consists of closely packed cells covered by a thickened mesothelium called the germinal epithelium. During embryonic development certain cells of the germinal epithelium enlarge, push into the mass of cells below, and become **primordial germ cells.** According to one view, these cells are not derived from the mesothelium, but originate in the epithelium of the yolk sac and migrate to their final position in the gonad. Other investigators maintain that the functional eggs do not come from these primordial germ cells visible in the ovary at birth but arise by new proliferations from the germinal epithelium in the adult.

As each oöcyte develops, it becomes surrounded by other cells derived from the germinal epithelium which form a spherical follicle about it (Fig. 32.12). These cells proliferate and form a thick layer, called the **stratum granulosum,** around the egg. A cavity, the **antrum,** filled with liquid appears in the mass of follicle cells. The connective tissue of the ovary forms a sheath, the **theca,** around the follicle. As the follicle enlarges and its antrum becomes dilated with follicular fluid, it is pushed near the surface of the ovary. It finally bursts and releases the egg into the peritoneal cavity, whence it passes into the oviduct. The release of the egg is known as **ovulation.** If the egg is fertilized in the oviduct, it will subsequently become embedded in the lining of the uterus and begin development.

The follicular cells remaining after the rupture of the follicle multiply and increase in size, filling the cavity left by the follicle. Cells from the theca grow in along with the granulosa cells and the two form the **corpus luteum.** This yellowish structure, a solid mass of cells about the size of a pea, projects from the surface of the ovary. If the egg is fertilized the human corpus luteum persists for months, but if no fertilization takes place it regresses after about two weeks to a small patch of whitish scar tissue, the corpus albicans.

Histochemical evidence indicates that the thecal cells are the source of estrogen and that these plus the granulosa cells of the

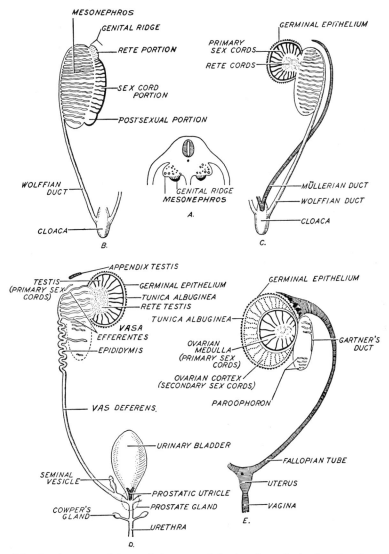

Figure 32.11   The development of the genital system. *A*, Section through the dorsal region of an early embryo. *B*, The wolffian body and genital ridge in frontal section. *C*, The indifferent stage. *D*, Differentiation of the male genitalia. *E*, Differentiation of the female genitalia. (Modified from Turner, 2nd ed.)

corpus luteum are the source of progesterone. The primary estrogen is 17-β-estradiol; other estrogens such as estrone and estriol may be metabolites of estradiol. Estradiol stimulates the changes which occur at sexual maturity: the growth of the accessory sex organs, uterus and vagina, the development of the breasts, changes in skeletal structure such as the broadening of the pelvis, the change in voice quality, the growth of pubic hair and the onset of the menstrual cycle. Both progesterone and estradiol are required for the growth of the uterine lining in each menstrual cycle to the stage at which implantation of the fertilized egg is possible. Progesterone is required for the maintenance of the developing embryo in the uterus and, together with estradiol, causes development of the breasts during pregnancy.

Progesterone is related chemically to the adrenal cortical hormones and is believed to be an intermediate in their synthesis, as well as an intermediate in the synthesis of estradiol and testosterone.

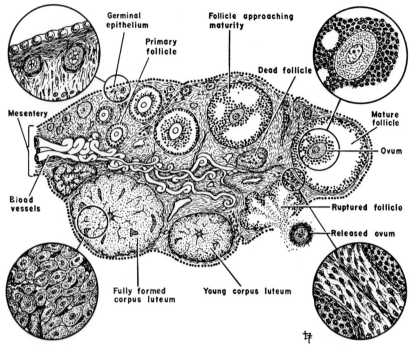

Figure 32.12 Stages in the development of an egg, follicle and corpus luteum in a mammalian ovary. Successive stages are depicted clockwise, beginning at the mesentery. Insets show the cellular structure of the successive stages. (Villee: Biology, 5th ed.)

32.10
The Estrous and Menstrual Cycles

The females of most mammalian species show cyclic periods of the sex urge and will permit copulation only at certain times, known as periods of **estrus** or "heat," when conditions are optimal for the union of egg and sperm. Most wild animals have one estrous period a year, the dog and cat have two, and rats and mice have estrous periods every five days. Estrus is characterized by heightened sex urge, ovulation and changes in the lining of the uterus and vagina. The uterine lining thickens, and its glands and blood vessels develop to provide optimal conditions for implantation.

The menstrual cycle of the primates is characterized not by periods of mating urge but by periods of bleeding caused by the degeneration and sloughing of the uterine lining. Ovulation occurs about midway between two successive menstruations, or periods of bleeding. Primates, unlike other mammals, permit copulation at any time in the menstrual cycle.

The menstrual cycle is controlled by the interaction of ovarian and pituitary hormones and includes events in the ovary, uterus and vagina. One menstrual cycle, from the beginning of one period of bleeding to the next, lasts 28 to 30 days in the human female (Fig. 32.13).

The lining of the uterus is almost completely sloughed off at each menstruation and thus is thinnest just after the menstrual flow. At that time, under the influence of FSH from the pituitary, one or more of the follicles in the ovary begin to grow rapidly. The follicular cells produce estradiol, which stimulates the growth of the uterine lining (the endometrium) and some growth of the uterine glands and blood vessels. The rupture of the follicle in ovulation does not occur automatically when a certain size is reached but is induced by the proper mixture of FSH and LH from the pituitary. Ovulation occurs about 15 days after the beginning of the previous period of menstruation. The corpus luteum develops and, under the stimulation of LH and prolactin, secretes progesterone. Progesterone, together with estradiol, promotes further growth of the endometrium. The endometrial glands grow further and become

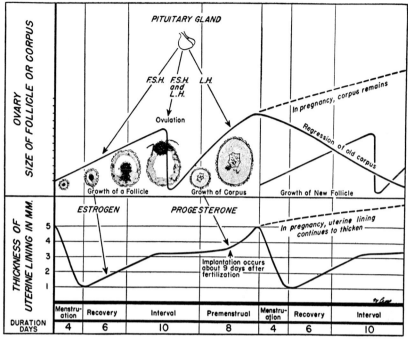

Figure 32.13 The menstrual cycle in the human female. The solid lines indicate the course of events if the egg is not fertilized; the dotted lines indicate the course of events when pregnancy occurs. The actions of the hormones of the pituitary and ovary in regulating the cycle are indicated by arrows. (Villee: Biology, 5th ed.)

secretory, and the blood vessels become long and coiled. Progesterone decreases the activity of the uterine muscles and brings the uterus into a condition such that the developing embryo formed from the fertilized egg can become implanted and develop. Progesterone inhibits the development of other follicles. If fertilization and implantation do not occur the corpus luteum begins to regress, it secretes less progesterone, and the endometrium, no longer provided with sufficient progesterone to be maintained, begins to slough. Thus menstruation ensues, completing the cycle.

If pregnancy occurs, the corpus luteum remains and continues secreting progesterone, which is necessary for the continuation of pregnancy. Removal of the ovary or of the corpus luteum results in the termination of pregnancy. In some animals the placenta produces enough progesterone so that loss of the corpus luteum does not result in abortion. Progesterone also stimulates the growth of the glands and ducts of the breasts during the latter months of pregnancy and prepares them for the action of prolactin secreted by the pituitary which, together with oxytocin, stimulates the flow of milk.

32.11
The Hormones of Pregnancy

The **placenta,** which develops in part from the extraembryonic membranes of the fetus and in part from the lining of the uterus (p. 577), is primarily an organ for the support and nourishment of the fetus. It is also an endocrine organ that produces hormones similar to those of the ovary, the adrenal cortex and the pituitary. These placental hormones, together with those of the maternal endocrine glands, control the many adaptations necessary for the continuation and successful termination of pregnancy.

The placenta secretes a protein hormone, **chorionic gonadotropin,** which is produced by the cells of the chorionic villi. Its effects are similar to, yet distinct from, those of the pituitary gonadotropins. It is known that the placenta secretes this and does not merely accumulate a hormone made elsewhere, for bits of placenta grown in tissue culture produce the hormone. One of the earliest signs of pregnancy is the appearance of this hormone in the blood and urine. The peak of chorionic gonadotropin production is reached in the second month of pregnancy, after

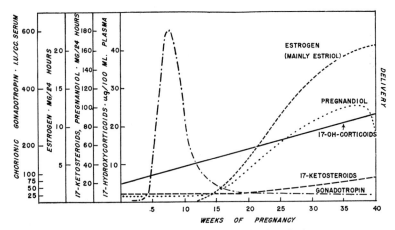

Figure 32.14   Hormone levels in blood and urine during pregnancy.

which the amount in blood and urine decreases to low levels (Fig. 32.14). Several pregnancy tests involve the effect of this gonadotropin, obtained from a sample of urine from the woman suspected of being pregnant, on sperm release in the frog or African toad or on the production of corpora lutea in rats or rabbits. These tests are quite accurate and make possible a diagnosis of pregnancy within a few weeks of conception. Chorionic gonadotropin stimulates the corpus luteum to remain functional and not regress as it would in the absence of pregnancy. The human placenta (and probably the placentas of other mammals, too) secretes another protein hormone, placental lactogen, with properties somewhat similar to those of pituitary lactogenic hormone. This hormone has marked lactogenic properties and also serves as a synergist to pituitary growth hormone.

The placenta also secretes estrogens and progesterone, which reinforce the ovarian hormones in the maintenance of pregnancy. There is good evidence that the placenta actually produces these hormones and does not accumulate them from the blood. There is a considerable body of evidence that the placenta may produce cortisol and other adrenal corticoids and a hormone very similar to ACTH.

In some animals, such as the rabbit, the placenta is a significant source of relaxin. This protein hormone, also produced by the ovary, functions to relax the ligaments of the pelvis to facilitate the birth of the young. Relaxin is effective only after the connective tissue of the pubic symphysis has been sensi-

tized by the action of estradiol. Relaxin also inhibits the motility of the uterine muscles.

The production of estrogens and progesterone, as reflected by the amount present in blood and urine, increases gradually throughout pregnancy, reaches a peak just before, or at the time of, parturition, and then abruptly declines after birth (Fig. 32.14). The factors which determine the onset of labor, the expulsion of the fetus from the uterus, remain a mystery. The possibility that oxytocin has a role in this was mentioned (p. 563). There are many hormonal changes which occur at about the time of parturition—decreases in estrogen and progesterone, and an increase in chorionic gonadotropin—but whether these are causes, effects, or unrelated phenomena remains to be determined.

32.12
Other Endocrine Glands

The thymus and pineal body may have endocrine functions. The thymus lies in the upper part of the chest, just above the heart. Its cells closely resemble lymph tissue. The thymus is large during the years of rapid growth but begins to regress after puberty. It has been postulated that it affects growth or sexual maturity, but extirpation of the gland or the administration of extracts fails to reveal any endocrine function.

The pineal body is a dorsal outgrowth of the diencephalon which lies on the upper surface of the thalamus. It has been suspected

Table 32.3   Hormones of the Digestive Tract

Hormone	Secreted by	Stimulus for Secretion	Target Organ	Response of Target Organ
Gastrin	Pyloric mucosa	Presence of food in stomach	Mucosa of stomach fundus	Secretion of gastric juice
Secretin	Duodenal mucosa	Presence of acid food in duodenum	Pancreas	Secretion of pancreatic juice
Enterogastrone	Duodenal mucosa	Neutral fat	Stomach	Decreased motility and secretion of HCl
Cholecystokinin	Duodenal mucosa	Acid food	Gallbladder	Contraction of gallbladder

of having some role in body growth and genital development, but the evidence is somewhat conflicting and no endocrine function can be ascribed to it with certainty.

The cells of certain parts of the digestive tract are known to secrete hormones in response to the presence of certain kinds of food which stimulate the production and release of digestive juices. These are summarized in Table 32.3.

32.13
Endocrine Interrelationships

In the course of our discussion some of the effects of one hormone on the production or action of another have been described. It is now becoming clear that each gland affects the functioning of almost every other one and that together they constitute an interrelated and interdependent system which coordinates body activities. When the role of the pituitary in regulating the activity of the thyroid, adrenals and gonads was first discovered, the pituitary was described as a "master controlling gland." But in view of the reciprocal effects of the hormones of these glands on the pituitary, and of the further control of the pituitary imposed by the hypothalamus, it is probably unwarranted to regard the pituitary as a special master gland.

The interplay of estradiol, progesterone, FSH and LH in regulating the menstrual cycle, and of estrogen, progesterone and prolactin in producing the development and functioning of the breasts, is now well established. The rate of cell metabolism and the relative rates of utilization of carbohydrates, fats and proteins are under the complex control of thyroxin, insulin, epinephrine, glucagon, growth hormone, cortisol, estradiol and testosterone. Normal growth requires not only growth hormone and thyroxin but also insulin, androgens and others.

Hans Selye, of the University of Montreal, has done much in recent years to investigate the role of hormones in adapting the body to environmental stresses. Stresses such as trauma, burns, cold, starvation, hemorrhage, intense sound or light and anoxia provoke a pattern of adaptation which tends to resist damage from the stress. The stress stimulates the release of epinephrine from the adrenal medulla which, in turn, leads to the release of ACTH by the anterior lobe of the pituitary. The adrenal cortical hormones released by the action of the ACTH produce changes in mineral and carbohydrate metabolism and in tissue reactivity which adapt the animal to resist the effects of the stress. Long-continued stresses eventually overcome the body's adaptive ability and produce exhaustion and shock. In the absence of either the hypophysis or the adrenal cortex, the body's ability to tolerate stress is greatly decreased.

32.14
Pheromones

In recent years it has been appreciated that the behavior of animals may be influenced not only by hormones—chemicals released into the internal environment by endocrine glands and which regulate and coordinate the activities of other tissues—but also by **pheromones**—substances secreted by *exocrine* glands, released into the *external* environment and which influence the behavior of other *animals* of the same species. We are used to thinking that information can be transferred from one animal to another by sight or sound; pheromones represent a means of communication, a means of transferring information, by smell.

Some pheromones act in some way on the recipient's central nervous system and produce an immediate effect on its behavior. Among these are the sex attractants of moths and the trail pheromones and alarm substances secreted by ants. Other pheromones act more slowly and trigger a chain of physiological events in the recipient which affect its growth and differentiation. These include the regulation of the growth of locusts and control of the numbers of reproductives and soldiers in termite colonies.

The sex attractants of moths provide one of the more spectacular examples of pheromones. Among the ones that have been isolated and identified are **bombykol,** a 16-carbon alcohol with two double bonds, secreted by female silkworms, and **gyplure,** 10-acetoxy-Δ^7-hexadecenol, secreted by female gypsy moths. The male has an extremely sensitive device in his antennas for sensing the attractant and responds by flying upwind to the source. He cannot determine the direction of the source by flying up a concentration gradient because the molecules are nearly uniformly dispersed except within a few meters of the source. With a gentle wind the attractant given off by a single female moth covers an area several thousand meters long and as much as 200 meters wide. An average silkworm contains some 0.01 mg. of sex attractant. It can be shown experimentally that when as little as 10,000 molecules of attractant are allowed to diffuse from a source 1 cm. from a male he responds appropriately. He can have received only a few hundred of these molecules, perhaps less. Thus the amount of attractant in one female could stimulate more than one billion males! The attractants are generally rather large molecules, containing 10 to 17 carbons in the chain, which provides for the specificity of the several kinds of attractants.

The fire ants, when returning to the nest after finding food, secrete a "trail pheromone" which marks the trail so that other ants can find their way to the food. The trail pheromone is volatile and evaporates within two minutes, so that there is little danger of ants being misled by old trails. Ants also release alarm substances when disturbed and this (rather like ringing the bell in a firehouse) in turn transmits the alarm to ants in the vicinity. These alarm substances have a lower molecular weight than the sex attractants and are less specific, so that members of several different species respond to the same alarm substance.

Worker bees, on finding food, secrete **geraniol,** a 10-carbon, branched chain alcohol, to attract other worker bees to the food. This supplements the information conveyed by their wagging dance (p. 749). Queen bees secrete 9-ketodecanoic acid which, when ingested by worker bees, inhibits the development of their ovaries and their ability to make royal cells in which new queens might be reared. This substance also serves as a sex attractant to male bees during the queen's nuptial flight.

In colonial insects, such as ants, bees and termites, pheromones play an important role in regulating and coordinating the composition and activities of the population. A termite colony includes morphologically distinct queen, king, soldiers and nymphs or workers. All develop from fertilized eggs; however, queens, kings and soldiers each secrete inhibitory substances, pheromones, that act on the corpus allatum of the nymphs and prevent their developing into the more specialized types. If the queen dies there is no longer any "antiqueen" pheromone released and one or more of the nymphs develop into queens. The members of each colony will permit only one queen to survive and will eat up any excess ones. Similarly the loss of the king termite or a reduction in the number of soldiers permits other nymphs to develop into the specialized castes to replace them. Males of migratory locusts secrete a substance from the surfaces of their skin which accelerates the growth of young locusts.

There are examples of pheromones in mammals as well as in insects. When female mice are placed four or more per cage there is a greatly increased frequency of pseudopregnancy. If their olfactory bulbs are removed this effect disappears. When more females are placed together in a cage their estrous cycles become very erratic. However, if one male mouse is placed in the cage his odor can initiate and synchronize the estrous cycles of all the females and reduce the frequency of reproductive abnormalities. Even more curious is the finding (the "Bruce effect") that the odor of a strange male will block pregnancy in a newly impregnated female mouse.

The question of whether there are human pheromones remains unanswered, but of interest in this respect is the observation of the French biologist, J. LeMagnen, that the odor of 14-hydroxytetradecanoic acid is perceived clearly by only sexually mature females and that it is perceived most sharply at about the time of ovulation! Males and young girls are relatively insensitive to this substance, but male subjects became more sensitive to it after an injection of estrogen.

QUESTIONS

1. Contrast the integrative effects of the nervous and endocrine systems.
2. Define a hormone. Distinguish between a hormone and a vitamin; a hormone and an enzyme.
3. What kinds of experiments might be used to determine whether a newly discovered gland in a vertebrate secretes a hormone?
4. Name and give the functions of the hormones secreted by the mammalian thyroid, parathyroid and adrenal medulla.
5. What radioactive substance is particularly useful in studying thyroid physiology? Why?
6. What hormone dysfunctions result in (a) myxedema, (b) Addison's disease, (c) diabetes insipidus, (d) diabetes mellitus, (e) Cushing's syndrome and (f) tetany?
7. Why can thyroxin be effective when administered orally, whereas insulin must be injected subcutaneously?
8. Describe the feedback mechanism that regulates the production of thyroxin and thyrotropin.
9. Describe the feedback mechanism that regulates the events of the menstrual cycle.
10. Contrast the effects of insulin and glucagon.
11. Compare the roles of parathormone and vitamin D in bone formation and dissolution.
12. Name and describe the effects of all the hormones that are required for normal growth.
13. Name and describe the effects of all the hormones that are required for the normal completion of pregnancy.
14. Name and give the functions of the main hormones of the adrenal cortex and the anterior lobe of the pituitary.
15. Discuss the theory that epinephrine has a special role in emergencies.
16. Describe the hormonal interrelations which control the development and functioning of the breasts.

ANNOTATED REFERENCES

Barrington, E. J. W.: Introduction to General and Comparative Endocrinology. Oxford, Clarendon Press, 1963. A comparative treatment of endocrine principles.

Gorbman, A., and H. A. Bern: A Textbook of Comparative Endocrinology. New York, John Wiley & Sons, Inc., 1962. An excellent presentation of the broad, evolutionary aspects of endocrine systems in vertebrate and invertebrate animals.

Prosser, C. L., and F. A. Brown: Comparative Animal Physiology. 2nd ed. Philadelphia, W. B. Saunders Company, 1961. Contains several chapters concerned with comparative endocrinology.

Turner, C. D.: General Endocrinology. 4th ed. Philadelphia, W. B. Saunders Company, 1966. An excellent, up-to-date treatment of the basic biological aspects of endocrinology.

Williams, R. H. (Ed.): Textbook of Endocrinology. 4th ed. Philadelphia, W. B. Saunders Company, 1968. A standard reference text by many specialists dealing primarily with medical endocrinology.

Young, W. C. (Ed.): Sex and Internal Secretions. 3rd ed. (2 vols.) Baltimore, Williams & Wilkins Company, 1961. A collection of essays by 28 experts dealing with many phases of reproductive physiology.

33

THE DEVELOPMENT OF MAMMALS

It is appropriate to conclude our consideration of the organ systems of vertebrates with a brief examination of their embryonic development. The general features of vertebrate development were discussed in Chapter 6 and should be reviewed at this time. We shall focus our attention on the early stages in the development of mammals, which differ in some respects from those of other vertebrates, and on the establishment of the organ systems.

33.1
Early Stages of Mammalian Development

Monotreme embryos derive their nutrients in reptilian fashion from the large accumulation of yolk stored in the cleidoic egg, but other mammalian embryos develop within the uterus and derive their nutrients from the mother through the placenta. These mammals do not provide their eggs with much yolk. The eggs are isolecithal and so small that they can barely be seen with the unaided eye. Indeed, they are so small that the early stages of mammalian development remained a mystery long after the early development of other vertebrates had been described. William Harvey, famed for his discovery of the circulation of the blood, searched the uteri of deer in vain for early embryos and finally concluded that the embryo might somehow be secreted by the uterus when seminal fluid was introduced.

In 1672, deGraaf discovered early cleavage stages (he called them eggs) in the fallopian tube of a rabbit, and concluded, correctly, that the eggs came from the ovary. The first mammalian egg to be seen, a dog's egg, was observed by von Baer in 1827. Human eggs free within the fallopian tube and early developmental stages implanted in the uterine lining have been described only in recent years.

Cleavage might be expected to be a very regular process in mammalian eggs as it is in other isolecithal eggs. The mammalian egg does cleave completely, and the first two or three cleavages in primates are regular and produce blastomeres of nearly equal size (Fig. 33.1). Subsequently, certain blastomeres divide faster than others, and cleavage becomes somewhat irregular. This may be a reflection of the irregular cleavage characteristic of the reptilian telolecithal egg, which was, of course, the type of egg present in mammalian ancestors.

A solid ball of cells, the **morula,** is produced, and as the cells continue to divide, they arrange themselves about a central cavity. This stage, known as the **blastocyst,** can be compared to the blastula of other vertebrates. However, only a group of cells at one pole of the blastocyst, the **inner cell mass,** forms the embryo (Fig. 33.2). The peripheral layer of cells, known as the **trophoblast,** comes in contact with the uterine lining and begins to form a placenta before the embryo itself has developed to any great extent. The value of the precocious development of this layer in a yolkless embryo that is not free to forage for

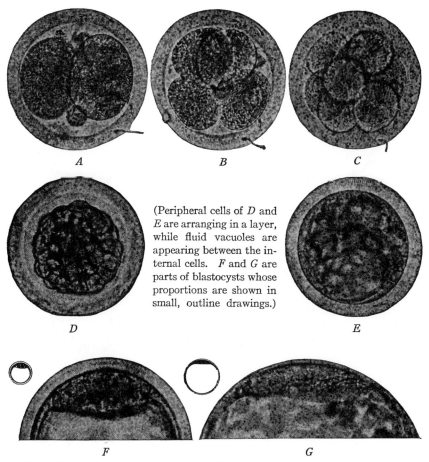

(Peripheral cells of *D* and *E* are arranging in a layer, while fluid vacuoles are appearing between the internal cells. *F* and *G* are parts of blastocysts whose proportions are shown in small, outline drawings.)

Figure 33.1 Photomicrographs of cleavage in mammalian eggs developing in a tissue culture. *A–C*, Two-, four- and eight-celled stages of the monkey; *D*, morula of a rabbit; *E–G*, blastocysts of a rabbit. Observe the thick membrane that surrounds the early stages. Several sperm are entrapped in this in *A* and *B*. (After Lewis, Hartman and Gregory.)

itself is obvious. The trophoblast is comparable to the ectoderm of the chorion, which is the outermost of the extraembryonic membranes of all amniotes. Bushy projections called **villi** develop on its surface and penetrate the uterine lining in most mammals. The placenta is formed by the intimate union of a portion of the chorion and the allantoic blood vessels present with the adjacent uterine lining.

In vertebrates such as the frog (Fig. 6.10), gastrulation involves an inpushing of certain cells of the vegetal hemisphere (invagination), a growth of cells from the animal hemisphere over the vegetal cells (epiboly), and an inturning of certain of these cells (involution). These complex processes are largely bypassed in mammalian development, and gas-

trulation is greatly abbreviated. In primates, cells on the lower part of the inner cell mass simply differentiate as **endoderm,** and a small space, the **yolk sac,** appears in their midst (Fig. 33.2). The dorsal endodermal cells of the yolk sac will contribute to the formation of the gut, but most of the yolk sac is simply an embryonic vestige devoid of yolk. Its presence is a holdover from the reptilian stage in the ancestry of mammals. The rest of the cells of the inner cell mass are prospective ectoderm and mesoderm. An **amniotic cavity** appears among the ectoderm cells at about the same time that the yolk sac develops (Fig. 33.2). The double-layered plate of cells lying between the yolk sac and amniotic cavity is the **embryonic disc.** A **primitive streak,** similar to that of reptiles and birds,

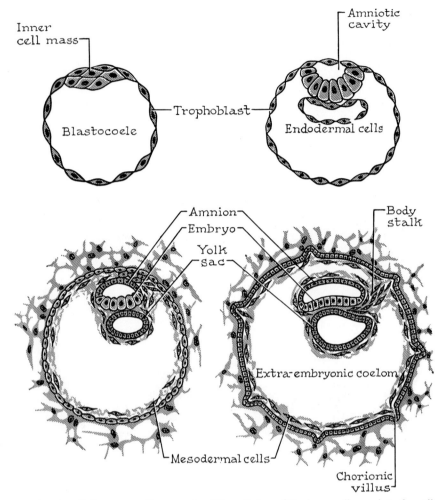

Figure 33.2 A series of diagrams to illustrate the differentiation of the inner cell mass into the yolk sac, amnion and embryonic disc, and to show the migration of the mesoderm. These changes occur in a human embryo during the second week. (Modified after Patten.)

develops upon the upper surface of the embryonic disc and establishes the longitudinal axis of the embryo (Fig. 33.3). Cells destined to become **mesoderm** move inward through, and proliferate from, the primitive streak. They spread out between the endoderm of the yolk sac and the ectoderm that forms the surface of the embryonic disc. Mesodermal proliferation from a primitive streak is similar to the proliferation of prospective mesoderm from the blastopore of a frog, for the primitive streak and the blastopore are homologous. As mesodermal cells continue to spread, they form a layer beneath the trophoblastic ectoderm, and this becomes a fairly typical **chorion** composed of ecto-

derm and mesoderm. Mesodermal cells also surround the endoderm of the yolk sac and the ectoderm lining the amniotic cavity (Fig. 33.2). A group of mesodermal cells known as the **body stalk** extends between the embryonic disc and the chorion, and an endodermal evagination grows into it from the posterior part of the yolk sac (Figs. 33.3 and 33.5). This evagination and the surrounding mesoderm constitute the **allantois.** The part of the yolk sac from which this evagination arises is destined to become the hindgut, so the allantois of mammals has the same relationship to the gut that the allantois has in reptiles and birds. The proximal part of the allantois becomes the urinary bladder.

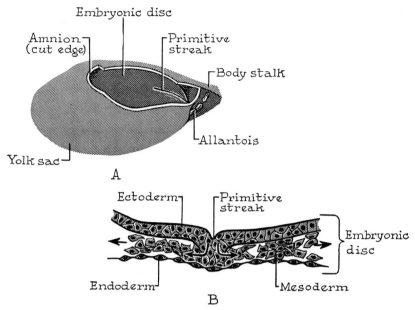

Figure 33.3 Mesoderm formation. *A,* A surface view of the embryonic disc of a 16-day human embryo showing the primitive streak. *B,* A cross section through the primitive streak. Prospective mesoderm, which originally lies on the surface of the embryonic disc, moves in through the primitive streak and spreads out between the ectoderm and endoderm in the manner shown by the arrows. (After Arey.)

33.2

Formation of the Notochord and Neural Tube

All of the extraembryonic membranes characteristic of amniotes (amnion, chorion, allantois and yolk sac) are now present, and the embryo itself is beginning to take shape. A **notochord** develops beneath the surface ectoderm in the longitudinal axis as the primitive streak shortens and retreats toward the posterior end of the embryonic disc. The ec-

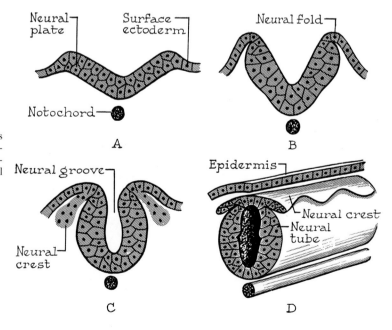

Figure 33.4 A series of cross sectional diagrams through the surface ectoderm to show the formation of the neural tube and neural crest. (After Arey.)

toderm overlying the notochord thickens and becomes a **neural plate.** The lateral edges of the neural plate are elevated as a pair of **neural folds,** which gradually come together (Fig. 33.4). The inner limbs of the folds become the **neural tube,** which differentiates into the spinal cord and brain; the outer limbs, along with the rest of the surface ectoderm, become the epidermis of the skin. Ectodermal cells that are pinched off near the apex of each neural fold form a ridge, the **neural crest,** on each side of the neural tube. The cells of the neural crest become segmentally arranged and many of them differentiate into the afferent neurons of the spinal and cranial nerves. Other neural crest cells migrate and form postganglionic sympathetic fibers (other types of efferent neurons grow out from the neural tube), the medullary cells of the adrenal gland, the neurilemmal sheath cells of peripheral neurons, and certain other structures. Surface ectoderm that does not contribute to the neural tube forms the epidermis, hair and skin glands.

33.3
The Digestive Tract and Its Derivatives

The neural tube and embryo elongate faster than the embryonic disc upon which the embryo is developing. As a result, the embryonic disc buckles at each end. The embryo continues to elongate, and the parts of the embryonic disc that originally lay anterior or posterior to the neural tube fold underneath the embryo (Fig. 33.5). Folds first separate the head and tail from surrounding structures. These folds deepen, and the folding process continues along each side until the embryo is more or less cylindrical in shape and remains connected to its surrounding membranes only by a narrow umbilical cord. The folding process is somewhat analogous to the gradual tightening of a pair of purse strings.

These folding processes gradually pinch off the dorsal part of the yolk sac and convert it into the primitive gut, or **archenteron,** of the

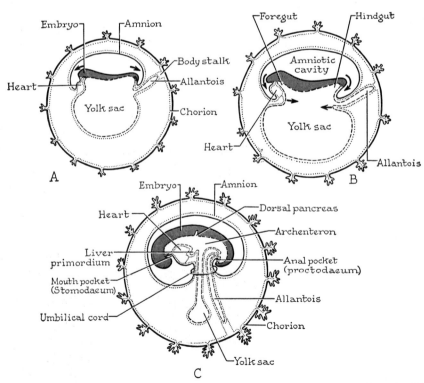

Figure 33.5 A series of diagrams of sagittal sections of embryos of different ages to show the folding processes that separate the embryo from its extraembryonic membranes. Solid lines represent ectoderm, broken lines endoderm, and stippled lines and shaded areas mesoderm. (Modified after Arey.)

embryo. The archenteron remains connected with the yolk sac by a narrow stalk that extends through the umbilical cord. The anterior part of the archenteron, the **foregut,** differentiates into the pharynx, esophagus, stomach and a small portion of the duodenum. The rest of the archenteron, the **hindgut,** forms most of the intestinal region and much of the embryonic cloaca. Only the linings of these organs are endodermal; the connective tissue and muscles in their wall are derived from mesoderm.

The pharyngeal pouches, thyroid gland, trachea and lungs develop as outgrowths from the pharynx, as described in section 27.2. A ventral outgrowth from the posterior end of the foregut differentiates into the liver and much of the pancreas, but part of the pancreas develops as a separate dorsal outgrowth (Figs. 33.5 and 33.6). This explains why the pancreas has two ducts, one entering the intestine with the bile duct and one independently.

The most anterior and posterior ends of the digestive tract develop from ectodermal pockets that invaginate and meet the archenteron. Initially, plates of tissue separate these pockets from the archenteron, but these plates eventually break down. The lining of the mouth, the enamel of the teeth and the secretory cells of the salivary glands are ectodermal in origin. The anterior and intermediate lobes of the pituitary gland develop as an ectodermal evagination from the roof of the mouth pocket, as described in Chapter 32, but the posterior lobe of the pituitary develops as an evagination from the floor of the diencephalic region of the brain. Part of the embryonic cloaca is of ectodermal origin. A cloaca persists in the adults of most vertebrates but is divided in most mammals to form the dorsal rectum and the more ventral

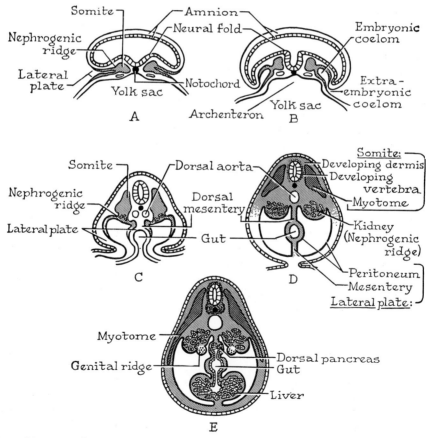

Figure 33.6 Diagrammatic cross sections through vertebrate embryos of different ages. The separation of the embryo from the yolk sac, the differentiation of the mesoderm, and the formation of the liver and dorsal pancreas are shown. (Modified after Patten.)

urogenital passages (part of the urethra in the male; part of the urethra and vagina in the female).

33.4

Differentiation of the Mesoderm

As the mesoderm spreads out from the primitive streak, its lateral portion splits into two layers (Fig. 33.6). This part of the mesoderm is known as the **lateral plate,** and the space between the two layers is the **embryonic coelom.** The embryonic coelom is continuous with the large **extraembryonic coelom,** or chorionic cavity, until the folding processes described above separate the embryo from surrounding structures. The inner layer of the lateral plate mesoderm, which lies next to the archenteron, forms the connective tissue and musculature (visceral muscles) of the digestive tract, the visceral peritoneum and the mesenteries. The outer layer forms the lateral wall of the coelom, that is, the parietal peritoneum, and may contribute to the musculature of the body wall.

Unlike the lateral plate, the mesoderm on each side of the neural tube and notochord becomes segmented and forms a series of paired **somites.** Some of the mesoderm of the somites spreads out beneath the surface ectoderm to form the dermis of the skin, some migrates around the neural tube and notochord and differentiates into the vertebral column and much of the skull, and the rest forms the segmented, embryonic skeletal muscle blocks, or **myotomes.** The myotomes extend out between the surface ectoderm and the lateral plate and develop into most of the musculature of the body wall and appendages (somatic muscles). The segmentation of the muscles is retained in adult fishes, but muscle segmentation is largely lost during the later development of most higher vertebrates.

The resemblance of certain of the embryonic stages of the higher vertebrates to the adults of lower vertebrates, such as we see in the segmentation of the muscles, is regarded as strong evidence for evolution. In the late nineteenth century, Ernst Haeckel postulated that embryos pass through stages during their embryonic development (ontogeny) that resemble the adult stages of their evolutionary ancestors (phylogeny). In other words, "ontogeny recapitulates phylogeny, or the embryo climbs its own family tree." This generalization is no longer taken as literally as Haeckel intended. It is now clear that the embryos of higher vertebrates resemble the *embryos* and not necessarily the adults of lower vertebrates. Early vertebrates evolved a series of developmental stages that resulted in their characteristic organs. Higher vertebrates have certain differences, but these develop by introducing changes in the later stages of development rather than by altering the whole complex and intricately interrelated developmental sequence. Development, therefore, tends to be conservative, and the early embryos of different animals may bear marked resemblances to each other. However, the early development of an embryo may be altered and correlated with special conditions to which the embryo has become adapted. The extraembryonic membranes of mammals, for example, develop in advance of the main body of the embryo, and the placenta is formed very early. This is an adaptation of the embryo to intrauterine life. In reptiles the extraembryonic membranes develop only after the body of the embryo is well established.

A narrow band of mesoderm, known as the **nephrogenic ridge,** lies between the somites and the lateral plate. This part of the mesoderm differentiates into the kidney, as described in section 29.1, and helps to form the gonads.

The entire circulatory system develops from the mesoderm, and its development is rapid in all vertebrates. Transporting vessels are necessary for the embryo to obtain nutrients from the placenta, or yolk, as the case may be. The blood vessels differentiate by the hollowing out and coalescence of cords and knots of mesodermal cells that appear first in the mesodermal layer next to the yolk sac. A pair of vessels that are destined to become the heart develop in the anterior part of the embryonic disc before the neural tube is completely formed (Fig. 33.7). Subsequent foldings that give the embryo its shape carry these vessels beneath the front of the embryo. They fuse to form a single **cardiac tube,** and the cardiac tube differentiates into the series of chambers found in fish hearts (sinus venosus, atrium, ventricle, and conus arteriosus). Since the cardiac tube grows in length faster

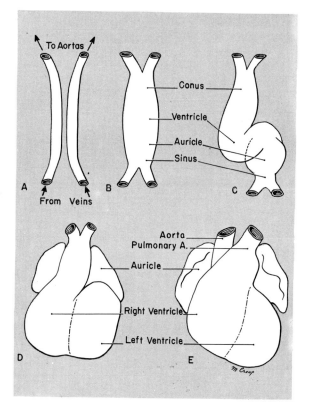

Figure 33.7 Stages in the development of a mammalian heart, seen in ventral view. (From Villee: Biology, 5th ed.)

than the part of the coelom (the pericardial cavity) in which it lies, it folds and forms an S-shaped tube. The atrium, which originally lay posterior to the ventricle, thus comes to lie in front of the ventricle. Gradually, the cardiac tube differentiates into the adult heart. The atrium and ventricle become divided in mammals, the sinus venosus is incorporated into the right atrium, and the conus arteriosus forms part of the pulmonary artery and the arch of the aorta.

A series of paired **aortic arches,** which are similar in arrangement to those of a fish but are not interrupted by capillaries, carry blood from the heart up through the pharyngeal region to the **dorsal aorta** (Fig. 33.8). **Vitelline**

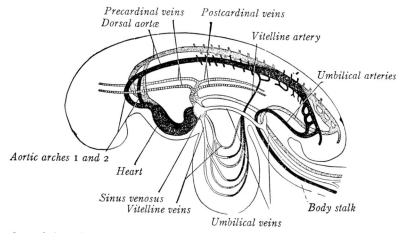

Figure 33.8 Lateral view of the major blood vessels of an early mammalian embryo. (From Arey after Felix.)

arteries extend from the aorta to the yolk, and **umbilical arteries** follow the allantois to the chorion and developing placenta. Veins develop in a similar manner and return blood to the heart from the yolk sac, chorionic villi and the embryo itself. In the early mammalian embryo, the pattern of the veins resembles the pattern seen in fishes. **Cardinal veins** are present and the venae cavae do not develop until later. The pattern of the circulation in a late fetus, and the changes that occur at birth, were considered in sections 28.10 and 28.11.

33.5
Growth of the Embryo

The main morphologic changes in embryonic development take place with surprising speed. A human embryo four weeks old is only 5 mm. long, but it has already developed enough to be recognized as some sort of a vertebrate embryo (Fig. 33.9*A*). The development of all the organ systems is well under way, the heart has begun to beat, limb buds that will differentiate into arms and legs are protruding from the surface, and a small tail is present. Pregnancy may only be suspected at this time. At eight weeks (Fig. 33.9*B*), the embryo can be recognized as human. The face and distinct fingers and toes have developed. The organ systems are approaching their adult condition. Some of the bones are beginning to ossify and taste buds are developing on the tongue. The embryo is arbitrarily called a **fetus** from this age on.

Only relatively small changes occur in the organ systems during the remaining seven months of pregnancy, but a great increase in size takes place. An eight-week fetus has a crown-rump length of 30 mm. At term, its crown-rump length is about 35 cm. Among the morphologic changes that occur during this period are differentiation of the external genitalia, development of body hair, muscularization of the digestive tract, and myelinization of the neurons. Though the infant is well developed at the time of birth, development does not cease. Changes in the organ systems and in the relative size of body parts continue throughout infancy, childhood and adolescence. Human development is not really completed until the late teens.

33.6
Twinning

Many offspring are born at the same time in pigs, rats and a number of other mammals. The number of piglets in a litter, for example, ranges from seven to 23. But many other mammals, including man and the other higher primates, whales and horses, normally have only one offspring at a time. Occasionally, multiple births occur in these mammals. Twins are produced about once in every 86 human births. Approximately three-fourths of these are **dizygotic,** or **fraternal twins.** Two eggs have been ovulated and fertilized at about the same time. Such twins do not resemble each other any more closely than brothers or sisters born at different times, for they have somewhat different genetic constitutions. Fraternal twins occur more frequently in some families than in others, so it is possible that there are certain hereditary tendencies for the maturation and ovulation of more than one ovum during a single menstrual cycle.

More rarely, **monozygotic** or **identical twins** are formed. Only one egg is fertilized, but two embryos develop from it. Identical twins are always of the same sex and resemble each other closely, for they have identical genetic constitutions. Monozygotic twinning may occur in one of several ways. The two blastomeres produced by the first cleavage may separate and each become an embryo, the inner cell mass may subdivide, or two primitive streaks may develop upon a single embryonic disc (Fig. 33.10). Twins have been produced experimentally by the first method in lower vertebrates. This method is a possibility in mammals, but it is not so likely to occur as the others, for the mammalian egg and cleavage stages are surrounded by a strong membrane, the **zona pellucida,** that should prevent the blastomeres from separating (Fig. 33.1). If embryos share the chorion, twinning occurs at the blastocyst stage or later.

A particularly interesting case of twinning is seen in the armadillo. This animal always has quadruplets and the four individuals are always of the same sex. The fact that only one corpus luteum is found in the ovary, which means that only one follicle and egg matured and ovulated, indicates that all are identical twins. When the blastocyst is examined, it is

A

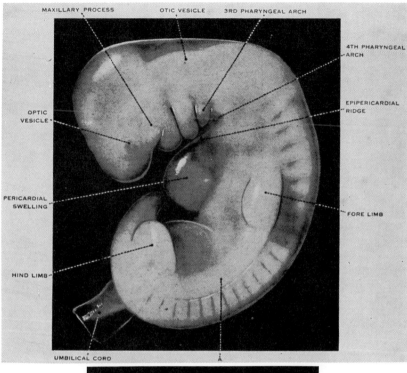

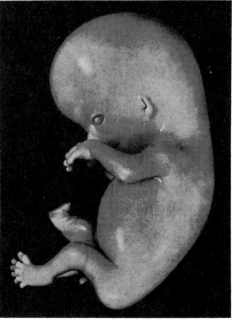

B

Figure 33.9 *A,* Side view of a human embryo about four weeks old; its crown-rump length is 5 mm. *B,* A human fetus about eight weeks old; its crown-rump length is 30 mm. (From Hamilton, Boyd and Mossman: Human Embryology, The Williams & Wilkins Co., Inc.)

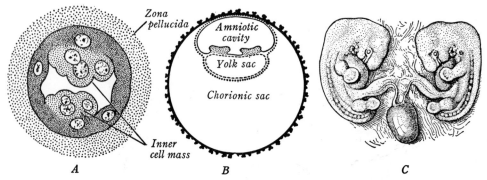

Figure 33.10 Two methods of monozygotic twinning: *A*, by division of inner cell mass; *B*, by the formation of two primitive streaks. In the latter case, the twins would be connected to a single yolk sac, as in *C*. (After Arey.)

discovered that the inner cell mass has subdivided into four parts.

If identical twins are produced by subdivision of the inner cell mass, or by the formation of two primitive streaks, one would expect to find occasional cases in which the separation is incomplete. Though fortunately rare, **conjoined twins** are born from time to time. All degrees of union have been found. Usually such individuals die in infancy, but the most famous pair, Chang and Eng, lived to be 63. Though Chinese, Chang and Eng were born in Siam. They worked for a circus, married and fathered 22 children! Their fame led to the popular term "Siamese twins" for such conjoined twins.

QUESTIONS

1. How has the early development of mammals been modified by the retention of the embryo in a uterus?
2. Compare the formation of endoderm and mesoderm in a mammal and a frog.
3. To what extent does ontogeny recapitulate phylogeny?
4. How does it happen that certain parts of the digestive tract are of ectodermal origin?
5. What structures develop from the somites, the nephrogenic ridge and the lateral plate mesoderm?
6. Describe the pattern of circulation of an early mammalian embryo. How does this resemble and differ from the circulatory pattern of an adult fish?
7. What sort of changes occur in the human fetus after the second month?
8. Distinguish between fraternal and identical twins. How may identical twins be formed?

ANNOTATED REFERENCES

Arey, L. B.: Developmental Anatomy. 7th ed. Philadelphia, W. B. Saunders Co., 1965. A standard text on human development. Morphology is emphasized.

Balinsky, B. I.: An Introduction to Embryology. 2nd ed. Philadelphia, W. B. Saunders Co., 1965. Functional and experimental aspects of embryology are stressed in this excellent text.

Corner, G. W.: Ourselves Unborn. An Embryologist's Essay on Man. New Haven, Yale University Press, 1944. A fascinating account of human development written for the layman by a leading embryologist.

DeBeer, G. R.: Embryos and Ancestors. 3rd ed. London, Oxford University Press, 1958. A careful analysis of evolution and embryology.

Newman, H. H., F. N., Freeman and K. J. Holzinger: Twins, a Study of Heredity and Evolution. Chicago, University of Chicago Press, 1937. An old but classic account of the biology of twinning and the differences between fraternal and identical twins.

Willier, B. H., P. A., Weiss, and V. Hamburger: Analysis of Development. Philadelphia, W. B. Saunders Co., 1955. A very valuable source book on experimental embryology.

Part Four

GENETICS
AND
EVOLUTION

34 PRINCIPLES OF HEREDITY

34.1
History of Genetics

It must have been thousands of years ago when man first made one of the fundamental observations of heredity—that "like tends to beget like." But his curiosity as to why this is true and how it is brought about remained unsatisfied until the beginning of the present century. A number of breeders, such as Kölreuter, who worked with tobacco plants about 1770, crossed different varieties of plants and produced hybrids. Kölreuter recognized that parental characters were transmitted by both the pollen and the ovule. Mendel's careful work with peas revealed the fundamental principles of heredity, but the report of his work, published in 1866, was far ahead of his time. It is clear that his work was known to a number of the leading biologists of the time, such as the botanist Nägeli, but in the absence of our present knowledge of chromosomes and their behavior, its significance was unappreciated.

The chromosomal details of mitosis were described by Eduard Strasburger in 1876. Eduard van Beneden (1887) discovered the process of meiosis and understood its significance. Earlier that same year Weismann had pointed out, simply from theoretical considerations, that the chromosome number in gametes must be half of that in somatic cells. It is conceivable that some brilliant theoretical biologist with these facts at hand might have postulated that, if hereditary factors were units located in the chromosomes, the mating of different parental types would yield offspring in predictable ratios. However, no such mental synthesis was made, and the existence of these defi-

nite ratios of the types of offspring resulting from a given mating remained to be demonstrated experimentally.

In 1900, three different biologists, working independently—de Vries in Holland, Correns in Germany and von Tschermak in Austria—rediscovered the phenomenon of regular, predictable ratios of the types of offspring produced by mating pure-bred parents. They then found Mendel's published report and, realizing his priority in these discoveries, gave him credit for his work by naming two of the fundamental principles of heredity **Mendel's laws.**

With the genetic and cytologic facts at hand, W. S. Sutton and C. E. McClung independently came to the conclusion (1902) that the hereditary factors are located in the chromosomes. They also pointed out that, since there is a much greater number of hereditary factors than of chromosomes, there must be more than one hereditary factor per chromosome. By 1911, T. H. Morgan was able to postulate, from the regularity with which certain characters tended to be inherited together, that the hereditary factors (which he named "genes") were located in the chromosomes in linear order, "like the beads on a string."

34.2
Mendel's Discoveries

Gregor Johann Mendel (1822–1884) was an Austrian abbot who spent some eight years breeding peas in the garden of his monastery at Brünn, now part of Czechoslovakia. He succeeded in reaching an understanding of the basic principles of heredity because (1) he studied the inheritance of single contrasting characters (such as green versus yellow seed color, wrinkled versus smooth seed coat), instead of attempting to study the complete inheritance of each organism; (2) his studies were quantitative; he counted the number of each type of offspring and kept accurate records of his crosses and results; and (3) by design or by good fortune, he chose a plant, and particular characters of that plant, that gave him clear ratios. If he had worked with other plants or with certain other characters of peas, he would have been unable to get these ratios. Now that the principles of heredity have been established, the explanation for these more complicated types of inheritance is clear.

Mendel established pure-breeding strains of peas with contrasting characters — yellow seed coat versus green seed coat, round seeds versus wrinkled ones — and then made crosses of the contrasting varieties. He found that the offspring of a cross of yellow and green all had yellow seed coats; the result was the same whether the male or the female parent had been the yellow one. Thus, the character of one parent can "dominate" over that of the other, but which of the contrasting characters is dominant depends upon the specific trait involved, not upon which parent contributes it. This observation, repeated for several different strains of peas, led Mendel to the generalization — the "law of dominance" — that, when two factors for the alternative expression of a character are brought together in one individual, one may be expressed completely and the other not at all. The character which appears in the first generation is said to be **dominant;** the contrasting character is said to be **recessive.**

Mendel then took the seeds produced by this first generation of the cross (called the **first filial generation,** abbreviated F_1), planted them and had the resulting plants fertilize themselves to produce the second filial generation, the F_2. He found that both the dominant and the recessive characters appeared in this generation, and upon counting the number of each type (Table 34.1) he found that, whatever set of characters he used, the ratio of plants with the dominant character to those with the recessive character was very close to 3:1. From such experiments Mendel concluded that (1) there must be discrete unit factors which determine the inherited characters, (2) these unit factors must exist in pairs, and (3) in the formation of gametes the members of these pairs separate from each other, with the result that each gamete receives only one member of the pair. The unit factor for green seed color is not affected by existing for a generation within a yellow seeded plant (e.g., the F_1 individuals). The two separate during gamete formation and, if a gamete bearing this factor for green seed coat fertilizes another gamete with this factor, the resulting seed has a green color. The generalization known as Mendel's first law, the **law of segregation,** may now be stated as: Genes exist in pairs in individuals, and in the formation of gametes each gene separates or segregates from the other member of the pair and passes into a different gamete, so that each gamete has one, and only one, of each kind of gene.

In other experiments Mendel observed the inheritance of two pairs of contrasting characters in a single cross. He mated a pure-breeding strain with round yellow seeds and one with wrinkled green seeds. The first filial generation all had round yellow seeds, but when these were self-fertilized he found in the F_2 generation all four possible combinations of seed color and shape. When he

Table 34.1 An Abstract of the Data Obtained by Mendel from His Breeding Experiments with Garden Peas

Parental Characters	First Generation	Second Generation	Ratios
Yellow seeds × green seeds	All yellow	6022 yellow: 2001 green	3.01:1
Round seeds × wrinkled seeds	All round	5474 round: 1850 wrinkled	2.96:1
Green pods × yellow pods	All green	428 green: 152 yellow	2.82:1
Long stems × short stems	All long	787 long: 277 short	2.84:1
Axial flowers × terminal flowers	All axial	651 axial: 207 terminal	3.14:1
Inflated pods × constricted pods	All inflated	882 inflated: 299 constricted	2.95:1
Red flowers × white flowers	All red	705 red: 224 white	3.15:1

counted these he found 315 round yellow seeds, 108 round green seeds, 101 wrinkled yellow seeds, and 32 wrinkled green seeds. There is a close approximation of a 3:1 ratio for seed color (416 yellow to 140 green) and for seed shape (423 round to 133 wrinkled). Thus, the inheritance of seed color is independent of the inheritance of seed shape; neither one affects the other. When the two types of traits are considered together, it is clear that there is a ratio of 9 with two dominant traits (yellow and round): 3 with one dominant and one recessive (round and green): 3 with the other dominant and recessive (yellow and wrinkled): 1 with the two recessive traits (green and wrinkled). Mendel's second law, the **law of independent assortment,** may now be given as: The distribution of each pair of genes into gametes is independent of the distribution of any other pair.

34.3
Chromosomal Basis of
the Laws of Heredity

Each cell of every member of a given species of animal or plant contains a definite number of chromosomes; the constancy of the chromosome number is assured by the precise and regular events of mitotic division (p. 36). Many widely different species of animals and plants have the same number of chromosomes. It is not the number of chromosomes, but the nature of the hereditary factors within them, that differentiates species.

The constancy of the chromosome number in successive generations of the same species is assured by the precise separation of the members of the pairs of homologous chromosomes in the meiotic divisions leading to the formation of gametes. The normal number of chromosomes for somatic cells is reconstituted in fertilization, when the egg and sperm nuclei fuse.

The laws of heredity follow directly from the behavior of the chromosomes in mitosis, meiosis and fertilization. Within each chromosome are numerous hereditary factors, the **genes,** each of which controls the inheritance of one or more characteristics. Each gene is located at a particular point, called a **locus** (plural, loci), along the chromosome. Since the genes are located in the chromosomes, and each cell has two of each

kind of chromosome, it follows that each cell has two of each kind of gene. The chromosomes separate in meiosis and recombine in fertilization and so, of course, do the genes within them. We currently believe that the genes are arranged in a linear order within the chromosomes; the **homologous chromosomes** have similar genes arranged in a similar order. When the chromosomes undergo synapsis during meiosis (p. 104) the homologous chromosomes become attached point by point and, presumably, gene by gene.

34.4
Genes and Alleles

Studies of inheritance are possible only when there are two alternate, contrasting conditions, such as Mendel's yellow and green peas or round and wrinkled ones. These contrasting conditions, inherited in such a way that an individual may have one or the other but not both, were originally termed allelomorphic traits or alleles. However, now the terms allele and gene are used more or less interchangeably, both referring to the hereditary factor responsible for a given trait. Thus, curly hair and straight hair are alleles, for a person's hair is one or the other, but curly and blond are not alleles, for hair may be both blond and curly. Used in this sense the term allele emphasizes that there are two or more alternative kinds of genes at a specific locus in a specific chromosome.

Brown and black coat color are allelomorphic traits in guinea pigs. Each body cell of the guinea pig has a pair of chromosomes which contain genes for coat color; since there are two chromosomes, there are two genes per cell. A "pure" black guinea pig (one of a pedigreed strain of black guinea pigs) has two genes for black coat, one in each chromosome, and a "pure" brown guinea pig has two genes for brown coat. The brown gene controls certain chemical reactions which lead to the formation of a brown pigment in the hair cells, whereas the black gene directs the chemical reactions toward the formation of black pigment. In working genetic problems, letters are conventionally used as symbols for the genes. A pair of genes for black pigment is represented as **BB,** and a pair of genes for brown pigment by **bb.** A capital letter is used for one gene and the corresponding lower case letter is used to represent the gene for the contrasting trait, the allele.

34.5

A Monohybrid Cross

The events of a hypothetical mating of a pure-bred brown male guinea pig **(bb)** with a pure black female **(BB)** are given in Figure 34.1. During meiosis in the male the two **bb** genes separate and each sperm receives only one **b** gene. Similarly, during meiosis in the female, the **BB** genes separate and each egg receives only one **B** gene. There is only one type of sperm, those containing a **b** gene, and one type of egg, those with a **B** gene, and their union leads to a single type of individual, **Bb.** Since these individuals have one gene for black color and one gene for brown color, you might guess that the offspring would be dark brown, or gray, or perhaps spotted. However, all the F₁ individuals are just as black as the mother. The black gene is **dominant** to the brown one and produces black coat color even in the presence of the other gene. The brown gene is said to be **recessive** to the black one. By convention, the dominant gene is symbolized by a capital letter and the recessive allele by the corresponding lower case letter. The phenomenon of dominance supplies part of the explanation as to how it is that an offspring may resemble one of its parents much more than the other, despite the fact that both parents make equal contributions to its genetic constitution.

An animal or plant with two genes exactly alike, two blacks **(BB)** or two browns **(bb),** is said to be **homozygous** or "pure" for the character. An organism with one dominant and one recessive gene **(Bb)** is said to be **heterozygous** or "hybrid." Thus, in the mating under consideration the black and brown parents were homozygous, **BB** and **bb,** respectively, and the offspring in the F₁ were all heterozygous, **Bb. Recessive genes** are those which will produce their effect only when homozygous; a **dominant gene** is one which will produce its effect whether it is homozygous or heterozygous.

In the process of gamete formation in these heterozygous black F₁ guinea pigs,

the chromosome containing the **B** gene undergoes synapsis with, and then separates from, the homologous chromosome containing the **b** gene, so that each sperm or egg has a **B** gene or a **b** gene. No sperm or egg is without one or the other and none has both. Since there are two kinds of eggs and two kinds of sperm, the mating of two of these heterozygous black guinea pigs permits four different combinations of eggs and sperm. To see these possible combinations of eggs and sperm it is conventional to arrange them in a Punnett square (Fig. 34.1), devised by the English geneticist, R. C. Punnett. Gametes containing **B** genes and ones containing **b** genes are formed in equal numbers. There is no special attraction or repulsion between an egg and a sperm containing similar genes; an egg containing a **B** gene is just as likely to be fertilized by a

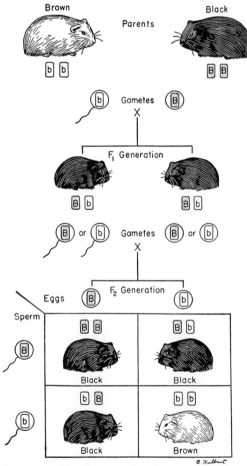

Figure 34.1 An example of a monohybrid cross: the mating of a brown with a black guinea pig. (Villee: Biology, 5th ed.)

B sperm as by a **b** sperm. The four possible combinations occur with equal frequency.

The possible types of eggs are written across the top of the Punnett square and the possible types of sperm are arranged down its left side, then the squares are filled in with the resulting zygote combinations (Fig. 34.1). Three-fourths of the offspring are either **BB** or **Bb,** and consequently have a black coat color, and one-fourth are **bb,** with a brown coat color. This 3:1 ratio is characteristically obtained in the second generation of a **monohybrid cross,** i.e., a mating of two individuals which differ in a single trait governed by a single pair of genes. The genetic mechanism responsible for the 3:1 ratios obtained by Mendel in his pea breeding experiments is now evident.

The appearance of an individual with respect to a certain trait, the end result of the action of the gene, is known as its **phenotype;** the individual's genetic constitution is called its **genotype.** In the F_2 generation of the guinea pig mating, the phenotypic ratio is 3 black : 1 brown; the genotypic ratio is 1 **BB** : 2 **Bb** : 1 **bb.** Guinea pigs which are **BB** and **Bb** have similar phenotypes—both have black coat color—but they have different genotypes, which could be distinguished only by further breeding tests. It is also possible, as we shall see later, for individuals to have similar genotypes but different phenotypes.

34.6
Laws of Probability

It is important to realize that all genetic ratios are expressions of probability, based on the laws of chance or probability; they do not express certainties. One can state, perhaps more exactly, that in the mating of two individuals heterozygous for a given trait there are three chances out of four that any particular offspring will show the dominant trait and one chance out of four that it will show the recessive one. If two heterozygous black guinea pigs are mated and have exactly four offspring there is no guarantee that there will be exactly three black ones and one brown one. All might be black, or all might be brown. Since the probability that each offspring will be black is $3/4$, the probability that all four will be black is the product of the individual probabilities, $3/4 \times 3/4$

$\times 3/4 \times 3/4$ or $81/256$. The probability that all four will be brown is $1/4 \times 1/4 \times 1/4 \times 1/4$ or $1/256$. Any of the combinations of 3 black : 1 brown, 2 black : 2 brown, or 1 black : 3 brown might appear. But if enough similar matings are made to produce a total of 400 offspring, the ratio of black to brown among the offspring will be very close to 300 to 100. The theoretical 3 : 1 ratio is approximated more and more exactly as the total number of individuals increases; this is predicted by the laws of probability and is actually found when genetic tests are made. Each mating, each union of an egg and a sperm, is an **independent event** which is not influenced by the results of previous matings. No matter how many black-coated offspring have been produced by the mating of two heterozygous black ones, the probability that the next offspring to be born will have a brown coat is one chance in four, and the probability that it will have a black coat is three chances in four.

34.7
Test Crosses

In the F_2 generation of a monohybrid cross, one-third of the individuals with the dominant phenotype are homozygous and two-thirds are heterozygous. In the guinea pig mating (Fig. 34.1) the black-coated individuals in the F_2 generation include some with the genotype **BB** and some with the genotype **Bb.** These can be distinguished by a test cross, in which the black-coated guinea pig is mated with a brown-coated one (genotype **bb**). If all of the offspring are black, the parent is probably homozygous (**BB),** but if any of the offspring are brown the black parent is heterozygous (**Bb).**

Test crosses are of obvious importance to the commercial breeder of animals or plants who is trying to establish a strain which will "breed true" for a certain trait. Formerly, farmers and commercial breeders could select plants to be used for seed, or animals to be used as breeding stock, only by their phenotypes. Without some means of differentiating homozygous and heterozygous individuals this method is unsatisfactory, for the heterozygous individuals would bear some offspring with the recessive trait.

In the more modern method, the breeder tests the genotypes of his breeding stock by observing the qualities of their offspring. If the offspring have the traits desired, then these same parents are used for further breeding. Two bulls, for example, may look equally healthy and vigorous, yet one may have daughters with qualities of milk production which are distinctly superior to the daughters of the other bull. By this method, called **progeny selection,** the desirable qualities of a strain of animals can be increased rapidly. One geneticist, for example, by progeny selection over a period of eight years increased the average annual egg production of a flock of hens from 114 to 200.

34.8

Incomplete Dominance

In many different species and for a variety of traits it has been found that one gene is not completely dominant to the other. Heterozygous individuals have a phenotype which can be distinguished from that of the homozygous dominant; it may be intermediate between the phenotypes of the two parental strains. The mating of red shorthorn cattle with white ones yields offspring which have an intermediate, roan-colored coat. The mating of two roan-colored cattle yields offspring in the ratio of 1 red : 2 roan : 1 white; thus the genotypic and phenotypic ratios are the same; each genotype has a recognizably different phenotype. This phenomenon, called **incomplete dominance,** is found with a number of traits in different animals and with some human characteristics. Studies of a number of human diseases inherited by recessive genes — sickle cell anemia, Mediterranean anemia, gout, epilepsy and many others — have shown that the individuals who are heterozygous for the trait have slight but detectable differences from the homozygous normal individual.

34.9

A Dihybrid Cross

The mating of individuals that differ in two traits, called a **dihybrid cross,** follows the same principles as those of the simpler monohybrid cross, but since there are a greater number of types of gametes, the number of different types of zygotes is correspondingly larger.

If two pairs of genes are located in different (nonhomologous) chromosomes, each pair is inherited independently of the other; each pair separates during meiosis independently of the other. Another pair of genes in the guinea pig governs the length of the hair in the coat; the gene for short hair **(S)** is dominant to the gene for long hair **(s).** The genes for hair color and hair length are located in different chromosomes. Each guinea pig has two of each kind of gene; thus the genotype of a homozygous black short-haired animal is **BBSS** and the genotype of a homozygous brown long-haired animal is **bbss.** The black short-haired animal produces only one kind of gamete, for all of them are **BS.** Similarly, the brown long-haired animals produce only **bs** eggs or sperm.

The mating of a black short-haired animal with a brown long-haired one produces offspring all of which have short black hair; they are heterozygous for both hair length and hair color genes and have the genotype **BbSs.** Each of the F_1 individuals will produce four kinds of gametes, **BS, Bs, bS** and **bs,** and there will be equal numbers of each type. When two of these F_1 individuals are mated, there will be 16 possible combinations in the F_2 (Fig. 34.2). There are nine chances out of 16 that any particular offspring will have black short hair, three chances out of 16 that it will have black long hair, three chances out of 16 that it will have brown short hair, and one chance in 16 that it will have brown long hair. The genetic mechanism underlying Mendel's second law, the law of independent assortment, should now be clear.

The results of crosses with three or more different pairs of genes may be predicted by similar reasoning. The F_1 individuals of a trihybrid cross will produce eight different kinds of gametes in equal numbers, and the random union of eight types of sperm and eight types of eggs gives 64 different combinations of genes in the F_2 generation. In the pea plant studied by Mendel, the crossing of a plant with round yellow seeds and long stems **(YYRRLL)** and a plant with wrinkled green seeds and short stems **(yyrrll)** yields F_1 individuals with the genotype **YyRrLl,** all with round yellow seeds and long stems. When these plants are self-fertilized, offspring are produced in the ratio of 27 yellow, round, long : 9 yellow, round, short : 9 yellow, wrinkled, long : 9 green, round, long : 3 yellow, wrinkled, short : 3 green, round,

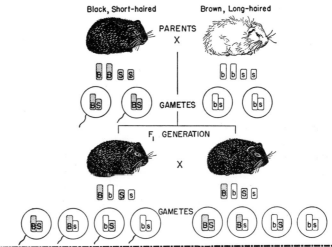

Black, Short-haired   Brown, Long-haired

PARENTS X

GAMETES

F₁ GENERATION

X

GAMETES

Figure 34.2 An example of a dihybrid cross: the mating of a black, short-haired guinea pig and a brown, long-haired one, illustrating independent assortment. (Villee: Biology, 5th ed.)

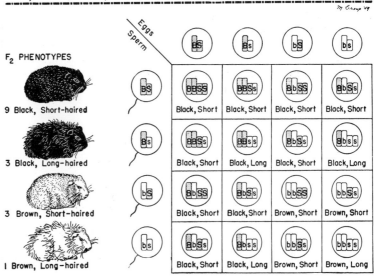

F₂ PHENOTYPES

9 Black, Short-haired

3 Black, Long-haired

3 Brown, Short-haired

1 Brown, Long-haired

short : 3 green, wrinkled, long : 1 green, wrinkled, short.

Set up a Punnett square with the eight types of eggs across the top and the eight types of sperm down the sides. Fill in the 64 squares with the appropriate F₂ genotypes and add up the phenotypes. Compare the phenotypic ratio you obtain with the one given here.

34.10
Deducing Genotypes

The science of genetics resembles mathematics in that when one has a firm grasp of the few basic principles involved he can solve a wide variety of problems. These basic principles include: (1) Inheritance is

biparental; both parents contribute to the genetic constitution of the offspring. (2) Genes are not altered by existing together in a heterozygote. (3) Each individual has two of each kind of gene, but each gamete has only one of each kind. (4) Two pairs of genes located in different chromosomes are inherited independently. (5) Gametes unite at random; there is neither attraction nor repulsion between an egg and a sperm containing identical genes.

In working genetics problems, it is helpful to use the following procedure:

1. Write down the symbols used for each pair of genes.

2. Determine the genotypes of the parents, deducing them from the phenotypes of the parents and, if necessary, from the phenotypes of the offspring.

3. Derive all of the possible types of gametes each parent would produce.

4. Prepare the appropriate Punnett square and write the possible types of eggs across its top and the types of sperm along its side.

5. Fill in the squares with the appropriate genotypes and read off the genotypic and phenotypic ratios of the offspring.

As an example of the method of solving a problem in genetics, let us consider the following: The length of fur in cats is an inherited trait; the gene for long hair (**1**), as in Persian cats, is recessive to the gene for short hair (**L**) of the common tabby cat. Let us suppose that a short-haired male is bred to three different females, two of which, A and C, are short-haired and one, B, is long-haired (Fig. 34.3). Cat A gives birth to a short-haired kitten, but cats B and C each produce a long-haired kitten. What offspring could be expected from further mating of this male with these three females?

Since the long-haired trait is recessive we know that all the long-haired cats must be homozygous. We can deduce, then, that cat B and the kittens produced by cats B and C have the genotype **ll**. All the short-haired cats have at least one **L** gene. The fact that any of the offspring of the male cat has long hair proves that he is heterozygous, with the genotype **Ll**. The kitten produced by cat B received one **l** gene from its mother but must have received the other from its father. The fact that cat C gave birth to a long-haired kitten proves that she, too, is heterozygous, and has the genotype **Ll**. It is impossible to decide, from the data at hand, whether the short-haired cat A is homozygous **LL** or heterozygous **Ll**. A test cross with a long-haired male would be helpful in deciding this. Further mating of the short-haired male with cat B would give half long-haired and half short-haired kittens, whereas further mating of the short-haired male with cat C would give three times as many short-haired kittens as long-haired ones.

Figure 34.3 An example of problem-solving in genetics: deducing parental genotypes from the phenotypes of the offspring. See text for discussion.

34.11

The Genetic Determination of Sex

The sex of an organism is a genetically determined trait. There is an exception to the general rule that all homologous pairs of chromosomes are identical in size and shape: the so-called **sex chromosomes.** In one sex of each species of animals there is either an unpaired chromosome or an odd pair of chromosomes, the two members of which differ in size and shape. In most species the females have two identical chromosomes, called X chromosomes, and males have either a single X chromosome or one X plus a generally somewhat smaller one called the Y chromosome. The existence of these un-

paired chromosomes was discovered by C. E. McClung, in 1902, when he was studying the process of meiosis in the testes of grasshoppers. He made the shrewd guess that these might play some role in sex determination. In a few animals, the butterflies and birds, the system is reversed and the male has two X chromosomes and the female one X and one Y. The Y chromosome usually contains few or no genes and in most species the X and Y chromosomes are distinguished by their different size and shape. Yet in meiosis the X and Y chromosomes act like homologous chromosomes; they undergo synapsis, separate, pass to opposite poles, and become incorporated into different gametes (Fig. 34.4). Human beings have 23 pairs of chromosomes; males have 22 pairs

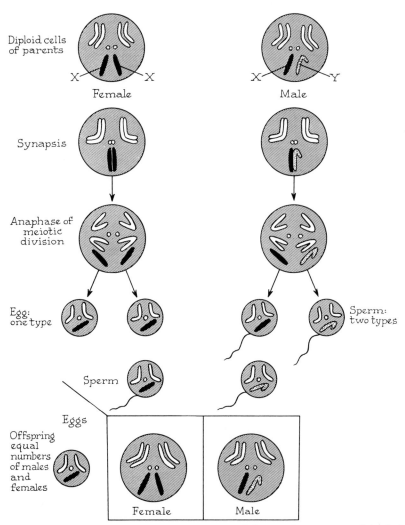

Figure 34.4 Diagram illustrating the transmission of the sex chromosomes of the fruit fly.

of ordinary chromosomes, called **autosomes,** one X and one Y chromosome, whereas females have 22 pairs of autosomes and two X chromosomes.

The experiments of C. B. Bridges revealed that the sex of fruit flies. *Drosophila,* is determined by the ratio of the number of X chromosomes to the number of haploid sets of autosomes. Males have one X and two haploid sets of autosomes, a ratio of 1:2, or 0.5. Females have two X and two haploid sets of autosomes, a ratio of 2:2, or 1.0. By genetic techniques possible in fruit flies, Bridges established abnormal flies with one X and three sets of autosomes. These flies, with a ratio of 0.33, had all their male characteristics exaggerated; Bridges called them "supermales." Other abnormal individuals, with three X and two sets of autosomes were "superfemales," with all the female characteristics exaggerated. Individuals with two X chromosomes and three sets of autosomes, a ratio of 0.67, were intersexes, with characters intermediate between those of normal males and normal females. All of these unusual flies, supermales, superfemales and intersexes, were sterile.

In man, and perhaps in other mammals, maleness is determined in large part by the presence of the Y chromosome. An individual with an XXY constitution is a nearly normal male in external appearance, though with underdeveloped gonads (Klinefelter's syndrome). An individual with one X but no Y chromosome has the appearance of an immature female (Turner's syndrome). It is possible to determine the "nuclear sex" of an individual by careful microscopic examination of some of his cells. Individuals with two X chromosomes have a "chromatin spot" at the edge of the nucleus which is evident in cells from the skin or from the mucosal lining of the mouth (Fig. 34.5). Cells from male individuals with only one X chromosome do not show a chromatin spot.

The chromatin spot represents one of the two X chromosomes, which becomes condensed and dark-staining. The other X chromosome, like the autosomes, is a fully extended thread not evident by light microscopy. Mary Lyon has suggested that only one of the two X chromosomes in the female is active; the condensed chromatin spot represents the inactive X chromosome. Which of the two becomes inactive in any given cell is a matter of chance; thus the cells in the body of a female are of two types, according to which X chromosome is inactive. Since the two X chromosomes may have different genetic complements, the cells may differ in the effective genes present. Mice have several genes for coat color in the X chromosome, and females heterozygous for two such genes may show patches of one coat color in the midst of areas of the other, a phenomenon termed variegation. The inactivation of one X chromosome apparently occurs early in embryonic development and thereafter all the progeny of that cell have the same inactive X chromosome. Although one X chromosome appears to be inactive, there are marked abnormalities of development when one X chromosome is completely missing from the chromosomal complement of the cell, as in the XO condition of Turner's syndrome.

All the eggs produced by XX females have one X chromosome. Half of the sperm produced by XY males contain an X chromosome and half contain a Y chromosome.

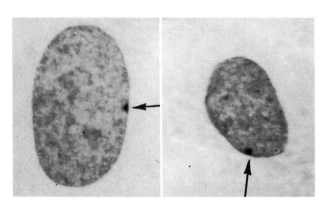

Figure 34.5 Sex chromatin in human fibroblasts cultured from skin of a female. The chromatin spot at the periphery of each nucleus is indicated by the arrow. (Feulgen, × 2200. Courtesy Dr. Ursula Mittwoch, Galton Laboratory, University College, London.) (Villee: Biology, 5th ed.)

The fertilization of an X-bearing egg by an X-bearing sperm results in an XX, or female, zygote, and the fertilization of an X-bearing egg by a Y-bearing sperm results in an XY, or male, zygote. Since there are equal numbers of X- and Y-bearing sperm, there are equal numbers of male and female offspring. In human beings, there are approximately 107 males born for every 100 females, and the ratio at conception is said to be even higher, about 114 males to 100 females. One possible explanation of the numerical discrepancy is that the Y chromosome is smaller than the X chromosome, and a sperm containing a Y chromosome, being a little lighter and perhaps able to swim a little faster than a sperm containing an X chromosome, would win the race to the egg slightly more than half of the time. Both during the period of intrauterine development and after birth, the death rate among males is slightly greater than that among females, so that by the age of 10 or 12 there are equal numbers of males and females. In later life there are more females than males in each age group.

34.12
Sex-linked Characteristics

The X chromosome contains many genes, and the traits controlled by these genes are said to be **sex-linked,** because their inheritance is linked with the inheritance of sex. The Y chromosome contains very few genes, so that the somatic cells of an XY male contain only one of each kind of gene in the X chromosome instead of two of each kind as in XX females. A male receives his single X chromosome, and thus all of his genes for sex-linked traits, from his mother. Females receive one X from the mother and one from the father. In writing the genotype of a sex-linked trait it is customary to write that of the male with the letter for the gene in the X chromosome plus the letter Y for the Y chromosome. Thus AY would represent the genotype of a male with a dominant gene for trait "A" in his X chromosome.

The phenomenon of sex-linked traits was discovered by T. H. Morgan and C. B. Bridges in the fruit fly, *Drosophila*. These flies normally have eyes with a dark red

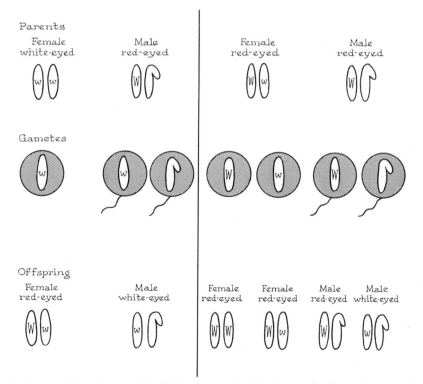

Figure 34.6 Diagram illustrating sex-linked inheritance, the inheritance of red vs. white eye color in fruit flies. See text for discussion.

color, but Morgan and Bridges discovered a strain with white eyes. The gene for white eye, **w,** proved to be recessive to the gene for red eye, **W,** but in certain types of crosses the male offspring had eyes of one color and the female offspring had eyes of the other color. Morgan reasoned that the peculiarities of inheritance could be explained if the genes for eye color were located in the X chromosome; later work proved the correctness of this guess. Crossing a homozygous red-eyed female with a white-eyed male (**WW** × **wY**) produces offspring all of which have red eyes (**Ww** females and **WY** males). But crossing a homozygous white-eyed female with a red-eyed male (**ww** × **WY**) yields red-eyed females and white-eyed males (**Ww** and **wY**) (Fig. 34.6).

In man, **hemophilia** (bleeder's disease) and **color blindness** are sex-linked traits. About four men in every hundred are color-blind, but somewhat less than one per cent of all women are color-blind. Only one gene for color-blindness produces the trait in males, but two such genes (the trait is recessive) are necessary to produce a color-blind female.

Not all the characters which differ in the two sexes are sex-linked. Some, the **sex-influenced traits,** are inherited by genes located in autosomes rather than X chromosomes, but the expression of the trait, the action of the gene which produces the phenotype, is altered by the sex of the animal, presumably by the action of one of the sex hormones. The presence or absence of horns in sheep, mahogany-and-white spotted coat versus red-and-white spotted coat in Ayrshire cattle, and pattern baldness in man are examples of such sex-influenced traits.

34.13
Linkage and Crossing Over

In the discussion of Mendel's law of independent assortment, we stressed the fact that this law is valid only for two pairs of genes located in different, nonhomologous chromosomes. The ratio of 9:3:3:1 is obtained in the F_2 generation of a dihybrid cross only if the pairs of genes are located in different chromosomes. Since there are many hundreds of inherited traits and a very limited number of pairs of chromosomes (23 in

man, four in the fruit fly), it is obvious that each chromosome must contain many genes. All the genes located in the same chromosome tend to be inherited as a group and are said to be **linked.** In meiosis the members of the pairs of homologous chromosomes separate as units and go to opposite poles. Hence, all the genes lying in one chromosome go to one pole and become incorporated into one gamete, and all the genes in the other member of the homologous pair go to the opposite pole and become incorporated in another gamete.

The linkage between the genes in a given chromosome is usually not complete. During the process of synapsis, when the homologous chromosomes are twisted around one another and attached point by point, whole segments of chromosomal material together with the genes located within that part of the chromosome may be exchanged. The exact mechanism of this exchange is still unknown, but it appears to occur at random along the length of the chromosome. The chance that an exchange of segments will occur between the loci of any two genes in a chromosome depends on the distance between the loci: the greater the distance, the greater the opportunity for exchange. The exchange of segments between homologous chromosomes, called **crossing over,** makes possible new combinations of linked genes. Evidence from genetic experiments indicates that crossing over occurs when the pairs of homologous chromosomes have doubled to form a total of four strands. Crossing over occurs as though two of the four strands break and then heal together after an exchange of segments has occurred (Fig. 34.7).

The genes for plant size and fruit shape in tomatoes are located in the same chromosome and therefore are linked; they tend to be inherited together. The gene for tall plants (**T**) is dominant to dwarf (**t**) and the gene for spherical fruit (**S**) is dominant to the one for pear-shaped fruit (**s**). The mating of a homozygous **TTSS** plant with a homozygous **ttss** plant yields an F_1 generation all of which are **TtSs,** tall plants with spherical fruit (Fig. 34.8). So far, there appears to be no difference from the ordinary dihybrid cross in which the genes are located in different chromosomes. The difference becomes apparent, however, when one of these **TtSs** plants is crossed to a homozygous

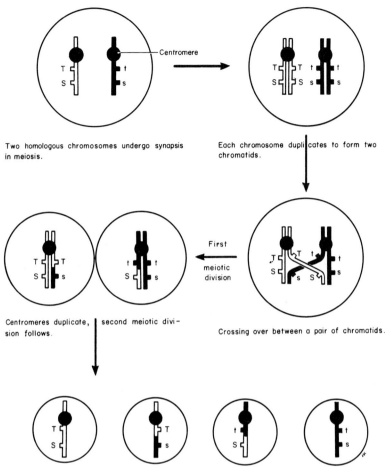

Two homologous chromosomes undergo synapsis in meiosis.

Each chromosome duplicates to form two chromatids.

First meiotic division

Centromeres duplicate, second meiotic division follows.

Crossing over between a pair of chromatids.

Four haploid gametes produced; here two crossover and two noncrossover gametes.

Figure 34.7 Diagram illustrating crossing over, the exchange of segments between chromatids of homologous chromosomes. Crossing over permits recombination of genes (e.g., tS and Ts); the farther apart genes are on a chromosome, the greater is the probability that crossing over between them will occur. (Villee: Biology, 5th ed.)

recessive one, **ttss.** If the two pairs of genes were located in different chromosomes, the four classes of offspring—tall, spherical; dwarf, spherical; tall, pear; and dwarf, pear—would be found in equal numbers. If the two pairs of genes were completely linked, that is, if no crossing over occurred between them, only two classes, tall plants with spherical fruit and dwarf plants with pear-shaped fruit, would be found and these two classes would occur in equal numbers. When the cross is actually made, most of the offspring are either tall plants with spherical fruit or dwarf plants with pear-shaped fruit (the noncrossovers) and only a few are either tall plants with pear-shaped fruit or dwarf plants with spherical fruit (the crossovers). Crossing over between these two pairs of genes occurs, on the average, in 20 per cent of the chro-

mosomes; the offspring are found in the ratio of 40 tall plants with spherical fruit: 40 dwarf plants with pear-shaped fruit: 10 tall plants with pear-shaped fruit: 10 dwarf plants with spherical fruit. The distance between two genes in a chromosome is measured in units of the percentage of crossing over that occurs between them; thus **T** and **S** are said to be 20 units apart on the chromosome.

The facts of crossing over provide proof that the genes lie in a linear order in the chromosomes. If three genes, A, B and C, lie in the same chromosome and tests show that crossing over between A and B occurs 5 per cent of the time (A and B are five units apart) and crossing over between B and C occurs 3 per cent of the time (B and C are three units apart), the percentage of crossing

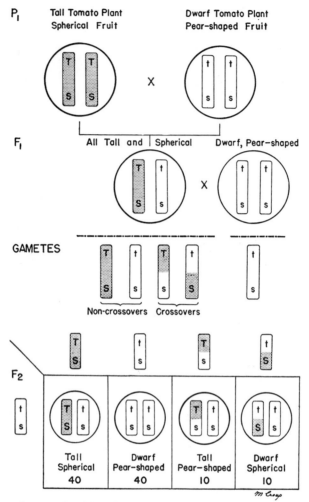

Figure 34.8 Diagram of a cross involving linkage and crossing over. The genes for tall vs. dwarf plants and spherical vs. pear-shaped fruits in tomatoes are linked; they are located in the same chromosome. (Villee: Biology, 5th ed.)

over between A and C is found to be either 8 per cent or 2 per cent. If it is 8 per cent, C lies to the right of B and the order is:

$$\overset{8}{\overbrace{\underset{\underset{5\quad\quad3}{}}{A\quad B\quad C}}}.$$ If A and C are two units apart,

then C lies between A and B and the order is: $\overset{5}{\overbrace{\underset{\underset{2\quad\quad3}{}}{A\quad C\quad B}}}$. In all such tests, the percentage of crossing over between the first and third genes is either the sum or the difference between the percentages of crossing over of the first and second, and the second and third. These facts are best explained by the assumption that the genes lie in a linear order in the chromosome.

Since crossing over occurs at random, more than one crossover may occur in a single chromosome at a given time. One can observe among the offspring only the frequency of recombination of characters, not the actual frequency of crossovers. The frequency of crossing over will be somewhat larger than the observed frequency of recombination because of the simultaneous occurrence of two crossovers between two particular genes, which leads to the reconstitution of the original combination of genes. (Fig. 34.9).

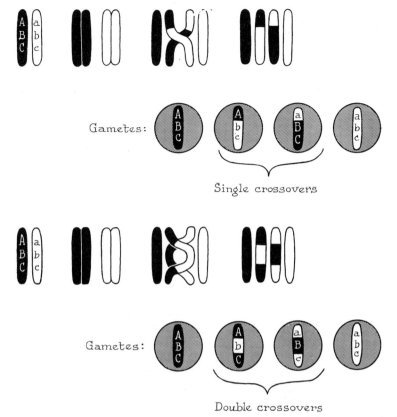

Figure 34.9 Diagram illustrating crossing over, the exchange of segments of chromosomes during synapsis. See text for discussion.

34.14
Chromosome Maps

All the genes in a particular chromosome constitute a **linkage group.** In all the species tested the number of linkage groups determined by genetic tests and the number of pairs of chromosomes observed under the microscope are the same. This is another bit of evidence that the genes are located in the chromosomes and not elsewhere within the cell. The genes which make up a linkage group remain constant from generation to generation and are altered only by some major change in chromosome morphology such as a **translocation** (p. 63), in which a piece of one chromosome breaks off and becomes attached to a different, nonhomologous chromosome.

In the species whose inheritance has been studied most extensively, fruit flies, corn and mice, the data on crossing over have been assembled, and chromosome maps, showing the relative location of the genes within a given chromosome, have been made (Fig. 34.10). The only human chromosome which has been even partially mapped is the X chromosome.

34.15
The Interactions of Genes

The relationship between the genes and their phenotypes discussed so far is simple and clear: each gene produces a single trait. Genetic research with many different kinds of animals and plants has revealed that the relationship between gene and trait may be quite complex. Several pairs of genes may interact to affect the production of a single trait; one pair of genes may inhibit or reverse the effect of another pair; or a given gene may produce different effects when

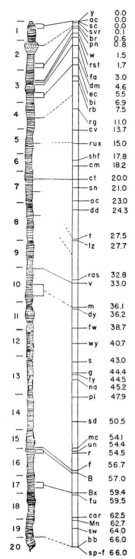

1	y	0.0
	ac	0.0
	sc	0.0
	svr	0.1
	br	0.6
	pn	0.8
2	w	1.5
	rst	1.7
3	fa	3.0
	dm	4.6
	ec	5.5
	bi	6.9
4	rb	7.5
	rg	11.0
	cv	13.7
5	rux	15.0
6	shf	17.8
	cm	18.2
7	ct	20.0
	sn	21.0
	oc	23.0
	dd	24.3
8		
	t	27.5
9	lz	27.7
10	ras	32.8
	v	33.0
11	m	36.1
	dy	36.2
	fw	38.7
12	wy	40.7
	s	43.0
13	g	44.4
	ty	44.5
	na	45.2
	pl	47.9
14		
	sd	50.5
15	mc	54.1
	un	54.4
	r	54.5
16	f	56.7
17	B	57.0
	Bx	59.4
18	fu	59.5
	car	62.5
19	Mn	62.7
	sw	64.0
	bb	66.0
20	sp-f	66.0

Figure 34.10 Diagram of the X chromosome of a fruit fly as seen in a cell of the salivary gland together with a map of the loci of the genes located in the X chromosome, with the distances between them as determined by frequency of crossing over. (Hunter and Hunter: College Zoology.)

the environment is altered in some way. The genes are inherited as units but may interact with one another in some complex fashion to produce the trait.

Complementary Genes. Two independent pairs of genes which interact to produce a trait in such a way that neither dominant can produce its effect unless the other is present too are called **complementary genes.** The presence of at least one dominant gene from each pair produces one character;

the alternative condition results from the absence of either dominant or of both dominants.

Several different varieties of sweet peas with white flowers are known, and the mating of most white-flowered plants produces only white-flowered offspring. However, when plants from two particular white-flowered varieties were crossed, all the offspring had purple flowers! When two of these purple F_1 plants were crossed, or when they were self-fertilized, an F_2 generation was produced in the ratio of 9 purple to 7 white (Fig. 34.11). Subsequent analysis has shown that two pairs of genes located in different chromosomes are involved; one **(C)** regulates some essential step in the production of a raw material, and the other **(E)** controls the formation of an enzyme which converts the raw material into purple pigment. The homozygous recessive **cc** is unable to synthesize the raw material, and the homozygous recessive **ee** lacks the enzyme to convert the raw material into purple pigment. One of the white-flowered varieties was genotypically **ccEE** — lacked the gene for the synthesis of raw material — and the other was **CCee,** without the gene for the enzyme required for pigment synthesis. Crossing **CCee** and **ccEE** produces an F_1 generation all of which are **CcEe** and have purple flowers because they have both raw material and enzyme for the synthesis of the pigment. A pure-breeding variety of purple-flowered sweet peas could be established by self-fertilization of a plant with the genotype **CCEE.**

Supplementary Genes. The term **supplementary genes** is applied to two independent pairs of genes which interact in the production of a trait in such a way that one dominant will produce its effect whether or not the second is present, but the second gene can produce its effect only in the presence of the first. In guinea pigs, in addition to the pair of genes for black versus brown coat color (**B** and **b**), the gene **C** controls the production of an enzyme which converts a colorless precursor into the pigment melanin and, hence, is required for the production of any pigment at all in the coat. The homozygous recessive, **cc,** lacks the enzyme, no melanin is produced and the animal is a white-coated, pink-eyed **albino,** no matter what combination of **B** and **b** genes may be present. The eyes have no pigment in the

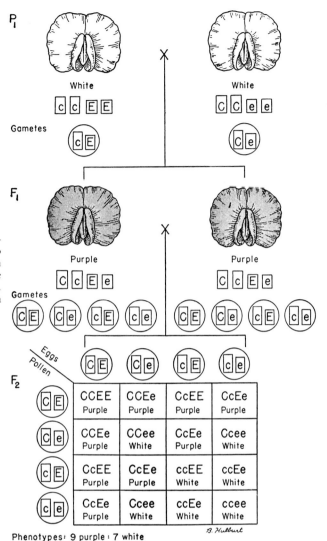

Figure 34.11 Diagram of a cross illustrating the action of complementary genes, the two pairs of genes which regulate flower color in sweet peas. At least one C gene and one E gene must be present to produce a colored flower. The absence of either one or both results in a white flower. (Villee: Biology, 5th ed.)

iris and the pink color results from the color of the blood in the tissues of the eye. The mating of an albino, **ccBB,** with a brown guinea pig, **CCbb,** produces offspring all of which are genotypically **CcBb** and have black-colored coats! When two of these F_1 black guinea pigs are mated, offspring appear in the F_2 in the ratio of 9 black : 3 brown : 4 albino. Make a Punnett square to prove this.

Some combination of complementary and supplementary genes may be involved in the inheritance of a single trait. The dominant genes **C** and **R** are both necessary for the production of red kernels in maize, and the absence of either dominant results in white-colored kernels. There is, in addition, a **P** gene which produces purple-colored kernels if both **C** and **R** genes are present. The **P** gene is supplementary to the other two pairs of genes and **C** and **R** are complementary.

The coat color of Duroc-Jersey pigs represents a slightly different type of gene interaction. Two independent pairs of genes (**R-r** and **S-s**) regulate coat color; at least one dominant of each pair must be present to give the full red-colored coat. Partial color, sandy, results when only one type of dominant is present, and an animal which is homozygous for both recessive (**rrss**) has a white-colored coat. The mating of two

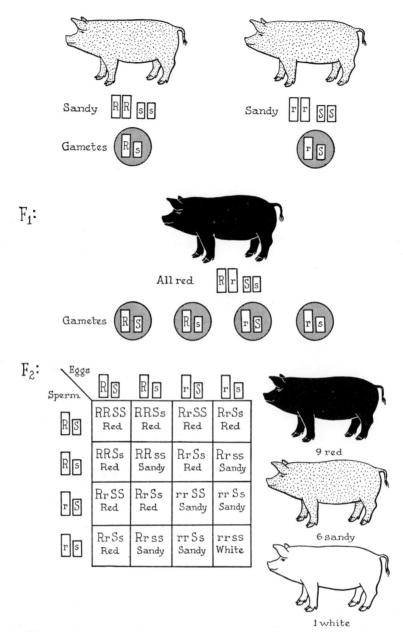

Figure 34.12 Diagram of the mode of inheritance of coat color in Duroc-Jersey pigs, illustrating inheritance by "mutually supplementary" genes.

different strains of sandy-colored pigs, **RRss × rrSS,** yields offspring all of which are red, and the mating of two of these red F_1 individuals produces an F_2 generation in the ratio of 9 red : 6 sandy : 1 white (Fig. 34.12). Genes which interact in this fashion have been termed "mutually supplementary."

The inheritance of comb type in poultry provides an interesting example of genic interaction. Leghorns have single combs,

Wyandottes have rose combs, and Brahmas have pea combs (Fig. 34.13). Each of these types is true breeding. Suitable crosses demonstrate that the gene for rose comb **(R)** is dominant to single **(r)** and that the gene for pea comb **(P)** is also dominant to its allele **(p)** for single comb. However, when a pea-combed fowl is mated with a rose-combed one, all of the offspring have a different type of comb, resembling half of

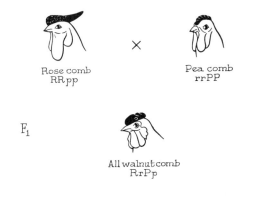

F₁

34.16
Polygenic Inheritance

Many human characteristics, height, body form, intelligence and skin color, and many commercially important characters of animals and plants, such as milk production in cows, egg production in hens, the size of fruits, and the like, are not separable into distinct alternate classes and are not inherited by single pairs of genes. Nonetheless these traits are governed by genetic factors; there are several, perhaps many, different pairs of genes which affect the same characteristic. The term **polygenic inheritance,** or multiple factor inheritance, is applied to two or more independent pairs of genes which affect the same character in the same way and in an additive fashion. When two varieties which differ in some trait controlled by polygenes are crossed, the F_1 are very similar to one another and are usually intermediate in the expression of this character between the two parental types. Crossing two F_1 individuals yields a widely variable F_2 generation, with a few members resembling one grandparent, a few resembling the other grandparent, and the rest showing a range of conditions intermediate between the two.

The inheritance of human skin color was carefully investigated by C. B. Davenport in Jamaica. He concluded that the inheritance of skin color in man is controlled by two pairs of genes, **A-a** and **B-b,** inherited independently. The genes for dark pigmentation, **A** and **B,** are incompletely dominant, and the darkness of the skin color is proportional to the sum of the dominant genes present. Thus, a full Negro has four dominant genes, **AABB,** and a white person has four recessive genes, **aabb.** The F_1 offspring of a mating of white and Negro are all **AaBb,** with two dominant genes and a skin color (mulatto) intermediate between white and Negro. The mating of two such mulattoes produces offspring with skin colors ranging from full Negro to white (Table 34.2). A mulatto with the genotype **AaBb** produces four kinds of eggs or sperm with respect to the genes for skin color: **AB, aB, Ab** and **ab.** From a Punnett square for the mating of two doubly heterozygous mulattoes **(AaBb)** it will be evident that there are 16 possible zygote combinations: one with four dominants (black), four with three dominants (dark brown skin), six with two dominants (mulatto),

The F₂ Punnett square:

	RP	Rp	rP	rp
RP	RRPP Walnut	RRPp Walnut	RrPP Walnut	RrPp Walnut
Rp	RRPp Walnut	RRpp Rose	RrPp Walnut	Rrpp Rose
rP	RrPP Walnut	RrPp Walnut	rrPP Pea	rrPp Pea
rp	RrPp Walnut	Rrpp Rose	rrPp Pea	rrpp Single

9 walnut

3 rose

3 pea

1 single

Figure 34.13 Diagram of the inheritance of comb types in chickens. See text for discussion.

a shelled walnut and called walnut. When two of these walnut-combed F_1 individuals are mated, offspring appear in the ratio of 9 walnut : 3 pea : 3 rose : 1 single. We can deduce from this that the genotype of a single-combed fowl must be **rrpp;** a pea-combed fowl is either **PPrr** or **Pprr;** a rose-combed fowl is either **ppRR** or **ppRr,** and a walnut comb develops in animals with at least one **P** and one **R** gene. Thus, the genotypes **PPRR, PpRR, PPRr** and **PpRr** all yield walnut combs. Certain Malay varieties of chicken have walnut combs.

It is clear that there is nothing unusual about the method of inheritance of any of these genes; the phenotypic ratios observed are simply the result of some variation in the interaction of the genes in the production of the phenotype.

Table 34.2   Polygenic Inheritance of Skin Color in Man

Parents		AaBb (Mulatto)	AaBb (Mulatto)
Gametes . . . . .AB Ab aB ab			AB Ab aB ab

Offspring:

 1 with 4 dominants – AABB – phenotypically Negro
 4 with 3 dominants – 2 AaBB and 2 AABb – phenotypically "dark"
 6 with 2 dominants – 4 AaBb, 1 AAbb, 1 aaBB – phenotypically mulatto
 4 with 1 dominant – 2 Aabb, 2 aaBb – phenotypically "light"
 1 with no dominants – aabb – phenotypically white

four with one dominant (light brown skin) and one with no dominants (white skin). The genes **A** and **B** produce about the same amount of pigmentation and the genotypes **AaBb, AAbb** and **aaBB** produce the same phenotype, mulatto skin color.

This example of polygenic inheritance is fairly simple, for only two pairs of genes appear to be involved. With a larger number of pairs of genes, perhaps 10 or more, there are so many classes and the differences between them are so slight that the classes are not distinguishable; a continuous series is obtained.

The inheritance of human stature is governed by a large number of pairs of genes, with shortness dominant to tallness. Since height is affected not only by these genes but also by a variety of environmental agents, there are adults of every height from perhaps 55 inches (140 cm.) up to 84 inches (203 cm.). If we measure the height of 1083 adult men selected at random and draw a graph of the number having each height, we will obtain a bell-shaped normal curve, or **curve of normal distribution** (Fig. 34.14). It is evident that there are few extremely tall or extremely

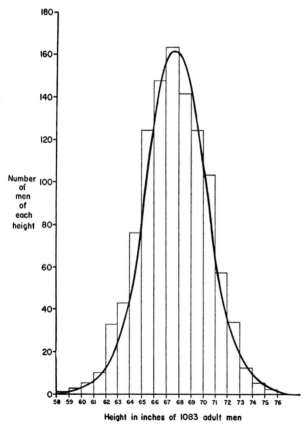

Figure 34.14 An example of a "normal curve," or curve of normal distribution: the heights of 1083 adult white males. The blocks indicate the actual number of men whose heights were within the unit range. For example, there were 163 men between 67 and 68 inches in height. The smooth curve is a normal curve based on the mean and standard deviation of the data. (Villee: Biology, 5th ed.)

short men, but many of intermediate height. This resembles the F_2 of the simpler situation with skin color, for there were few individuals with black or white skin but many with mulatto skin.

All living things show comparable variations in certain of their characteristics. If one were to measure the length of 1000 shells from the same species of clam, or the weight of 1000 hens' eggs, or the amount of milk produced per year by 1000 dairy cows, or the intelligence quotient (I.Q.) of 1000 grade school children, and make graphs of the number of individuals in each subclass, one would obtain a normal curve of distribution in each instance. The variation is due in part to the action of polygenes and in part to the effects of a variety of environmental agents. In a few species it has been possible to establish strains which are genetically identical—all the individuals have exactly the same genetic constitution. Human identical twins (p. 584) have identical sets of genes. The individuals of these strains, and human identical twins, are not identical in all of their characters, however, for the variations due to environmental influences remain. One method of estimating the relative importance of genetic and environmental factors on a given character is to compare the variability of that character in a genetically heterogeneous group and in a genetically homogeneous one.

When a commercial breeder attempts to establish a new strain of hens that will lay more eggs per year, or a strain of turkeys with more breast meat, or a strain of sheep with longer, finer wool, he selects individuals which show the desired trait in greatest amount for further breeding. There is a limit, of course, to the effectiveness of selective breeding in increasing some desirable trait or in decreasing some undesirable one. When the strain becomes homozygous for all the genetic factors involved, further selective breeding will be ineffective.

The inheritance of certain traits depends not only on a single pair of genes which determines the presence or absence of the trait but also on a number of polygenes which determine the extent of the trait. For example, the presence or absence of spots in the coat of most mammals is determined by a single pair of genes. The size and distribution of the spots, however, are determined by a series of polygenes. The term **modifying factors**

has been suggested for polygenes which affect the degree of expression of another gene.

34.17
Multiple Alleles

In all the types of inheritance discussed so far, there have been only two possible alleles, one dominant and one recessive gene, which could be represented by capital and lower case letters respectively. In addition to a dominant and a recessive gene, there may be one or more additional kinds of gene found at that same location in the chromosome that affect the same trait in an alternative fashion. The term **multiple alleles** is applied to the type of inheritance in which there are three or more different kinds of gene, three or more alternative conditions at a single locus in the chromosome, each of which produces a distinctive phenotype. In the population as a whole, there are distributed three or more different alleles, but each individual has any two, and no more than two, of the possible types of alleles, and any gamete has only one. The members of an allelic series are indicated by the same letter, with suitable distinguishing superscripts.

One series of multiple alleles which affects coat color in rabbits includes the dominant gene **C** for normal coat color, the recessive gene **c** which produces albino coat color when homozygous, and two other alleles, c^h and c^{ch}. The gene c^h, when homozygous, produces the "Himalayan" pattern of white coat over the body but with a dark color on the tips of the ears, nose, tail and legs. The gene c^{ch}, when homozygous, produces the "chinchilla" pattern of light gray fur all over the body. These alleles may be arranged in the series **C,** c^{ch}, c^h and **c,** in which each gene is dominant to the succeeding genes but recessive to the preceding ones. In other series of multiple alleles the genes may be incompletely dominant so that the heterozygote has a phenotype intermediate between those of its two parents, or one which is some combination of the two parental phenotypes.

Multiple alleles govern the inheritance of the human blood groups O, A, B and AB (p. 487). The three alleles of the series, a^A, a^B and **a,** regulate the kind of agglutinogen in the red blood cells (Table 34.3). Gene a^A produces agglutinogen A, gene a^B produces agglutinogen B, and gene **a** produces no ag-

Table 34.3 The Inheritance of the Human Blood Groups

Blood Group	Genotypes	Agglutinogen in Red Cells	Agglutinin in Plasma	Can Give Blood to Groups	Can Receive Blood from Groups
O	aa	none	a and b	O, A, B, AB	O
A	$a^A a^A$, $a^A a$	A	b	A, AB	O, A
B	$a^B a^B$, $a^B a$	B	a	B, AB	O, B
AB	$a^A a^B$	A and B	none	AB	O, A, B and AB

glutinogens. Gene **a** is recessive to the other two, but neither a^A nor a^B is dominant to the other; each produces its characteristic agglutinogen independently of the other. Transfusions of blood from one person to another are successful only when the two bloods are compatible, when the agglutinins in the plasma of the recipient do not react with the agglutinogens in the red cells of the donor to cause agglutination, clumping of the red cells. People with type O blood (no agglutinogens in their red cells) are known as "universal donors"; their blood can be transfused into the veins of persons with any of these blood groups. People with type AB blood are called "universal recipients"; they have no agglutinins in the plasma and hence their plasma will not cause agglutination of the red cells from any person.

Since blood types are inherited, and do not change in a person's lifetime, they are useful indicators of parentage. In cases of disputed parentage, genetic evidence can show only that a certain man or woman *could be* the parent of a particular child, and never that he *is* the parent. In certain circumstances, however, the genetic evidence can definitely exclude a particular man or woman as the parent of a given child. Thus, if a child of

blood group A is born to a type O woman, no man with type O or type B blood could be its father (Table 34.4).

We now know of 11 different sets of blood groups, inherited by different pairs of genes, all of which are helpful in establishing paternity. The most important of these are the Rh alleles, which determine the presence or absence of a different agglutinogen, the **Rh factor,** first found in the blood of rhesus monkeys. There are actually several alleles at the **Rh** locus, but to simplify matters we shall consider just two: **Rh,** which produces the Rh positive antigen, and the recessive **rh,** which does not produce the antigen. Genotypes **RhRh** and **Rhrh** are phenotypically Rh positive and genotype **rhrh** is phenotypically Rh negative. An Rh negative woman married to an Rh positive man may have an Rh positive child. If some blood manages to pass across the placenta from the fetus to the mother it will stimulate the formation, in her blood, of antibodies to the Rh factor. Then, in a subsequent pregnancy, some of these Rh antibodies may pass through the placenta to the child's blood, and react with the Rh antigen in the child's red cells. The red cells are agglutinated and destroyed and a serious, often fatal, anemia, called **erythroblastosis fetalis,**

Table 34.4 Exclusion of Paternity Based on Blood Types

Child	Mother	Father Must Be of Type	Father Cannot Be of Type
O	O	O, A, or B	AB
O	A	O, A, or B	AB
O	B	O, A, or B	AB
A	O	A or AB	O or B
A	A	A, B, AB, or O	————
B	B	A, B, AB, or O	————
A	B	A or AB	O or B
B	A	B or AB	O or A
B	O	B or AB	O or A
AB	A	B or AB	O or A
AB	B	A or AB	O or B
AB	AB	A, B, or AB	O

ensues. This is now treated by massive blood transfusions in which essentially all of the blood of the newborn is replaced.

Extensive surveys have shown that approximately 41 per cent of native white Americans are type O, 45 per cent are type A, 10 per cent are type B, and 4 per cent are type AB. The frequency of the blood groups in other races may be quite different; American Indians, for example, have a low frequency of group A and a high frequency of group B. No one blood type is characteristic of a single race; the racial differences lie in the *relative frequency* of the several blood types. Studies of the relative frequencies of the blood groups found in different races living today and in mummies and skeletons have provided valuable evidence as to the relationships of the present races of man.

34.18
Inbreeding and Outbreeding

It is commonly believed that the mating of two closely related individuals—brother and sister or father and daughter—is harmful and leads to the production of monstrosities. The marriage of first cousins is forbidden by law in some states. Carefully controlled experiments with many different kinds of animals and plants have shown that there is nothing harmful in the process of inbreeding itself. It is, in fact, one of the standard procedures used by commercial breeders to improve strains of cattle, corn, cats and cantaloupes. It is not necessarily a bad practice in the human species. In all animals or plants it simply tends to make the strain homozygous. All natural populations of individuals are heterozygous for many traits; some of the hidden recessive genes are for desirable traits, others are for undesirable ones. **Inbreeding** will simply permit these genes to become homozygous and lead to the unmasking of

the good or bad traits. If a stock is good, inbreeding will improve it; but if a stock has many undesirable recessive traits, inbreeding will lead to their phenotypic expression.

The crossing of two completely unrelated strains, called **outbreeding,** is another widely used genetic maneuver. It is frequently found that the offspring of such a mating are much larger, stronger and healthier than either parent. Much of the corn grown in the United States is a special hybrid variety developed by the United States Department of Agriculture from a mating of four different inbred strains. Each year, the seed to grow this uniformly fine hybrid corn is obtained by mating the original inbred lines. If the hybrid corn were used in mating, it would give rise to many different kinds of corn since it is heterozygous for many different traits. The mule, the hybrid offspring of the mating of a horse and donkey, is a strong, sturdy animal, better adapted for many kinds of work than either of its parents. This phenomenon of **hybrid vigor,** or **heterosis,** does not result from the act of outbreeding itself, but from the heterozygous nature of the F_1 organisms which result from outbreeding. Each of the parental strains is homozygous for certain undesirable recessive traits, but the two strains are homozygous for *different* traits, and each one has dominant genes to mask the undesirable recessive genes of the other. As a concrete example, let us suppose that there are four pairs of genes, **A, B, C** and **D;** the capital letters represent the dominant gene for some desirable trait, and the lower case letters represent the recessive gene for its undesirable allele. If one parental strain is then **AAbbCCdd** and the other **aaBBccDD,** the offspring will all be **AaBbCcDd** and have all of the desirable and none of the undesirable traits. The actual situation in any given cross is undoubtedly much more complex and involves many pairs of genes.

QUESTIONS

1. Define in your own words: dominant, recessive, homozygous, heterozygous, genotype, phenotype, gene, allele, locus and test-cross.
2. Discuss Mendel's studies of heredity as an example of the scientific method.
3. Give briefly the implications of Mendel's two laws of heredity.
4. In peas, the gene for smooth seed coat is dominant to the one for wrinkled seeds. What would be the result of the following matings: heterozygous smooth × heterozygous smooth? Heterozygous smooth × wrinkled? Heterozygous smooth × homozygous smooth? Wrinkled × wrinkled?

5. In peas, the gene for red flowers is dominant to the one for white flowers. What would be the result of mating heterozygous red-flowered, smooth-seeded plants with white-flowered, wrinkled-seeded plants?

6. The mating of two black short-haired guinea pigs produced a litter which included some black long-haired and some white short-haired offspring. What are the genotypes of the parents and what is the probability of their having black short-haired offspring in subsequent matings?

7. Human color blindness is a sex-linked, recessive trait. What is the probability that a woman with normal vision whose husband is color-blind will have a color-blind son? a color-blind daughter? What is the probability that a woman with normal vision whose father was color-blind but whose husband has normal vision will have a color-blind son? a color-blind daughter?

8. The gene for white eye color (w) in fruit flies is sex-linked and recessive to normal red eye color (W). Give the results of mating (a) a heterozygous red-eyed female with a red-eyed male, (b) a white-eyed female with a red-eyed male and (c) a heterozygous red-eyed female with a white-eyed male.

9. A blue-eyed man, both of whose parents were brown-eyed, marries a brown-eyed woman whose father was blue-eyed and whose mother was brown-eyed. Their first child has blue eyes. Give the genotypes of all the individuals mentioned and give the probability that the second child will also have blue eyes.

10. Outline a breeding procedure whereby a true-breeding strain of red cattle could be established from a roan bull and a white cow.

11. Suppose you learned that shmoos may have long, oval or round bodies and that matings of shmoos gave the following results:
    long × oval gave 52 long and 48 oval
    long × round gave 99 oval
    oval × round gave 51 oval and 50 round
    oval × oval gave 24 long, 53 oval and 27 round.
    What hypothesis about the inheritance of shmoo shape would be consistent with these results?

12. A mating of an albino guinea pig and a black one gave six white (albino), three black and three brown offspring. What are the genotypes of the parents? What kinds of offspring, and in what proportions, would result from the mating of the black parent with another animal that has exactly the same genotype as it has?

13. Mating a red Duroc-Jersey hog to sow A (white) gave pigs in the ratio of 1 red : 2 sandy : 1 white. Mating this same hog to sow B (sandy) gave 3 red : 4 sandy : 1 white. When this hog was mated to sow C (sandy) the litter had equal numbers of red and sandy piglets. Give the genotypes of the hog and the three sows.

14. A walnut-combed rooster is mated to three hens. Hen A (walnut-combed) has offspring in the ratio of 3 walnut : 1 rose. Hen B (pea-combed) has offspring in the ratio of 3 walnut : 3 pea : 1 rose : 1 single. Hen C (walnut-combed) has only walnut-combed offspring. What are the genotypes of the rooster and the three hens?

15. The size of egg laid by one variety of hens is determined by three pairs of genes; hens with the genotype **AABBCC** lay eggs weighing 90 gm. and hens with the genotype **aabbcc** lay eggs weighing 30 gm. Each dominant gene adds 10 gm. to the weight of the egg. When a hen from the 90 gm. strain is mated with a rooster from the 30 gm. strain, the hens in the F_1 generation lay eggs weighing 60 gm. If a hen and rooster from this F_1 generation are mated, what will be the weights of the eggs laid by the hens of the F_2 generation?

16. Mrs. Doe and Mrs. Roe had babies at the same hospital and at the same time. Mrs. Doe took home a girl and named her Nancy. Mrs. Roe received a boy and named him Harry. However, she was sure that she had had a girl and brought suit against the hospital. Blood tests showed that Mr. Roe was type O, Mrs. Roe was type AB, Mr. and Mrs. Doe were both type B, Nancy was type A and Harry was type O. Had an exchange occurred?

17. A woman who is type O and Rh negative is married to a man who is type AB and Rh possitive. The man's father was type AB and Rh negative. What are the genotypes of the man and woman and what blood types may occur among their offspring? Is there any danger that any of their offspring may have erythroblastosis fetalis?

18. What are the advantages and disadvantages of inbreeding?

ANNOTATED REFERENCES

Bonner, D. M., and S. E. Mills: Heredity. 2nd ed. Englewood Cliffs, N. J., Prentice-Hall, Inc., 1964. A brief survey of genetics in paperback.

Carlson, E.: The Gene: A Critical History. Philadelphia, W. B. Saunders Company, 1966. Traces the development of the concept of the gene.

Gardner, E. J.: Principles of Genetics. New York, John Wiley & Sons, Inc., 1960. An excellent presentation of basic genetic principles.

Srb, A. M., R. D. Owen, and R. S. Edgar: General Genetics. 2nd ed. San Francisco, W. H. Freeman & Co., 1965. One of the standard texts with excellent coverage of the fundamentals of genetics.

Stern, C.: Principles of Human Genetics. 2nd ed. San Francisco, W. H. Freeman & Co., 1960. A standard text with an excellent treatment of the genetics of man.

35 CHEMICAL AND MATHEMATICAL ASPECTS OF GENETICS

Attempts to discover the physical and chemical mechanisms involved in the transmission of inherited traits have led to the formulation of the science of **biochemical genetics,** which deals with two basic problems: the chemical and physical nature of the genetic material, and the mechanisms whereby genes control the development and maintenance of the organism.

According to the current working hypothesis, each gene contains information coded in the form of a specific sequence of purine and pyrimidine nucleotides within its **DNA (deoxyribonucleic acid)** molecule. The unit of genetic information is a group of three adjacent nucleotides, termed a **codon,** that ultimately specify a single amino acid; thus the genetic code is a **triplet code.** The DNA molecule consists of two complementary chains of polynucleotides twisted about each other in a regular helix and joined by specific hydrogen bonds between the purine and pyrimidine bases. The DNA molecule is replicated when the two strands separate and each acts as a template for the formation of a new complementary strand.

The DNA of each gene has a sequence of nucleotides which differs from that of every other gene. This information is transferred from the genic DNA to a particular kind of RNA (ribonucleic acid) termed **messenger RNA** (Fig. 35.1) which is synthesized in the nucleus and passes to the ribosomes in the

endoplasmic reticulum. There the messenger RNA combines with the ribosomal RNA and provides a template for the synthesis of an enzyme or some other specific protein. The information originally coded as a specific sequence of nucleotides in the DNA is translated via a specific sequence of nucleotides in messenger RNA into the specific order of amino acids in the protein molecule.

35.1
The Chemistry of Chromosomes

Chromosomes have been shown to contain DNA, RNA and several kinds of proteins. By homogenizing cells and isolating the nuclei by centrifugation, and then homogenizing the nuclei and isolating chromosomes by further centrifugation, A. E. Mirsky has obtained pure chromosomal material for analysis. There is about 6×10^{-9} milligrams of DNA per nucleus in somatic cells and 3×10^{-9} milligrams of DNA per nucleus in egg or sperm cells (Table 35.1). In tissues known to be polyploid (having more than two sets of chromosomes per nucleus) the amount of DNA per nucleus corresponds to the multiple of chromosomes known to be present. Tetraploid cells, with four sets of chromosomes, have been found to have 12×10^{-9} milligrams of DNA per nucleus. The amount per nucleus of DNA and of a protein termed

614

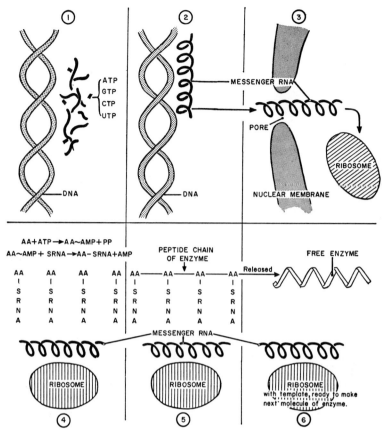

Figure 35.1 Diagram of mechanism by which genetic information may be passed from DNA in the nucleus via messenger RNA to the ribosomes, where amino acids are assembled in specific sequence to make a specific enzyme. *1,* Messenger RNA is synthesized in the nucleus from nucleoside triphosphates (ATP, GTP, CTP and UTP) with its specificity determined by the DNA. *2* and *3,* It passes through a nuclear pore to the ribosomes in the cytoplasm. *4,* Amino acids are activated by reacting with ATP, then transferred to transfer RNA (SRNA). The amino acid-transfer RNA complexes are lined up on the messenger RNA. The peptide chain is formed by the formation of peptide bonds between adjacent amino acids (*5*), then the completed protein molecule is peeled off the RNA template (*6*). (Villee: Biology, 5th ed.)

histone are essentially the same in all the cells of a given organism (Table 35.1). In marked contrast, the amounts of RNA and of several other proteins vary considerably from cell to cell. That the amount of DNA, like the number of genes, is constant in all the cells of the body, and the amount of DNA in germ cells is only half the amount in somatic cells, is taken as evidence that DNA is an essential part of the gene. From the amount of DNA per cell, one can estimate the number of nucleotide pairs per cell and thus the amount of genetic information present (Table 35.2).

Treating chromosomes with **deoxyribonuclease,** an enzyme that specifically hydrolyzes DNA, removes the DNA, but a shadow of the chromosome structure remains. In contrast, a chromosome treated with proteolytic enzymes breaks into fragments. This suggests that the chromosome consists of a continuous protein core along which are local concentrations of DNA. Treating chromosomes with Versene (EDTA), an agent that removes and binds divalent cations such as calcium, yields small particles the size of a chromosome band, which suggests that the DNA and protein of the chromosome are normally held together by divalent cations such as calcium and magnesium. When these cations are removed by Versene, the nucleic acid and protein disaggregate.

The chromosomes of some of the simpler organisms appear to be enormous single molecules of DNA, with molecular weights of 1.2×10^8 (bacteriophage) or 2×10^9

Table 35.1   Amount of Deoxyribonucleic Acid (DNA) per Nucleus in Animal Tissues, Expressed as Mg. $\times 10^{-9}$

Species	Sperm	Red Cell	Liver	Heart	Kidney	Pancreas	Spleen
Shad	0.91	1.97	2.01				
Carp	1.64	3.49	3.33				
Brown trout	2.67	5.79					
Toad	3.70	7.33					
Frog		15.0	15.7				
Chicken	1.26	2.49	2.66	2.45	2.20	2.61	2.55
Dog			5.5		5.3		
Rat			9.47	6.50	6.74	7.33	6.55
Ox	3.42		7.05		6.63	7.15	7.26
Man	3.25	7.30	10.36		8.6		

(*Escherichia coli*). In these organisms the molecule of DNA appears to be circular, without any free ends. It has been suggested that this circularity prevents replication of the DNA and that the DNA molecule is converted from the circular to a linear form for only a brief moment during the replication process. The possibility remains that individual DNA molecules in the chromosomes of higher organisms are circular. However, electron micrographs published in 1966 by Dr. Margit Nass showed that the DNA in the nuclei of mouse fibroblasts is in linear fibrous strands 10 to 15 microns long. The mitochondria of many, perhaps all, cells contain a small amount of DNA (about 1 or 2 per cent of the total), and Dr. Nass's electron micrographs revealed that the mitochondrial DNA consists of circular strands some 5 microns long.

Table 35.2   The Amount of DNA per Cell in Animal and Plant Cells and in Virus Particles

	DNA (Mg. $\times 10^{-9}$ per Cell)	Nucleotide Pairs per Cell
Mammals	6	5.5×10^9
Birds	2	2×10^9
Reptiles	5	4.5×10^9
Amphibia	7	6.5×10^9
Fish	2	2×10^9
Insects	0.17–12	0.16×10^9
Crustacea	3	2.8×10^9
Mollusks	1.2	1.1×10^9
Echinoderms	1.8	1.7×10^9
Sponges	0.1	0.1×10^9
Higher plants	2.5–40	2.3×10^9
Fungi	0.02–0.17	0.02×10^9
Algae	3	2.8×10^9
Bacteria	0.002–0.06	2×10^6
T_2 bacteriophage	0.00024	2.2×10^5
λ bacteriophage	0.00008	7×10^4
Papilloma virus	—	6×10^3

35.2
The Role of DNA in Heredity

Direct evidence that DNA transmits genetic information has come from experiments with bacteria, viruses and molds. Substances termed "transforming agents" can be isolated from pneumococci and certain other bacteria. A transforming agent isolated from strain III of pneumococcus (the bacteria causing pneumonia) will, when added to the culture medium, transform strain II organisms into strain III pneumococci. This is a "permanent" transformation; the strain II organisms so produced multiply to give only strain III offspring. Similar transforming agents have been found in other types of bacteria and, in each case, when they have been isolated and characterized, they have been found to be pure DNA.

DNA has been shown to be the carrier of genetic information in bacterial viruses that consist of a "head," made up of a protein membrane around a DNA "core," and a tail composed of protein. The virus becomes attached to the bacterial cell by the tip of its tail. The DNA present in the head of the virus is transferred inside the bacterial cell, but most of the tail and the head membrane remain outside. The viral protein on the outside of the bacterial cell can be sheared off by stirring the infected bacteria in a Waring Blendor. The bacteria containing the viral DNA will then produce a large number of virus particles identical with the one used for infection. Thus, most of the viral protein can be eliminated without interfering with the replication process, indicating that the protein is not important in the formation of new virus particles.

Experiments using labeled atoms have

shown further that the atoms of the protein in the parent virus do not appear in the progeny, whereas more than 50 per cent of the atoms of the parental DNA do appear in the progeny. Within the bacterial cell the nucleic acid leads to the production both of additional nucleic acid cores and of protein coats, and many virus particles are formed and released when the infected bacterial cell bursts. In other experiments pure nucleic acid has been prepared from plant viruses and shown to have the viral activity characteristic of that species of virus.

Further evidence that DNA is the carrier of genetic information comes from experiments in which genetic recombination has been demonstrated between different strains of bacteria. On rare occasions two bacteria come together, a cytoplasmic bridge forms between them and DNA passes across this bridge from the donor to the recipient cell. The amount of DNA transferred is proportional to the amount of genetic information transferred as measured on a genetic map. If the bacteria are left undisturbed, as much as one-third of the genetic material is transferred from donor to recipient. However, if bacteria are placed in a Waring Blendor at various times after the cytoplasmic bridge has formed and the cells are separated, varying amounts of DNA and of genetic material will be transferred. The proportionality between the amount of DNA and the length of the genetic map transferred indicates that genetic information is contained in DNA.

Nucleic acids absorb ultraviolet light very strongly with a maximum at 260 millimicrons. The production of mutations by ultraviolet light is also maximal at 260 millimicrons. When one compares the number of mutations produced per unit of energy delivered and the wave length at which the energy is delivered, an action spectrum for mutations is obtained. There is a close correlation between the action spectrum for the production of mutations and the absorption spectrum for nucleic acids. The simplest explanation of this phenomenon is that genes are composed of nucleic acids, that mutations are produced as nucleic acids absorb energy, and that the absorbed energy is effective in changing the nucleic acid molecule to yield a mutant gene.

35.3
The Watson-Crick Model of DNA

Highly purified DNA has been prepared from a wide variety of animals, plants and bacteria and found in each case to consist of a sugar—**deoxyribose,** phosphoric acid and nitrogenous bases. Four major kinds of bases have been found in DNA: two purines, **adenine** and **guanine,** and two pyrimidines, **cytosine** and **thymine.** The ratios of these purine and pyrimidine bases differ in different samples of DNA (Table 35.3), but in all the total amount of purines equals the total amount of pyrimidines ($A + G = T + C$), the amount of adenine equals the amount of thymine ($A = T$), and the amount of guanine equals the amount of cytosine ($G = C$). DNA from mammalian tissues is generally rich in adenine and thymine and relatively poor in guanine and cytosine, whereas nucleic acid from bacterial sources is, in general, rich in guanine and cytosine and relatively poor in adenine and thymine.

On the basis of these analytical results, and from a study of the x-ray diffraction patterns of a number of samples of DNA, Watson and Crick proposed in 1953 a model of the DNA

Table 35.3   Relative Amounts of Purines and Pyrimidines in Samples of DNA

Source	Adenine	Guanine	Cytosine	Thymine
Beef thymus	29.0	21.2	21.2	28.5
Beef liver	28.8	21.0	21.1	29.0
Beef sperm	28.7	22.2	22.0	27.2
Human thymus	30.9	19.9	19.8	29.4
Human liver	30.3	19.5	19.9	30.3
Human sperm	30.9	19.1	18.4	31.6
Hen red cells	28.8	20.5	21.5	29.2
Herring sperm	27.8	22.2	22.6	27.5
Wheat germ	26.5	23.5	23.0	27.0
Yeast	31.7	18.3	17.4	32.6
Vaccinia virus	29.5	20.6	20.0	29.9
Bacteriophage T_2	32.5	18.2	16.7	32.6

molecule. The great usefulness of this model in providing a chemical explanation for the properties of DNA led to the awarding of Nobel prizes to Watson and Crick in 1962. In DNA the adjacent nucleotides are joined together in a chain by phosphodiester bridges linking the 5′ carbon of the deoxyribose of one nucleotide with the 3′ carbon of the deoxyribose of the next nucleotide (Fig. 35.2). Watson and Crick suggested that the DNA molecule consists of two such polynucleotide chains wrapped helically around each other, with the sugar-phosphate chain on the outside of the helix and the purines and pyrimidines on the inside. The two chains are held together by hydrogen bonds between specific pairs of purines and pyrimidines (Fig. 35.3).

The hydrogen bonds between purines and pyrimidines are such that adenine can bond to thymine and guanine can bond to cytosine but other combinations are not possible; they would not fit into the repeating lattice formed by the two helical polynucleotide chains. Adenine could not form hydrogen bonds with guanine for there would not be enough

room for these two relatively large molecules to be bonded and yet form parts of the helical chains. On the other hand, thymine could not be bonded to cytosine while both were parts of these helical chains because the distance between the two would be too great. Hydrogen bonds could not form between a thymine that was part of one chain and a cytosine that was part of another. *Two* hydrogen bonds form between adenine and thymine and *three* between guanine and cytosine (Fig. 35.3).

The specificity of the kind of hydrogen bonds that can be formed provides assurance that for every adenine in one chain there will be a thymine in the other, for every guanine in the first chain there will be a cytosine in the other, and so on. Thus, the two chains are complementary to each other; that is, the sequence of nucleotides in one chain dictates specifically and precisely the sequence of nucleotides in the other. The two strands run in opposite directions (have opposite polarities) and have their terminal phosphate groups at opposite ends of the double helix. When exactly scaled molecular models are made (Fig. 35.4), it can be seen that these

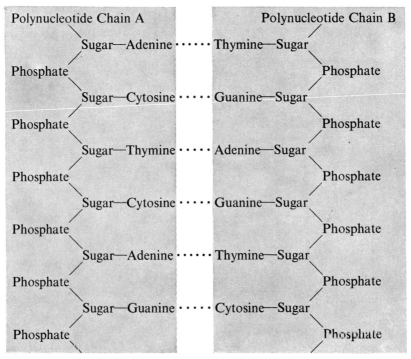

Figure 35.2 Schematic diagram of a portion of a DNA molecule, showing the two polynucleotide chains joined by hydrogen bonds (. . . . . .). The chains are not flat, as represented here but are coiled around each other in helices (see Fig. 35.4). (Villee: Biology, 5th ed.)

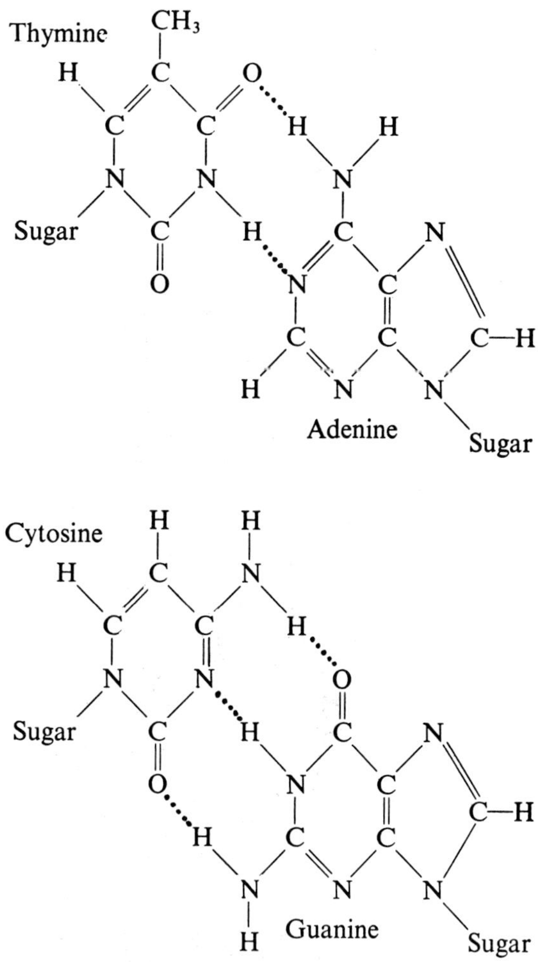

Figure 35.3 Diagram showing the specific pairing of adenine and thymine (above), joined by two hydrogen bonds (. . . . . .), and of guanine and cytosine (below), linked by three hydrogen bonds. (Villee: Biology, 5th ed.)

combinations, adenine-thymine and guanine-cytosine, will fit into the space available whereas other combinations will not.

This model explains how a DNA molecule may be able to undergo replication. It is part of the Watson-Crick theory that when the DNA molecule undergoes replication, these two chains separate, each one causes the formation of a new chain which is complementary to it and, thus, two new chains are established (Fig. 35.5). Genic specificity is believed to reside in the specific sequence of purine and pyrimidine bases in the double helix of the DNA chain. When the DNA molecule undergoes replication, the two chains must somehow uncoil, and each chain carries out the synthesis of a new chain. The nucleotides in the new chain are assembled in a specific order because each purine or pyrimidine in the original chain forms hydrogen bonds with the complementary purine or pyrimidine nucleotide triphosphates from the surrounding medium and lines them up. Phosphate ester bonds are formed in a reaction catalyzed by **DNA polymerase** to join adjacent nucleotides in the chain, and a new polynucleotide chain results. The new and the original chain then are wound round each other, and a new DNA molecule is formed.

The DNA has two prime functions: first, to carry out **replication** sometime before cell division so that each daughter cell has the same amount of DNA that the parent cell had. Second, sometime between cell divisions the DNA must make one or more **transcriptions** of the information contained in its specific sequence of nucleotides. This transcription termed **"messenger RNA"** or **mRNA** then combines with ribosomes to carry out the synthesis of enzymes and other specific pro-

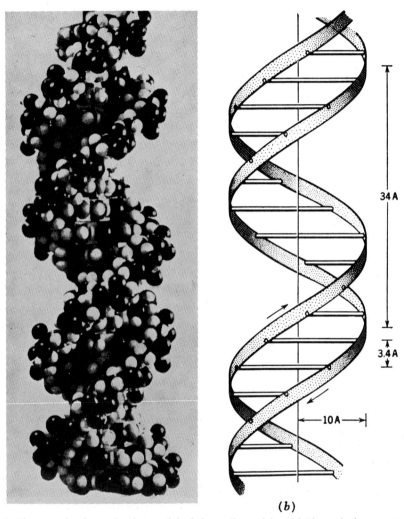

(*b*)

Figure 35.4 Photograph of a molecular model of deoxyribonucleic acid (through the courtesy of Dr. M. H. F. Wilkins). A schematic drawing of this two-stranded structure is shown on the right, together with certain of its dimensions in Ångstrom units. (Anfinsen: Molecular Basis of Evolution, John Wiley & Sons.)

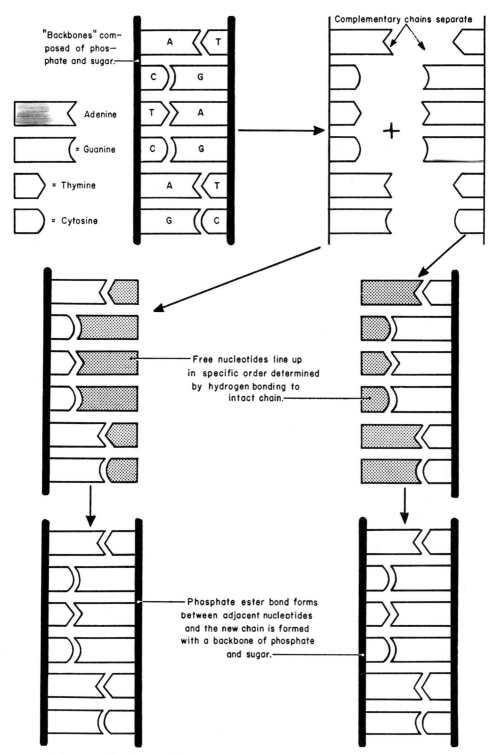

Figure 35.5 Diagrammatic scheme of how DNA molecules may undergo replication. (Villee: Biology, 5th ed.)

teins. In this way, one can picture how each gene can lead to the production of a specific enzyme. We shall return to this subject later.

35.4
What is a Gene?

The term gene has been applied to any hereditary unit that can undergo mutation and then be detected by the change it produces in the phenotype of the organism. It is now possible to define the gene somewhat more precisely in chemical terms. With the techniques of classical genetics, two genes can be defined as being alleles or nonalleles — the same gene or different genes — on the basis of whether they can undergo recombination or whether they affect the same biochemical function.

In an organism that is haploid as an adult, the recombination test is fairly simple. Let us suppose that two genes, a_1 and a_2, affect the same phenotype. If the two genes are at different loci, then the cross $a_1 A_2 \times A_1 a_2$ should yield some wild type organisms, $A_1 A_2$, as well as the double mutant, $a_1 a_2$, as a result of recombination. Genes a_1 and a_2 are presumed to be nonallelic if some wild type organisms are obtained (by recombination) as a result of crossing the two strains; they are presumed to be alleles if only organisms with the mutant phenotype appear. In diploid organisms the same test can be applied, but the situation is more complicated because of the phenomenon of dominance. If two recessive mutant strains are crossed and the mutant genes are located in the same locus, then the offspring should show only the mutant phenotype. If the two mutant genes are at different loci, each strain would have dominant alleles for the recessive mutant genes of the other strain and all of the offspring will be of the wild type. This definition assumes that crossing over and recombination do not occur within a gene. The sharpness of this definition depends upon how many progeny from a single cross can be examined. If the genes are indeed separate but are located close together so that recombinations will occur only rarely, then in an organism with relatively few offspring they might be considered to be the same gene, whereas in the same genetic situation in an organism in which it is easily possible to score millions of progeny, the rare recombinations could be found and the genes would be identified as being separate.

The genetic analysis by Green and Green in 1949 of the genes which produce "lozenge" eyes in *Drosophila* revealed an interesting phenomenon. There are three different loci, all very close together in one chromosome, which produce the same phenotype, a change in pigmentation and shape of the eye which is termed **lozenge.** These lozenge genes are recessive; the heterozygotes have normal eyes. However, double heterozygotes with two mutant alleles present had different phenotypes, depending upon whether the two mutant alleles were in the same chromosome strand or were in opposite members of the pair of homologous chromosomes (Fig. 35.6). Two mutant alleles in the same chromosome resulted in normal eyes, whereas two mutant genes in different members of the homologous pair of chromosomes produced

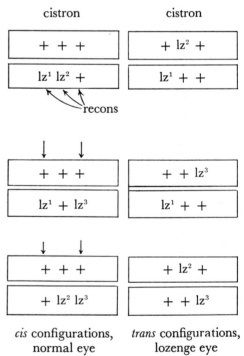

cistron　　　　　　　cistron

| + + + |
| lz¹ lz² + |

| + lz² + |
| lz¹ + + |

recons

| + + + |
| lz¹ + lz³ |

| + + lz³ |
| lz¹ + + |

| + + + |
| + lz² lz³ |

| + lz² + |
| + + lz³ |

cis configurations,　　*trans* configurations,
　　normal eye　　　　　　lozenge eye

Figure 35.6 Diagrams of the possible arrangements of the three lozenge genes, lz¹, lz² and lz³, within the lozenge cistron. In the *cis* configurations, one of the members of the homologous pair of chromosomes contains only wild type alleles (+ + +) and thus can produce the wild type (normal eye). In the *trans* configurations, neither of the two homologous chromosomes has a complete set of normal alleles, a complete wild type cistron, and the eyes are the lozenge phenotype.

the mutant phenotype (lozenge eyes). It would appear that this entire region is one genetic functional unit and that these separate loci are substructures of the parent gene. A mutation at any one of the three loci may lead to an impairment of the gene so that it cannot produce a normal eye. When the mutant alleles are both present in the same chromosome strand (the so-called *cis* position), then the opposite chromosome strand is composed entirely of wild type alleles (Fig. 35.6) and is able to function and produce a wild type eye. When the two lozenge genes are in opposite members of the chromosome pair (the *trans* position) there is no complete normal gene that is able to function and the result is the lozenge phenotype.

Seymour Benzer has suggested three terms which sharpen these different aspects of the gene. He has defined a **cistron** as the genetic unit of biochemical function. Two genes are different in a biochemical sense, i.e., they belong to different cistrons, if they lead to the production of different enzymes. A cistron may be a very complex structure containing many subunits distinguishable by genetic tests. It is defined as that part of a chromosome within which recessive mutants determine a mutant phenotype when in combinations of two in the trans position but not in the cis position.

A cistron can be subdivided by appropriate genetic tests into the ultimate units of recombination, termed by Benzer the **recon.** The recon is defined as "the smallest element in a one dimensional array that is interchangeable, but not divisible, by recombination." The **muton** is defined as "the smallest portion of a chromosome which, when altered, gives rise to a mutant form of the organism."

At one time it was believed that the gene was a truly indivisible unit and that all three of these definitions should refer to the same portion of the chromosome. However, it has been found in experiments with microorganisms that these three definitions lead to quite different estimates of the size of the genes. From his experiments with mutant bacteriophages, Benzer has estimated that the recon, the smallest element which can be interchanged but not divided by genetic recombination, may be as small as a single nucleotide pair. The unit of mutation, the muton, may also be as small as a single nucleotide pair, but the cistron, the functional gene, is a very

complex structure with several hundred or even a thousand or more pairs of nucleotides.

Pontecorvo has used similar methods to calculate the size of different genetic elements in the mold *Aspergillus* and in the fruit fly *Drosophila*. For *Aspergillus* the number of nucleotide pairs in the smallest unit, the recon, came out to be three, whereas for *Drosophila* the recon was calculated to contain 40 nucleotide pairs. Evidence from several different types of organisms suggests that a cistron contains about 1000 nucleotide pairs. It is estimated that the total number of nucleotide pairs per cell in man and other higher organisms is about 100,000,000,000 — equal to a nucleotide chain about 2 meters long!

A modern definition of the gene, then, might be that it is a "unit of function" as determined by the *cis-trans* test or by some suitable biochemical test. Within this gene there may be a number, indeed a large number, of independently mutating sites, and the various parts of the gene may undergo separation and recombination by crossing over. Recombination can occur not only between genes, as had been believed before, but also within genes. Indeed, recombination could theoretically give rise to a unit composed in part of one allele and in part of another. This carries the implication that recombination might give progeny with properties that are different from either parent, and examples of this have been observed.

A gene could be defined as that part of the hereditary material which has to do with determining the amino acid sequence of a specific protein. Although this definition of a gene is difficult to apply in many cases, it remains the best theoretical definition — "a gene is that section of the DNA which is involved in the determination of the amino acid sequence of a single peptide chain."

A number of attempts have been made to obtain estimates of the total number of genes in any given organism. In *Drosophila* it has been estimated that there are about 3000 to 4000 genes, and estimates have placed the number in *Neurospora* at about 6000. In each case, the number is about 1000 genes per chromosome. If we assume that the number of genes per chromosome in man is comparable, man would have perhaps 23,000 genes in the nucleus of each cell. The error of this estimate is probably no more than fivefold and the true number of genes is somewhere between 5000 and 125,000. It seems unlikely that the true number of genes in man could be as few as 100 or less, or as many as several million.

35.5
The Genetic Code

The Watson-Crick model of the DNA molecule implied that genetic information is transmitted by some specific sequence of its constituent nucleotides. Since there are only four types of nucleotides—A, T, G and C—in the DNA and 20 or more kinds of amino acids in a peptide chain, it was obvious that there could not be a one-to-one correlation between nucleotide and amino acid in the coding process. If the code involved two nucleotides to specify an amino acid, the various combinations of four symbols taken two at a time would provide only 16 different combinations; again, this is not enough to account for the 20 or more different types of amino acids.

A triplet code of three nucleotides for each amino acid would permit 64 different combinations of four nucleotides taken three at a time. At first glance this would seem to provide for many more code symbols than are actually needed; however, experiments have shown that the code is "degenerate" and each amino

acid may be specified by two to as many as six different triplets.

The fundamental characteristics of the genetic code of DNA are now well established: It is a triplet code with three adjacent nucleotide bases, termed a **codon,** specifying each amino acid (Table 35.4) Adjacent codons do not overlap; they do not share a given base. Each single base is part of only one codon. *The genetic code appears to be universal;* that is, the codons in the DNA and RNA specify the same amino acid in all the organisms that have been studied, from viruses to man.

Early in 1961 Crick postulated that three consecutive nucleotides in a strand of messenger RNA provide the code that determines the position of a single amino acid in a polypeptide chain. Experimental evidence to support this was quickly forthcoming from experiments of Nirenberg and Matthaei regarding the incorporation of specific labeled amino acids into protein by purified enzyme systems under the direction of artificial messenger RNA's of known composition.

Nirenberg used a synthetic polyuridylic acid (UUUUU . . .)—prepared by using the enzyme polynucleotide phosphorylase—as messenger and found that phenylalanine was incorporated into protein. The addition of poly U to a ribosomal protein synthesizing system led to the production of a polypeptide

Table 35.4   The Genetic Code: The Sequence of Nucleotides in the Triplet Codons of Messenger RNA Which Specify a Given Amino Acid

First Position (5' end)	Second Position	Third Position (3' end)			
		U	C	A	G
U	U	Phe	Phe	Leu	Leu
	C	Ser	Ser	Ser	Ser
	A	Tyr	Tyr	Nonsense	Nonsense
	G	Cys	Cys	Try	Try
C	U	Leu	Leu	Leu	Leu
	C	Pro	Pro	Pro	Pro
	A	His	His	Glu·NH₂	Glu·NH₂
	G	Arg	Arg	Arg	Arg
A	U	Ileu	Ileu	Met	Met
	C	Thr	Thr	Thr	Thr
	A	Asp·NH₂	Asp·NH₂	Lys	Lys
	G	Ser	Ser	Arg	Arg
G	U	Val	Val	Val	Val
	C	Ala	Ala	Ala	Ala
	A	Asp	Asp	Glu	Glu
	G	Gly	Gly	Gly	Gly

containing only phenylalanine. The inference that UUU is the code for phenylalanine was inescapable.

Comparable experiments by Nirenberg and by Severo Ochoa showed that polyadenylic acid provided the code for lysine and polycytidylic acid coded for proline. Further experiments with mixed nucleotide polymers (such as poly AC) as artificial messenger permitted the assignment of many other nucleotide combinations to specific amino acids.

These experiments did not reveal the *order* of the nucleotides within the triplets but this has been inferred from other kinds of experiments. Even when protein synthesis is not occurring, specific transfer RNA molecules will attach to ribosomes only when mRNA is present. Very fortunately this effect does not require a long molecule of mRNA (which would be difficult to synthesize); synthetic messenger RNA as short as a trinucleotide will suffice to promote specific binding of transfer RNA to the ribosome. Since it is possible to synthesize trinucleotides of known sequence, it has been possible to determine the coding assignments of all 64 possible triplets. Thus GUU but not UGU or UUG induced the binding of valine-tRNA to ribosomes.

It is also possible to prepare nucleotide copolymers of known repeating sequences that will serve in protein-synthesizing systems. Using a polynucleotide with the repeating sequence CUCUCUCUCU ..., a polypeptide was produced in which leucine and serine alternated. From this and other evidence it was inferred that CUC is the codon, the triplet sequence, for leucine and that UCU is the codon for serine.

It is apparent from Table 35.4 that the first two bases of the triplet have greater specificity than the third. Both AUU and AUC code for isoleucine; both bind isoleucine-transfer RNA to ribosomes. CCX and CGX code for proline and arginine respectively; the third base in the triplet, X, can be any of the four nucleotides.

Two of the 64 codons, UAA and UAG, are termed "nonsense" codons which do not specify any amino acid but appear to signal the end of the message. Either of these stops the ribosome from reading the message further and leads to the release of the peptide chain from the ribosome. What signals the beginning of the message, what tells the ribosome to "start here," is not yet known but it might also be some specific codon.

The specific properties of each protein depend in part on the sequence of the amino acids in the peptide chain or chains. A gene is a linear polynucleotide molecule and a protein is also a linear molecule with respect to its amino acid sequence. The essence of the genetic code is that the sequence of amino acids in the peptide chain is dictated by the order of the corresponding nucleotide bases in one of the two polynucleotide chains of the DNA molecule. Thus, the DNA molecule and the resulting polypeptide chain are said to be **colinear.**

This concept of colinearity was implicit in the original Watson-Crick model of the DNA molecule. Direct evidence of colinearity has come from analyses carried out by Charles Yanofsky of the genetic control of the enzyme tryptophan synthetase in bacteria. Yanofsky showed that the relative position of mutational sites within a cistron, as determined by genetic analysis of the mutants, corresponds to the relative position of the altered amino acids in the peptide chain of the enzyme molecule, as determined by direct chemical analysis of the peptide. Other examples of colinearity are derived from analyses of the genetic control of hemoglobin synthesis in man.

It is now clear that DNA does not control the production of a polypeptide by any direct interaction with the amino acid. Instead, it forms an intermediate template, an RNA molecule, which in turn directs the synthesis of the peptide chain. The DNA has been compared to a master model that is carefully preserved in the nucleus and used only to synthesize secondary working models which pass out to the ribosomal mechanism in the cytoplasm and are utilized for the actual synthesis of proteins.

The coding relationships between DNA, RNA and protein involve (1) the **replication** of DNA to form new DNA, (2) the **transcription** of DNA to form a messenger RNA template, and (3) the **translation** of the code of the messenger RNA template into the specific sequence of amino acids in a protein. The arrows in the formula indicate the direction of transfer of genetic information:

$$DNA \xrightarrow{\text{transcription}} RNA \xrightarrow{\text{translation}} Protein$$

$$\downarrow \text{replication}$$

$$DNA$$

35.6

The Synthesis of DNA: Replication

The synthesis of DNA is catalyzed by an enzyme system, **DNA polymerase,** first isolated from the cells of *Escherichia coli* by Kornberg and colleagues in 1957. DNA polymerase requires the triphosphates of all four deoxyribonucleosides (abbreviated dATP, dGTP, dCTP and dTTP) as substrates, magnesium ions, and a small amount of high molecular weight DNA polymer to serve as a primer and template for the reaction. The product of the reaction is more DNA polymer and a molecule of pyrophosphate for each molecule of deoxyribonucleotide incorporated.

$$\left.\begin{array}{l} \text{dATP} \\ \text{dGTP} \\ \text{dCTP} \\ \text{dTTP} \end{array}\right\} \xrightarrow[\text{DNA polymerase}]{\substack{\text{DNA} \\ \text{Mg}^{++}}} \text{DNA} + n\text{PPi}$$

The DNA polymerase from *Escherichia coli* can use template DNA prepared from a wide variety of sources—bacteria, viruses, mammals and plants—and will produce DNA with a nucleotide ratio comparable to that of the template used. Thus the sequence of nucleotides in the product is dictated by the sequence in the primer and not by the properties of the polymerase nor by the ratio of the substrate molecules present in the reaction mixture.

Khorana and his colleagues prepared synthetic deoxyribonucleotide polymers containing adenylic and cytidylic acids and other polymers containing alternating thymidylic and guanylic acids. Neither one alone could serve as a template for DNA polymerase, but a mixture of the two, which forms a synthetic double stranded helix with conventional pairing of the bases, can serve as a template.

The DNA template appears to have two functions in the DNA polymerase system: first, to provide 3′-OH groups which are free to serve as the growing end or primer of the polymer and, second, to provide coded information. A double-stranded molecule is required because each strand of the pair serves as a template for the extension of the complementary strand and as a primer for its own extension. The DNA-like polymer that is produced by the action of the DNA polymerase in the presence of double-stranded template is also double-stranded and has the same base composition as the template DNA. The ratios of the bases are those predicted by the Watson-Crick model.

In the cells of higher organisms, the synthesis of DNA occurs only during the interphase, when chromosomes are in their extended form and are not readily visible. Thus, if an enzyme similar to the Kornberg enzyme catalyzes the synthesis of DNA in vivo, there must be some sort of biological signal which initiates DNA synthesis at this time and turns it off at other times. It appears that both the enzyme DNA polymerase and the substrates, dATP, dGTP, dCTP and dTTP, are present all the time, and hence there must be some change in the DNA template which initiates DNA synthesis and then turns it off.

During DNA replication two new strands are formed, each complementary to one of the existing DNA strands in the double-stranded helix. The double-stranded helix unwinds; one strand provides a template for one new one and the other original strand also provides a template for a second new strand. This is called a **semi-conservative** mechanism: the two original strands of DNA are retained in the product, one in each of the two daughter helices.

The experiment of Meselson and Stahl (Fig. 35.7) provided evidence that DNA replication is carried out by a semi-conservative mechanism, at least in bacteria. Bacteria were grown for several generations in a medium containing heavy nitrogen, ^{15}N. Thus, all of the nitrogen in the DNA of those bacteria was ^{15}N. When a sample of the DNA was isolated and centrifuged in a cesium chloride density gradient, the DNA collected at a level which reflected the presence of the heavy nitrogen in the DNA molecules.

The bacteria were then removed from the ^{15}N medium, placed in a medium containing ordinary nitrogen, ^{14}N, and allowed to divide once in this medium. When some of the DNA from this generation was isolated and centrifuged, all the DNA was lighter and had a density corresponding to its being half labeled with ^{15}N and half labeled with ^{14}N. If the Watson-Crick theory is correct and replication is semi-conservative, this result would be expected because one strand of the double-stranded DNA in each organism is ^{15}N-labeled and the other is ^{14}N-labeled.

When the organisms were allowed to divide again in ^{14}N medium, each molecule of progeny DNA again received one parental strand and made one new strand containing ^{14}N. As a result, some double-stranded DNA containing only ^{14}N was formed and appeared as

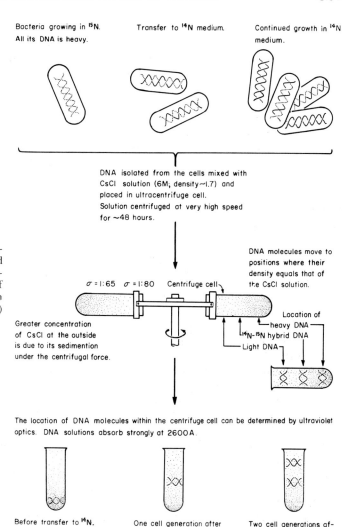

Figure 35.7 Diagram of the experiment of Meselson and Stahl which indicated that DNA is replicated by a semi-conservative mechanism: the two original strands of DNA are retained in the product, one in each daughter helix. (Villee: Biology, 5th ed.)

a light DNA on centrifugation. The parental ^{15}N-containing strands made complementary strands containing ^{14}N and appeared on centrifugation with a density characteristic of the half ^{15}N, half ^{14}N double-stranded state.

If the replication of the strands begins as the strands begin to untwist, Y-shaped molecules of DNA should be evident during the replication process. Such Y-shaped regions have been found by autoradiography of chromosomes of *Escherichia coli*.

35.7

Transcription of the Code:
The Synthesis of Messenger RNA

Messenger RNA is synthesized by a **DNA-dependent RNA polymerase** found first in the nuclei of rat liver and subsequently in plants, bacteria and other animals. It requires DNA as a template and uses as substrate the four triphosphates of the ribonucleotides commonly found in RNA. The products are RNA and inorganic pyrophosphate. The reaction system can utilize single-stranded or native DNA or synthetic deoxyribopolynucleotides as template. These can be polymers of a single nucleotide or polynucleotides with some kind of repeating sequence.

The RNA that is produced by the use of these carefully defined templates is exactly that predicted by the kinds of base pairing permitted in the Watson-Crick model. Although the DNA template is double-stranded and contains two different but complementary template sequences (which would have quite different genetic information), it appears that only one DNA strand is selected for transcription and only one kind of mRNA is produced. The molecular basis for this distinction between the two strands is unknown.

Transfer RNA and ribosomal RNA as well as messenger RNA have complementary sequences in DNA and are produced by DNA-dependent RNA synthesizing systems.

35.8

Types of RNA: Messenger, Ribosomal and Transfer

Chemical analyses show that, in contrast to DNA, molecules of RNA do not usually have complementary base ratios and the inference is that RNA is not a double helix like DNA but is single-stranded. It is a long, unbranched molecule containing four kinds of ribonucleotides linked by 3'-5' phosphodiester bonds. RNA contains ribose instead of deoxyribose and uracil rather than thymine.

Three kinds of RNA molecules are required for protein synthesis: **messenger RNA,** which transmits genetic information from the DNA molecule in the nucleus to the cytoplasm; **ribosomal RNA,** which serves some nonspecific function in connection with the cytoplasmic particles called ribosomes on which the protein synthesis occurs; and **transfer RNA,** which acts as an adaptor to bring amino acids into line in the growing polypeptide chain in the appropriate place.

Electron microscopy has established that most cells contain an extensive system of tubules with thin membranes termed the endoplasmic reticulum. Associated with the endoplasmic reticulum or floating freely in the cytoplasm are small particles termed ribosomes. Ribosomes are about half protein and half RNA. The RNA of ribosomes after extraction with phenol appears to consist of two components with molecular weights of about 600,000 and 1,300,000.

Transfer RNA is a smaller molecule than messenger or ribosomal RNA and functions as an adaptor in protein synthesis. A specific amino acid is attached to a specific kind of transfer RNA. A particular section of the transfer RNA molecule contains an **anticodon,** a triplet complementary to the codon in messenger RNA that specifies that amino acid. Thus, there is at least one specific transfer RNA for each amino acid. Transfer RNA is also unusual in containing not only the four

nucleotides, adenylic, guanylic, cytidylic and uridylic, but also small amounts of unusual nucleotides such as 6-methylamino adenylic acid, dimethylguanylic acid and thymine ribotide.

Transfer RNA's are polynucleotide chains of about 70 nucleotides. The chain is doubled back on itself so that some 25 bases on one limb are hydrogen bonded and paired with an equal number on the other limb to form a double helix. These base paired limbs are joined by a loop in the center of the chain, and the loop contains the minor components such as the methylated bases. The triplet that is complementary to the codon is believed to be located in the loop.

All the 20 or so different kinds of transfer RNA have a similar sequence of nucleotides (CCA) at the end to which the amino acid is attached and a guanine at the opposite end. The first complete analysis of a transfer RNA was carried out by Holley and his co-workers. They showed that the transfer RNA for alanine obtained from yeast cells has 77 nucleotides arranged in a unique sequence. Nine of these 77 are unusual bases, ones other than A, G, C or U. These unusual bases typically have one or more methyl groups which are added enzymatically after the nucleotides are linked together by phosphodiester linkages. These unusual bases in general cannot form conventional base pairs and therefore may serve to disrupt the base pairing in other parts of the transfer RNA and to expose specific chemical groups which form secondary bonds to messenger RNA, to the ribosome, or perhaps to the enzyme needed to attach a specific amino acid to its specific transfer RNA molecule.

It should be noted that since the exact sequence of this transfer RNA is known, this means that the sequence of the gene that specifies this particular kind of transfer RNA is also known, for it can be inferred on the basis of specific base pairing. The gene specifying this transfer RNA would also be only 77 nucleotides long.

35.9

The Synthesis of a Specific Polypeptide Chain

The first step in the synthesis of a peptide requires the activation of the amino acid by an enzyme system in the cytoplasm (Fig. 35.8). There is a separate specific amino acid acti-

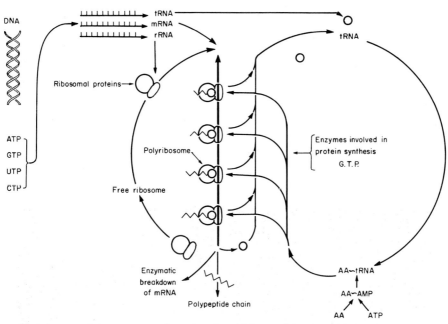

Figure 35.8 Diagram of the sequence of reactions by which specific amino acids are activated and transferred to specific transfer RNAs (aa-tRNA) and then, on the ribosome, transferred to a specific spot in the growing polypeptide chain. (Villee: Biology, 5th ed. Redrawn after Watson.)

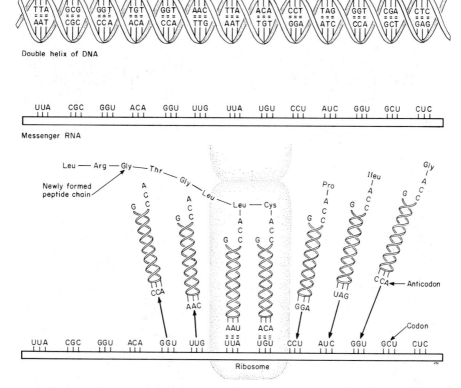

Figure 35.9 Diagram of the postulated mechanism of protein synthesis on the ribosome, illustrating the relationship between the triplet code of the DNA helix, the complementary triplet code of messenger RNA and the complementary triplet code (anticodon) of transfer RNA. Molecules of tRNA charged with specific amino acids are depicted coming from the right, assuming their proper place on mRNA at the ribosome, transferring the amino acid to the growing peptide chain, and then (*left*) leaving the ribosome to be recharged with amino acids for further reactions. The growing polypeptide chain remains attached to its original ribosome. (Villee: Biology, 5th ed.)

vating enzyme for each amino acid. The enzyme first catalyzes the reaction of the amino acid (aa) and ATP to form the amino acid adenylic acid compound (aa-AMP) and release pyrophosphate. The same enzyme then catalyzes the transfer of the amino acid to the specific transfer RNA for the amino acid, yielding the transfer RNA-amino acid compound and free adenylic acid. The amino acid is attached at the end of the transfer RNA which contains cytidylic, cytidylic and adenylic

acid; the amino acid is attached to the ribose of the terminal adenylic acid.

The next step in protein synthesis is not clearly understood but it involves the diffusion of the amino acid-transfer RNA complex to the ribosomes. The function of the ribosomes is to provide the proper orientation of the amino acid transfer RNA precursor, the messenger RNA and the growing polypeptide chain so that the genetic code on the template on the messenger RNA can be read accurately.

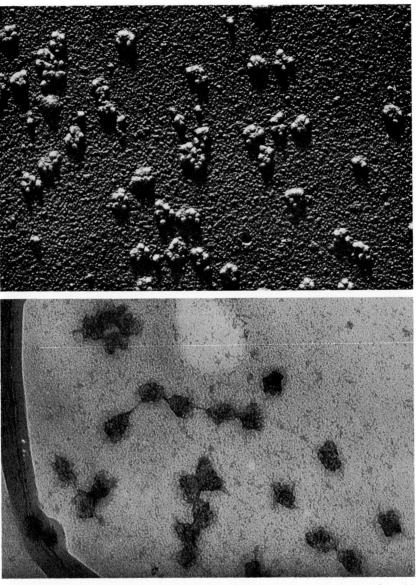

Figure 35.10 Electron micrographs of polyribosomes isolated from the reticulocytes of a rabbit. The upper preparation was shadowed with gold and the lower one was stained with uranyl nitrate. The electron micrographs show that polyribosomes tend to occur in clusters of four, five or six and the clusters are connected by a thin strand of mRNA. (Photographs courtesy of Dr. Alexander Rich.)

There are some 15,000 ribosomes in a rapidly growing cell of *Escherichia coli,* each with a molecular weight of nearly 3,000,000. The ribosomes account for nearly a quarter of the total cell mass. It seems clear that only one polypeptide chain can be formed at a time on a given ribosome.

The template or the genetic information is supplied by the messenger RNA formed on one chain of the double helix of DNA. The messenger RNA passes to the cytoplasm and becomes associated with a ribosome. The messenger RNA appears to move across the site on a ribosome at which protein synthesis occurs, and brings successive codons into a position on which the appropriate amino acid transfer RNA anti-codons can be arranged (Fig. 35.9). The transfer of the amino acid to the growing peptide chain on a ribosome requires guanosine triphosphate, one or two specific enzymes and glutathione.

Protein synthesis has been studied intensively in preparations of rabbit reticulocytes which are engaged primarily in making just one protein, hemoglobin. Rich and his co-workers showed that the ribosomes most active in protein synthesis are ones that interact in clusters of five which he termed **polyribosomes** (Fig. 35.10). These are held together by a strand of messenger RNA. It has been known that peptides are synthesized by the sequential addition of amino acids beginning at the N-terminal end. The distribution of the polyribosomes favors the interpretation that individual ribosomes are attached to one end of a polyribosome cluster and gradually move along the messenger RNA strand as the polypeptide chain attached to it increases in length by the sequential addition of amino acids. Each ribosome appears to ride along the extended messenger RNA molecule, "reading the message" as it goes. It is believed to play a part in bringing the transfer RNA molecule into line at the right position. After completing the reading of one molecule of messenger RNA and releasing the polypeptide that is synthesized, the ribosome appears to jump off the end of one messenger RNA chain and find a new messenger RNA chain to read.

At the other end of the messenger chain the ribosomes detach, and the completed polypeptide chain is released. Thus, the mechanism involves no transfer of a polypeptide chain from one ribosome to another; instead the growing peptide chain remains attached to its original ribosome. A number of ribosomes may be working simultaneously on a single strand of messenger RNA, each reading a different part of the "message."

All the processes of gene replication, gene transcription and protein synthesis depend upon the formation of specific, though relatively weak, hydrogen bonds between specific base pairs. The specificity of these bonds ensures the remarkable accuracy of the processes; mistakes in base pairing occur less than one time in a thousand.

35.10
Changes in Genes: Mutations

Although genes are remarkably stable and are transmitted to succeeding generations with great fidelity, they do from time to time undergo changes called **mutations.** After a gene has mutated to a new form this new form is stable and usually has no greater tendency to mutate again than the original gene. A mutation has been defined as any inherited change not due to segregation or to the normal recombination of unchanged genetic material. Mutations provide the diversity of genetic material which makes possible a study of the process of inheritance, and investigations of the nature of the mutation process have provided important clues as to the nature of the genetic material itself.

Some mutations, termed **chromosomal mutations,** are accompanied by a visible change in the structure of the chromosome. A small segment of the chromosome may be missing (a **deletion**) or be represented twice in the chromosome (a **duplication**) (Fig. 35.11). A segment of one chromosome may be translocated to a new position on a new chromosome (a **translocation**), or a segment may be turned end for end and attached to its usual chromosome (an **inversion**). Point mutations or gene mutations produce no visible change in chromosome structure, and it is assumed that these involve such small changes at the molecular level that they are not evident under the microscope. From the current theory that the genic material is DNA arranged in a double helix, and that genic specificity resides in a particular sequence of nucleotides, it would follow that a gene mutation is some change in the sequence of nucleotides within a particular region of the DNA.

It would follow from these theories that the

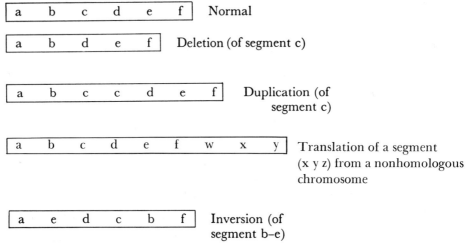

Figure 35.11 Diagram illustrating types of chromosome mutations.

replacement in the DNA of one of these specific purine or pyrimidine nucleotides by an analogue such as azaguanine or bromouracil would result in a mutation. In several experiments in which analogues were incorporated into bacteriophages, no mutations were evident. Study of the genetic code (Table 35.4) shows that because of the degeneracy of the code certain changes in base pairs could occur without changing the amino acid specified.

In other organisms, the incorporation of bromouracil into DNA does lead to an increased rate of mutation. The chemical properties of the substances known to be mutagenic—nitrogen mustards, epoxides, nitrous acid, alkylating agents—are such that they could react with specific nucleotide bases in DNA and change their nature. The incorporation of an analogue into DNA may lead to mistakes in the pairing of nucleotides in subsequent replication processes (Fig. 35.12). Bromouracil, when incorporated into DNA in place of thymine, would pair with guanine more often than with adenine, the normal pairing partner of the natural base thymine. This would lead to the substitution of a G-C pair of nucleotides at the point in the sequence previously occupied by an A-T pair of nucleotides.

The presence of a mutagenic analogue may increase the frequency of mistakes in nucleotides pairing, and this would result in the production of DNA molecules containing only natural bases (no analogues are present) but with a different base order. The change

in the normal base order is significant because, in subsequent replications, this altered base sequence will be reproduced by the normal process of DNA synthesis. By definition, a mutation has occurred only when a change has been introduced in the DNA molecule which can be propagated subsequently for an indefinite number of times.

"Spontaneous" gene mutations may result from errors in base pairing during the replication process; thus the A-T normally present at a given site may be replaced by G-C, C-G or T-A. The altered DNA will be transcribed to give an altered mRNA, and this will be translated into a peptide chain with one amino acid different from the normal sequence. If the altered amino acid is located at or near the active site of the enzyme, the altered protein may have markedly decreased or altered catalytic properties. If the altered amino acid is elsewhere in the protein, it may have little or no effect on the properties of the enzyme and may thus go undetected. The true number of gene mutations may be much greater than the number observed.

If a single nucleotide pair were inserted into or deleted from the DNA molecule, it would shift the reading of the genetic message, alter all the codons lying beyond that point, and change completely the nature of the resulting peptide chain and its biological activity. Thus if the normal sequence is CAG TTC ATG, read (CAG)(TTC)(ATG), the insertion of a G between the two T's results in CAG TGT CAT G, read (CAG) (TGT) (CAT) (G . .).

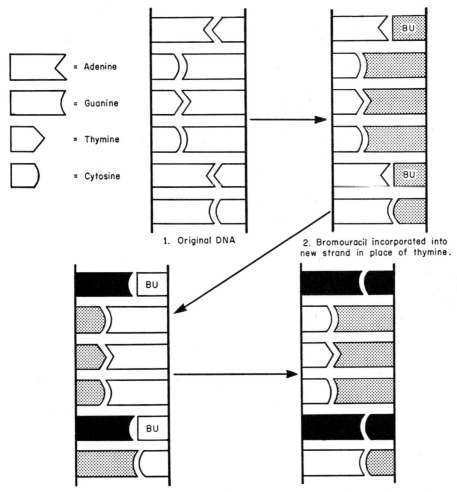

1. Original DNA

= Adenine

= Guanine

= Thymine

= Cytosine

2. Bromouracil incorporated into new strand in place of thymine.

3. Strand with bromouracil leads to production of new strand with guanine paired to the bromouracil.

4. New, mutant DNA which contains no analogue bases, but has nucleotide sequence different from original, with GC pairs in place of AT.

Figure 35.12 Diagrammatic scheme of how an analogue of a purine or pyrimidine might interfere with the replication process and cause a mutation, an altered sequence of nucleotides in the DNA, indicated in black. The nucleotides of the new chain at each replication are indicated by the dotted blocks. In this instance, two new GC pairs are indicated. Probably a single substitution of a GC pair for an AT pair would be sufficient to cause a mutation if it occurred in one of the triplet codes and not in the "nonsense" part of the nucleotide sequence. (Villee: Biology, 5th ed.)

Gene mutations can be induced not only by exposing the cell to certain chemicals but by a variety of types of radiation — x-rays, gamma rays, cosmic rays, ultraviolet rays, and the several types of radiation that are by-products of atomic power. Mutations occur spontaneously at low, but measurable, rates which are characteristic of the species and of the gene; some genes are much more prone to undergo mutation than others. Natural radiations, such as cosmic rays, probably play some role in causing "spontaneous muta-tions," but other factors, such as errors in base pairing, play a role. The rates of spon-

taneous mutation of different human genes range from 10^{-3} to 10^{-5} mutations per gene per generation. Since man has a total of some 2.3×10^4 genes, this means that the total mutation rate is on the order of one mutation per person per generation. Each one of us, in other words, has some mutant gene that was not present in either of our parents.

35.11
Gene–Enzyme Relations

If we assume that a specific gene leads to the production of a specific enzyme by the method outlined above, we must next inquire how the presence or absence of a specific enzyme may affect the development of a specific trait. The expression of any trait is the result of a number, perhaps a large number, of chemical reactions which occur in series, with the product of each reaction serving as the substrate ʼfor the next: A→B→C→D. The dark color of most mammalian skin or hair is due to the pigment **melanin** (D), produced from dihydroxyphenylalanine (dopa) (C), produced in turn from tyrosine (B) and phenylalanine (A). Each of these reactions is controlled by a particular enzyme; the conversion of dopa to melanin is mediated by **tyrosinase. Albinism,** characterized by the absence of melanin, results from the absence of tyrosinase. The gene for albinism (a) does not produce the enzyme tyrosinase but its normal allele (A) does.

The earliest attempts to connect the action of a particular gene with a particular reaction were studies of the inheritance of flower colors, in which the specific flower pigments could be extracted and analyzed. Other studies of the inheritance of coat color in mammals and eye color in insects were also able to relate specific genes with specific

enzymic reactions in the synthesis of these pigments.

A major advance was made when George Beadle and Edward Tatum conceived the idea of looking for mutations in the mold, *Neurospora*, which interfere with the reactions by which chemicals essential for its growth are produced. The wild type *Neurospora* requires as nutrients only sugar, salts, inorganic nitrogen and biotin. A mixture of these comprises the so-called "minimal medium" for the growth of the wild type *Neurospora* (Fig. 35.13). Exposure of the conidia (haploid asexual spores) to x-rays or ultraviolet rays produces many mutations. After irradiation the mold is supplied with a "complete" medium, an extract of yeast which contains all the known amino acids, vitamins, purines, pyrimidines, and so on. Any nutritional mutant produced by the irradiation is thus able to survive and reproduce to be tested subsequently.

Some of the cells from the irradiated mold are then placed on minimal medium. If these are unable to grow we know that a mutant has been produced which is unable to produce some compound essential for growth. By trial and error, by adding substances to

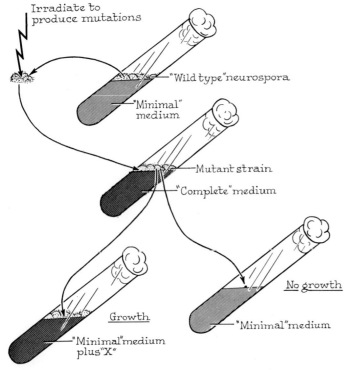

Figure 35.13 The method of producing and testing biochemical mutants in *Neurospora*. See text for discussion.

the minimal medium in groups or singly, the required substance is identified. In each instance genetic tests show that the mutant strain produced by irradiation differs from the normal wild type by a single gene, and chemical tests show that the addition of a single chemical substance to the minimal medium will enable the mutant strain to grow normally. The obvious inference is that each normal gene produces a single enzyme which regulates one step in the biosynthesis of this particular chemical; the mutant gene does not produce this enzyme. It has been possible in certain instances to show that the particular enzyme can be extracted from the cells of normal *Neurospora* but not from cells of the mutant strain. The synthesis of each of these nutritional substances involves a number of different steps, each mediated by a separate, gene-controlled enzyme. An estimate of the minimal number of steps involved can be obtained from the number of different mutants

that will interfere with the production of that substance.

Similar one-to-one relationships of gene, enzyme and biochemical reaction in man were first described by the English physician A. E. Garrod in 1908. **Alkaptonuria** is a trait, inherited by a recessive gene, in which the patient's urine turns black on exposure to air. The urine contains homogentisic acid, a normal intermediate in the metabolism of phenylalanine and tyrosine. The tissues of normal people have an enzyme which oxidizes homogentisic acid so that it is eventually excreted as carbon dioxide and water (Fig. 35.14). Alkaptonuric patients lack this enzyme because they lack the gene which controls its production. As a result, homogentisic acid accumulates in the tissues and blood and spills over into the urine. Garrod used the term "inborn errors of metabolism" to describe alkaptonuria and comparable conditions such as phenylketonuria and albinism.

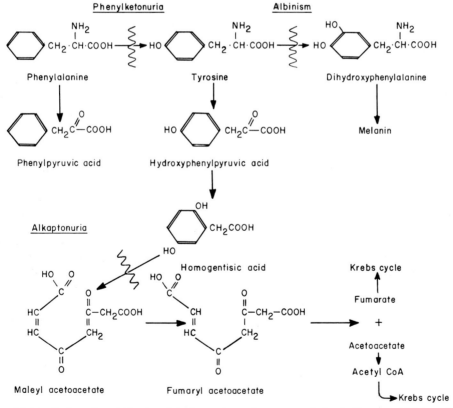

Figure 35.14   Pathway by which phenylalanine and tyrosine are metabolized. Mutants which interfere with the production of the enzymes that catalyze each of these steps may result in "inborn errors of metabolism" such as phenylketonuria, albinism and alkaptonuria. (Villee: Biology, 5th ed.)

The question of whether the genes normally operate so as to lead to the production of the *maximum* number of enzymes all the time has been given consideration in recent years. From a variety of experimental evidence it would appear that this is not the case. Each gene is probably "repressed" to a greater or lesser extent under normal conditions and then, in response to some sort of environmental demand for that particular enzyme, the gene becomes "derepressed" and leads to an increased production of the enzyme. When a single gene is fully derepressed it can lead to the synthesis of fantastically high amounts of enzymes—one enzyme may comprise 5 to 8 per cent of the total protein of the cell! If all enzymes were produced at this same fantastically high rate, metabolic chaos would result. Thus, the phenomena of gene repression and derepression would appear to be necessary to prevent this chaos and to provide a means for increasing or decreasing the rate of synthesis of one particular enzyme in response to variations in environmental requirements.

35.12
Genes and Differentiation

The present theory of the genetic code provides a detailed working hypothesis as to how biological information is transferred from one generation of cells to the next and how this information is transcribed and translated in each cell so that specific enzymes and other proteins are synthesized. This mechanism provides an explanation of how each cell in a multicellular organism has the same assortment of enzymes as every other cell. Additional mechanisms are required to regulate (1) how much of any given enzyme is produced in a given cell, (2) when in the course of development each enzyme appears, and (3) how certain cells may contain a given enzyme or protein whereas other cells in the same organism with the same genetic information do not produce that protein.

Cellular differentiation might be explained if genetic material were parceled out differentially at cell division so that daughter cells actually had different kinds of genetic information. Although there are a few clear instances of differential nuclear divisions in animals such as *Ascaris* and *Sciara*, this does not appear to be the general mechanism of

differentiation. The generalization that the mitotic process ensures the exact distribution of genes to each cell of the organism appears to be valid. Thus, the differences in enzymes and other proteins found in different cells must arise by differences in the *activity* of the same set of genes in different cells.

Some striking evidence regarding the differential activity of genes comes from studies of insects. In certain tissues of insects the chromosomes undergo repeated duplication, and the daughter strands line up exactly in register locus by locus so that characteristic bands appear along the length of the giant chromosome. When these bands are examined carefully, either in the same tissue at different times or in different tissues at the same time, certain differences in appearance become evident. A particular section of a chromosome may have the appearance of a diffuse **puff** (Fig. 35.15) and histochemical tests reveal that these puffs are RNA. It has been inferred that these puffs represent the specific kind of messenger RNA produced by the gene in that band. It has been possible to correlate the appearance of puffs at specific regions in the chromosome with specific cellular events such as the initiation of molting and pupation.

The turning on and off of the synthesis of a specific protein—differentiation at the molecular level—could occur by some process involving the DNA of the gene, the transcription of the DNA to form messenger RNA, the combination of messenger RNA with the ribosome during protein synthesis, or even some transformation of the ultimate protein product.

In view of the tremendous number of kinds of DNA that are represented by the genic complement of a cell such as a human cell, we might ask what prevents that cell from producing continuously all of the tremendous variety of messenger RNAs and the corresponding protein products that are possible. What determines which molecules of DNA are to be transcribed at any given moment in a given cell?

A mechanism which controlled the transcription of DNA to regulate the production of messenger RNA would probably be the most economical one biologically, for it would clearly be to the cell's advantage not to have its ribosomes encumbered with nonfunctional molecules of messenger RNA. A cell optimally should produce only those kinds of mes-

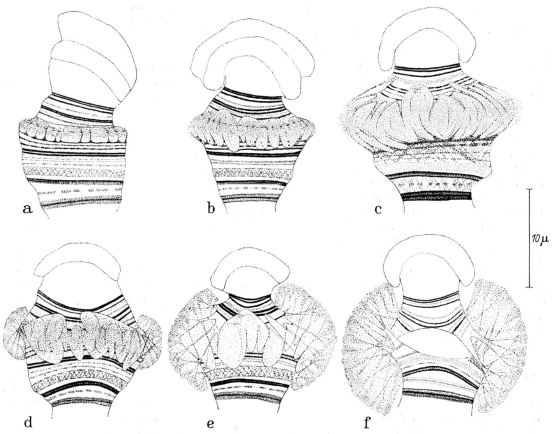

10 μ

Figure 35.15 Diagrams illustrating changing appearance of a polytene chromosome of a salivary gland of *Chironomus tentans* as a chromosome puff gradually appears. The material comprising the puff has been shown by histochemical tests and by autoradiography with tritium labeled uridine to be largely ribonucleic acid. (From Beermann: Chromosoma, 5:139–198, 1952.)

senger RNA that would produce the specific proteins required at that moment.

The continued synthesis of any protein requires the continued synthesis of its corresponding messenger RNA. Each kind of messenger RNA has a half life ranging from a few minutes in certain microorganisms to 12 or 16 hours in man and other mammals. Although each molecule of RNA template can probably serve to direct the synthesis on a ribosome of many molecules of its protein, the RNA is eventually degraded and must be replaced. This provides a mechanism by which a cell can alter the kind of protein being synthesized as new types of messenger RNA replace the previous ones. Thus the cell can respond to exogenous stimuli with the production of new types of enzymes.

The DNA of the genes that are not being transcribed at any given moment may be bound to a histone or to some other kind of protein which makes the DNA unavailable for the transcription system. There is some evidence suggesting that in the nucleus some genes are free and can be transcribed and others are bound and not transcribable.

Studies of the control of the production of a specific globulin by the pea seed provide an example of such regulation of gene activity. This specific protein is synthesized in the seed but not in any other part of the pea plant. James Bonner has provided evidence that the DNA which codes for the synthesis of **pea seed globulin** is bound to histone in the cells elsewhere in the plant but within the pea seed the histone is removed; that particular segment of the DNA becomes free and can be transcribed, and ultimately forms messenger RNA which leads to the production of the globulin. The question of what controls the binding and release of a specific segment of DNA remains to be answered.

An alternative hypothesis suggests that DNA may be transcribed to form messenger RNA but the mRNA is "masked" and inactive as a template for protein synthesis until it is subsequently unmasked by a separate process. There is some evidence that this form of control may be operative especially during early embryonic development. The mRNA may be synthesized in the egg but be inactive until activated by the fertilization process and freed to undergo translation.

There may be marked qualitative and quantitative differences in the kinds of enzymes present in different cells and tissues of the same organism. Mammalian liver cells, for example, have a glucose-6-phosphatase and can convert glycogen and other precursors to free glucose, whereas skeletal muscle cells lack this enzyme. Enzymes that catalyze the same reaction in different tissues may differ in their molecular size, their amino acid composition, their immunologic properties and their responses to hormones and other control mechanisms.

Even within a single tissue or a single cell, multiple molecular forms of an enzyme, termed **isozymes,** may be found. All of these proteins catalyze the same general reaction but have distinct chemical and physical properties. The different molecular forms may bear a different net charge and thus be separable by the process of electrophoresis.

Studies of the lactic dehydrogenases indicate that each enzyme molecule is composed of four subunits bound together. There appear to be two kinds of subunits, A and B, each of which is a polypeptide chain with a specific sequence of amino acids. The entire molecule is analogous to a hemoglobin molecule which is composed of two α and two β polypeptides. However, in the lactic dehydrogenase molecule any combination of the two types of subunits is permissible. The combinations of two kinds of subunits taken four at a time (A_4, A_3B, A_2B_2, AB_3, B_4) add up to the five kinds of lactic dehydrogenases that are typically observed in different tissues.

It appears that there are two genes, one for each of the subunits, but the question of why different types of tissues have characteristically different ratios of the different chains in the tetramers remains unanswered. A very curious observation, one that requires explanation, is that the lactic dehydrogenase in the breast muscle of chickens changes during embryonic development from a pure B_4 isozyme through a series of intermediates to a pure A_4 type in the adult.

The experiments of Clifford Grobstein and others emphasize that complex cellular interactions may be involved in regulating differentiation and that extrinsic factors as well as nuclear factors may play a role in this process. Grobstein found that embryonic pancreatic epithelium will continue to differentiate in organ culture only in the presence of mesenchyme cells. This requirement can be met not only by pancreatic mesenchyme from the mouse but by mesenchyme from a variety of other sources, even embryonic chick mesenchyme.

The mesenchyme can be replaced by a chick embryo juice, and the active principle of the juice appears to be a protein, for it is inactivated by trypsin but not by ribonuclease or deoxyribonuclease. It can be sedimented by high speed centrifugation, and appears to be a large protein molecule. This factor is only weakly effective in causing differentiation of salivary gland epithelium in culture and is ineffective in inducing the formation of kidney tubules or of cartilage from their respective mesenchymes. From these and other experiments there appears to be a spectrum of protein factors, each of which is more or less specific for the differentiation of one kind of cell.

Embryonic tissues have differential sensitivities to changes in nutrients, to the presence of inhibitors and antimetabolites, and to various environmental agents. These factors may change the course of differentiation and mimic the phenotype of a mutant gene, producing what is termed a **phenocopy.**

One of the clearest demonstrations that the same genes operating in dissimilar environments may have different morphologic effects was provided by experiments with races of frogs found in nature in Florida, Pennsylvania and Vermont. Each of these races normally develops at a speed which is adapted to the normal length of the spring and summer seasons. Southern frogs develop slowly and northern frogs develop more rapidly. When northern frogs are raised under southern environmental conditions their development is overaccelerated, whereas when southern frogs are raised under northern conditions their development is over-retarded.

It is possible to fertilize an egg with sperm from a different race and remove the original egg nucleus before the sperm nucleus can unite with it. In this way it was possible to set up a cell with "northern" genes in "southern" cytoplasm and the reverse. Northern genes operating in southern cytoplasm resulted in a poorly regulated development. The animal's head grew more rapidly than the posterior region and was disproportionately large. When southern genes were introduced into northern cytoplasm, development was again poorly regulated but the head rather than the posterior region was retarded and was disproportionately small.

Genes from the Pennsylvania race of frog acted as "northern" with Florida cytoplasm and as "southern" with Vermont cytoplasm. Thus the same set of genes produced quite opposite morphologic effects when operating in different cytoplasmic environments.

Cellular differentiation may involve the differential activation of specific genetic sites in different tissues, and it may involve mechanisms operating at the ribosomal level or even at the cell surface where the transport of substances into and out of the cell is regulated.

Differentiation may be controlled at least in part by influences originating outside the cell, from neighboring cells in early differentiation or from distant cells by materials such as hormones or the mesenchymal proteins studied by Grobstein. Such systemic influences participate in the integration of the differentiation of individual cells into the larger pattern of differentiation of the tissues of the whole organism. Eventually, it should be possible to bridge the gap between studies of development at the level of the whole organism and studies at the molecular level and trace in detail the sequence of events from the initial action of the gene to the final expression of its phenotype.

Certain genes produce such a tremendous deviation from the normal development of an organism that it is unable to survive. The presence of these **lethal genes** can be detected by certain upsets in the expected genetic ratios. For example, some mice in a certain strain had yellow coat color, but experimenters found it impossible to establish a true-breeding strain with yellow coat. Instead, when two yellow mice were bred, offspring were produced in the ratio of 2 yellow : 1 nonyellow. A yellow mouse bred to a black mouse gave half yellow mice and half black mice among the offspring. Then

investigators noticed that the litters of yellow × yellow matings were somewhat smaller than other litters of mice, being only about three-quarters as large. They reasoned that one-quarter of the embryos, those homozygous for yellow, did not develop. When the uterus of the mother was opened early in pregnancy the abnormal embryos, those homozygous for the yellow trait, were found. Embryos homozygous for yellow color begin development, then cease developing, die and are resorbed.

"Creeper" fowl have short legs and short wings and, when two "creeper" fowl are bred, the offspring are in the ratio of two "creepers" to one normal. One-quarter of the embryos—those homozygous for "creeper"—have marked abnormalities of the vertebrae and spinal cord and die without hatching.

These lethal genes, yellow and "creeper," produce a phenotypic effect when heterozygous and hence are said to be dominant. Many, perhaps most, of the lethal genes appear to have no effect when heterozygous but cause death when homozygous and are called recessive lethal genes. These can be detected only by special genetic techniques. When wild populations of fruit flies and other organisms are analyzed, the presence of many recessive lethals is revealed. In the light of our present theory about the relations between genes and development we can suppose that a lethal gene is a mutant which causes the absence of some enzyme of primary importance in intermediary metabolism. The absence of this enzyme prevents the proper development of the organism.

Each recessive gene described so far produces its trait when it is homozygous, and each dominant gene produces its effect when it is homozygous or heterozygous, but other genes are known which do not always produce their expected phenotypes. Genes which always produce the expected phenotype are said to have complete penetrance. If only 70 per cent of the individuals of a stock homozygous for a certain recessive gene show the character phenotypically, the gene is said to have 70 per cent penetrance. The term **penetrance** refers to the statistical regularity with which a gene produces its effect when present in the requisite homozygous (or heterozygous) state. The percentage of penetrance of a given gene may be altered by changing the conditions of temperature, moisture, nutrition, and so forth, under which the organism develops.

Some stocks which are homozygous for a recessive gene may show wide variations in the appearance of the character. Fruit flies homozygous for a recessive gene which produces shortening and scalloping of the wings exhibit wide variations in the *degree* of shortening and scalloping. Such differences are known as variations in the **expressivity** or expression of the gene. The expressivity of the gene may also be altered by changing the environmental conditions during the organism's development. In view of the long and sometimes tenuous connection between the gene in the nucleus of the cell and the final production of the trait, it is easy to understand why the expression of the trait might vary or why the mutant trait might be completely absent.

35.13

The Mathematical Basis of Genetics: The Laws of Probability

The discussions of heredity in Chapter 34 were concerned with inheritance in individuals, with the appearance of the offspring of two individuals with specific traits. Geneticists may also be concerned with the genetic characteristics of a population as a whole. It is possible, with the aid of simple mathematical methods, to make inferences about the mode of inheritance of a trait from its distribution in a population. All genetic events are governed by the laws of probability and, although the outcome of any single event is highly uncertain, in a large number of events the laws of probability provide a reasonable prediction of the fraction of those events which will be of one type or the other. In tossing a coin, where the probability, p, of obtaining a "heads" is one chance in two, or $\frac{1}{2}$, one cannot predict the outcome of any *single* toss of the coin. But in 100 tosses about 50 will come up "heads" and 50 will come up "tails." Probabilities are usually expressed as the fraction obtained by dividing the number of "favorable" events by the total number of possible events. If you are engaged in a game of chance in which the favorable event involves turning up a "three" on a die, the probability of this favorable event is one in six. If a bag contains 10 red, 40 black and 50 white marbles, the chance of

picking a single red marble out of the bag is 10 in 100 or $\frac{1}{10}$.

Three types of probabilities can be distinguished. **A priori probabilities** are those which can be specified in advance from the nature of the event. For example, in flipping a coin the probability of obtaining a head is one in two and in casting a die the probability of obtaining a six is one in six; these probabilities are independent of whether the event actually occurs. In contrast, **empiric probabilities** are obtained by counting the number of times a given event occurs in a certain number of trials. For example, if a surgeon performs a certain type of operation on 500 people and 40 of them succumb, then the probability of death in this type of operation is 40 in 500 or 0.08. Such empiric probabilities have to be used in many fields of research where there is no theoretical basis, no *a priori* basis, for predicting the outcome. This type of probability is used in setting up the "risk tables" widely used by insurance firms. If a scientist collects data about the number of individuals with a certain trait in a given population and wants to know the probability that these numbers agree with the ratio expected on the basis of some genetic theory (1:1 or 3:1, etc.), he uses the methods of **sampling probability.**

If two events are independent the probability of their coinciding is the *product* of their individual probabilities. For example, the probability of obtaining a head on the first toss of a coin is $\frac{1}{2}$ and the probability of obtaining a head on the second toss of a coin (an independent event) is $\frac{1}{2}$. The probability of obtaining two heads on successive tosses of the coin is the product of their probabilities, $\frac{1}{2} \times \frac{1}{2}$, or $\frac{1}{4}$. There is one chance in four of obtaining two heads on two successive tosses of a coin. This "product rule" of probability also holds for three or more independent events. For example, the probability of choosing at random an individual who is male, has blood group A and was born in June is $0.5 \times 0.45 \times 0.084 = 0.0189$.

The probability that one or another of two mutually exclusive events will occur is the sum of their separate probabilities. For example, in rolling a die the probability that the die will come up *either* two or five is $\frac{1}{6} + \frac{1}{6} = \frac{1}{3}$.

The application of these considerations to genetics is illustrated in Figure 35.16. Let us consider the probability that a child will in-

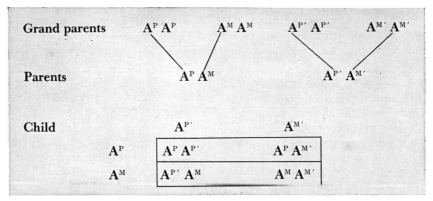

Figure 35.16   An example of the application of the laws of probability to genetics, illustrating both the "product law" of independent events and the "sum law" of mutually exclusive events. See text for discussion. (Villee: Biology, 5th ed.)

herit from his father the particular allele that the father inherited in turn from his father, the child's grandfather. The father has two alleles, A^P and A^M, obtained from the grandfather and grandmother respectively. He will pass onto his son one of these two. The "favorable" event is the transmission of the A^P gene and the total number of events is two; thus, the probability that the son will receive from his father the same allele that the father received from his grandfather is one in two. The probability that the child will receive from his father the allele that the father obtained from the grandfather (A^P) and also will obtain from his mother the allele that she received from the grandmother ($A^{M'}$) is the product of their independent occurrences, $\frac{1}{2} \times \frac{1}{2} = \frac{1}{4}$. The probability that the child will obtain either the two alleles from the two grandfathers $A^P A^{P'}$ or the two alleles from the two grandmothers $A^M A^{M'}$ is the sum of their independent probabilities, $\frac{1}{4} + \frac{1}{4} = \frac{1}{2}$.

When expressed in this fashion, the limits of probability are from 0 to 1. A probability of 0 indicates that the event is impossible; there is no favorable possibility. A probability of 1 represents a certainty; that is, all of the possible events are favorable ones.

35.14
Population Genetics

The question that sometimes puzzles beginning geneticists is: Why, if brown eye genes are dominant to blue eye genes, haven't all the blue eye genes disappeared? The answer lies partly in the fact that a recessive gene, such as the one for blue eyes, is not changed by having existed for a generation next to a brown eye gene in a heterozygous individual, **Bb.** The remainder of the explanation lies in the fact that as long as there is no selection for either eye color, that is, as long as people with blue eyes are just as likely to marry and have as many children as people with brown eyes, successive generations will have the same proportion of blue- and brown-eyed people as the initial one.

A brief excursion in mathematics will show why this is true. If we consider the distribution of a single pair of genes, **A** and **a,** any member of the population will have the genotype **AA, Aa** or **aa.** No other possibilities exist. Now let us suppose that these genotypes are present in the population in the ratio of $\frac{1}{4}$ **AA** : $\frac{1}{2}$ **Aa** : $\frac{1}{4}$ **aa.** If all the members of the population select their mates at random, without regard to whether they are **AA, Aa,** or **aa,** and if all of the types of pairs produce, on the average, comparable numbers of offspring, the succeeding generations will also have genotypes in the ratio $\frac{1}{4}$ **AA** : $\frac{1}{2}$ **Aa** : $\frac{1}{4}$ **aa.** This can be demonstrated by putting down all the possible types of matings, the frequency of their occurrence at random, and the kinds and proportions of offspring produced by each type of mating. When all the types of offspring are summed, it will be found that the next generation will also have genotypes in the ratio $\frac{1}{4}$ **AA** : $\frac{1}{2}$ **Aa** : $\frac{1}{4}$ **aa** (Table 35.5).

Hardy, a mathematician, and Weinberg, a physician, independently observed in 1908 that the frequencies of the members of a pair of allelic genes in a population are described by the expansion of a binomial equation. If we let p be the proportion of **A** genes in the

Table 35.5   The Offspring of the Random Mating of a Population Composed of $\frac{1}{4}$ **AA**, $\frac{1}{2}$ **Aa** and $\frac{1}{4}$ **aa** Individuals (Villee: Biology, 5th ed.)

Mating Male Female	Frequency	Offspring
AA × AA	1/4 × 1/4	1/16 AA
AA × Aa	1/4 × 1/2	1/16 AA + 1/16 Aa
AA × aa	1/4 × 1/4	1/16 Aa
Aa × AA	1/2 × 1/4	1/16 AA + 1/16 Aa
Aa × Aa	1/2 × 1/2	1/16 AA + 1/8 Aa + 1/16 aa
Aa × aa	1/2 × 1/4	1/16 Aa + 1/16 aa
aa × AA	1/4 × 1/4	1/16 Aa
aa × Aa	1/4 × 1/2	1/16 Aa + 1/16 aa
aa × aa	1/4 × 1/4	1/16 aa
		Sum: 4/16 AA + 8/16 Aa + 4/16 aa

population and q be the proportion of **a** genes in the population, since a gene must be either **A** or **a**, $p + q = 1$. Thus, if we know the value of either p or q, we can calculate the value of the other.

When we consider all of the matings in any given generation, a p number of **A**-containing eggs and a q number of **a**-containing eggs are fertilized by a p number of **A**-containing sperm and a q number of **a**-containing sperm: $(p\mathbf{A} + q\mathbf{a}) \times (p\mathbf{A} + q\mathbf{a})$. The proportion of the types of offspring of all these matings is described by the algebraic product: $p^2\mathbf{AA} + 2pq\mathbf{Aa} + q^2\mathbf{aa}$. If p, the frequency of gene **A**, equals $\frac{1}{2}$, then q, the frequency of gene **a**, equals $1 - p$ or $1 - \frac{1}{2}$ or $\frac{1}{2}$. From the formula, the frequency of genotype **AA**, p^2, equals $(\frac{1}{2})^2$ or $\frac{1}{4}$; the frequency of **Aa**, $2pq$, equals $2 \times \frac{1}{2} \times \frac{1}{2}$, or $\frac{1}{2}$, and the frequency of **aa**, q^2, equals $(\frac{1}{2})^2$ or $\frac{1}{4}$. Any population in which the distribution of alleles **A** and **a** conforms to the relation $p^2\mathbf{AA} + 2pq\mathbf{Aa} + q^2\mathbf{aa}$ is in genetic equilibrium. The proportions of these alleles in successive generations will be the same (unless altered by selection or mutation). This concept of the mathematical basis of genetic equilibrium in a population and the changes in equilibrium produced by mutation and selection, is fundamental to the modern concept of the operation of natural selection in evolution (see Chapter 36).

From this it follows that if either p^2, the frequency of genotype **AA**, or q^2, the frequency of genotype **aa**, is known, the frequencies of the other genotypes can be calculated. To obtain an estimate of the number of individuals in a population that are genetic

carriers for a given trait, one need know only that it is inherited by a single pair of genes and know the frequency with which the homozygous recessive individuals appear. For example, surveys have shown that the frequency of **albinism** (genetically **aa**) in human populations is about 1 in 20,000. Using the Hardy-Weinberg equation, the frequency of **aa** individuals, q^2, is $\frac{1}{20,000}$. The square root of $\frac{1}{20,000}$ is about $\frac{1}{141}$, thus q is equal to $\frac{1}{141}$. Since $p + q = 1$, $p = 1 - q$ or $1 - \frac{1}{141}$ or $\frac{140}{141}$. Since we know both p and q we can calculate the value of $2pq$, the frequency of occurrence of individuals genetically **Aa**, heterozygous for albinism: $2 \times \frac{140}{141} \times \frac{1}{141} = \frac{1}{70}$. That is, one person in 70 is a carrier for albinism although only one person in 20,000 is homozygous for the trait. It may come as a surprise that there are so many carriers for such a rare trait. H. J. Muller has calculated that each of us is, on the average, heterozygous for eight recessive undesirable genes.

The ability or inability to taste **phenylthiocarbamide** (PTC) and related compounds with the

$$\mathrm{N\!-\!C\!\!=\!\!S}$$

group is an inherited trait. Some people find that this substance has a bitter taste, others report it to be completely tasteless. L. H. Snyder examined 3643 people and found that 70.2 per cent were "tasters" and 29.8 per cent were "nontasters" for PTC. If this trait is inherited by a single pair of genes, with "tasting" dominant to "nontasting," then the mathematics underlying population genetics would predict that in a population of mar-

Table 35.6 The Inheritance of the Ability to Taste Phenylthiocarbamide

Marriage	No. of Families	Offspring		Proportion of Nontasters	
		Tasters	Nontasters	Observed	Calculated*
taster × taster	425	929	130	0.123	0.124
taster × nontaster	289	483	278	0.336	0.354
nontaster × nontaster	86	5	218	0.979	1.0

*From the Hardy-Weinberg Law, it follows that among marriages of parents with unlike traits (i.e., taster × nontaster), the fraction of the offspring with the recessive trait is $q/1 + q$. Among marriages of parents with like traits (i.e., taster × taster), the fraction of offspring with the recessive trait, nontaster, is $(q/1 + q)^2$. Since 29.8 per cent of the population were nontasters, $q^2 = 0.298$, $q = 0.545$, $q/1 + q = 0.354$ and $(q/1 + q)^2 = 0.124$. (Villee: Biology, 5th ed.)

riages of tasters with tasters, 12.4 per cent of the children will be nontasters (Table 35.6). It similarly predicts that in a population of marriages of tasters with nontasters, 35.4 per cent of the children will be nontasters. In Snyder's study the percentages actually found were 12.3 per cent and 33.6 per cent, respectively. From this close agreement, we may conclude that the original assumption, that the tasting-nontasting trait is inherited by a single pair of genes, is correct. Although some 30 per cent of whites are nontasters, they are very rare in populations of Negroes, Eskimos and American Indians.

As another example of the use of the Hardy-Weinberg Law, let us consider the inheritance of the blood groups M, MN and N. In the United States, among the white population 29.16 per cent have blood type M, 49.58 per cent have blood type MN, and 21.26 per cent have blood type N. Applying the Hardy-Weinberg Law to these data, $q^2 = 0.2126$, from which we calculate that $q = 0.46$. To estimate the value for p, we subtract 0.46 from 1 and arrive at 0.54. The square of this estimate of p, $(0.54)^2$, is equal to 0.29 and $2 pq = 2 \times 0.54 \times 0.46$ or 0.49. The excellent agreement between the values observed and the theoretical values is evidence that M and N blood types are inherited by a single pair of genes, with neither gene being dominant to the other (they may be termed **codominants**) so that the heterozygote shows the two kinds of blood antigens.

35.15
Human Cytogenetics

Many of the basic principles of genetics were discovered by experiments in lower organisms in which it was possible to relate genetic data with cytologic events. This involved making smears of cells and examining them under the microscope to see the number and the structure of the chromosomes present. Some of the organisms used in genetics, such as the fruit fly *Drosophila*, have few chromosomes (four pairs) and, at least in certain cells of the body (for example, the salivary glands), the chromosomes are quite large and the details of their structure are readily evident. Not only are the chromosomes of mammals more numerous and rather small, but mammalian cells are difficult to fix for cytologic examination. Advances in recent years in the techniques of fixing and staining cells, however, have made possible cytologic examination of human cells as well as those of other mammals. This led in 1956 to the finding that the chromosome number for man is 46 rather than 48, the number which had been quoted for the previous 30 years or more.

Although the normal chromosome number in man is 46, some rare instances of abnormal chromosome numbers have been reported. These usually are associated with some change in the phenotype of the individual. Changes in chromosome number are termed *ploidy*. An individual may be polyploid, having one or more complete extra sets of chromosomes, or he may have one or two extra chromosomes with the total chromosome number of 47 or 48. A severely defective male child was found to be a *triploid* individual with a total of 69 chromosomes. He had 66 autosomes, two X chromosomes and one Y chromosome. It seems likely that this zygote was formed from a normal haploid egg which was fertilized by an unusual diploid sperm or from an exceptional diploid egg fertilized by a normal haploid sperm.

A number of cases have now been reported

of individuals who show a gain or a loss of a single chromosome, presumably caused by "nondisjunction." **Nondisjunction** refers to the failure of a pair of homologous chromosomes to separate normally during the reduction division. Two X chromosomes, for example, might fail to separate and both might enter the egg nucleus, leaving the polar bodies with no X chromosome. Alternatively, the two joined X chromosomes might go into the polar body, leaving the female pronucleus with no X chromosomes. Nondisjunction of the XY chromosomes in the male might lead to the formation of sperm which have both an X and a Y chromosome or to sperm with neither an X nor a Y chromosome. Chromosomal nondisjunction may occur during either the first or second meiotic division; it may also occur during mitotic divisions and lead to the establishing of a group of abnormal cells in an otherwise normal individual.

Cytogenetic studies have clarified the origin of one of the more distressing abnormal conditions in man, that of **mongolism** or mongolian idiocy. Individuals suffering from this have abnormalities of the face, eyelids, tongue and other parts of the body, and are greatly retarded in both their physical and mental development. The term "mongolism" was originally applied to this condition because affected individuals often show a fold of the eyelid similar to that typical of members of the Mongolian race. Mongolism is a relatively common congenital malformation, occurring in 0.15 per cent of all births. It had been known for some time that the appearance of mongolism is related to the age of the mother and that it increases greatly with maternal age. For example, mongolism is a hundredfold more likely in the offspring of women 45 years or older than in the offspring of mothers under 19. The occurrence of mongolism, however, is independent of the age of the father, and it is also independent of the number of preceding pregnancies in the woman. Cytogenetic studies revealed that mongols have one extra chromosome, a total of 47. The presence of this extra small chromosome is believed to arise by nondisjunction in the maternal oöcyte. It had long been known that in fruit flies the tendency for nondisjunction to occur increases greatly in older females and perhaps this is also true in human females.

Mongolism should be inherited as though it were a dominant gene, since a mongoloid would form gametes half of which have the normal complement of 23 chromosomes and half of which have 24 chromosomes. In the rare cases where mongols have had offspring they have produced normal and mongol children in about equal proportions.

Another condition caused by an upset in chromosome number is that of individuals who are outwardly nearly normal males but have small testes. They produce few sperm, they have seminiferous tubules which are very aberrant in appearance, and they usually have gynecomastia (a tendency for formation of female-like breasts). This condition, called **Klinefelter's syndrome,** usually becomes apparent only after puberty, when the small testes and gynecomastia may bring the individual to the attention of his physician. The cells of these individuals show a chromatin spot, and at one time they were thought to be XX individuals, i.e., genetic females. However, when their chromosomes were examined cytologically and counted it was found that they have 47 chromosomes; their cells have *two* X and one Y chromosome. The fact that they are nearly normal males in their external appearance emphasizes the male-determining effect of the Y chromosome.

Another condition resulting from changes in chromosome number is **Turner's syndrome,** in which the external genitalia, though feminine, are those of an immature female. The internal reproductive tract is present and resembles that of an immature but perfectly formed female. The uterus is present but small, and the gonads may be absent. The cells of these individuals are "chromatin negative," which suggests that they are males. However, they have only one X chromosome but no Y chromosome. This type of individual again emphasizes the importance of the Y chromosome in determining the male characteristics.

An individual with an extra chromosome, with three of one kind, is said to be **trisomic,** and an individual lacking one of a pair is said to be **monosomic.** Thus mongols are trisomic for chromosome 21, and individuals with Turner's syndrome are monosomic for the X chromosome.

In summary, the primary genetic material in all living systems is nucleic acid. The genetic material is DNA in all organisms except a few of the viruses in which only RNA is present.

Genetic information is transferred from one generation to the next in the form of specific sequences of nucleotides in the nucleic acid chain. It would appear that the number of nucleotides that form a unit in this informational code, a codon, is three. A gene is a localized sequence of nucleotides in a nucleic acid which carries the information for the synthesis of a peptide chain with a specific sequence of amino acids. The function of the gene is to transfer this specificity to some non-genic macromolecule, presumably messenger RNA. The model of DNA proposed by Watson and Crick provides for gene specificity, gene replication and gene mutation. A gene mutation is believed to be an alteration of the specific sequence of nucleotides in the nucleic acid molecule which leads to the formation of a different type of protein or perhaps prevents the formation of that protein. Each gene is believed to control the production of a single specific protein.

QUESTIONS

1. Discuss the evidence that deoxyribonucleic acid is an integral part of the gene.
2. What types of substances are present in the chromosomes? What is known about their respective functions?
3. What is the nature of a "transforming agent"? What importance may this phenomenon have for our understanding of the chemical basis of inheritance?
4. What evidence regarding the nature of the genetic material has been derived from experiments with bacterial viruses?
5. Discuss the chemical composition of DNA. How does the Watson-Crick model of DNA account for its properties? How does it explain the process of gene replication?
6. Distinguish between a cistron, a recon and a muton. Which of these is the largest and which is the smallest genic unit?
7. Define the term mutation. What types of mutations can be distinguished? How may mutations be produced?
8. Discuss the problem of the "coding" of information in the gene.
9. Distinguish between "messenger" RNA and "transfer" RNA. What is the role of each in the synthesis of proteins?
10. Distinguish between penetrance and expressivity.
11. What are some of the current theories of the genetic basis of differentiation?
12. Compare and contrast a priori probability, empiric probability and sampling probability.
13. Discuss the "product rule" of probability.
14. What is the Hardy-Weinberg Law?
15. How does one determine whether a given population is in genetic equilibrium?
16. What is meant by "nondisjunction"? What human abnormalities appear to be the result of nondisjunction?

ANNOTATED REFERENCES

Frisch, L. (Ed): The Genetic Code. Cold Spring Harbor Symposium on Quantitative Biology. Cold Spring Harbor, N. Y. Vol. 31, 1966. A rich source of facts and theories detailing the state of our knowledge of biochemical genetics as of June 1966.

Hartman, P. E. and S. R. Suskind: Gene Action. Englewood Cliffs, N. J. Prentice-Hall, Inc., 1964. A brief paperback presentation of molecular genetics.

Ingram, V.: The Biosynthesis of Macromolecules. New York, W. A. Benjamin, 1965. A clear, logically presented discussion of the genetic control of protein synthesis.

Markert, C. L.: Developmental Genetics. Englewood Cliffs, N. J., Prentice-Hall, Inc., 1964. A summary of the application of current genetic theories to the problem of differentiation.

Watson, J. D.: Molecular Biology of the Gene. New York, W. A. Benjamin, 1965. A masterful summary of biochemical genetics based on experiments with bacteria and viruses.

Wolstenholme, G. E. W., and C. M. O'Connor: The Biochemistry of Human Genetics. Boston, Little Brown and Company, 1959. The proceedings of a Ciba symposium on the chemical aspects of human inheritance.

36

THE CONCEPT OF EVOLUTION

The preceding chapters have served as an introduction to the immense variety of forms of life which inhabit every conceivable place on land and in the water and exhibit tremendous variations in size, shape, degree of complexity, and methods of obtaining food, of evading predators and of reproducing their kind. How all these species came into existence, how they came to have the particular adaptations which make them peculiarly fitted for survival in a particular environment, and why there are orderly degrees of resemblance between forms which permit their classification in genera, orders, classes and phyla, are fundamental problems of zoology. From detailed comparisons of the structures of living and fossil forms, from the sequence of the appearance and extinction of species in times past, from the physiologic and biochemical similarities and differences between species, and from the analyses of heredity and variation in many different animals and plants have come one of the great unifying concepts of biology, that of **evolution.** Evolution is not a new topic at this point for it has been fundamental, both implicitly and explicitly, to many of the subjects discussed previously.

36.1

The Principle of Organic Evolution

The term evolution means an unfolding, or unrolling, a gradual, orderly change from one state to the next. The planets and stars, the topography of the earth, and the chemical compounds of the universe have undergone gradual, orderly changes some-

times called **inorganic evolution.** The principle of **organic evolution,** now universally accepted by biologists, simply applies this concept to living things: all the various plants and animals living today have descended from simpler organisms by gradual modifications which have accumulated in successive generations.

Evolution is continuing to occur; indeed, it is occurring more rapidly today than in many of the past ages. In the last few hundred thousand years, hundreds of species of animals and plants have become extinct and other hundreds have arisen. The process is usually too gradual to be observed, but there are some remarkable examples of evolutionary changes which have taken place within historic times. For example, some rabbits were released early in the fifteenth century on a small island near Madeira called Porto Santo. There were no other rabbits and no carnivorous enemies on the island and the rabbits multiplied at an amazing rate. In 400 years they became quite different from the ancestral European stock; they were only half as large, had a different color pattern, and were more nocturnal animals. Most important, they could not produce offspring when bred with members of the European species. They were, in fact, a new species of rabbit.

36.2

Development of Ideas About Evolution

The idea that the present forms of life have arisen from earlier, simpler ones was far from new when Charles Darwin published *The Origin of Species* in 1859. The oldest speculations about evolution are found in the writings of certain Greek philosophers, Thales (624–548 B.C.), Anaximander (588–524 B.C.), Empedocles (495–435 B.C.) and Epicurus (341–270 B.C.). The spirit of this age of Greek philosophy was somewhat similar to that of our own age, for simple, natural causes were sought to explain all phenomena. Since they knew very little biology, however, their ideas about evolution were extremely vague and can scarcely be said to foreshadow our present theory of organic evolution. Aristotle (384–322 B.C.), who was a great biologist as well as a philosopher, knew a great deal about animals and plants and wrote detailed, accurate descriptions of many of them. He observed that organisms could be arranged in graded series from lower to higher and drew the correct inference that one evolved from the other. However, he had the metaphysical belief that the gradual evolution of living things occurred because nature strives to change from the simple and imperfect to the more complex and perfect. An evolutionary explanation of the origin of plants and animals was given by the Roman poet Lucretius (99–55 B.C.) in his poem *De Rerum Natura.*

With the Renaissance, interest in the natural sciences quickened and the increasing knowledge of the many kinds of animals led more and more scientists to consider the concept of evolution favorably. Among these were Hooke (1635–1703), Ray (1627–1705), Buffon (1707–1788), Erasmus Darwin (1731–1802) and Lamarck (1744–1829). Even before the Renaissance men had discovered shells, teeth, bones and other parts of animals buried in the ground. Some of these corresponded to parts of familiar living animals, but others were strangely unlike any known form. Many of the objects found in rocks high in the mountains, far from the sea, resembled parts of marine animals. In the fifteenth century, the versatile artist and scientist, Leonardo da Vinci, gave the correct explanation of these curious finds, and gradually his conclusion, that they were the remains of animals that had existed at one time but had become extinct, was accepted. This evidence of former life suggested to some people the theory of **catastrophism** — the idea that a succession of catastrophes, fires and floods, have periodically destroyed all living things, followed each time by the origin of new and higher types by acts of special creation.

Three Englishmen in the eighteenth and early nineteenth centuries laid the foundations of modern geology, and by their careful, cogent arguments advanced the theory of **uniformitarianism** to replace the concept of catastrophism. In 1785 James Hutton developed the concept that the geologic forces at work in the past were the same as those operating now. He arrived at this conclusion after a careful study of the erosion of valleys by rivers and the formation of sedimentary deposits at the mouths of rivers. He demonstrated that the processes of erosion, sedimentation, disruption and uplift, carried on over long periods of time, could account for the formation of fossil-bearing rock strata. The publication of John Playfair's *Illustrations of the Huttonian Theory of the Earth* in 1802 gave further explanation and examples of the idea of uniformitarianism in geologic processes. Sir Charles Lyell, one of the most influential geologists of his time, finally converted most of the contemporary geologists to the theory of uniformitarianism by the publication of his *Principles of Geology* (1832). A necessary corollary of the idea that slowly acting geologic forces have worn away mountains and filled up seas is that geologic time has been immensely long. This idea, completely revolutionary at the time, paved the way for the acceptance of the theory of organic evolution, for the process of evolution requires an extremely long time.

The earliest theory of organic evolution to be logically developed was that of Jean Baptiste de Lamarck, the great French zoologist whose *Philosophie Zoologique* was published in 1809. Lamarck, like most biologists of his time, believed that all living things are endowed with a vital force that controls the development and functioning of their parts and enables them to overcome handicaps in the environment. He believed that any trait acquired by an organism during its lifetime was passed on to succeeding generations—that acquired characters are inherited. Developing the notion that new organs arise in response to the demands of the environment, he postulated that the size of the organ is proportional to its use or disuse. The changes produced by the use or disuse of an organ are transmitted to the offspring and this process, repeated for many generations, would result in marked alterations of form and function. Lamarck explained the evolution of the giraffe's long neck by suggesting that some short-necked ancestor of the giraffe took to browsing on the leaves of trees, instead of on grass, and that, in reaching up, it stretched and elongated its neck. The offspring, inheriting the longer neck, stretched still farther, and the process was repeated until the present long neck was achieved.

Both Buffon and Erasmus Darwin had similar ideas about the role in evolution of the direct response of the organism to its environment but had not expressed them so clearly. This theory, called **Lamarckism,** provides an explanation for the remarkable adaptation of many plants and animals to their environment but is completely unacceptable because of the overwhelming genetic evidence that acquired characteristics cannot be inherited. The theoretical distinction between somatoplasm and germ plasm made by Weismann (1887) refuted all theories of evolution based on the inheritance of acquired characters. Acquired characters are present only in the body cells (somatoplasm) and not in the germ cells (germ plasm), and only traits present in the germ plasm are transmitted to the next generation.

36.3
Background for The
Origin of Species

Charles Darwin made two great contributions to the body of scientific knowledge: he presented a wealth of detailed evidence and cogent arguments to show that organic evolution had occurred, and he formulated a theory, that of **natural selection,** to explain the mechanism of evolution.

Darwin was born in 1809 and was sent at the age of 15 to study medicine at the University of Edinburgh. Finding the lectures intolerably dull, he transferred, after two years, to Christ's College, Cambridge University, to study theology. Many of Darwin's friends at Edinburgh were interested in geology and zoology, and at Cambridge he joined a circle of friends interested in collecting beetles. Through them he came to know Professor Henslow, the naturalist. Shortly after leaving college, and upon the recommendation of Professor Henslow, Darwin was appointed naturalist on the ship Beagle, which was to make a five-year cruise around the world preparing navigation charts for the British Navy. The Beagle left Plymouth in 1831 and cruised slowly down the east coast and up the west coast of South America. While the rest of the company mapped the coasts and harbors, Darwin studied the animals, plants and geologic formations of both coastal and inland regions. He made extensive collections of specimens and copious notes of his observations. The Beagle then spent some time at the Galápagos Islands, west of Ecuador, where Darwin continued his observations of the flora and fauna, comparing them to those on the South American mainland. These observations convinced Darwin that the theory of special creation was inadequate and set him to thinking about alternative explanations.

Upon his return to England in 1836, Darwin spent his time assembling the notes of his observations for publication and searching for some reasonable explanation for the diversity of organisms and the peculiarities of their distribution. As Darwin wrote in his notebook:

On my return home in the autumn of 1836 I immediately began to prepare my journal for publication, and then saw how many facts indicated the common descent of species. . . . In July (1837) I opened my first notebook for facts in relation to the origin of species, about which I had long reflected, and never ceased working for the next twenty years. . . . Had been greatly struck from the month of March on character of South American fossils, and species on Galápagos Archipelago. These facts (especially latter) origin of all my views. . . .

In October (1838), that is fifteen months after I had begun my systematic inquiry, I happened to read for amusement Malthus on Population, and being well prepared to appreciate the struggle for existence which everywhere goes on, from long-continued observation of the habits of animals and plants, it at once struck me that under these circumstances favorable variations would tend to be preserved, and unfavorable ones to be destroyed. The result of this would be the origin of new species. Here then I had at last got a theory by which to work.

Darwin spent the next 20 years accumulating data from many fields of biology, examining it critically, and building up a tremendous body of facts that demonstrated that evolution had occurred and formulating his arguments for natural selection. In 1857 he submitted a draft of his theory to a number of scientific friends for comment and criticism. Alfred Russel Wallace, a naturalist and explorer who was studying the flora and fauna of Malaya and the East Indies, was similarly struck by the diversity of living things and the peculiarities of their distribution. Like Darwin, he happened to read Malthus' treatise and came independently to the same conclusion, that evolution occurred by natural selection. In 1858 Wallace sent a manuscript to Darwin, and asked him, if he thought it of sufficient interest, to present it to the Linnaean Society. Darwin's friends persuaded him to present an abstract of his own work along with Wallace's paper and this was done at a meeting of the Linnaean Society in July, 1858. Darwin's monumental *On the Origin of Species by Means of Natural Selection* was published in November, 1859.

The time was ripe for the formulation and acceptance of the theory of organic evolution. The publication of Lyell's *Principles of Geology* and the subsequent acceptance of the idea of geologic evolution, the publication of Malthus' ideas on population growth and pressure and the struggle for existence, together with the vast accumulation of information about the distribution of living and fossil forms of life, and studies of comparative anatomy and embryology, all showed the inadequacy of the theory of special creation. Because the time was ripe, Darwin's theory rapidly gained acceptance.

36.4
The Darwin-Wallace Theory of Natural Selection

Darwin's explanation of the way in which evolution occurs can be summarized as follows:

1. Variation is characteristic of every group of animals and plants, and there are many ways in which organisms may differ. (Darwin and Wallace did not understand the cause of variation, and assumed it was one of the innate properties of living things. We now know that inherited variations are caused by mutations.)

2. More organisms of each kind are born than can possibly obtain food and survive. Since the number of each species remains fairly constant under natural conditions, it must be assumed that most of the offspring in each generation perish. If all the offspring of any species remained alive and reproduced, they would soon crowd all other species from the earth.

3. Since more individuals are born than can survive, there is a struggle for survival, a competition for food and space. This contest may be an active kill-or-be-killed struggle, or

one less immediately apparent but no less real, such as the struggle of plants or animals to survive drought or cold. This idea of competition for survival in an overpopulated world was derived from Malthus.

4. Some of the variations exhibited by living things make it easier for them to survive; others are handicaps which bring about the elimination of their possessors. This idea of "the survival of the fittest" is the core of the theory of natural selection.

5. The surviving individuals will give rise to the next generation and, in this way, the "successful" variations are transmitted to the succeeding generations. The less fit will tend to be eliminated before they have reproduced.

Successive generations in this way tend to become better adapted to their environment; as the environment changes, further adaptations occur. The operation of natural selection over many generations may produce descendants which are quite different from their ancestors, different enough to be separate species. Furthermore, certain members of a population with one group of variations may become adapted to the environment in one way, while others, with a different set of variations, become adapted in a different way, or become adapted to a different environment. In this way two or more species may arise from a single ancestral stock.

Animals and plants exhibit many variations which are neither a help nor a hindrance to them in their struggle for survival. These are not affected directly by natural selection but are transmitted to succeeding generations.

Darwin's theory of natural selection was so reasonable and well documented that most biologists soon accepted it. One of the early, serious objections to the theory was that it did not explain the appearance of many apparently useless structures in an organism. We now know that many of the visible differences between species are not important for survival but are simply incidental effects of genes that have other physiologic effects of great survival value. Other nonadaptive differences may be controlled by genes that are closely linked in the chromosomes to genes for traits which are important for survival. Still other nonadaptive characteristics may become fixed in a population by chance, by the phenomenon of "genetic drift" (p. 651).

Another of the early objections to the

theory was that new variations would be lost by "dilution" as the individuals possessing them bred with others without them. We now know that although the phenotypic expression of a gene may be altered when the gene exists in combination with certain other genes, the gene itself is not altered and is transmitted unchanged to succeeding generations.

36.5
Populations and Gene Pools

The concepts of the "struggle for survival" and "survival of the fittest" were key points in the Darwin-Wallace theory of natural selection, but it is now realized that the actual physical struggle between animals for survival or the competition between plants for space, sun and water is much less important as an evolutionary force than Darwin believed. The evolution of any given kind of organism occurs over many generations during which individuals are born and die, but the population has a certain continuity. Thus, the unit in evolution is not the individual but rather a *population* of individuals.

A population of similar individuals living within a circumscribed area and interbreeding is termed a **deme** or a **genetic population.** The territorial limits of any given deme may be quite vague and difficult to define and the number of individuals in the deme may fluctuate widely with time. A deme commonly overlaps with one or more adjacent demes to some extent. The next larger unit of population in nature is the **species,** composed of a series of intergrading demes.

The Hardy-Weinberg Law states that gene frequencies in a population remain constant from generation to generation if (1) the population is large, (2) there is no selection (i.e., mating occurs at random), and (3) mutations do not occur. Stated in its simplest terms evolution is a gradual change in the gene frequencies of a population when the Hardy-Weinberg equilibrium is upset either because mutations occur, because reproduction is nonrandom or because the population is small (resulting in genetic drift).

The demes and species occurring in nature tend to continue unchanged for many generations or centuries. This implies that there has been no change in the genetic constitution of the deme and no change in the environmental factors. When a change in a population does occur, this reflects either a change in the genetic factors brought about by mutation or a change in the environmental factors, which lead to selective survival of one or another kind of individual or both.

One of the basic concepts of population genetics and of evolution is that each population is characterized by a certain **genetic pool.** Each individual in the population is genetically unique and has a specific genotype. However, if we count all the alleles of a given gene (A_1, A_2, A_3 . . .) in a population (or in a valid sample of the population) we could then calculate the fraction of the total represented by allele A_1, allele A_2 and so on. A population in genetic equilibrium has a gene pool which is constant from one generation to the next; i.e., the frequency of each allele in the population remains unchanged.

In contrast, a population undergoing evolution is one in which the gene pool is changing from generation to generation. The gene pool of a population may be changed (1) by mutation, (2) by hybridization, that is, by the introduction into the population of genes from some outside population, or (3) by natural selection. Recombination brought about by crossing over and by the assortment of chromosomes in meiosis may also lead to new combinations of genes and phenotypes with some specific advantage or disadvantage for survival that would be reflected in a change in the genetic pool.

Evolution by natural selection simply means that those individuals with certain traits have more surviving offspring in the next generation and so contribute a proportionately greater percentage of genes to the gene pool of the next generation than organisms with other traits. New inherited variations arise primarily by mutation, and if the organisms with a new mutation survive and have, on the average, more offspring that survive than the organisms without that mutation, then in successive generations the gene pool of the population will gradually change.

This process, termed **nonrandom reproduction** or **differential reproduction,** implies that the conditions of the Hardy-Weinberg equilibrium do not apply to that population. The individuals that produce more surviving offspring in the next generation are usually, but not necessarily, those that are best adapted to the given environment. Well adapted individuals may be healthier, better able to obtain food and mates and better able to care for their offspring, but the primary factor in evolution is how many of their offspring survive to be parents of the next generation.

The ultimate raw material of evolution is a mutation which establishes an alternative allele at a given locus and makes possible an alternative phenotype. Evolutionary changes are possible only when there are alternative phenotypes that may survive or perish. However, the process of selection does not in general operate gene by gene but rather individual by individual and on the basis of the effects of the individual's entire genetic system.

When a mutation first appears, only one or a few organisms in the population will bear the mutant gene, and these will breed with other members of the population from which the mutant arose. The change in the gene pool so that the mutant gene appears with greater and greater frequency in the population is a gradual process which may occur only over many generations. When one is considering evolutionary changes in a larger population, the success or lack of success of some new mutant gene will depend largely on its ability to confer on its possessors the capacity to leave a larger number of surviving individuals in the next generation.

In the reproduction of small populations chance alone may play a considerable role in determining the composition of the succeeding generation. The equilibrium of the genetic pool of the population can be changed by chance processes rather than by natural selection. This role of chance in the evolution of small breeding populations has been described by Sewall Wright as **genetic drift.** Within small interbreeding populations, heterozygous gene pairs tend to become homozygous for one allele or the other by chance rather than by selection. This may lead to the accumulation of certain disadvantageous characters and the subsequent elimination of the group possessing those characters.

The role that genetic drift actually plays in the evolution of organisms in nature has been the subject for debate among biologists, but there seems little doubt that it does play at least a minor role. Certainly, many animal and plant populations in nature are divided into subgroups small enough to be affected by the chance events underlying genetic drift.

Genetic drift represents an exception to the Hardy-Weinberg Law underlying the tendency for a population to maintain its proportion of homozygous and heterozygous individuals. The Hardy-Weinberg Law is based on statistical events and, like all statistical laws, holds only when the number of individuals involved is large enough. Genetic drift may explain the common observation that closely related species in different parts of the world frequently differ in curious, even bizarre, ways which appear to have no particular adaptive value.

The role of chance in evolution is particularly evident when a species moves into a new area, for the number of individuals moving into that area is usually small. These first colonizers from which the entire new population develops rarely constitute a representative sample of the gene pool of the original population, but instead differ from the parent population in the frequencies of specific genes. These differences may be quite marked but the new colonizing generation differs from the parent population in ways which are random.

This effect is most apparent on islands and other areas of geographic isolation, and helps to account for the differences evident in island populations as compared to their mainland relatives. When a species is expanding continuously, the populations at the edge of the range, invading new areas, are likely to be small and differ genetically from the main body of the population. In all these situations, when the breeding population is small, chance rather than selection may play a large role in determining the evolution of a particular group.

36.6
Differential Reproduction

The evolutionary forces of mutation, genetic drift and the migration of genes from one population to another by hybridization can lead to the establishment of diversity among living things, but these processes operate by and large at random. In contrast, a key feature of evolution is the tendency of organisms to become adapted so as to survive and reproduce in the particular environment that they inhabit. The evolutionary process, then, is not random with respect to the establishing of adaptive features of organisms.

The process of differential reproduction may be nonrandom with respect to (1) the union of male and female gametes, (2) the production of viable zygotes, or (3) the development and survival of the zygotes until they are adults and capable of producing their own offspring. Nonrandom reproduction tends to produce nonrandom, directional changes in the genetic pool which lead to nonrandom, directional evolution. Random mating implies that any given male must be as likely to mate with any one female in the population as with any other, or that the gametes of any two individuals must be equally likely to unite. However, mating in nature is seldom completely at random.

Differential reproduction, i.e., a change in the gene pool in successive generations, usually occurs in some way that is correlated with the genotypes of the individuals concerned and tends to produce directional changes in evolution. Differential reproduction may result from nonrandom mating—that is, the union of male and female gametes by the mating of specific individuals—from the differential viability of the resulting zygotes or from differences in the development and survival of the offspring until they are in turn the parents of the next generation.

Behavior patterns of courtship and mating within a given species which lead to the acceptance or refusal of one individual by another in mating comprise one kind of force directing differential reproduction through **nonrandom mating.** Any gene mutation that causes a change from the usual pattern of courtship will generally have a negative selective advantage and tend to be eliminated. In many fishes and birds some brightly colored part on the male serves as a stimulus to the opposite sex which is necessary before copulation can be begun. Mutations that lead to the formation of bigger, brighter spots may confer a selective advantage on their possessors. Darwin recognized this evolutionary force and termed it **sexual selection.** However, it is clear that this is just one kind of natural selection, one factor that may result in differential reproduction.

A second aspect of differential reproduction is **differential fecundity,** which refers to the number of viable zygotes that are produced by a given mating. There may be genetic differences in the number of gametes produced by individuals and in the proportion of those gametes that can unite with others to form viable zygotes. In organisms with a low probability of individual survival, high fecundity will be an evolutionary advantage. However, in other organisms where the chances of the survival of an individual are high, an extremely high fecundity may actually reduce the chances of survival of any given individual by reducing the opportunity for parental care and feeding of the offspring.

Even after two gametes have united to produce a viable zygote, the resulting organism must go through a fairly long period of development and growth before becoming sexually mature and able to contribute to the next generation. It is this aspect of differential reproduction that has played perhaps the largest role in determining the course of evolution. It is the differential success of organisms in a population in surviving to the reproductive age and contributing to the next generation's gene pool that has been responsible for the more obvious features of organic adaptation.

The survival of an organism to sexual maturity and its reproductive performance obviously require its competence to withstand a variety of elements in the physical and biological environment. The physical factors of sunlight, moisture, temperature, gravity, light and darkness may be of prime importance in determining the survival or elimination of certain genotypes. Each organism has to live amid other organisms, which leads to competition to eat and avoid being eaten.

Plants must compete for room in the soil and for sunlight as well as for water and inorganic salts. Each is constantly threatened by animals that may eat it before it has the opportunity to reach sexual maturity and release the spores or seeds for the next generation. Animals are under similar pressure to avoid being eaten or killed and to find food for themselves. Any adaptation that improves an organism's ability to find food and avoid being eaten will, of course, play a role in its differential reproduction.

Thus, evolutionary changes resulting from differential reproduction are of such a nature as to maintain or improve the average ability of that population to produce successive generations under the conditions of the environment. Since there are a great many different ways by which the process of differential reproduction can be facilitated, there are a great many different ways in which natural selection may operate.

Natural selection, in general, does not operate upon the phenotypes of single genes but upon the phenotypic effects of the whole genetic system. One group of organisms may survive despite some obviously disadvantageous character while another may be eliminated despite some traits that are highly advantageous for its getting along in life. The plants and animals that ultimately survive and are the parents of the next generation are those with qualities whose sum total renders them a little better able than their competitors to survive and reproduce their kind. The environment itself may change from time to time; thus, a characteristic of adaptive value at one time may be useless or even deleterious at another.

36.7

Mutations, The Raw Material of Evolution

The Dutch botanist Hugo de Vries, one of the three rediscoverers of Mendel's laws, was the first to emphasize the importance in evolution of sudden large changes rather than the gradual accumulation of many small changes postulated by Darwin. In his experiments with plants, such as the evening primrose, de Vries found that many unusual forms, which differed markedly from the ancestral wild plant, appeared and bred true thereafter. He applied the term **mutations** to these sudden changes in the characteristics of an organism (earlier breeders had called them "sports"). Darwin had observed such changes but thought they occurred too rarely to be of importance in evolution. Darwin believed that these sudden changes would upset the harmonious relations between the various parts of an organism and its adaptation to the environment. Thousands of breeding experiments with plants and animals since the turn of the century have shown that such mutations do occur constantly and that their effects may be of adaptive value. With the development of the gene theory, the term mutation has come to refer to sudden, discontinuous, random changes in the genes and chromosomes, although it is still used to some extent to refer to the new type of plant or animal.

In the plants and animals most widely used in breeding experiments—corn and fruit flies—some 400 to 600 mutations, respectively, have been detected. The fruit fly mutations are tremendously varied and include all shades of body color from yellow through brown and gray to black; red, white, brown or purple eyes; crumpled, curled, shortened, and peculiarly shaped wings—even the complete absence of wings; oddly shaped legs and bristles; and such extraordinary changes as a pair of legs growing on the forehead in place of the antennae (Fig. 36.1). Mutations are found in domestic animals; the six-toed cats of Cape Cod and the short-legged Ancon sheep are two of many examples of the persistence of a single mutation.

Early in the present century there was a heated discussion as to whether evolution was the result of natural selection or of mutation. As more was learned about heredity, it became clear that natural selection can operate only when there is something to be selected, that is, when mutations present alternative ways of coping with the environment. The evolution of new species, then, involves both mutation and natural selection.

One of the current controversies in evolutionary theory concerns the possible role of small and large mutations in the origin of new species. The Neo-Darwinists argue that new species (and all the higher categories) evolve by the gradual accumulation of many small mutations; thus, there should exist many forms intermediate between the original species and the new one. Other biologists believe that new species and genera arise in a single step by a **macromutation,** a major change in the genetic system which produces a major change in the pattern of development. This results in an adult that is morphologically and physiologically quite different from its parents. The macromutationists would hold that one should not expect to find forms which are intermediate between the original species and the new one. Many macromutations result only in "monsters" which would be unable to survive. (The term monster simply means any form which is markedly different from the usual type of the species and does not necessarily imply that it is ugly.) Other macromutations may give rise to what Richard Goldschmidt called "hopeful monsters," organisms which are enabled by their mutation to occupy some new environment. The evolution of the extinct ancestral bird, *Archaeopteryx,* into modern birds, Goldschmidt believed, may have occurred by a macromutation. *Archaeopteryx* (Fig. 24.16) had a long reptile-like tail covered with feathers; a macromutation which altered

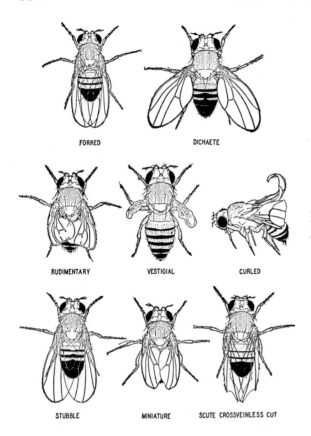

FORKED   DICHAETE

RUDIMENTARY   VESTIGIAL   CURLED

STUBBLE   MINIATURE   SCUTE CROSSVEINLESS CUT

Figure 36.1 Some wing and bristle mutants in the fruit fly, *Drosophila melanogaster*. (Drawn by E. M. Wallace; Sturtevant and Beadle: An Introduction to Genetics.)

development so that the tail was greatly shortened would result in a "hopeful monster" with the fan-shaped arrangement of tail feathers seen in modern birds. This new shape of the tail, which is better suited for flying than the long tail of *Archaeopteryx*, gave its possessors an advantage in the struggle for existence. There is, of course, no proof that modern birds evolved in this way, but there is ample evidence that similar marked skeletal changes may result from a single mutation. The stubby tail of the Manx cat is the result of a mutation which causes the tail vertebrae to shorten and fuse. Professor Goldschmidt did not deny that small mutations may occur and accumulate but held that they can lead only to varieties or geographic races and not to species, genera and the higher taxonomic divisions.

The causes of natural or spontaneous mutations are unknown. Both gene and chromosome mutations can be produced artificially by a variety of agents: x-rays and alpha, beta and gamma rays emitted by radioactive elements, neutrons, ultraviolet rays, chemicals such as the war gas known as nitrogen mustard, even heat and cold are slightly effective.

Cosmic rays and other particles bombarding the earth may account for some of the spontaneous mutations. Errors in the process of gene replication could lead to the production of mutant genes.

Both spontaneous and artificially induced mutations occur at random; the appearance of a mutation bears no relationship to the kind of inducing agent or to the particular need of the organism at that time. There is no way of producing to order a particular kind of mutation—a particular kind of biochemical mutant in *Neurospora,* for example. An investigator who wants to use some particular mutant has no choice but to irradiate many organisms, produce hundreds or even thousands of mutations, and then select the one he particularly wants.

Whatever the causes of mutations may be, their central role in evolution as the raw material for natural selection is now generally accepted. Some evolutionists have in the past objected that the spontaneous or induced mutations observed in the laboratory could not be the basis for evolution because almost all of them are deleterious, and because the differences between species are usually slight variations, affecting many different parts of the organism and inherited by means of multiple factors, whereas the mutations observed in the laboratory are usually large variations, involving a single organ and inherited by single gene differences. Studies in the genetics of wild populations have shown that mutations that occur in the wild, like the ones observed in the laboratory, are usually for detrimental traits. We must keep clearly in mind that the animals and plants living today are the result of a long and rigorous process of natural selection. In the course of their evolution, most of the possible mutations have occurred, and the beneficial ones have been selected and preserved. The organisms are well adapted to their surroundings and further mutations are much more likely to be harmful than helpful. However, a few of the mutations seen in the laboratory and in wild populations are beneficial and have survival value. Mutations may produce traits which are deleterious in one environment but advantageous in another. Sickle cell anemia, for example, is generally disadvantageous, but its resistance to malaria is advantageous in regions such as Central Africa where malaria is very widespread.

Closer study of populations has shown that the sort of variations which differentiate a species do appear in stocks bred in the laboratory. However, being somewhat more difficult to detect and study, they were missed in some of the earlier work. More recent experiments indicate that such mutations occur at an even greater rate than the larger, more obvious ones.

36.8
Balanced Polymorphism

It might be assumed that selection would inevitably result in a population completely homozygous for whichever pair of alleles at a given locus provides for a trait of the greatest adaptive value. Although this indeed may happen, it is not the only possibility in differential reproduction. Variation itself may be adaptive for a population, because a completely homozygous population would have no genetic substratum on which natural selection could act. A population with a good prognosis for survival is one that has maintained enough variation to permit further adaptive changes. Observations on wild populations of flies and other organisms have shown that their genetic pools do change adaptively in response to such changes in the environment as the alternations of the seasons.

There are instances in which the heterozygote is fitter for reproductive efficiency and survival than either of the corresponding homozygous individuals; however, the heterozygous state cannot be maintained in the population unless a certain number of the comparatively less fit homozygous individuals are also produced. Depending on the relative selective values of the heterozygous and homozygous states, there is a particular ratio of alleles in the genetic pool that will result in the optimal proportion of heterozygotes and homozygotes. The preservation of variation by selection in this way is termed a **balanced polymorphism.** More and more evidence is coming to light that the populations that are most effective reproductively do maintain a fairly high degree of heterozygosity.

36.9
Adaptive Radiation

The phenomenon termed adaptive radiation is a general feature of the evolution of most plants and animals. Whenever a group of organisms has been provided with the opportunity to spread into a number of new ecological habitats to which it has physical access and in which it has the possibility of surviving, these radiations have occurred. Because of the competition for food and living space, there is a tendency for each group of organisms to spread out and occupy as many different habitats as they can reach and which will support them. This evolution, from a single ancestral species, of a variety of forms which occupy different habitats is called **adaptive radiation.** It is obviously advantageous in enabling organisms to tap new sources of food and to escape from some of their enemies.

The placental mammals provide a classic illustration of the process, for from a primitive, insect-eating, five-toed, short-legged creature that walked with the soles of its feet flat on the ground have evolved all the present-day types of placental mammals (Fig. 36.2). There are dogs and deer, adapted for terrestrial life in which running rapidly

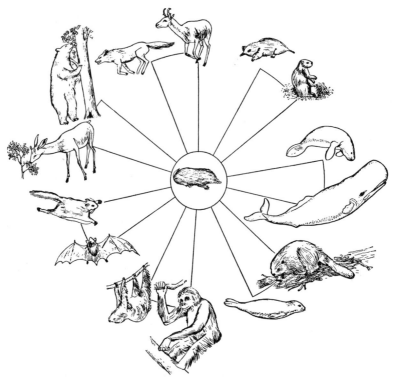

Figure 36.2 Adaptive radiation. All the various mammals shown have evolved from the common ancestor shown in the center, but have become adapted to a wide variety of habitats.

is important for survival; squirrels and primates, adapted for life in the trees; bats, equipped for flying; beavers and seals, which maintain an amphibious existence; the completely aquatic whales, porpoises and sea cows; and the burrowing animals, moles, gophers and shrews. The number and shape of the teeth, the length and number of leg bones, the number and attachment sites of muscles and the thickness and color of the fur are some of the structures that are involved in adaptation.

There was a comparable major adaptive radiation of the reptiles in earlier geologic ages. Adaptive radiation may take place on a much smaller scale, as represented by the variety of ground finches found today on the Galápagos Islands west of Ecuador. Some of these are ground birds that feed mainly on seeds, others feed mainly on cactus, and still others have taken to living in trees and eating insects. There have been evolutionary changes in the size of the beak and in its structure. The essence of adaptive radiation, then, is the evolution of a variety of different forms from a single ancestral form with each of the descendants being adaptively specialized in

a unique way to survive in a particular habitat.

Adaptive radiation in which a single ancestral type gives rise to several descendant lines adapted in different ways to different environments may be termed **divergent evolution.** The opposite phenomenon is also fairly frequent in evolution—that is, two or more unrelated groups become adapted to similar environments and tend to develop features that are at least superficially similar. The evolution of similar sets of characteristics in groups of quite different evolutionary ancestry is termed **convergent evolution.** An often quoted example of convergent evolution is the development of wings in flying reptiles, in birds and in mammals as well as in insects.

The dolphins and porpoises (which are mammals), the extinct ichthyosaurs (which were reptiles) and both bony and cartilaginous fishes have all evolved streamlined shapes, dorsal fins, tail fins and flipper-like fore and hind limbs which make them look much alike (Fig. 36.3). The moles and gophers, in adapting to a burrowing life, have evolved similar fore and hind leg struc-

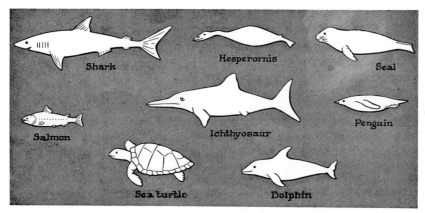

Figure 36.3 Convergent evolution. All of these aquatic vertebrates have a marked superficial similarity despite their distant relationship, because of their adaptations to similar environments.

tures adapted for digging, but the mole is an insectivore and the gopher is a rodent. The eye of the squid and the eye of the simpler vertebrates such as the fish are also very similar in structure and provide yet another example of convergent evolution.

36.10
Speciation

We have defined a species as a collection of demes or populations within which interbreeding may occur, a group of populations with a common gene pool. It is implicit in this definition that there is no free flow of genes between two such species, that reproductive barriers isolate one species from the next. These barriers need not be absolute and an occasional hybrid between species does not alter their status as separate species.

The problem of speciation is to explain how unit evolutionary changes in a population may eventually culminate in the establishment of new species, genera, families and orders and to explain how reproductive barriers between species may arise. When interbreeding between subgroups of a population becomes less and less frequent and the resulting hybrids become less and less fertile, the several groups eventually become different species. Any factor that decreases the amount of interbreeding between groups or organisms is called an **isolating mechanism.**

Perhaps the most common type of isolation is **geographic,** whereby groups of related organisms become separated by some physical barrier such as a sea, mountain, desert, glacier or river (Fig. 36.4). In moun-

tainous regions the individual ranges provide effective barriers between the valleys, and there are usually more different species for a given area than on the plains. In the mountains of western United States 23 species and subspecies of rabbits are known, while in the larger plains area of the Midwest and East there are only eight species. Valleys only a short distance apart, but separated by ridges perpetually covered with snow, have species of plants and animals peculiar to them.

One of the most striking examples of geographic isolation is provided by the seas divided by the Isthmus of Panama. On either side of the Isthmus, the phyla and classes of marine invertebrates are made up of different, but closely related species—a situation brought about by the fact that for some 16,000,000 years, during the Tertiary period, there was no connection between North and South America. This made it possible for animals to migrate freely between what is now the Gulf of Mexico and the Pacific Ocean. With the emergence of the Isthmus of Panama the closely related groups of animals were isolated, and the differences between the two fauna today represent the subsequent accumulation of hereditary differences.

Geographic isolation is usually not permanent; hence two previously isolated groups may come into contact again and interbreed unless **genetic isolation** or interspecific sterility has arisen in the meantime. The various races of man are the result of isolation and the accumulation of chance mutations, but since interracial sterility has not developed, the differences disappear when geographic isolation breaks down. That they do not disappear even more quickly and com-

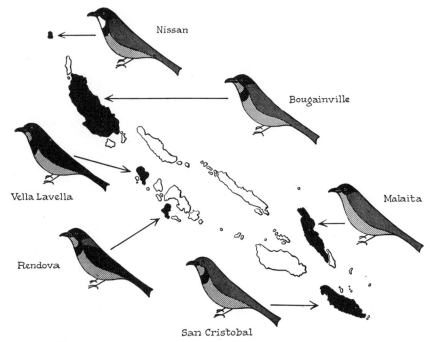

Figure 36.4 The distribution of the subspecies of the golden whistler (*Pachycephala pectoralis*) in the Solomon Islands. A major factor in the evolution of these subspecies has been their geographic isolation on separate islands. Green-colored plumage is indicated by cross-hatching; yellow by light gray tone. (Modified from Dobzhansky.)

pletely is due largely to social taboos against intermarriage—itself a form of isolation.

Genetic isolation results from one or more mutations occurring by chance, independently of other mutations. It may arise only after a long period of geographic isolation has produced marked differences between two groups of organisms, or it may arise within a single, otherwise homogeneous group. Such a mutation for genetic isolation occurred in a species of fruit fly, *Drosophila pseudoobscura,* producing two groups of flies, externally indistinguishable, yet completely sterile when mated with each other. The two groups are isolated as effectively as if they lived on different continents, and as generations pass and different mutations accumulate by chance and selection, they will undoubtedly become visibly different. Biologists usually do not consider two closely related but different groups of organisms to be different species unless genetic isolation has developed.

Another type of isolation, called **ecologic,** depends upon the fact that two groups of animals living in the same geographic area may occupy different habitats. Marine animals living only in the intertidal zone are effectively isolated from others living only a few feet away, below the low-tide mark. Or ecologic isolation may be due to the fact that two groups breed at different times of the year.

36.11
The Origin of Species by Hybridization

The crossing of two different varieties or species, called **hybridization,** provides another way in which new species may originate. The new species may combine the best characters of each of the parental species, thereby becoming better able to survive than either of its parents. Hybridization is used routinely by animal and plant breeders to establish new combinations of desirable characters.

When two different species are crossed, and especially ones with different chromosome numbers, the offspring are usually sterile. The unlike chromosomes cannot pair properly, cannot undergo synapsis in the process of meiosis, and the resulting eggs and sperm do not receive the proper assortment of chromosomes. However, if one of these interspecific hybrids undergoes a chromosome mutation which results in the doubling of the chromosome number, meiosis can then occur normally and fertile eggs and sperm are produced. The hybrid will breed true thereafter and will generally not produce fertile offspring when bred with either of the parental species. It is widely believed that this process has been quite important in the evolution of the higher plants; more than half of the higher plants appear to be polyploids. There are species of wheat with 14, 28 and 42 chromosomes, species of roses with 14, 28, 42 and 56 chromosomes, and species of violets with every multiple of 6 from 12 to 54. The fact that similar series of plants with related numbers of chromosomes can be established by experimental breeding lends credence to the idea that these natural series arose by successive hybridization and chromosome doubling.

One of the more famous experimental hybrids was the radish × cabbage cross made by Karpechenko. Although radishes and cabbages belong to different genera, each has 18 chromosomes. The resulting hybrid also had 18 chromosomes, nine from the radish parent and nine from the cabbage parent. The radish and cabbage chromosomes were not sufficiently alike to permit synapsis to occur normally and the hybrid was almost completely sterile. The chance distribution of the chromosomes led to the formation of a few eggs and sperm that had 18 chromosomes each, and the union of such eggs and sperm resulted in a plant with 36 chromosomes. This new plant was fertile; in meiosis the homologous radish chromosomes paired with each other and the homologous cabbage chromosomes paired with each other. The new hybrid had some of the characteristics of each of its parents and bred true for them. It was not valuable commercially, however, for it had roots like a cabbage and a top like a radish. Since this hybrid could not be crossed readily with either of its parental species, *Raphanus sativus*, the radish, or *Brassica oleracea,* the cabbage, Karpechenko named this new, experimentally produced genus *Raphanobrassica.*

There are many other examples of species of plants produced by hybridization and chromosome doubling, but this process appears to have played a negligible role in the evolution of animals. Two explanations of this have been advanced: the gametes of animals are more sensitive to imbalances of chromosomes and are nonviable unless a normal haploid set is present; since the sexes are separate in most animals, the random segregation of several pairs of sex chromosomes in a polyploid animal might lead to the formation of sterile combinations.

36.12
Straight-line Evolution

Many of the earlier paleontologists and other students of evolution were led to the conclusion that there are trends in evolution, that evolution tends to progress in a straight line. The term **orthogenesis** was coined to refer to straight-line evolution; some investigators had the somewhat mystical belief that organisms have an inherent tendency to evolve in a predetermined direction. Fuller examination of the accumulating fossil data, however, has shown that many of the instances often quoted as examples of orthogenesis are not truly evolution in a straight line. The horse is often said to have evolved in a straight line from the primitive *Hyracotherium* (a small animal, the size of a fox, with four toes on the front feet and three toes on the hind feet) to the modern *Equus,* but the complete fossil record shows that there were many side branches in horse evolution (Fig. 36.5). The evolution of the present-day horse is not at all the simple progression along a single straight line of evolution that it was once thought to be. The evolution of the horse was said to show the following "trends": an increase in size, a lengthening of the legs, enlargement of the third digit and reduction of the others, an increase in the size of the molar teeth and in the complexity of the patterns of ridges on their crowns, and increases in the size of the lower jaw and the skull. More recent work has shown that there are so many exceptions to each of these that the concept of a straight-line evolution of the horse has been abandoned.

The term orthogenesis is sometimes applied to the evolutionary overdevelopment of some characteristic. The classic example of this is the development of the antlers of the extinct Irish deer. In successive generations the antlers became larger, and although this may have been of adaptive significance at first, the antlers eventually became so big, with a total spread of 3.5 meters, that they may have been a factor contributing to the extinction of the species.

Our increasing knowledge of how genes act

EOCENE OLIGOCENE MIOCENE PLIOCENE PLEISTOCENE-RECENT

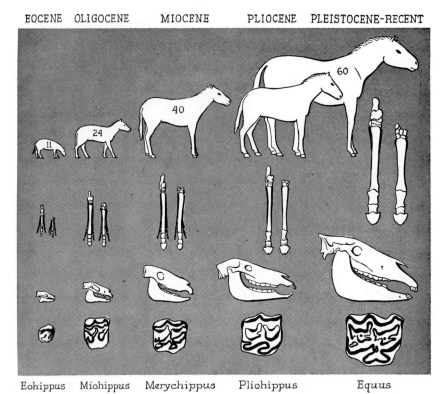

Eohippus Miohippus Merychippus Pliohippus Equus

Figure 36.5 Stages in the evolution of the horse, illustrating (top) the changes in size and shape (the numbers indicate the shoulder height in inches), (second row) the bones of the fore and hind feet, (third row) the skull, and (bottom) the grinding surfaces of the second upper molar tooth. *Eohippus* is a synonym of *Hyracotherium*.

in controlling development has enabled us to explain whatever straight-line trends in evolution may be real in terms of conventional evolution by mutation and selection. Many different types of developmental patterns may arise by random mutation, yet most of them will result in unharmonious processes, ones which will not interdigitate properly and will lead to the death of the organism. Others, with no particular value for survival, will remain or be eliminated by chance. The ones most likely to survive, perhaps, are those which provide for further improvement in some peculiar adaptive structure already present. Thus, orthogenetic series can be explained as the result of random mutation and selection occurring along one of the few possible lines of development. An explanation for the overdevelopment of parts is now possible as well: genes do not function independently but must operate against the background of many other genes also present. Those controlling larger horns, for example, might cause the horns to be proportionately larger than the rest of the body, and if other

genes cause an increase in total body size, the horns might become lethal to their possessors.

36.13
The Origin of Life

The modern theories of mutation, natural selection and population dynamics provide us with a satisfactory explanation of how the present-day animals and plants evolved from previous forms by descent with modification. The question of the ultimate origin of life on this planet has been given serious consideration by many different biologists. Some have postulated that some kind of spores or germs may have been carried through space from another planet to this one. This is unsatisfactory, not only because it begs the question of the ultimate source of these spores, but because it is extremely unlikely that any sort of living thing could survive the extreme cold and intense irradiation of interplanetary travel. Evidence for life in other parts of the cosmos has come from the discovery in 1961 of what appear to be fossils of microscopic organisms, somewhat like algae, in meteorites. This does not provide evidence, however, that living organisms could be transported through space in a meteorite.

The concept that the first living things *did* evolve from nonliving things has been put forward by Pflüger, J. B. S. Haldane, R. Beutner, and especially by the Russian biochemist A. I. Oparin in his book, *The Origin of Life* (1938). The earth originated some 3.5 to 5 billion years ago, either as a part broken off from the sun or by the gradual condensation of interstellar dust. Most authorities seem agreed that the earth at first was very hot and molten and that conditions consistent with life arose only perhaps a billion and a half years ago. At that time the earth's atmosphere contained essentially no free oxygen; all the oxygen was combined as water and as oxides.

A number of reactions by which organic substances can be made from inorganic ones are known. It is believed that originally much of the earth's carbon was in the form of metallic carbides; these could react with water to form acetylene, which would subsequently polymerize to form compounds containing long chains of carbon atoms. It has been shown experimentally that high energy radiation, such as that of cosmic rays, can produce organic compounds. This has been demonstrated by M. Calvin, who irradiated solutions of carbon dioxide and water in a cyclotron and obtained formic, oxalic and succinic acids, which contain one, two and four carbons respectively. These are important intermediates in the metabolism of living organisms. Irradiation of solutions with ultraviolet light, or with electric charges to simulate lightning, also produces organic compounds. Harold Urey and Stanley Miller, at the University of Chicago, showed in 1953 that amino acids such as glycine and alanine, and even more complex organic substances, can be formed in vitro by exposing a mixture of water vapor, methane, ammonia and hydrogen gases to electric discharges for a mere week. All of these gases are believed to have been present in adequate amounts in the earth's atmosphere in prebiotic times.

The spontaneous origin of living things at the present time is believed to be extremely improbable, yet that this same event occurred in the past is quite probable. The difference lies in the conditions existing on the earth: the accumulation of organic molecules was possible before there were living things because there were no molds, no bacteria, no living things of any kind to bring about their decay. Furthermore, there was little or no oxygen in the atmosphere to bring about their spontaneous oxidation.

The details of the chemical reactions which could give rise, without the intervention of living things, to carbohydrates, fats and amino acids have been worked out by Oparin and extended by Calvin and others. Most of the reactions by which the more complex organic substances were formed probably occurred in the sea, in which were dissolved and mixed the organic molecules formed. The sea, we may postulate, became a sort of dilute broth in which these molecules collided, reacted, and aggregated to form new molecules of increasing size and complexity. As more has been learned of the role of specific hydrogen-bonding and other weak intermolecular forces in the pairing of specific nucleotide bases, and the effectiveness of these processes in the transfer of biological information, it has become clear that similar forces could have operated early in evolution, before the appearance of "living" organisms.

The known forces of intermolecular attraction, and the tendency for certain molecules to form liquid crystals, provide us with means by which large, complex, specific molecules can form spontaneously. Oparin suggested that natural selection can operate at the level of these complex molecules before anything recognizable as life is present. As the molecules came together to form colloidal aggregates, these aggregates began to compete with one another for raw materials. Some of the aggregates, which had some particularly favorable internal arrangement, would acquire new molecules more rapidly than others and would eventually become the dominant types.

Once some protein molecules had formed and had achieved the ability to catalyze reactions, the rate of formation of additional molecules would be greatly stepped up. Next, in combination with molecules of nucleic acid, these complex protein molecules probably acquired the ability to catalyze the synthesis of molecules like themselves. These hypothetic, autocatalytic particles composed of nucleic acids and proteins would have some of the properties of a virus, or perhaps of a free-living gene. The next step in the development of a living thing was the addition of the ability of the autocatalytic particle to undergo inherited changes — to mutate. Then, if a number of these free genes had joined to form a single larger unit, the resulting organism would have been similar to certain present-day viruses. A major step in early evolution was the development of a protein-lipid membrane around this aggregate which permitted the accumulation of some and the exclusion of other molecules. All the known viruses are parasites that can live only within the cells of higher animals and plants. However, a little reflection will suggest that free-living viruses, ones which do not produce a disease, would be very difficult to detect; such organisms may indeed exist.

The first living organisms, having arisen in a sea of organic molecules and in contact with an atmosphere free of oxygen, presumably obtained energy by the fermentation of certain of these organic substances. These heterotrophs could survive only as long as the supply of organic molecules in the sea broth, accumulated from the past, lasted. Before the supply was exhausted, however, the heterotrophs evolved further and became autotrophs, able to make their own organic molecules by chemosynthesis or photosynthesis. One of the by-products of photosynthesis is gaseous oxygen, and it is likely that all the oxygen in the atmosphere was produced and is still produced in this way. It is estimated that all the oxygen of our atmosphere is renewed by photosynthesis every 2000 years and all the carbon dioxide molecules pass through the photosynthetic process every 300 years. All the oxygen and carbon dioxide in the earth's atmosphere are the products of living organisms and have passed through living organisms over and over again in times past.

An explanation of how an autotroph may have evolved from one of these primitive, fermenting heterotrophs was presented by N. H. Horowitz in 1945. According to Horowitz' hypothesis, an organism might acquire, by successive mutations, the enzymes needed to synthesize complex from simple substances, in the reverse order to the sequence in which they are used in normal metabolism. Let us suppose that our first primitive heterotroph required organic compound Z for its growth. Substance Z, and a variety of other organic compounds, Y, X, W, V, U, etc., were present in the organic sea broth which was

the environment of this heterotroph. They had been synthesized previously by the action of nonliving factors of the environment. The heterotroph would survive nicely as long as the supply of compound Z lasted. If a mutation occurred which enabled the heterotroph to synthesize substance Z from substance Y, the strain of heterotroph with this mutation would be able to survive when the supply of substance Z was exhausted. A second mutation, which established an enzyme catalyzing a reaction by which substance Y could be made from the simpler substance X, would again have great survival value when the supply of Y was exhausted. Similar mutations, setting up enzymes enabling the organism to use successively simpler substances, W, V, U, . . . and finally some inorganic substance, A, would eventually result in an organism able to make substance Z, which it needs for growth, out of substance A by way of all the intermediate compounds. When, by other series of mutations, the organism was able to synthesize all of its requirements from simple inorganic compounds, as the green plants can, it would have become an autotroph. Once the first simple autotrophs had evolved, the way was clear for the further evolution of the vast variety of green plants, bacteria, molds and animals that inhabit the world today.

These considerations lead us to the conclusion that the origin of life, as an orderly natural event on this planet, was not only possible, it was almost inevitable. Furthermore, with the vast number of planets in all the known galaxies of the universe, many of them must have conditions which permit the origin of life. It is probable, then, that there are many other planets on which life as we know it exists. Wherever life is possible, it should, if given enough time, appear and ramify into a wide variety of types. Some of these may be quite dissimilar from the ones on this planet, but others may be quite like those found here; some may, perhaps, be like ourselves.

It seems unlikely that we will ever know how life originated, whether it happened only once or many times, or whether it might happen again. The theory (1) that organic substances were formed from inorganic substances by the action of physical factors in the environment; (2) that they interacted to form more and more complex substances, finally enzymes, and then self-reproducing systems ("free genes"); (3) that these "free genes" diversified and united to form primitive, perhaps virus-like heterotrophs; and (4) that autotrophs then evolved from these heterotrophs, has the virtue of being quite plausible. Many of the parts of this theory have been subjected to experimental verification.

36.14

Principles of Evolution

However much students of evolution may disagree as to the nature of mutations, the kind of mutations involved in evolution, and the degree to which such factors as natural selection, isolation, genetic recombination and population dynamics may affect the evolution of some particular organism, there are several fundamental principles upon which they are agreed: changes within the genes and chromosomes are the raw material of evolution, some sort of isolation is necessary for the establishment of a new species, and natural selection by differential reproduction is involved in the survival of some, but not all, of the mutations which occur. In addition, there are five principles of evolution to which nearly all biologists would subscribe.

1. Evolution occurs more rapidly at some times than at others. At the present time it is occurring rapidly, with many new forms appearing and many old ones becoming extinct.

2. Evolution does not proceed at the same rate among different types of organisms. At one extreme are the brachiopods, some species of which have been exactly the same for the last 500,000,000 years at least, for fossil shells found in rocks deposited at that time are identical with those of animals living today. In contrast, several species of man

have appeared and become extinct in the past few hundred thousand years. In general, evolution tends to occur rapidly when a new species first appears, and then gradually slows down as the group becomes established and adapted to its particular environment.

3. New species do not evolve from the most advanced and specialized forms already living, but from relatively simple, unspecialized forms. The mammals, for example, did not evolve from the large, specialized dinosaurs, but from a group of rather small and unspecialized reptiles.

4. Evolution is not always from the simple to the complex. There are many examples of "regressive" evolution, in which a complex organism has given rise to simpler ones. Most parasites have evolved from free-living ancestors which were more complex than they; wingless birds, such as the cassowary and emu, have descended from birds that could fly; many wingless insects have evolved from winged ones; the legless snakes came from reptiles with appendages; the whale, which has no hind legs, evolved from a mammal that had the customary two pairs of legs and so on. These are all reflections of the fact that mutations occur at random and not necessarily from the simple to the complex or from the imperfect to the perfect. If there is some advantage to a species in having a simpler structure, or in doing without some structure altogether, any mutations which happen to occur for such conditions will tend to accumulate by natural selection.

5. Evolution occurs by *populations*, not by individuals; evolutionary processes are brought about by the processes of mutation, nonrandom reproduction, natural selection and genetic drift.

QUESTIONS

1. What were Darwin's chief contributions to the theory of evolution?
2. Discuss the essential points of Lamarckism. What has led to the rejection of this theory?
3. Discuss the advances in the science of geology that paved the way for the theory of evolution.
4. Describe in your own words what Darwin meant by natural selection.
5. What changes in the theory of natural selection have been made necessary by discoveries since Darwin's time?
6. What contributions to the principle of evolution were made by Erasmus Darwin, Alfred Russel Wallace, Thomas Huxley, Thomas Malthus and Hugo de Vries?
7. Discuss the role of isolation in the origin of species.
8. What is meant by "genetic drift"? Under what circumstances is it important in evolution?
9. What evolutionary advantage may result if a population of animals becomes a balanced polymorphism?
10. Compare the Neo-Darwinian and the macromutation theories of the origin of species.

11. Distinguish between the several types of mutations. What physical and chemical agents are known to produce mutations in the laboratory? What agents may produce spontaneous mutations in natural populations?

12. What explanation may be given for the observation that most spontaneous and induced mutations produce phenotypes which are less well adapted for survival than the original form?

13. Describe the steps by which simple inorganic substances may have undergone chemical evolution to yield the complex system of organic chemicals we recognize as "living matter." Which of these has been duplicated experimentally?

14. List the general principles of evolution. Are there any you think should be deleted or added?

ANNOTATED REFERENCES

Blum, H. F.: Time's Arrow and Evolution. Princeton, Princeton University Press, 1951. A discussion of theories of the origin of life.

Bryson, V., and H. J. Vogel (Eds.): Evolving Genes and Proteins. New York, Academic Press, 1965. Proceedings of a symposium relating biochemistry, genetics and evolution, especially the evolutionary implications of our expanding knowledge of the structure and function of macromolecules.

Carter, G. S.: Animal Evolution: A Study of Recent Views on Its Causes. London, Sidgwick & Jackson, 1951. A detailed, technical account of the evolution of animals.

Darwin, C.: The Origin of Species. 1859. Available in a number of recent reprint editions. This classic is well worth sampling for its clear, logical arguments and for its wealth of examples.

Dobzhansky, T.: Genetics and the Origin of Species. 3rd ed. New York, Columbia University Press, 1951. A detailed, technical presentation of the neo-Darwinian viewpoint of the role of small mutations and natural selection in evolution.

Goldschmidt, R. B.: The Material Basis of Evolution. New Haven, Yale University Press, 1940. Presents in detail Goldschmidt's views on the importance of large mutations in the evolution of species.

Irvine, W.: Apes, Angels and Victorians. New York, McGraw-Hill Book Co., 1955. Presents a clear picture of the impact of the theory of evolution on Victorian England and a vivid portrayal of Thomas Huxley's championing of Darwin's theory.

Jukes, T. H.: Molecules and Evolution. New York, Columbia University Press, 1966. An account of certain biochemical reactions responsible for the structure, function and survival of organisms and their bearing on evolution.

Mayr, E.: Animal Species and Evolution. Cambridge, Harvard University Press, 1963. A scholarly account of the problem of speciation.

Oparin, A. I.: The Origin of Life. New York, Macmillan, 1938. A translation of Oparin's classic arguments as to how life may have evolved from nonliving systems.

Osborn, H. F.: From the Greeks to Darwin. New York, Macmillan, 1913. An interesting and classic account of the history of ideas on evolution.

Ross, H. H.: A Synthesis of Evolutionary Theory. Englewood Cliffs, N. J., Prentice-Hall, Inc., 1964. A short book summarizing current views of the theory of evolution.

Savage, J. M.: Evolution. New York, Holt, Rinehart and Winston, 1963. A readable, relatively brief presentation of the evidence for and theories of evolution.

Simpson, G. G.: The Meaning of Evolution. New Haven, Yale University Press, 1950. An excellent, nontechnical presentation of evolutionary concepts.

Williams-Ellis, A.: Darwin's Moon. London and Edinburgh, Blackie & Son, 1966. An excellent biography of Alfred Russel Wallace with a vivid portrayal of Wallace's life and times which reemphasizes his solid contributions to the advancement of the theory of evolution.

37 THE EVIDENCE FOR EVOLUTION

The evidence that organic evolution has occurred is so overwhelming that no one who is acquainted with it has any doubt that new species are derived from previously existing ones by descent with modification. The fossil record provides direct evidence of organic evolution and gives the details of the evolutionary relationships of many lines of descent. In addition, there are vast quantities of facts from all the subdivisions of biologic science which acquire significance, and make sense, only when viewed against the background of evolution.

37.1
The Fossil Evidence

The evidence of life in former times is now both abundant and diverse. The science of **paleontology,** which deals with the finding, cataloguing and interpretation of **fossils,** has aided immensely in our understanding of the lines of descent of many vertebrate and invertebrate stocks. The term "fossil" (Latin *fossilium* something dug up) refers not only to the bones, shells, teeth and other hard parts of an animal's body which may survive, but to any impression or trace left by previous organisms. In view of the large number of fossils that have been found to date, it is sobering to realize that only a small fraction of animals died under conditions that favored their preservation as fossils.

Footprints or trails made in soft mud, which subsequently hardened, are a common type of fossil. For example, the tracks of an amphibian from the Pennsylvanian period, discovered in 1948 near Pittsburgh, revealed that the animal moved by hopping rather than by walking, for the footprints lay opposite each other in pairs.

The commonest vertebrate fossils are skeletal parts. From the shape of bones, and the position of the bone scars which indicate points of muscle attachment, paleontologists can make inferences about an animal's posture and style of walking, the position and size of its muscles, and hence the contours of its body. Careful study of fossil remains has enabled paleontologists to make reconstructions of what the animal must have looked like in life (Figs. 24.16 and 37.1).

In some fossils, the original hard parts, or more rarely the soft tissues of the body, have been replaced by minerals, a process called **petrifaction.** Iron pyrites, silica and calcium carbonate are some of the common petrifying minerals. The petrified muscle of a shark more than 300,000,000 years old was so well preserved by petrifaction that not only individual muscle fibers, but even their cross striations, could be observed in thin sections under the microscope. A famous example of the process of petrifaction is the Petrified Forest in Arizona.

Molds and casts are superficially similar to petrified fossils but are produced in a different way. **Molds** are formed by the hardening of the material surrounding a buried organism, followed by the decay and removal of the body of the organism. The mold may subsequently be filled by minerals which harden to form **casts** which are exact replicas of the original structures. Some animal remains have been exceptionally well preserved by being embedded in tar, amber, ice or volcanic ash. The remains of woolly mammoths,

Figure 37.1　An example of a fossil, the remains of *Archaeopteryx*, a tailed, toothed bird from the Jurassic Period. (Courtesy of the American Museum of Natural History.)

deep frozen in Siberian ice for more than 25,000 years, were so well preserved that the meat was edible!

37.2
The Geologic Time Table

Studies of the earth's crust have shown that it consists of sheets of rock lying one on top of the next. There are five major rock strata and each of these is subdivided into minor strata. These layers were generally formed by the accumulation of sediment—sand or mud—at the bottom of oceans, seas or lakes. Each rock stratum contains certain characteristic kinds of fossils which can now be used to identify deposits made at the same time in different parts of the world. Geologic time has been divided, according to the succession of these rock strata, into eras, periods and epochs (Table 37.1). The duration of each period or epoch can be estimated from the thickness of the sedimentary deposits, although, of course, the rate of deposition was not exactly the same in different places and at different times.

The layers of sedimentary rock should occur in the sequence of their deposition, with the newer strata on top of the older ones,

but subsequent geologic events may have changed the relationship of the layers. Not all of the expected strata may occur in some particular region, for that land may have been exposed rather than submerged during one or more geologic ages. In some regions the strata formed previously have subsequently emerged, been washed away, and then relatively recent strata have been deposited directly on very ancient ones. Certain sections of the earth's crust, in addition, have undergone massive foldings and splittings, so that early layers have come to lie on top of later ones. The age of a rock stratum may be determined by a study of its fossils, for some kinds of fossils were deposited in only one era or period.

Rock deposits are now dated largely by taking advantage of the fact that certain radioactive elements are transformed into other elements at rates which are slow and essentially unaffected by the pressures and temperatures to which the rock has been subjected. Half of a given sample of uranium will be converted to a special isotope of lead in 4.5 billion years. Hence, by measuring the proportion of uranium and lead in a bit of crystalline rock, its age can be measured. In this way, the oldest rocks of the earliest geologic period are calculated to be about

3,500,000,000 years old and the latest Cambrian rocks to be 500,000,000 years old. These dates have been confirmed by newer methods in which the radioactive decay of rubidium 87 (half-life 47 billion years!) and potassium 40 has been utilized to measure the ages of micas and feldspars. Events in more recent times can be dated quite accurately by the decay of carbon 14, which has a half-life of 5568 years.* Relatively short periods of geologic time are estimated by measuring the rate at which waterfalls recede upstream as they wear away the rocks over which they tumble or by counting the annual deposits of clay on the bottoms of ponds and lakes.

Between the major eras there were widespread geologic disturbances, called **revolutions,** which raised or lowered vast regions of the earth's surface and created or eliminated shallow inland seas. These revolutions produced great changes in the distribution of sea and land organisms and wiped out many of the previous forms of life. The Paleozoic era ended with the revolution that raised the Appalachian mountains and, it is believed, killed all but 3 per cent of the forms of life existing then. The Rocky Mountain revolution (which raised the Andes, Alps and Himalayas as well as the Rockies) annihilated most reptiles of the Mesozoic.

37.3
The Geologic Eras

Archeozoic Era. The rocks of the oldest geologic era are very deeply buried in most parts of the world but are exposed at the bottom of the Grand Canyon and along the shores of Lake Superior. The oldest geologic era, the Archeozoic, begins not with the origin of the earth but with the formation of the earth's crust, when rocks and mountains were in existence and the processes of erosion and sedimentation had begun. The Archeozoic era lasted about two billion years, about as long as all the succeeding eras combined. It was characterized by widespread volcanic activity and large upheavals which resulted

in the raising of mountains. The heat, pressure and churning associated with the movements of the earth's crust probably destroyed most of whatever fossil remains there may have been, but a few traces of life remain. Scattered through the Archeozoic rocks are flakes of graphite, pure carbon, which are probably the transformed remains of plants and animal bodies. Although graphite can originate inorganically, its distribution in the rocks suggests that it was formed organically. If the amount of graphite in these rocks can be taken as a measure of the amount of living things in the Archeozoic, and there are reasons for believing that this is justified, then life must have been abundant in the Archeozoic seas, for there is more carbon in these rocks than in the coal beds of the Appalachians.

Proterozoic Era. The second geologic era, which lasted about one billion years, was characterized by the deposition of large quantities of sediment and by at least one great period of glaciation during which ice sheets stretched to within 20 degrees of the equator. There was less volcanic activity in this than in the preceding era, and the rocks are better preserved. Only a few fossils have been found in Proterozoic rocks but they show not only that life was present but that evolution had proceeded quite far before the end of the era. Plants and animals were differentiated, multicellular forms had evolved from unicellular ones and some of the major groups of plants and animals had appeared. Sponge spicules, jellyfish, and the remains of fungi, algae, brachiopods and annelid worm tubes have been found in Proterozoic rocks. Several rich deposits of Pre-Cambrian fossils have been found in South Australia. These include jellyfish, corals, segmented worms and two animals with no resemblance to any known fossil or living form. The bodies of these animals were soft and were strengthened only by spicules of calcium carbonate.

Paleozoic Era. A second great revolution ended the Proterozoic era. During the ensuing 370,000,000 years of the Paleozoic every phylum and class of animals except birds and mammals appeared. Some of these animals appeared and became extinct in a short time (geologically speaking), and their fossils provide convenient markers by which rocks of the same era in different localities can be correlated.

---

*Organic carbon is derived by CO_2 fixation from atmospheric CO_2 and the ratio of ^{12}C to ^{14}C in living organisms is the same as that in the atmosphere. No exchange of carbon atoms with the atmosphere occurs after death and the ^{14}C in the body is slowly transformed into ^{14}N. The age of organic remains can be estimated from their $^{12}C/^{14}C$ ratio and the half-life of ^{14}C.

Table 37.1 Geologic Time Table

Era	Period	Epoch	Duration in Millions of Years	Time from Beginning of Period to Present (Millions of Years)	Geologic Conditions	Plant Life	Animal Life
Cenozoic (Age of Mammals)	Quaternary	Recent	0.011	0.011	End of last ice age; climate warmer	Decline of woody plants; rise of herbaceous ones	Age of man
		Pleistocene	1	1	Repeated glaciation; four ice ages	Great extinction of species	Extinction of great mammals; first human social life
	Tertiary	Pliocene	12	13	Continued rise of mountains of western North America; volcanic activity	Decline of forests; spread of grasslands; flowering plants, monocotyledons developed	Man evolved from manlike apes; elephants, horses, camels almost like modern species
		Miocene	13	25	Sierra and Cascade mountains formed; volcanic activity in northwest U.S.; climate cooler		Mammals at height of evolution; first manlike apes
		Oligocene	11	36	Lands lower; climate warmer	Maximum spread of forests; rise of monocotyledons, flowering plants	Archaic mammals extinct; rise of anthropoids; forerunners of most living genera of mammals
		Eocene	22	58	Mountains eroded; no continental seas; climate warmer		Placental mammals diversified and specialized; hoofed mammals and carnivores established
		Paleocene	5	63			Spread of archaic mammals

Rocky Mountain Revolution (Little Destruction of Fossils)

Era	Period	Epoch	Duration in Millions of Years	Time from Beginning of Period to Present (Millions of Years)	Geologic Conditions	Plant Life	Animal Life
Mesozoic (Age of Reptiles)	Cretaceous		72	135	Andes, Alps, Himalayas, Rockies formed late; earlier, inland seas and swamps; chalk, shale deposited	First monocotyledons; first oak and maple forests; gymnosperms declined	Dinosaurs reached peak, became extinct; toothed birds became extinct; first modern birds; archaic mammals common
	Jurassic		46	181	Continents fairly high; shallow seas over some of Europe and Western U.S.	Increase of dicotyledons; cycads and conifers common	First toothed birds; dinosaurs larger and specialized; primitive mammals
	Triassic		49	230	Continents exposed; widespread desert conditions; many land deposits	Gymnosperms dominant, declining toward end; extinction of seed ferns	First dinosaurs, pterosaurs and egg-laying mammals; extinction of primitive amphibians

Table 37.1 Geologic Time Table (*Continued*)

Era	Period	Epoch	Duration in Millions of Years	Time from Beginning of Period to Present (Millions of Years)	Geologic Conditions	Plant Life	Animal Life

Appalachian Revolution (Some Loss of Fossils)

Era	Period	Epoch	Duration in Millions of Years	Time from Beginning of Period to Present (Millions of Years)	Geologic Conditions	Plant Life	Animal Life
Paleozoic (Age of Ancient Life)	Permian		50	280	Continents rose; Appalachians formed; increasing glaciation and aridity	Decline of lycopods and horsetails	Many ancient animals died out; mammal-like reptiles, modern insects arose
	Pennsylvanian		40	320	Lands at first low; great coal swamps	Great forests of seed ferns and gymnosperms	First reptiles; insects common; spread of ancient amphibians
	Mississippian		25	345	Climate warm and humid at first, cooler later as land rose	Lycopods and horsetails dominant; gymnosperms increasingly widespread	Sea lilies at height; spread of ancient sharks
	Devonian		60	405	Smaller inland seas; land higher, more arid; glaciation	First forests; land plants well established; first gymnosperms	First amphibians; lungfishes, sharks abundant
	Silurian		20	425	Extensive continental seas; lowlands increasingly arid as land rose	First definite evidence of land plants; algae dominant	Marine arachnids dominant; first (wingless) insects; rise of fishes
	Ordovician		75	500	Great submergence of land; warm climates even in Arctic	Land plants probably first appeared; marine algae abundant	First fishes, probably fresh-water; corals, trilobites abundant; diversified mollusks
	Cambrian		100	600	Lands low, climate mild; earliest rocks with abundant fossils	Marine algae	Trilobites, brachiopods dominant; most modern phyla established

Second Great Revolution (Considerable Loss of Fossils)

Era	Period	Epoch	Duration in Millions of Years	Time from Beginning of Period to Present (Millions of Years)	Geologic Conditions	Plant Life	Animal Life
Proterozoic			1000	1600	Great sedimentation; volcanic activity later; extensive erosion, repeated glaciations	Primitive aquatic plants—algae, fungi	Various marine protozoa; towards end, mollusks, worms, other marine invertebrates

First Great Revolution (Considerable Loss of Fossils)

Era	Period	Epoch	Duration in Millions of Years	Time from Beginning of Period to Present (Millions of Years)	Geologic Conditions	Plant Life	Animal Life
Archeozoic			2000	3600	Great volcanic activity; some sedimentary deposition; extensive erosion	No recognizable fossils; indirect evidence of living things from deposits of organic material in rock	

The fossil deposits of the first three periods of the Paleozoic era, the Cambrian, Ordovician and Silurian, were mostly laid down in the seas. Large shallow seas covered most of the continents during these three periods and they teemed with life. Many of these forms had hard skeletons or armor coverings which left a good fossil record. The organisms living in the Cambrian were so varied and complex that they must have evolved from ancestors dating back to the Proterozoic era. Apparently, both plants and animals lived in the sea, and the land was a curious lifeless waste until the Ordovician, when plants became established on land. The Cambrian seas contained small floating plants and animals that were eaten by primitive shrimplike crustaceans and swimming annelid worms. The sea floor was covered with simple sponges, corals, echinoderms growing on stalks, snails, pelecypods and primitive cephalopods. An exceptionally well-preserved collection of Cambrian fossils was found in the mountains of British Columbia; it included annelids, crustaceans, and a connecting link similar to peripatus. The most numerous animals were brachiopods and trilobites. Brachiopods, sessile, bivalved plankton feeders, flourished in the Cambrian and the rest of the Paleozoic. One of the present-day brachiopods, *Lingula,* is the oldest known genus of animals and is almost identical with its Cambrian ancestors. The trilobites (see Fig. 16.2) were primitive arthropods, with flattened, elongated bodies covered dorsally by a hard shell. The shell had two longitudinal grooves that divided the body into three lobes. On the ventral side of the body was a pair of legs on each somite but the last, and each leg was biramous, had an outer gill branch and an inner walking or swimming branch. Most trilobites were only 5 to 8 cm. long but the largest was about 60 cm. They reached their peak of importance in the late Cambrian and then dwindled and became extinct in the Permian.

Evolution since the Cambrian has been characterized by the elaboration and ramification of the lines already present rather than by the establishment of entirely new forms. The original, primitive members of most lines were replaced by more complex, better adapted ones. The Ordovician seas contained, among other forms, giant cephalopods, squidlike animals with straight shells 5 to 7 meters long and 30 cm. in diameter. The Ordovician seas were apparently quite warm, for corals, which grow only in warm waters, lived as far north as Ontario and Greenland. The first vertebrates, the jawless, limbless, armored, bottom-dwelling fishes called **ostracoderms,** appeared in the Ordovician. These lived in fresh water and their bony armor may have served as a defense against their chief predator, the carnivorous giant arachnids called **eurypterids.** Two important events of the Silurian were the evolution of land plants and of the first air-breathing animals, primitive scorpions.

The evolution of the vertebrates, from ostracoderms to placoderms, cartilaginous and bony fishes, amphibians, reptiles, birds and mammals has been traced in Chapters 22 to 25. The Devonian seas contained corals, sea lilies and brachiopods in addition to a great variety of fishes. Trilobites were still present but were declining in numbers and importance. The first land vertebrates, the amphibians called **labyrinthodonts,** appeared in the latter part of the Devonian; this period also saw the first true forests of ferns, "seed ferns," club mosses and horsetails and the first wingless insects and millipedes.

The Mississippian and Pennsylvanian periods are frequently grouped together as the Carboniferous, for during this time there flourished the great swamp forests whose remains gave rise to the major coal deposits of the world. The earliest stem reptiles appeared in the Pennsylvanian and from these there evolved in the succeeding Permian period a group of early, mammal-like reptiles, the **pelycosaurs,** from which the mammals eventually evolved (Fig. 37.2). Two important groups of winged insects, the ancestors of the cockroaches and the ancestors of the dragonflies, evolved during the Carboniferous.

The Permian period was characterized by widespread changes in topography and climate. The land began to rise early in the period, so that the swamps and shallow seas were drained, and the Appalachian revolution that ended the period, together with widespread glaciation, killed off a great many kinds of animals. The trilobites finally disappeared and the brachiopods, stalked echinoderms, cephalopods, and many other kinds of invertebrates were reduced to small, unimportant, relict groups.

Mesozoic Era. The Mesozoic era, which began some 230,000,000 years ago and lasted some 167,000,000 years, is subdivided into the Triassic, Jurassic and Cretaceous

Figure 37.2 Texas in the Permian period, about 280,000,000 years ago. Various pelycosaurs are shown. Some had large fins, others were essentially like lizards. In the lower illustration is a salamander-like amphibian with a flat, triangular skull. (Copyright, Chicago Natural History Museum, from the painting by Charles R. Knight.)

periods. During the Triassic and Jurassic most of the continental area was above water, warm and fairly dry. During the Cretaceous the Gulf of Mexico expanded into Texas and New Mexico, and the sea once again overspread large parts of the continents. There were great swamps from Colorado to British Columbia (Fig. 37.3). In the latter part of the Cretaceous the interior of the North American continent was further submerged and cut in two by the union of a bay from the Gulf of Mexico and one from the Arctic Sea. The Rocky Mountain revolution ended the Cretaceous with the upheaval of

the Rockies, Alps, Himalayas and Andes mountains. The Mesozoic is characterized by the tremendous evolution, diversification and specialization of the reptiles and is commonly called the Age of Reptiles. Mammals originated in the Triassic and birds in the Jurassic. Most of the modern orders of insects appeared in the Triassic, and snails, bivalve mollusks and sea urchins underwent important evolutionary advances.

At the end of the Cretaceous a great many reptiles became extinct; they were apparently unable to adapt to the marked changes brought about by the Rocky Mountain revo-

Figure 37.3　Western Canada in the Cretaceous period, about 110,000,000 years ago. The land was low, well watered, and covered with numerous swamps. Most of the dinosaurs were harmless, plant-eating Ornithischians, reptiles with bird-like pelvic bones. Two types of duck-billed dinosaurs can be seen—three large, uncrested ones in the upper portion, and two kinds of crested ones in the lower portion. In the upper right foreground is a heavily armored, four-footed dinosaur covered with bony plates and spines. In the upper right and lower left background are ostrich dinosaurs—tall slender animals, with the general proportions of an ostrich, but with short forelegs and a long, slender tail. (Copyright, Chicago Natural History Museum, from the painting by Charles R. Knight.)

lution. As the climate became colder and drier, many of the plants which served as food for the herbivorous reptiles disappeared. Some of the herbivorous reptiles were too large to walk about on land when the swamps dried up. The smaller, warm-blooded mammals which appeared were better able to compete for food, and many of these ate reptilian eggs. The demise of the many kinds of reptiles was probably the result of a combination of a whole host of factors rather than any single one.

Cenozoic Era. The Cenozoic era, extending from the Rocky Mountain revolution to the present, is subdivided into the earlier Tertiary period, which lasted some 62,000,-000 years, and the present Quaternary period, which includes the last million or million and one-half years.

The Tertiary is subdivided into five epochs, the Paleocene, Eocene, Oligocene, Miocene and Pliocene. The Rockies, formed at the beginning of the Tertiary, were considerably eroded by the Oligocene, and the North American continent had a gently rolling topography. Another series of uplifts in the Miocene raised the Sierra Nevadas and a new set of Rockies, and resulted in the formation of the western deserts. The climate of the Oligocene was rather mild, and palm trees grew as far north as Wyoming. The uplifts of the Miocene and Pliocene, and the successive ice ages of the Pleistocene, killed off many of the mammals that had evolved.

The last elevation of the Colorado Plateau, which initiated the cutting of the Grand Canyon, occurred almost entirely in the short Pleistocene and Recent epochs, the two subdivisions of the Quaternary period. Four periods of glaciation occurred in the Pleistocene, between which the sheets of ice retreated. At their greatest extent, these ice sheets extended as far south as the Missouri and Ohio rivers and covered 4,000,000 square miles of North America. The Great Lakes, which were carved out by the advancing glaciers, changed their outlines and connections several times. It is estimated that at one time, when the Mississippi river drained lakes as far west as Duluth and as far east as Buffalo, its volume was more than 60 times as great as at present. During the Pleistocene glaciations enough water was removed from the oceans and locked in the vast sheets of ice to lower the water level as much as 100 meters.

This created land connections, highways for the dispersal of many land forms, between Siberia and Alaska at Bering Strait and between England and the continent of Europe. Many mammals, including the saber-toothed tiger, the mammoth and the giant ground sloth, became extinct in the Pleistocene after primitive man had appeared.

The fossil record available today makes it impossible to doubt that the present species arose from previously existing, different ones. For many lines of evolution the individual steps are well known; other lines have some gaps which remain to be filled by future paleontologists.

Even if there were no fossil record at all, the results of the detailed studies of the morphology, physiology and biochemistry of present-day animals and plants, of their mode of development, of the transmission of inherited characteristics, and of their distribution over the earth's surface would provide overwhelming proof that organic evolution has occurred.

37.4

The Evidence from Taxonomy

The science of naming, describing and classifying organisms, **taxonomy,** was discussed in Chapter 7. The science of taxonomy began long before the doctrine of evolution was accepted; indeed the founders of scientific taxonomy, Ray and Linnaeus, were firm believers in the fixity, the unchangingness, of species. Present-day taxonomists are concerned with the naming and describing of species primarily as a means of discovering evolutionary relationships, based upon the assumption that the degree of resemblance in homologous structures is a measure of the degree of relationship. The fact that the characteristics of living things are such that they can be fitted into a hierarchical scheme of categories, each more inclusive than the previous one—species, genera, families, orders, classes and phyla, can best be interpreted as proof of evolutionary relationship. If the kinds of animals and plants were not related by evolutionary descent, their characters would be present in a confused, random pattern and no such hierarchy of forms could be established.

The basic unit of taxonomy is the **species,** a

population of closely similar individuals, which are alike in their morphologic, embryologic and physiologic characters, which in nature breed only with each other and which have a common ancestry. It is difficult to give a definition of species that is universally applicable. The definition must be modified slightly to include species whose life cycle includes two or more quite different forms (many coelenterates, parasitic worms, larval and adult insects and amphibians, for example). A population that is spread over a wide territory may show local or regional differences which may be called subspecies. Many instances are known in which a species is broken up into a chain of subspecies, each of which differs slightly from its neighbors but interbreeds with them. The subspecies at the two ends of the chain, however, may be so different that they cannot interbreed. Such a series of geographically distributed subspecies is called a *Rassenkreis* (German, race-circle).

The classification of living organisms into well-defined groups is possible because most of the intermediate forms have become extinct. If representatives of every type of animal and plant that have ever lived were still living today, there would be many series of intergrading forms and the division of these into neat taxonomic categories would be difficult indeed. The present-day species have been compared to the terminal twigs of a tree whose main branches and trunk have disappeared. The fascinating puzzle for the taxonomist is to reconstruct the missing branches and put each twig on the proper branch.

37.5
The Evidence from Morphology

Comparisons of the anatomy of different animals have been made throughout this text. In each instance it has been found that if we study the details of the structure of any particular organ system in the diverse members of a given phylum, it is clear that there is a basic similarity of form which is varied to some extent from one class to another. The skeletal, muscular, circulatory and excretory systems of the vertebrates provide especially clear illustrations of this principle, but this is generally true of all systems in all phyla. You will recall that not all similarities can be used in classification but only those based on **homologous organs** (p. 356), ones which are basically similar in their structure, in their relationship to adjacent structures, in their embryonic development, and in their nerve and blood supply. A seal's front flipper, a bat's wing, a cat's paw, a horse's front leg and a human hand, though superficially dissimilar and adapted for quite different functions, nevertheless are homologous organs. Each consists of almost the same number of bones, muscles, nerves and blood vessels arranged in the same pattern, and their mode of development is very similar. The existence of such homologous organs implies a common evolutionary origin.

Many species of animals have organs or parts of organs which are useless and often small or lacking some essential part; in related organisms, the organ is full-sized, complete and functional. There are more than 100 such **vestigial organs** in the human body,

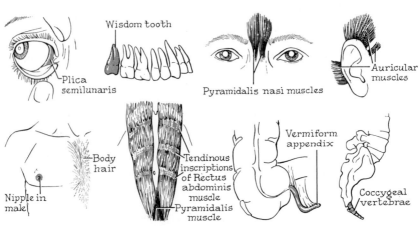

Figure 37.4   Diagrams of some of the vestigial organs of the human body.

including the appendix, the coccyx (fused tail vertebrae), the wisdom teeth, the nictitating membrane of the eye, body hair, and the muscles that move the ears (Fig. 37.4). Such organs are the remnants of ones which were functional in the ancestral forms, but when some change in the environment rendered the organ no longer necessary for survival it gradually became reduced to a vestige. This appears at first glance to be an application of Lamarck's idea of the role of "use and disuse" of an organ in evolution, but the underlying mechanism is quite different. Mutations for the decrease in the size and functional importance of an organ are occurring constantly; as long as the organ is necessary for survival, such mutations are lethal and eliminate their possessors. But if the organ is no longer needed for survival, such mutations will not be lethal, and they may accumulate and lead to the reduction of the organ.

37.6

The Evidence from Comparative Physiology and Biochemistry

The study of the physiologic and biochemical traits of organisms generally requires complex apparatus and is more difficult than the direct observation of morphologic characters. Yet, as such studies have been made using a wide variety of animal types, it has become clear that there are functional similarities and differences which parallel closely the morphologic ones. Indeed, if one were to establish taxonomic relationships based on physiologic and biochemical characters instead of on the usual structural ones, the end result would be much the same

The fundamental similarity of the chemical constituents and patterns of enzymes present in cells of different animals was presented in Chapter 4. There are, however, certain chemical constituents, certain enzymes and certain hormones that are found in some animals and not in others. The distribution of these biochemical characters strongly parallels the evolutionary relationships inferred from other evidence.

The blood serum of each species of animal contains certain specific proteins. The degree of similarity of these serum proteins can be determined by **antigen-antibody** reactions. To perform the test, an experimental animal, usually a rabbit, is injected with a small

amount of the serum, as, for example, a sample of human serum. The proteins of the injected serum are foreign to the rabbit's blood and hence act as antigens, stimulating the production of antibodies which are specific for human serum antigens. These antibodies are then obtained by withdrawing blood from the rabbit and allowing it to clot; the antibodies are in the serum. When a dilute sample of this serum is mixed with a drop of human serum, the antibody for human serum reacts with the human serum antigen and produces a visible precipitation. The strength of the reaction can be measured by making successive dilutions of the human serum, mixing each dilution with a fresh sample of the antibody solution (the rabbit serum), and observing at what point the precipitation no longer occurs. When serum from an animal other than man is mixed with rabbit serum containing antibodies for human serum proteins, there is either no precipitation at all, or else a precipitation occurs only with concentrated antigen solutions. By testing, in turn, the sera of a variety of animals with rabbit serum containing antibodies for human serum proteins, the degree of similarity between the proteins can be determined. If the serum of another animal contains proteins which are similar to those of man, a precipitation will occur. In this way, man's closest "blood relations" have been found to be the great apes, and then, in order, the Old World monkeys, the New World monkeys, and finally the tarsioids. The serum of the lemur gives the smallest amount of precipitation when mixed with antibodies specific for human serum.

The biochemical relationships of a variety of forms, tested in this way, correlate with and complement the relationships determined by other means. Cats, dogs and bears are closely related, as determined by this test; cows, sheep, goats, deer and antelopes constitute another closely related group. This test reveals that there is a closer relationship among the modern birds than among the mammals, for all of the several hundred species of birds tested give strong and immediate reactions with serum containing antibodies for chicken serum. From other tests it was concluded that birds are more closely related to the crocodile line of reptiles than to the snake-lizard line, which corroborates the paleontologic evidence. Similar tests of the sera of crustaceans, insects and mollusks have shown that those forms regarded as being closely related from morphologic or paleontologic evidence also show similarities in their serum proteins.

Investigations of the sequence of amino acids in the α and β chains of hemoglobins from different species have revealed great similarities, of course, and specific differences, the pattern of which demonstrates the order in which the underlying mutations, the changes in nucleotide base pairs, must have occurred in evolution. The evolutionary relationships inferred from these studies agree completely with those based on morphologic studies. Analyses of the amino acid sequence in the protein portion of the cytochromes provide further concurring evidence of evolutionary relationships. Thus evidence of evolutionary relationships can be adduced from similarities and differences in *molecular* structure as well as from gross morphology.

The properties of specific enzymes, which reflect their molecular structure, also provide evidence of evolutionary relationships. The pattern and rates of reaction of lactate dehydrogenase and certain other enzymes with the normal pyridine nucleotide coenzyme (DPN) and with analogues of DPN can be used to demonstrate evolutionary relationships.

It might seem unlikely that an analysis of the urinary wastes of different species would provide evidence of evolutionary relationship, yet this is true. The kind of waste excreted depends upon the particular kinds of enzymes present, and the enzymes are determined by genes, which have been selected in the course of evolution. The waste products of the metabolism of purines, adenine and guanine, are excreted by man and other primates as uric acid, by other mammals as allantoin, by amphibians and most fishes as urea, and by most invertebrates as ammonia. Vertebrate evolution has been marked by the successive loss of enzymes required for the stepwise degradation of uric acid. Joseph Needham made the interesting observation that the chick embryo in the early stages of development excretes ammonia, later it excretes urea, and finally it excretes uric acid. The enzyme uricase, which catalyzes the first step in the degradation of uric acid, is present in the early chick embryo but disappears in the later stages of development. The adult frog excretes urea, but the larval form excretes ammonia. These are biochemical examples of the principle of recapitulation.

37.7
The Evidence from Embryology

The importance of the embryologic evidence for evolution was emphasized by Darwin and brought into even greater prominence by Ernst Haeckel in 1866, when he developed his theory that embryos, in the course of development, repeat the evolutionary history of their ancestors in some abbreviated form. This idea, succinctly stated as "Ontogeny recapitulates phylogeny," stimulated research in embryology and focused attention on the general resemblance between embryonic development and the evolutionary process, but it now seems clear that the embryos of the higher animals resemble the *embryos* of lower forms, not the adults, as Haeckel had believed. The early stages of all vertebrate embryos, for example, are remarkably similar, and it is not easy to differentiate a human embryo from the embryo of a fish, frog, chick or pig (Fig. 37.5).

In recapitulating its evolutionary history in a few days, weeks or months the embryo must eliminate some steps and alter and distort others. In addition, some new characters have evolved which are adaptive and enable the embryo to survive to later stages. For example, mammalian embryos, which have many early characteristics in common with those of fish, amphibia and reptiles, have other structures which enable them to survive and to develop within the mother's uterus rather than within an egg shell. Such secondary traits may alter the original characters common to all vertebrates so that the basic resemblances are blurred. The concept of recapitulation must be used with due caution, rather than rigorously, but it does provide an explanation for many otherwise inexplicable events in development.

Studies of the embryonic forms may provide the only means for identifying the relationships of certain organisms. *Sacculina*, for example, is an extremely aberrant barnacle which parasitizes crabs. The adult form is a saclike structure which sends processes into the tissues of the host to absorb nourishment. It resembles no other organism and its relationship became clear only when it was found

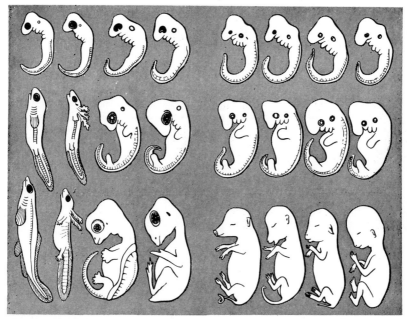

Fish Salamander Turtle Chicken   Pig   Cow   Rabbit   Man

Figure 37.5 Comparison of early and later stages in the development of vertebrate embryos. Note the similarity of the earliest stages of each.

that its larva is like that of other barnacles until it becomes attached to the abdomen of the host. Then it loses its appendages and other structures and becomes the adult, saclike creature.

The concept of recapitulation is very helpful in understanding the curious and complex development of the vertebrate circulatory and excretory systems. It is also useful, when not taken too literally, in getting a broad picture of the whole of development. Thus, the fertilized egg can be compared to the putative single-celled flagellate ancestor of all animals, and the blastula can be compared to a colonial protozoan or to some hypothetic blastula-like animal which has been postulated to be the ancestor of all Metazoa. Haeckel believed that the ancestor of coelenterates and all the higher animals was a gastrula-like organism with two layers of cells and a central cavity connected by a blastopore to the outside. After gastrulation, development follows one of two main lines. In the echinoderms and chordates the blastopore becomes the anus, or comes to lie near the anus. In the annelid-mollusk-arthropod line the blastopore becomes the mouth or comes to lie near the mouth. In both lines the mesoderm develops between the ectoderm and endoderm.

In the chordate-echinoderm line the mesoderm develops, at least in part, as pouches from the primitive digestive tract, whereas in the annelid-mollusk line the mesoderm usually originates from special cells differentiated early in development.

All chordate embryos develop, shortly after the mesoderm begins to appear, a dorsal hollow nerve cord, a notochord and pharyngeal pouches. The early human embryo at this stage resembles a fish embryo, with gill pouches, pairs of aortic arches, a fishlike heart with a single atrium and ventricle, a primitive fish kidney, and a well-differentiated tail complete with muscles for wagging it (Fig. 37.6). At a slightly later stage the human embryo resembles a reptilian embryo. Its gill pouches regress; the bones which make up each vertebra, and which had been separate as in the most primitive fishes, fuse; a new kidney, the mesonephros, forms and the pronephros disappears or becomes incorporated into other structures; and the atrium becomes divided into right and left chambers. Still later in development the human embryo develops a mammalian, four-chambered heart and a third kidney, the metanephros. During the seventh month of intrauterine development the human embryo, with its coat

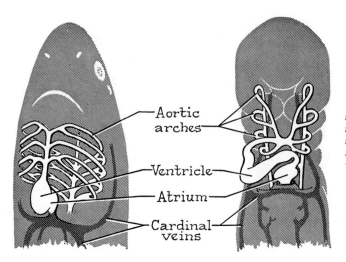

Figure 37.6 Ventral views of the heart and aortic arches of a human embryo (right) and an adult shark (left). Both have a single atrium and single ventricle, several aortic arches, and anterior and posterior cardinal veins emptying into the heart.

of embryonic hair and in the relative size of body and limbs, resembles a baby ape more than it resembles an adult human.

Our increasing understanding of physiologic genetics provides us with an explanation of the phenomenon of recapitulation. All chordates have in common a certain number of genes which regulate the processes of early development. But, as our ancestors evolved from fish, through amphibian and reptilian stages, they accumulated mutations for new characteristics but kept some of the original "fish" genes, which still control early development. Later in development the genes which the human shares with amphibians influence the course of development so that the embryo resembles a frog embryo. Subsequently, some of the genes which we have in common with reptiles come into control. Only after this do most of the peculiarly mammalian genes exert their influence, and these are followed by the action of genes we have in common with other primates. The anthropoid apes, which have the most immediate ancestors in common with us, have the most genes in common with us and their development is identical with ours except for some fine details. A pig or rat, whose ancestors are the same as ours only up to the stage of the primitive placental mammals, has fewer genes in common and has developmental processes that diverge at an earlier time. In general, during development, the general characters that distinguish phyla and classes appear before the special characters that distinguish genera and, finally, species. Within each phylum, the higher forms pass through a sequence of developmental stages

which are similar to those of lower forms but achieve a different final form by adding changes at the end of the original sequence and by altering certain of the earlier embryonic stages they share with the lower forms.

37.8
The Evidence from Genetics and Cytology

For the past several thousand years man has been selecting and breeding animals and plants for his own uses, and a great many varieties, adapted for different purposes, have been established. These results of artificial selection provide striking models of what may be accomplished by natural selection. All of our breeds of dogs have descended from one, or perhaps a very few, species of wild dog or wolf, yet they vary so much in color, size and body proportions that if they occurred in the wild they would undoubtedly be considered separate species. They are all interfertile and are known to come from common ancestors, so they are regarded as varieties of a single species. A comparable range of varieties has been produced by artificial selection in cats, chickens, sheep, cattle and horses. Plant breeders have established by selective breeding a tremendous variety of plants. From the cliff cabbage, which still grows wild in Europe, have come cultivated cabbage, cauliflower, kohlrabi, Brussels sprouts, broccoli and kale.

Geneticists have been able to trace the ancestry of certain modern plants by a combination of cytologic techniques in which the morphology of the chromosomes is compared and by breeding techniques which compare the kinds of genes and their order in particular chromosomes in a series of plants. In this way, the present cultivated tobacco plant, *Nicotiana tabacum*, was shown to have arisen from two species of wild tobacco, and corn was traced to teosinte, a grasslike plant which grows wild in the Andes and Mexico. The cytologic details of the structure of the giant chromosomes of the salivary glands of fruit flies have been of prime importance in unraveling the evolutionary history of the many species of *Drosophila*.

37.9

The Evidence from the Geographic Distribution of Organisms

In the course of the voyage of the *Beagle*, Darwin was greatly impressed by his observations that the plants and animals of South America and the Galápagos Islands were *not* found everywhere that they could exist if climate and topography were the only factors determining their distribution. The facts of biogeography, the geographic distribution of plants and animals, were of prime importance in leading both Darwin and Alfred Russel Wallace to the conclusion that organic evolution had occurred by natural selection. The present distribution of organisms, and the sites at which their fossil remains are found, are understandable only on the basis of the evolutionary history of each species.

The **range** of each species is that particular portion of the earth in which it is found. The range of a species may be restricted to a few square miles or less or, as with man, may include almost the entire earth. In general, the ranges of closely related species or subspecies are not identical, nor are they widely separated, but are adjacent and separated by a barrier of some sort. This generalization was stated by David Starr Jordan and is known as **Jordan's rule.** The explanation for this should be clear from the discussion of the role of isolation in species formation. A single species cannot be subdivided as long as interbreeding can occur throughout the whole population. But when some barrier is interposed between two parts of the population so that interbreeding is prevented, the two populations will, in the subsequent course of time, accumulate different gene mutations.

One of the fundamental assumptions of biogeography is that each species of animal or plant originated only once. The place where this occurred is known as its **center of origin.** The center of origin is not a single point, but the range of the population when the new species was formed. From this center of origin each species spreads out, under the pressure of an increasing population, until it is halted by a barrier of some kind: a physical one such as an ocean, mountain or desert, an environmental one such as unfavorable climate, or a biologic barrier such as the absence of food or the presence of other species which prey upon it or compete with it for food or shelter.

As one might expect, regions which have been separated from the rest of the world for a long time, such as South America and Australia, have a unique assemblage of animals and plants. Australia has a mammalian population of monotremes and marsupials that is found nowhere else. Australia became separated from Malaya during the Mesozoic, before placental mammals evolved, and its primitive mammals were not eliminated, as were the monotremes and most of the marsupials in the other parts of the world, by the competition of the better adapted placental mammals. The Australian marsupials evolved into a wide variety of forms, each adapted to some particular combination of environmental factors.

The kinds of animals and plants found on oceanic islands resemble, in general, those of the nearest mainland, yet include species found nowhere else. Darwin studied the flora and fauna of the Cape Verde Islands, some 400 miles west of Dakar in Africa, and of the Galápagos Islands, a comparable distance west of Ecuador. On each archipelago the plants and the nonflying animals were indigenous, but those of Cape Verde resembled African species and those of the Galápagos resembled South American ones. It is clear that species from the neighboring continent migrated or were carried to the island and that by subsequent evolution they became differentiated from their ancestral forms. The animals and plants found on oceanic islands are only those that could survive the trip there. There are, for example, no frogs or toads on the Galápagos and no terrestrial mammals, even though conditions would favor their survival.

There are many facts of the present-day distribution of animals and plants which can be explained only by knowledge of their history. Alligators, for example, are found only in the rivers of southeastern United States and in the Yangtse River in China. Sassafras, tulip trees and magnolias are found only in the eastern United States, Japan, and eastern China. The explanation for these curious patterns of distribution lies in the fact that early in the Cenozoic era the northern hemisphere was much flatter than at present and the North American continent was connected with eastern Asia by a land bridge at what is now Bering Strait. The climate of the whole region was much warmer than at present, and fossil evidence shows that alligators, magnolia trees and sassafras were distributed over the entire region. Later in the Cenozoic, as the Rockies increased in height, the western part of North America became much colder and drier. During the Pleistocene the ice sheets moving down from the north met the desert and mountain regions of western North America, and the animals and plants that had lived in that region either became extinct or migrated. In southeastern United States and in eastern China were regions untouched by the glaciations and here the alligators and magnolia trees survived. Because the alligators and magnolias of the two regions have been separated for several million years, they have had the opportunity to accumulate different random mutations. They are, thus, slightly different but closely related species of the same genera.

37.10
The Biogeographic Realms

Careful studies of the distribution of plants and animals over the earth have revealed the existence of six major biogeographic realms, each characterized by the presence of certain unique organisms. These realms were originally defined on the basis of the distribution of mammals, but they have proved to be valid for many other kinds of animals and plants as well. The various parts of each realm may be widely separated and have quite different conditions of climate and topography, but it has been possible, during most geologic eras, for organisms to pass more or less freely from one part to another. In contrast, the six realms are separated from each other by major barriers of sea, desert or mountains (Fig. 37.7).

The **Palearctic** realm includes Europe, Africa north of the Sahara desert, and Asia north of the Himalaya and Nan-Ling mountains, plus Japan, Iceland and the Azores and Cape Verde Islands. The animals indigenous to the Palearctic are moles, deer, oxen, sheep, goats, robins and magpies.

The **Nearctic** realm includes Greenland and North America north of the northern plateau of Mexico. This contains many of the same animals as the Palearctic, plus species of mountain goats, prairie dogs, opossums, skunks, raccoons, bluejays, turkey buzzards and wren-tits found nowhere else. The land bridge connecting North America and Asia at Bering Strait in former geologic times permitted the migration back and forth of many kinds of animals and plants. The flora and fauna of the Palearctic and Nearctic realms are similar in many respects and the two are sometimes combined as the **Holarctic** region.

The **Neotropical** realm consists of South America, Central America, southern Mexico and the islands of the West Indies. Its distinctive fauna includes alpacas, llamas, prehensile-tailed monkeys, blood-sucking bats, sloths, tapirs, anteaters, and a host of bird species—toucans, puff birds, tinamous and others—found nowhere else in the world.

The part of Africa south of the Sahara, plus the island of Madagascar, comprises the **Ethiopian** realm. The gorilla, chimpanzee, zebra, rhinoceros, hippopotamus, giraffe, aardvark, and many birds, reptiles and fishes live only in this realm.

The **Oriental** realm includes India, Ceylon, southeast Asia, southern China, the Malay peninsula and some of the islands of the East Indies—the Philippines, Borneo, Java and Bali. Some of the animals peculiar to it are the orangutan, black panther, Indian elephant, gibbon and tarsier.

Australia, New Zealand, New Guinea, and the remaining islands of the East Indies, those east of Celebes and Lombok, make up the **Australian** realm. The line separating the Oriental and Australian realms, known as Wallace's Line, separates Bali and Lombok, goes through the straits of Macassar between Borneo and Celebes, and passes east of the Philippines. Although the islands of Bali and Lombok are separated by a channel only 30 kilometers wide, their respective animals and

Figure 37.7 A polar projection map of the world showing the biogeographic realms. (After Matthew.)

plants are more unlike than are those of England and Japan, almost on the opposite sides of the world from each other. Native to the Australian realm are the duck-billed platypus, echidna, kangaroo, wombat, koala bear, and other marsupials. Its assortment of curious birds includes the cassowary and emu, the lyre-bird, cockatoo and bird-of-paradise.

Why certain animals appear in one region yet are excluded from another in which they are well adapted to survive (and in which they flourish when introduced by man) can be explained only by their evolutionary history.

QUESTIONS

1. What methods are used for estimating the age of rocks?
2. What is a geologic revolution? What effects have such revolutions on the course of evolution?
3. Describe the life of the Cambrian period. What are the biggest differences between the animal life of that time and the present?
4. Discuss the thesis that the hierarchical scheme of animal classification is evidence for organic evolution.
5. How would you define a species? What difficulties might be encountered in trying to decide whether two populations of animals are one or two species?
6. Define: homologous organs, vestigial organs, Rassenkreis, petrifaction.
7. Describe the method used to determine evolutionary relationship by the nature of serum proteins. By the nature of tissue enzymes.
8. Discuss the implications of the phrase "Ontogeny recapitulates phylogeny." What changes in Haeckel's theory have been made necessary by subsequent research?

9. Discuss the genetic explanation for the phenomenon of recapitulation.
10. What is Jordan's rule?
11. Define the terms "range" and "center of origin."
12. If, in tracing evolutionary relationships, anatomic evidence pointed one way and biochemical evidence another, which do you think would be the more reliable? Why?

ANNOTATED REFERENCES

Baldwin, E. B.: An Introduction to Comparative Biochemistry. 3rd ed. Cambridge, Cambridge University Press, 1957. A classic exposition of some of the biochemical similarities among animals that aid in defining evolutionary relationships.

Berrill, N. J.: The Origin of Vertebrates. London, Oxford University Press, 1955. Contains excellent descriptions of fossil vertebrates and presents the theory that vertebrates evolved from ascidians.

Bryson, V., and H. J. Vogel (Eds.): Evolving Genes and Proteins. New York, Academic Press, 1965. The proceedings of a symposium held at Rutgers University, containing a series of articles which compare the structures of specific proteins and nucleic acids in different species and show how this evidence may be used to deduce evolutionary relationships.

Colbert, E. H.: Evolution of the Vertebrates. New York, John Wiley & Sons, Inc., 1955. A text recommended for its presentation of information regarding vertebrate fossils.

Dodson, E. O.: Evolution: Process and Product. New York, Reinhold Publishing Corp., 1960. A good introductory text describing the general field of evolutionary phenomena.

Jukes, T. H.: Molecules and Evolution. New York, Columbia University Press, 1966. A readable introductory text that relates modern genetics and the evolution of specific molecular structures.

Moore, R. C., C. G. Lalicker and A. G. Fischer: Invertebrate Fossils. New York, McGraw-Hill Book Co., 1952. An excellent source of information regarding extinct invertebrate animals.

Raymond, P. E.: Prehistoric Life. Cambridge, Harvard University Press, 1939. A very readable description of the important vertebrate fossils.

Romer, A. S.: Vertebrate Paleontology. 3rd ed. Chicago, University of Chicago Press, 1966. A comprehensive, well-written text, highly recommended as a source book for further reading.

Shrock, R. R., and W. H. Twenhofel: Principles of Invertebrate Paleontology. New York, McGraw-Hill Book Co. 1953. An excellent text describing the evolution of the invertebrates.

38 THE EVOLUTION OF MAN

The line of evolution that led from the ostracoderms to the primates was traced in Chapters 22 to 25. Although the fossil records of horses, elephants, camels and many other mammals are quite good, those of the primates are regrettably fragmentary. Most of our primate ancestors lived in tropical forests, where animals are not likely to be fossilized. However, there are representatives of several primitive groups of primates alive today from which we can get some idea of what our ancestral primates might have looked like. The earliest placental mammals were small, tree-dwelling, insect-eating animals; from these insectivores have evolved every kind of placental mammal alive today. The primates remained mostly arboreal and are relatively unspecialized.

38.1
The Primates

There are four groups (suborders) of primates: the **lemuroids,** which include the tree shrews, lemurs and lorises; the **tarsioids,** the tarsier; the **platyrrhines,** New World monkeys with flat, broad noses; and **catarrhines,** Old World monkeys, great apes and man. Lemuroids and tarsioids are often collectively called prosimians, and the platyrrhines and catarrhines are called anthropoids. The primates are, in general, rather unspecialized mammals; the specializations they do have are adaptations for arboreal life; grasping hands and feet (with opposable thumbs and great toes); some or all of the fingers and toes

with flattened nails; very flexible, mobile arms and legs; well-developed brains (especially the cerebrum); and binocular vision.

The primate line appears to have begun with the **tree shrews,** which are intermediate between the primitive insectivores and the primates. There are fossil tree shrews known from the Oligocene, and some tree shrews, such as *Tupaia* (Fig. 25.10), which still survive in the forests of Malaya and the Philippines. The tree shrew looks a bit like a squirrel with a long snout and tail, but has opposable first toes. During most of primate evolution, the trend was toward greater adaptation for an arboreal life. Only in some of the larger apes and man has this trend been reversed.

38.2
Prosimians

The earliest primates, called **prosimians,** were abundant in the early Paleocene over much of the world except Australia and South America. The lemurs, bush babies and tarsiers living today in Africa and southeastern Asia are prosimians that have descended with relatively little change from the early forms.

The **lemurs** are small nocturnal, arboreal animals with long tails, long flexible limbs and grasping hands and feet (Fig. 38.1). Lemurs are found today in the tropics of Africa and Asia, and are especially abundant on the island of Madagascar. Fossil lemurs have been found in deposits from the Paleocene and Eocene of Europe and North Amer-

Figure 38.1 The varied lemur, *Lemur variegatus.* (Courtesy of the American Museum of Natural History.)

ica. A complete skeleton of the Eocene lemur, *Notharctus,* shows that it was quite similar to the modern forms such as *Lemur.*

The **tarsioids** are represented today by a single genus, *Tarsius,* found in the East Indies. Tarsiers are also small, nocturnal and arboreal; they have large ears and distinctive,

Figure 38.2 The tarsier, *Tarsius,* found in the East Indies. Note the large, forward-directed eyes and the adhesive pads on the tips of the digits which facilitate its clinging to the branches of trees. (Courtesy of the American Museum of Natural History.)

enormous eyes, set close together and directed forward (Fig. 38.2). The hind legs are long and specialized for hopping; *Tarsius* is noted for its ability to leap great distances through the treetops. Its toes are long and slender and supplied with adhesive pads for grasping. Fossil tarsioids have been found in Eocene deposits in both North America and Europe. These primitive tarsioids are intermediate in many respects between lemurs and the anthropoids, and the latter probably evolved from some early tarsioid group.

38.3

Anthropoids

Three major groups evolved from the prosimians in the Oligocene, the **Ceboidea** or New World monkeys, the **Cercopithicoidea** or Old World monkeys, and the **Hominoidea** or great apes and man. Monkeys, apes and man have many characteristics in common and are grouped in the suborder Anthropoidea. The anthropoids have larger, more complicated brains than the prosimians, and large, forward-directed eyes enclosed in complete bony sockets. Most of the anthropoids walk on all four legs, but tend to sit upright so that the hands are free to manipulate objects. The opposability of the thumb and great toe is highly developed.

The ceboids, found in South and Central America, have widely separated nostrils directed forward and sideward. These primates became isolated in South America during the Tertiary and evolved independently of the other anthropoids. They include the marmosets, which are primitive and resemble lemurs in general body form, and the capuchin, squirrel and spider monkeys, most of which have strongly prehensile tails which serve as "fifth hands" in climbing (Fig. 38.3).

The cercopithicoids, or Old World monkeys, have a much narrower nose, with nostrils set close together and directed downward. They all have the same dental formula, a large brain, flattened nails on all digits, and a tail which may be long, short or absent but is never prehensile (Fig. 38.4).

The oldest fossil cercopithicoid is *Parapithecus,* whose remains have been found in the lower Oligocene in Egypt. It was a small monkey and is believed to represent the common ancestor of today's Old World monkeys, apes and man. The present-day Old

Figure 38.3 Spider monkey, a New World monkey with a strong prehensile tail, used in swinging from tree to tree. (Courtesy of the San Diego Zoo.)

Figure 38.4   Old World monkeys (*Nilgiri langur*). (Courtesy of the American Museum of Natural History.)

World monkeys are a large group, which includes the macaque, guenon, mandrill, mangabey, baboon, langur and others. They all tend to sit upright and have buttocks with bare, hardened sitting pads, called **ischial callosities,** which are frequently a brilliant red or blue. The mandrills and baboons have taken to living on the ground and walking on all fours. They have an elongated snout and large canine teeth. Baboons are intelligent animals that travel in troops and cooperate in obtaining food and protecting the females and young.

In the same Oligocene deposits in which *Parapithecus* was found occur fossils of the first anthropoid ape, *Propliopithecus*. This small, gibbon-like animal probably descended from *Parapithecus* and is widely believed to be close to the common ancestor of all the anthropoid apes and man. In the evolution of the apes there has been a trend toward a general increase in body size and in the size of the brain and skull. Most apes move by swinging from one branch to the next and have developed long arms and fingers. The hind legs are rather short.

Apes were widely distributed throughout Europe, Asia and Africa during the middle and later Cenozoic. Fossils of *Limnopithecus,* believed to be ancestral to the gibbons, and *Proconsul,* on the line of evolution of the other apes, have been found in lower Miocene deposits in Africa. *Paleosimia,* apparently the ancestor of the orangutan, is known from Miocene deposits in India. The genus *Dryopithecus* includes anthropoid apes that flourished in Europe and Asia during the Miocene and Pliocene; they were probably the ancestors of modern gorillas, chimpanzees and man. Early Pliocene deposits in northern Italy have yielded fossil remains of *Oreopithecus,* an apelike animal with manlike teeth and jaws. *Oreopithecus* appears to be fairly close to the evolutionary line that led to man.

38.4

The Modern Great Apes

The hominoids include a variety of fossil apes and ape-men plus man and four genera of living great apes, members of the family Pongidae — the gibbon, orangutan, chimpanzee and gorilla. These apes have rudimentary tails or none at all, arms that are longer than their legs, opposable thumbs and great toes, a

semierect posture, and chests which are broad and flat like man's rather than thin and deep like the monkey's.

The gibbon, found in Malaya, is the smallest and perhaps most primitive of the great apes. It has extraordinarily long arms, which reach to the ground when it stands erect (Fig. 38.5). Its slender, graceful body is covered with fur. Gibbons are the most skillful "brachiators," swinging gracefully and surely from branch to branch, clearing as much as 13 meters at each swing and using the arms alternately. The spectacular aerial acrobatics of the gibbon require great agility, coordination, keen eyesight and the ability to make rapid judgments of distance and possible landing sites.

The orangutan, a native of Borneo and Sumatra, is a bulky and powerful animal covered with long reddish-brown hair. Although it is short-legged and scarcely 150 cm. tall, it may weigh as much as 75 kg. Orangutans have enormously long arms, with a span of 2.5 meters and long slender hands and feet. They are successful arboreal animals, but because of their considerable weight they move more deliberately than the gibbons do.

Figure 38.5 The white-banded gibbon. These anthropoid apes use their long arms to swing from tree to tree with great agility. (Courtesy of the San Diego Zoo.)

Orangs eat fruit and leaves and build nests in trees on which to sleep.

Chimpanzees and gorillas both live in Africa, are closely related, and have many characteristics in common. Both are more terrestrial and less arboreal than the other apes and have relatively shorter arms and longer, stronger legs than gibbons and orangs. Both are large powerful animals; a male chimpanzee is about 150 cm. tall and weighs about 50 kg., and a male gorilla may be over 180 cm. tall and weigh as much as 230 kg. Chimpanzees are primarily tree-dwellers but are quite at home on the gound and walk in a semierect position. The hands and feet of the chimpanzee are long and narrow, with small thumbs and great toes, but those of the gorilla are shorter and broader, more closely resembling those of man. The gorilla has a massive head, with large bony crests on top of the skull for the attachment of the neck and jaw muscles and with prominent bony ridges over the eyes. The gorilla, like man, walks on the soles of his feet with the toes extended, rather than on the outer edge of the foot with the toes curled underneath as do other apes. Both chimpanzees and gorillas may build nests in low trees.

Psychologic studies of chimpanzees and gorillas have shown that they are curious, perceptive, able to reason, and have strong emotions and social instincts.

Man is more nearly similar to the chimpanzee and gorilla than to any other primate, yet differs in enough characters to be placed in a separate family, the Hominidae. The anatomic differences between the great apes and ourselves are rather small, and are generally differences in proportion of parts correlated with our adaptation to terrestrial life. Some of the characters which distinguish man from the other primates are (1) man's posture is fully erect; (2) his legs are longer than his arms; (3) his great toe is not opposable but is in line with the others and adapted for walking; (4) the human foot is adapted for bearing weight by the presence of lengthwise and transverse arches; (5) man's brain is large—two to three times larger than the gorilla's; (6) the human nose has a prominent bridge and a peculiar elongated tip; (7) the upper lip has a median furrow, and both lips are rolled outward so that the mucous membrane is visible; (8) man has a jutting chin; (9) his canine teeth project slightly, if at all, beyond the level of the others; and (10) man is relatively hairless.

There is no single ape that resembles man in all respects more than the other apes. The hands, feet and pelvis of the gorilla most closely resemble man's, but the skull and hair color of the chimpanzee are nearest to the human. The orang is the only ape to have the same number of ribs we have, and the posture and gait of the gibbon is most nearly human. With respect to any structure or proportion of parts, however, the difference between man and any of the great apes is less than between any of these and the monkeys.

38.5
The Man-Apes

Fossil anthropoids that almost bridge the gap from ape to man were found in Tanganyika in 1959. These deposits date from the late Pliocene or early Pleistocene and were estimated to be about 1,750,000 years old on the basis of their content of radioactive potassium. These man-apes have been named *Zinjanthropus*. They are forms that apparently came down out of the trees and made and used simple stone tools and wooden clubs. Their brain volume was small, about 600 ml., and they had essentially no forehead. From the nature of their teeth it has been inferred that they were vegetarians.

From Pleistocene cave deposits in South Africa about one million years old have come fossils of other man-apes that are believed to be related to the evolutionary line that gave rise to modern man. These man apes probably existed too recently to be man's ancestors, but they show the kind of changes by which the transition from ape to man was made. They are now regarded as "progressive apes," adapted for walking upright on the ground, which evolved independently of the human line from common dryopithecine ancestors in the Miocene.

The first of these fossils, the skull of a baby man-ape, was found in the Transvaal by Dart in 1925 and named *Australopithecus* (Fig. 38.6). Subsequently, Dart and Broom found adult skulls and parts of skeletons, and although these were given separate names, *Plesianthropus* and *Paranthropus,* they probably represent animals very closely related to, if not identical with, the original *Australopithecus*. These australopithecines have an interesting mixture of apelike and human characteristics. The head was apelike, with a low-vaulted

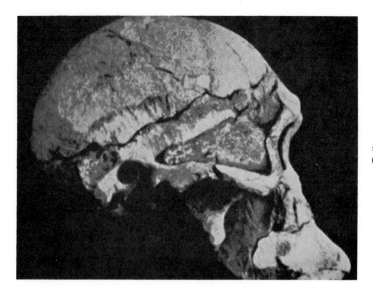

Figure 38.6 Reconstruction of the skull of the man ape *Australopithecus*. (Clark: The History of the Primates.)

skull, protruding muzzle and heavy jaws, but the brain capacity was 650 ml., greater than that of any known ape and almost as large as that of the earliest ape man. The cheekbone, jaw hinge and teeth were very similar to man's; the small canine teeth and molars resemble ours. These man-apes lived in caves, hunted animals, and may have learned how to use fire. From the structure of the pelvis and leg bones, and from the fact that the foramen magnum (the hole in the skull through which the spinal cord emerges) is located far under the skull, we conclude that these man-apes had a fairly erect posture. The largest of the australopithecines, the Swartkrans man-ape found in 1949, appears to have been a veritable giant, larger and heavier than the largest gorillas.

38.6
Fossil Ape-Men

The hominid stock appears to have diverged from the great apes some time after the Miocene, and the remains of a number of creatures with characters intermediate between the fossil apes and living man have been found in Pliocene and Pleistocene deposits in widely scattered parts of Europe, Asia and Africa (Fig. 38.7). The evidence from these fossils indicates that the characteristics which distinguish man from the apes did not appear simultaneously in a single form, for these ape men show a mixture of apelike and human traits. Whether these are apes or men is, perhaps, a matter of definition, but they were large-brained anthropoids who walked erect, had well-formed hands, and made and used tools of stone and bone. We have a fairly clear idea of what

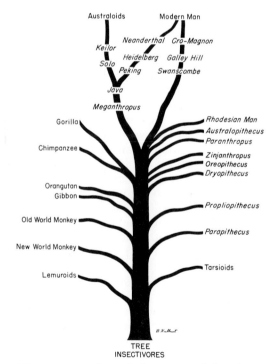

Figure 38.7 An evolutionary tree of the primates, beginning with the primitive tree insectivores. The forms known only as fossils are indicated in italics. (Villee: Biology, 5th ed.)

these ape-men looked like from their fossil remains, and we also know quite a bit about how they lived from the tools, weapons, ornaments and other cultural remains that have been discovered.

It is understandable that the fossil record of man's immediate ancestors is incomplete, for those animals were too intelligent to be caught in quicksands or tarpits. They were primarily forest-dwellers and their dead bodies were quickly devoured by other animals. In addition it was at about this stage of evolution that burial customs arose, involving cremation of the dead.

One of the most primitive ape-men was *Pithecanthropus erectus,* the **Java man,** whose remains were found in 1891 in Pleistocene deposits on the banks of the Solo River in eastern Java (Fig. 38.10). Several other skulls and leg bones found since give us a good idea of what Java man looked like. He was of stocky build, about 170 cm. tall, weighed 70 kg., walked erect, and probably traveled in small family groups, living in caves and hunting in the forests. His face was rather apelike, with massive, protruding, chinless jaws equipped with a set of huge teeth (although the canine teeth were not enlarged tusks as in the apes). The nose was broad and low-bridged and there was a heavy, bony protruding ridge over the eyes. The skull had a cranial capacity of about 900 ml., intermediate between the 1500 ml. which is average for modern man, and the 600 ml. of the gorilla and australopithecines. By studying casts of the interior of the skull, the contours and relative proportions of the various parts of the brain can be determined. *Pithecanthropus* appears to have had the part of the brain which controls speech, though we have no way of knowing whether he could speak. The frontal lobes of the brain, which were the last parts to appear in evolution, were smaller in Java man than in modern man, but larger than in any living ape. Java man's brain was more human than simian, larger and more convoluted than that of any of the primitive or present apes.

Other remains found in limestone caves near Peking, China, are those of a primitive ape-man of the middle Pleistocene, some half million years ago. Their discoverer, Davidson Black, named them *Sinanthropus pekinensis.* The skeletons of more than 40 individuals have now been found, and it is possible to make fairly complete reconstructions of their

form. **Peking man** had a skull very similar to that of Java man, with heavy bony ridges over the eyes, a low slanting forehead, a broad flat nose and a massive chinless jaw (Fig. 38.8). The remains fall into two groups, one considerably larger than the other, which suggests that the difference between the size of males and females was greater than at present. The cranial capacity of Peking man ranged from 850 to 1300 ml. and averaged about 1075 ml., distinctly larger than that of Java man. The fact that many of the skulls are found with their bases broken open suggests that Peking man was a cannibal with a taste for brains.

As more specimens of Java and Peking men have been found, it has become clear that the two are really quite similar and represent two races or subspecies of the same species rather than separate genera. The anthropologist who has studied them most intensively, Franz Weidenreich, found that Java and Peking man are identical in 57 of 74 characters of the skull, and that there are clear differences in only four characters, one of which is the difference in size. He has suggested that they be named *Homo erectus erectus* and *Homo erectus pekinensis,* respectively.

Traces of other ape-men, much larger than Java and Peking men, have also been found in southern Asia. The lower Pleistocene deposits of Java have yielded a large lower jaw with molar teeth that appears to have belonged to an ape-man as big as a gorilla. Probably this Javanese giant, named *Meganthropus,* was exceeded in size by another giant, named *Gigantopithecus,* known only from some extremely large, human-like fossil teeth found in a Hong Kong drugstore! These were traced back to cave deposits from the lower Pleistocene in southern China. The largest molar found is some six times larger than a human molar and must have belonged to an exceptionally large ape-man. Whether these giants represent ancestors of modern man or side branches of anthropoid evolution cannot be decided at present.

Remains of another primitive man have been found on the banks of the Solo River in Java, only a few miles from the spot where Java man was found. Eleven skulls of **Solo man** have been found since 1936, all with their bases bashed in, suggesting that Solo man inherited a taste for human brains along with other traits from his ancestral Javan man. These Solo skulls retain many brutish

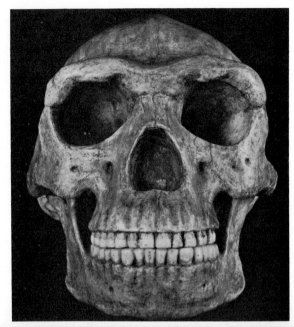

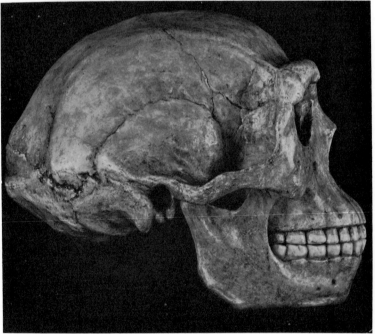

Figure 38.8   Front and side views of a reconstructed skull of Peking man, *Sinanthropus pekinensis.* Note the massive bony ridges over the eyes, the low, retreating forehead, the protruding jaws and the absence of a chin. (Courtesy of the American Museum of Natural History, New York.)

characteristics, with heavy brow ridges and a sloping forehead, but the head is somewhat rounder and more like modern man's in shape. The Australian bushmen are believed to be descendants of Solo man, a conclusion strengthened by the finding in 1940 of two Pleistocene skulls at Keilor, near Melbourne, Australia, which were intermediate in character between Solo man and the present aboriginal Australians.

Another primitive skull, to which the name Rhodesian man has been given, was found in

1921 in a limestone cave at Broken Hill, Rhodesia. The skull was well preserved and has thick bones, very large eyebrow ridges and a low, receding forehead but a cranial capacity of about 1300 ml. The teeth are large, but human rather than apelike, and are badly decayed, an unusual condition in apes and primitive man. The relations of this finding to other primitive men are obscure.

38.7
Fossil Members of the Genus Homo

The fossils of primitive man found in Europe, Asia and Africa are slightly different but similar enough to be grouped together as the Neanderthaloids. The Neanderthaloids, which include Heidelberg man, Neanderthal man, Solo man and Rhodesian man, probably are descended from the pithecanthropoids, Java and Peking men.

Heidelberg man (originally described as *Homo heidelbergensis*) is known only from a massive lower jaw found buried under 25 meters of sand in a pit near Heidelberg, Germany. The jaw is large and heavy and lacks a chin, but the teeth are of moderate size and generally like modern man's. Since it resembles the jaw of Neanderthal man in many respects, Heidelberg man, who lived more than 500,000 years ago, may have been an ancestor of Neanderthal and other later men. The fossils found with this jaw are those of animals from a warm climate—lions and rhinoceroses—and Heidelberg man must have lived during one of the interglacial periods. Although it is not clear which interglacial period was graced by Heidelberg man, it was at least 500,000 years ago and he was a contemporary of *Homo erectus* and is sometimes placed in the *erectus* assemblage.

The first human fossils to be discovered, a skull and some bones, were found in the Neander valley near Düsseldorf, Germany, in 1856. Similar skulls and skeletons have been found in widely separated parts of Europe, Asia Minor, North Africa, Siberia and the islands of the Mediterranean. Neanderthal remains are associated with a particular Stone Age culture known as the **Mousterian** (named after le Moustier cave on the bank of the Vézère River in France). Neanderthal man (originally described as *Homo neanderthalensis*) lived in Europe for thousands of years during and after the third interglacial period, about 150,000 years ago, and became extinct only about 25,000 years ago. A typical Neanderthal man was short, stocky, and powerfully built, about 150 cm. tall, with stooped shoulders and bent knees (Fig. 38.9). The head jutted forward from a short thick neck and massive shoulders. The massive skull had a thick bony ridge over the eyes and a receding forehead. The nose was broad and short, and the jaws were large and strong with a very little chin. Despite these primitive features, Neanderthal man's cranial capacity was as large as or larger than modern man's,

Figure 38.9 An artist's reconstruction of a Neanderthal family living in a cave in the Rock of Gibraltar. (Courtesy of the Chicago Natural History Museum. Frederick Blaschke, sculptor; Charles A. Corwin, artist.)

averaging 1550 ml., and he was probably quite intelligent. He lived primarily in caves, used fire, made beautiful chipped stone tools and weapons, and buried his dead reverently with food and ornaments. As more of the weapons, tools, utensils and ornaments made by Neanderthal man have been found, we are coming to realize that he was indeed a very capable and intelligent fellow.

Human fossils found in caves in Mount Carmel in Galilee include some that are typically Neanderthaloid and others that have characters more like those of modern man—greater height, smaller face, less receding forehead, and so on. It is clear that these were all contemporaneous, but whether they represent a connection between later types of man and Neanderthal man, or hybridization between two separate stocks, is unknown.

38.8
Modern Man (Homo sapiens)

The species *Homo sapiens* includes all the living races of man and some extinct ones such as the Cro-Magnons. The idea that this species appeared relatively recently in the late Pleistocene, when the Neanderthalers were vanishing, is no longer valid, for the Swanscombe man is now known to have existed in the middle Pleistocene. This skull, essentially modern in shape and size, though having somewhat thicker bones, was found in 1935 in the Thames Valley at Swanscombe in a gravel deposit from the Middle Pleistocene. Its antiquity was confirmed in 1949 by the fluorine test, which depends on the fact that buried bones and teeth gradually accumulate fluorine. The age of a fossil can be estimated from its fluorine content. Other remains of *Homo sapiens* which bridge the long gap between Swanscombe man and the Cro-Magnon races have been found in central France in 1948 and in northern Iran in 1951.

More than 100 fossils of *Homo sapiens* have been found from the period between 15,000 and 60,000 or so years ago. The first of these were found in the Cro-Magnon rock shelters in the Vézère valley in south central France, and these are all referred to as Cro-Magnon men, even though they fall into several different groups. The Cro-Magnons were tall and large-boned, with massive long skulls, a high forehead, prominent chin, no eyebrow ridges, and brain volumes as great as 1800 ml. (Fig. 38.10). They lived in rock shelters and caves and drew superb pictures of the con-

Figure 38.10 Restorations by Dr. J. H. McGregor of what prehistoric men probably looked like. From left to right, the Java ape man, Neanderthal man and Cro-Magnon man. (Courtesy of Dr. J. H. McGregor and the American Museum of Natural History, New York.)

temporary animals on the walls of these caves (see Fig. 1.1). Cro-Magnon man was a contemporary of the Neanderthalers and may have displaced and exterminated them or may have hybridized with them. The heterogeneity of the skeletal remains found in single sites suggests that there was extensive hybridization among the various types existing at the time.

The center of origin of modern man appears to have been in Asia, in the general region of the Caspian Sea. The white races spread westward around both shores of the Mediterranean to Europe, Southwestern Asia and North Africa, displacing the Cro-Magnons who had, in turn, displaced the earlier Neanderthalers. Some of the inhabitants of Ireland and Scandinavia, and the Basques of southern France and northern Spain, show marked similarities to Cro-Magnons and may represent their descendants who were pushed westward by the migrating neolithic man.

The Negroid races spread south on both sides of the Indian Ocean to Africa and Melanesia. It appears that they, too, displaced more primitive races and pushed the Bushmen to the tip of South Africa and the Australoids into Australia.

The Mongoloids spread east and north, occupying Siberia and China. About 40,000 years ago they crossed the Bering Strait to occupy North and South America.

There are four basic stocks of modern man, all of which belong to the species *Homo sapiens.* The Australian aborigines appear to be the most primitive and perhaps have a slightly different line of descent from the others. The other three, the whites, the negroids and the mongoloids, are each subdivided into a number of races. A **race,** whether of human beings or some other animal or plant, may be defined genetically as a population which differs significantly from other populations with respect to the frequency of one or more of the genes it possesses. Or it may be defined phenotypically as a population whose members, though varying individually, are distinguished as a group by a certain combination of morphologic and physiologic characteristics which they share because of their common descent.

In the course of his evolution from the ape-men, man has increased slightly in height but his frame has become much less massive. He now stands completely erect and his head

is balanced on a relatively slender neck, instead of jutting forward from the shoulders and being held in place by massive neck muscles. His cranial capacity has increased, the frontal lobes of the brain have enlarged and the skull is more rounded, the forehead is more vertical and the bony ridges over the eyes have become smaller. The face and jaws have become smaller and the reduction in jaw size is correlated with a reduction in the size and complexity of the teeth. There is a strong tendency for the third molars, the **wisdom teeth,** to become vestigial. These changes probably follow, directly or indirectly, from the evolutionary trend towards larger brains and greater intelligence. These more intelligent descendants were less dependent upon sheer physical strength for getting food and fighting enemies, animals and other men. Speech was invented, tools and weapons were made, man began to live in clans and tribes and progressed beyond his former state of being a tree-dwelling primate to that of a ground-dwelling, civilized animal.

38.9
Cultural Evolution

Corroborative evidence for the relationships and temporal order of these primitive and modern men comes from the objects they made and used, called **artifacts,** which were deposited along with the fossils. The science of **archeology** is concerned with the finding, identifying and interpreting of the tools, weapons, cooking utensils, ornaments and other objects made by man.

Although early man must have learned to pick up and use stones of a convenient size and shape, it was not until the middle Pleistocene, apparently, that he learned how to chip pieces of flint to make hand axes. The culture characterized by these chipped stone tools is called the **Lower Paleolithic** and was the culture of Java and Peking men. These men lived in caves and were hunters and food gatherers who had learned how to use fire. The association of certain kinds of axes and scraping tools with the Java and Peking men provides clues for the study of their distribution, for similar artifacts without skeletal remains have been found in India and Burma.

More advanced tools from the third interglacial and the last glacial periods represent the **Middle Paleolithic** culture. Neanderthal man is associated with the Mousterian culture, a Middle Paleolithic one. Each of these cultures is recognized by the style of tools and weapons made. The Mousterian implements were made by chipping flakes from a piece of flint and then sharpening the edges by removing more flakes with a bone tool. The common weapon of this time was a triangular piece of stone, the forerunner of both the spear and arrowhead.

Later, in the **Upper Paleolithic** culture, an improved method of tool making was discovered, in which the flakes were removed from the piece of flint by means of steadily and carefully applied pressure, rather than by blows. This produced long, slender, knife-like blades, many of which were elaborately and skillfully carved and were true works of art. These Upper Paleolithic men, Cro-Magnons and others, were painters as well as skilled craftsmen; their cave paintings, found in France and Spain, show a remarkable grasp of the principles of design. These men of the Upper Paleolithic introduced bone needles and other tools and probably invented the bow and arrow.

The **Mesolithic,** or Middle Stone Age, shows no important advance over the Paleo-lithic cultures. Mesolithic man was still a hunter and food gatherer, living in small isolated breeding groups, which would favor the occurrence of genetic drift, and lead to the formation of divergent groups.

The **Neolithic** or New Stone Age culture originated in the Near East, between Egypt and Iran. This culture is marked not only by tools which were carefully ground and polished, but by the beginnings of agriculture and animal husbandry. The earliest animals to be domesticated, after the dog, were the pig, sheep, goat and cow; the horse was not domesticated until much later. Man gradually changed from a wandering hunter and food gatherer to a settled food producer, raising grain, making pottery and cloth, and living in villages. The increase in the food supply led to an increase in population, breeding groups became larger and interbred with neighboring ones, and the tendency toward genetic drift was greatly decreased. The evolution of social organization from the family groups and clans of the Old Stone Age to the present-day large nations, which are dependent upon man's social behavior, his ability to cooperate with others and to restrain his own behavior, has been an important factor in the evolutionary success of *Homo sapiens.*

QUESTIONS

1. List and discuss the characters of the human body which are remnants of our former adaptation for living in trees.
2. Indicate the current belief as to the course of evolution from primitive insectivores to man.
3. Distinguish between ceboid and cercopithicoid anthropoids.
4. List the characters which distinguish man from the great apes.
5. Compare the structures and functions of gibbons, orangs and gorillas. Which shows the best adaptation to arboreal life?
6. Do you consider any of the ape-men or man-apes to be the "missing link" in human evolution?
7. Compare the appearance of Neanderthal and Cro-Magnon men. What became of each?
8. Why is the structure of the human body said to be "relatively unspecialized"?
9. Why is it incorrect to say that man came from monkeys? What is the correct statement?
10. What characters distinguish the present races of man?
11. What is an archeologic artifact? Of what use are they in tracing human evolution?
12. In what ways do the Upper Paleolithic and Neolithic cultures differ?
13. Why is genetic drift less important in human evolution at present than it was 10,000 or more years ago?

ANNOTATED REFERENCES

Clark, W. E. LeGros: The Antecedents of Man. Edinburgh, Edinburgh University Press, 1959. This book, also published as a paperback by Harper, 1963, is an excellent popular presentation of human evolution.

Coon, C. S.: The Races of Europe. New York, Macmillan, 1939. A well-written, comprehensive treatise describing the many subdivisions of the white race.

Dobzhansky, T.: Evolution, Genetics and Man. New York, John Wiley & Sons, Inc., 1955. An interesting discussion of human heredity and evolution.

Hooton, E. A.: Up from the Ape. 2nd ed. New York, Macmillan, 1945. An amusing and informative discussion of the primates and their evolution.

Howells, W. W.: Mankind So Far. New York, Doubleday, Doran and Co. 1944. Excellent presentation of the status of our knowledge of prehistoric man some 25 years ago.

Osborn, H. F.: Men of the Old Stone Age. 3rd ed. New York, Charles Scribner's Sons, 1918. A very readable account of some of the early discoveries of fossils of our ancestral apes and ape-men.

Romer, A. S.: The Vertebrate Story. 4th ed. Chicago, University of Chicago Press, 1959. A well-illustrated text of vertebrate evolution.

Weidenreich, F.: Apes, Giants and Men. Chicago, University of Chicago Press, 1947. A fascinating account of studies of fossil ape-men by one of the major researchers in the field.

Part Five

ANIMALS AND THEIR ENVIRONMENT

39   ECOLOGY

The animals and plants living today are related not only by evolutionary descent, as described in the preceding three chapters, but also by their relations to each other and to the physical environment. One form may provide food or shelter for another; it may produce some substance beneficial or harmful to the second; or the two may compete for food and shelter. The study of the interrelationships between living things—both within species and between species—and their physical environment is known as **ecology.** Each organism, in the course of evolution, has become adapted to survive in some particular kind of environment, has developed a tolerance for a certain range of moisture, light, temperature, wind and so on, and has developed certain relationships with other animals and plants in its immediate vicinity. Because the study of ecologic principles and an appreciation of the prime importance of ecology require a good background knowledge of the anatomy and physiology of a wide variety of animals, the discussion of this topic has been reserved for these concluding chapters.

39.1
Ecosystems

When any species of animal is carefully studied in the wild, it becomes clear that it is not independent of other living things but is one of a system of interacting and interdependent parts which form a larger unit. Ecologists use the term **ecosystem** to indicate a natural unit of living and nonliving parts that interact to form a stable system in which the exchange of materials between living and nonliving parts follows a circular path. Eco-

systems may be as large as a lake or forest, or one of the cycles of the elements (p. 701), or as small as an aquarium jar containing tropical fish, green plants and snails.

A small lake or pond is a classic example of an ecosystem small enough to be investigated easily (Fig. 39.1). The nonliving parts of the lake include the water, dissolved oxygen, carbon dioxide, inorganic salts such as phosphates and chlorides of sodium, potassium and calcium, and a host of organic compounds. The living organisms may be subdivided into producers, consumers and decomposers, according to their role in keeping the ecosystem operating as a stable interacting whole. The **producer organisms** are the green plants that manufacture organic compounds from simple inorganic substances. There are two kinds of producer organisms in a typical small lake: the larger plants growing along the shore or floating in shallow water, and the microscopic floating plants, mostly algae, distributed throughout the water, as far down as light will penetrate. Such small plants are collectively known as **phytoplankton;** they are usually invisible unless present in great abundance, when they give the water a greenish tinge. The phytoplankton are usually much more important as food producers for the lake than are the larger plants.

The consumer organisms include insects and insect larvae, crustacea, fish, and perhaps some fresh-water clams. The plant eaters are called **primary consumers,** the carnivores that eat the primary consumers are called **secondary consumers,** and so on. The ecosystem is completed by **decomposer organisms,** bacteria and fungi, which break down the organic compounds of dead cells from producer and consumer organisms

699

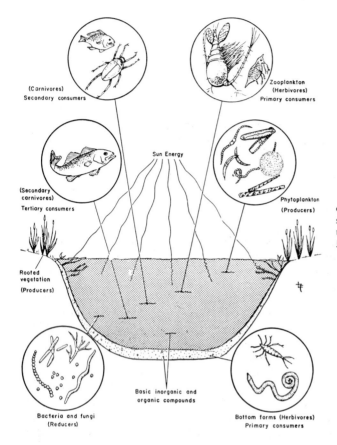

Figure 39.1 A small fresh-water pond as an example of an ecosystem. The producer, consumer and decomposer (reducer) organisms plus the nonliving parts are indicated. (Villee: Biology, 5th ed.)

into inorganic substances that can be used as raw materials by green plants.

No matter how large and complex an ecosystem may be, it can be shown to consist of these same major parts—producer, consumer and decomposer organisms, and nonliving components.

39.2
Habitat and Ecologic Niche

Two important concepts which are basic to the description of the ecologic relations of organisms are the habitat and the ecologic niche. The **habitat** of an organism is the place where it lives—a physical area, some specific part of the earth's surface, air, soil or water. It may be as large as the ocean or a prairie, or as small as the underside of a rotten log or the intestine of a termite, but it is always a tangible, physically demarcated region. More than one animal or plant may live in a single habitat.

The **ecologic niche** is the status of an organism within the community or ecosystem and depends upon the organism's structural adaptations, physiologic responses and behavior. E. P. Odum has made the analogy that the habitat is an organism's "address" and the ecologic niche is its "profession," biologically speaking. The ecologic niche is an abstraction that includes all the physical, chemical, physiologic and biotic factors that an organism requires to live. To describe an organism's ecologic niche, one must know what it eats, what eats it, its range of movement, and its effects on other organisms and on the nonliving parts of the surroundings.

The difference between these two concepts may be made clearer by an example. In the shallow waters at the edge of a lake one could find many different kinds of water bugs, all of which have the same habitat. Some of these, such as the backswimmer, *Notonecta*, are predators, catching and eating other animals of about its size, while others, such as *Corixa*, feed on dead and decaying organisms. Each has a quite different role in the biologic economy of the lake and, thus, each occupies an entirely different ecologic niche.

A single species may occupy somewhat

different niches in different regions, depending on the available food supply and the number and kinds of competitors. Some organisms, such as animals with distinct stages in their life history, occupy different niches in succession. A tadpole is a primary consumer, feeding on plants, but an adult frog is a secondary consumer, feeding on insects and other animals.

39.3
The Cyclic Use of Matter

The total mass of the organisms that have lived in the past billion or so years is much greater than the mass of carbon and nitrogen atoms present on the planet. The Law of the Conservation of Matter assures us that matter is neither created nor destroyed; obviously, then, the carbon and nitrogen atoms must have been used over and over again in the formation of new generations of animals and plants. The earth neither receives any great amount of matter from other parts of the universe nor does it lose significant amounts of matter to outer space. Each element — carbon, hydrogen, oxygen, nitrogen, phosphorus, sulfur, and the rest — is taken from the environment, made a part of living material and finally, perhaps by a quite circuitous route involving a number of other

organisms, is returned to the environment to be used again. An appreciation of the roles of animals, green plants and bacteria in this cyclic use of the elements can be gained from a consideration of the details of the more important cycles.

39.4
The Carbon Cycle

There are about six tons of carbon (in the form of carbon dioxide) in the atmosphere over each acre of the earth's surface. Yet each year an acre of luxurious plant growth, such as sugar cane, will extract as much as 20 tons of carbon from the atmosphere and incorporate it into plant bodies. If there were no way to renew the supply, the green plants would use up the entire supply of atmospheric carbon dioxide in a few centuries. Carbon dioxide fixation by bacteria and animals is another, but quantitatively minor, drain on the supply of carbon dioxide. Carbon dioxide is returned to the atmosphere by respiration. Plants carry on respiration continuously, and green plant tissues are eaten by animals who, by respiration, return more carbon dioxide to the air. But respiration alone would be unable to return enough carbon dioxide to the air to balance that withdrawn by photosynthesis; vast amounts

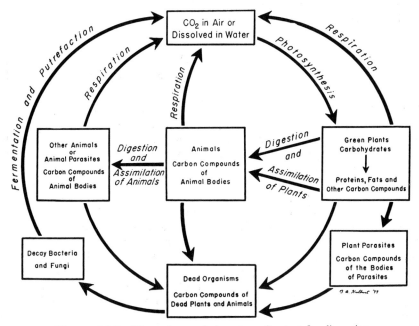

Figure 39.2 The carbon cycle in nature. See text for discussion.

of carbon would accumulate in the dead bodies of plants and animals. The carbon cycle is balanced by the decay bacteria and fungi which break down the carbon compounds of dead plants and animals and convert the carbon to carbon dioxide (Fig. 39.2).

Investigators at the University of Notre Dame have been able to raise bacteria-free animals in special sterile incubators. This has been done to study problems such as the synthesis of vitamins by the bacteria normally present in the intestines. In time, these animals age and die, but their bodies do not decompose—the carbon atoms have been withdrawn (temporarily) from the cycle.

When the bodies of plants are compressed under water they undergo a series of chemical changes to form **peat,** then brown coal or **lignite** and, finally, **coal.** The bodies of certain marine plants and animals may undergo somewhat similar changes to form petroleum. These processes remove some carbon from the cycle temporarily, but eventually geologic changes or man's mining and drilling bring the coal and oil to the surface to be burned to carbon dioxide and restored to the cycle.

Much of the earth's carbon is present in rocks as carbonates—limestone and marble. These rocks are gradually worn down and the carbonates are, in time, added to the carbon cycle; but other rocks are forming at the bottom of the sea from the sediments of dead animals and plants, so that the amount of carbon in the carbon cycle remains about the same.

39.5
The Nitrogen Cycle

The nitrates of the soil and water are taken up by plants and are the source of nitrogen for the synthesis of amino acids and proteins. The plants may then be eaten by animals that, in turn, use the amino acids from the plant proteins in synthesizing their own amino acids, proteins, nucleic acids and other nitrogenous compounds. When animals and plants die, the decay bacteria convert these nitrogenous compounds into ammonia. Animals excrete several kinds of nitrogenous wastes—urea, uric acid, creatinine and ammonia—and decay bacteria convert these into ammonia. Most of the ammonia is converted

by nitrite bacteria to nitrites and this, in turn, is converted by nitrate bacteria into nitrates, thus completing the cycle (Fig. 39.3). Denitrifying bacteria convert some of the ammonia to atmospheric nitrogen. Atmospheric nitrogen can be converted to amino acids and other organic nitrogen compounds by some algae (*Nostoc*) and by the soil bacteria *Azotobacter* and *Clostridium*. Other bacteria of the genus *Rhizobium*, though unable to fix atmospheric nitrogen by themselves, can carry out this process in combination with cells from the roots of legumes such as peas and beans. The bacteria invade the roots and stimulate the formation of **root nodules,** a sort of benign tumor. The combination of legume cell and bacteria is able to fix nitrogen, something neither can do alone. For this reason legumes are often planted to restore soil fertility by increasing the content of fixed nitrogen. Nodule bacteria may fix as much as 2.5 kilograms of nitrogen per acre per year and soil bacteria as much as 3 kilograms per acre per year. Atmospheric nitrogen can also be fixed by electrical energy, either by lightning or by man-made electricity. Although 80 per cent of the gases in the atmosphere is nitrogen, no animals and only these few plants can utilize it in this form. When the bodies of the nitrogen-fixing bacteria are decayed, the amino acids are metabolized to ammonia and this, in turn, is converted by the nitrite and nitrate bacteria to complete the cycle.

39.6
The Water Cycle

The seas are the world's great reservoir of water. The sun's heat vaporizes water and forms clouds; these are blown over the land, where they are cooled enough to precipitate the water as rain or snow. Some of the precipitated water soaks into the ground, some runs off the surface into streams and goes directly back to the sea. The ground water is returned to the surface by springs, by pumps, and by the activities of the roots and stems of plants. Water inevitably ends up in the sea, but it may become incorporated into the bodies of several successive organisms en route. The energy to run the cycle—the heat needed to evaporate water—comes from sunlight.

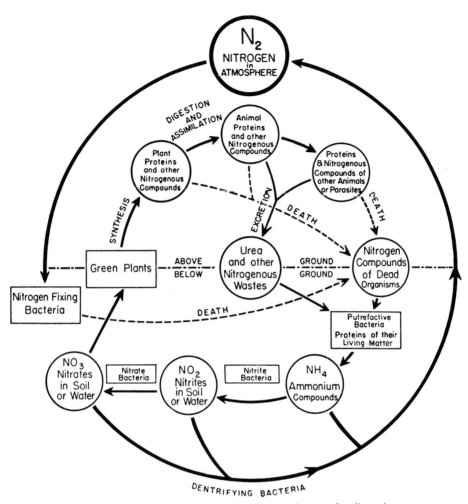

Figure 39.3 The nitrogen cycle in nature. See text for discussion.

39.7
Mineral Cycles

As water runs over rocks it gradually wears away the surface and carries off a variety of minerals, some in solution and some in suspension. Some of these minerals, such as the phosphates, sulfates, and other salts of calcium, magnesium, sodium and potassium, are essential for the growth of plants and animals. Phosphorus, an essential component of many of the compounds present in cells, enters plants as inorganic phosphate and is converted to a variety of organic phosphates which are intermediates in the metabolism of carbohydrates and other substances (p. 66). Animals obtain their phosphorus as inorganic phosphate in the water they drink or as inorganic and organic phosphates in the food they eat. The phosphorus cycle is not completely balanced, for phosphates are being carried into the sediments at the bottom of the sea faster than they are being returned by the actions of fish and marine birds. Sea birds play an important role in returning phosphorus to the cycle by depositing phosphate-rich **guano** on land. Man and other animals, by catching fish, also recover some phosphorus from the sea. Minerals are recovered from the sea bottom and made available for use once more when geologic upheavals bring some of the sea bottom back to the surface and raise new mountains.

39.8
The Energy Cycle

The cycles of matter are closed: the atoms are used over and over again. Keeping the cycles going does not require new matter, but it does require energy, for *the energy cycle is not a closed one*. Although energy is neither created nor destroyed, but converted from one form to another (first law of thermodynamics), there is a decrease in the amount of *useful* energy whenever one of these transformations occurs; some energy is degraded into heat and dissipated (second law of thermodynamics).

Only a small fraction of the light energy reaching the earth is trapped; considerable areas of the earth have no plants, and plants can utilize in photosynthesis only about 3 per cent of the incident energy. This is converted into the chemical energy of the bonds of the organic substances made by the plant. When an animal eats the plant, or when bacteria decompose the plant material, and these organic substances are oxidized, the energy liberated is just equal to the amount used in synthesizing the substances (first law of thermodynamics) but some of the energy is heat and is not useful energy (second law of thermodynamics). If the animal's flesh is eaten by another animal, a further decrease in useful energy occurs as the second animal oxidizes the organic substances of the first to liberate energy to synthesize its own cellular constituents.

Eventually, all the energy originally trapped by plants in photosynthesis is converted to heat and dissipated to outer space, and all the carbon of the organic compounds ends up as carbon dioxide. The only important source of energy on earth is sunlight—energy derived from nuclear reactions, largely the conversion of hydrogen to helium, occurring at extremely high temperatures in the interior of the sun. When this energy is exhausted and the radiant energy of the sun can no longer support photosynthesis, the carbon cycle will stop, all plants and animals will die, and organic carbon will be converted to carbon dioxide.

39.9

Factors Limiting the Ranges of Animals

No species of animal or plant is found everywhere in the world; some parts of the earth are too hot, too cold, too wet, too dry, or too something else for the organism to survive there. Some factor in the environment may kill the animal or plant directly, or

it may keep the species from becoming established by preventing its reproduction or by killing off the egg, embryo, or some other peculiarly sensitive stage in the life cycle. Most species of organisms are not even found in all the regions of the world where they could survive. The existence of barriers prevents their further migration and enables us to distinguish the major biogeographic realms (p. 680), characterized by certain assemblages of plants and animals.

Biologists were aware more than a century ago that each kind of animal requires certain materials for growth and reproduction and is unable to survive if the environment does not provide a certain minimum of each of the materials required. V. E. Shelford pointed out in 1913 that *too much* of a certain factor would act as a limiting factor just as effectively as too little of it. Thus, the distribution of each species is determined by its **range of tolerance** to variations in each of the environmental factors. Much ecologic research has been done to define the limits of tolerance, the limits within which species can exist, and the results have been very helpful in understanding the pattern of distribution of animals and plants. One stage in the life cycle—perhaps the larvae or eggs—is usually more sensitive to some environmental factor and is effective in limiting the distribution of the species. The adult blue crab, for example, can survive in water of low salt content and can migrate for some distance up river from the sea, but the larvae cannot survive low salinity and the species cannot become permanently established there.

Some organisms have very narrow ranges of tolerance to environmental changes; others can survive within much broader limits. Any particular species, of course, may have narrow limits of tolerance for one factor and wide limits for another. Ecologists use the prefixes **steno-** and **eury-,** respectively, to refer to species with narrow and wide ranges of tolerance to a given factor. A stenothermic organism is one which will tolerate only narrow variations in temperature. The housefly, in contrast, is eurythermic, tolerating temperatures ranging from 6° to 45° C.

Temperature. Temperature is an important limiting factor, as the relative sparseness of life in the desert and arctic testifies. Even birds and mammals with temperatures kept relatively constant by physiologic thermostats and body insulation may be limited by extremes of temperature. Extreme heat or cold may limit their food supplies or act in some other indirect fashion to prevent their survival. Most of the animals found in the desert have adapted to the rigors of the environment by living in burrows during the day and foraging only at night. Many animals escape the bitter cold of the northern winter by migrating southward or by burrowing beneath the snow. Measurements made in Alaska show that when the surface temperature is −50° C. the temperature 60 cm. under the snow, at the surface of the soil, is −7° C. Animals such as deer and elk that spend the summer in the high mountains migrate to lower levels during the winter. Certain bats, rodents and shrews survive the winter in a state of markedly reduced metabolism, known as **hibernation** (p. 715). The body temperature falls to just a degree or two above that of the surrounding air, metabolism is greatly decreased, and the heart beat and respiration become very slow. No food is eaten, and the metabolic demands of the body are met from the stores of body fat. Crocodiles, certain frogs and fishes survive periods of high temperature and dryness by undergoing **aestivation,** a torpid, inactive state comparable to hibernation.

Birds and mammals have physiologic mechanisms which keep body temperature constant despite wide fluctuations in the environmental temperature (p. 428). These thermostated animals are said to be **homoiothermic** ("warm-blooded" is not quite the proper synonym; they are really "constant temperature-blooded"). Reptiles, amphibia, fish and all invertebrates are **poikilothermic;** their body temperature fluctuates with that of the environment. "Cold-blooded" is not properly descriptive, for a lizard sitting in the sun may have warmer blood than ours. All the metabolic processes in poikilotherms are directly influenced by the environmental temperature. Such animals move, feed and grow in warm weather and become inactive in cold weather. Many marine organisms have seasonal north-south migrations to find water with the optimal temperature.

Light. The amount of light is an important factor in determining the distribution and behavior of both plants and animals. Light is, of course, the ultimate source of energy for life on this planet, yet prolonged direct exposure of cells to light of high intensity may be fatal. Both plants and animals have evolved mechanisms and responses to protect them against too much (or too little) light.

The amount of daylight per day, known as the **photoperiod,** has a marked influence on the time of flowering of plants, the time of migration of birds, the time of spawning of fish, and the seasonal change of color of certain birds and mammals. The effects of the photoperiod on vertebrates appear to occur via some hormonal mechanism involving the hypothalamus and pituitary. Knowledge of photoperiod phenomena has proved to be of considerable economic importance. Chicken farmers have found that artificial illumination in the hen house, by extending the photoperiod, stimulates the hens to lay more eggs.

Water. Water is a physiologic necessity for all living things but is a limiting factor primarily for land organisms. The total amount of rainfall, its seasonal distribution, the humidity, and the ground supply of water are some of the factors limiting distribution of animals and plants. Some lakes and streams, especially in the western and southwestern United States, periodically become dry or almost dry, and the fish and other aquatic animals are killed. During periods of low water, the water temperature may rise sufficiently to kill off the aquatic forms. Many of the protozoa form thick-walled cysts which enable them to survive the drying of the puddles in which they normally live. Some desert animals have adapted to desert conditions by digging and living in burrows where the temperature is lower and the humidity is higher than at the surface. Measurements have shown that the burrow of a kangaroo rat 60 cm. underground may have a temperature of only 16° C. when the surface temperature is over 38° C.

An excess of water is fatal to certain animals; earthworms, for example, may be driven from their burrows by heavy rainfall because oxygen is only sparingly soluble in water and they are unable to get enough oxygen when immersed. Knowledge of the limits of water tolerance is helpful in attacking insect and other pests. Wire worms have rather narrow limits of tolerance to water and are most sensitive as larvae and pupae. They can be killed by flooding the infested fields or by planting alfalfa or wheat to dry out the soil below the limit of tolerance of the wire worm larvae.

Other Factors. The supply of oxygen and carbon dioxide is usually not limiting for land organisms except for animals living deep in the soil, on the tops of mountains, or within the bodies of other animals. Animals living in aquatic environments may be limited by the amount of dissolved oxygen present; the oxygen tension in stagnant ponds or in streams fouled by industrial wastes may become so low as to be incompatible with many forms of life. Some parasites have adapted to the low oxygen tension within the host's body by evolving special metabolic pathways by which energy can be released from foodstuffs without the utilization of free oxygen.

The trace elements necessary for plant and animal life are limiting factors in certain parts of the world. The soil in certain parts of Australia, for example, is extremely deficient in copper and cobalt and is unsuitable for raising cattle or sheep. Other trace elements which may be a limiting factor are manganese, zinc, iron, sulfur and boron.

The amount of carbon dioxide in the air is remarkably constant, but the amount dissolved in water varies widely. An excess of carbon dioxide may be a limiting factor for fish and insect larvae. The hydrogen ion concentration, pH, of water is related physicochemically to the carbon dioxide concentration, and it, too, may be an important limiting factor in aquatic environments.

Water currents are limiting for a number of kinds of animals and plants; the fauna and flora of a still pond and of a rapidly flowing stream are quite different. Winds may have a comparable limiting effect upon land organisms.

The type of soil, the amount of topsoil, its pH, porosity, slope, water-retaining properties, and so on, are limiting factors for a variety of plants, and hence indirectly for animals. The ability of many animals to survive in a given region depends upon the presence of certain plants to provide shelter and cover, as well as food. Grasses, shrubs and trees on land each provide shelter for certain kinds of animals, and seaweeds and fresh-water aquatic plants have a similar role for aquatic animals. Some animals require special shelter for breeding places and the care of the young. In many different kinds of birds, mammals, crustaceans and other animals, each animal or pair establishes a **territory,** a region which supplies food and shelter for it and its offspring, and which it

defends vigorously against invasion by other members of the same species.

In summary, whether an animal can become established in a given region is the result of a complex interplay of such physical factors as temperature, light, water, winds and salts, and biotic factors such as the plants and other animals in that region which serve as food, compete for food or space, or act as predators or disease organisms.

39.10
Types of Interactions Between Species

The members of two different species may affect each other in any one of several different ways. If neither population is affected by the presence of the other, so that there is no interaction, the situation is termed **neutralism.** If each population is adversely affected by the other in its search for food, space, shelter, or some other fundamental requirement for life, the interaction is one of **competition.** If each population is benefited by the presence of the other, but can survive in its absence, the relationship is termed **protocooperation.** But if each population is benefited in some way by the other, and cannot survive in nature without it, the relationship is termed **mutualism. Commensalism** refers to the relationship in which one species is benefited and the second is not effected by existing together, and **amensalism** to the relationship where one species is inhibited by the second but the second is unaffected by the first. Where one species affects the second adversely but cannot live without it, the relationship is one of **pasasitism** or **predation;** parasitism if one species lives in or on the body of the second and predation if the first species catches, kills and feeds upon the second. The older term **symbiosis,** "living together," is used by some authors as a synonym of mutualism and by others in a wider sense as a term including mutualism, commensalism and even parasitism.

39.11
Competition

Two species may compete for the same space, food or light, or in escaping from pred-

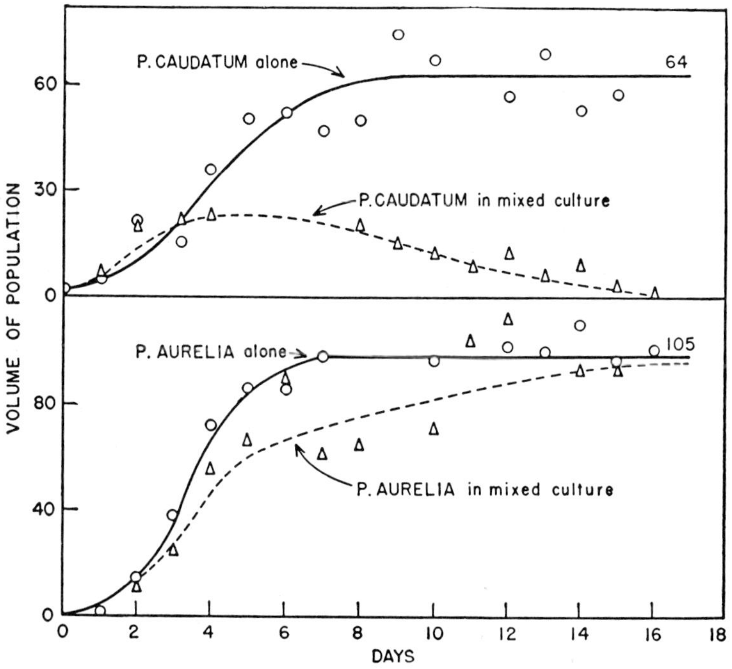

Figure 39.4 An experiment to demonstrate the competition between two closely related species of paramecia which have identical niches. When grown separately in controlled cultures with a fixed supply of food (bacteria), both *Paramecium caudatum* and *P. aurelia* show normal S-shaped growth curves (solid lines). When grown together, *P. caudatum* is eliminated (dotted lines). (After Gause, from Allee et al.: Principles of Animal Ecology.)

ators or disease; this may be summarized as competition for the same ecologic niche. Competition may result in one species dying off or being forced to move to a different space or use a different food. Careful ecologic studies usually reveal that there is only one species in an ecologic niche (Gause's rule). One of the clearest examples of competition was provided by the classic experiments of Gause with populations of paramecia. When either of two closely related species, *Paramecium caudatum* or *Paramecium aurelia*, was cultured separately on a fixed amount of bacteria as food, it multiplied and finally reached a constant level (Fig. 39.4). But when both species were placed in the same culture vessel with a limited amount of food, only *Paramecium aurelia* was left at the end of 16 days (Fig. 39.4). The *Paramecium aurelia* had not attacked the other species or secreted any harmful substance; it simply had been more successful in competing for the limited food supply. Studies in the field generally corroborate Gause's rule. Two fish-eating, cliff-nesting birds, the cormorant and the shag, which seemed at first glance to have survived despite occupying the same ecologic niche, were found upon analysis to have slightly different niches. The cormorant feeds on bottom-dwelling fish and shrimps, whereas

the shag hunts fish and eels in the upper levels of the sea. Further study showed that these birds typically have slightly different nesting sites on the cliffs as well.

39.12
Beneficial Associations

Commensalism, the living together of two species one of which (the commensal) derives benefit from the association whereas the other is unharmed by it, is especially common in the sea. Practically every worm burrow and shellfish contains some uninvited guests that take advantage of the shelter, and possibly of the abundant food, provided by the host organism but do it neither good nor harm. Certain flatworms live attached to the gills of the horseshoe crab and get their food from the scraps of the crab's meals. They obtain shelter and transportation from the host but apparently do it no harm. Many oysters and other bivalves have small crabs living in their mantle cavity, and there is a species of small fish that lives in the posterior end of the digestive tract of the sea cucumber!

If both species gain from an association, but are able to survive without it, the association is termed **protocooperation.** A number of crabs put coelenterates of one sort or another on top of their shells, presumably as camouflage. The coelenterates benefit from the association by getting bits of food when the crab captures and eats an animal. Neither crab nor coelenterate is absolutely dependent upon the other.

When both species gain from an association and are unable to survive separately, the association is termed **mutualism.** It is probable that associations begin as commensalism and then evolve through a stage of protocooperation to one of mutualism. A striking example of mutualism is provided by the relationship of termites and their intestinal flagellates. Termites have no enzymes for the digestion of wood, yet that is their staple diet. Certain flagellate protozoa that live only in their intestines do have the enzymes to digest the cellulose of wood to sugars. Although the flagellates require some of this sugar for their own metabolism, there is enough left over for the termite. Termites are unable to survive without their intestinal inhabitants; newly hatched termites instinctively lick the anus of another termite to get a supply of flagellates. Since a termite loses all of its flagellates along with most of its gut lining at each molt, termites must live in colonies so that a newly molted individual will be able to get flagellates from a neighbor. The flagellates are provided with plenty of food in a well-protected, relatively constant environment; they can, in fact, survive only in the intestines of termites.

39.13
Negative Interactions

Commensalism, protocooperation and mutualism are types of **positive interactions,** ones in which one or both members of the associated pair derive benefit from the association yet neither is harmed by it. **Negative interactions** between species—amensalism, parasitism and predation—are those in which one species is harmed by the association. If the second species is unaffected, the relationship between the two is termed **amensalism.** Organisms that produce antibiotics and the species inhibited by the antibiotic are examples of amensalism. The mold *Penicillium* produces the antibiotic penicillin which inhibits the growth of a variety of bacteria, but the mold is unaffected by the bacteria. The

clinical use of these bacteria-inhibiting agents has had the unexpected effect of increasing the incidence of fungus-induced diseases in man which are normally kept in check by the presence of the bacteria. When the bacteria are killed off by the antibiotics, the pathogenic fungi have a golden opportunity.

It is incorrect to assume that the host-parasite and predator-prey relationships are invariably harmful to the host or prey *as a species.* This is usually true when such relationships are first established, but the forces of natural selection tend, in time, to decrease the detrimental effects. If this did not occur the parasite would eventually exterminate the host species and, unless it found a new species to parasitize, would die itself.

Studies of many examples of parasite-host and predator-prey associations show that, in general, when the associations have been established for a long time, evolutionarily speaking, the long-term effect on the host or prey species is not very detrimental. Conversely, newly acquired predators or parasites are usually quite damaging. The plant parasites and insect pests that are most troublesome to man and his crops are usually those which have recently been introduced into some new area and thus have a new group of organisms to attack.

The role of the predator-prey relationship in maintaining a balance between the number of predators and of prey is beautifully illustrated by the story of the Kaibab deer. The Kaibab plateau is located on the north side of the Grand Canyon of the Colorado River. In 1907 there were some 4000 deer living on the plateau, together with a considerable population of predators, mountain lions and wolves. When a concerted effort was made to "protect" the deer by killing off the predators, the deer population increased tremendously and by 1925 some 100,000 deer roamed the plateau, far more than the supply of vegetation could support. The deer ate everything in reach—grass, tree seedlings and shrubs—and there was marked damage to the vegetation. Over the next two winters large numbers of the deer died of starvation, and the size of the herd fell to about 10,000. In the wild, the size of the predator population varies with the size of the population of the species which is preyed upon, with the swings in the size of the predator population lagging somewhat behind those of the prey.

39.14
Intraspecific Relations

In addition to the associations between the members of two different species just described, aggregations of animals or plants of a single species frequently occur. Some of these aggregations are temporary, for breeding; others are more permanent. Despite the fact that the crowding which accompanies dense aggregations of animals is ecologically undesirable and deleterious, both laboratory experiments and field observations show that such aggregations of individuals are able to survive when a single individual of the same species placed in the same environment dies. A herd of deer, with many noses and pairs of eyes, is less likely to be surprised by a predator than is a single one. A pack of wolves hunting together are more likely to make a kill than is a lone wolf. The survival value of aggregations is less obvious, but nonetheless real, in some of the lower animals. It can be shown experimentally that a group of insects is less likely to dry up and die in a dry environment than is a single insect, and a group of planaria is less likely to be killed by a given dose of ultraviolet light than is a single flatworm. When a dozen goldfish are placed in one bowl and a single one in a second bowl, and the same amount of a toxic agent such as colloidal silver is added to each bowl, the single fish will die but the group will survive. The explanation for this has proved to be that the slime secreted by the group of fish is enough to precipitate much of the colloidal silver and render it nontoxic, whereas the amount secreted by a single fish is not.

Such animal aggregations do have survival value for the species. Allee has called this "unconscious cooperation." When genes governing a tendency toward aggregation arise in a species and prove to have survival value, natural selection will tend to preserve this inherited behavior pattern. The occurrence of many fish in schools, of birds in flocks, and so on, are examples of this "unconscious cooperation" which occurs very widely in the animal kingdom.

From such simple animal aggregations there may evolve complex animal societies, composed of specialized types of individuals, such as the colonies of bees, ants and termites. Man is another example of a social animal.

39.15
Food Chains

Once a given species has reached and become established in a certain area, the number of organisms—or more precisely their total mass—is determined by the rate of flow of energy through the biological part of the ecosystem which includes them. Although carbon, nitrogen and the other elements are reused cyclically, energy is not and can be used only once by a given organism. It is ultimately degraded to heat and lost to the ecosystem.

The ultimate source of all the energy used by living things is sunlight, the energy of which is converted to a biologically useful form by the process of photosynthesis carried on by green plants. Only a small fraction, about 3 per cent, of the light energy striking the leaves of a green plant is transformed by photosynthesis into the potential energy of a food substance; the rest escapes as heat. This loss is not the result of inefficiency of the biochemical processes involved, but of the operation of the laws of thermodynamics. The second law of thermodynamics may be stated as "whenever energy is transformed from one form into another there is a decrease in the amount of useful energy; some energy is degraded into heat and dissipated." In other words, no transformation of energy can be 100 per cent efficient.

When an animal eats a plant, much of the energy is again dissipated as heat and only a fraction is used to synthesize the animal's tissues. When a second animal eats the first, there is a further loss of energy as heat, and so on. The transfer of energy from its ultimate source in plants through a series of organisms, each of which eats the preceding and is eaten by the following, is known as a **food chain.** The number of steps in a food chain is limited to perhaps four or five because of the great decrease in available energy at each step. The percentage of the energy in the food consumed that is converted to new cellular materials, and thus is available as energy for the next organism in the food chain, is known as the percentage **efficiency of energy transfer.**

The flow of energy in ecosystems from sunlight through photosynthesis in autotrophic producers, through the tissues of herbivorous primary consumers and the tissues of carnivorous secondary consumers, determines the number and total weight, the **biomass,** of organisms at each level in the ecosystem. The flow of energy is greatly reduced at each successive level of nutrition because of the heat losses at each transformation of energy, and this decreases the biomass in each level.

The first step in any food chain, the capture of light energy by photosynthesis and the production of energy-containing foods by plants, is relatively inefficient; only about 0.2 per cent of the incident light energy is stored as food. The efficiency of energy transfer when one animal eats a plant or another animal is higher, ranging from 5 to 20 per cent. Some animals eat but one kind of food and, therefore, are members of a single food chain. Other animals eat many different kinds of food and are not only members of different food chains but may occupy different positions in different food chains. An animal may be a primary consumer in one chain, eating green plants, but a secondary or tertiary consumer in other chains, eating herbivorous animals or other carnivores.

Man is the end of a number of food chains. For example, man eats a fish such as a black bass, which ate smaller fish, which in turn ate small crustacea, which in turn ate algae. The ultimate size of the human population, or of the population of any animal, is limited (1) by the length of the food chain, (2) by the percentage efficiency of energy transfer at each step in the chain, and (3) by the amount of light energy falling on the earth. Since man can do nothing about increasing the amount of incident sunlight, and very little about the percentage efficiency of energy transfer, he can increase his supply of food energy only by shortening his food chain, i.e., by eating the primary producers, plants, rather than animals. In overcrowded countries such as India and China, men are largely vegetarians because this food chain is shortest, and a given area of land can in this way support the greatest number of people. Steak is a luxury ecologically as well as economically!

In addition to predator food chains, such as the man–black bass–minnow–crustacean one, there are parasite food chains. For example, mammals and birds are parasitized by fleas; in the fleas live protozoa which are, in turn, the hosts of bacteria. Since the bacteria might be parasitized by viruses, there could be a five-step parasite food chain.

A third type of food chain is one in which plant material is converted into dead organic matter, **detritus,** before being eaten by animals such as millipedes and earthworms on land, by marine worms and mollusks, or by bacteria and fungi. In a shallow sea community, about 30 per cent of the total energy flows via detritus chains, but in a forest community, with a large biomass of plants and a relatively small biomass of animals, as much as 90 per cent of energy flow may be via detritus pathways. In an intertidal salt marsh, where most of the animals—shellfish, snails and crabs—are detritus eaters, 90 per cent or more of the energy flow is via detritus chains.

Since, in any food chain, there is a loss of energy at each step, it follows that there is usually a smaller biomass in each successive step. H. T. Odum has calculated that 8100 kilograms of alfalfa plants are required to provide the food for 1000 kilograms of calves, which provide enough food to keep one 12-year-old 48 kilogram boy alive for one year. Although boys eat many things other than veal, and calves other things besides alfalfa, these numbers illustrate the principle of a food chain. A food chain may be visualized as a pyramid; each step in the pyramid is much smaller than the one on which it feeds. Since the predators are usually larger than the ones on which they prey, the **pyramid of numbers** of individuals in each step of the chain is even more striking than the **pyramid of the mass** of individuals in successive steps: one boy requires 4.5 calves, which require 20,000,000 alfalfa plants.

39.16
Communities and Populations

Each region of the earth—sea, lake, forest, prairie, tundra, desert—is inhabited by a characteristic assemblage of animals and plants which are interrelated in many and diverse ways as competitors, commensals, predators, and so on. The members of each assemblage are not determined by chance but by the total effect of the many interacting physical and biotic factors of the environment. The ecologist refers to the organisms living in a given area as a **biotic community;** this is composed of smaller groups, or **populations,** groups of individuals of any one kind of organism.

The intermeshings of the food chains in

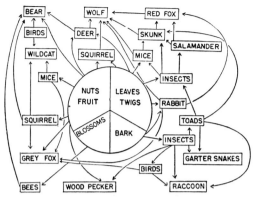

Figure 39.5 Diagram of a food chain in an Illinois deciduous forest. (After Shelford.) (Courtesy of Dr. V. E. Shelford.)

any biotic community are very complex and are sometimes called a food web, or "web of life." Some of the interrelated food chains of a deciduous forest in eastern North America are indicated in Figure 39.5. The basic principles of the ecologic relations of biotic communities have been elucidated by the study of somewhat simpler communities such as the arctic tundra or desert. The producer organisms of the tundra are lichens, mosses and grasses. Reindeer and caribou feed on the lichens and are preyed upon by wolves and man. Grasses are eaten by the arctic hare and the lemming, which are eaten by the snowy owl and the arctic fox, which is preyed upon by man for its fur. During the brief arctic summer the food web is enlarged by many insects and by migratory birds which feed upon them.

39.17
Populations and Their Characteristics

A **population** may be defined as a group of organisms of the same species which occupy a given area. It has characteristics which are a function of the whole group and not of the individual members; these are **population density, birth rate, death rate, age distribution, biotic potential, rate of dispersion,** and **growth form.** Although individuals are born and die, individuals do not have birth rates or death rates; these are characteristics of the population as a whole. Modern ecology deals especially with the community and population aspects of the science, and the study of group organization is the unique

part of the science of ecology. Population and community relationships are often more important in determining the occurrence and survival of organisms in nature than are the direct effects of physical and chemical factors in the environment.

One important attribute of a population is its **density**—the number of individuals per unit area or volume, e.g., the number of animals per square mile, of trees per acre in a forest, or millions of diatoms per cubic meter of sea water. This is a measure of the population's success in a given region. Frequently, in ecologic studies it is important to know not only the population density but whether it is changing and, if so, what the rate of change is. Population density is often difficult to measure in terms of individuals, but estimates such as the number of insects caught per hour in a standard trap, the number of sea urchins caught in a standard "sea mop," or the number of birds seen or heard per hour, are usable substitutes. A method that will give good results when used with the proper precautions is that of capturing, let us say, 100 animals, tagging them in some way, and then releasing them. On some subsequent day, another 100 animals are trapped and the proportion of tagged animals is determined. This assumes that animals caught once are neither more nor less likely to be caught again, and that both sets of trapped animals are random samples of the population. If the 100 animals caught on the second day include 20 tagged ones, the total population of tagged and untagged animals in the area of the traps is 500; x/100 = 100/20, hence x = 500.

For many kinds of ecologic investigations, an estimate of the number of individuals per total area or volume, known as the **"crude density,"** is not exact enough. Only a fraction of that total area may be a habitat suitable for the population, and the size of the individual members of a population may vary tremendously. Ecologists, therefore, calculate an **ecologic density,** defined as the number, or more exactly as the mass, of individuals per area or volume of habitable space. Trapping and tagging experiments might give an estimate of 500 rabbits per square mile, but if only half of that square mile actually consists of areas suitable for rabbits to inhabit, then the ecologic density would be 1000 rabbits per square mile of rabbit habitat. With species whose individuals vary greatly in size, such as fish, live weight or some other estimate of the total mass of living fish is a much more satisfactory estimate of density than simply the total number of individuals present.

A graph in which the number of organisms, or its logarithm, is plotted against time is a **population growth curve** (Fig. 39.6). Such curves are characteristic of populations, rather than of a single species, and are amazingly similar for populations of almost all organisms from bacteria to man.

Population growth curves have a characteristic shape. When a few individuals enter a previously unoccupied area, growth at first is slow (the positive acceleration phase), then becomes rapid and the population increases exponentially (the logarithmic phase). The growth rate eventually slows as environmental resistance increases (the negative acceleration phase) and finally reaches an equilibrium. This upper asymptote of the sigmoid curve is termed the "carrying capacity" of the environment.

The **birth rate,** or natality, of a population is simply the number of new individuals produced per unit time. The **maximum birth rate** is the largest number of individuals that could be produced per unit time under ideal conditions, when there are no limiting factors. This is a constant for a species and is determined by physiologic factors such as the number of eggs produced per female per unit time, the proportion of females in the species, and so on. The actual birth rate is usually considerably less than this, for not all the eggs laid are able to hatch, not all the larvae or young to survive, and so on. The size and composition of the population and a variety of environmental conditions affect the actual birth rate. It is difficult to determine the maximum natality, for it is difficult to be sure that all limiting factors have been removed. However, under experimental conditions, or by careful field studies, one can get an estimate of this value which is useful in predicting the rate of increase of the population and in providing a yardstick for comparison with the actual birth rate.

The **mortality rate** of a population refers to the number of individuals dying per unit time. There is a theoretical **minimum mortality,** somewhat analogous to the maximum birth rate, which is the number of deaths that would occur under ideal conditions—deaths caused simply by the physiologic changes of old age. This minimum mortality rate is also a constant for a given population. The actual mortality rate will, of course, depend upon physical factors and upon the size and composition of the population. By plotting the number of survivors in a population against time, one gets a **survival curve** (Fig. 39.7). If the units of the time axis are the percentage of total life span, one can compare the survival curves for organisms with very different total life spans. Civilized man has improved his average life expectancy greatly by modern medical practices, and the curve for human survival approaches the curve for minimum mortality. From such curves one can determine at what stage in the life cycle a particular species is most vulnerable. Reducing or increasing the mortality in this vulnerable period will have the greatest effect on the

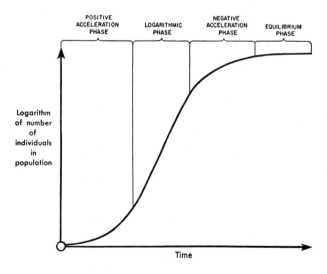

Figure 39.6 showing a curve divided into POSITIVE ACCELERATION PHASE, LOGARITHMIC PHASE, NEGATIVE ACCELERATION PHASE, and EQUILIBRIUM PHASE. Y-axis: Logarithm of number of individuals in population. X-axis: Time.

Figure 39.6 A typical growth curve of a population, one in which the logarithm of the total number of individuals is plotted against time. The absolute units of time and the total number in the population would vary from one species to another, but the shape of the growth curve would be similar for all populations.

Figure 39.7 Survival curves of four different animals, plotted as the number of survivors left at each fraction of the total life span of the species. The total life span for man is about 100 years; the solid curve indicates that about 10 per cent of the babies born die during the first few years of life. Only a small fraction of the human population dies between ages five and 45 but after 45 the number of survivors decreases rapidly. Starved fruit flies live only about five days, but almost the entire population lives the same length of time and dies at once. The vast majority of oyster larvae die, but the few that become attached to the proper sort of rock or to an old oyster shell survive. The survival curve of hydras is one typical of most animals and plants, in which a relatively constant fraction of the population dies off in each successive time period. (Villee: Biology, 5th ed.)

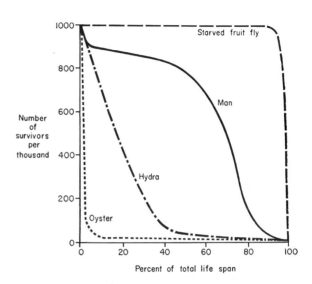

future size of the population. Since the death rate is more variable and more affected by environmental factors than the birth rate, it has a primary role in population control.

It is quite obvious that populations that differ in the relative numbers of young and old will have quite different characteristics, different birth and death rates, and different prospects. Death rates typically vary with age, and birth rates are usually proportional to the number of individuals able to reproduce. Three ages can be distinguished in a population in this respect: prereproductive, reproductive and postreproductive. A. J. Lotka has shown from theoretical considerations that a population will tend to become stable and have a constant proportion of individuals of these three ages. Censuses of the ages of plant or animal populations are thus valuable in predicting population trends. Rapidly growing populations have a high proportion of young forms. The age of fishes can be estimated from the growth rings on their scales, and studies of the age ratios of commercial fish catches are of great use in predicting future catches and in preventing overfishing of a region.

The term **biotic potential,** or reproductive potential, refers to the inherent power of a population to increase in numbers, when the age ratio is stable and all environmental conditions are optimal. The biotic potential is defined mathematically as the slope of the population growth curve during the logarithmic phase of growth (Fig. 39.6). When environmental conditions are less than optimal,

the rate of population growth is less. The difference between the potential ability of a population to increase and the actual change in the size of the population is a measure of environmental resistance. Even when a population is growing rapidly in numbers, each individual organism of the reproductive age carries on reproduction at the same rate as at any other time; the increase in numbers is due to increased survival. At a conservative estimate, one man and one woman, with the cooperation of their children and grandchildren, could produce 200,000 progeny within a century, and a pair of fruit flies could increase to 3368×10^{52} individuals in a year. Since optimal conditions are not maintained, such biologic catastrophes do not occur, but the situations, in India, China and elsewhere indicate the tragedy implicit in the tendency toward overpopulation.

The sum of the physical and biologic factors which prevent a species from reproducing at its maximum rate is termed the environmental resistance. Environmental resistance is often low when a species is first introduced into a new territory, and the species increases in number at a fantastic rate. The introduction of the rabbit into Australia, and the English sparrow or Japanese beetle into the United States, are examples of these. As a species increases in numbers, the environmental resistance to it also increases in the form of organisms which prey upon it or parasitize it, and the competition between the members of the species for food and living space.

In an essay published in 1798 the Englishman Robert Malthus pointed out this tendency for populations to increase in size until checked by the environment. He realized that the same principles control human populations and suggested that wars, famines and pestilences are inevitable and necessary as brakes on population growth. Since Malthus' time man's productive capacity has increased tremendously, as has the total human population. But Malthus' basic principle, that there are physical limits to the amount of food that can be produced for any species, remains valid. As environmental resistance increases, the rate of increase of the human population will eventually have to decrease so that an equilibrium is reached, either by decreasing the birth rate or by increasing the mortality rate.

39.18
Population Cycles

Once a population becomes established in a certain region and has reached its equilibrium level, the numbers will vary up and down from year to year, depending on variations in environmental resistance or on factors intrinsic to the population. Some of these population variations are completely irregular, but others are regular and cyclic. One of the best known of these is the regular 9 to 10 year cycle of abundance and scarcity of the snowshoe hare and the lynx in Canada which can be traced by the records of the number of pelts received by the Hudson's Bay Company. The peak of the hare population oc-

curs about a year before the peak of the lynx population (Fig. 39.8). Since the lynx feeds on the hare, it is obvious that the lynx cycle is related to the hare cycle.

A three to four year cycle of abundance is shown by lemmings and voles, small mouse-like animals living in the northern tundra region. Every three or four years there is a great increase in the number of lemmings; they eat all the available food in the tundra and then migrate in vast numbers looking for food. They invade villages in hordes and, finally, many reach the sea and drown. The numbers of arctic foxes and snowy owls, which feed on lemmings, increase similarly; when the lemming population decreases, the foxes starve and the owls migrate south— there is an invasion by snowy owls of the United States every three or four years.

Although some cycles recur with great regularity, others do not. For example, in the carefully managed forests of Germany the numbers of four species of moths whose caterpillars feed on pine needles were estimated from censuses made each year for the period from 1880 to 1940. The numbers varied from less than one to more than 10,000 per thousand square meters. The cycles of maxima and minima of the four species were quite independent and were irregular in their frequency and duration.

Attempts to explain these vast oscillations in the numbers of a species on the basis of climatic changes have been unsuccessful. At one time it was believed that the cycles were caused by sunspots, and the sunspot and lynx cycles do appear to correspond during the early part of the nineteenth century. How-

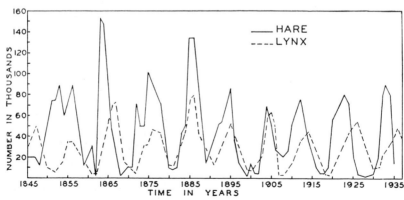

Figure 39.8 Changes in the abundance of the lynx and snowshoe hare, as indicated by the number of pelts received by the Hudson's Bay Company. This is a classic example of cyclic oscillation in population density. (Redrawn from MacLulich, 1937.)

ever, the cycles are of slightly different lengths and by 1920 were completely out of phase, with sunspot maxima corresponding to lynx minima. Attempts to correlate these cycles with other periodic weather changes or with cycles of disease organisms have been unsuccessful.

The snowshoe hares, for example, die off cyclically even in the absence of predators and in the absence of known disease organisms or parasites. The animals apparently die of "shock," characterized by low blood sugar, exhaustion, convulsions and death, symptoms which resemble the "alarm response" induced in laboratory animals subjected to physiologic stress. This similarity led J. J. Christian in 1950 to propose that their death, like the alarm response, is the result of an upset in the adrenal-pituitary system. As the population density increases, there is increasing physiologic stress on individual hares caused by crowding and competition for food. Some individuals are forced into poorer habitats, where the food is less abundant and predators more abundant. The physiologic stresses stimulate the adrenal medulla to secrete epinephrine which stimulates the pituitary to secrete more ACTH (adrenocorticotropic hormone). This, in turn, stimulates the adrenal cortex to produce corticoids, an excess or imbalance of which produces the alarm response or physiologic shock. In the latter part of the winter of a peak year, with the stress of cold weather, lack of food and the onset of the new reproductive season putting additional demands on the pituitary to secrete gonadotropins, the adrenal-pituitary system fails, becomes unable to maintain its normal control of carbohydrate metabolism, and low blood sugar, convulsions and death ensue. This is an attractive theory, but the appropriate experiments and observations in the wild to test it have not yet been made.

39.19

Cyclic Phenomena in Biology: Circadian Rhythms

In addition to cycles of recurring abundance and scarcity of certain species over periods covering several years, there are other cyclic phenomena in biology which recur each year, each lunar month, each day, or with the tides. In recent years, there has been much interest in these cycles and in the possibility that intrinsic "biologic clocks" may be involved in regulating such cyclic phenomena.

The organisms living in the temperate zones of the world typically show marked seasonal cycles of activity. Most animals have a breeding season at one time of the year—usually in the spring; some show a pronounced decrease in activity and metabolism during the winter, a phenomenon termed **hibernation.** The adult forms of many plants and animals, especially insects, die at the end of each summer season, and the species is carried over the winter in the form of seeds, eggs or pupae. In the tropics, although there is no sharp change in temperature from one month to the next, there is usually a period of heavy rain which alternates with a period of little or no rain. The plants and animals in such regions have cycles that are geared to these changes in the environment.

There are other cycles of animal, and perhaps plant, activity which reflect the phases of the moon but these are usually less well marked than the annual cycles. The most striking ones are those in marine organisms that reflect the changes in the tides that are correlated with the phases of the moon. The swarming of the palolo worm at a particular time of the year is governed by a combination of an annual and a lunar cycle.

Organisms (and even the several parts of an organism) usually do not function at a constant rate over the entire 24 hours of a day. Frequently, there appear to be repeated sequences of events which occur at about 24 hour intervals. These have been termed "circadian rhythms" (*circa,* about; *dies,* day). These rhythms are composed of events which occur in a given order and at similar intervals and are not simply the repetition of specific changes after some precisely fixed period.

Some animals are **diurnal,** having their greatest degree of activity during the day; others are **crepuscular** and have their greatest activity during the twilight hours; and still others are **nocturnal** and show their greatest degree of activity during the hours of darkness. Certain insects exhibit diurnal variations in pigmentation, and continue to show these cyclic variations even when placed in continuous darkness. There is a diurnal cycle of the deposition and utilization of glycogen in the liver of the rabbit and the mouse, and probably of other mammals.

The diurnal cycles of many organisms are firmly entrenched and are not easily upset even by prolonged exposure to constant light or constant darkness, or to abnormal cycles (e.g., 8 or 10 hours instead of 24) of alternating light and darkness. Man also has circadian rhythms; many people, for example, find that a quick airplane flight east or west to a time zone several hours different from the one they are used to may upset certain physiologic functions.

Many marine organisms living in the intertidal zone show marked differences in their activity, some being active only when the tide is in, others when the tide is out. The vertical distribution of many small marine organisms is subject to a diurnal cycle—they tend to concentrate near the surface at night and to go to deeper water during the day. Since many fish feed on these small organisms, the fish, in turn, tend to move nearer the surface at night and to swim farther down in the water during the day.

Many different kinds of animals have evolved "biologic clocks," by means of which their activities are adapted to the regularly recurring changes in the external physical conditions, and perhaps to changes in their internal milieu as well. These clocks, together with other signals received from the external environment, indicate to the organism the time of day that is most appropriate for some particular activity or physiologic process. In a few animals, such as birds and bees, these timing devices have been highly evolved and can serve for navigation.

Bees are not only able to find their way from hive to feeding ground using the direction of the sun to determine their direction (p. 749), but they can make suitable corrections for the sun's position as the day advances; that is, they can correct their celestial navigation for the time of day just as man does. One type of experiment that indicates this is the following: A colony of bees is trained one *afternoon* to go to a feeding table 150 meters northwest of the hive. Then, during the night, the colony is moved to an entirely new region, with quite different landmarks. Four feeding tables are set up 150 meters to the northwest, northeast, southwest and southeast respectively. The bees are released in the *morning*, yet the vast majority of them fly to the feeding table to the north-

west. From this and other evidence it appears that bees (a) navigate using the sun as a guide and (b) make allowance in their navigation for the changing position of the sun as the day advances. This "time memory" makes it possible for a bee to store information (over a period of rainy days, for example) regarding the best time of day to visit a given species of plant whose nectar is secreted only during certain hours of the day.

At one time it was believed that the timing mechanisms of organisms generally operated on some kind of "hourglass" principle—some regularly recurring stimulus, such as sunrise, triggered some physiologic process which required a certain length of time for its completion, at which time a signal was sent to the appropriate organ. More recent evidence favors the theory that the timing mechanisms are based on intrinsic processes with some sort of cyclic oscillation. The exact nature of the "clockwork" underlying these biologic clocks is unknown. It would appear that it is not simply an oscillation of some set of enzyme-controlled metabolic reactions, for it is only slightly altered by variations in temperature. Biologic clocks do require a small, but definite, amount of biologically useful energy for their operation. The clock could involve a biophysical mechanism, for example, an alternation in the physical state of a complex molecule such as a protein, or an alternation in the tension and relaxation of some physical structure. There is now evidence that processes in which energy is transferred by the transport of electrons, in contrast to those involving the thermal movements of molecules, are relatively insensitive to temperature changes.

The existence of these biologic clocks was discovered when it was found that certain organisms which normally have rhythms coordinated with daily changes in their environment will have a persistence of these rhythms even in the absence of the stimulus. It was known as long ago as 1729 that plants placed in continuous complete darkness at constant temperature would show the same diurnal leaf movements they normally have when exposed to the daily alternation of light and dark. Further interest in biologic clocks was aroused when it was discovered that marine organisms which normally show variations in their activity with the tide would continue to show such cyclic variations, at the proper time, when removed to an aquarium away from the influence of the tide and when protected from changes in light, temperature and other factors. The survival value of such mechanisms for intrinsic rhythms is that certain physiologic and biochemical adjustments can take place preceding the time of the change in the environment. This may enable the organism to synchronize its activities more efficiently with the various periodicities in the environment.

39.20
Population Dispersal

Populations have a tendency to disperse, or spread out in all directions until some barrier is reached. Within the area, the members of the population may occur at random (this is rarely found), they may be distributed more or less uniformly throughout the area (this occurs when there is competition or antagonism to keep them apart) or, most commonly, they may occur in small groups or clumps. Aggregation in clumps may increase the competition between the members of the group for food or space, but this is more than counterbalanced by the greater survival power of the group during unfavorable periods. Aggregation may be caused by local differences in habitat, by weather changes, reproductive urges or social attractions. Certain animals are regularly found spaced apart; they establish and defend certain **territories.** Many species of birds, some mammals, reptiles, fish, crabs and insects establish such territories, either as regions for gathering food or as nesting areas.

39.21
Biotic Communities

A **biotic community** is an assemblage of populations living in a defined area or habitat; it can be either large or small. The interactions of the various kinds of organisms maintain the structure and function of the community and provide the basis for the ecologic regulation of community succession.

The concept that animals and plants live together in an orderly manner, not strewn haphazardly over the surface of the earth, is one of the important principles of ecology. Sometimes adjacent communities are sharply defined and separated from each other; more frequently they blend imperceptibly together.

The unraveling of why certain plants and animals comprise a given community, how they affect each other, and how man can control them to his advantage are some of the major problems of ecologic research. In trying to control some particular species, it has frequently been found more effective to modify the community than to attempt direct control of the species itself. For example, the most effective way to increase the quail population is not to raise and release birds (artificially "stocking" the area) or to kill off predators but to develop and maintain the particular biotic community in which quail are most successful.

Although each community may contain hundreds or thousands of species of plants and animals, most of these are relatively unimportant and only a few, by their size, numbers or activities, exert a major control of the community. In land communities these major species are usually plants, for they both produce food and provide shelter for many other species, and many land communities are named for their dominant plants—sagebrush, oak-hickory, pine, and so on. Aquatic communities, with no conspicuous large plants, are usually named for some physical characteristic—stream rapids community, mud flat community and sandy beach community.

In ecologic investigations it is unnecessary (in fact it is usually impossible) to consider all the species present in a community. Usually a study of the major plants which control the community, the larger populations of animals, and the fundamental energy relations—food chains—of the ecosystem will define the ecologic relations within the community. For example, in studying a lake one would first investigate the kinds, distribution and abundance of the important producer plants, and the physical and chemical factors which might be limiting. Then the reproductive rate, mortality rate, age distribution and other important population characteristics of the important game fish would be determined. A study of the kinds, distribution and abundance of the primary and perhaps secondary consumers of the lake, which constitute the food of the game fish, and the nature of other organisms which compete for food with these fish, would elucidate the basic food chains in the lake. Quantitative studies of these would reveal the basic energy relationships of the whole ecosystem and show how efficiently the incident energy is being converted into the desired end product, the flesh of game fish. On the basis of this knowledge, the lake could intelligently be managed to increase the production of game fish.

Most of the studies of biotic communities made to date have been of regions in the arctic or desert, where there are fewer organisms, and their relatively simpler interrelations are more easily analyzed and understood. A thorough ecologic investigation of a particular region requires that it be studied throughout the year for a period of several years. The physical, chemical, climatic and other factors of the region are carefully evaluated, and an intensive study is made of a number of carefully delimited areas which are large enough to be representative of the region but small enough to be studied quantitatively. The number and kinds of plants and animals in these "study areas" are estimated by suitable sampling techniques. Estimates are made periodically throughout the year to learn not only the components of the community at any one time but also their seasonal and annual variations. Finally, the biologic and physical data are correlated, the major and minor communities of the region are identified, and the food chains and other important ecologic relations of the communities and the particular adaptations of the animals and plants for their role in the community are studied.

39.22
Community Succession

With time, any given area tends to have an orderly sequence of communities that change together with the physical conditions and lead eventually to a stable mature community or **climax community.** The entire series of communities is known as a **sere,** and the individual transitional communities as **seral stages** or seral communities. In successive stages there is not only a change in the species of organisms present but an increase in the number of species and in the total biomass. These series are so regular in many parts of the world that an ecologist, recognizing the particular seral community present in a given area, can predict the sequence of future changes. The ultimate causes of these successions are not clear. Climate and other physical factors play some

role, but the succession is directed in part by the nature of the community itself, for the action of each seral community is to make the area less favorable for itself and more favorable for other species until the stable, climax community is reached.

Occasionally the organisms that man wants to encourage for his own ends—timber, game birds, fresh-water game fish—are members of a seral stage in community succession rather than of the climax community. Then the ecologist has the difficult problem of trying to manipulate the community to halt the succession and maintain the desired seral community.

One of the classic studies of ecologic succession was made on the shores of Lake Michigan (Fig. 39.9). As the lake has become smaller it has left successively younger sand dunes, and one can study the stages in ecologic succession as one goes away from the lake. The youngest dunes, nearest the lake, have only grasses and insects; the next older ones have shrubs such as cottonwoods, then evergreens, and finally a beech-maple climax community with a rich soil full of earthworms and snails. As the lake retreated it also left a series of ponds. The youngest of these contain little rooted vegetation and lots of bass and bluegills. Later, the ponds become choked with vegetation and smaller in size as the basins fill. Finally, the ponds become marshes and then dry ground, invaded by shrubs and ending in the beech-maple climax forest. Man-made ponds, such as those impounded by dams, similarly tend to become filled up, becoming first marshes, then dry land.

Ecologic succession can be demonstrated in the laboratory. If a few pieces of dry hay are placed in some pond water, a population of bacteria will appear in a few days. Next, flagellates appear and eat the bacteria, then ciliated protozoa such as paramecia followed by predator protozoa such as *Didinium* emerge. The protozoa, present as spores or cysts in the pond water or attached to the hay, emerge in a definite succession of protozoan communities.

Biotic communities typically show a marked **vertical stratification,** determined in large part by vertical differences in physical factors such as temperature, light and oxygen. The operation of such physical factors in determining vertical stratification in lakes and the ocean is quite evident. In a forest there is

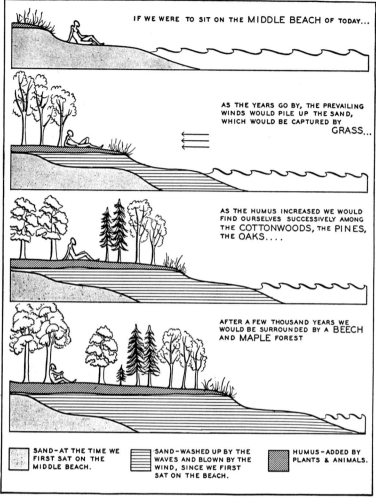

IF WE WERE TO SIT ON THE MIDDLE BEACH OF TODAY...

AS THE YEARS GO BY, THE PREVAILING WINDS WOULD PILE UP THE SAND, WHICH WOULD BE CAPTURED BY GRASS...

AS THE HUMUS INCREASED WE WOULD FIND OURSELVES SUCCESSIVELY AMONG THE COTTONWOODS, THE PINES, THE OAKS....

AFTER A FEW THOUSAND YEARS WE WOULD BE SURROUNDED BY A BEECH AND MAPLE FOREST

SAND – AT THE TIME WE FIRST SAT ON THE MIDDLE BEACH.

SAND – WASHED UP BY THE WAVES AND BLOWN BY THE WIND, SINCE WE FIRST SAT ON THE BEACH.

HUMUS – ADDED BY PLANTS & ANIMALS.

Figure 39.9 Diagram of the succession of communities with time along the shores of Lake Michigan in northern Indiana. (Redrawn after Buchsbaum, Readings in Ecology, from Allee et al.: Principles of Animal Ecology.)

a vertical stratification of plant life, from mosses and herbs on the ground, then shrubs, low trees and tall trees. Each of these strata has a distinctive animal population. Even such highly motile animals as birds have been found to be restricted to certain layers. Some birds are found only in shrubs, others only in the tops of tall trees. There are daily and seasonal changes in the populations found in each stratum, and many animals are found first in one layer and then in another as they pass through their life history. These strata are strongly interdependent and most ecologists consider them to be subdivisions of one large community rather than separate communities. Vertical stratification, by increasing the number of ecologic niches in a given surface area, reduces competition between species and enables more species to exist in a given area.

39.23
The Dynamic Balance of Nature

The concept of the dynamic state of the body constituents was discussed in Chapter 4, and we learned that the protein, fat, carbohydrate and other constituents of both animal and plant bodies are constantly being broken down and resynthesized. Biotic communities are constantly undergoing an analogous reshuffling, and the concept of the **dynamic state of communities** is an important ecologic principle. Not only are plant and animal populations constantly subject to changes in their physical and biotic environment to which they must adapt or die, but communities undergo a number of rhythmic changes—daily, lunar, seasonal, tidal, etc.—in the activities or movements of their component organisms which result in periodic changes in the composition of the community as a whole. A population may vary in size, but if it outruns its food supply, like the Kaibab deer or the lemmings, equilibrium is quickly restored. Communities of organisms are comparable in many ways to a many-celled organism and exhibit growth, specialization and interdependence of parts, characteristic form, and even development from immaturity to maturity, old age and death.

QUESTIONS

1. Define an ecosystem. Discuss an aquarium of tropical fish as an example of an ecosystem.
2. Differentiate clearly between a habitat and an ecologic niche.
3. Discuss the various pathways of the nitrogen cycle. What can man do to increase the supply of nitrates?
4. Define: range of tolerance, hibernation, photoperiod, biologic potential, environmental resistance.
5. Define and give examples of commensalism, mutualism and parasitism.
6. What is meant by a food chain? Why are the number of steps in a food chain limited? Describe a food chain ending in a bird hawk.
7. What is meant by a survival curve? Discuss the importance of such curves to a life insurance company.
8. Discuss the factors that tend to keep relatively constant the size of a population of animals in the wild.
9. What factors tend to cause cyclic variations in the size of a population of animals in the wild?
10. Define circadian rhythm. Discuss an example from your own observation.
11. Define and give an example of a biotic community. What information is required to define a particular biotic community?
12. Explain why there is a tendency for there to be an orderly sequence of communities leading to a climax community. What is the climax community in your region?

ANNOTATED REFERENCES

Kendeigh, S. C.: Animal Ecology. Englewood Cliffs, N. J., Prentice Hall, Inc., 1961. A brief account of the principles of ecology.

Odum. E. P.: Fundamentals of Ecology. 2nd ed. Philadelphia, W. B. Saunders Co. 1959. An excellent treatise of the principles of ecology, a classic in the field.

Odum E. P.: Ecology. New York, Holt, Rinehart & Winston, 1963. A brief description, in paperback form, of the essentials of ecology.

40 ADAPTATIONS, BIOMES AND ECOSYSTEMS

A complete discussion of the many ways in which living things have become adapted to overcome or to neutralize deleterious aspects of the environment or to take advantage of favorable factors would fill a large library. In this chapter we shall describe and give examples of some of the general types of adaptations developed by animals to the physical environment and to other living things. These adaptations permit certain animals and plants to live together in definable communities, biomes and ecosystems which are described in the latter part of the chapter. Careful ecologic studies of these biomes have brought to light many fascinating interrelations among the organisms present, each of which has become adapted to its respective ecologic niche.

40.1
Structural Adaptations

Careful study of any group of animals shows that some have generalized structures which can be used to survive in a wide range of environments. Other animals are highly specialized for some particular mode of life. Many insects, for example, have become adapted to feeding on one or a few kinds of plants. The mouth parts of certain insects are adapted for sucking nectar from certain kinds of plants; others are specialized for sucking blood, for biting or for chewing vegetation. The bills of various kinds of birds and the teeth of various kinds of mammals may be highly adapted for particular kinds of food (Fig. 40.1).

Animals that are highly specialized, adapted for a very narrow ecologic niche, will have some advantage as long as that environment is present but are at a great evolutionary disadvantage when the environment changes. In the course of time, organisms have had to become readapted many times as their environment changed or as they migrated to a new environment. As a result, many animals today have structures or physiologic mechanisms that are useless, or even somewhat deleterious, but which were useful for survival in earlier times, when the organism was adapted to a rather different environment.

Animals may become adapted for a particular mode of life in a particular environment by specializations of structure, function, color, chemical composition or behavior. Structural adaptations are, perhaps, the most easily recognized; changes in the size, shape, relative proportion, and so on, of the bones and muscles of the body which adapt for running, jumping, climbing, gliding, flying, burrowing or swimming are, in general, readily evident. The adaptive nature of certain other structural modifications becomes clear only when an animal is studied in its environment.

In many animals, the specialized adaptation to a certain way of life now evident is simply the latest stage in a series of adaptations. For example, both man and the baboon, whose immediate ancestors were tree-dwellers, have returned to the ground and have become readapted for walking rather than climbing trees. The process of readaptation may be quite complicated. The contemporary Aus-

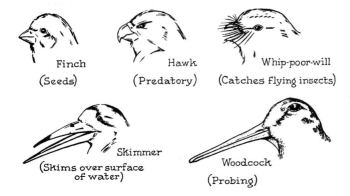

Finch
(Seeds)

Hawk
(Predatory)

Whip-poor-will
(Catches flying insects)

Skimmer
(Skims over surface
of water)

Woodcock
(Probing)

Figure 40.1 Diagrams of the bills of a variety of birds, illustrating their adaptation to the type of food eaten.

tralian tree-climbing kangaroos are the descendants of an original ground-dwelling marsupial. From these ground-dwellers evolved forms which, in the course of adaptive radiation, took to the trees and developed limbs adapted to tree climbing (or perhaps the sequence of events was the reverse—first the evolution of specialized limbs and then the adoption of an arboreal life). Some of these tree-dwellers eventually left the trees and became readapted for ground life, accumulating, by mutation and selection, genes for hind legs which were longer, stronger, and adapted for leaping. Some of these readapted ground-dwellers then returned to the trees in the course of further evolution, but their legs were so highly specialized for leaping that they could not be used for grasping a tree trunk. In consequence, the present-day tree kangaroos must climb like bears by bracing their feet against the tree trunk. A comparison of the feet of the existing Australian marsupials reveals all the stages in this complicated process of adaptation and readaptation.

40.2
Physiologic Adaptations

Since one of the major struggles among organisms stems from the competition for food, any mutation which enables an animal to utilize a new type of food will be extremely advantageous. This might involve the evolution of a new digestive enzyme or of a new energy-liberating enzyme system. The evolution of a new enzyme system enabled the sulfur bacteria to obtain biologically useful energy from hydrogen sulfide, a substance which is poisonous to almost all other organisms. The evolution of a special enzyme for reducing disulfide bridges gave the clothes moth its unique ability to digest wool, the protein molecules of which are held together by such disulfide bridges.

A mutation that decreases the growing season of a plant or the total length of time required for an insect or other animal to complete development will enable it to survive farther from the equator, thus opening up new areas of living space and new sources of food for the new organism. Any mutation that increases the limits of temperature tolerance of a species—makes it more eurythermic—may enable it to inhabit a new part of the earth, at a higher latitude or higher altitude. Other organisms have adapted to life in the arctic by evolving either an ability to become dormant during the cold season or a behavior pattern that includes migration southward during the winter.

Marine fish are usually adapted to survive within a certain range of pressures and thus are found at a particular depth. Animals adapted to live near the surface are crushed by the terrific pressures of the deep, and deep-sea animals usually burst when brought to the surface. The whale has a remarkable ability to withstand changes in pressure, and can dive to depths of 800 meters without injury. Presumably, its lung alveoli collapse when the pressure on the body reaches a certain point and then gases are no longer absorbed into the blood.

A man can survive pressures as great as six atmospheres if the pressure is increased and subsequently decreased slowly. The increase in pressure increases the amount of gas dissolved in the blood, in body fluids and within the cells. If the pressure is decreased suddenly, the gases come out of solution and form bubbles throughout the body. Those in the blood impede circulation and bring about the symptoms of diver's disease, or "the bends." The pilot of a jet plane may gain altitude so quickly that the atmospheric pressure is reduced rapidly enough to bring bubbles of gas out of solution in his blood and produce a type of the bends.

40.3
Color Adaptations

Adaptations for survival are evident in the color and color pattern of animals and plants as well as in their structure and physiologic processes. Ecologists recognize three types of color adaptation: **concealing** or **protective coloration,** which enables the organism to blend with its background and be less visible to predators; **warning coloration,** which consists of bright, conspicuous colors and is assumed by poisonous or unpalatable animals to warn off potential predators; and **mimicry,** in which the organism resembles some other living or nonliving object—a twig, leaf, stone, or perhaps some other animal which, being poisonous, has warning coloration.

Concealing coloration may serve to hide an animal which wants to escape the notice of a potential predator or it may hide a predator from his intended prey. Examples of such coloration are legion—the white coats of arctic animals, and the stripes and spots of tigers, leopards, zebras and giraffes which, though conspicuous in a zoo, blend imperceptibly with the moving pattern of light and dark typical of their native savanna. Some animals—frogs, flounders, chameleons, crabs and others—can change color and pattern as they move from a dark to a light background or from one that is uniform to one that is mottled (Fig. 40.2).

To demonstrate experimentally that concealing coloration does have survival value—that what looks to a man like a good match between animal and background will also fool the animal's predators—investigators fastened grasshoppers with different body colors to plots of different colored soils—light, dark, grassy or sandy. After these plots have been exposed to the predatory activities of chickens or wild birds for a given length of time, the survivors were tabulated. It was found that there was a significantly higher percentage of survivors among those grasshoppers which matched their background.

When an animal is protected by poison fangs, stinging mechanisms, or some chemical which gives it a noxious taste, it is to its advantage to have this fact widely advertised. In fact, many animals with such protective adaptations do have warning colors. A European species of toad, for example, has skin glands which secrete an unpleasant, unpalatable substance. Its belly is bright scarlet, and whenever a potential predator, such as a stork, swoops over a congregation of these toads, they flop on their backs, exposing their scarlet bellies as a warning. The storks and other birds apparently become conditioned to the association of the red color and the bad taste and do not try to eat the toads.

Other animals survive by mimicking one of these protectively colored animals. Some harmless, defenseless and palatable animals have evolved to be almost identical in shape and color with a poisonous or noxious animal of quite a different family or order and, being mistaken for it by predators, are left alone. Examples of mimicry are particularly common among tropical insects. This type of adaptation is successful only where there are many more genuinely disagreeable or dangerous organisms than forms which mimic them. Obviously, if a predator finds that any

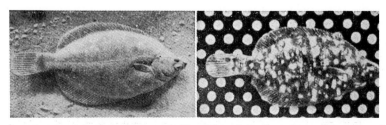

Figure 40.2   An experiment to show the remarkable ability of the flounder to change its color and pattern to conform with its background. Left, a flounder on a uniform, light background; right, the same fish after being placed on a spotted, darker background. (Villee: Biology, 5th ed.)

considerable percentage of the animals with a particular shape and color *are* palatable, he will not be conditioned to avoid them.

The reality of the selective advantage of color adaptations has been much debated. It has been argued that animal vision may be quite different from human vision; that animals may be color-blind, or perhaps able to see light in the ultraviolet or infrared part of the spectrum, and, therefore, that an animal which appears to be protectively colored to human eyes may be readily evident to its natural predators. However, many experimental studies, such as the grasshopper experiment cited previously, have shown that protective coloration does have survival value.

Color and patterns may serve to attract other organisms when such attraction is necessary for survival. The red and blue ischial callosities of monkeys, and the extravagantly colored plumage of many birds, apparently have an attraction for the members of the opposite sex. The vivid colors of flowers appear to attract the birds or insects whose activities are needed to ensure the pollination of the plant or the dispersal of its seed.

40.4
Adaptations of Species to Species

The evolutionary adaptation of each species has not occurred in a biologic vacuum, independently of other organisms. On the contrary, the adaptation of each species has been influenced markedly by the concurrent adaptations of other species. As a result of this, many types of cross-dependency between species have arisen. Some of the clearest and best understood of these involve insects.

Insects are necessary for the pollination of a great many plants; the plants are so dependent on these insects that they are unable to become established in a given region unless those particular insects are present. The Smyrna fig, for example, could not be grown in California, even though all climatic conditions were favorable, until the fig insect, which pollinates the plant, was introduced. Birds, bats and even snails serve as pollinators for some plants, but insects are the prime animals with this function. Flowering plants have evolved bright colors and strong fragrances, presumably to attract insects and

birds and ensure pollination. There has been some doubt as to whether insects can detect these colors and odors, but the experiments of Karl von Frisch (p. 286) show that honeybees, at least, can differentiate colors, shapes and scents and are guided in their visits to flowers by these stimuli.

Some of the species-to-species adaptations are so exact that neither one can exist without the other. The yucca plant and the yucca moth have evolved to a state of complete interdependence. The yucca moth, by a series of instinctive acts, goes to a yucca flower, collects some pollen and takes it to a second flower. There it pushes its ovipositor through the wall of the ovary of the flower and lays an egg. It then carefully places some pollen on the stigma. The yucca plant is fertilized and produces seeds, on a few of which the larva of the yucca moth feeds. The plant produces a large number of seeds and can easily spare the ones eaten by the moth larva.

40.5
The Distribution of Animals

Three major habitats can be distinguished, **marine, fresh water** and **terrestrial.** No animal is found in all three major habitats and, indeed, no animal is found everywhere within any one of these. Every species of animal and plant tends to produce more offspring than can survive within the normal range of the organism. There is a strong **population pressure** tending to force the individuals to spread out and become established in new territories. Competing species, predators, lack of food, adverse climate and the unsuitability of the adjacent regions, perhaps due to lack of some requisite physical or chemical factor, act to counterbalance the population pressure and to prevent the spread of the species. Since all of these factors are subject to change, the range of a species tends to be dynamic rather than static and may change quite suddenly. The spread of a species is prevented by geographic **barriers** such as oceans, mountains, deserts and large rivers and is facilitated by **"highways"** such as land connections between continents. The present distribution of the species of animals is determined by the barriers and highways that exist and have existed in the geologic past.

The biogeographic realms, discussed on page 680, are regions made up of whole continents, or of large parts of a continent, separated by major geographic barriers, and characterized by the presence of certain unique animals and plants. Within these biogeographic realms (and established by a complex interaction of climate, other physical factors and biotic factors) are large, distinct, easily differentiated community units called **biomes.**

A biome is a large community unit characterized by the kinds of plants and animals present. In contrast the term ecosystem is defined as a natural unit of living and non-living parts that interact to form a stable system in which the exchange of materials follows a circular path. Thus an ecosystem might be a small pond or a large area coextensive with a biome but including the physical environment as well as the populations of animals, plants and microorganisms.

In each biome the *kind* of climax vegetation is uniform—grasses, conifers, deciduous trees—but the particular *species* of plant may vary in different parts of the biome. The kind of climax vegetation depends upon the physical environment, and the two together determine the kinds of animals present. The definition of a biome includes not only the actual climax community of a region but also the several intermediate seral communities that precede the climax community.

There is usually no sharp line of demarcation between adjacent biomes; instead, each blends with the next through a fairly broad transitional region termed an **ecotone.** The ecotonal community typically consists of some organisms from each of the adjacent biomes plus some that are characteristic of, and perhaps restricted to, the ecotone. There is a tendency (called the **edge effect**) for the ecotone to contain both a greater number of species and a higher population density than either adjacent biome.

40.6
Terrestrial Life Zones

Some of the biomes recognized by ecologists are **tundra, coniferous forest, deciduous forest, broad-leaved evergreen subtropical forest, grassland, desert, chaparral** and **tropical rain forest.** These biomes are distributed, though somewhat irregularly, as belts around the earth (Fig. 40.3), and as one

travels from the equator to the pole he may traverse tropical rain forest, grassland, desert, deciduous forest, coniferous forest, and finally reach the tundra in northern Canada, Alaska or Siberia. Since climatic conditions at higher altitudes are in many ways similar to those at higher latitudes, there is a similar succession of biomes on the slopes of high mountains (Fig. 40.4). As one ascends from the San Joaquin Valley of California into the Sierras, one passes from desert and chaparral through deciduous forest and coniferous forest to, above the timberline, a region resembling the tundra of the arctic.

40.7
The Tundra Biome

Between the Arctic Ocean and polar icecaps and the forests to the south lies a band of treeless country called the **tundra** (Fig. 40.5). Some five million acres of tundra stretch across northern North America, northern Europe and Siberia. The primary characteristics of this region are the low temperatures and a short growing season. The amount of precipitation is rather small but water is usually not a limiting factor because the rate of evaporation is also very low.

The ground usually remains frozen except for the uppermost 10 or 20 cm., which thaw during the brief summer season. The rather thin carpet of vegetation includes lichens, mosses, grasses, sedges and a few low shrubs. The animals that have adapted to survive in the tundra are caribou or reindeer, the arctic hare, arctic fox, polar bear, wolves, lemmings, snowy owls, ptarmigans and, during the summer, swarms of flies, mosquitoes and a host of migratory birds.

The caribou and reindeer are highly migratory because there is not enough vegetation produced in any one local area to support them. Although casual inspection might suggest that tundras are rather barren areas, a surprisingly large number of organisms have become adapted to survive the cold. During the long daylight hours of the brief summer, the rate of primary production is quite high. The production from the vegetation on the land, from the plants in the many shallow ponds that dot the landscape and from the phytoplankton in the adjacent Arctic Ocean provides enough food to support both a

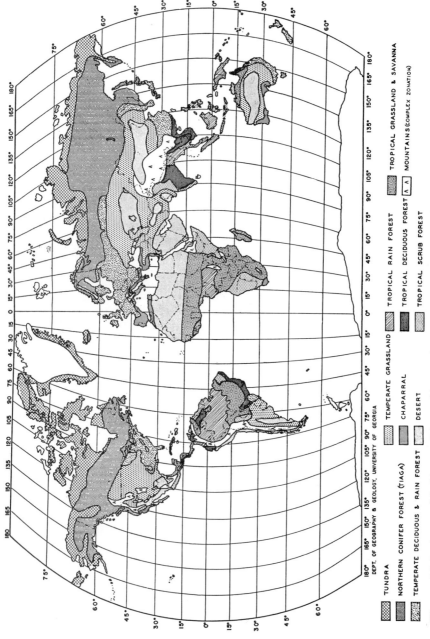

Figure 40.3 A map of the biomes of the world. Note that only the tundra and northern conifer forest are more or less continuous bands around the world. Other biomes are generally isolated in different biogeographic realms and may be expected to have ecologically equivalent but taxonomically unrelated species. (Odum: Fundamentals of Ecology.)

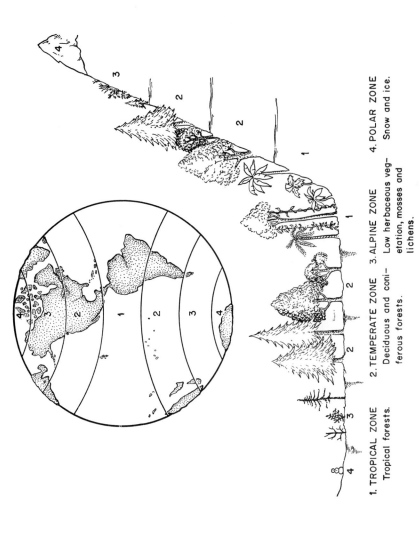

Figure 40.4 Diagram showing correspondence of life zones at successively higher altitudes at the same latitude (*1 to 4*, right), and at successively higher latitudes at the same altitude (*1 to 4*, left, and inset). (Villee: Biology, 5th ed.)

1. TROPICAL ZONE
Tropical forests.

2. TEMPERATE ZONE
Deciduous and coni-
ferous forests.

3. ALPINE ZONE
Low herbaceous veg-
etation, mosses and
lichens.

4. POLAR ZONE
Snow and ice.

Figure 40.5   The tundra biome. Above, View of the low tundra near Churchill, Manitoba, in July. Note the numerous ponds. Below, View of tundra vegetation showing "lumpy" nature of low tundra and a characteristic tundra bird, the willow ptarmigan. (Lower photo by C. Lynn Haywood.)

variety of permanent resident mammals and many kinds of migratory birds and insects.

40.8
The Forest Biomes

Several different types of forest biomes can be distinguished and these are arranged generally on a gradient from north to south or from high altitude to lower altitude. Adjacent to the tundra region either at high latitude or high altitude is the **northern coniferous forest** (Fig. 40.6), which stretches across both North America and Eurasia just south of the tundra. This is characterized by spruce, fir and pine trees and by animals such as the snowshoe hare, the lynx and the wolf.

The fact that the trees are evergreen means

that there is a dense shade throughout the year, which tends to inhibit development of shrubs and a herbaceous undergrowth. The continuous presence of green leaves permits photosynthesis to occur throughout the year despite the low temperature during the winter and results in a fairly high annual rate of primary production.

These coniferous forests are the major source of commercial lumber around the world. After they have fallen, the needles decay very slowly and the soil develops a characteristic condition with relatively little humus. The northern coniferous forest, like the tundra, shows a very marked seasonal periodicity, and the populations of animals tend to show marked peaks and depressions in numbers.

Along the west coast of North America

Figure 40.6 The coniferous forest biome covers parts of Canada, northern Europe and Siberia and extends southward at higher altitudes on the larger mountain ranges. (Orr: Vertebrate Biology, 2nd ed.)

from Alaska south to central California is a region termed the **moist coniferous forest biome,** characterized by a much greater humidity, somewhat higher temperatures and smaller seasonal ranges than the classic coniferous forest farther north. There is high rainfall and, in addition, a great deal of moisture is contributed by the frequent fogs. There are forests of Sitka spruce in the northern section, western hemlock, arbor vitae, and Douglas fir in the Puget Sound area, and the coastal redwood, *Sequoia sempervirens,* in California. The potential production of this region is very great, and with careful foresting and replanting, the annual crop of lumber is very high.

The **temperate deciduous forest biome** (Fig. 40.7) is found in areas with abundant evenly distributed rainfall (75 to 150 cm. annually) and moderate temperatures with distinct summers and winters. Temperate deciduous forest biomes originally covered eastern North America, all of Europe, parts of Japan and Australia, and the southern portion of South America.

The trees present — beech, maple, oak, hickory and chestnut — lose their leaves during half the year; thus, the contrast between winter and summer is very marked. The undergrowth of shrubs and herbs is generally well developed. The animals originally present in the forest were deer, bears, squir-

rels, gray foxes, bobcats, wild turkeys and woodpeckers. Much of this forest region has now been replaced by cultivated fields and cities.

In regions of fairly high rainfall but where temperature differences between winter and summer are less marked, as in Florida, is the **broad-leaved evergreen subtropical forest biome.** The vegetation includes live oaks, magnolias, tamarinds and palm trees, with many vines and epiphytes such as orchids and Spanish moss.

The variety of life reaches its maximum in the **tropical rain forests** (Fig. 40.8), which occupy low-lying areas near the equator with annual rainfalls of 200 cm. or more. The thick rain forests, with a tremendous variety of plants and animals, are found in the valleys of the Amazon, Orinoco, Congo and Zambesi rivers and in parts of Central America, Malaya, Borneo and New Guinea.

The extremely dense vegetation makes it difficult to study or even photograph the rain forest biome. The vegetation is vertically stratified with tall trees often covered with vines, creepers, lianas and epiphytes.

No single species of animal or plant is present in large enough numbers to be dominant. The diversity of species is remarkable; there may be more species of plants and insects in a few acres of tropical rain forest than in all of Europe. The trees of the tropical

Figure 40.7   An example of a temperate deciduous forest, Noble County, Ohio. The dominant trees are white and red oaks with an understory of hickory. (Photograph by U. S. Forest Service.)

rain forest are usually evergreen and rather tall. Their roots are often shallow and have swollen bases or flying buttresses.

The tropical rain forest is the ultimate of jungles although the low light intensity at the ground level may result in sparse herbaceous vegetation and actual bare spots in certain areas. Many of the animals live in the upper layers of the vegetation. Among the characteristic animals are monkeys, sloths, termites,

Figure 40.8 The rain forest biome: border of a clearing in the Ituri Forest of Nala, Belgian Congo. (Photograph by Herbert Lang; courtesy of The American Museum of Natural History.)

ants, anteaters, many reptiles and many brilliantly colored birds — parakeets, toucans and birds of paradise.

40.9
The Grassland Biome

The **grassland** biome (Fig. 40.9) occurs where rainfall is about 25 to 75 cm. per year, insufficient to support a forest, yet greater than that of a true desert. Grasslands are usually found in the interiors of continents — the prairies of western United States and those of Argentina, Australia, southern Russia and Siberia. It appears that early human civilizations developed in this grasslands region, where early man raised grazing animals and cultivated and selected the grasses to produce his prime food plants, the cereals such as wheat and rye. The animals of the grasslands are either grazing or burrowing mammals — bison, antelope, zebras, rabbits, ground squirrels, prairie dogs and gophers — and birds such as prairie chickens, meadow larks and rodent hawks.

The species of grasses present in a grassland may range from tall species 150 to 250 cm. in height to short species of grass that do not exceed 15 cm. in height. Some species of grass grow in clumps or bunches and others spread out and form sods with underground rhizomes. The roots of grasses penetrate deeply in the soil and the weight of the roots

of a healthy plant will be several times the weight of the shoot.

Trees and shrubs may occur in grasslands as scattered individuals or in belts along the streams and rivers. The soil of grasslands is very rich in humus because of the rapid growth and decay of the individual plants. The grasslands are excellent pastures for cattle, sheep and goats as well as for the indigenous grazing animals.

There is a broad band of tropical grassland or **savanna** in Africa lying between the Sahara desert and the tropical rain forest of the Congo basin. Although the annual rainfall is high, as much as 125 cm., there is a distinct dry season from June to August which prevents the development of forests. There are great numbers and many different kinds of grazing animals in this region (Fig. 40.10), together with predators such as lions. This is the storied "big game country" of Africa. Kangaroos and wallabies are the grazing animals of the Australian grasslands that are ecologically comparable to the antelope and zebras of the African savanna.

How to make the best use of these African grasslands is a problem now facing the new nations of Africa as they work to raise the level of nutrition of their human populations. Many ecologists are of the opinion that it would be better to harvest the native herbivores — antelope, hippopotamuses, and wildebeests — on a sustained yield basis rather than attempt to exterminate them and substitute

Figure 40.9 A region of short-grass grassland with a herd of bison, originally one of the major grazing animals in the grassland biome of western United States and Canada. The bison in the center is wallowing. (Odum: Fundamentals of Ecology.)

Figure 40.10   The grassland biome; characteristic animals of the African grasslands, zebra and wildebeest, Kruger National Park, Transvaal. (Photograph by Herbert Lang.)

cattle. The diversity of the native population would mean broader use of all the resources of primary production, and the native species are largely immune to the many tropical parasites and diseases that plague the cattle that have been introduced.

40.10
The Chaparral Biome

In mild temperate regions of the world with relatively abundant rain in the winter but with very dry summers, the climax community includes trees and shrubs with hard, thick evergreen leaves (Fig. 40.11). This type of vegetation is called "chaparral" in California and Mexico, "macchie" around the Mediterranean and "mellee scrub" on Australia's south coast.

The trees and shrubs common in California's chaparral are chamiso and manzanita. Eucalyptus trees introduced from Australia's south coast into California's chaparral region have prospered mightily and have replaced to a considerable extent the native woody vegetation in areas near cities.

Mule deer and many kinds of birds live in the chaparral during the rainy season but move north or to higher altitudes to escape the hot dry summer. Brush rabbits, wood rats, chipmunks, lizards, wren-tits and brown

towhees are characteristic animals of the chaparral biome. During the hot dry season, there is an ever present danger of fire, which may sweep rapidly over the chaparral slopes. Following a fire, the shrubs sprout vigorously after the first rains and may reach maximum size within 20 years.

Figure 40.11   An example of the chaparral biome in California. The shrubs in the picture are *Eriodictyon tomentosum*. (Photograph by U. S. Forest Service.)

40.11

The Desert Biome

In regions with less than 25 cm. of rain per year, or in certain hot regions where there may be more rainfall but with an uneven distribution in the annual cycle, vegetation is sparse and consists of greasewood, sagebrush or cactus. The individual plants in the desert are typically widely spaced with large bare areas separating them. In the brief rainy season, the California desert becomes carpeted with an amazing variety of wild flowers and grasses, most of which complete their life cycle from seed to seed in a few weeks. The animals present in the desert are reptiles, insects and burrowing rodents such as the kangaroo rat and pocket mouse, both of which are able to live without drinking water by extracting the water from the seeds and succulent cactus they eat.

The small amount of rainfall may be due to continued high barometric pressure, as in the Sahara and Australian deserts; a geographical position in the rain shadow of a mountain, as in the western North American deserts; or to high altitude, as in the deserts in Tibet and Bolivia. The only absolute

Figure 40.12 Two types of desert in western North America, a "cool" desert in Idaho dominated by sagebrush (above) and (below) a rather luxuriant "hot" desert in Arizona, with giant cactus (Saguaro) and palo verde trees, in addition to creosote bushes and other desert shrubs. In extensive areas of desert country the desert shrubs alone dot the landscape. (Upper photograph by U. S. Forest Service, lower by U. S. Soil Conservation Service.)

deserts, where little or no rain ever falls, are those of northern Chile and of the central Sahara.

Careful measurements of the amount of dry matter produced for a given area in the course of a year show a clear linear relationship with the amount of rainfall, at least up to 60 cm. per year. This illustrates clearly the primary role of moisture as a limiting factor in the productivity of the desert. Where the soil is favorable, an irrigated desert can be extremely productive because of the large amount of sunlight.

Two types of deserts can be distinguished on the basis of their average temperatures: "hot" deserts, such as that found in Arizona, characterized by the giant saguaro cactus, palo verde trees and the creosote bush; and "cool" deserts, such as that present in Idaho, dominated by sagebrush (Fig. 40.12).

Certain reptiles and insects are well adapted for survival in deserts because of their thick, impervious integuments and the fact that they excrete dry waste matter. A few species of mammals have become secondarily adapted to the desert by excreting very concentrated urine and they avoid the sun by remaining in their burrows during the day. The camel and the desert birds must have an occasional drink of water but can go for long periods of time using the water stored in the body.

When deserts are irrigated, the large volume of water passing through the irrigation system may lead to the accumulation of salts in the soil as some of the water is evaporated, and this will eventually limit the area's productivity. The water supply itself can fail if the watershed from which it is obtained is not cared for appropriately. The ruins of old irrigation systems and of the civilizations they supported in the deserts of North Africa and the Near East remind us that the irrigated desert will retain its productivity only when the entire system is kept in appropriate balance.

40.12
The Edge of the Sea:
Marshes and Estuaries

Where the sea meets the land there may be one of several kinds of ecosystems with distinctive characteristics: a rocky shore, a sandy beach, an intertidal mud flat or a tidal estuary containing salt marshes. The word estuary refers to the mouth of a river or a coastal bay where the salinity is less than in the open ocean, intermediate between sea and fresh water.

The waters of estuaries are among the most naturally fertile in the world, frequently having a much greater productivity than the adjacent sea or the fresh water up the river. This high productivity is brought about by the action of the tides, which promote a rapid circulation of nutrients and aid in the removal of waste products, and by the presence of many kinds of plants, which provide for an extensive photosynthetic carpet. These include the phytoplankton, the algae living in and on the mud, sand, rocks or other hard surfaces, and the large attached plants, "seaweeds," eel grasses and marsh grasses.

Some of the marsh grass is eaten by insects and other terrestrial herbivores but most of it is converted to detritus and is consumed by the clams, crabs and other marine detritus eaters. Estuaries may have a high productivity of fish, oysters, shrimp and other seafood.

40.13
Marine Life Zones

The recent marked upsurge of interest in oceanography in general and in marine ecology in particular reflects our growing appreciation of the importance of the seas as a reservoir of nutrients for land as well as marine organisms.

The oceans and seas cover about 70 per cent of the earth's surface and have an enormously rich fauna and flora. The total weight of living things, the biomass, in the ocean far exceeds the mass of terrestrial animals and plants. Living animals are found in even the greatest depths of the ocean. The temperature of the oceans ranges from about −2° C. in the polar seas to 32° C. or more in the tropics, but the annual range of variation in any locality is usually not more than 6 degrees. The oceans are in continuous circulation brought about by the trade winds and the rotation of the earth. These currents, such as the famous Gulf Stream, Japan current and Humboldt current, not only play a major role in the ecology of the oceans but also have marked effects on the climate and other ecologic factors of the adjacent land masses. The major currents circulate in a clockwise fashion in the northern hemisphere and in a counterclockwise direction in the southern hemisphere. The combination of these currents and the prevailing winds tends to cause upwellings of cool water laden with nutrients from the depths to the surface on the west coasts of the continents. These upwellings on the coasts of California, Peru and Portugal support large populations of sardines, tuna and other fish.

Although the saltiness of the sea is relatively uniform, the concentrations of phosphates, nitrates and other nutrients vary widely in different parts of the sea and at different times of the year. These are among the prime factors limiting the biologic productivity of the sea in a given region.

All the phyla except the Onychophora, and all the classes except the amphibians, centipedes, millipedes and insects, are well represented in the oceans; ctenophores, brachiopods, echinoderms, chaetognaths and a few lesser phyla are found only in the oceans. The ocean has clearly demarcated regions characterized by different physical conditions and, consequently, inhabited by different kinds of animals and plants. A gently sloping **continental shelf** usually extends some distance offshore; beyond this the ocean floor (the continental slope) drops steeply to the abyssal region (Fig. 40.13). The region of shallow water over the continental shelf is called the **neritic zone;** it can be subdivided into **supra-**

tidal (above the high tide mark), **intertidal** (between high and low tide lines, a region also known as the "littoral") and **subtidal regions** (Fig. 40.13).

The open sea beyond the edge of the continental shelf is the **oceanic zone.** The upper part of the ocean, into which enough light can penetrate to be effective in photosynthesis, is known as the **euphotic region.** The average lower limit of this is at about 100 meters, but in a few regions of clear tropical water this may extend to twice that depth. The regions of the ocean beneath the euphotic zone are called the **bathyal zone** over the continental slope, to a depth of perhaps 2000 meters; the depths of the ocean beyond that comprise the **abyssal zone.**

The floor of the ocean is not flat but is thrown into gigantic ridges and valleys. Some of the ridges rise nearly to the surface (or above it where there are oceanic islands), and some of the valleys lie 10,000 meters below the surface of the sea. Huge underwater avalanches occur from time to time as parts of the ridges tumble into the valleys.

The marine organisms are classified ecologically as **plankton,** organisms that float and are moved passively by the currents, winds and waves; **nekton,** animals that swim actively; and **benthos,** the bottom-dwellers that crawl over, burrow into, or are attached to the bottom. The plankton are generally very small protozoa, algae, small larval forms of a vari-

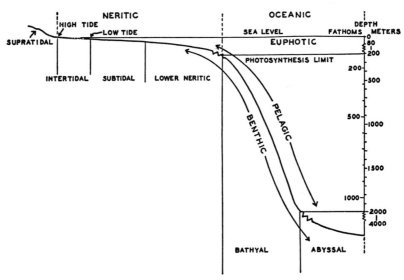

Figure 40.13 Diagram illustrating zonation in the sea. (After Hedgpeth, from Odum. Fundamentals of Ecology.)

ety of animals, and a few worms. The nekton include the jellyfish, squid, fishes, turtles, seals and whales. Some of the benthic animals, crabs, snails, starfish and some worms, crawl over the substrate; clams and worms burrow into the sand, mud or rock of the sea bottom; and a third group, including sponges, sea anemones, corals, bryozoans, crinoids, oysters, barnacles and tunicates, are attached to the substrate.

The intertidal zone is one of the most favorable of all the habitats of the world, with an abundance of light, oxygen, carbon dioxide and minerals to foster a rich growth of plants, and the plants, providing food and shelter, make it an excellent habitat for animals. The plant life is largely composed of algae, with only a few grasses in addition.

Members of every phylum of the animal kingdom are found in the intertidal zone, many of which are sessile and more or less permanently attached to the sea bottom, although they may be pelagic at some stage of their life cycle. These sessile animals are typically restricted to certain depths of the intertidal zone. There is keen competition among the plants for space and among the animals for space and food, so the forms living here have had to evolve special adaptations to survive.

The intertidal zone is exposed to the air twice daily and its inhabitants have had to develop some sort of protection against desiccation. Some animals avoid this by burrowing into the damp sand or rocks until the tide returns; others have evolved shells which can be closed to retain a supply of water within them. Many plants contain jelly-like substances such as agar which absorb and retain large quantities of water.

One of the outstanding characteristics of this region, of course, is the ever-present action of the waves, and the organisms in adapting to life here have evolved ways of resisting wave action. The many seaweeds have tough pliable bodies, able to bend with the waves without breaking, while the animals are either encased in hard calcareous shells, such as those of mollusks, bryozoa, starfish, barnacles and crabs, or are covered by a strong leathery skin that can bend without breaking, such as that of the sea anemone and octopus.

The subtidal zone, just beyond the intertidal zone, is also thickly populated, for it has plenty of light and an abundance of minerals and other nutrients for plant growth. The absence of the periodic exposure to air

and the lesser wave action permit many plants and animals to live here which could not survive in the intertidal zone. Here live many species of fish and many single-celled algae; the larger sea weeds, which require a substrate for attachment, are found in the shallower parts of the region. Most of the world's great commercial fishing areas are in the neritic region, at places where the upwelling of cold bottom water brings nutrients up from the depths.

The euphotic region, distinguished by the presence of sunlight and the absence of a substrate, is populated by plankton and nekton. There are no large seaweeds, except occasional pieces torn from their anchorage in the shallow sea, and fewer microscopic algae, generally, than in the shallow sea. There are protozoa such as foraminifera and radiolaria, small crustacea and many larval forms. The larger animals include the Portuguese man-of-war, jellyfish, squid, fishes and whales. Some whales are equipped with strainers and feed upon the microscopic plankton; others have teeth and prey upon fish, squid and other whales.

The bathyal and abyssal zones, lying below the euphotic, are characterized by the absence of light and the consequent absence of living green plants. The waters are quiet and very cold and the pressure is stupendous. The animals that live here feed upon each other and upon the bodies of dead plants and animals that are constantly settling down from above. Most of the fish of the abyssal region are small and peculiarly shaped; many are equipped with luminescent organs, which may serve as lures for their prey. The majority of the deep-sea creatures are related to shallow-sea forms and are believed to have migrated to their present habitat relatively recently (by geologic standards), for none is older than the Mesozoic.

Since the number of members of any one species in these vast, dark depths is small, reproduction is more of a problem than in any other region, and some fish have evolved a curious adaptation to ensure that the two sexes will be in proximity to reproduce. At an early age the male becomes attached to the head of the female and fuses with it. There he continues to live as a small (2.5 cm.) parasite (Fig. 40.14). In due course he becomes sexually mature and when the female lays her eggs, he releases his sperm into the water to fertilize them.

The bottom of the sea is a soft ooze, com-

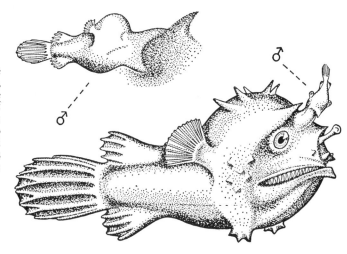

Figure 40.14 Sexual parasitism in the deep-sea angler fish, *Photocorynus spiniceps*, in which the difficulty of one sex finding the other is met by permanent attachment of the much smaller male to the female. The union is so complete that the male has no independent existence at all, being nourished by the blood of the female to which he is attached. (After Norman, from Allee et al.: Principles of Animal Ecology.)

Figure 40.15 Photographs (by means of a special underwater camera called the benthograph) of the ocean bottom at three different depths off southern California (San Diego Trough). *A*, At 90 meters. Note abundant sea urchins (probably *Lytechinus*) appearing as globular, light-colored bodies, and the long curved sea whips (probably *Acanthoptilum*). Burrowing worms have built the conical piles of sediment at the mouth of their burrows. (Emery, 1952.) *B*, At 1097 meters. Vertical photograph of about 3.34 square meters of bottom composed of green silty mud having a high organic content. Note the numerous brittle stars (Ophiuroidea) and several large sea cucumbers (Holothuroidea). The latter have not been identified as to species as they have never been dredged from the sea and have only been seen in bottom photographs! (Official Navy photo, courtesy of U. S. Navy Electronics Laboratory, San Diego.) *C*, At 1335 meters. Note in the right foreground the 10 arms of what is probably a comatulid crinoid (a relative of the starfish which is attached to the bottom by a stalk-like part). Small worm tubes and brittle stars litter the surface, and two sea cucumbers may be seen in the left foreground. Continual activity of burrowing animals keeps the sea bottom "bumpy." The bottom edge of the picture represents a distance of about 1.8 meters. (Emery, 1952.)

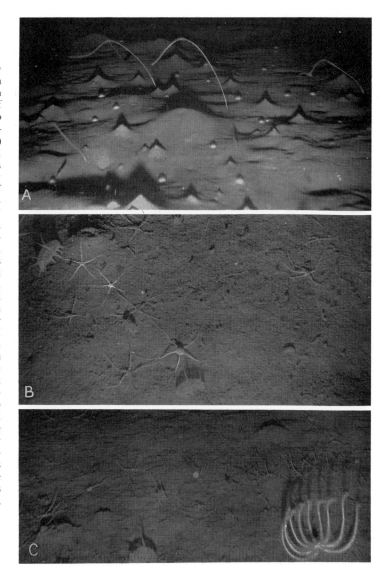

posed of the organic remains and shells of foraminifera, radiolaria and other animals and plants. Many invertebrates live at great depths on the ocean floor (Fig. 40.15) and characteristically have thin, almost transparent shells, whereas the related shallow-sea forms, exposed to wave action, have hard thicker shells. Even the greatest depths are inhabited, for tube-dwelling worms have been dredged from depths of 8000 meters, and sea urchins, starfish, bryozoa and brachiopods have been found at depths of 6000 meters.

40.14

Fresh-water Life Zones

Fresh-water habitats may be divided into **standing water**—lakes, ponds and swamps— and **running water**—springs, creeks and rivers—though, of course, each intergrades with the other. The biologic communities of fresh-water habitats are, in general, more familiar than the marine ones, and many of the animals used as specimens in zoology classes are from fresh water—amebas and other protozoa, hydras, planarians, crayfish and frogs.

A lake or other large body of standing water can be subdivided, much as the zones of the ocean are distinguished, into the shallow water near the shore—the **littoral** zone; the surface waters away from the shore —the **limnetic** zone; and the deep waters under the limnetic zone. Some aspects of the ecology of a fresh-water lake were discussed in section 39.1. The ecologic factors which may be limiting to a fresh-water habitat are temperature, turbidity of the water, the amount of the current and the concentration of oxygen, carbon dioxide and salts, especially phosphates and nitrates. The organisms of the fresh-water community may also be subdivided into plankton, nekton and benthos. The most important animal members of the community are fish, insects and crustacea, and the plant members are algae and aquatic seed plants.

Fresh-water habitats change much more rapidly than other life zones; ponds may become swamps and swamps become filled in and form dry land in a few hundred years. Streams are constantly eroding their banks and changing their course. Consequently, the kinds of plants and animals present may

change markedly and show ecologic successions analogous to those on land. The large lakes, such as the Great Lakes, are relatively stable habitats, and their populations of animals and plants change much less rapidly. Lake Baikal in the Soviet Union is the oldest and deepest lake in the world, formed during the Mesozoic era. It contains many species of fish and other animals found nowhere else in the world.

A large, deep lake will show vertical stratification with marked differences in temperature, dissolved gases, light and other factors. Particular species of fish and other animals are more or less restricted to a certain range of depths. The deeper waters of many lakes become almost depleted of oxygen during the summer. In the summer the top layer becomes much warmer than the water below and the circulation of water is essentially restricted to the warm upper layer. The increased activity of decomposer organisms in the lake depths exhausts the supply of oxygen, and the lack of circulation prevents its renewal by the algae and other plants in the upper layers.

The ecologic factors which are most important in limiting the distribution of animals in running water are the speed of the current, the degree to which basic nutrients can be obtained from the adjacent land or from connected lakes, and the amount of oxygen present. Running streams are, in general, well oxygenated, and the animals living there usually have a very low tolerance to reduced oxygen tension. The pollution of streams by sewage or industrial wastes may kill the fauna either by direct toxic effect of one of the chemicals or indirectly by encouraging the growth of decomposer organisms which reduce the oxygen tension in the water.

The adaptations made by animals for survival in streams are concerned primarily with ways of maintaining their position in the current. Some have developed permanent connections with the substrate by evolving hooks, suckers or glands for the secretion of threads or sticky masses with which to attach to the substrate. Others have evolved streamlined, flattened bodies and behavior patterns by which they normally orient themselves so as to head upstream and swim against the current.

In studying any animal it is important to consider whether it is a generalized or specialized representative of its group, what adaptations it has made for survival in its habitat, and what its ecologic role is in the population, community, biome or ecosystem of which it is a member.

QUESTIONS

1. Define and give an example of adaptive radiation.
2. Define the term convergent evolution. Discuss convergent evolution of flying animals and of burrowing animals.
3. Differentiate between protective coloration and mimicry. Give examples of each.
4. What experiments could you devise to determine whether color adaptations have a selective advantage?
5. Discuss the subdivisions of the marine habitat and give examples of animals found typically in each.
6. What is a biome? How does it differ from a biotic community?
7. Define the term ecotone. Give an example of one and discuss its primary characteristics.
8. What adaptations are needed for survival in the intertidal zone?
9. Differentiate between plankton and nekton. Give examples of each.
10. Compare the adaptations made by barnacles, snails and starfish which enable them to survive in the intertidal zone.
11. Why are similar biomes found at high latitudes and high altitudes? Would you expect to find exactly the same species of plants and animals in the tundra region of Alaska and in the tundra region of the Andes? Why?
12. Describe briefly the characteristics of the temperate deciduous forest biome; of the desert biome.

ANNOTATED REFERENCES

Darlington, P. J.: Zoogeography. New York, John Wiley & Sons, Inc., 1957. A description of the principles of zoogeography and details of the major life zones of the world.

Hazen, W. E. (Ed.): Readings in Population and Community Ecology. Philadelphia, W. B. Saunders Co., 1964. A collection of articles by 25 experts on a variety of topics in ecology.

Lack, D.: The Natural Regulation of Animal Numbers. Oxford, Oxford University Press, 1954. A description of the principles of ecologic regulation is given in a very interesting fashion.

Descriptions of the major biomes and life zones can be found in the following:

Bates, M.: The Forest and the Sea. New York, Random House, 1960.

Bourliere, F.: The Tropics. New York, Alfred A. Knopf, Inc., 1957.

Carson, R.: The Sea Around Us. New York, Oxford University Press, 1952.

Carson, R.: The Edge of the Sea. Boston, Houghton Mifflin Co., 1955.

Coker, R. E.: Lakes, Streams and Ponds. Chapel Hill, University of North Carolina Press, 1954.

Farb, P.: The Forest. New York, Time-Life Nature Library, 1961.

Reid, G.: Ecology of Inland Waters and Estuaries. New York, Reinhold Publishing Corp., 1961.

Richard, P. W.: The Tropical Rain Forest. New York, Cambridge University Press, 1952.

41 ANIMAL BEHAVIOR

By Brian A. Hazlett

Behavior is "what an animal does"; more explicitly, behavior patterns are coordinated sequences of neuromuscular activity such as the hunting movements of a lion, the pattern of crawling of a flatworm, the courtship movements of a male stickleback fish, or the cries of young birds when they are hungry. All animals exhibit behavior patterns, although their detection in sponges and some sessile pelecypods requires extreme patience on the part of the observer. Similar general types of behavior are apparent in many different groups of animals, and the behavior of diverse groups is influenced by certain common factors. The activity of the nervous system provides the physiologic basis of behavior. All movements may ultimately be analyzed in terms of the patterns of nervous activity and the patterns of neuromuscular connections. In the following sections, we shall first describe certain behavior patterns, grouped according to the biologic functions with which they are associated, and then consider some of the factors controlling these acts.

All the existing patterns of behavior are the result of evolution. Even when a particular behavior pattern is learned rather than innate, the nervous system which permits the learning of the behavior pattern is the result of natural selection. When the ability to learn rapidly helps the animal to survive and to produce more offspring, the genes that give rise to that type of nervous system will be favored in successive generations.

41.1
Behavior Patterns: Feeding

All animals take in food during their life cycle and show characteristic behavior patterns in finding and consuming their sources of energy. Sessile suspension feeders do not hunt their food, but have filtering mechanisms, sense organs and coordinated muscle contractions that enable them to obtain particles of food of the correct size. Most animals search actively for food and, when certain physical characteristics are detected by the animal's sense organs, the object is treated as food and is eaten. Some insects feed on particular plants only when specific receptors located on hairs on their mouth parts are stimulated by a particular chemical substance. Frogs are visually stimulated by small, dark, moving forms; the identification of such forms by the frog's nervous system appears to result from the properties of special interneurons in the visual pathway which fire only when specific types of movement occur across the frog's retina. Young birds initially peck at any small round object which contrasts with the background. By trial and error, their pecking movements become more accurate, and they learn to avoid pecking at objects such as pebbles which offer no nutritive value.

Predatory behavior, in which one animal kills another for food, is of special interest because of the interactions between the attack patterns of the predator and the defense patterns of the prey. Lions and leopards show a

740

complex of movements as they move along downwind from a herd of antelope, creep toward an animal and run down the prey with one short burst of speed. If the antelope is not caught during this short burst, it usually escapes.

Many birds are attracted to the visual patterns presented by insects. In an evolutionary response to this, a number of larval and adult insects have "eyespot" patterns which are suddenly exposed when the insect is disturbed, and create a "non-insect" pattern.

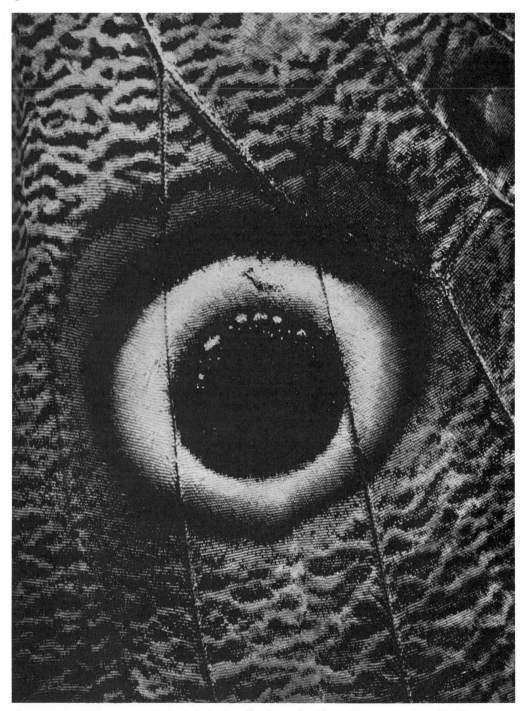

Figure 41.1 Eyespot on the hind wing of a Brazilian butterfly. The sudden appearance of such eyespots, when the insect is disturbed, often elicits retreat by a predator. (Courtesy of H. B. Cott.)

Figure 41.2 Cryptic resemblance of several different types of insects to leaves. (Courtesy of H. B. Cott.)

(Fig. 41.1). Other insects resemble their environment closely and become immobile when disturbed (Fig. 41.2). Since predators are usually attracted by movement, simply being still is an excellent defense. In a number of arthropods (whip scorpions, many insects, most millipedes) and some vertebrates (toads, skunks), behavior patterns involving **chemical warning** and **defensive devices** have evolved as a means of protection against predators (Fig. 41.3).

A common type of predator-prey interaction, termed **protean behavior,** occurs when the prey appears to go through a sequence of possible escape patterns at random, and the predator cannot predict the exact path of the prey's movements. A stickleback fish being chased by a duck follows an erratic path that is very difficult to follow and apparently impossible to predict.

Conversely, a very well ordered sequence of movements is exchanged between a fish infested with ectoparasites and a cleaning organism such as a shrimp of the genus *Periclimenes* (Fig. 41.4). In this **cleaning symbiosis,** the shrimp feeds on the ectoparasites, and the fish has its parasites removed and its wounds cleaned. Such shrimp often advertise

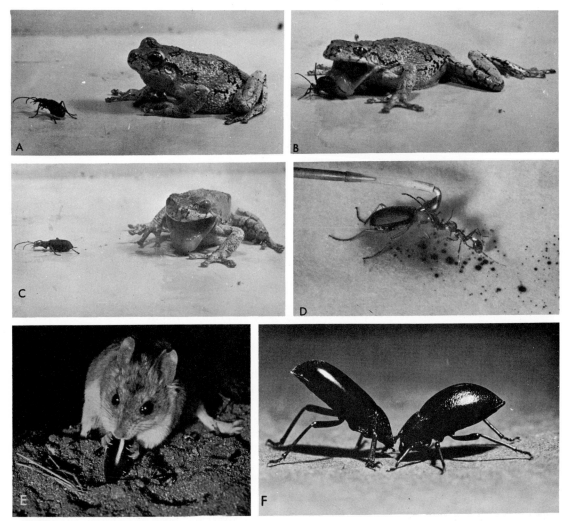

Figure 41.3 Chemical defense systems in arthropods. The bombardier beetle produces a noxious chemical spray when attacked by ants (*D*) or a toad (*A, B* and *C*). When the toad tastes the beetle's spray, it rejects the insect (*C*). The beetle *Eleodes* does a headstand as it ejects its defensive spray (animal to the left in *F*); a mimic of *Eleodes*, *Megasica* also does the headstand, although it has no defensive chemical spray (animal to the right in *F*). The grasshopper mouse avoids the spray of *Eleodes* by sticking the beetle's abdomen toward the ground (*E*). (Courtesy of T. Eisner)

Figure 41.4 The cleaning shrimp, *Periclimenes*, removing ectoparasites from a squirrelfish. The very conspicuous antennae and body markings are characteristic of cleaning animals. (Courtesy of C. Limbaugh.)

that they are "open for business" by waving their long conspicuous antennae up and down. The fish approaches and assumes a special posture ("I'm next") and the shrimp begins cleaning. When all the cleaning organisms are removed from a reef area, the fish are soon in poor health as a result of heavy infestations of ectoparasites and wounds that do not heal.

41.2
Behavior Patterns: Orientation

The behavioral activities of animals are in large measure directed by sensory information about the environment. If a sequence of muscle contractions is to bring about a biologically effective movement, the animal must have information about where it is and where its limbs are. Input from proprioceptors indicates where limbs are, and input from other sense organs indicates the body's position in space. For example, at any time you are aware of where your arms and legs are in relation to your body, and whether you are sitting, tilting your head to one side, or lying down.

The octopus can be readily trained to attack only when stimulated by certain visual patterns. However, when its gravitational sensory input is cut off by removal of the statocysts, the octopus has great difficulty responding to the visual patterns in the correct way. The central nervous system must integrate visual and gravitational information before the proper responses can occur.

Most animals **orient** themselves in a particular way in the area in which they move about. Amphipods living on the beach use visual stimuli (the sun during the day, the moon at night) to determine the direction back to the ocean. That these crustaceans use the position of the sun or moon as an indicator of compass direction was demonstrated by experiments in which a screen and mirrors were used to change the apparent position of the sun or moon (Fig. 41.5). Some wolf spiders, which live along river banks and escape from enemies by running across the water, also use the position of the sun to determine escape direction. It has been shown that the correct escape direction is learned. All young spiders of a brood tend to show a particular directional response, but when they are moved to

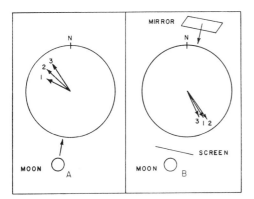

Figure 41.5 Lunar orientation in an amphipod crustacean. The animals initially moved as shown in *A*. When the apparent lunar position was altered by a screen and a mirror, the direction of escape was altered (*B*). (Courtesy of J. T. Enright.)

a new location, their responses are altered so that their movements take them in the correct direction relative to the water in that locality.

Mammals frequently mark the limits of their home range (the area of their daily movements) or territory (the area an animal defends) by chemical marks. Some animals have special scent glands with which they regularly mark the limits of their territory. The familiar sight of a dog at a fire hydrant or shrub is not so much the result of pressure on the dog's bladder as it is an attempt to provide a chemical marker for later orientation.

In addition to those movements involved in daily life, many vertebrates and some arthropods have special migratory behavior patterns, in the performance of which they cover relatively great distances and usually move to a different type of environment. Often, environmental changes bring about certain physiologic changes in the animals which are followed by the extended periods of locomotor activity that constitute the migration. In locusts, increased tactile contacts due to crowding bring about physiologic changes which precede the formation of migratory swarms. Spiny lobsters (Fig. 41.6) may use tactile stimuli to become entrained in long migrating columns. The migrations of birds have been described extensively, and have been the subject of many analyses. This vast subject has already been introduced in the chapter on birds.

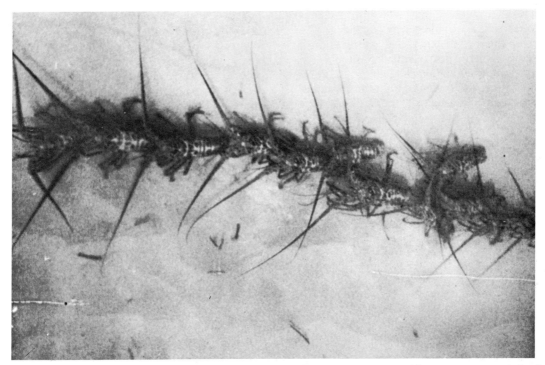

Figure 41.6 Single file chain of migrating spiny lobsters, *Panulirus argus*. Over 100 lobsters may move together in one file. (Courtesy of W. F. Hernnkind.)

41.3
Behavior Patterns: Aggression

Competition for food, mating partners and nesting space results in fighting. These **aggressive behavior patterns** are exchanged primarily between members of the same species. When any other individual comes too close, the first response is often a defensive posture (Fig. 41.7). Most arthropod and vertebrate animals have such an **individual distance,** which is the minimum distance that can separate two animals without a fight ensuing. It can be pictured as a space around an animal into which only sexual partners may enter without eliciting aggressive behavior.

This space is distinct from an animal's **territory,** which is the environmental area it will defend. In its territory, an animal obtains the food, nest materials and space that are necessary for the rearing of its young. Since only members of the same species are likely to utilize the same portions of the environment, territorial defense is usually shown only toward members of the same species, and aggressive interactions are especially frequent at territorial boundaries. Such "boundary encounters" are usually longer and more complex than fights well within an individual's territory. One animal will quickly retreat from a second when the meeting occurs within the second's territory. At the boundary between territories, neither animal retreats and complex exchanges occur. The animals may show **ambivalent behavior patterns** as they are simultaneously motivated to attack and retreat. Under such confusing conditions, the animals often do something totally unrelated to the situation. Herring gulls, after a series of aggressive postures at a territorial boundary, may begin pulling grass from the ground, an activity usually associated with nest building. The birds may simply go through motions similar to grass pulling. Such **displacement activities** may be quite ineffective in the circumstances. Grass pulling has secondarily become part of the gull's aggressive repertoire.

An important characteristic of intraspecific fighting is that it rarely results in any physical damage to the combatants. Through evolutionary selection the acts have become **ritualized,** the movements have a social, communicatory function and interactions are exchanges of signals or **displays.** The wrestling of rattlesnakes (Fig. 41.8) produces even less damage to the interacting animals than the shows put on by "wrestlers" on television. When one individual wins an encounter, the loser frequently assumes a **submissive posture** which inhibits further attack by the winner. When a dog loses a fight it turns its neck toward the winner, exposing the vulnerable throat area; the attack then ceases. In some species of hermit crabs, exchanges of aggressive movements stop when one or both crabs suddenly squat down on the sand. Fighting may, in some species, continue to the point where damage is done. Equally paired mice will sometimes fight to the point of bloodshed; large male seals regularly lose blood in fights for the possession of a harem

Figure 41.7 Defensive display of the ghost crab, *Ocypode*. The bright white mani of the chelipeds are ordinarily held under the body, out of sight. (Courtesy of K. Daumer.)

Figure 41.8 Fighting among rattlesnakes. The snakes do not bite one another but wrestle, pushing against each other with their heads (*a* and *b*) or ventral parts of their bodies (*c* and *d*) until one is pinned (*e*). (From The Fighting Behavior in Animals by I. Eibl-Eibesfeldt. Copyright © by Scientific American, Inc. All rights reserved.)

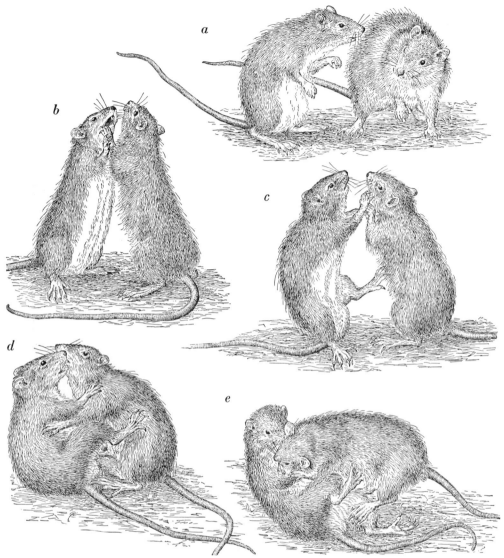

Figure 41.9 Fighting in the common rat, *Rattus norvegicus*. The aggressor initially arches its back (*a*), the pair then push back and forth (*b*), sometimes kicking with the hind feet (*c*). When one is pushed backward (*d*), it may give up, but if not continued fighting may lead to biting (*e*). (From The Fighting Behavior in Animals by I. Eibl-Eibesfeldt. Copyright © by Scientific American, Inc. All rights reserved.)

of females. But the great majority of intra-specific fights do not result in physical damage (Fig. 41.9).

41.4
Behavior Patterns: Communication

Animals often communicate by behavior patterns which mutually affect one another's behavior. In many instances the behavior is of an aggressive nature or is concerned with mating. Two of the most interesting exam-

ples of nonaggressive, nonsexual communication are the systems by which honeybees and fire ants direct other members of the group to a source of food. Members of a bee-

Figure 41.10 The round dance, an alternation of circling first one way and then the other. (After von Frisch.)

hive transmit information regarding the location of a source of food to one another by a special sequence of movements. When a worker bee has found a source of food, it collects food and flies back to the hive. On the vertical surface of the hive, it goes through a dance. If the food is close to the hive the common honeybee circles first in one direction and then in the other in a **round dance** (Fig. 41.10). Other workers then fly out and search in all directions near the hive.

If the food is located at a greater distance, the bee executes a **waggle dance.** She goes through a half circle, then moves in a straight line, wiggling her abdomen from side to side, and finally does a half circle in the other direction. During the straight portion of the dance, the bee produces a series of sounds. The angle that the straight, wiggling portion of the dance makes with the vertical is the same as the angle of flight relative to the sun (Figs. 41.11 and 41.12). Information on the distance to be traveled in that direction is also transmitted by the waggle dance. As shown in Figure 41.12 there is a correlation between the number of waggle dances executed in a

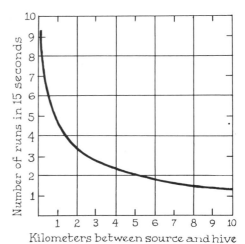

Figure 41.12 The relation between the distance of the food source from the hive and the number of straight rushes per 15 seconds in the wagging dance. As the distance becomes shorter the dance merges into the round dance. (After von Frisch.)

given time and the distance of the food from the hive. An even closer correlation, however, is found between distance and the sound pulses the dancing bee produces. Bees can "hear" substrate vibrations, and sound would seem to be a good way to communicate in the dark of the hive.

The distance to be traveled is "calculated" by the bee on the basis of the flight to the food source, not the return trip. Moreover, the instructions include corrections for wind and large obstacles (Fig. 41.13). The dancing bee also indicates the richness of the food source by how long and vigorously it repeats the dance, and the other bees gain further information about the food source by the smell of the flowers the bee has recently visited. The more primitive social bees, the stingless bees, lay down an odor trail, a series of chemical marks, to the food source; in addition, the collector bee guides other individuals along the trail.

In the food-directing system of the fire ant, communication by chemicals is of prime importance. These chemicals, called **pheromones,** when produced by an individual have an effect on the behavior of other individuals of the same species. When one member of a group has located a source of food, it gathers what it can and starts back toward the nest. As it moves along the ground, it periodically extrudes its stinger and places a small amount of pheromone on the substrate. This substance is produced in a special gland, Dufor's gland,

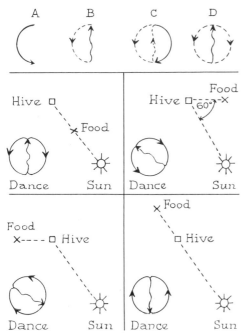

Figure 41.11 The wagging dance. *A* to *D*, The four successive steps of the dance. The following four figures demonstrate the relation of the straight rush to the direction of the food, in which *upward* (toward top of page here) on the vertical surface inside the hive is substituted for *sunward* outdoors. (After von Frisch.)

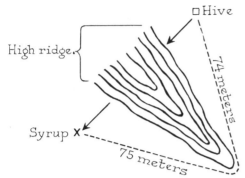

Figure 41.13 The contour lines indicate a high ridge separating the hive from a syrup source. Bees returned to the hive along the dotted line, and in their wagging dance indicated the true direction (heavy arrows), but 149 meters distance. (After von Frisch.)

located in the abdomen of the worker ant. When another fire ant comes across this trail of chemical dashes it becomes very active, follows the trail, and is led to the source of the food.

Other examples of communication between members of a group can be seen in the schooling of fish and the group flight patterns of birds. The importance of visual cues has been established for schooling in some fish, but what controls the sudden group movements of flocks of birds is still a mystery. In both fishes and birds it appears that grouping is an antipredator mechanism. Predators are often able to catch isolated individuals but

are confused by the many movements of the animals making up a group.

Some animals give off chemicals which attract other members of the species to the same area, but not for sexual purposes. Such **aggregation pheromones** are given off by some noxious insects which have warning coloration. Birds and other predators must learn to avoid insects with warning coloration. The crowding of the insects facilitates the learning process.

41.5
Behavior Patterns: Mating

All bisexual animals possess mechanisms for getting egg and sperm together to continue the existence of the species. For some sessile marine animals, such as clams, urchins and tunicates, courtship and mating are simply the releasing of many sperm or eggs into the surrounding waters (where external fertilization takes place) when the animals are chemically stimulated by the presence of a few gametes in the water. Changes in the physical environment induce (via hormones) physiologic changes in many species which prepare the animals so that subsequently specific stimuli elicit the appropriate mating patterns. In other species the presence and movements of individuals of the opposite sex initiate the physiologic changes. Mutual exchanges of

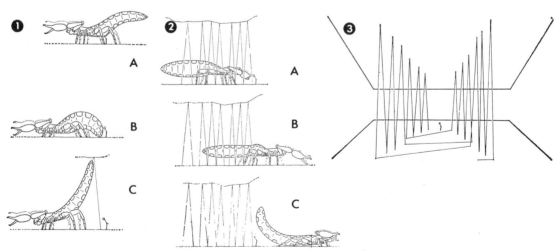

Figure 41.14 Mating in the pseudoscorpion, *Serianus*. Unlike many species of pseudoscorpion, in which the male and female go through a complex dance, a *Serianus* male, in the presence of a female, deposits a spermatophore (*1A* and *B*) and then weaves a web (*1C, 3*) which guides the female to the spermatophore (*2A, B* and *C*). (Courtesy of P. Weygoldt.)

early courtship movements not only **initiate** but also **synchronize** physiologic changes, so that the sexes are ready to mate at the same time.

Further precopulatory behavior patterns (or repetition of the ones effective in physiologic priming) serve two important functions: (1) they **decrease aggressive tendencies** and (2) they establish species and sexual **identification.** The former is needed if two animals are to avoid fighting long enough to mate. Where this condition has not been completely fulfilled, special adaptations are necessary. For example, the male praying mantis is smaller than the female and subject to predatory attack by her. However, mating can continue even after the male's head has been eaten by the female, since the nervous activities controlling copulatory movements are centered in an abdominal ganglion. In some cockroaches and other primitive insects, the female feeds on a special secretion on a part of the male's back, which diverts her attention during copulation. The males of certain predatory flies present the females with little packages of food wrapped up with silken threads. Other members of this group don't bother with the food; the male diverts the female's attention by the presentation of an empty ballon of silk. The ballon both decreases the female's aggressive tendencies and identifies the sex and species of the male presenting it. A web of silk is used by some pseudoscorpions to form a "hallway" to guide the female (Fig. 41.14).

The singing of male birds is well known as a pattern advertising the presence of a territorial male. The song pattern of each species is distinct and presumably functions both to keep other males of that species away and to attract a female of the species to the singing male. Certain fishes, frogs and insects also have mating calls which provide effective cues for **species discrimination.** Female frogs are attracted to calling males of their own species and not to calling males of other, closely related species. This ethologic isolating mechanism prevents the wasting of genetic material.

The bowerbirds of tropical jungles have a very complex courtship behavior. In an

Figure 41.15 Courtship in one species of bower bird. The male builds a bower of sticks (*A*) and decorates it with pebbles and berries (*B*). The female bower bird enters the construction (*C*) and, after the male displays, she sits (*D*) and the birds mate (*E*). The female leaves, builds the nest (*F*) and rears the young birds by herself. (From the Evolution of Bower Birds by E. T. Gilliard. Copyright © by Scientific American, Inc. All rights reserved.)

arena, a special territory where mating takes place, the male sings and displays his bright colors in special short flight movements. (In most birds, nesting and the rearing of young also occur in the territory, and the male shares the tasks of incubating the eggs and feeding the young birds.) After mating, the female bowerbird builds the nest and cares for the brood. In other species, the male's plumage is less brilliantly marked, but he builds and decorates an elaborate display area, thus attracting a female not by his own color, but by forms and colors added to the display area (Fig. 41.15).

41.6
Behavior Patterns: Parental Care

Most animals give little or no care to their offspring. This lack of parental behavior is usually correlated with the production of great numbers of eggs and sperm. Some reptiles and insects place their eggs in special burrows or nests to complete their development, but do not aid the young after they hatch. Female crayfish and other decapod crustaceans attach their eggs to their abdominal pleopods and aerate them until the eggs hatch. The young of some scorpions remain with the mother, clinging to her back, until after their first molt. Care-giving behavior between one generation and the next is well developed in the social insects, birds and mammals. Many young birds respond to tactile and visual stimuli given by the adult by gaping—stretching upward toward the parent with open mouth. The parent responds to this gaping by feeding the young.

The extensive exchanges between mother and young in primates often have long-term effects on the behavioral development of the

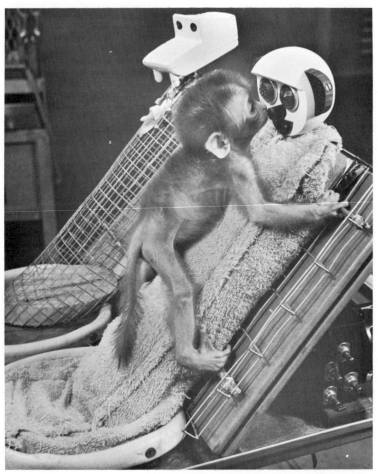

Figure 41.16   Young rhesus monkey, reared without a real mother, clinging to the surrogate used in raising it. (Photography by Gordon Coster. *In* H. F. Harlow: Scientific American, *200*:68−74, 1959. Copyright © 1959 by Scientific American, Inc. All rights reserved.)

Figure 41.17 Abnormal grouping of rhesus monkeys. These young animals were raised without real mothers. For many months when placed together in a cage, they did not play as normal monkeys do, but spent almost all their time huddled in odd positions. (Photography by Gordon Coster. *In* H. F. Harlow, and M. K. Harlow: Scientific American, *207*:136−146, 1962. Copyright © 1962 by Scientific American, Inc. All rights reserved.)

young. Indeed, contact between a young rhesus monkey and its mother is necessary if the animal is to develop socially. Monkeys reared by artificial mothers (Fig. 41.16) do not interact normally with other members of the species (Fig. 41.17), nor are they able to mate when mature. The young of some primates receive attention from several of the adult females of the troop, which is the social unit, consisting of several adult males, three to four adult females and their offspring. Initially the mother will not allow others to hold the infant, but soon it is held and carried by other females, each of which nudges, touches, smells and licks it. If the infant squeals or begins to struggle, another female (usually the mother) comes over and takes it. The touch and color of the fur and the movements of the mother elicit a clinging response in the infant; the infant's color pattern elicits the interest and movements of the female, which then facilitates clinging.

41.7

Behavior Patterns: Dominance Hierarchies

In many vertebrates and a few arthropods, members of a local group have well organized social interactions, which help to decrease aggressive activity among members of the group. In the simplest form of social hierarchy, one individual (α) is dominant over all others, a second (β) is dominant over all except α, etc. **Dominance** is expressed by win-

ning in aggressive interaction, by having first chance at the available food and mating partners, and by having first choice of nesting locations. The other animals are **subordinate** and either retreat from a more dominant individual or assume a submissive posture. The most dominant animal is often, though not necessarily, a leader of the group.

An animal's position in a hierarchy may be a function not only of its size, but also of its sex, individual temperament, immediate physiologic condition, and behavioral interactions outside its social group. A chicken can maintain distinct positions in a number of groups at the same time, but its positions in all groups can be altered by interactions with chickens outside these groups. Thus when a chicken loses an encounter with a very aggressive animal outside its usual social group, it subsequently may lose additional encounters within its social group.

Hierarchies have been observed in a number of invertebrates, but the organization within small groups of crayfish appears to be the clearest case of individual recognition-dependent structure. Straight-line hierarchies develop after a small number of fights and subsequent interactions are mostly exchanges of displays of mild threats.

41.8

Social Systems

True social systems occur only in certain insects, birds and mammals. In these, care of some sort or exchanges of special intragroup behavior are extended to overlapping generations, and specialization of roles occurs. In insect colonies, reproduction is limited to one or a few individuals and there is a separation of duties among the nonreproductive individuals. Chemical communication by pheromones is well developed in social insects. The social structure of the colony is developed and maintained by **trophallaxis,** a mutual exchange of food and licking of secretions among the members of the colony.

Termites. The termite colony begins when a pair of winged primary reproductives shed their wings and set up housekeeping (Fig. 41.18). The first young raised by this pair retain the nymphal morphology throughout life and are sterile workers. They take over all the work, including nest building and feeding the primaries. The primaries continue to reproduce, increasing the population of the colony. If the colony becomes large, a few of the nymphs (the secondary reproductives) develop wing buds and become sexually mature.

All the termites produce some secretions and these are continually licked by the workers and young nymphs. In this way, the colony as a whole develops a blended odor, distinct from that of any other colony, and it is used by the members of a colony in recognizing strangers. The reproductives produce especially copious secretions that are sought after by the workers. The secretions of the primary reproductives contain a pheromone that prevents sexual maturity in their offspring. Secondary reproductives appear only after the colony is so large that the secretions of the king and queen are extremely diluted among the colony members.

Ants. Each ant colony is founded by a winged queen after she has mated with a winged male shortly after leaving the parent colony. She sheds her wings and uses the nourishment of stored fat and degenerating wing muscles while rearing the first group of workers, which are small, stunted individuals. These workers take care of the subsequent young, leaving the nest, gathering food, and doing all the work of the colony. As nourishment becomes more plentiful, later offspring are of normal size. Most of the larvae mature as workers, but in certain species soldiers, honey ants, and other kinds **(castes)** appear (Fig. 41.19). Trophallaxis is again the major integrating mechanism of the colony.

Honeybees. The queen honeybee is unable to establish a colony or to survive at all without workers. She appears in an established colony, flies out of the hive, is fertilized, and then returns to the hive. The presence of more than one queen in a colony does not last long; swarming occurs, in which part of the colony leaves with the old queen. Al-

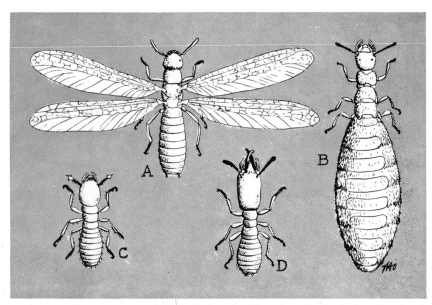

Figure 41.18 Castes of termites. *A,* Male (king), before shedding wings. *B,* Female (queen), after shedding wings. *C,* Worker. *D,* Soldier. Workers and soldiers are sterile individuals of either sex.

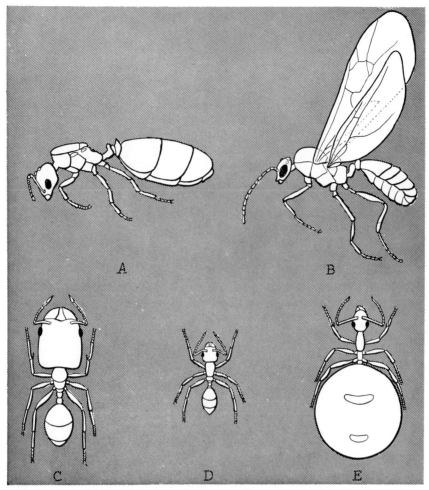

Figure 41.19   Castes of ants. *A*, Female (queen), after shedding wings. *B*, Male. Note large eyes and long antennae. *C*, Soldier. *D*, Worker (stunted workers may be still smaller). *E*, Honey ant, which hangs motionless in the nest, is fed excessively when food is plentiful and serves as a food source when food is scarce. The last three categories are all sterile females.

though there is only one caste of sterile female bees, these workers are differentiated by age into physiologically different groups, as described on page 267. If one age group is removed from the colony, however, the time scale of development in the others is altered; sometimes individuals will revert to a younger stage so as to restore the hive's balance.

The only substance known to influence the structure of a bee colony is secreted by the mandibular glands of the queen. This secretion prevents the sexual maturity of workers and also prevents the raising of new queens by workers. If the queen, or her mandibular glands, is removed, a number of the younger workers will develop sexually to the point where they can produce a few eggs. Such reproductive workers apparently also secrete

the antiqueen substance, since no more appear after the first few. In the meantime, however, the workers have also modified the environment of some of the last eggs or larvae produced by the queen so that they eventually mature as full-fledged queens. New queens may also appear in normal, queen-containing colonies. If the population becomes very large, the nurse bees set aside a few eggs to be raised as queens. Cell walls are removed to make larger chambers and the larvae in these chambers are fed exclusively on royal jelly for the full six days of their larval life.

When a queen and a portion of a colony fly away from the hive to find a new home, an interesting democratic process occurs. The **swarm** moves away and temporarily settles on

Figure 41.20   Grooming in the rhesus monkey. One monkey is looking for and removing ectoparasites and dead tissue from the other. The roles of groomer and groomee will be reversed after a few minutes. (Courtesy of S. Altmann.)

a branch or shrub. Most of the swarm remains there, but scouts fly out in all directions, seeking a suitable place to build the new hive. As they find locations, they fly back to the swarm and do a tail-wagging dance to indicate the location of the potential hive-site. Some of the other bees then fly off and inspect this site. The swarm does not take the "word" of the first scout to return; each site is inspected by a number of bees. Scouts inspect the sites indicated by other scouts, and may change the site they "advertise." When a large majority of the scouts indicate the same site, the swarm flies to that place and starts building a new hive.

The sex of termites is determined by the usual XX-XY chromosomal mechanism, and half of each caste are male and half female. Most ants and bees, however, are female. Males are produced only from unfertilized eggs and are haploid. They appear only with the female reproductives in the ant colony, as part of the seasonal swarming. Male bees are produced sporadically and remain in the hive as drones, doing no work. Their only function is to be there when a new queen emerges. They chase her on the nuptial flight and, high in the air, one of them mates with her. In the fall, as the colony prepares for winter, the drones are expelled from the hive.

Primates.   The social group of most primates, the **troop,** consists of a varying number of adult males and females and their offspring. Unlike insect colonies, a troop always includes several reproducing females. The troop is usually well organized as a dominance hierarchy and often the α male is a true **leader**—he determines the path of movement of the troop, helps to determine the outcome of intragroup flights, and initiates defensive action against predators. An important behavior in maintaining troop structure is **mutual grooming,** during which one animal parts the fur of another, cleans dead tissue from wounds, and removes all visible ectoparasites (Fig. 41.20).

41.9
Factors Affecting Behavior

Morphologic Limitations.   One factor that is often ignored in behavioral studies, perhaps because it seems so obvious, is the limitation that an animal's structure places upon the movements it can execute. Chimpanzees reared by humans and treated as "one of the family" show remarkable learning ability and adopt as many social graces as a human child during the first three or four years. However, the number of human words a chimp-child can utter is small, not so much from limitations in the ape's brain but as a result of the structure of its vocal cords.

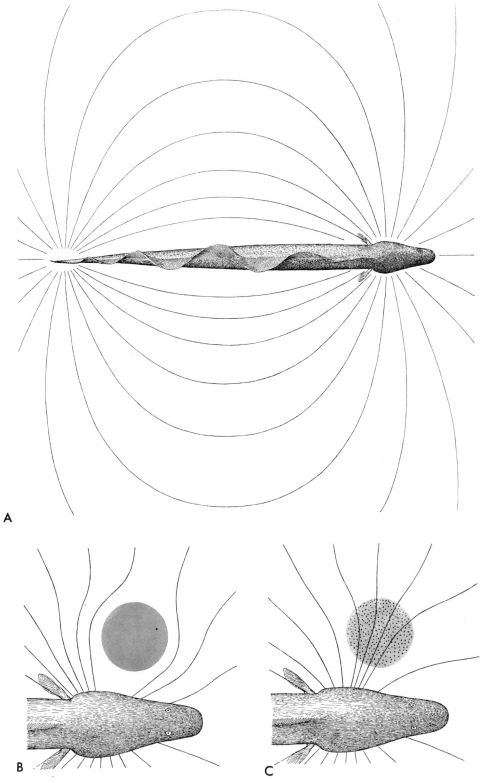

A

B   C

Figure 41.21 Electrolocation in the fish *Gymnarchus*. The fish generates an electric field, its tail negative to the head (*A*). Objects that conduct less (*B*) or more (*C*) electricity than the surrounding water distort the electric field and this is detected by special sense organs along the sides of the fish. (From Electric Location by Fishes by H. W. Lissmann. Copyright © by Scientific American, Inc. All rights reserved.)

Stimuli. What an animal does is markedly affected by changes in its surrounding environment. Such stimuli may **initiate** and **control** behavior patterns in many ways. Each sense organ has evolved sensitivity to some particular physical factor (sound, light, touch, taste, smell, heat, etc.). What elicits a change in behavior in one species may be totally ineffective in another. Although sounds of 70,000 cycles per second normally have no effect on our ears, bats produce such high frequency sounds and, by listening to the echos bounding back from objects in the area in front of them, they locate these objects by "echolocation" (see also p. 436). Noctuid moths, in turn, depend upon detecting these high frequency sounds to avoid bats. The entire sequence of hunting by bats and avoidance by moths is a silent show to us, but special electronic equipment can bring these sounds into our sensory world.

Many arthropods can detect and respond to ultraviolet light, which is undetectable by most vertebrates. An even more intriguing sensory system is found in several families of fish (Gymnotids and Mormoryids) which produce electric fields around themselves and detect changes in these fields which result from the presence of objects that are better or worse conductors of electricity than the waters the fish live in (Fig. 41.21). This **electrolocation** system is as ingenious as the echolocation systems used by bats in air and porpoises in water.

The question of stimulus discrimination is also of importance in understanding animal behavior. How much can a stimulus be altered before the change is detected by the animal? How accurate are the sense organs in detecting differences between stimuli? An octopus can readily distinguish a horizontal from a vertical rectangle, but has great difficulty in differentiating a rectangle leaning 45 degrees to the right from one leaning 45 degrees to the left. This may be correlated with the structure of the retinal units of the octopus eye. These units and the interneurons between the retina and the optic lobe of the brain are oriented in the dorsoventral and horizontal axes of the eye; almost none are oriented obliquely.

41.10
Types of Responses

The perception of a stimulus is often followed by a behavioral change, the **response.** However, a given environmental change may not elicit an identical response each time it occurs. Some of the reasons for this variability will be examined in later sections.

The simplest reaction an animal can give to a stimulus is an undirected change in its rate of movement. Such responses, termed **kineses,** may act to keep an animal in the appropriate microclimate. For example, the common wood louse tends to remain motionless when the relative humidity is high (Fig. 41.22). This simple reaction keeps the wood louse in an environment in which it does not

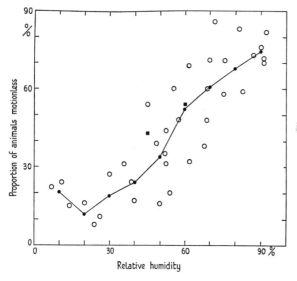

Figure 41.22 Locomotor activity of the woodlouse, *Porcellio*, relative to humidity. This simple kinesis keeps the animals in areas of high relative humidity. (Courtesy of Fraenkel & Gunn.)

lose much moisture. Klinokinesis is another type of reaction to a stimulus in which the rate of the animal's turning changes.

Other simple reactions to stimuli, termed **taxes,** are movements of the whole animal in relation to the location of the source of the stimulus. Such reactions often depend upon equalizing the input of the stimulus to two symmetrically placed sense organs. Some insects show a negative phototaxis, and move toward the side which is receiving less light and thus away from the light. Combinations of several taxes can produce more complex orienting movements (Fig. 41.23). Some animals maintain a constant angle to the source of a stimulus while they move. This **telotaxis** is observed in the daily movements of social insects, such as bees and ants. It is of particular importance to animals that use the sun as a reference point in maintaining direction.

Taxes and kineses adequately describe some elementary orientational movements, but most behavior patterns involve slightly more complex responses to stimuli. When an adequate stimulus affects a sense organ, a simple movement of one portion of the animal may result. These **reflexes** are characterized by the relatively simple role that the central nervous system plays in their execution (see also pp. 351 and 533). The knee jerk in man is a well known reflex, in which stimulus input–reaction output is not greatly affected by action potentials from the brain. Instances in which the sequence of input-output is not altered by influences from other parts of the nervous system are not very common.

Most behavior patterns involve some integrative action of the central nervous system. The brain or even a single ganglion may alter the pattern of nerve impulses so that the output is not simply a copy of the input. Such

Figure 41.24 Graylag goose retrieving and attempting to retrieve eggs. The stereotyped movements involved in egg retrieval can be elicited by oversized artificial eggs. (After Tinbergen.)

integration is a result of the nature of the synaptic connections between neurons. Stimuli may not only initiate but also control in part the execution of patterns of movement. The adaptive value of behavior patterns would be much less if they were not affected by the conditions present in the environment at the time of their execution.

The stimuli that initiate a complex pattern of movements are often complex themselves, and the integrative action of the central nervous system can be observed either on the input side (complex stimuli) or on the output side (complex patterns of muscle coordination). How complex movements can be altered by stimuli can be seen in the egg-retrieving behavior of the graylag goose (Fig. 41.24), which builds its nest on the ground. When an egg is beyond the edge of the nest, a bird sitting on the eggs in the nest will reach out and pull the egg into the nest with its bill. This movement is stereotyped in the outward movement of the bird's head, but the motion inward can be modified in its horizontal component by feedback from tactile receptors on the ventral surface of the bird's bill. This feedback enables the bird to alter its movement as the egg tends to roll to one side or the other. The stimulus that initiates the sequence of movements is visual (the sight of the egg), whereas the inputs that partially modify the execution of the movements are tactile.

In another experiment, model eggs were presented to birds to find out what "an-egg-

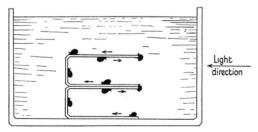

Figure 41.23 Orientation of the marine snail, *Littorina.* The animal shows a negative phototaxis when horizontal, negative geotaxis on the vertical wall, and a positive phototaxis when upside-down. (Courtesy of Fraenkel & Gunn.)

to-be-rolled-back" looks like. The visual characteristics of an "egg" could be widely varied. The model could be round, or even rectangular, although the normal oval shape was preferred. The size could be altered considerably, and there appeared to be no upper limit to the size of egg which a bird would try to retrieve. Amusing sequences were observed as birds tried in vain to pull in model eggs larger than the birds themselves. Similar reactions to **supernormal stimuli** have been observed in other situations in which selection pressure for closer stimulus discrimination is apparently missing. The color pattern of the test eggs could be varied from plain to checkered to speckled. The speckling present on normal eggs elicited more responses than a plain egg. In choosing between two eggs placed side by side, birds apparently add up the several visual parameters: the shape, size and coloration of the eggs, as well as their positions relative to the nest. The stimulus value of an object was found to be equal to the sum of the values of its various features.

In many behavior patterns, once the correct stimulus has been perceived a complex pattern of movements can be executed with minimal feedback from the environment. The perceiving of the stimulus appears to **release** the execution of the whole pattern. Many species of small fresh-water fish show a rapid flight reaction when chemicals from the damaged skin of various species of other small fish are detected. Predator damage to any small fish signals danger to all. Some shellfish show a complex escape reaction when the tube feet of a given (few) species of starfish touch their shell. The stimulus initiates the pattern, but does not further influence it.

The above examples concern the elicitation of a response by a stimulus, an increase in the probability of occurrence of the behavior pattern. But a stimulus may also **inhibit** a response, may decrease the probability of its occurrence. In some species of hermit crabs, attack by one crab is inhibited when the other crab lowers its body to the substrate.

The same stimulus may not consistently release the same behavior pattern in an animal because of changes in its physiologic condition, its past experience, or changes in the configurational or immediate **context.** An animal does not in general perceive an isolated stimulus, but rather many types of sensory input accompany any specific change in the environment and these accompanying

inputs may alter the response to the stimulus. A young thrush presents an open mouth to any projection above a certain size—this would normally be the parent's bill as it gets ready to feed the young bird. Yet the same projection is more effective in releasing the behavior if it is (1) moving slightly, (2) at a certain horizontal distance from the nest and (3) a certain vertical distance above the eye of the young bird.

The fact that a number of aspects of the environment may alter an animal's response in a given situation has led some workers to consider the configurational aspects of the many stimuli together to be of prime importance. In other words, the total configuration is the stimulus. Such **gestalt** perception is particularly evident in higher mammals. Infant human beings beyond 20 weeks of age appear to use a gestalt type of visual representation. The configurational effect of a complex pattern elicits a stronger response than the sum of the responses to the parts making up the pattern when the parts are presented separately. Infants of 10 weeks of age use heterogeneous summation in their response to visual objects; i.e., the response to a complex visual object equals the sum of the responses to the separate parts making up the object.

41.11
Physiologic Condition

The behavior shown by an animal may be greatly affected by its **physiologic condition.** A snake that has just eaten a rabbit is unlikely to show feeding behavior for some days, irrespective of the stimuli presented to the snake. Conversely a dog that has not ingested water for 24 hours will be very likely to show behavior associated with drinking.

The complex of organs which secrete hormones have a profound influence on behavior. The sex hormones secreted by the testes or ovaries of mammals **prime** the animal so that when the proper stimuli are detected, sexual behavior occurs. Without such priming, the stimuli would have little or no effect, or could elicit completely different responses. In turn, the secretion of hormones is affected by sensory input. In some birds, such as the Australian budgerigars, the hormonal systems of the female are activated when the female hears the song of the male, and this hormonal activation results in ovulation. Subsequently, following some days of hormonal action, the female will show sexual responses to the male. Females that have not heard the male song and have not been primed by hormonal action show no response to courting males.

Nesting and parental behavior is also strongly influenced by the levels of several hormones. In the canary, the male and female are initially affected by longer day length, and sex hormones are produced in both the male and female. The male begins showing courtship behavior, which stimulates the female to start building a nest. Her ovaries start developing rapidly at this time. Then, due to the presence of estrogens and other hormones, the feathers on the female's breast begin to shed, as a broodpatch is formed. After the nest is finished, the female assumes the copulatory position which elicits copulatory behavior in the male. The female is subsequently stimulated by the touch of the nest, and egg laying follows after further, hormonally controlled physiologic changes.

In many crustaceans, the hormonal interactions which prime the animal for sexual behavior are even more complex. Many crustaceans mate only during a short period following a female molt. Males show no interest in females that are not ready to molt, probably due to the lack of a male-stimulating chemical given off by the premolt female. Females vigorously fight any errant male that shows sexual behavior when she is not "ready." The hormones controlling molting thus affect both sexual responses and aggressive behavior (recently molted crustaceans retreat more readily in fights). The chain of hormonal control may extend even further in certain parasites and their vertebrate hosts. The parasites are affected by the hormone level of their host in such a way that the parasite's behavior is primed to show the appropriate patterns at the same time the host is altering its behavior owing to its own hormone level.

41.12
Rhythmic Phenomena

A number of biologic characteristics of animals fluctuate in some regular fashion. Certain kinds of behavior (mating, migrations) recur annually. Some animals show a pronounced decrease in activity and metabolism during winter—a phenomenon called **hibernation.** In some others there may be lunar, tidal or daily rhythms of change in behavior, correlated with the movement of the moon, the tides or the sun. **Tidal rhythms** are shown by many marine organisms living in the intertidal zone, whose activity patterns must be correlated with the movements of the tide if they are to obtain their food yet avoid the dangers of being stranded on dry land or being drowned. Some intertidal crabs continue to show tidal rhythms of activity even when removed to an aquarium in a laboratory and maintained under apparently constant conditions.

Organisms, and even parts of organisms, usually do not function at a constant rate over the entire 24 hours of a day. Repeated sequences of events which occur at about 24-hour intervals have been termed **circadian rhythms.** It is important to note that these rhythms have a period of *about* 24 hours, *almost never exactly* 24 hours, when the organism is placed in constant conditions. In nature, the activity cycle is entrained or lined up with the cycle of physical events which determine the length of our day. The daily changes in light are the physical phenomenon used by most organisms as a "zeitgeber" (*zeit,* time; *geben,* to give). Many animals, when placed under apparently constant conditions, continue to show rhythmic changes in activity but the period is often 23 or 25 hours. The animal's day tends to shift relative to the real day when the animal has no zeitgeber.

Some animals are diurnal, showing their greatest activity during the day, whereas others are nocturnal and are most active during the hours of darkness. Certain insects exhibit diurnal variations in pigmentation, and they continue to show these cyclic variations when placed in continuous darkness. A diurnal cycle of deposition and utilization of glycogen in the liver of the rabbit and the mouse has been detected. Some spiders show a daily rhythm of secretion of neurohormones; preparations of nervous tissues isolated from the animal and maintained in vitro continue to show such cyclic production. The vertical distribution of many small marine organisms is also subject to a diurnal cycle—they tend to concentrate near the surface at night and to go into deeper water during the day. Their movements, however, begin before any light cues are received.

In birds and bees, timing devices or "biologic clocks" are highly developed and can serve in navigation. Bees are not only able to find their way from hive to feeding ground by using the direction of the sun to guide them, but they can make suitable corrections for changes in the sun's position as the day advances, even when they remain in the hive. They can correct their celestial navigation for the time of day.

In addition to such cyclic phenomena, changes in activity at the neuronal level are equally significant in the behavior of animals. Most neurons have a low level of activity which is rather constant until a stimulus elicits a change in that level of activity. Sensory cells alter their rate of discharge when the proper environmental change stimulates them, and interneurons are stimulated by other neurons. Certain neurons or groups of neurons discharge very regularly at a somewhat higher rate. Such **pacemakers** are especially well known for vital body organs such as the heart of crustaceans. The heartbeat in the lobster is neurogenic, controlled by a small ganglion located in the dorsal wall of the heart. The ganglion is made up of only nine neurons, and of these the four smaller neurons appear to be the true pacemakers. Some property intrinsic to these cells regularly initiates the discharge of impulses which leads to a heartbeat.

41.13
Learning, Conditioning and Imprinting

Past events vary in their effects on an animal's behavior. In some cases they alter the individual's behavior for most of its life; in others they have an effect only on those events that immediately follow. The latter type is most obvious in **chains of interactions,** in which behavior by one individual is the stimulus for an act by a second animal, and this act is the stimulus for the next act by the first animal (Fig. 41.25). Often, if a chain of behavioral exchanges is interrupted, the two individuals must "go back to the first act and start over." Such chains of interactions, with a number of patterns executed by male and female, are especially common in mating behavior, for the wastage of genetic material is too serious to depend upon just one stimulus-response sequence.

Comparable sequences are also evident in predator-prey interactions. The bee-hunting digger wasp is initially attracted to a potential prey by a particular visual pattern. After moving toward the visual stimulus to about 10 cm. downwind from the bee, the wasp can then be stimulated by the odor of the bee. After this chemical stimulation, the wasp lunges forward and must then receive tactile stimuli. The final stinging movement is not carried out unless the wasp's touch receptors perceive the correct "bee pattern." Hermit crabs fight by exchanging visual displays, stereotyped movements which change the behavior of other members of the species. The reactions shown by one crab to the movements of another depend, to some degree, upon the previous acts executed by the pair. In the aggressive interactions of rhesus monkeys, the "meaning" of a display can be dependent upon acts which happened five or more acts previously.

Frequently when a stimulus is presented a number of times in succession, the animal's response to the stimulus gradually diminishes and becomes less frequent. This **habituation** is not a result of muscle fatigue or sensory failure, but of changes in the integrative action of the central nervous system. Marine polychaete worms living in tubes pull back into their tubes rapidly when a shadow passes over or when they are mechanically disturbed. On successive stimulations, the response becomes less regular and then no longer occurs. The curves of habituation to visual and tactile stimuli are different, illustrating that the decrease in response is not due to muscle fatigue.

Learning is a relatively long-lasting change in behavior as a result of past experience. Laboratory experiments have shown that learning is possible in almost all animal phyla, and field experiments have shown the importance of learning in many natural situations. Two general types of learning procedures have been used in the laboratory and illustrate two ways in which learning takes place in nature. In **classic conditioning,** a stimulus is presented and the natural response occurs. A second stimulus (the conditioned stimulus) is paired with the first and after a number of pairings, the second stimulus elicits the response that originally was shown only to the first stimulus. In **operant conditioning,** a particular act is rewarded (or punished) when it occurs, thus increasing (or decreasing) the subsequent probability of

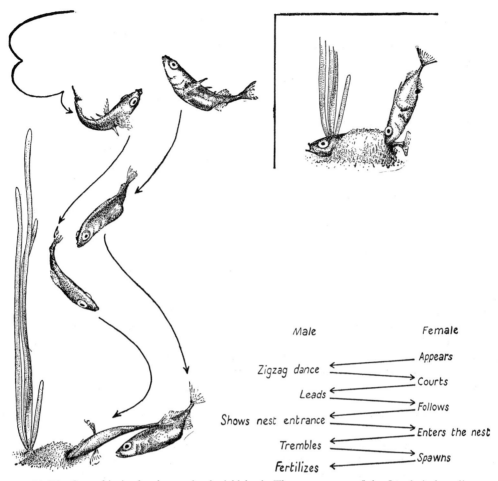

Figure 41.25 Courtship in the three-spined stickleback. The appearance of the female in breeding condition elicits a zigzag dance by a territory holding male. The female follows the male, who leads her to the entrance of the nest he has built. When the female is in the nest, the male's tactile prodding elicits egg laying (inset). (After Tinbergen.)

occurrence of that act. The trial-and-error type of learning which occurs in nature is usually more like operant conditioning than classic conditioning. In both types of conditioning, only the probability of occurrence of a certain act under certain conditions is changed. For example, young chicks initially peck at almost any small object, but they learn not to peck at inedible objects. The probability of pecking when certain visual stimuli are perceived is decreased.

Learning affects the behavior of vertebrates more frequently than that of invertebrates. Young chimpanzees learn from older individuals how to use a clump of lichens as a sponge to get water from within cracks in rocks and how to use a moistened twig to draw termites out of a hole. Sparrows in northern Europe regularly "steal" milk from bottles left on doorsteps. This pattern, first observed in England a few years ago, has spread rapidly to sparrows in other areas. Apparently the pattern is learned by one bird **mimicking** another. This involves the execution of a rather complex act following the observation of another animal performing that act. A similar action has been termed **local enhancement,** whereby the movements of one individual simply draws the attention of another to a certain area. A third, related phenomenon is **social facilitation,** whereby the execution of an act by one individual increases the probability that an observing individual will execute the same act. We have all experienced this; when one person in a room yawns, the probability of others yawning is increased embarrassingly.

Learning has been observed in the behavior of many invertebrates. Some species of digger wasp place captured prey in a burrow as food for their larvae. The female wasp learns to recognize the location of the burrow by objects near the entrance. After each trip to the burrow, she flys around the location several times, probably as an aid in memorizing the characteristics of the location. Moreover, in some species, the female remembers the locations of several burrows at the same time, as she is tending more than one larva. Even the neuronally deficient starfish has been shown to learn to alter its responses to light and thus increase the probability of finding food in a particular portion of its environment.

The effects of experience early in an animal's life are of particular importance. Certain insects lay their eggs only on the same species of plant which they fed upon as larvae. Similarly, adult salmon return, after several years in the ocean, to the stream in which they grew up, guided by chemical orientation. Often such experiences can have an effect only during limited **critical periods.** If the animal does not experience these events during these periods of its life, the later occurrence of the events has no effect or altered effects.

Many birds and mammals show a special learning phenomenon called **imprinting,** characterized by a very short critical period early in life. Experiences during a short period of early life restrict the social preferences the animal will show later in life. Young birds and mammals are stimulated by visual and/or sound patterns and follow such patterns as they move. Normally the pattern would be that of the animal's parent. The animals later preferentially show social responses to the pattern they themselves had followed. The idea of restricting sexual behavior by such early experiences has been overemphasized, but it is clear that the object a bird or mammal follows during certain hours after hatching or birth is later given some preference as a social partner. In other animals, **socialization** (learning which animals are to be reacted to as conspecific individuals) occurs more slowly and in several steps.

A critical period of the opposite type has been observed in young cuttlefish. Newly hatched *Sepia* normally attack and eat only one kind of shrimp. During the first month, *Sepia* cannot learn to stop attacking this kind of shrimp or to redirect their attacks. Later,

after certain parts of the brain have become interconnected, such learning is easily accomplished.

41.14
Genetic Control of Behavior

Behavior may be under genetic control on either the input or output side. Sensory input is limited by the genetically controlled capabilities of sense organs and their connections within the central nervous system. Similarly, the patterns of nervous activity responsible for a particular pattern of movement may be the result of the inherited characteristics of the nervous system. Cuttlefish, for example, attack certain species of shrimp without prior experience. The central nervous system appears to be structured from birth in such a way that the correct visual input elicits the attack pattern. It is clear that just as the ability to learn is built into a nervous system, the execution of innate behavior patterns is a result of the characteristics of a nervous system, which were determined during embryologic development by genetic directions interacting with the milieu of the embryo. To call behavior innate is misleading only if the label is considered a final answer and inhibits further research.

Innate acts in vertebrates vary from simple reflexes, such as removing one's hand from a hot stove, to complex patterns, such as bird songs. Although learning is important in the songs of some birds, others sing the proper pattern of sounds even when they have been raised from hatching in complete isolation. In other species the species' normal song is sung only if the singer is allowed to hear it a few times. Subsequent deafening does not alter the song pattern. Deafening before the bird has sung does prevent the development of the species' normal song. Apparently the neuromuscular and proprioceptive activity which produces the song must be compared to a sound template in the central nervous system.

Invertebrates show more **innate patterns** of behavior. The lack of parental care or even of contact with members of the same species during early development necessitates a certain degree of innate control. Recently metamorphosed young hermit crabs usually orient correctly and show all the elements of entering behavior the very first time they come in contact with an empty gastropod shell. The sounds produced by crickets reared in isolation and deafened to prevent their hearing even their own sounds are the same as the sounds produced by normal crickets.

Experiments in behavioral genetics have shown that acts can be affected by just a few genes, although most patterns are under polygenic control. Individuals of *Drosophila melanogaster* may be positively or negatively geotropic (tend to move down or up in a gravitational field) and this difference is controlled by just three genes. When selection for strong positive and negative geotropism has been carried out for five or six generations and the flies are subsequently put together, the positive individuals tend to mate with other positive individuals and negative ones with negative ones. The flies are sexually isolated after just a few generations of strong selection for this behavioral trait.

41.15
Methods of Studying Behavior

All behavior patterns are based ultimately upon neuronal activities. By removing, stimulating and recording the activity of neurons, neurophysiologists seek to understand this basis. Nerve recordings can establish the limits of sensory input available to the central nervous system of an animal. Behavioral tests may be unable to distinguish between an animal that is incapable of detecting a particular stimulus and an animal that simply is not responding under the particular test conditions. By monitoring neuronal activity one can determine what physical changes actually result in the generation of action potentials in a given sense organ (Fig. 41.26).

Electrical stimulation of parts of the central nervous system may produce complex patterns of behavior. Although the complexity of the central nervous system makes it difficult to interpret the results of such experiments, the location of the neural pathways involved in the control of the movements can be established. When **implanted electrodes** are left in place in the brain of an awake, freely moving animal (Fig. 41.27), the animal can be repeatedly stimulated with impulses of different strength. By observing the relation between stimulation of a known area and the observed behavior or mood of the animal, one can gain some insight into the actual workings of the brain.

In many species of mammals stimulation of a certain portion of the midbrain can serve as a reward. Human subjects report that this part of the brain is a "pleasure center," that

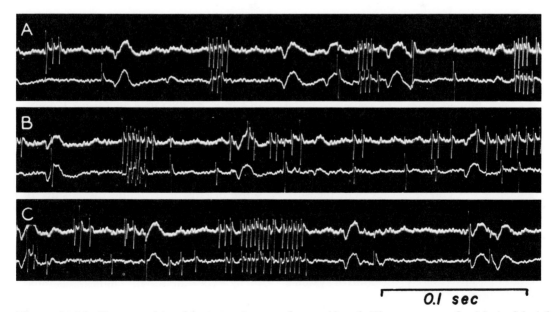

0.1 sec

Figure 41.26 Nervous activity of the tympanic nerve of a noctuid moth. The upper trace of activity is of the left "ear" of the moth, the lower trace the right. The response seen is due to the approach of an echolocating (moth-eating) bat. In records (*A*) and (*B*) the difference in left and right tympanic activity indicates that the bat is approaching from the left. A burst of activity (*C*) is the response to a bat "buzz" rather close to the moth. (Courtesy of K. D. Roeder.)

Figure 41.27 Electrical stimulation of attack behavior. The rooster is stimulated by electrodes implanted in a particular part of its brain. It starts to move toward the keeper and, as stimulation is continued, it attacks. (Courtesy of E. von Holst.)

electrical stimulation of this area does not produce sensations of sound, light or odor but of pure pleasure. This obviously potent means of controlling behavior has been used to a very limited extent to relieve suicidal tendencies in individuals with extreme manic-depressive tendencies. Before asking for such a means of "getting kicks," one should be aware of the fate of a rat permitted to stimulate implanted electrodes in its brain by pressing a bar at one end of its cage. The pleasure lasts as long as the rat is alive, but it slowly dies of starvation and exhaustion as it fails to sleep or eat—pleasuring itself to death.

Another method of studying behavior combines some concepts of neurophysiology, ethology and psychology; the **control systems analysis** method involves making systematic changes in the sensory input of an animal and observing the changes in output in a limited segment of its behavioral repertoire. The resulting diagrammatic representations

of input-output relationships often rely upon feedback loops and other cybernetic phenomena. As an example, the control of the attack movements in the praying mantis is outlined in Figure 41.28. Once the forward movement of the forelegs has started, there is no further guidance from the sensory inputs obtained during the strike. Visual and proprioceptive inputs determine the direction in which the legs move. By removing the proprioceptive sense organs or by fixing the posture of the mantis, the effect of specific patterns of input upon the attack pattern (output) can be determined.

Psychologists are also concerned with determining relationships of input to output. In their experiments the alterations imposed upon the animal often affect the central nervous system rather than the pattern of peripheral input, and in interpreting the results much emphasis is placed upon the influence of past experience. An attempt is

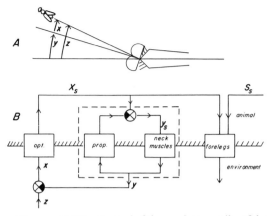

Figure 41.28 Control of the predatory strike of the praying mantis. Optic information is combined with proprioceptive information to determine a strike angle. The optic deficit (x) is a result of unequal input from the two eyes, while the proprioceptive deficit (y) is a result of unequal stimulation of hair plates, postural receptors on the neck. (After Mittelstaedt.)

made to control the environment of the animal as completely as possible in order to determine what factors are important in controlling behavior.

In the past, comparative psychologists were largely concerned with learning processes in the white rat. In recent years, their attention has turned to the behavior of other species and to a variety of behavioral phenomena. One idea which arose from early psychologic work was the all-pervading stimulus-response theory, which sought to explain all behavior as a series of reactions to stimuli. It was axiomatic that every stimulus caused a response and to explain behavior one looked simply for the proper stimulus or set of stimuli. The importance of stimuli and responses is readily apparent, but animals are more than a collection of sets of stimulus-response reactions.

The **ethologic** school demands that the natural behavior of a species be carefully observed before experimentation is initiated. Knowledge of an animal's behavior in nature makes it possible to recognize those patterns (or the lack of them) under experimental conditions. The ethologist, perhaps more than other students of behavior, is interested in the evolution of behavior. A concern for the biologic significance of behavior patterns follows from this interest in how the patterns have evolved. Because many of the biologically important behavior patterns studied by ethologists appeared to be more the product of genetic expression and less a result of learning, early ethologists tended to overemphasize the innate qualities of behavior. Most workers today recognize the importance of both genes and experience.

The behavior an animal shows at any moment is the result of many factors. As a result of past selective forces (evolution) the animal has a particular morphologic, biochemical and neuronal structure. To a greater or lesser extent, this structure is continually altered in its functional characteristics by experience and by hormonal and other physiologic changes. If the sum of these factors results in maintaining the animal in the proper condition, stimuli from the biotic and abiotic environment will then elicit particular behavior patterns.

QUESTIONS

1. Why should precopulatory behavior often consist of a long sequence of interactions?
2. How can the ability to learn help animals in their daily life?
3. What is the function of aggressive behavior?
4. What are the similarities and differences between cleaning symbiosis and grooming behavior?
5. Give examples of the use of the different sense organs in animal communication.
6. What are some similarities in the orientation systems of bats and the fish *Gymnarchus*?
7. Distinguish between gestalt and heterogeneous summation as types of perception.

ANNOTATED REFERENCES

Hinde, R. A.: Animal Behaviour. New York, McGraw-Hill Book Co., 1966. A good, recent textbook combining psychologic and ethologic data.

Marler, P., and W. J. Hamilton: Mechanisms of Animal Behavior. New York, John Wiley & Sons, Inc., 1966. An excellent and readable textbook on most aspects of behavior.

Tinbergen, N.: Social Behaviour in Animals. London, Methuen & Co. Ltd., 1953. Easy reading on the behavior of animals in their natural environment.

Young, J. Z.: A Model of the Brain. London, Oxford University Press, 1964. An interesting approach to understanding the bases of behavior.

42 PARASITISM

The relationship between two species of organisms in which one species lives in or on the body of the second and at its expense is termed **parasitism.** The species that derives benefit from the relationship, and usually cannot survive otherwise, is called the **parasite,** and the species which is injured or affected adversely in some way is called the **host.** This relationship is distinguished from **mutualism** (p. 708), in which both species derive some benefit from the association and cannot survive in nature without it. The term **symbiosis** has been used with several different meanings in the past, but it is now widely used as a general term to indicate a persistent physical association between two different species of animals, plants or microorganisms without special connotation of harm or of benefit to the host species.

Green plants, fungi, bacteria and viruses, as well as animals of many different phyla, may be parasites. There are animals parasitic on plants and plants which are parasites of animals.

42.1
The Origin of Parasitism

The ecologic relationship of parasitism may arise by any of several evolutionary paths. Predation, commensalism or competition between species for food may develop into parasitism. Animals which are saprozoic or bacterial feeders are, to some extent, adapted beforehand to living in the digestive tract and can become parasites directly on their first contact with the host species.

Predation and Parasitism. When predation evolves into parasitism, the diet is usually changed from small prey to a large host species. The mites, for example, which are small relatives of the spiders, include many predators that hunt down and kill small arthropods, sucking out their body juices. Some of these attack larger arthropods and vertebrates and, in the process of removing a full meal, do not kill the prey. These have taken the first step toward parasitism. Still other mites not only do not remove enough juice to kill the host at one meal but remain on the host between meals, so that much of their life is spent there. These are fully evolved parasites.

Leeches show a similar progression from predation to parasitism. Some leeches feed primarily on small arthropods, snails and worms. Others feed upon vertebrates when they are available, removing a meal of blood and then falling off. A few species are completely parasitic and live in continuous association with the host without killing it. Again, predation is associated with small invertebrates, parasitism with vertebrates.

Bats provide a third example of this, but only the first step toward parasitism has been taken. Most bats are insectivorous and feed upon insects which they capture in flight. Certain South American bats have changed their food source to large mammals and, instead of killing and consuming their prey, they draw blood from the neck. Vampire bats feed like parasites, but in their failure to remain with the host and their hunting activities they are still predators.

Commensalism and Parasitism. Commensalism and parasitism are easily distinguished in theory, but in practice we know so little about many organisms that we cannot be sure whether an association that appears to be commensalism may not, in fact, be parasitism. We can only say, for example, that peritrich ciliates *appear* to be commensals on hydras, feeding upon stray bits of debris without harming the host. The same is true for many of the associations found in the sea. In some cases, however, the innocence of the commensal is dubious. Certain marine annelids live on echinoderms, especially in the ambulacral grooves of starfishes. In general, these are commensals, seeking shelter on the host and feeding on "leftovers" at mealtime. At least one species, however, has been observed to feed on more than leftovers, poking its head into the host's stomach in its enthusiasm to share the meal. The evolutionary path from shelter-seeking commensalism to food-robbing parasitism appears to have been followed frequently.

In another type of commensalism, the commensal feeds upon materials shed and no longer wanted by the host. This may develop into parasitism if the commensals become more aggressive, feeding first upon the materials before they are shed and finally feeding on living tissues. Certain kinds of mites are common in the nests of birds and mammals and feed upon the shed hair, feathers and flakes of skin. This is a loose type of commensalism, since the mites do not live directly on the hosts. Other mites do live directly on the hosts; those feeding mostly on flaked skin do little if any harm, but those feeding on feathers or hair may impair the plumage or fur. These might be called commensals with parasitic tendencies. Some mites have extended their diet to include the living tissues of the host and, thus, are completely parasitic.

Food Competition and Parasitism.

The development of parasitism from food competition has occurred many times in the nematodes. Both free-living and parasitic nematodes are covered by a thick cuticle which undoubtedly has facilitated their evolution as intestinal parasites. Many species feed on fruits and vegetables in competition with other herbivores. Related to these are intestinal parasites still feeding on food bits, but from the security of the host's digestive tract. They may have evolved from free-living forms that were inadvertently eaten.

Saprozoic Animals and Bacterial Feeders. Saprozoic animals may become parasitic if they can withstand the digestive enzymes of the host and the low oxygen tension in its digestive tract. Many of the free-living saprozoic flagellates have parasitic relatives which are specialized so that they can grow only within the digestive tract of particular hosts. Other relatives are intracellular parasites, especially of other protozoa. Other saprozoic parasites such as cestodes and acanthocephalans apparently became saprozoic after they became parasites, for they do not have free-living saprozoic relatives.

The bacterial feeders that can withstand digestive enzymes and low oxygen tension may become intestinal commensals and feed on the bacterial population of the large intestine which otherwise becomes a part of the feces. Such commensals are found among flagellates, ciliates, amebas and roundworms. Many of these groups have close relatives that either have become saprozoic and rob the host of digested nutrients or directly attack

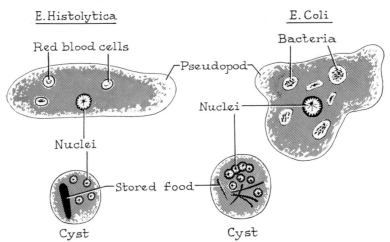

Figure 42.1 A parasite, *Entamoeba histolytica* (left), and a commensal, *E. coli* (right), of the human large intestine. Active amebas above, cysts below, that are passed in the feces and can infect new individuals.

the host tissues. The most striking case of this kind is found in the amebic genus, *Entamoeba* (Fig. 42.1). *E. coli* lives in the large intestine of man and feeds upon bacteria. Although it is abundant in the tropics and by no means rare in temperate regions, it appears to be harmless. It has a close relative, *E. histolytica,* which also appears to be a bacterial feeder normally but which, at times, destroys the lining of the large intestine and feeds on red blood corpuscles. An acute attack by these parasites can produce severe dysentery and riddle the entire large intestine with deep ulcers and abscesses.

Parasites may begin as ectoparasites on the host surface or as endoparasites in the digestive tract. From either of these initial positions the parasites may become endoparasitic among the tissues and organs of the body, or even become intracellular, living within the host cells.

42.2

Ectoparasites

Parasites that feed at the surface of the host fall into three major categories: those that eat dead material such as hair, feathers, flakes of skin; those that suck blood; those that feed on living tissue.

Parasites Feeding on Dead Material. The largest group of ectoparasites that feed on dead surface material is an order of insects, the **Mallophaga** (Fig. 42.2). These are known as **bird lice,** since most of them are found on birds, or **biting lice,** because they have jaws for biting and chewing. A few species are found on mammals. They do not directly injure the host, but the constant irritation of their presence as they feed on feathers or fur can produce restlessness and

insomnia with loss of vigor and weight. A few of the species chew down into the shafts of the feathers until they reach live tissues and draw blood.

Bloodsuckers. The list of animals that suck blood but do not remain with the host between meals is long: leeches, mites, ticks, lice, fleas, bedbugs, mosquitoes, sandflies, midges, blackflies, horseflies, tsetse flies and vampire bats. The true parasites that remain with the host are a much smaller group, including a few of the leeches, a few ticks and mites, the sucking lice and fleas. The two major groups are the sucking lice (order **Anoplura**) and the fleas (order **Siphonaptera**) in the class Insecta.

Sucking lice spend their entire life cycle on the same host and are transferred to new host individuals through body contact or by migration from hosts that die. All of the species parasitize mammals. The head louse, the body louse and the pubic or "crab" louse parasitize man (Fig. 42.3). Fleas are free-living as larvae (Fig. 42.4). The eggs are dropped, usually in the nest or sleeping place of the host, where they hatch into small worms that feed on debris. After pupation they emerge as full-grown adults that seek the proper host. Although a few species parasitize birds, most fleas are found on mammals.

Bloodsuckers are not only harmful as parasites but are dangerous as carriers of disease organisms. During the fourteenth century about 25 million people died of bubonic and pneumonic plagues. This disease is caused by a bacterium that can be carried in rats and other rodents where it is relatively harmless. It is transmitted from individual to individual by rat fleas. Unfortunately, rat fleas occasionally bite man and, in this way, transmit the disease to a host in which its effects are deva-

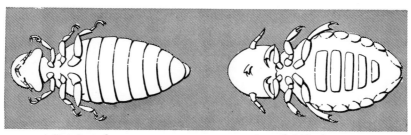

Chicken louse   Cattle louse

Figure 42.2 Mallophaga. Ventral views showing biting mandibles. Most species infect birds and have two claws on each foot (left). The few that infect mammals have single claws (right) resembling those of the Anoplura. (After Borror and DeLong.)

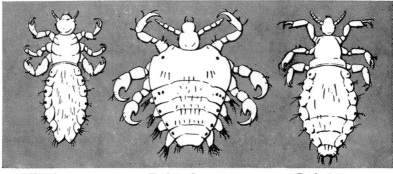

Head louse   Pubic louse   Body louse

Figure 42.3 Anoplura. The three varieties of human lice. The head louse, *Pediculus humanus* var. *capitis*, and body louse, *P. h.* var. *corporis*, are interfertile varieties of one species that rarely interbreed because one lives on the head, laying eggs on the hairs, while the other lives on the clothed portion of the body, laying eggs in the clothing. The pubic louse, *Phthirus pubis*, lives in the pubic region and occasionally in the armpits. (After Patton and Evans.)

stating. Fleas can transmit typhus fever, tularemia, undulant fever and other diseases as well as the plague. The human louse will transmit typhus, but the disease kills both the humans and the lice. In regions where lice are abundant the spread of typhus can reach epidemic proportions. During World War I louse-borne typhus killed at least 3,000,000 men. The common tick *Dermacentor andersoni* (Fig. 42.5) carries more pathogens than any other parasite, including those that produce spotted fever, Colorado tick fever, Q fever, tularemia, undulant fever and several forms of virus encephalitis.

Bloodsuckers may serve as alternate hosts for the pathogens they carry. The role of the mosquito in malaria has already been described. Dog tapeworms use the dog flea as an intermediate host, and a few of the nematodes pass parts of their life cycles in blackflies and horseflies. African sleeping sickness, a disease caused by protozoan parasites, includes the tsetse fly as an alternate host, and leishmaniasis, a related disease, involves sandflies.

Parasites Feeding on Living Tissues. Ectoparasites that feed directly on living flesh include trematodes, crustaceans, mites and fly maggots. Many of these feed on blood as well as flesh. Certain trematodes parasitize the gills of fishes; crustaceans parasitize a variety of animals including other crustaceans, annelids, mollusks, echinoderms and fishes; and the mites and flies parasitize terrestrial vertebrates. Man may be infested with the mange or itch mites (Fig. 42.6) that burrow in the skin, or with chiggers, a mite

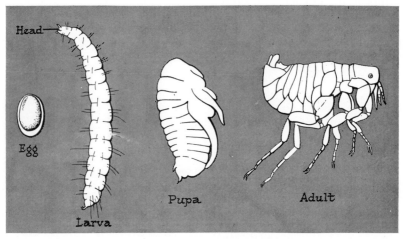

Head Egg Larva Pupa Adult

Figure 42.4 Siphonaptera. Life cycle of the rat flea, *Xenopsylla cheopis*. Eggs fall to the ground and hatch into free-living larvae. These feed on debris, eventually pupate, and emerge as adults that seek out the proper host. (Adult after Chandler; others after Patton and Evans.)

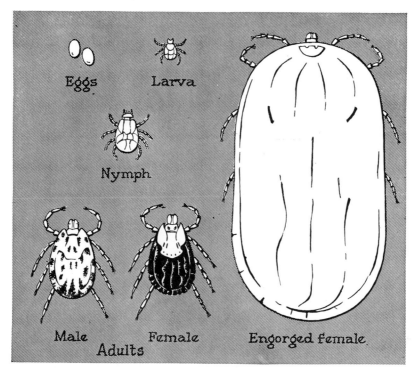

Figure 42.5 The common tick, *Dermacentor andersoni*. Eggs laid on the ground hatch into six-legged larvae that feed on small mammals. These drop off, molt into eight-legged nymphs that return to small mammals. After molting on the ground again the adults attack large mammals. The females become enormous after mating and eventually fall to the ground to lay a thousand or more eggs. (After Chandler.)

that secretes enzymes which dissolve small holes in the host's skin for feeding.

The maggots of several kinds of flies burrow in the skin of mammals. One of the common and curious species is the skin botfly, *Dermatobia hominis* (Fig. 42.7). The maggots burrow into the skin and feed on dissolved flesh and blood. In Central and South America it may be so abundant that the hides of cows are riddled. The flies burrow in man as easily as in other mammals. When the maggots are mature they drop to the ground and

pupate. The female fly lays her eggs not on the mammalian host but on the lower side of a bloodsucking arthropod, usually a mosquito. The eggs are ready to hatch in eight or 10 days. When the mosquito feeds, the warmth of the mammal stimulates the maggots to emerge and drop onto the host.

Some of the parasitic copepods (class Crustacea) are attached to the host by their antennae while they feed upon the host with the mouth parts. In other species the antennae grow into the host to serve as an anchor, and

Figure 42.6 The mange mite, *Sarcoptes scabiei*. These pass their entire life cycle on the host. Eggs laid in the burrows hatch into young mites that begin burrows of their own. Note the suckers on the anterior legs. (After Craig and Faust.)

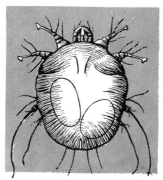

Adult female

Mange mite burrowing in skin

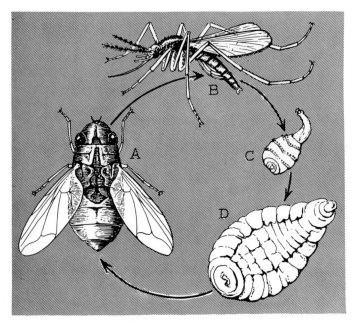

Figure 42.7 The skin botfly, *Derma-tobia hominis*. The adult (*A*) lays its eggs on blood-sucking arthropods (*B*). When this carrier feeds the young larvae hatch and burrow into the skin (*C*). After feeding and growing beneath the skin the full-grown larva (*D*) drops to the ground, pupates, and emerges later as an adult.

in still others this anchor serves as a nutritive organ and soaks up nourishment from the host. Finally, in several groups of parasitic copepods the mouth parts are degenerate, and the antennae form a root system that spreads throughout the host. In the barnacles this type of parasitism has developed directly from nonparasitic forms. Barnacles usually attach to inanimate objects, but a few species attach to other organisms. In some of these the attachment organ, the antenna of the larva, extends into the host as an anchor, and in other species it becomes a nutritive organ. In some species of both groups the root system becomes much developed while the body left outside degenerates completely, giving rise to endoparasitism.

42.3
Parasites of the Digestive Tract

These can be divided into several categories: those that eat the host's food, those that are saprozoic, soaking up food the host has digested, those that feed on the digestive tissues and those that suck blood. Intestinal organisms feeding on bacteria are usually commensals and do little or no harm to the host, who is usually unaware of their presence.

Intestinal parasites that compete with the host for food may cause malnourishment. Nematodes are the most numerous of these parasites. As far as we know, all nematodes swallow food, and many species live in the small intestine eating partially digested material supplied by the host. They are often harmless in the sense that the host can usually eat enough for everybody, but if they become too numerous or if the host is starved, the host suffers. *Ascaris lumbricoides* is so prevalent throughout the world that Chandler has described it as "one of man's most faithful and constant companions from time immemorial." Most mammals have their species of ascaris-like roundworms, and it is unusual to open a mammalian intestine and not find them.

Saprozoic intestinal parasites live in the small intestine, where food is digested by the host. The tapeworms (class Cestoda) and spiny-headed worms (phylum Acanthocephala) are the two large groups of such parasites. A number of flagellates are also saprozoic. In man the flagellate *Giardia lamblia* (Fig. 42.8) applies its concave ventral surface to an intestinal cell and attaches by suction. It feeds by absorbing nutrients from fluid that is swept past by the flagella. If this species is so abundant as to carpet the gut wall, absorption by the host may be impaired. Tapeworms attach by suckers or hooks and spiny-headed worms bury the head in the intestinal

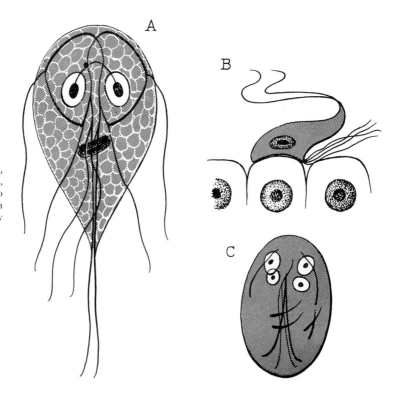

Figure 42.8 *Giardia lamblia. A,* Ventral view showing two nuclei. *B,* Lateral view showing attachment to host intestinal cell. *C,* Cyst passed in the feces, capable of infecting a new host. (After Chandler.)

wall. Both groups lack digestive tracts and soak up nutrients through the integument. Their major harm is in the injuries caused by attachment, which may become infected and ulcerated. They may also produce systemic disorders such as allergy and anemia.

Those intestinal parasites that feed on the intestinal wall include protozoa, the intestinal flukes, a few roundworms and a few fly larvae. Man is attacked by an ameba, a flagellate and a ciliate, all of which live in the large intestine. The ameba, *Entamoeba histolytica,* is the most harmful and has already been described. The flagellate, *Trichomonas hominis,* is the least harmful. It feeds primarily on bacteria and debris and only occasionally produces diarrhea or other signs of distress. At such times it is suspected of feeding on the intestinal lining. The ciliate, *Balantidium coli,* is injurious but uncommon. It digests the intestinal mucosa, produces ulcers like those of the ameba, and can cause death.

Several families of flukes live in the intestine and its associated passages (bile ducts, etc.). Like their ectoparasitic relatives on the gills of fishes, these trematodes attach by the ventral or posterior sucker and feed through the oral sucker, scraping off the superficial

layer of cells. Their damage is slight unless they become numerous.

The most injurious group of intestinal parasites is the bloodsucking hookworms, a group of nematodes. Their effect is seldom sudden or catastrophic but chronic and insidious, sapping the vitality of the host and undermining his health year after year. Two species are common in the small intestine of man, *Ancylostoma duodenale* and *Necator americanus* (Fig. 42.9). The adult gathers a bit of intestinal lining in its mouth and sucks blood from the capillaries. These are one-host parasites with a free-living larva. Eggs pass out in the feces and hatch in the soil, where the larvae develop to the infective stage. Once on the host they bore through the skin into the blood, are swept through the circulatory system to the lungs, where they burrow into the air cavities, crawl up the bronchial tubes, and are swallowed. In warm, moist climates where people are often barefoot, hookworms are common and contribute greatly to the lethargy, indifference and poverty of man. In recent years, the prevalence of hookworm in southeastern United States has been greatly decreased through improved health habits and economic status.

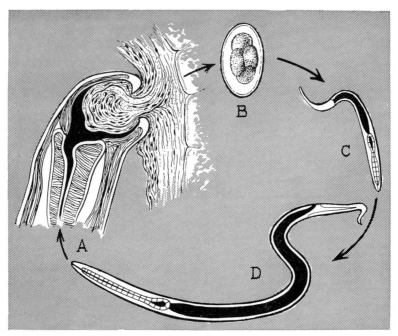

Figure 42.9 Hookworm. *A*, Longitudinal section through head of adult showing mouthful of intestinal wall being sucked. Eggs (*B*) pass out in the host feces, hatch in the soil (*C*) and grow to the infective stage (*D*). These penetrate the host skin and migrate by way of the blood, lungs, and throat to the small intestine. (*A* after Ash and Spitz; others after Chandler.)

42.4

Parasites in Body Tissues

Parasites that live within the tissues of the host may enter through the skin or from the digestive tract. Some of these feed upon the tissues; others lie among the cells and are saprozoic. The two largest and most important groups are the trypanosomes (class Flagellata) and the blood flukes (class Trematoda), both of which live in the blood stream. Parasites that burrow extensively in body organs include some trematodes, nematodes, and a few fly maggots.

Trypanosomes. Trypanosomes live in the blood of all kinds of vertebrates and usually are transmitted by blood-sucking arthropods in which a part of the life cycle is passed. Most of them do little harm to their hosts, and those that are dangerous are believed to represent instances in which the trypanosomes have invaded new hosts. Such may be the case with **African sleeping sickness,** a disease of man caused by two species of the genus *Trypanosoma* (Fig. 42.10). The ancestral species, *T. brucei,* is common in many African wild mammals, where it is harmless. It is virulent in domestic animals

such as horses and camels but is unable to attack man. Early in this century in Rhodesia, however, the population of native mammals was greatly reduced and the tsetse flies that carry *T. brucei* were forced to feed more frequently on humans. In 1909 a case of human sleeping sickness caused by a trypanosome very similar to *T. brucei* was discovered. Since then there have been numerous instances of human infection by this strain of protozoa called *T. rhodesiense* although it is probably only a variety of *T. brucei. Trypanosoma gambiense* has had a longer association with man and also is found in monkeys, antelopes and pigs. It originally was found in central Africa, where it produces a serious but not devastating disease of man. Late in the nineteenth century, apparently as a result of exploration by whites, the organisms were carried north into Uganda and the lake region, where the human population had not previously been exposed to the disease and where tsetse flies were abundant. The result was a terrible epidemic of sleeping sickness that killed two-thirds of the population and rendered large areas of land uninhabitable. Today a major activity of the Uganda government is the gradual

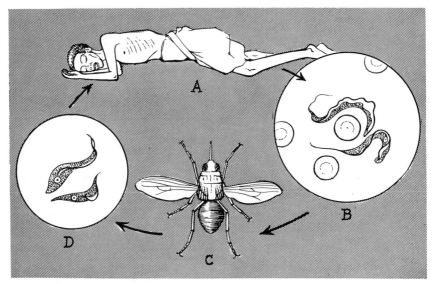

Figure 42.10 *A,* African sleeping sickness victim. Active trypanosomes in the blood *(B)* are sucked up by the tsetse fly *(C)*. The protozoa reproduce in the digestive tract, migrate to the salivary glands where they attach to the walls and finally become infective *(D),* passing into a new host during salivary secretion.

reclamation of its land by systematically killing off all the large mammals that carry the disease and infect the tsetse flies.

African sleeping sickness begins with fever and headache, followed by weakness and anemia. The patient may then recover partially or completely. Often, however, the trypanosomes reach the central nervous system, and then the host becomes progressively less active, repeatedly falling asleep and abhorring exertion. Emaciation, coma and death follow after several weeks. In South America, trypanosomes cause a disease involving fever, anemia and mental disturbances. The parasites are normally found in small mammals and are transmitted to man by a bloodsucking bug (order Hemiptera).

Blood Flukes. Blood flukes belong to the family **Schistosomatidae** and infect birds and mammals. Two characteristics distinguish them from other trematodes: the sexes are separate, and the cercariae penetrate directly through the skin of the final host rather than being eaten. Man may be infected by three species of the genus *Schistosoma* (Fig. 42.11). Two species live in blood vessels near the digestive tract, and their eggs appear in the feces; the third lives in vessels near the bladder, and its eggs appear in the urine. They are frequently found in pairs, the broad male folded around the long slender female.

Infection is widespread in Africa, the Near East and the Orient, where more than 90 per cent of the human population may carry the worms. The disease usually passes through several stages of fever, pain and diarrhea without serious harm and then continues for years as an insidious drain on body vigor. Occasionally, however, infection may become acute, with internal bleeding, secondary bacterial infection and death. The Egyptian government considers this disease to be a major obstacle in the path of the country's economic progress. At the request of the governments concerned, the World Health Organization has major research programs aimed at the control of this disease in Egypt and in the Philippines.

Blood flukes infecting birds and mammals are common everywhere. Several species in North America are able to penetrate the skin of man should he enter the water where the cercariae occur. They burrow in the skin, producing "swimmer's itch," but are unable to develop properly and soon perish.

Filariae. Of parasites that live in tissues other than blood the most harmful group are the filarial roundworms, slender nematodes several centimeters long and no thicker than a coarse thread. Adults burrow beneath the skin or live in the lymph nodes and connective tissue, releasing minute larvae into the blood stream. The larvae may be picked up by some bloodsucking arthro-

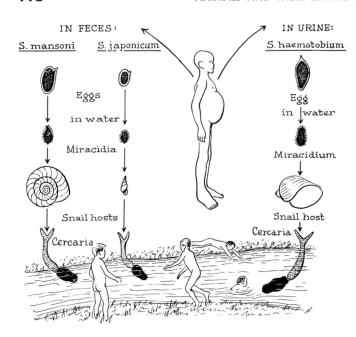

Figure 42.11 Three species of *Schistosoma* that infect man. In severe cases (top figure) the body is emaciated and the feet edematous while the spleen is greatly enlarged. Eggs hatch on contact with water and each species enters its own particular kind of snail host. Emerging cercariae penetrate directly into the human skin. In regions where these parasites are prevalent, children usually become infected as soon as they start playing in water.

pod and thus be transmitted to a new host. A common but relatively harmless example is the African eye worm, *Loa loa* (Fig. 42.12), which burrows beneath the skin near the eyes and often can be seen coiled in the white of the eye.

The filarial genus *Wuchereria*, especially *W. bancrofti* (Fig. 42.13), can produce a serious disease. These live in the lymph nodes and lymph ducts and in the connective tissue associated with various glands. They may produce little effect, but the interaction of parasite and host often results in repeated inflammation of the lymphatic ducts. If the ducts become obstructed the tissues begin to swell, producing a progressive enlargement known as **elephantiasis.** The disorder is commonly localized in a lower part of the

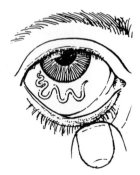

Figure 42.12 Adult of the African eye worm, *Loa loa*, visible in the white of the eye. (After Fülleborn.)

body such as a leg or the scrotum, which may become very enlarged.

Trichinella. Another kind of nematode, *Trichinella spiralis*, burrows in the host body during a portion of its life cycle (Fig. 42.14). The adult is a small intestinal parasite, females 3 to 4 mm. long, males 1.5 mm. long. They are ovoviviparous, and the female usually burrows slightly into the intestinal wall so that the young are released into the tissues. These larvae (0.1 mm. long) are distributed throughout the body by the circulatory system and eventually burrow into striated muscles. Within the muscle they grow rapidly to a length of 1 mm. and then roll into a spiral form embedded in cysts within the muscle cells. This is a waiting stage, for the worms will develop no further unless the meat is eaten by another host. They will survive in this condition for periods ranging from several months to several years. If the meat is eaten by an appropriate host (man, swine, rodents, cats, sometimes other mammals), the worms are digested free of the cyst and mature in about four days in the new host's intestine. The disease **trichinosis** is caused by a sudden heavy infestation and is manifested in two stages. While the adult females are burrowing into the intestinal wall, various intestinal and systemic disorders, including diarrhea, pain and fever, may result. The second stage is caused by the activities of the larvae as they penetrate the muscles and is accompanied by intense

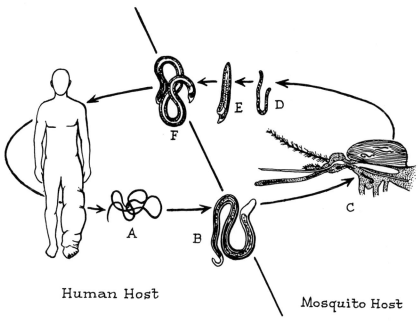

Figure 42.13 *Wuchereria bancrofti.* Adult worms in human lymphatic tissue (*A*) release microscopic larvae into the blood (*B*). If these are taken up by a mosquito (*C*) they migrate to the thoracic muscle, where they metamorphose and grow (*D, E* and *F*). The infective stage (*F*) migrates to the proboscis where it can penetrate into man while the insect is feeding.

muscular pain, disturbances of muscular activity, and sometimes death. Unlike most parasites *Trichinella* is most abundant in temperate climates. Although its natural reservoir is probably in rodents, wild pigs and carnivorous mammals, it is common only where it has found especially suitable conditions on swine farms where pigs are fed raw garbage, including pig scraps and dead rodents. It is more abundant in this country than elsewhere.

Botflies. Maggots of many botflies bur-

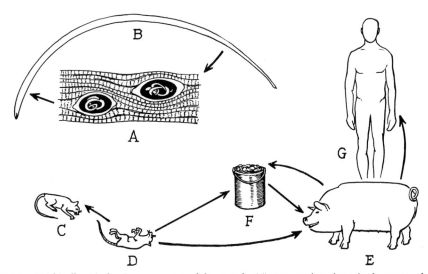

Figure 42.14 *Trichinella spiralis.* Larvae encysted in muscle (*A*) mature into intestinal worms when eaten (*B*). These give birth to larvae that burrow into the host, encysting in muscle. The natural reservoir is rodents (*C*) and similar animals which eat their dead (*D*). Pigs (*E*) will also eat dead rodents. Furthermore, killed rodents and pig scraps are fed to them in garbage (*F*). Man can become infected by eating insufficiently cooked meat containing larvae.

row throughout the body. The skin botfly described previously stays beneath the skin but others, such as cattle bots, burrow deep into the body and wander at will. Eventually, they migrate to the skin of the back and produce blisters or **warbles.** When full grown they drop off and pupate in the ground. Head bots of sheep and goats penetrate the lining of the nose and burrow in the face, sometimes destroying an eye.

42.5
Intracellular Parasites

Only the protozoa and nematodes have given rise to intracellular parasites. Probably the first parasites were ones living within the cells of other protozoa, possibly forms like some of the dinoflagellates that are endoparasites of ciliates. Among the intracellular parasites of metazoans are a genus of flagellates related to trypanosomes, *Leishmania,* and the entire class of sporozoans.

Trypanosomes themselves are to some extent intracellular, especially in the arthropod host where they may grow and reproduce in the cells lining the intestine. One species (*T. cruzi*) is intracellular in the vertebrate host, but several species are completely extracellular in both hosts. In the related genus, *Leishmania,* the parasites are entirely intracellular in the vertebrate host. These are responsible for a variety of tropical sores and ulcers where the skin and underlying tissue have been destroyed. One species, *L. donovani,* invades the inner body tissues, especially the spleen, producing a disease known as **kala-azar.** Fever, pain and anemia are followed by progressive emaciation of the body while the spleen becomes enlarged. Untreated cases are 95 per cent fatal. Within the last 20 years, however, drugs have been found which reduce the mortality rate to 5 per cent or less.

Sporozoans are common parasites of the intestinal tract of arthropods, infecting the individual cells of the lining. Other species infect the intestinal cells of vertebrates, including all the domestic mammals and birds. The most important of these belong to the order Coccidia and produce a disease called **coccidiosis.** In wild animals they are not a serious problem because the spores are shed in the feces and must be eaten to cause reinfection. Domestication often forces animals

into a closer association with their excrement than is natural, and the contamination of food by feces is common. Chickens, particularly, suffer from the conditions imposed upon them. If too many of the intestinal cells are destroyed at once, the animal suffers weakness, diarrhea, bloody feces, loss of appetite and, often, death.

Another group of sporozoans, the order Haemosporidia, pass a part of their life cycle as intracellular parasites of blood cells and another part in an arthropod bloodsucker. The malarial parasites of man, described earlier (Fig. 6.1), belong to this group. In regions where malaria is common it is typically a chronic disease. Those infected suffer periodic relapses of fever, weakness and a general decrease in resistance to other diseases. The fever produced when malarial parasites burst from one set of blood cells and infect a new set is high enough to be deleterious to other parasites, notably the bacterial spirochete producing syphilis. In fact, several tropical tribes have been found in which all the individuals have both syphilis and malaria. The people have some resistance to malaria so that it is not a serious illness, and suffer very little from syphilis because the malarial fevers keep it under control. When some of these individuals were cured of malaria their syphilis immediately became worse. Before the discovery of penicillin a mild form of malaria was sometimes used in American hospitals as one means of controlling advanced cases of syphilis.

Intracellular nematodes are common and sometimes economically serious parasites of plants.

The insidious parasitic diseases of man which have a widespread distribution are preponderantly blood diseases. Malaria has been the most serious world-wide parasitic disease, but modern medical and public health practices have reduced its prevalence. Schistosomiasis, caused by trematodes which live in blood vessels and eat blood, remains a medical challenge. The extent of its damage in regions where most people are infected is unknown. Hookworm disease, caused by bloodsucking parasites in the intestine, and amebiasis, caused by *Entamoeba histolytica* which erodes the intestine and eats red blood cells, are both extremely widespread diseases. Both undoubtedly weaken the host but their actual damage is difficult to estimate. Both

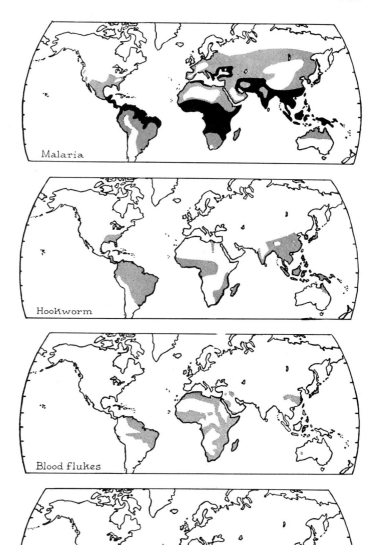

Figure 42.15 The world distribution of malaria, hookworm, blood flukes and sleeping sickness. For malaria, solid black indicates extreme prevalence, shaded areas show moderate or occasional presence.

can be controlled. Sleeping sickness, caused by a blood saprozoite, is the scourge of much of Africa. These five diseases are probably the most important, if both the seriousness of the disease and the number of people affected are taken into consideration. The extent to which four of these parasites are distributed in the world is shown on the accompanying maps (Fig. 42.15). *Entamoeba histolytica* is virtually world-wide in distribution but is a serious problem only in tropical regions.

42.6
Adaptations to Parasitism

Adaptations that are common among parasitic animals include the development of devices for attachment and of methods of transmission, and simplification or loss of sensory, locomotor and digestive structures. These adaptations are found in other organisms, of course, and none of them is found in all parasites.

Means for Attachment. Devices for

attachment such as the suckers of trematodes (Fig. 11.11) and leeches (Fig. 15.1) are especially common among ectoparasites and intestinal parasites. The burrowing habit of some of the skin mites is a less obvious way of solving the attachment problem. Most of the fleas and lice have legs and claws adapted for gripping hair or feathers. In the human crab louse, for example (Fig. 42.3), the second and third pairs of legs are chelate in such a way that when the claw closes against the "hand" a hole is left that is slightly smaller than the diameter of a pubic hair. This enables the louse to grip pubic hairs tightly without cutting them through. These lice are limited to the pubic region primarily because the head and body hairs are too fine to be gripped, but men with luxuriant coarse body hair can be infested from head to toe. The head and body lice (Fig. 42.3) have more delicate claws.

The ventral sucker of intestinal trematodes is used for attachment inside the body just as the posterior sucker of their ectoparasitic relatives is used on the outside. The suckers or hooks of tapeworms, the spiny heads of acanthocephalans, and the ventral concavity of Giardia have already been described. Hookworms are securely attached by the mouthful of intestinal wall through which they suck blood (Fig. 42.9). Prominent among intestinal parasites that are not attached are Ascaris and its relatives. These continually crawl "upstream" as a means of staying in the host (they occasionally crawl too far and come out the mouth or nose).

Means for Transmission.   Two problems are involved in the transfer of the parasite from one host to another: the development of stages in the life cycle that can survive crossing the ecologic desert that lies between hosts and the production of sufficient numbers of such stages to enhance the chance of locating a new host. The first problem is associated with the survival of the individual, the second with the survival of the species.

Organisms that are only partially modified as parasites, for example, leeches and mosquitoes, have no difficulty getting from host to host. Fleas and lice that are wingless have a greater problem. Fleas are free-living as larvae and have powerful jumping legs as adults so that they can move rapidly through a considerable distance. Lice cannot move fast and will perish in a short time if removed from the host. They seldom attempt to cross voids between hosts and rely on body contacts between hosts as a means of transmission.

Most ectoparasites have no serious problem in transmission. Internal parasites, however, are adapted to an environment very different from that outside the host and must produce stages in the life cycle able to withstand external conditions if they are to infect new hosts. Most intestinal parasites produce resistant spores, cysts or eggs, which pass out in the feces of the host. These stages may survive long periods of exposure and are infective when eaten by the next host. Others require an alternate host that frequently is part of the food chain of the final host. Thus, some tapeworm eggs hatch when eaten by an arthropod host and develop to the next stage, which continues to develop only when the arthropod is eaten by a vertebrate host. In a sense, the arthropod is used as a means of transmission from the vertebrate's feces to its mouth. Some of the intestinal parasites take an active role in transmission. The resistant stages expelled in the feces by hookworms and certain trematodes develop into active stages that seek out the next host and penetrate through its skin rather than waiting to be eaten.

Parasites of body tissues use two routes of dispersal. Some, such as blood flukes, release stages which make their way into the intestine and pass out with the feces. Their subsequent problems of transmission are the same as those of intestinal parasites. Others release stages into the blood that will survive passage through arthropod bloodsuckers. They usually develop through several stages of the life cycle in these arthropods. The use of this route by malarial parasites, trypanosomes and filariae has been described. These parasites avoid the problems of the outside world by remaining inside hosts throughout the life cycle.

Filarial nematodes release their larvae into the blood stream only during those hours of the day in which the arthropod vectors are active. In regions where the insects bite in the daytime the larvae are found in the blood only in the daytime. Strains of Wuchereria occur on different islands in the South Pacific, some of which have diurnal, others nocturnal, insects. The strains of parasites found on the different islands have evolved to conform with these patterns.

If the transmission stages are passive, or if the sojourn between hosts is at all protracted, the odds that an individual parasite released from one host will successfully arrive at another host are small. To balance these odds many parasites produce tremendous numbers of such stages. Tapeworms, roundworms, acanthocephalans and internal trematodes all produce millions of eggs. Protozoan parasites such as *Giardia* and *Entamoeba* produce "showers" of encysted stages. The number of filarial larvae in the blood at the appropriate time of day can be enormous. These adaptations not only assure the survival of the species but, if environmental conditions are such that transmission becomes more probable, such parasites can rapidly produce extremely high infection rates.

In many cases in which the parasite is found in more than one kind of host, reproduction takes place in all hosts. The mosquito that picks up a few infective malarial parasites from one person shortly has enough parasites to infect all the people it may bite after that. Similarly, the trematode miracidium lucky enough to get from its vertebrate host to a snail reproduces so as to produce many cercariae, not just one. The eggs of many of the insect parasites of other insects go through a process called **polyembryony** to produce a number of larvae from each egg that successfully reach a new host.

The remarkable rate of reproduction, often at more than one point in the life cycle, makes it difficult to control parasites. Although all but a few parasites may be eliminated by intensive medical treatment, those few can shortly replace the entire population.

Selective Modification of Organs. The intimate association of a parasite with its host may eliminate the usefulness of certain of its organs. The selective disadvantage of some structures is obvious, such as the cumbersome wings of ectoparasitic insects that crawl through feathers or fur. Useless structures tend to become reduced or absent in parasites because there is no longer any positive selection in their favor, and the gene complexes responsible for their existence gradually are dispersed. A mouth, gut and digestive glands are not required for the survival of an organism living in the host's digestive tract, where saprozoic nutrition is possible.

Locomotor organs may also be useless. Most adult tapeworms do not move again once the head is attached, and these tapeworms have such poor musculature that they cannot crawl effectively. Although larval parasitic copepods and barnacles have typical larval legs in the free-swimming stage, in many species the legs rapidly disintegrate as soon as the individual attaches to its host. Even the protozoan Sporozoa have lost their original locomotor organelles. Most of the ectoparasites, however, have fair to good locomotor organs, and the insects that have lost their wings still have well-developed legs.

Sense organs become somewhat less useful as the locomotor organs of ectoparasites decrease in size. Fleas, which have strong jumping legs, have well-developed eyes and an excellent sense of the warmth of mammals at a distance. The latter is shown by waving first a cold object and then the hand past fleas on the floor. The fleas show little response to the cold object, but as the hand approaches they all turn to face it and then jump upon it at the appropriate moment. Lice have weak legs, and most of them are blind, but they retain a good chemical sense for use as they crawl over the host.

Internal parasites have even less use for eyes, ears and other sense organs. The only sense found in many internal parasites is a little understood ability to migrate to a specific portion of the body, which is presumably a form of chemical sense. Internal parasites with complex life cycles including a free-living stage, such as the miracidium and cercaria of trematodes, may have various organs including eyes in the free-living stage, but these are absent in the parasitic stage.

The evolutionary reduction of organs is called simplification or degeneration. It would be a mistake, however, to consider that parasitic organisms are "degenerate" because they have lost some organs or have ones that are reduced in size and complexity. Degenerate organisms are ineffective, inefficient individuals. Parasites are both efficient and effective. The degeneration—simplification or loss—of some of their organs is balanced by other adaptations with which they exploit the parasitic way of life. Sucking lice, for example, are abundant wherever mammals are found and, in spite of their weak bodies and near or total blindness, they live with remarkable security, having longer lives and requiring fewer offspring for perpetuation of the species than many free-living insects of their size.

42.7

Host Specificity

Many parasites can infect a variety of animals. The common tick (Fig. 42.5) will feed on almost any mammal, and a single acanthocephalan species may be found in the intestines of birds belonging to several different orders. Most parasites, however, are more restricted and infect only a group of species that are closely related. One genus of tapeworms is found only in carnivores, another only in rodents and a third only in marsupials. Some parasites are still more restricted and can infect only one host species or possibly a few species of the same genus. This extreme host specificity is common in malarial parasites (those of man will not infect any other animal), sucking lice (the crab louse can live on the gorilla, but the head and body lice live only on man), and nematodes (the human *Ascaris* can live in other mammals but will not reproduce there), and it is not rare in other groups such as fleas and tapeworms.

Where host specificity is extreme, the parasites may have been associated with their hosts for a considerable period of geologic history and, as the host evolved into a number of species, the parasites evolved with them. In such cases, the taxonomic arrangement of the hosts and the parasites often shows similar or identical patterns. This phenomenon has been used as a means of settling certain taxonomic problems. In the last century, for example, it was observed that the llamas of the South American Andes were similar to the camels of northern Africa and central Asia, but the geographic distance between the two groups was considered to be a barrier to placing them in the same family. When their lice were studied it was discovered that they also were similar to each other and different from other lice. On the strength of this concordance the llamas and camels were grouped in the family Camelidae and the lice were grouped in the genus *Microthoracius*. This decision was shown to be correct later when an abundance of fossil camels was found in North America. Today, in fact, it is believed that the group,

together with its lice, arose in North America and spread to both South America and Asia before becoming extinct on this continent.

The extent to which the taxonomic schemes of parasites and their hosts agree can be used as an indication of the age of the association between parasites and hosts. The conclusion that ancestral camels were infested with ancestors of *Microthoracius*, together with the age of camel fossils, indicates that this association has existed for at least 30 million years. The Australian fauna was isolated about 75 million years ago, and the Australian marsupials were separated from their relatives in America. The tapeworms of these two marsupial groups are similar, suggesting that tapeworms were parasitizing them before their separation. On the other hand, their internal trematodes are not similar, and it is concluded that these parasites have infected marsupials for less than 75 million years. The same conclusion is reached for the sucking lice, which are found on all the American marsupials but which are entirely absent from Australia.

Concordance in the evolution of parasites and their hosts is often marred, however, by occasional "jumps" to new hosts. Most of the species of sucking lice in the genus *Linognathus* are found on ungulates, and the genus is believed to have evolved with this mammalian group. One species, however, is found on the fox and dog. This does not suggest that the latter evolved from ungulates but rather that the lice established a new beachhead on the predators of their usual hosts. These changes are often associated with ecologic relationships. One species of a genus of rabbit fleas is a parasite of birds that nest in rabbit holes. The relationship is less obvious in the case of malarial parasites of the genus *Plasmodium*. Some species are found in man and a few other primates, while other species are found in several different groups of birds. All of these parasites use mosquitoes as the alternate host, and it is the mosquitoes that provide the ecologic link, sucking the blood of warm-blooded birds as well as that of mammals. Since jumps to new hosts by parasite groups with extreme host specificity are known to occur occasionally, agreement of taxonomic relationship among parasites and their hosts can never be used as absolute proof for the course of evolution implied in the taxonomy.

42.8

Social Parasites

Animal societies may be subjected to a kind of parasitism in which the parasite does not feed on individuals but intrudes itself into the social economy. The American cowbird and European cuckoo are examples of this. These birds lay their eggs in the nests of other species where the involuntary foster parents obligingly feed and care for the young. The rightful nestlings are often smaller and less vigorous than the social parasites and may be crowded out of the nest. These parasites successfully invade the social family life of the host birds.

Insect societies are invaded by a variety of beetles and wasps that in one way or another become accepted as a part of the colony. Some of these parasites are food-robbers, masquerading as colony members while they actually do nothing but steal food when hungry. Others enter into the trophallaxis of the colony, offering secretions in return for being fed so that the hosts appear content with their presence. They are worse than commensals since they use up some of the food supply of the colony. Other insects that actually eat larvae are tolerated and to some extent protected by the colony. This is predation against the larvae, but in relation to the whole colony may be regarded as a form of parasitism, since the invaders remain with the colony and do not kill it.

QUESTIONS

1. Give examples of ectoparasitism, intestinal parasitism, blood parasitism and intracellular parasitism.
2. Describe the evolutionary pathways by which an animal may become a parasite.
3. Name an ectoparasite and an endoparasite which eat the flesh of man and describe the life history of each.
4. Discuss three adaptations common in parasites.
5. Distinguish between biting and sucking lice according to both their taxonomy and their hosts.
6. Describe the life cycle of the common tick.
7. Where are hookworms prevalent? What countermeasures are effective against hookworms?

ANNOTATED REFERENCES

Baer, J. G.: Ecology of Animal Parasites. Urbana, University of Illinois Press, 1951. The only text emphasizing the environmental relations of parasites. Includes many interesting examples.

Chandler, A. C., and C. P. Read: Introduction to Parasitology. 10th ed. New York, John Wiley & Sons, Inc., 1961. A standard, widely used undergraduate text on parasitology.

Cheng, T. C.: The Biology of Animal Parasites. Philadelphia, W. B. Saunders Co., 1964. A textbook of parasitology for undergraduate students.

Hunter, G. W., W. W. Frye, and J. C. Swartzwelder: A Manual of Tropical Medicine. 4th ed. Philadelphia, W. B. Saunders Co., 1966. An excellent source book of tropical parasites.

Rothschild, M., and T. Clay: Fleas, Flukes, and Cuckoos. London, William Collins Sons & Co. Ltd., 1952. A fascinating, semipopular account of parasitism.

Zinsser, H.: Rats, Lice, and History. Boston, Little, Brown and Co., 1935. A popular and authoritative account of typhus down through the ages.

43 _____ CONSERVATION

There are many ways in which a knowledge of the principles of ecology can be used to further human society, one of the most important of which is the rational conservation of our natural resources. Conservation does not mean simply hoarding—not using the resources at all—nor does it imply a simple rationing of our supplies so that some will be left for the future. True conservation implies taking full advantage of our knowledge of ecology and managing our ecosystems so as to establish a balance of harvest and renewal, thus ensuring a continuous yield of useful plants, animals and materials. In general, man is still acting as though he had not yet learned that he is part of a complex environment which must be studied and treated as a whole and not in terms of isolated "projects," for in attempting to carry out one project he may nullify or completely overcome the results of another one.

The record of man's past squandering of natural resources is indeed a dark one. The slaughter of the bison that once roamed the western plains, the decimation of the whales, the depletion of our supplies of many kinds of fresh-water and marine fishes, the extinction of birds such as the passenger pigeon, the razing of thousands of square miles of forests and the burning of more by careless use of fire, the pollution of streams with sewage and industrial wastes, the careless cultivation of land which has resulted in the complete ruin of many square miles of land, and the silting of streams are some of the more flagrant examples of natural resources wasted beyond hope of reclamation. State and federal departments of conservation and professional ecologists have been aware of the problem for many years and have begun countermeasures, but the chief task at present is to make the population at large realize

786

the urgency and the magnitude of the job to be done and to get general support for the measures which must be taken. For many aspects of the conservation problem, additional basic ecologic research is needed to determine the possible effects of some proposed conservation measure on the whole ecology of the region.

43.1
Agriculture

Wind and water have caused soil erosion through all geologic ages but unwise farming practices in the last few centuries have greatly increased the rate of erosion in certain parts of the globe. After decades of the destructive exploitation of farmlands by planting one crop such as corn or cotton year after year, the soil conservation program sponsored jointly by federal and local agencies and based on sound ecologic principles is beginning to be effective in countering erosion. The rotation of crops, contour farming, the establishment of windbreaks to prevent soil erosion by winds, and the use of proper fertilizers to renew the soil are all measures which are effective in maintaining a balanced ecosystem. Successful farming must follow the principles of good land use. It is not conservation to reclaim marginal land for agricultural purposes or to build expensive dams and canals to irrigate land unless the land can produce crops which will make the irrigation worthwhile. If the grasslands of regions with slight rainfall are plowed and planted with wheat, a "dust bowl" will inevitably develop; but if the land is kept as grassland and grazed in moderation, the soil will be kept in place, no dust bowl will develop, and the land can be used economically year after year. Overgrazing, by destroy-

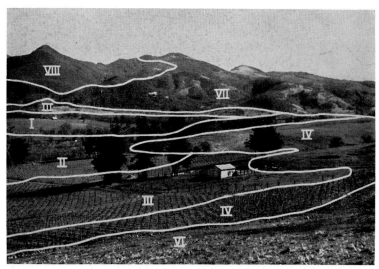

Figure 43.1 Classification of land according to its usefulness. Types I and II may be cultivated continuously; types III and IV are subject to erosion and must be cultivated with great care; types V, VI and VII are suitable for pasture or forests but not for cultivation; type VIII is productive only as a habitat for game. (U. S. Soil Conservation Service.)

ing the grass covering the soil, can lead to destructive erosion just as plowing does. Overgrazing also leads to the invasion of the grassland by undesirable weeds and desert shrubs. These are difficult to eradicate so that grass may grow again. It is now evident that poor land use affects not only the unwise farmer but the whole population, which is eventually taxed to pay for rehabilitation.

The ecologists specializing in the management of land have classified land on the basis of its slope, kind of soil and natural biotic communities into eight categories, from type I, which is excellent for farming and can be cultivated continuously, through three classes that can be used for farming only with special care, and another three classes that are suitable only for permanent pasture or forest, to type VIII, suitable only to be left as it is for game (Fig. 43.1).

The control of insect pests by chemicals such as DDT must be carried out cautiously, with possible ecologic upsets in mind. Spraying orchards, forests and marshes may destroy not only the pests but also useful insects such as honeybees which pollinate many kinds of fruit trees and crops, and useful insect parasites. In some cases, the insect pests have actually increased after the use of DDT because the chemical killed off greater numbers of insect enemies of the pest than of the pests themselves. A number of strains of insects resistant to DDT have developed.

DDT and related chemicals kill other animals in addition to insects; amphibians and reptiles are the most vulnerable vertebrates. The vertebrates are less sensitive than insects, and DDT applied at a level of about 1 pound per acre is effective in insect control without endangering the vertebrates. However, when applied at a level of 5 to 10 pounds per acre, some of the useful animals are killed along with the insects. Some of the newer, stronger insecticides have been used without adequate testing of their effects on other animals.

43.2
Forestry

The management of our forests is an important aspect of applied ecology. Careful forest management has been carried on in Europe for many decades but is only beginning in this country. Proper timber management in our national and state forests has been important in demonstrating to the owners of private forests the results that can be obtained in this way. Since, in some regions, the desirable timber trees are members of the climax community, the ecologic problem is simply to find the best way to speed the return of the climax community after the trees have been cut. In other regions, the desirable trees are earlier seral stages of the ecologic succession, and forest management involves establishing means of preventing the succession to the climax community. This is also true of many kinds of animals; most game birds and many of the most valuable game fish are members of, and thrive best in, an early seral stage of their community.

43.3
Wildlife

The management of our fish and wildlife resources is a field of applied ecology which is supported by wide public interest, especially by sportsmen's clubs and associations. "Wildlife" used in this connection usually means game and fur-bearing animals. Since the various types of wildlife are adapted to different stages of ecologic succession, their management requires a knowledge of and the proper use of these stages. As the Middle West became more and more intensively farmed, and the original forests and prairies were reduced to small patches, the prairie chickens and ruffed grouse which were adapted to these habitats were greatly decreased in numbers. However, this region has been partially restocked with game birds by introducing pheasants and partridges, which had become adapted to living in the intensively farmed regions of Europe.

Of the three general methods used to increase the population of game animals—laws restricting the number killed, artificial stocking and the improvement of the habitat—the latter is the most effective. If the game habitats are destroyed or drastically altered, protective laws and artificial stocking of the region are useless.

Protective laws must operate to prevent a population from getting too large as well as too small. Deer populations, in the absence of natural predators but subject to a constant, moderate amount of hunting, may increase to a point where they actually ruin the vegetation of the forest. Hunting should be restricted, of course, when populations are small and increased when they are larger. This requires accurate annual estimates of the population density of the game species.

Stocking a region artificially with game animals is effective only if they are being introduced into a new region or into one from which they have been killed off. Beavers, for example, were trapped to extermination in Pennsylvania, but restocking with Canadian beavers has been very successful, and it is estimated that there are some fifteen to twenty thousand beavers busy building dams in Pennsylvania. These are now an important factor in flood control in that region. The principles of population growth make it clear that if game animals of a certain species are already present, artificially stocking that region with additional members of the species will be futile. Stocking a region with a completely new species must be done cautiously, or the species may succeed so well as to become a pest and upset the biotic community, as has happened with rabbits in Australia and the English sparrow in the United States.

The management of the fish in a pond may be directed toward providing sport for hook and line fishermen or toward raising a crop of food fish and draining the pond at regular intervals to harvest the crop. To provide the best sport fishing it has been found that a lake or pond should be stocked with a combina-

Table 43.1 A Comparison of a Single Main River Reservoir Plan with a Plan for Multiple Smaller Headwaters Reservoirs

	Main Stream Reservoir	*Multiple Headwaters Reservoirs*
Number of reservoirs	1	34
Drainage area, square miles	195	190
Flood storage, acre feet	52,000	59,100
Surface water area for recreation, acres	1,950	2,100
Flood pool, acres	3,650	5,100
Bottom farmland inundated, acres	1,850	1,600
Bottom farmland protected, acres	3,371	8,080
Total cost	$6,000,000	$1,983,000

From E. P. Odum: Fundamentals of Ecology.

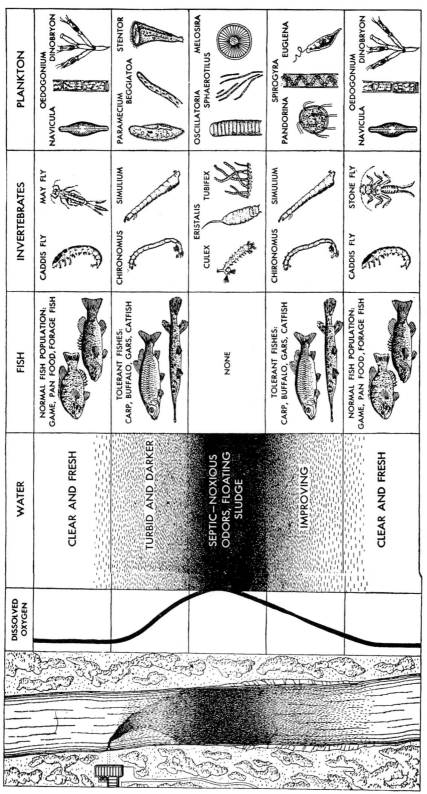

Figure 43.2 Pollution of a stream with untreated sewage and its subsequent recovery. As the amount of oxygen dissolved in the water decreases (left), fishes disappear and only organisms able to obtain oxygen from the surface, or those which tolerate low oxygen tensions, are able to survive. When the sewage has been reduced by bacteria, the population of animals and plants in the stream returns to normal. (After Eliassen, from Odum: Fundamentals of Ecology.)

tion of the sport fish and its natural prey; stocking a pond with large-mouth bass plus bluegills gives seven to ten times more bass in three years than does stocking with bass alone. Stocking with fish must be done with care, for if a lake that already has about as many fish occupying a certain ecologic niche as possible is stocked with more of the same kind, there will be a decrease in the rate of growth and the average size of the fish. It has been found that sport fishing with hook and line is not likely to overfish a lake; the lake is more likely to be underfished, and the resulting crowding leads to a decrease in the average size of the fish population.

The building of dams raises intricate ecologic problems, for dams may be intended for power, for flood control, for the prevention of soil erosion, for irrigation or for the creation of recreational areas. Since no one dam can satisfactorily accomplish all of these objectives, the primary objective must be clearly delineated and the secondary results must be understood. A contrast of two proposals for dealing with the same watershed (Table 43.1) shows that the multiple dam plan costs less, destroys a smaller area of productive farmland, impounds more water and is more effective in controlling floods and soil erosion.

To be most effective, the building of a dam must be accompanied by additional measures to decrease soil erosion upstream or the storage reservoir will fill with silt in a few years.

The management of the fish population in the lakes created by large dams is more difficult than the management of a pond. Sport fishing is usually very good when a dam has first been built, but gradually the silting up of the reservoir and the decrease in productivity change the nature of the fish community from game fish to less desirable catfish and shiners.

The three chief sources of stream pollution are industrial materials which are either directly toxic themselves or which reduce the oxygen supply in the water, sewage and other materials which decrease the oxygen content of the water and introduce bacteria and other septic organisms (Fig. 43.2), and turbidity caused by soil erosion in the watershed. As the silt settles out downstream it may cover up the spawning grounds of fish and have other direct deleterious effects. Erosion can be prevented by proper soil management, industrial wastes can be prevented by suitable design of the manufacturing process, and properly treated sewage can be emptied into a stream without deranging its ecologic relations.

43.4
Marine Fisheries

The primary productivity of the sea, as measured by the pounds of organic carbon produced per year per acre of surface, is very high. The productivity of the western Atlantic off the coast of North America is 2.5 to 3.5 tons of organic carbon per acre and that of Long Island Sound is 2.5 to 4.5 tons per acre. The productivity of the average forest is about 1 ton per acre; most cultivated land fixes only about ¾ ton of organic carbon per acre; and only the rich, intensively cultivated cornfields of Ohio produce as much as 4 tons per acre. Despite this high productivity, man's actual harvest from the ocean, in terms of pounds of fish caught per acre of surface, is very low. Only the rich fishing grounds of the North Sea produce as much as 15 pounds of fish per acre. The ecologic reasons for this are clear: the fish are secondary or tertiary consumers and are on top of a vast pyramid of producers. There are many organisms competing for the food energy fixed by the algae in addition to the edible fish and crustacea harvested from the sea.

Man could undoubtedly recover for his use much more of the biologic productivity of the sea. Although he might be reluctant to eat marine algae himself, they might be filtered from sea water and processed so as to be suitable as feed for cattle or some other gastronomically acceptable animal. Careful studies by the U. S. Fish and Wildlife Service of the fish population of George's Bank and other commercially fished areas have led to recommendations about the rate of fishing and the size of nets used which ensure that the fish are harvested at an optimal size for greatest yield at present and in the future. These areas, which had been fished so extensively that some of the most desirable species were reduced greatly in numbers, are now beginning to revive under careful management.

The shellfish—oysters, clams, shrimps and lobsters—present somewhat different and more difficult problems, for their habitat is more limited than that of commercial fish and they are more affected by adverse environmental changes. Oysters, whose food consists of algae or detritus of a certain size filtered from the sea water by their gills, are unable to use algae of a different size. Oysters were unable to survive in certain bays of Long Island Sound when ducks were raised in large numbers commercially on the adjacent shore. The wastes from the duck farms were washed into the bays, and the addition of this organic matter changed the community ecology in such a way that the normal food of the oyster, diatoms, was replaced by other algae which could not be used by the oysters. Once an oyster bed has been seriously depleted it may fail to recover even if seeded with oyster larvae, because the larvae require a favorable surface for attachment and the most favorable is the shell of an old oyster. In commercial oyster farms the larvae are provided with artificial sites for attachment. Once they have become attached they may be moved to other waters, even from one ocean to another, to complete their growth in waters that are favorable for feeding although not favorable for the reproduction of the species.

43.5

Public Health

Many aspects of the field of public health require the application of ecologic principles; the prevention of the spread of diseases carried by animals is an ecologic as well as a medical problem. The most effective way of eliminating malaria, for example, is to eliminate the particular species of mosquito which is the vector of the malaria parasite, yet this must be done without destroying the useful insects of the region. The mosquitoes which transmit malaria in different parts of the world have quite different ecologic niches and, therefore, measures that may be effective in mosquito control in one region may be quite ineffective in another. The malaria of the southeastern United States is transmitted by mosquitoes living in marshes; Italian malarial mosquitoes live in cool running water in the uplands; and Puerto Rican malarial mosquitoes live in brackish (slightly salty) water. Careful ecologic surveys of each region are necessary to formulate the proper measures to control the insects.

The size of the populations of rats, mice and many insect pests increases with the size of cities and the correlated tendency toward the development of slums in the older parts of the town. A survey in England in 1953 reported that only 0.1 per cent of the houses in towns with less than 25,000 houses were infested with bedbugs, but over 1.0 per cent were infested in towns with more than 100,-000 houses! Careful ecologic studies in Baltimore showed that although professional crews of rat trappers might catch as much as half of the rat population, it quickly returned to its former level. Cats proved to be much overrated as rat predators and were not effective in controlling the rat population. However, by changing the essential elements of the rats' habitat, by improving sanitation, thus decreasing the garbage on which the rats fed and the wastes in which they hid, the rat population was reduced to about 10 per cent of its former size. It remained at this lower level because that was the total number of rats which could survive in the altered environment.

43.6

Human Ecology

No great amount of thought is required to realize that the ecologic principles discussed in these pages apply to human populations as well as to populations of animals and plants. Human ecology deals not only with the dynamics of human populations but also with the relationship of man to the many physical and biotic factors which impinge upon him. By appreciating that human populations are a part of larger units — of biotic communities and ecosystems — man can deal with his own special problems more intelligently. Man has a great deal of control over his environment and has modified the communities and ecosystems of which he is a part. However, this control is far from complete, and man must, like other animals, adapt to those situations which he cannot change. By understanding and cooperating with the various cycles of nature, man has a better chance of surviving in the future than if he blindly attempts to change and control them.

There is a lively controversy at present as to whether the human population is in danger of multiplying beyond the ability of the earth to support it. In the past several centuries the population of the world has increased tremendously as new territories have been opened for exploitation and as methods of food production have become more efficient. Part of the disagreement involves the question of whether comparable increases in the "carrying capacity" of the earth may be expected in the future. Most biologists and social scientists believe that the danger of overpopulation is both great and imminent, but some hold the opposite view. It has been amply shown that the Malthusian principle that populations have an inherent ability to grow exponentially is true for organisms generally, and the growth of the human population in the past 300 years does follow an exponential curve. Whether other factors will come into play to prevent the biologic catastrophe of human overpopulation remains to be seen.

The productivity and carrying capacity of the earth for man can be maintained and increased somewhat, but eventually the human biomass must be brought into equilibrium with the space and food available. Some limitation of human reproduction is clearly inevitable; it remains to be seen whether man will do this voluntarily or involuntarily.

QUESTIONS

1. What is meant by conservation? What conservation measures are being taken in your state?
2. What methods may be used to increase the number of game fish in a large lake? The number of game birds in a forest?
3. What ecologic problems may be raised by the damming of a river, by mining operations and by the establishment of a large chemical factory?
4. Discuss the ecologic principles involved in the operation of an oyster farm.
5. In what ways are ecology and public health related?
6. What is meant by human ecology? How is it related to sociology?

ANNOTATED REFERENCES

Brown, H.: The Challenge of Man's Future. New York, Viking Press, 1954. An able and fascinating discussion of some important aspects of human ecology.

Osborn, F.: Our Plundered Planet. Boston, Little, Brown and Co., 1948. The problems associated with the proper conservation of our natural resources are ably reviewed.

Sears, P.: Deserts on the March. Norman, University of Oklahoma Press, 1935. An excellent discussion of the conservation problems of the dust bowls of the world.

Vogt, W.: Road to Survival. New York, William Sloane Associates, 1948. A further discussion of some of the measures that must be taken to conserve our dwindling natural resources.

GLOSSARY

Important and widely used terms and concepts whose meanings or pronunciations may not be well known are included in this glossary. Relatively common and better known terms have not been included, nor have many of those not so widely used; pages on which these are defined can be found in the index. Names of the major taxa, generally down to class, are included; others can be found through the index.

A simplified, phonetic respelling of terms appears in parentheses. Unless indicated to the contrary, an unmarked vowel ending a phonetic syllable is long; an unmarked vowel in a syllable ending with a consonant is short. In cases where these rules do not apply, the vowel is marked long (ē) or short (ĕ). Primary (′) and secondary (″) accents are indicated.

Derivations of terms are given in brackets. The student's understanding of the terms will be facilitated if he studies these and learns to recognize the common roots used in etymology.

absorption (ab-sorp′shun) [L. *ab* away + *sorbere* to suck in]. The taking up of a substance, as by the skin, mucous surfaces or lining of the digestive tract.

absorption spectrum A measure of the amount of energy at specific wave lengths that has been absorbed as light passes through a substance. Each type of molecule has a characteristic absorption spectrum.

acanthocephala (ah-kan″tho-sef′ah-lah) [Gr. *akantha* thorn + *cephalon* head]. Spiny-headed parasitic worms, a class of the Aschelminthes.

accommodation (ah-kom″o-da′shun) [L. *accommodere* to fit to]. Adjustment of the lens of the eye for various distances; accomplished in fishes and amphibians by lens movements and in higher vertebrates by a change in the shape of the lens.

acetylcholine (as″ĕ-til-ko′lēn). The acetic acid ester of the organic base choline, normally secreted at the ends of many neurons; responsible for the transmission of a nerve impulse across a synapse.

achondroplasia (ah-kon″dro-pla′ze-ah) [*a* neg. + Gr. *chondros* cartilage + *plassein* to form + *-ia*]. A hereditary disturbance of growth and maturation of the bones which results in inadequate bone formation and a characteristic type of dwarfism.

acid (as′id) [L. *acidus*, from *acere* to be sour]. A substance whose molecules or ions release hydrogen ions (protons) in water. Acids have a sour taste, turn blue litmus paper red and unite with bases to form salts.

acidosis (as″ĭ-do′sis). A pathologic condition resulting from the accumulation of acid or the loss of base in the body; characterized by an increased hydrogen ion concentration (decreased pH).

acromegaly (ak″ro-meg′ah-le) [Gr. *akron* extremity + Gr. *megalē* great]. A condition characterized by overgrowth of the extremities of the skeleton, the nose, jaws, fingers and toes. This may be produced by excessive secretion of growth hormone from the pituitary.

acrosome (ak′ro-sōm) [*acro-* + Gr. *sōma* body]. A

793

caplike structure covering the head of the spermatozoon.

actin (ak'tin). A protein found in muscle which together with myosin is responsible for the contraction and relaxation of muscle.

actinopterygian (ak″tĭ-nop′tēr-ij-ĭ-an) [Gr. *actinos* ray + *pterygos* wing]. A member of a subclass of the Osteichthyes in which the fins are supported by bony rays; includes sturgeons, gars and teleosts.

action current A slight current which can be detected with appropriate sensitive devices when any tissue becomes active—as when a muscle contracts, a gland secretes or a nerve conducts an impulse.

active transport The transfer of a substance into or out of a cell across the cell membrane against a concentration gradient by a process which requires the expenditure of energy.

adaptation The fitness of an organism for its environment; the process by which it becomes fit; a characteristic which enables the organism to survive in its environment.

adaptive radiation The evolution from a single ancestral species of a variety of species which occupy different habitats.

adductor (ad-duk′ter) [L. that which draws toward]. A muscle that draws a structure toward the midline of the body, as in bringing the legs together or closing a shell.

adenine (ad′ĕ-nīn) [Gr. *aden* a gland]. A purine (nitrogenous base) which is a component of nucleic acids and of nucleotides important in energy transfer—adenosine triphosphate (ATP), adenosine diphosphate (ADP) and adenylic acid (AMP).

adenosine triphosphate (ah-den′o-sin). An organic compound containing adenine, ribose and three phosphate groups; of prime importance for energy transfers in biological systems.

adipose (ad′ĭ-pōs) [L. *adiposus* fatty]. Referring to the tissue in which fat is stored or to the fat itself.

aerobic (a-er-o′bik) [Gr. *aero* air]. Growing or metabolizing only in the presence of molecular oxygen.

aestivation (es″tĭ-va′shun) [L. *aestivus* summer]. The dormant state of decreased metabolism in which certain animals pass hot, dry seasons.

afferent (af′er-ent) [L. *ad* to + *ferre* to carry]. Conveying toward a center; designating vessels or neurons that transmit blood or impulses toward a point of reference; afferent neurons are sensory neurons conducting impulses toward the central nervous system.

agglutination (ah-gloo″tĭ-na′shun) [L. *agglutinare* to glue to a thing]. The collection into clumps of cells or particles distributed in a fluid.

agnatha (ag′na-thah) [*a-* not + Gr. *gnathos* jaw]. The jawless fishes. A class of vertebrates including lampreys, hagfishes and many extinct forms.

agnosia (ag-no′se-ah) [Gr. *a* neg. + *gnosis* perception]. The loss of the ability to recognize the significance of sensory stimuli.

allantois (ah-lan′to-is) [Gr. *allas* sausage + *eidos* form]. One of the extraembryonic membranes of reptiles, birds and mammals; a pouch growing out of the posterior part of the digestive system and serving as an embryonic urinary bladder or as a source of blood vessels to and from the chorion or placenta.

allele (ah-lēl′) [Gr. *allēlon* of one another]. One of a group of alternative forms of a gene that may occur at a given site (locus) on a chromosome.

allergy A hypersensitivity to some substance in the environment, manifested as hay fever, skin rash or asthma.

alveolus (al-ve′o-lus) [L. dim. of *alveus* hollow]. A small saclike dilatation or cavity; the terminal chamber of air passages in the mammalian lung.

amebocyte (ah-me′bo-sīt″) [Gr. *amoibe* change + *kytos* hollow vessel]. In a metazoan, a cell that wanders through the body in ameboid fashion.

ameboid motion (ah-me′boid) [Gr. *amoibē* change + *eidos* form]. The movement of a cell by means of the slow oozing of the cellular contents.

amensalism (a-men′sal-izm). A relationship between two species whereby one is adversely affected by the second, but the second species is unaffected by the presence of the first.

amino acid (am′ĭ-no). An organic compound containing an amino group ($-NH_2$) and a carboxyl group ($-COOH$); amino acids may be linked together to form the peptide chains of protein molecules.

amnion (am′ne-on) [Gr. *amnion* lamb]. One of the extraembryonic membranes of reptiles, birds and mammals; a fluid-filled sac around the embryo.

amniote (am′ne-ōt) [Gr. *amnion* lamb]. A vertebrate characterized by having an amnion during its development; a reptile, bird or mammal.

amphibian (am-fib′e-an) [Gr. *amphi* on both sides + *bios* life]. A member of a class of vertebrates in which the larvae are usually aquatic and the adults terrestrial; includes frogs, toads, salamanders and their allies.

amphiblastula (am″fĭ-blas′tu-lah) [Gr. *amphi* on both sides + *blastos* germ]. Larval sponge blastula composed of two kinds of cells.

amphineura (am″fĭ-nu′rah) [Gr. *amphi* on both sides + *neuron* nerve]. A class of primitive mollusks of sluggish habit, with a bilaterally symmetrical nervous system.

amylase (am′ĭ-lās) [L *amylum* starch]. An enzyme that catalyzes the hydrolysis of starches; it cleaves α-1 → 4 glucosidic bonds of polysaccharides.

anabolism (ah-nab′o-lizm) [Gr. *anabolē* a throwing up]. Chemical reactions in which simpler substances are combined to form more complex substances, resulting in the storage of energy, the production of new cellular materials and growth.

anaerobic (an″a-er-o′bik) [*an* neg. + Gr. *aero* air + *bios* life]. Growing or metabolizing only in the absence of molecular oxygen.

analogous (ah-nal′o-gus) [Gr. *analogos* according to a due ratio, conformable, proportionate]. Similar in function or appearance but not in origin or development.

anamniote (an-am′ne-ōt) [Gr. *an* not + *amnion* lamb]. A vertebrate characterized by the absence of an amnion during its development; a fish or amphibian.

anaphase (an′ah-fāz) [Gr. *ana* up, back, again + *phasis* phase]. Stage in mitosis or meiosis, following the metaphase, in which the chromosomes move apart toward the poles of the spindle.

androgen (an′dro-jen) [Gr. *andros* man + *gennan* to produce]. Any substance which possesses masculinizing activities, such as testosterone or one of the other male sex hormones.

anhydro bonds (an-hī′dro) [Gr. *ahydros* waterless]. Bonds formed by the removal of water between two molecules, i.e., by removing an OH ion from one molecule and an H ion from the other.

anion (an′i-on) [Gr. *ana* up + *iōn* going]. An ion carrying a negative charge.

annelida (a-nel′ĭ-dah) [F. *anneler* to arrange in rings]. The phylum of segmented worms including earthworms, clamworms and leeches.

antenna (an-ten′ah) [L. a spar projecting from the mast of a boat, supporting a sail; a sail yard]. A projecting, usually filamentous organ equipped with sensory receptors.

anthozoa (an″tho-zo′ah) [Gr. *anthos* flower + *zoia* animal]. A class of coelenterates with large polyps and no medusa stage; includes corals.

antibiotics (an″ti-bi-ot′ik) [Gr. *anti* against + *bios* life]. Substances produced by microorganisms which have the capacity, in dilute solutions, to inhibit the growth of or to destroy bacteria and other microorganisms; used largely in the treatment of infectious diseases of man, animals and plants.

antibody (an′ti-bod″e). A protein produced in response to the presence of some foreign substance in the blood or tissues.

antidiuretic hormone (an″tĭ-di″u-ret′ik hor′mōn) [Gr. *anti* against + *diouretikos* promoting urine; *hormaein* to set in motion, spur on]. A hormone produced in the hypothalamus and stored and released from the posterior lobe of the pituitary which controls the rate at which water is reabsorbed by the kidney tubules.

antigen (an′tĭ-jen) [Gr. *anti* against + *gennan* to produce]. A foreign substance, usually protein or protein-polysaccharide complex in nature, which elicits the formation of specific antibodies within an organism.

antimetabolites (an″tĭ-mĕ-tab′o-līt) [Gr. *anti* against + *metaballein* to turn about, change,

alter]. Substances bearing a close structural resemblance to ones required for normal physiological functioning; exert their effect by replacing or interfering with the utilization of the essential metabolite.

antitoxin (an″ti-tok′sin) [Gr. *anti* against + *toxicon* poison]. An antibody produced in response to the presence of a toxin (usually protein) released by a bacterium.

aorta (a-or′tah) [Gr. *aortē* the aorta]. One of the primary arteries of the body, e.g., the ventral aorta of fishes which distributes blood to the gills, or the dorsal aorta which distributes blood to the body.

aphasia (ah-fa′ze-ah) [*a* neg. + Gr. *phasis* speech]. Inability to recognize certain kinds of symbols (such as writing or speech) due to injury or disease of the brain centers.

apoenzyme (ap″o-en′zīm) [Gr. *apo* from + *en* in + *zymē* leaven]. Protein portion of an enzyme; requires the presence of a specific coenzyme to become a complete functional enzyme.

archenteron (ar-ken′ter-on) [Gr. *archē* beginning + *enteron* intestine]. The central cavity of the gastrula, lined with endoderm, which forms the rudiment of the digestive system.

archinephric duct (ar″ke-nef′ric) [Gr. *archaios* ancient + *nephros* kidney]. The primitive kidney duct; drains the pronephros, mesonephros and opisthonephros.

arteriole (ar-te′re-ōl) [Gr. *arteria* artery]. A minute arterial branch, especially one just proximal to a capillary.

artery A vessel through which the blood passes away from the heart to the various parts of the body; typically has thick, elastic walls.

arthropod (ar′thro-pod) [Gr. *arthron* joint + *pous* foot]. An invertebrate, such as an insect or a crustacean, which has jointed legs.

arthropoda (ar-throp′o-dah) [Gr. *arthron* joint + *podos* foot]. The phylum of invertebrates with jointed legs, including insects and crustaceans.

aschelminthes (ask″hel-minth′ēz) [Gr. *askos* bladder + *helminthes* worms]. A phylum of pseudocoelomate animals with mosaic development and a remarkable degree of cell constancy.

asconoid (as′kon-oid) [Gr. *askos* bladder + *eidos* form]. In sponges, a simple vaselike body plan with no folding of the body wall.

asteroidea (as″ter-oi′de-ah) [Gr. *asteroeides* like a star]. The starfishes, a class of common and familiar echinoderms.

atom The smallest quantity of an element which can retain the chemical properties of the element, composed of an atomic nucleus containing protons and neutrons together with electrons that circle the nucleus in specific orbits.

atomic orbital Distribution of an electron around the atomic nucleus.

atresia (ah-tre′ze-ah) [Gr. *a* neg. + *trēsis* a hole + *-ia*]. Absence or closure of a normal body orifice, passage or cavity.

atrium (a′tre-um) [Gr. *atrion* hall]. A chamber affording entrance to another structure or organ; a chamber of the heart receiving blood from a vein and pumping it into a ventricle.

auditory ossicle (os′sĭ-k′l) [L. *ossiculum* a small bone]. One of three small bones (malleus, incus and stapes) which transmit vibrations across the middle ear cavity from tympanic membrane to the inner ear.

auricle (aw′ri-k′l) [L. *auricula* small ear]. A receiving chamber of the heart that pumps blood into the ventricle; a synonym for atrium.

auricularia (aw-rik″u-la′rĭ-ah). One of several kinds of echinoderm larvae that show strong resemblances to hemichordate larvae.

autosome (aw′to-sōm) [Gr. *autos* self + *soma* body]. Any ordinary paired chromosome, as distinguished from a sex chromosome.

avian (a′ve-an) [L. *avis* bird]. Pertaining to the Aves, the class of flying vertebrates consisting of birds.

avicularia (a-vik″u-la′ri-a) [L. *avicula* small bird]. Specialized members of a colony of ectoproct bryozoa which resemble the head of a bird.

axon (ak′son) [Gr. *axōn* axle]. Nerve fiber which conducts nerve impulses away from the cell body.

bacteriophage (bak-te′re-o-fāj″) [L. *bactērion* little rod + Gr. *phagein* to eat]. Virus which infects and may kill bacteria.

bacterium (bak-te′re-um) [L. *bactērion* little rod]. Small, typically one-celled microorganisms characterized by the absence of a formed nucleus.

basal body A structure at the base of a flagellum or cilium that controls its activity; similar in several ways to a centriole.

basal metabolic rate The amount of energy expended by the body just to keep alive, when no food is being digested and no muscular work is being done.

base A compound which releases hydroxyl ions (OH⁻) when dissolved in water; turns red litmus paper blue.

benthos (ben′thos) [Gr. *benthos* bottom of the sea]. The flora and fauna of the bottom of oceans or lakes.

bicuspid (bi-kus′pid) [L. *bi* two + *cuspis* point]. Having two cusps, flaps or points.

binary fission (bi′na-re) [L. *binarius* two at a time]. Simple cell division into two equal daughter cells.

binomial system System of naming organisms by the combination of the names of genus and species.

bioassay (bi″o-as-sa′) [Gr. *bios* life]. Determination of the effectiveness of a biologically active substance by noting its effect on a living organism.

biologic clock Means by which activities of plants or animals are adapted to the regularly recurring changes in the external physical conditions, and perhaps to changes in internal milieu as well.

biological oxidation Process in which electrons removed from an atom or molecule are transferred through the electron transmitter system of the mitochondrion.

bioluminescence (bi″o-loo″mĭ-nes′ens) [Gr. *bios* life + L. *lumen* light]. Emission of light by living cells or by enzyme systems prepared from living cells.

biome (bi′ōm) [Gr. *bios* life + *ome* mass]. Large, easily differentiated community unit arising as a result of complex interactions of climate, other physical factors and biotic factors.

biotic potential Inherent power of a population to increase in numbers when the age ratio is stable and all environmental conditions are optimal.

birefringence (bi″re-frin′jens) [L. *bi* two + *refringere* to break up]. Property of a substance in solution to refract light differently in different planes.

blastocoele (blas′to-sēl) [Gr. *blastos* germ + *koilos* hollow]. The fluid-filled cavity of the blastula, the mass of cells produced by cleavage of a fertilized ovum.

blastocyst (blas′to-sist) [Gr. *blastos* germ + *kystis* bladder]. The modified blastula stage of embryonic mammals; it consists of an inner cell mass, which develops into the embryo, and a peripheral layer of cells, the trophoblast, which contributes to the placenta.

blastopore (blas′to-pōr) [Gr. *blastos* germ + *poros* opening]. The opening, in the gastrula stage of development, from the archenteron to the surface.

blastula (blas′tu-lah) [Gr. *blastos* germ]. Usually spherical structure produced by cleavage of a fertilized ovum, consisting of a single layer of cells surrounding a fluid-filled cavity.

blood plasma (plaz′mah) [Gr. *plasma* to mold]. The liquid portion of the blood in which the corpuscles are suspended; differs from blood serum in that it contains fibrinogen.

book gill A respiratory organ composed of many lamellae, like the pages of a book, found in both aquatic (gill) and terrestrial (lung) chelicerates.

book lung See *book gill.*

Bowman's capsule Double-walled, hollow sac of cells which surrounds the glomerulus at the end of each kidney tubule.

brachiopoda (bra″ke-op′o-da) [L. *brachium* arm]. A phylum of marine organisms which possess a pair of shells and, internally, a pair of coiled arms which bear ciliated tentacles.

brachycephalic (brak″e-se-fal′ik) [Gr. *brachys* short + *kephalē* head]. Having a skull which is broad; roundheaded; with a cranial index of 80 or more.

brachydactyly (brak″e-dak′tǐ-le) [Gr. *brachys* short + *daktylos* finger]. Abnormal shortness of the fingers and toes.

brachyphalangy (brak″e-fah-lan′je) [Gr. *brachy* short + *phalanx* log]. Abnormal shortness of one or more of the phalanges of a finger or toe.

branchial (brang′ke-al) [Gr. *branchion* a gill]. Pertaining to the gills or gill region.

brownian movement Motion of small particles in solution or suspension resulting from their being bumped by water molecules.

bryozoa (bri″o-zo′a) [Gr. *bryo* moss + *zoe* life]. Moss animals; the colonies of some species, delicately branched and beautiful, are sometimes mistaken for seaweed; other species form colonies which appear as thin, lacy encrustations on rocks.

budding Asexual reproduction in which a small part of the parent's body separates from the rest and develops into a new individual, eventually either taking up an independent existence or becoming a more or less independent member of the colony.

buffers Substances in a solution which tend to lessen the change in hydrogen ion concentration (*p*H), which otherwise would be produced by adding acids or bases.

calorie The amount of heat required to raise one gram of water one degree centigrade (strictly, from 14.5° to 15.5° C.). A kilocalorie or Calorie is a unit 1000 times larger, the amount of heat required to raise one kilogram of water one degree centigrade.

capillaries (kap′ǐ-lar″e) [L. *capillaris* hairlike]. Microscopic thin-walled vessels located in the tissues, connecting arteries and veins and through the walls of which substances pass to the tissue fluid.

carapace (kar′ă-pās) [Sp. *carapacho*]. A bony or chitinous shield covering the back of an animal.

carbohydrate (kar″bo-hi′drāt). Compounds containing carbon, hydrogen and oxygen, in the ratio of 1C:2H:1O; e.g., sugars, starches and cellulose.

carbonic anhydrase (kar′bon-ik an-hi′drās) [Gr. *an* not + *hydor* water]. An enzyme which catalyzes the reaction carbon dioxide + water ⇌ carbonic acid; abundant in erythrocytes.

carnivore (kar′nǐ-vōr) [L. *carno* flesh + *vorare* to devour]. An animal that eats flesh.

carotene (kar′o-tēn) [L. *carota* carrot]. Yellow to orange-red pigments found in carrots, sweet potatoes, leafy vegetables, etc., which can be converted in the animal body to vitamin A.

cartilage replacement bone (kar′tǐ-lij) [L. *cartilago* cartilage]. Bone which develops in and around a cartilaginous rudiment, which it gradually replaces.

catabolism (kah-tab′o-lizm) [Gr. *katabolē* a throwing down]. Chemical reactions by which complex substances are converted, within living cells, into simpler compounds with the release of energy.

catalyst (kat′ah-list) [Gr. *katalysis* dissolution]. A substance which regulates the speed at which a chemical reaction occurs without affecting the end point of the reaction and without being used up as a result of the reaction.

cation (kat′i-on) [Gr. *kata* down + *ion* going]. An ion bearing a positive charge.

ceboids New World prehensile-tailed monkeys.

cecum (se′kum) [L. *caecum* blind]. A blind pouch into which open the ileum, the colon, and the vermiform appendix.

cell constancy An extreme example of mosaic development which results in all individuals in a species having exactly the same number of cells in comparable tissues performing similar functions.

cell lineage In embryos with mosaic development, the tracing of cell histories through successive cleavages.

cell theory The generalization that all living things are composed of cells and cell products, that new cells are formed by the division of pre-existing cells, that there are fundamental similarities in the chemical constituents and metabolic activities of all cells, and that the activity of an organism as a whole is the sum of the activities and interactions of its independent cell units.

cells The microscopic units of structure and function that comprise the bodies of plants and animals.

centriole (sen′trǐ-ōl) [L. *centrum* center]. Small, dark-staining organelle lying near the nucleus in the cytoplasm of animal cells, and forming the spindle during mitosis and meiosis.

centromere (sen′tro-mēr) [Gr. *kentro* center + *meros* part]. The point on a chromosome to which the spindle fiber is attached; during mitosis or meiosis it is the first part of the chromosome to pass toward the pole.

cephalochordata (sef″ah-lo-kor-dā′tah) [Gr. *kephalē* head + L. *chorda* string]. A subphylum of chordates characterized by the extension of the notochord to the anterior end of the body; includes *Amphioxus*.

cephalopoda (sef″ah-lop′o-dah) [Gr. *kephalē* head + *podos* foot]. The squids and octopuses, a class of mollusks with arms or tentacles surrounding the head.

cercaria (ser-ka′re-ah) [Gr. *kerkos* tail]. The final free-swimming larval stage of a trematode parasite, which encysts in a fish.

cercopithecoid An Old World monkey; has a tail but does not use it as a limb.

cerebellum (ser″e-bel′um) [L. dim of *cerebrum* brain]. The part of the vertebrate brain which controls muscular coordination.

cerebrum (ser′e-brum) [L. *cerebrum* brain]. A major portion of the vertebrate brain, occupying the upper part of the cranium; the two cerebral hemispheres, united by the corpus callosum, form the largest part of the central nervous system in man.

cestoda (ses-to′dah) [Gr. *kestos* girdle]. The tapeworms, a class of parasitic flatworms.

chaetognatha (ke″to-gna′thah) [Gr. *chaite* hair + *gnathos* jaw]. The arrow worms, a phylum of enterocoelous marine predators.

chelicera (ke-lis′er-a) [Gr. *chele* claw + *keras* horn]. A pair of pincer-like head appendages found in spiders, scorpions and other arachnids.

chemoreceptor (ke″mo-re-sep′tor). A sense organ or sensory cell that responds to chemical stimuli.

chemotropism (ke-mot′ro-pizm) [Gr. *chemeia* chemistry + *tropos* a turning]. A growth response to a chemical stimulus.

chilopoda (ki-lop′o-dah) [Gr. *cheilos* lip + *podos* foot]. Centipedes, a class of arthropods whose first pair of legs have evolved as poison fangs.

chimaera (ki-me′rah) [Gr. *chimaira* a mythological fire-spouting monster with a lion's head, goat's body and serpent's tail]. An individual organism whose body contains cell populations derived from different zygotes of the same or of different species; occurring spontaneously, as in twins, or produced artifically, as an organism which develops from combined portions of different embryos, or one in which tissues or cells of another organism have been introduced. Also, a cartilaginous fish belonging to the subclass Holocephali.

chitin (ki′tin) [Gr. *chitōn* tunic]. An insoluble, horny protein-polysaccharide that forms the exoskeleton of arthropods and the cell walls of many fungi.

choanocyte (ko′ă-no″sīt) [Gr. *choane* funnel + *kytos* hollow vessel]. A unique cell type with a flagellum surrounded by a thin cytoplasmic collar; characteristic of sponges and one group of protozoa.

chondrichthyes (kon″drik′thi-ēz) [Gr. *chondros* cartilage + *ichthys* fish]. A class of fishes with cartilaginous skeletons; includes sharks, skates and their allies.

chordate (kor′dāt) [L. *chorda* string]. A member of the phylum of animals characterized by the presence of a notochord at some stage of development; includes urochordates, *Amphioxus* and vertebrates.

chorion (ko′re-on). An extraembryonic membrane in reptiles, birds and mammals that forms an outer cover around the embryo and in mammals contributes to the formation of the placenta.

choroid coat (ko′roid) [Gr. *chorion* the outermost extraembryonic membrane of an amniote embryo + *eidos* form]. The middle, pigmented and vascular layer of the eyeball; its anterior portion contributes to the iris and ciliary body.

chromatin (kro′mah-tin) [Gr. *chroma* color]. The readily stainable portion of the cell nucleus, forming a network of fibrils within the nucleus; composed of DNA and proteins.

chromatin spot An aggregation of chromatin at the periphery of the nucleus, evident in cells of human skin or from the mucosal lining of the mouth; makes possible the determination of the "nuclear sex" of an individual. Most of the cells of a female and none of the cells of a male have a chromatin spot.

chromatophore (kro′mah-to-fōr″) [Gr. *chroma* color + *pherein* to bear]. Any pigmentary cell or color-producing plastid, such as those of the deep layers of the epidermis.

chromomere (kro′mo-mēr) [Gr. *chroma* color + *meros* part]. One of a linear series of beadlike structures composing a chromosome.

chromosomes (kro′mo-sōm) [Gr. *chroma* color + *sōma* body]. Filamentous or rod-shaped bodies in the cell nucleus which contain the hereditary units, the genes.

cilia (sil′e-ah) [L. *cilium* eyelid]. Small, bristle-like, cytoplasmic projections on the free surface of cells; they beat in coordinated fashion to move the cell or its environment.

ciliata (sil″e-a′tah) [L. *cilium* eyelid]. A class of protozoa having cilia throughout life.

circadian rhythms (ser″kah-de′an) [L. *circa* about + *dies* a day]. Repeated sequences of events which occur at about 24 hour intervals.

cistron (sis′tron). The genetic unit of biochemical function; the sequence of nucleotide pairs in DNA that specify the amino acid sequence of a single peptide chain.

class In taxonomy, a major subdivision of a phylum. Each class is composed of one or more related orders.

cleidoic egg (kli-do′ik) [Gr. *kleidouchos* holding the keys]. The eggs of reptiles, birds and primitive mammals which are self-sufficient, and in which the embryo develops directly to the miniature adult without passing through a larval stage.

cline (klin) [Gr. *klin-*, stem of *klinein* to slope, and of *klinē* bed]. Continuous series of differences in structure or function exhibited by the members of a species along a line extending from one part of their range to another.

clitoris (kli′to-ris) [Gr. *kleitoris*]. A small, erectile body at the anterior part of the vulva which is homologous to the male penis.

cloaca (klo-a′kah) [L. a sewer]. A common chamber receiving the discharge of the digestive, excretory and reproductive systems in most of the lower vertebrates.

cobalamin (ko-bal′ah-min). Vitamin B_{12}; substance essential to the manufacture of red cells.

cocci (kok′si) [L.; Gr. *kokkos* berry]. Spherical bacterial cells, usually less than 1 μ in diameter.

cochlea (kok′le-ah) [Gr. *kochlias* snail]. The part of the inner ear consisting of the cochlear duct, which contains the receptive organ of Corti and the scala vestibuli and tympani; a spirally coiled tube of two and a half turns, resembling a snail's shell.

coelenterata (se-len″ter-ah′tah) [Gr. *koilos* hollow + *enteron* intestine]. A phylum including hydra, jellyfish and corals.

coelom (se′lom) [Gr. *koilia* cavity]. Body cavity of triploblastic animals lying within the mesoderm and lined by it.

coenzyme (ko-en′zīm) [L. *cum* with + Gr. *en* in + *zymē* leaven]. A substance which is required for some particular enzymatic reaction to occur; participates in the reaction by donating or accepting some reactant; loosely bound to enzyme.

collagen (kol′ah-jen) [Gr. *kolla* glue + *gennan* to produce]. Protein in connective tissue fibers which is converted to gelatin by boiling.

colloblast (kol′o-blast) [Gr. *kolla* glue + *blastos* bud]. An adhesive cell used by ctenophores to capture prey.

colloid (kol′oid) [Gr. *kollōdēs* glutinous]. A two-phase system in which particles of one phase, ranging in size from 1 to 100 mμ, are dispersed in the second phase; a gelatinous material secreted by cuboidal epithelial cells, arranged in hollow spheres one cell thick, in the thyroid.

colony (kol′o-ne) [L. *colonus* farmer]. An association of unicellular or multicellular organisms of the same species; each individual is separate or essentially so, but sometimes there are connections among the members of the colony and some division of labor among them, e.g., feeding and reproductive polyps of certain hydrozoa.

commensalism (kǒ-men′sal-izm″) [L. *cum* together + *mensa* table]. A relationship between two species in which one is benefited and the second is neither harmed nor benefited by existing together.

cone (kōn) [L. *conus*]. In zoology, the cone-shaped photoreceptive cells of the retina which are particularly sensitive to bright light and, by distinguishing light of various wave lengths, mediate color vision.

conjugation (kon″ju-ga′shun) [L. *conjugatio* a blending]. The act of joining together; form of sexual reproduction in which nuclear material is exchanged during the temporary union of two cells; occurs in many ciliate protozoa and in bacteria.

conservation of energy, law of A fundamental law of physics which states that in any given system the amount of energy is constant; energy is neither created nor destroyed, but only transformed from one form to another.

conservation of matter, law of A fundamental law of physics which states that in any chemical reaction atoms are neither created nor destroyed but simply change partners.

"consumer" organisms Those elements of an ecosystem, plants or animals, that eat other plants or animals.

contraception (kon-trah-sep′shun) [L. *contra*

against + *conceptus* conceiving]. Method of birth control which involves the use of mechanical or chemical agents to prevent the sperm from reaching and fertilizing the egg.

conus arteriosus (ko′nus ar-te″re-o′sus) [L. *conus* cone + *arteriosus* arterial]. The terminal chamber of the heart of many fishes and amphibians; receives blood from the ventricle and delivers it to the ventral aorta.

convergent evolution (kon-ver′jent) [L. *cum* together + *vergere* to incline]. The independent evolution of similar structures, which carry on similar functions, in two or more organisms of widely different, unrelated ancestry.

copulation (kop″u-la′shun) [L. *copulatio*]. Sexual union; act of physical joining of two animals during which sperm cells are transferred from one to the other.

cornea (kor′ne-ah) [L. *corneus* horny]. The transparent structure forming the anterior part of the fibrous layer of the eyeball; it is continuous posteriorly with the sclera.

corpus callosum (kor′pus kah-lo′sum) [L. *corpus* body + *callosus* hard]. A large commissure of fibers interconnecting the two cerebral hemispheres in mammals.

corpus luteum (kor′pus lu′tĭ-um) [L. *corpus* body + *luteus* yellow]. A yellow glandular mass in the ovary formed by the cells of an ovarian follicle that has matured and discharged its ovum.

corpus striatum (stri-a′tum) [L. *corpus* body + *striatum* striped]. A large subcortical mass of neuron cell bodies and fibers in the base of each cerebral hemisphere.

cortex (kor′teks) [L. *cortex* bark]. The outer layer of an organ.

covalent bond Chemical bond involving one or more shared pairs of electrons.

cranium (kra′ne-um) [Gr. *kranion* head]. The part of a skull which surrounds the brain; the brain case.

cretinism (kre′tin-izm). A chronic condition in the young due to congenital lack of thyroid secretion; retarded physical and mental development.

crinoidea (kri-noi′de-ah) [Gr. *krinoeides* like a lily]. The sea lilies, a class of ancient echinoderms, some of which survive today.

crop A sac in the digestive tract in which food is stored before digestion begins.

crossing over Process during meiosis in which the homologous chromosomes undergo synapsis and exchange segments.

crossopterigian (krŏ-sop′tĕ-rij″ĭ-an) [Gr. *krossoi* a fringe + *pterygos* wing]. A member of an order of sarcopterygian fishes ancestral to terrestrial vertebrates; now nearly extinct.

crustacea (krus-ta′she-ah) [L. *crusta* a hard surface]. A large subphylum of arthropods having typically biramous limbs and two pairs of antennae.

ctenophores (tēn′o-fors) [Gr. *ktenos* comb]. Marine animals ("comb jellies") whose bodies consist of two layers of cells enclosing a mass of jelly; the outer surface is covered with eight rows of cilia, resembling combs, by which the animal moves through the water.

cutaneous (ku-ta′ne-us) [L. *cutis* skin].   Pertaining to the skin.

cytochromes (si′to-krom) [Gr. *kytōs* hollow vessel + *chroma* color].   The iron-containing heme proteins of the electron transmitter system that are alternately oxidized and reduced in biological oxidation.

cytokinesis (si″to-ki-ne′sis) [Gr. *kytōs* hollow vessel + *kinesis* motion].   The division of the cytoplasm during mitosis or meiosis.

cytoplasmic bridge   A cytoplasmic connection between cells that occurs occasionally in tissues and also in some colonial protozoa.

deamination (de-am′ĭ-na′shun).   Removal of an amino group (—NH₂) from an amino acid or other organic compound.

decarboxylation (de″kar-bok″sĭ-la′shun).   Removal of a carboxyl group (—COOH) from an organic compound.

defecation (def″e-ka′shun) [L. *defaecare* to deprive of dregs].   The elimination of excrement, much of which is undigested refuse that has not taken part in metabolism.

dehydrogenation (de-hi″dro-jen-a′shun) [L. *de* apart + Gr. *hydōr* water].   A form of oxidation in which hydrogen atoms are removed from a molecule.

delamination (de″lam-ĭ-na′shun) [L. *de* apart + *lamina* plate].   Separation of the blastoderm into an upper ectoderm and a lower endoderm during embryonic development.

deme (dēm).   A population of very similar organisms interbreeding in nature and occupying a circumscribed area.

denaturation (de-na-tūr-a′shun).   Alteration of physical properties and three dimensional structure of a protein, nucleic acid or other macromolecule by mild treatment that does not break the primary structure.

dendrite (den′drīt) [Gr. *dendron* tree].   Nerve fiber, typically branched, which conducts a nerve impulse toward the cell body.

deoxyribose (de-ok″se-ri′bōs).   A five-carbon sugar with one less oxygen atom than the parent sugar, ribose; constituent of DNA.

dermal bone (der′mal) [Gr. *derma* skin].   Bone that develops directly in connective tissue and is not preceded by a cartilaginous rudiment; found in the dermis of the skin, or just beneath the skin.

dermis (der′mis) [Gr. *derma* skin].   The deeper layer of the skin of vertebrates.

detoxification (de-tok″sĭ-fi-ka′shun).   Enzymatic processes which reduce the toxicity of a substance.

deuterostome (du′ter-o-stōm″) [Gr. *deuteros* second + *stoma* mouth].   An animal in which the site of the blastopore is posterior—far from the mouth, which forms anew at the anterior end.

diapause (di′a-pawz) [Gr. *dia* through + *pausis* a stopping].   Inactive state of an insect during the pupal stage.

diaphragm (di′ah-fram) [Gr. *diaphragnynai* to fence by a partition].   The fibromuscular partition separating the thoracic and abdominal cavities of mammals; its contraction plays the major role in inspiration.

diastole (di-as′to-le) [Gr. *diastole* a drawing asunder; expansion].   Relaxation of the heart muscle, especially that of the ventricle, during which the lumen becomes filled with blood.

diencephalon (di″en-sef′ah-lon) [Gr. *dia* through + *enkephalos* brain].   A major subdivision of the brain lying between the telencephalon and mesencephalon; includes the epithalamus, thalamus and hypothalamus.

differentiation   Development toward a more mature state; a process changing a relatively unspecialized cell to a more specialized cell.

diffusion   The movement of molecules from a region of high concentration to one of lower concentration, brought about by their kinetic energy.

digitigrade (dij′ĭ-tĭ-grād″) [L. *digitus* finger or toe + *gradi* to walk].   Locomotion by walking on the toes; applied to animals—dogs and cats—whose digits only touch the ground.

diploid (dip′loid) [Gr. *diploos* twofold].   A chromosome number twice that found in gametes; containing two sets of chromosomes.

diplopoda (dĭ-plop′o-dah) [Gr. *diploos* double + *podos* foot].   Millipedes, a class of arthropods in which many body segments appear to have two pairs of legs.

disaccharides (di-sak′ah-rid).   Sugars which yield two monosaccharides on hydrolysis; e.g., sucrose, lactose and maltose.

displacement activity   An act that is apparently irrelevant to the situation; it often occurs when two conflicting responses are called for at the same time.

distal (dis′tal) [L. *distans* distant].   Remote; farther from the point of reference.

DNA   Deoxyribose nucleic acid; is present in chromosomes and contains genetic information coded in specific sequences of its constituent nucleotides.

dolichocephalic (dol″ĭ-ko-se-fal′ik) [Gr. *dolichos* long + *kephalē* head].   Longheaded; pertaining to a skull with a breadth less than 75 per cent of its length.

DPN   Diphosphopyridine nucleotide; a coenzyme serving as a hydrogen donor or acceptor in many reactions.

ductus arteriosus (duk′tus ar-te″re-o′sus) [L. *ductus* conduit + *arteriosus* arterial].   A short vessel, derived from the dorsal part of the sixth aortic arch, which connects the pulmonary artery and dorsal aorta; normally present only in larval or embryonic stages and serving to divert blood from the developing lungs.

ecdyson (ek-di′son) [Gr. *ekdysis* a getting out]. The hormone that induces molting (ecdysis) in anthropods.

echinoderm (e-kin′o-derm) [L. *echinus* hedgehog, sea urchin + Gr. *derma* skin]. Phylum of spiny-skinned marine animals; e.g., starfish, sea urchins, sea cucumbers.

echinoidea (ek″in-oi′de-ah). The sea urchins, a class of echinoderms with rigid body walls and long spines.

echiuroidea (ek″i-u-roi′de-ah) [Gr. *echis* viper + *oura* tail]. A small phylum of marine worms related to annelids.

ecologic niche The status of an organism within a community or ecosystem; depends on the organism's structural adaptations, physiologic responses and behavior.

ecology (e-kol′o-je) [Gr. *oikos* house + *logos* word, discourse]. The study of the interrelations between living things and their environment, both physical and biotic.

ecosystem (ek″o-sis′tem) [Gr. *oikos* house]. A natural unit of living and nonliving parts that interact to produce a stable system in which the exchange of materials between living and non-living parts follows a circular path.

ecotone A fairly broad transition region between adjacent biomes; contains some organisms from each of the adjacent biomes plus some that are characteristic of, and perhaps restricted to, the ecotone.

ectoderm (ek′to-derm) [Gr. *ektos* without + *derma* skin]. The outer of the two germ layers of the gastrula; gives rise to the skin and nervous system.

effector (ef-fek′tor). Structures of the body by which an organism acts; the means by which it reacts to stimuli; e.g., muscles and glands.

efferent (ef′er-ent) [L. *ex* out + *ferre* to carry]. Conveying away; denoting certain vessels or neurons that transmit blood or impulses away from a point of reference; efferent neurons are motor neurons conducting impulses away from the central nervous system.

elasmobranch (e-las′mo-brank) [Gr. *elasmos* plate + L. *branchia* gill]. A member of a subclass of cartilaginous fishes in which the gills are plate-like and each gill slit opens independently on the body surface; sharks, skates and their allies.

electrolyte (e-lek′tro-līt) [Gr. *elektron* amber + *lytos* soluble]. Substance which dissociates in solution into charged particles, ions and thus permits the conduction of an electric current through the solution.

electron transmitter system System of enzymes localized within the mitochondria which transfer electrons from foodstuff molecules to oxygen.

element (el′ĕ-ment). One of the hundred or so types of matter, natural or man-made, composed of atoms all of which have the same number of protons in the atomic nucleus and the same number of electrons circling in the orbits.

embolus (em′bo-lus) [Gr. *embolos* plug]. A thrombus or any other particle carried by the bloodstream which blocks a blood vessel.

embryo (em′bre-o) [Gr. *en* in + *bryein* to swell]. The early stage of development of an organism; the developing product of fertilization of an egg.

emulsion (e-mul′shun) [L. *emulsum* to milk out]. A colloid in which one liquid phase is dispersed in another liquid phase.

endergonic (end″er-gon′ik) [Gr. *endon* within + *ergon* work]. A reaction characterized by the absorption of energy; requires energy to occur.

endocrine (en′do-krin) [Gr. *endon* within + *krinein* to separate]. Secreting internally; applied to organs whose function is to secrete into the blood or lymph a substance that has a specific effect on another organ or part.

endoderm (en′do-derm) [Gr. *endon* within + *derma* skin]. The inner germ layer of the gastrula, lining the archenteron; becomes the digestive tract and its outgrowths—the liver, lungs and pancreas.

endolymph (en′do-limf) [Gr. *endon* within + L. *lympha* lymph]. The lymphlike fluid contained within the semicircular canals, cochlear duct and other parts of the membranous labyrinth of the inner ear.

endopeptidase (en″do-pep′tĭ-dās) [Gr. *endon* within + *peptos* digested]. A proteolytic enzyme which cleaves peptide bonds within a peptide chain.

endopodite (en-dop′o-dīt) [Gr. *endon* within + *podos* foot]. The inner branch of a biramous crustacean limb.

endoskeleton (en″do-skel′ĕ-ton) [Gr. *endon* within + *skeleton* a dried body]. Bony and cartilaginous supporting structures within the body; provide support from within.

endostyle (en′do-stīl) [Gr. *endon* within + *stylos* a pillar]. A longitudinal groove in the floor of the pharynx of certain lower chordates and larval cyclostomes; its glandular and ciliated cells secrete mucus which is moved anteriorly and entraps minute food particles.

engram (en′gram) [Gr. *en* in + *gramma* mark]. The term is applied to the presumed change that occurs in the brain as a consequence of learning; a memory trace.

enterocoel (en′ter-o-sēl″) [Gr. *enteron* intestine + *koilia* cavity]. A body cavity formed by outpouches from the primitive gut.

entoprocta (en″to-prok′tah) [Gr. *entos* within + *proctos* anus]. A small phylum of pseudocoels having both mouth and anus within a circlet of feeding tentacles.

enzyme (en'zīm) [Gr. *en* in + *zymē* leaven]. A protein catalyst produced within a living organism which accelerates specific chemical reactions.

epiboly (e-pib'o-le) [Gr. *epibolē* cover]. A method of gastrulation by which the smaller blastomeres at the animal pole of the embryo grow over and enclose the cells of the vegetal hemisphere.

epidermis (ep'ĭ-der'mis) [Gr. *epi* on + *derma* skin]. The outermost layer of cells of an organism.

epididymis (ep'ĭ-did'ĭ-mis) [Gr. *epi* on + *didymos* testis]. Complexly coiled tube adjacent to the testis where sperm are stored.

epigenesis (ep'ĭ-jen'e-sis) [Gr. *epi* on + *genesis* to be born]. The theory that development proceeds from a structureless cell by the successive formation and addition of new parts which do not pre-exist in the fertilized egg.

epiglottis (ep'ĭ-glot'is) [Gr. *epi* on + *glottis* the tongue]. The lidlike structure which covers the glottis, the entrance to the larynx.

epithelium (ep'ĭ-the'le-um) [Gr. *epi* on + *thēlē* nipple]. The layer of tissue covering the internal and external surfaces of the body, including the lining of vessels and other small cavities; consists of cells joined by small amounts of cementing substances.

equilibrium (e"kwĭ-lib're-um) [L. *aequus* equal + *libra* balance]. A state of balance; a condition in which opposing forces exactly counteract each other.

erythrocyte (e-rith'ro-sīt) [Gr. *erythros* red + *kytos* hollow vessel]. Red blood cells; they contain hemoglobin and transport gases.

estivation Aestivation.

estrogen (es'tro-jen). One of the female sex hormones, produced by the ovarian follicle, which promotes the development of the secondary sex characteristics.

estrus (es'trus) [L. *oestrus* gadfly; Gr. *oistros* anything that drives mad, any vehement desire]. The recurrent, restricted period of sexual receptivity in female mammals, marked by intense sexual urge.

eustachian tube (u-sta'ke-an) [*Eustachio* an Italian anatomist of the sixteenth century]. The auditory tube passing between the middle ear cavity and pharynx of most terrestrial vertebrates; it permits the equalization of pressure on the tympanic membrane.

eutherian (u-thēr'ĭ-an) [Gr. *eu* good + *therion* beast]. One of the placental mammals in which a well formed placenta is present and the young are born at a relatively advanced stage of development; includes all living mammals except monotremes and marsupials.

excretion (eks-kre'shun) [L. *ex* out + *cernere* to sift, separate]. Removal of metabolic wastes by an organism.

exergonic (ek"ser-gon'ik) [L. *ex* out + Gr. *ergon* work]. A reaction characterized by the release of energy.

exopeptidase (ek"so-pep'tĭ-dās) [Gr. *exo* outside and *peptos* digested]. A proteolytic enzyme which cleaves only the bond joining a terminal amino acid to a peptide chain.

exopodite (eks-op'o-dīt) [Gr. *exo* outside + *podos* foot]. The outer branch of a biramous crustacean limb.

exoskeleton (ek"so-skel'ĕ-ton) [Gr. *exo* outside + *skeleton* a dried body]. Calcareous, chitinous or other hard material covering the body surface and providing protection or support.

expressivity (eks"pres-siv'ĭ-te) [L. *expressus*]. The extent to which a heritable trait is manifested by an individual carrying the principal gene conditioning it.

extensor (eks-ten'ser) [L. one that stretches]. A muscle that serves to extend or straighten a limb.

facilitation (fah-sil"i-ta'shun) [L. *facilis* easy]. The promotion or hastening of any natural process; the reverse of inhibition.

fallopian tube (fal-lo'pe-an) [*Fallopius* an Italian anatomist of the sixteenth century]. The uterine tube of mammals, which extends from a point near the ovary to the uterus; evolved from a part of the oviduct of lower vertebrates.

family In taxonomy, a major subdivision of an order. Each family is composed of one or more related genera.

feedback control System in which the accumulation of the product of a reaction leads to a decrease in its rate of production or a deficiency of the product leads to an increase in its rate of production.

fenestra (fĕ-nes'trah) [L. *fenestra* a window]. A moderate-sized opening in a structure, e.g., the fenestra ovalis (oval window) in the middle ear cavity.

fermentation (fer"men-ta'shun) [L. *fermentum* leaven]. Anaerobic decomposition of an organic compound by an enzyme system; energy is made available to the cell for other processes.

fertilization (fer"tĭ-lĭ-za'shun) [L. *fertilis* to bear, produce]. The fusion of a spermatozoon with an ovum to initiate development of the resulting zygote.

fetus (fe'tus) [L. *fetus* fruitful]. The unborn offspring after it has largely completed its embryonic development.

filtration (fil-tra'shun) [Fr. *filtre* a filter]. The passage of a liquid through a filter following a pressure gradient; occurs in capillary beds, including the glomeruli of the kidney.

fission (fish'un) [L. *fissio* to cleave]. Process of asexual reproduction in which an organism divides into two approximately equal parts.

flagellates (flaj'ĕ-lāt) [L. *flagellum* whip]. Microorganisms furnished with one or more slender, whiplike processes termed flagella.

flagellum (flă-jel′um) [L. *flagellum* whip]. A mobile whiplike, filamentous appendage of certain cells; usually longer and having a more sinuous movement than a cilium.

flexor (flek′sor). A muscle that serves to bend a limb.

fluorescence (floo″o-res′ens). The emission of light by a substance which has absorbed radiation of a different wave length; results when an excited singlet state decays to the ground state, an extremely rapid process which is independent of temperature.

follicle (fol′lĭ-k′l) [L. *folliculus* small bag]. A small sac of cells in the mammalian ovary which contains a maturing egg.

food chain A sequence of organisms through which energy is transferred from its ultimate source in a plant; each organism eats the preceding and is eaten by the following member of the sequence.

foramen (fo-ra′men) [L. *forare* to bore]. A small opening or perforation in a body structure.

foramen ovale The oval window between the right and left atria, present in the fetus and by means of which blood entering the right atrium may enter the aorta without passing through the lung.

foraminifera (fo-ram″ĭ-nif′er-ah) [L. *forare* to bore + *ferre* to bear]. Ameboid protozoa which secrete chalky, many-chambered shells with pores through which the animal extends its pseudopods.

fossa (fos′ah) [L. *fossa* a ditch]. A depression in a structure, e.g., the fossa ovalis or depression in the interatrial septum of the adult mammal; located at the site of the embryonic foramen ovale.

fossils (fos′ils) [L. *fossilis* to dig]. Any remains of an organism that have been preserved in the earth's crust.

fovea (fo′ve-ah) [L. a small pit]. A small pit in the surface of a structure or organ; specifically, a pit in the center of the retina which contains only cones and provides for keenest vision.

frustule (frus′tūl) [L. a small piece]. In coelenterates, a cylinder of tissue formed asexually that creeps away and forms a new individual.

fundus (fun′dus) [L. *fundus* bottom]. The bottom or base of an organ; the part of a hollow organ farthest from its opening.

gamete (gam′ēt) [Gr. *gametē* wife]. A reproductive cell; an egg or sperm whose union, in sexual reproduction, initiates the development of a new individual.

ganglion (gang′gle-on) [Gr. *gangli* knot]. A knotlike mass of the cell bodies of neurons located outside the central nervous system; in inverte-

brates, includes the swellings of the central nervous system.

gastrodermis (gas″tro-der′mis) [Gr. *gastēr* stomach + *derma* skin]. The tissue lining the gut cavity that is responsible for digestion and absorption.

gastropoda (gas-trop′o-dah) [Gr. *gaster* stomach + *podos* foot]. The snails, a class of mollusks that creep on a broad ventral foot.

gastrotricha (gas″tro-trĭ′kah) [Gr. *gastēr* stomach + *trichos* hair]. A class of minute aschelminthes with ciliated regions on the ventral surface.

gastrula (gas′troo-lah) [Gr. *gastēr* stomach]. Early embryonic stage which follows the blastula; consists initially of two layers, the ectoderm and the endoderm, and of two cavities, the blastocoele between ectoderm and endoderm and the archenteron, formed by invagination, lying within the endoderm, and opening to the exterior through the blastopore.

gastrulation (gas″troo-la′shun) [Gr. *gastēr* stomach]. The process by which the young embryo becomes a gastrula and acquires first two and then three layers of cells.

gel (jel) [L. from *gelare* to congeal]. A colloidal system in which the solid phase is continuous and the liquid phase is dispersed.

gemmule (jem′ūl) [L. *gemmula,* small bud]. In sponges, an asexually produced reproductive body surrounded by a protective cover.

gene (jēn) [Gr. *gennan* to produce]. The biologic unit of genetic information, self-reproducing and located in a definite position (locus) on a particular chromosome.

genetic drift The tendency, within small interbreeding populations, for heterozygous gene pairs to become homozygous for one allele or the other by *chance* rather than by selection.

genetic equilibrium The situation in which the distribution of alleles in a population is constant in successive generations (unless altered by selection or mutation).

genome (je′nōm) [Gr. *gennan* to produce + *ōma* mass, abstract entity]. A complete set of hereditary factors, contained in the haploid assortment of chromosomes.

genotype (jen′o-tip) [Gr. *geno-* from *gennan* to produce + *typos* type]. The fundamental hereditary constitution, assortment of genes, of any given organism.

genus (je′nus) [L. birth, race, kind, sort]. A rank in taxonomic classification in which closely related species are grouped together.

gestalt perception (gĕ-shtalt′) [G.]. Perception of objects in which the stimulus value of the whole is greater than the sum of the values of the parts.

gill slit An opening to the outside from the pharynx that arises during development. Water taken in at the mouth passes out through the gill slits, aiding respiration and the filtering of food.

gizzard (giz′erd) [L. *gigeria* cooked entrails of

poultry]. A portion of the digestive tract specialized for mechanical digestion.

globulin (glob'u-lin) [L. *globulus* globule]. One of a class of proteins in blood plasma, some of which (gamma globulins) function as antibodies.

glomerulus (glo-mer'u-lōs) [L. *glomus* ball]. A tuft of minute blood vessels or nerve fibers; specifically, the knot of capillaries at the proximal end of a kidney tubule.

glottis (glot'is) [Gr. *glossa* tongue]. The opening between the pharynx and larynx; it is bounded by the vocal cords in higher vertebrates.

glycolysis (gli-kol'ĭ-sis) [Gr. *glykys* sweet + *lysis* solution]. The metabolic conversion of sugars into simpler compounds.

goiter (goi'ter). An enlargement of the thyroid gland, causing a swelling in the front part of the neck; may result from overactivity of the thyroid or from deficiency of iodine.

Golgi bodies A type of cell organelle found in the cytoplasm of all cells except mature sperm and red blood cells; believed to play a role in the secretion of cell products.

gonad (gon'ad) [Gr. *gonē* seed]. A gamete-producing gland; an ovary or testis.

gordiacea (gor'dĭ-a'ce-ah) [After the Gordian knot of Greek mythology]. The hairworms, with free-living adults and larvae parasitic on insects; a class of aschelminths.

habitat (hab'ĭ-tat) [L. *habitus*, from *habere* to hold]. The natural abode of an animal or plant species; the physical area in which it may be found.

habituation A gradual decrease in response to successive stimulation due to changes in the central nervous system.

haploid (hap'loid) [Gr. *haploos* simple, single]. Having a single set of chromosomes, as normally present in a mature gamete.

Hardy-Weinberg Law The relative frequencies of the members of a pair of allelic genes in a population are described by the expansion of the binomial equation, $a^2 + 2ab + b^2$.

haversian canals (ha-ver'shan). Channels extending through the matrix of bone and containing blood vessels and nerves.

hemichordata (hem''ĭ-kor-dah'tah) [Gr. *hēmi* half + L. *chorda* cord]. A marine phylum related to the chordates; includes the acorn worms.

hemocoel (he'mo-sēl) [Gr. *haima* blood + *koilia* cavity]. A body cavity formed by expansions of the circulatory system, replacing the embryonic coelom.

hemocyanin (he''mo-si'an-in) [Gr. *haima* blood + *kyanos* dark blue]. A copper-containing respiratory pigment found in the blood of various invertebrates.

hemoglobin (he''mo-glo'bin) [Gr. *haima, haimatos* blood]. The red, iron-containing, protein pigment of the erythrocytes that transports oxygen and carbon dioxide and aids in regulation of *p*H.

hemophilia (he''mo-fil'e-ah) [Gr. *haima, haimatos* blood + *philein* to love]. Hereditary disease in which the formation of thromboplastin is impaired due to a deficiency of the so-called antihemophilic globulin; blood does not clot properly; "bleeder's disease."

hepatic (he-pat'ik) [Gr. *hēpatikos*]. Pertaining to the liver.

herbivore (her'bĭ-vōr) [L. *herba* herb + *vorare* to devour]. A plant-eating animal.

hermaphroditism (her-maf'ro-dit-izm) (Gr. god and goddess, Hermes and Aphrodite, whence *hermaphroditos* a person having the attributes of both sexes]. A state characterized by the presence of both male and female sex organs in the same organism.

heterogamy (het''er-og'ah-me) [Gr. *heteros* other + *gamōs* marriage]. Reproduction involving the union of two gametes which differ in size and structure; e.g., egg and sperm.

heterografts (het'er-o-grafts) [Gr. *heteros* other]. Grafts of tissue obtained from the body of an animal of a species other than that of the recipient.

heterotrophs (het'er-o-trofs) [Gr. *heteros* other + *trophos* feeder]. Organisms which cannot synthesize their own food from inorganic materials and therefore must live either at the expense of autotrophs or upon decaying matter.

heterozygous (het''er-o-zi'gus) [Gr. *heteros* other + *zygos* yoke]. Possessing two different alleles for a given character at the corresponding loci of homologous chromosomes.

hexapoda (heks-ah'po-dah) [Gr. *hex* six + *podos* foot]. The insects, a superclass of arthropods in which adults have three pairs of legs.

hibernation (hi''ber-na'shun) [L. *hiberna* winter]. The dormant state of decreased metabolism in which certain animals pass the winter.

hirudin (hi-ru'din) [L. *hirudo* leech]. A substance secreted by leeches that prevents the clotting of blood; used in medicine.

hirudinea (hi''ru-din'e-ah) [L *hirudo* leech]. The leeches, a class of annelids many of which suck blood.

holothuroidea (ho''lo-thu-roi'de-ah) [Gr. *holothurion* a sea polyp]. The sea cucumbers, a class of soft-bodied echinoderms.

homeostasis (ho''me-o-sta'sis) [Gr. *homois* unchanging + *stasis* standing]. The tendency to maintain uniformity or stability in the internal environment of the organism.

hominid Pertaining to the family of man; a living or extinct man or manlike type.

homograft reaction The rejection by the host organism of a graft of tissue from an organism of the same species but a different genotype.

homoiothermic (ho-moi'o-ther''mik) [Gr. *homois* unchanging + *thermē* heat]. Constant-temperature animals; e.g., birds and mammals which maintain a constant body temperature despite variations in environmental temperature.

homologous structures (ho-mol′o-gus) [Gr. *homologos* agreeing, corresponding]. Those structures of various animals which arise from common rudiments and are similar in basic plan and development.

homoplastic (ho″mo-plas′tik) [Gr. *homos* same + *plasma* a thing molded]. Pertaining to a type of analogy in which there is a superficial structural similarity between analogous organs, but there is no community of evolutionary origin.

homozygous (ho″mo-zi′gus) [Gr. *homos* same + *zygos* yoke]. Possessing an identical pair of alleles at the corresponding loci of homologous chromosomes for a given character or for all characters.

hormones (hor′mōns) [Gr. *hormaein* to set in motion, spur on]. Substances produced in cells in one part of the body which diffuse or are transported by the blood stream to cells in other parts of the body where they regulate and coordinate their activities.

humus (hu′mus) [L.]. Organic matter in the soil; a dark mold of decayed vegetable tissue which gives soil a brown or black color.

hybrid vigor (hi′brid) [L. *hybrida* mongrel]. The mating of genetically dissimilar individuals of totally unrelated strains which may yield offspring which are better adapted to survive than either parent strain.

hydrogen bond A weak bond between two molecules formed when a hydrogen atom is shared between two atoms, one of which is usually oxygen; of primary importance in the structure of nucleic acids and proteins.

hydrolysis (hi-drol′ĭ-sis) [Gr. *hydōr* water + *lysis* dissolution]. The splitting of a compound into parts by the addition of water between certain of its bonds, the hydroxyl group being incorporated in one fragment, and the hydrogen atom in the other.

hydrozoa (hi″dro-zo′ah) [Gr. *Hydra* a mythical nine-headed monster + *zōon* animal]. A class of coelenterates usually with colonial branching polyps and small medusae.

hyoid (hi′oid) [Gr. *hyo* the letter *υ* + *eidos* form]. One or more bones of visceral arch origin lodged in and supporting the base of the tongue.

hypersensitivity (hi″per-sen′sĭ-tiv′ĭ-te [Gr. *hyper* above]. A state of altered reactivity; abnormally increased sensitivity; ability to react with characteristic symptoms to the presence of certain substances (allergens) in amounts innocuous to normal individuals.

hypertonic (hi″per-ton′ik) [Gr. *hyper* above + *tonos* tone]. Having a greater concentration of solute molecules and a lower concentration of solvent (water) molecules and hence an osmotic pressure greater than that of the solution with which it is compared.

hypothalamus (hi″po-thal′ah-mus) [Gr. *hypo* under + *thalamos* inner chamber]. A region of the forebrain, the floor of the third ventricle, which contains various centers controlling visceral activities, water balance, temperature, sleep, etc.

hypothesis (hi-poth′ĕ-sis) [Gr. *hypo* under + *thesis* setting down]. A supposition assumed as a basis of reasoning which can then be tested by further controlled experiments.

hypotonic (hi″po-ton′ik) [Gr. *hypo* under + *tonos* tone]. Having a lower concentration of solute molecules and a higher concentration of solvent (water) molecules and hence an osmotic pressure lower than that of the solution with which it is compared.

ileum (il′e-um) [L. groin]. The terminal portion of the small intestine of higher vertebrates lying between the jejunum and colon.

immune reaction (ĭ-mūn′) [L. *immunis* safe]. The production of antibodies in response to antigens.

immunologic tolerance (im-mu″no-loj′ik). The ability of an organism to accept cells transplanted from a genetically distinct organism; results from exposure of the organism to an antigen before it has developed the capacity to react to it, thereafter development of capacity to react may be delayed or postponed indefinitely.

implantation (im″plan-ta′shun) [L. *in* into + *plantare* to set]. The insertion of a part of tissue in a new site in the body; the attachment of the developing embryo to the epithelial lining (endometrium) of the uterus.

imprinting A form of rapid learning by which a young bird or mammal forms a strong social attachment to an object within a few hours after hatching or birth.

induction (in-duk′shun) [L. *inductio* from *inducere* to lead in]. The production of a specific morphogenetic effect in one tissue of a developing embryo through the influence of an organizer or another tissue.

inflammation (in″flah-ma′shun) [L. *inflammare* to set on fire]. The reactions of tissues to injury: pain, increased temperature, redness and accumulation of leukocytes.

ingestion (in-jes′chun) [L. *in* into + *gerere* to carry]. The act of taking food into the body by mouth.

integument (in-teg′u-ment) [L. *integumentum* from *in* on + *tegere* to cover]. Skin, the covering of the body.

interferon (in″ter-fēr′on). A protein formed during the interaction of animal cells with viruses, which is capable of conferring on fresh animal cells of the same species resistance to infection with a wide range of viruses.

intermedin (in″ter-me′din) [L. *inter* between + *medius* middle]. A hormone secreted by the intermediate lobe of the pituitary which regulates the degree of extension of pigment cells in the skin of certain vertebrates such as frogs.

internuncial (in″ter-nun′she-al) [L. *inter* between + *nuncius* messenger]. Denoting a neuron that lies between the afferent and efferent neurons and transmits impulses within the central nervous system; often the term is shortened to interneuron.

invagination (in-vaj"ĭ-na'shun) [L. *invaginatio* from *in* within + *vagina* sheath]. The infolding of one part within another, specifically a process of gastrulation in which one region infolds to form a double-layered cup.

inversion, chromosomal Turning a segment of a chromosome end for end and attaching it to the same chromosome.

ion (i'on) [Gr. *iōn* going]. An atom or a group of atoms bearing an electric charge, either positive (cation) or negative (anion).

isomer (i'so-mer) [Gr. *isos* equal + *meros* part]. Molecule with the same molecular formula as another but a different structural formula; e.g., glucose and fructose.

isotonic or **isosmotic** (i-so-ton'ik, i-sos-mot'ik). Having identical concentrations of solute and solvent molecules and hence the same osmotic pressure as the solution with which it is compared.

isotopes (i'so-tōps) [Gr. *isos* equal + *topos* place]. Alternate forms of a chemical element having the same atomic number (that is, the same number of nuclear protons and orbital electrons) but possessing different atomic masses (that is, different numbers of neutrons).

isozymes (i'so-zīms) [Gr. *isos* equal + *zymē* leaven]. Different molecular forms of proteins with the same enzymatic activity.

jejunum (je-joo'num) [L. *jejunus* empty]. The middle portion of the small intestine of higher vertebrates lying between the duodenum and ileum.

juvenile hormone An arthropod hormone that preserves juvenile morphology during a molt. Without it, metamorphosis toward the adult form takes place.

karyokinesis (kar"e-o-ki-ne'sis) [Gr. *karyon* nucleus or nut + *kinesis* motion]. The phenomena involved in division of the nucleus in mitosis.

keratin (ker'ah-tin) [Gr. *keratos* horn]. A horny, water-insoluble protein found in the epidermis of vertebrates and in nails, feathers, hair, horn and the like.

ketone bodies Incompletely oxidized fatty acids which are toxic in high concentrations; excreted in the urine, causing an acidosis.

kinesis (ki-ne'sis) [Gr. *kinēsis* movement]. The activity of an organism in response to a stimulus; the direction of the response is not controlled by the direction of the stimulus (in contrast to a taxis).

kinesthesis (kin"es-the'sis) [Gr. *kinēsis* movement + *aisthēsis* perception]. Sense which gives us our awareness of the position and movement of the various parts of the body.

kinins (ki'nins). Group of polypeptides produced in blood and tissues and acting on blood vessels, smooth muscles and certain nerve endings; e.g., bradykinin or kallidin; one of a group of compounds containing adenine that stimulates cell division and growth of plant cells in tissue culture.

labyrinthodont (lab"ĭ-rin'tho-dont) [Gr. *labyrinthos* labyrinth + *odontos* tooth]. A member of a subclass of extinct amphibians in which the enamel of the tooth was complexly invaginated into the dentin; included the first terrestrial vertebrates and the ancestors of modern amphibians and reptiles.

lamella (lah-mel'ah) [L. dim. of *lamina* plate, leaf]. A thin leaf or plate, as of bone.

larva (lar'vah) [L.]. An actively feeding immature stage in the life history of an animal in which it is unlike the parent.

larynx (lar'inks) [Gr. "the upper part of the windpipe"]. The cartilaginous structure located at the entrance of the trachea which functions secondarily as the organ of voice.

latent period An interval, lasting about 0.01 second, between the application of a stimulus and the beginning of the visible shortening of a muscle.

leuconoid (lu'kon-oid) [Gr. *leukos* white + *eidos* form]. In sponges, a body plan similar to that of the white sponge leucon, with a complex body wall having secondary indentations.

leukemia (lu-ke'me-ah) [Gr. *leukos* white + *haima* blood]. A type of cancer, characterized by the abnormally rapid growth of white blood cells.

leukocytes (lu'ko-sīts) [Gr. *leukos* white + *kytos* cell]. White blood cells; colorless cells exhibiting phagocytosis and ameboid movement.

linkage The tendency for a group of genes located in the same chromosome to be inherited together in successive generations.

lipase (lip'ās) [Gr. *lipos* fat]. An enzyme that catalyzes the hydrolysis of fats; it cleaves the ester bonds joining fatty acids to glycerol.

littoral (lit'o-ral) [L. *litoralis* the seashore]. The region of shallow water near the shore between the high and low tide marks.

locus (lo'kus) [L. place]. The particular point on the chromosome at which the gene for a given trait occurs.

loop of Henle (hen'lē) [*Henle* German anatomist of the nineteenth century]. The U-shaped loop of a mammalian kidney tubule which dips down into the medulla; lies between the proximal and distal convoluted tubules.

lophophore (lof'o-for) [Gr. *lophos* crest, tuft + *phore*, from *phorein*, to bear]. The horseshoe-shaped ridge with a set of ciliated tentacles around the mouth of bryozoa.

luciferin (lu-sif′er-in) [L. *lux* light + *ferre* to bear]. Substrate present in certain organisms capable of bioluminescence, producing light, when acted upon by the enzyme luciferase.

lumen (lu′men) [L. *lumen* light or an opening through which light passes]. The cavity of a tubular organ such as the intestine.

lymph (limf) [L. *lympha* lymph]. The colorless fluid which is derived from blood plasma and resembles it closely in composition; contains white cells, some of which enter the lymph capillaries from the tissue fluid, others of which are manufactured in the lymph nodes.

lymph node (limf nōd) One of the nodules of lymphatic tissue that occur in groups along the course of the lymphatic vessels; produces and contains lymphocytes and phagocytic cells.

lysis (li′sis) [Gr. *lysis* lossening]. The process of disintegration or solution of a cell or some other structure.

macromere (mak′ro-mēr) [Gr. *makros* long in extent + *meros* a portion]. The larger cell resulting from unequal cell division.

macronucleus (mak″ro-nu′kle-us) [Gr. *makros* + L. *nucleus* kernel]. The large nucleus in ciliates that governs activities not associated with reproduction.

make-ready reaction A term for metabolic reactions that result in the formation of a configuration of the substrate molecule suitable for a subsequent dehydrogenation reaction.

malpighian tubule The excretory organ of many arthropods, named for the seventeenth century Italian anatomist Marcello Malpighi.

mammal (mam′al) [L. *mamma* breast]. A member of a class of vertebrates characterized by having hair and mammary glands; includes such diverse types as shrews, bats, cats, whales, cattle and man.

marsupials (mar-su′pe-als) [L. *marsupium* a pouch]. A group of mammals characterized by the possession of an abdominal pouch in which the young are carried for some time after being born in a very immature condition.

mating type In Protozoa, a sex. As many as eight sexes are known in some species.

matrix (ma′triks) [L. *mater* mother]. Nonliving material secreted by and surrounding the connective tissue cells; frequently contains a thick, interlacing matted network of microscopic fibers.

medulla (me-dul′lah) [L. from *medius* middle]. The inner part of an organ, e.g., the medulla of the kidney; the most posterior part of the brain, lying next to the spinal cord.

medusa (me-du′sah) [Gr. *medousa*]. A jellyfish; a free-swimming, umbrella-shaped form in the life cycle of certain coelenterate animals.

meiosis (mi-o′sis) [Gr. *meiōsis* diminution]. Kind of nuclear division, usually two successive cell divisions, which results in daughter cells with the haploid number of chromosomes, one half the number of chromosomes in the original cell.

melanin (mel′ah-nin) [Gr. *melas* black]. A dark-brown to black pigment common in the integument of many animals and sometimes found in other organs; usually occurs within special pigment cells.

membranelle An organelle formed by the fusion of a row of cilia to produce a small membrane.

menopause (men′o-pawz) [Gr. *men* month; *meniaia* the menses + *pausis* cessation]. The period (from 40 to 50 years of age) when the recurring menstrual cycle ceases.

menstruation (men″stroo-a′shun) [L. *menstrualis* monthly]. The cyclic, physiologic uterine bleeding which normally recurs, usually at approximately four-week intervals, in the absence of pregnancy during the reproductive period of the female.

merozoite (mer″o-zo′īt) [Gr. *meros* part + *zōon* animal]. One of the young forms derived from the splitting up of the schizont in the human cycle of the malarial parasite, plasmodium; it is released into the circulating blood and attacks new erythrocytes.

mesencephalon (mes″en-sef′ah-lon) [Gr. *mesos* middle + *enkephalos* brain]. The middle subdivision of the brain lying between the diencephalon and metencephalon; includes the superior and inferior colliculi.

mesenchyme (mes′eng-kīm) [Gr. *mesos* middle + *enchyme* an infusion]. A meshwork of loosely associated, often stellate cells; found in the embryos of vertebrates and the adults of some invertebrates.

mesentery (mes′en-ter″e) [Gr. *mesos* middle + *enteron* intestine]. One of the membranes in vertebrates that extend from the body wall to the visceral organs or from one organ to another; consists of two layers of coelomic epithelium and enclosed connective tissue, vessels and nerves.

mesoderm (mes′o-derm) [Gr. *mesos* middle + *derma* skin]. The middle layer of the three primary germ layers of the embryo, lying between the ectoderm and the endoderm.

mesoglea (mes″o-gle′ah) [Gr. *mesos* middle + *gloia* glue]. A gelatinous matrix located between the ectoderm and endoderm of coelenterates.

mesonephros (mes″o-nef′ros) [Gr. *mesos* middle + *nephros* kidney]. An embryonic vertebrate kidney which succeeds the pronephros; its tubules develop adjacent to the middle portion of the coelom and drain into the archinephric duct.

mesozoa (mes″o-zo′ah) [Gr. *mesos* middle + *zōon* animal]. A small group of tiny parasites whose relationships to the Protozoa and Metazoa are uncertain.

messenger RNA A particular kind of ribonucleic acid which is synthesized in the nucleus and passes to the ribosomes in the cytoplasm; combines with RNA in the ribosomes and provides a template for the synthesis of an enzyme or some other specific protein.

metabolism (me-tab'o-lizm) [Gr. *metaballein* to turn about, change, alter]. The sum of all the physical and chemical processes by which living organized substance is produced and maintained; the transformations by which energy and matter are made available for the uses of the organism.

metamerism (met-am'er-izm) [Gr. *meta* with + *meros* part]. The state of being made up of serial segments, as in annelids and chordates.

metamorphosis (met"ah-mor'fo-sis) [Gr. *meta* after, beyond, over + *morphōsis* a shaping, bringing into shape]. An abrupt transition from one developmental stage to another, e.g., from a larva to an adult.

metanephros (met"ah-nef'ros) [Gr. *meta* after, beyond, over + *nephros* kidney]. The adult kidney of reptiles, birds and mammals.

metaphase (met'ah-fāz) [Gr. *meta* after, beyond, over + *phasis* to make to appear]. The middle stage of mitosis during which the chromosomes line up in the equatorial plate and separate lengthwise.

metazoa (met"ah-zo'ah) [Gr. *meta* after, beyond, over + *zōon* animal]. Division of the animal kingdom which embraces all multicellular animals whose cells become differentiated to form tissues; all animals except the protozoa.

metencephalon (met"en-sef'ah-lon) [Gr. *meta* after + *enkephalos* brain]. A major subdivision of the brain lying between the mesencephalon and myelencephalon; includes the cerebellum and pons.

micromere (mi'kro-mēr) [Gr. *mikros* small + *meros* part]. The smaller cell, following unequal cell division.

micron (mi'kron) [Gr. *mikros* small]. A unit of linear measure in the metric system; one-thousandth part of a millimeter.

micronucleus (mi"kro-nu'kle-us) [Gr. *mikros* + L. *nucleus* kernel]. A small nucleus that governs reproduction in ciliates.

mimicry (mim'ik-re") [Gr. *mimos* to imitate]. An adaptation for survival in which an organism resembles some other living or nonliving object.

miracidium (mir"ah-sid'ĭ-um) [Gr. *meirakidion* youthful person]. The first larval stage of parasitic flukes.

mitochondria (mīt"o-kon'dre-ah) [Gr. *mitos* thread + *chondrion* granule]. Spherical or elongate intracellular organelles which contain the electron transmitter system and certain other enzymes; site of oxidative phosphorylation.

mitosis (mi-to'sis) [Gr. *mitos* thread + *osis* state or condition]. A form of cell or nuclear division by means of which each of the two daughter nuclei receives exactly the same complement of chromosomes as the parent nucleus had.

mixture A solution made up of two or more kinds of atoms or molecules which may be combined in varying proportions.

mole (mōl) [L. *moles* a shapeless mass]. The amount of a chemical compound whose mass in grams is equivalent to its molecular weight, the sum of the atomic weights of its constituent atoms.

molecule (mol'ĕ-kul) [L. *molecula* little mass]. The smallest particle of a covalently bonded element or compound having the composition and properties of a larger part of the substance.

mollusca (mol-lus'kah) [L. *molluscus*, soft]. A phylum of soft-bodied animals usually enclosed in shells, including snails and clams.

molting [L. *mutare* to change]. The shedding and replacement of an outer covering such as hair, feathers and exoskeleton.

monera (mo-ne'rah) [Gr. *monērēs* single]. A category of organisms that includes the simplest microorganisms, the bacteria and blue-green algae, forms lacking true nuclei or plastids and in which sexual reproduction is very rare or absent.

mongolism (mon'go-lizm). A congenital malformation in which individuals have abnormalities of the face, eyelids, tongue and other parts of the body and are greatly retarded in both their physical and mental development; results from a trisomy of chromosome 21 or 18.

monomer (mon'o-mer) [Gr. *monos* single + *meros* part]. A simple molecule of a compound of relatively low molecular weight which can be linked with others to form a polymer.

monotreme (mon'o-trēm) [Gr. *monos* one + *trema* hole]. A member of the most primitive order of living mammals characterized by the retention of the cloaca, into which the digestive and urogenital tracts discharge, and an egg-laying habit; includes the duckbill platypus and spiny anteater.

morphogenesis (mor"fo-jen'ě-sis) [Gr. *morphe* form + *gennan* to produce]. The development of form, size and other features of a particular organ or part of the body.

mosaic development Embryonic development in which the capacities of the cells are restricted to the structures they normally form.

motor unit (mo'tor u'nit). All the skeletal muscle fibers that are stimulated by a single motor neuron.

mucosa (mu-ko'sah). Mucous membrane; e.g., the lining of the digestive tract.

multiple alleles Three or more alternate conditions of a single locus which produce different phenotypes.

mutation A stable, inherited change in a gene.

muton (mu'ton) [Gr. *mutation* + *on* neuter ending]. The smallest portion of a chromosome which, when altered, gives rise to a mutant form of the organism.

mutualism (mu'tu-al-izm). An association

whereby two organisms of different species each gain from being together and are unable to survive separately.

myelencephalon (mi″ĕ-len-sef′ah-lon) [Gr. *myelos* marrow + *enkephalos* brain]. The most posterior of the five major subdivisions of the brain; comprises the medulla oblongata.

myelin (mi′ĕ-lin) [Gr. *myelos* marrow]. The fatty material which forms a sheath around the axons of nerve cells in the central nervous system and in certain peripheral nerves.

myofibrils (mi″o-fi′brils) [Gr. *mys* muscle + L. *fibrilla* small fiber]. Microscopic, extended contractile fibers composed of the proteins myosin and actin.

myomere (mi′o-mēr) [Gr. *mys* muscle + *meros* part]. The muscle segment of an animal; sometimes restricted to the adult segment.

myopia (mi-o′pe-ah) [Gr. *myein* to shut + *ōps* eye]. Nearsightedness; the eyeball is too long and the retina too far from the lens; light rays converge at a point in front of the retina, and are again diverging when they reach it, resulting in a blurred image.

myosin (mi′o-sin) [Gr. *mys* muscle]. A soluble protein found in muscle; in combination with actin functions in the contraction and relaxation of muscle fibers.

myotome (mi′o-tōm) [Gr. *mys* muscle + *tomos* section]. The muscle segment of animal; sometimes restricted to the embryonic segment.

myxedema (mik″sĕ-de′mah) [Gr. *myxa* mucus + *oidēma* swelling]. A condition which results from a deficiency of thyroxin secretion in an adult; characterized by a low metabolic rate and decreased heat production.

nares (na′rēz) [L. *nares* nostrils]. The openings of the nasal cavities. External nares open to the body surface; internal nares, to the pharynx.

nauplius (no′plĭ-us) [L. a kind of shellfish]. A larva with three pairs of appendages—future head limbs—characteristic of the crustaceans.

nekton (nek′ton) [Gr. *nēktos* swimming]. Collective term for the organisms which are active swimmers.

nematocyst (nem′ah-to-sist) [Gr. *nematos* thread + *kystis* bladder]. A minute stinging structure found on coelenterates and used for anchorage, for defense and for the capture of prey.

nematoda (nem″ah-to′dah) [Gr. *nematos* thread]. The roundworms, a large class of aschelminths, many of which are parasitic.

nemertea (nem-ur′te-ah) [After Nemertes, one of the Nereids of Greek mythology]. The ribbon worms, a phylum with many marine and a few fresh-water species.

nephridium (nĕ-frid′e-um) [Gr. *nephros* kidney]. The excretory organ of the earthworm and other annelids which consists of a ciliated funnel,

opening into the next anterior coelomic cavity and connected by a tube to the outside of the body.

nephron (nef′ron) [Gr. *nephros* kidney]. The anatomical and functional unit of the vertebrate kidney.

nerve (nerv) [L. *nervus* nerve]. A cordlike collection of neurons and associated connective tissue that extends between the central nervous system and other parts of the body; most nerves contain both afferent and efferent neurons.

nerve net A relatively unorganized, diffuse net of nerve cells with no obvious directionality in the transmission of impulses.

neurohumor (nu″ro-hu′mor) [Gr. *neuron* nerve + L. *humor* a liquid]. A substance secreted by the tip of a neuron which is able to activate a neighboring neuron or muscle.

neuron (nu′ron) [Gr. *neuron* nerve]. A nerve cell with its processes, collaterals and terminations; the structural unit of the nervous system.

neurosecretion (nu″ro-se-kre′shun) [Gr. *neuron* nerve + L. *secretio*, from *secrenere* to secrete]. The production of hormones by nerve cells.

neuroses (nu-ro′sēs) [Gr. *neuron* nerve + *osis* state or condition]. Comparatively mild and common psychic disorders with a great variety of symptoms: anxiety, fear, shyness and oversensitiveness.

neurula (nu′roo-lah) [Gr. *neuron* nerve]. The early embryonic stage during which the primitive nervous system forms.

neutrons (nu′trons). Electrically uncharged particles of matter existing along with protons in the atomic nucleus of all elements except the mass 1 isotope of hydrogen.

nondisjunction (non″dis-junk′shun). The failure of a pair of homologous chromosomes to separate normally during the reduction division at meiosis; both members of the pair are carried to the same daughter nucleus and the other daughter cell is lacking in that particular chromosome.

notochord (no′to-kord) [Gr. *noton* back + *chorde* cord]. The rod-shaped body in the anteroposterior axis which serves as an internal skeleton in the embryos of all chordates and in the adults of some; replaced by a vertebral column in most adult chordates.

notum (no′tum) [Gr. *nōton* back]. The dorsal part of the body. In arthropods, the dorsal element of each segment.

nuclease (nu′kle-ās) [L. *nucleus* a kernel]. An enzyme that facilitates the hydrolysis of nucleic acids.

nucleolus (nu-kle′o-lus) [L. dim. of *nucleus*, dim. of *nux* nut]. A spherical body found within the cell nucleus; rich in ribonucleic acid and believed to be the site of synthesis of ribosomes.

nucleotide (nu′kle-o-tīd). A molecule composed of a phosphate group, a 5-carbon sugar—ribose or deoxyribose—and a nitrogenous base—a purine or a pyrimidine; one of the subunits into which nucleic acids are split by the action of nucleases.

nucleus (nu′kle-us) [L. *nucleus* a kernel]. The organelle of a cell containing the hereditary material; a group of nerve cell bodies in the central nervous system.

nutrient (nu′tre-ent) [L. *nutriens*]. A general term for any substance which can be used in the metabolic processes of the body.

nymph (nimf) [L. *nympha* young woman]. A juvenile insect that often resembles the adult and that will become an adult without an intervening pupal stage.

olfaction (ol-fak′shun) [L. *olfacere* to smell]. The act of smelling.

oligochaeta (ol″ig-o-ke′tah) [Gr. *oligos* scant + *chaite* hair]. A class of annelids bearing few bristles; includes earthworms.

ommatidium (om″ah-tid′ĭ-um) [Gr. diminutive of *omma* eye]. One of the elements of a compound eye, itself complete with lens and retina.

ontogeny (on-toj′ĕ-ne) [Gr. *ōn* existing + *gennan* to produce]. The complete developmental history of the individual organism.

onychophora (on-ĭ-kof′o-rah) [Gr. *onyx* nail + *phoros* bearing]. Rare, tropical, caterpillar-like animals, structurally intermediate between annelids and arthropods, possessing an annelid-like excretory system, an insect-like respiratory system and claw-tipped short legs.

oögenesis (o″o-jen′e-sis) [Gr. *ōon* egg + *genesis* production]. The origin and development of the ovum.

oögonium (o″o-go′ne-um) [Gr. *ōon* egg + *gonē* generation]. The primordial cell from which the ovarian egg arises; undergoes growth to become a primary oöcyte.

ophiuroidea (o″fi-u-roi′de-ah) [Gr. *ophis* snake + *oura* tail + *eidos* form]. The brittle stars, a class of echinoderms with snakelike prehensile arms.

opisthonephros (o″pis-tho-nef′ros) [Gr. *opisthen* behind + *nephros* kidney]. The adult kidney of most fishes and amphibians; its tubules extend from the mesonephric region to the posterior end of the coelom; drained by the archinephric duct and sometimes also by accessory urinary ducts.

order In taxonomy, a major subdivision of a class. Each order is composed of one or more related families.

organ of Corti (cōr′tĭ) [*Corti* Italian anatomist of the nineteenth century]. The organ attached to the basilar membrane in the cochlear duct which contains the cells receptive to sound.

organelle (or″gan-el′) [Gr. *organon* bodily organ]. One of the specialized structures within a cell, e.g., the mitochondria, Golgi complex, ribosomes, contractile vacuole, etc.

organizer A part of an embryo which influences some other part and directs its histological and morphological differentiation.

orthogenesis (or″tho-jen′ĕ-sis) [Gr. *orthos* straight + *genesis* production]. Evolution progressing in a given direction; straight-line evolution.

osculum (os′ku-lum) [L. little mouth]. In sponges, the large excurrent openings.

osmosis (os-mo′sis)]Gr. *ōsmos* impulsion]. The passage of solvent molecules from the lesser to the greater concentration of solute when two solutions are separated by a membrane which selectively prevents the passage of solute molecules but is permeable to the solvent.

osteichthyes (os″te-ik′thĭ-ēz) [Gr. *osteon* bone + *ichthys* fish]. A class of fishes in which the skeleton is composed, at least in part, of bone; includes sturgeons, teleosts, lungfish.

ostracoderm (os′tră-ko-derm″) [Gr. *ostrakon* shell + *derma* skin]. A member of one of several orders of primitive jawless fishes which were abundant during the Devonian; the ancestral vertebrates.

outbreeding The mating of individuals of unrelated strains.

ovary (o′vah-re) [L. *ovaria*]. The female gonad which produces eggs.

ovulation (ōv″u-la′shun) [L. *ovulum* little egg + *atus* process or product]. The discharge of a mature ovum from the graafian follicle of the ovary.

ovum (o′vum) [L. *ovum* egg]. The female reproductive cell, which after fertilization by a sperm, develops into a new member of the same species.

oxidation The process in which electrons are removed from an atom or molecule.

oxidative phosphorylation (ok″sĭ-da′tiv fos″fōr-ĭ-la′shun). The conversion of inorganic phosphate to the energy-rich phosphate of ATP by reactions coupled to the transfer of electrons in the electron transmitter system of the mitochondria.

oxygen debt The accumulation of lactic acid in muscles during violent exercise.

pacemaker The part whose rate of reaction sets the pace for a series of interrelated reactions; e.g., the sinoatrial node initiates the heart beat and regulates the rate of contraction of the heart.

parallel evolution (par′ă-lel) [Gr. *para* beside + *allos* other]. The independent evolution of similar structures in two or more rather closely related organisms, e.g., the independent evolution of quills from hair by American and African porcupines.

paramylum Carbohydrate storage compound present in the euglenoids, chemically distinct from both starch and glycogen.

parapodia (par″ah-po′de-ah) [L. *para* beyond + Gr. *podion* little foot]. Paired, thickly bristled paddles extending laterally from each segment of polychaete worms.

parasitism (par'ah-sīt"izm) [Gr. *parasitos* one who eats at the table of another + *ismos* condition]. A type of heterotrophic nutrition found among both plants and animals; a parasite lives in or on the living body of a plant or animal (host) and obtains its nourishment from it.

parasympathetic (par'ah-sim"pah-thet'ik) [Gr. *para* beyond + *sym* with + *pathos* feeling]. A segment of the autonomic nervous system; fibers originate in the brain and the pelvic region of the spinal cord and innervate primarily the internal organs.

parathyroids (par"ah-thi'roids) [Gr. *para* beyond + *thyreoeidēs* shieldlike]. Small, pea-sized glands situated in the substance of the thyroid gland; their secretion is concerned chiefly with regulating the metabolism of calcium and phosphorus by the body.

parthenogenesis (par"thĕ-no-jen'ĕ-sis) [Gr. *parthenos* virgin + *genesis* production]. The development of an unfertilized egg into an adult organism; common among honeybees, wasps and certain other arthropods.

parturition (par"tu-rish'un) [L. *parturito* childbirth]. The process of giving birth to a child.

pelagic (pe-laj'ik) [Gr. *pelagios* living in the sea]. An organism which inhabits open water, as in midocean.

pelecypoda (pel"e-sip'o-dah) [Gr. *pelekys* hatchet + *podos* foot]. The bivalves, a class of mollusks with a spadelike foot for digging.

penetrance (pen'ĕ-trans) [L. *penetrare* to enter into]. The expression of the frequency with which a heritable trait is shown in individuals carrying the principal gene or genes conditioning it.

penis (pe'nis) [L.]. The copulatory organ of the male; found in most of those species of animals in which fertilization is internal.

pepsin (pep'sin) [L. *pepsinum* from Gr. *pepsis* digestion]. A proteolytic enzyme secreted by the cells lining the stomach: functions only in a very acid medium and works optimally at *p*H 2.

pericardium (per"ĭ-kar'de-um) [Gr. *perikardios*, near the heart]. The lining of that part of the coelom that forms a separate chamber containing the heart.

perilymph (per'ĭ-limf) [Gr. *peri* around + L. *lympha* lymph]. The lymphlike fluid which lies between the membranous labyrinth and the bone or cartilage encapsulating the inner ear; the scala tympani and scala vestibuli of the mammalian cochlea are perilymphatic channels.

peripheral resistance The state of constriction or relaxation of the blood vessels; plays an important role in determining blood pressure.

peristalsis (per"ĭ-stal'sis) [Gr. *peri* around + *stalsis* contraction]. Powerful, rhythmic waves of muscular contraction and relaxation in the walls of hollow tubular organs such as the ureter or the parts of the digestive tract; serve to move the contents through the tube.

peritoneum (per"ĭ-to-ne'um) [Gr. *peritonos* stretched over]. Coelomic epithelium and supporting connective tissue which lines the abdominal cavity of vertebrates and covers the abdominal viscera.

peritrophic membrane (per"ĭ-trof'ic) [Gr. *peri* around + *trophe* food]. In many arthropods, a cylindrical sheath of chitin continuously secreted from the posterior edge of the foregut (stomadeum); encloses the gut contents.

*p***H** The negative logarithm of the hydrogen ion concentration, by which the degree of acidity or alkalinity of a fluid may be expressed.

phagocytosis (fag"o-si-to'sis) [Gr. *phagein* to eat + *kytos* hollow vessel + *osis* state or condition]. The engulfing of microorganisms, other cells and foreign particles by a cell such as a white blood cell.

pharynx (far'inks) [Gr.]. That part of the digestive tract from which the gill pouches or slits develop; in higher vertebrates it is bounded anteriorly by the mouth and nasal cavities and posteriorly by the esophagus and larynx.

phenocopy (fe'no-kop"e) [Gr. *phainein* to show + L. *copia* abundance, number]. The simulation by an individual of traits characteristic of another genotype resulting from physical or chemical influences in the environment which change the course of development and produce a trait which mimics that of an individual with a different genotype.

phenotype (fe'no-tīp) [Gr. *phainein* to show + *typos* type]. The outward, visible expression of the hereditary constitution of an organism.

pheromone (fēr'o-mōn) [Gr. *phorein* to carry]. A substance secreted by one organism to the external environment which influences the development or behavior of other members of the same species.

phoronida (fo-ro'nid-ah) [From Phoronis, the surname of Io in Greek mythology]. A small phylum of lophophorate worms related to brachiopods.

phosphorescence (fos"fo-res'ens) [Gr. *phōs* light + *phorein* to carry]. The emission of light without appreciable heat, caused by the decay of a molecule in the triplet state to the ground state.

phosphorylation (fos"fōr-ĭ-la'shun) [Gr. *phōs* light + *phorein* to carry]. The introduction of a phosphate group into an organic molecule.

photon (fo'ton) [Gr. *phōs* light + *ton* slice]. A particle of electromagnetic radiation, one quantum of radiant energy.

photoperiodism (fo"to-pe're-od-izm) [Gr. *phōs* light + *peri* around + *hodos* way + *ismos* state]. The physiologic response of animals and plants to variations of light and darkness.

photosynthesis (fo"to-sin'the-sis) [Gr. *phōs* light + *synthesis* putting together]. The process of synthesizing carbohydrates from carbon dioxide and water, utilizing the radiant energy of light captured by the chlorophyll in plant cells.

phylogeny (fi-loj′e-ne) [Gr. *phylon* tribe + *genesis* generation]. The complete evolutionary history of a group of organisms.

phylum (fi′lum) [Gr. *phylon* race]. A primary, large, main division of the animal or plant kingdom, including organisms which are assumed to have a common ancestry.

phytoplankton (fi″to-plank′ton) [Gr. *phyton* plant + *planktos* wandering]. Microscopic floating plants, most of which are algae, which are distributed throughout the ocean or a lake.

pi electrons Mobile electrons located in a system of conjugated single and double bonds which are associated not with a single atom or bond but with the conjugated system as a whole.

pinocytosis (pi″no-si-to′sis) [Gr. *pinein* to drink + *kytos* cell + *osis* state or condition]. "Cell drinking"; the engulfing and absorption of droplets of liquids by cells.

pituitary (pĭ-tu′ĭ-tār″e) [L. *pituitarius* secreting phlegm]. A small gland which lies just below the hypothalamus of the brain, to which it is attached by a narrow stalk; the anterior lobe forms in the embryo as an outgrowth of the roof of the mouth and the posterior lobe grows down from the floor of the brain.

placenta (plah-sen′tah) [L. a flat cake]. A structure formed in part from tissues derived from the embryo and in part from maternal tissues—the lining of the uterus—by means of which the embryo receives nutrients and oxygen and eliminates wastes.

placodermi (plak′o-der″mi) [Gr. *plakos* a tablet, a flat plate + *derma* skin]. The earliest of the jawed fishes, known only from fossils; believed to be ancestral to both bony and cartilaginous fishes.

plankton (plank′ton) [Gr. *planktos* wandering]. Minute, free-floating organisms, both plants and animals, which live in practically all natural waters.

plantigrade (plan′tĭ-grād) [L. *planta* sole + *gradi* to walk]. Locomotion adapted for a comparatively slow gait, characterized by walking on the full sole of the foot.

plasma membrane (plaz′mah mem′brān) [Gr. *plasma* anything formed or molded + L. *membrana* skin covering]. A living, functional part of the cell through which all nutrients entering the cell and all waste products or secretions leaving it must pass.

plasmodium (plaz-mo′de-um) [Gr. *plasma* anything formed + *odēs* like]. Multinucleate, ameboid mass of living matter that comprises the diploid phase of slime molds; single-celled animals that reproduce by spore formation and cause malaria.

plasmolysis (plaz-mol′ĭ-sis) [Gr. *plasma* anything formed + *lysis* dissolution]. Contraction of the

cytoplasm of a cell due to the loss of water by osmotic action.

platelet (plāt′let) [Gr. *platē* a flattened surface]. A small colorless blood corpuscle of mammals that plays an important role in blood coagulation and in the contraction of the clot.

platyhelminthes (plat″ĭ-hel-min′thēz) [Gr. *platys* flat + *helminthos* worms]. The phylum of flatworms, flukes and tapeworms.

pleurum (ploor′um). [L. one of the sides of an animal]. In arthropods, a lateral skeletal piece of any segment.

plexus (plek′sus) [L. *plexus* a braid]. A network of interconnecting structures such as nerves, e.g., the brachial plexus of nerves supplying the arm.

ploidy (ploi′de) [Gr. *ploos* fold + *odēs* like, resembling]. Relating to the number of sets of chromosomes in a cell.

poikilothermic (poi″kĭ-lo-ther′mik) [Gr. *poikilos* varied + *thermē* heat]. Having a body temperature that fluctuates with that of the environment; "cold-blooded."

polar body Small cell which consists of practically nothing but a nucleus; formed during oögenesis, maturation of the egg, and appears as a speck at the animal pole of the egg.

polarity In biology, the tendency of a piece of an organism to retain its original body orientation, regenerating a head at the original anterior end, etc.

polychaeta (pol″e-ke′tah) [Gr. *polys* many + *chaite* hair]. A class of annelids with parapodia bearing numerous bristles.

polygenes (pol″e-jēns′) [Gr. *polys* many + *gennan* to produce]. Two or more pairs of genes that affect the same trait in an additive fashion.

polymorphism (pol″e-mor′fizm) [Gr. *poly* + *morphē* form]. Differences in form among the members of a species; occurrence of several distinct phenotypes in a population.

polyploids (pol″e-ploids′) [Gr. *polys* many + *ploos* folds]. Organisms which have more than two full sets of homologous chromosomes.

polyps (pol′ips) [Gr. *polypous* morbid excrescences]. Hydra-like animals; the sessile stage in the life cycle of certain coelenterates; protruding growths from a mucous membrane.

pons (ponz) [L. bridge]. The ventral portion of the metencephalon; it relays certain impulses from the cerebrum to the cerebellum and interconnects the two sides of the cerebellum.

population The group of individuals of a given species inhabiting a specified geographic area.

porifera (po-rif′ĕ-rah) [L. *porus* pore + *ferre* to bear]. The phylum of sponges; the body is perforated with many pores to admit water, from which food is strained.

portal system (por′tal) [L. *porta* a gate]. A group of veins which drain one region and lead to a capillary bed in another organ rather than directly to the heart, e.g., the renal portal system and hepatic portal system.

precursor (pre-kur'sor) [L. *praecursor* to run before]. A substance which precedes another substance in a metabolic pathway; a substance from which another substance is synthesized.

predation (pre-da'shun) [K. *praedatio* to plunder]. Relationship in which one species adversely affects the second but cannot live without it; the first species kills and devours the second.

priapuloidea (pri-ap"u-loi'de-ah) [Gr. *priapus* phallus]. A small phylum of large fleshy marine worms whose taxonomic position in the animal kingdom is uncertain.

primitive streak (prim'ĭ-tiv) [L. *primitivus* first in point of time]. A longitudinal groove which develops on the embryonic disc of the eggs of fishes, reptiles, birds and mammals as a consequence of the movement of cells and formation of mesoderm; it is homologous to the lips of the blastopore and marks the future longitudinal axis of the embryo.

primordium (pri-mor'de-um) [L. "the beginning"]. The earliest discernible indication during embryonic development of an organ or part.

proboscis (pro-bos'is) [Gr. *pro* before + *boskein* to feed, graze]. Any tubular process of the head or snout of an animal, usually used in feeding.

progeny selection (proj'e-ne se-lek'shun) [L. *progignere* to bring forth]. A breeding program in which the genotype is determined by making test matings and observing the offspring.

progesterone (pro-jes'ter-ōn) [L. *pro* before + *gestus* to bear, carry, conduct]. The hormone produced in the corpus luteum of the ovary and in the placenta; acts with estradiol to regulate estrous and menstrual cycles and to maintain pregnancy.

proglottid (pro-glot'id) [L. *pro* before, in front of + *glottis* the tongue]. The body sections of a tapeworm.

pronephros (pro-nef'ros) [Gr. *pro* before + *nephros* kidney]. The first formed kidney of embryonic or larval vertebrates; its tubules develop adjacent to the cranial end of the coelom and form the archinephric duct.

prophase (pro'fāz) [L. *pro* before + Gr. *phasis* an appearance]. The first stage in mitosis, during which the chromatin threads condense, distinct chromosomes become evident, and a spindle forms.

prosimian (pro"sim'ĭ-an) [L. *pro* before, in front of + *simia* an ape]. A primitive living primate or an early ancestral primate.

prostate (pros'tāt) [Gr. *prostates* one who stands before]. The largest accessory sex gland of male mammals; it surrounds the urethra at the point where the vasa deferentia join it, and it secretes a large portion of the seminal fluid.

prosthetic group (pros-thet'ik) [Gr. "a putting to,

addition"]. A cofactor tightly bound to an enzyme.

protean behavior (pro'te-un) [From Proteus, the sea god of Greek mythology who changed shape unpredictably when seized]. An irregular, unpredictable sequence of movements by prey when pursued by predators.

protease (pro'te-ās). An enzyme that catalyzes the digestion of proteins.

proteins (pro'te-ins) [Gr. *prōtos* first]. Macromolecules containing carbon, hydrogen, oxygen, nitrogen and usually sulfur and phosphorus; composed of chains of amino acids bound in peptide bonds; one of the principal types of compounds present in all cells.

protista (pro-tis'tah) [Gr. *prōtista* the very first, from *prōtos* first]. Kingdom of living organisms, including the protozoa, flagellates, slime molds, certain algae and fungi.

protocooperation (pro"to-co-op"er-a'shun) [Gr. *prōtos* first + L. *cooperatio* to work]. Relationship in which each of two populations benefits by the presence of the other but can survive in its absence.

proton (pro'ton) [Gr. *prōtos* first]. A basic physical particle present in the nuclei of all atoms which has a positive electric charge and a mass similar to that of a neutron; a hydrogen ion.

protonephridium (pro"to-nef-rid'e-um) [Gr. *prōtos* first + *nephridios* kidneys]. The flame-cell excretory organs of lower invertebrates and of some larval higher animals.

protopodite (pro-top'o-dīt) [Gr. *prōtos* + *podos* foot]. The basal portion of a biramous crustacean limb.

protostome (pro'to-stōm) [Gr. *prōtos* + *stoma* mouth]. An animal in which the blastopore is in a ventral site and contributes to the formation of the mouth as well as the anus.

protozoa (pro"to-zo'ah) [Gr. *prōtos* first + *zōon* animal]. The phylum of single-celled animals, includes amebas, ciliates, flagellates, and sporozoa.

pseudocoelom (su"do-se'lom) [Gr. *pseudēs* false + *koilia* cavity]. A body cavity between the mesoderm and endoderm; a persistent blastocoel.

pseudopod (su'do-pod) [Gr. *pseudes* false + *podos* foot]. A temporary cytoplasmic protrusion of an ameba or ameboid cell, functions in locomotion and feeding.

pterygota (ter"ĭ-go'tah) [Gr. *pteryos* wing]. The group of insects having wings, including species that have secondarily lost wings.

pupa (pu'pah) [L. "a doll"]. A stage in the development of an insect, between the larva and the imago (adult); a form which neither moves nor feeds.

purines (pu'rēns) [blend of *pure* and *urine*]. Organic bases with carbon and nitrogen atoms in two interlocking rings; components of nucleic acids, ATP, DPN and other biologically active substances.

putrefaction (pu"trĕ-fak'shun) [L. *putrefactio* decaying]. The enzymatic anaerobic degradation of proteins and amino acids.

pyrenoid (pi′rĕ-noid) [Gr. *pyrēn* fruit stone + *eidos* form]. Starch-containing granular bodies seen in the chromatophores of certain protozoa.

pyrimidines (pi-rim′ĭ-dins). Nitrogenous bases composed of a single ring of carbon and nitrogen atoms; components of nucleic acids.

quantum (kwon′tum) [L. "as much as"]. A unit of radiant energy; has no electric charge and very little mass; the energy of a quantum is an inverse function of the wavelength of the radiation.

race A division of a species; a population which differs from other populations with respect to the frequency of one or more genes; a subgroup of a species distinguished by a certain combination of morphologic and physiologic traits.

radula (raj′oo-la) [L. a scraper]. A rasplike structure in the alimentary tract of chitons, snails, squids and certain other mollusks.

range The portion of the earth in which a given species is found.

rassenkreis [Ger. race-circle]. Series of geographic subspecies in a population that is spread over a wide territory; each subspecies differs in some respects from their neighboring ones but interbreeds with them, but the groups at the two ends of the series may be quite different and have markedly reduced interfertility.

reabsorption Term applied to the selective removal of certain substances from the glomerular filtrate by the cells of the convoluted tubules of the kidney and their secretion into the bloodstream.

recapitulation The tendency for embryos in the course of development to repeat, perhaps in an abbreviated fashion, the sequence of stages in the embryonic development of their evolutionary ancestors.

receptor A sensory cell, or sometimes a free nerve ending which responds to a given type of stimulus.

recessive genes Genes which do not express their phenotype unless carried by both members of a set of homologous chromosomes; i.e., genes which produce their effect only when homozygous, when present in "double dose."

recon (re′kon) [From *recombination* + Gr. *on* neuter ending]. The ultimate unit of genetic recombination; the smallest element in a one-dimensional array of genetic material that is interchangeable, but not divisible, by recombination.

redia (re′dĭ-ah) [After Francesco Redi, seventeenth century Italian naturalist]. The second stage of flukes. It reproduces asexually in snails.

reduction The addition of electrons to an atom or molecule; opposite of oxidation.

reflex (re′fleks) [L. *reflexus* bent back]. An inborn, automatic, involuntary response to a given stimulus which is determined by the anatomic relations of the involved neurons; the functional units of the nervous system.

reflex arc A sequence of sensory, internuncial and motor neurons which conduct the nerve impulses for a given reflex.

refractory period The period of time which elapses after the response of a neuron or muscle fiber to one impulse before it can respond again.

regeneration Regrowth of a lost or injured tissue or part of an organism.

renal (re′nal) [L. *renalis* the kidney]. Pertaining to the kidney.

renal corpuscle (re′nal) [L. *renalis* kidney]. The complex formed by a glomerulus and the surrounding Bowman's capsule of a kidney tubule; filtration, the first step in urine formation, occurs here.

rennin (ren′in). Enzyme secreted by the gastric mucosa which converts the milk protein, casein, from a soluble to an insoluble substance, thereby curdling the milk.

reptile (rep′tīl) [L. *repere* to creep]. A member of a class of terrestrial vertebrates which are covered with horny scales or plates; living representatives include turtles, lizards, snakes and crocodiles.

resonating system A system of atoms bonded together which includes many different ways of arranging the external electrons without moving any of the constituent atoms.

respiration (res″pĭ-ra′shun) [L. *respirare* to breathe]. Process by which animal and plant cells utilize oxygen, produce carbon dioxide and conserve the energy of foodstuff molecules in biologically useful forms such as ATP; the act or function of breathing.

reticulum (re-tik′u-lum) [L. dim. of *rete* net]. A network of fibrils or filaments, either within a cell or in the intercellular matrix.

retina (ret′ĭ-nah) [L. *rete* net]. The innermost of the three tunics of the eyeball, surrounding the vitreous body and continuous posteriorly with the optic nerve; contains the light-sensitive receptor cells, rods and cones.

Rh factor An agglutinogen, originally discovered in the rhesus monkey, which is found in the erythrocytes of about 85 per cent of the white population.

rhodopsin (ro-dop′sin) [Gr. *rhodon* rose + *opsis* sight]. A substance in the retina of the eye (visual purple) made up of retinene, a derivative of vitamin A, and a protein, opsin; undergoes a chemical reaction triggered by light which stimulates the receptor cell to send an impulse to the brain, resulting in the sensation of sight.

ribonucleic acid (RNA) (ri″bo-nu′kle-ik as′id). Nucleic acid containing the sugar ribose; present in both nucleus and cytoplasm and of prime importance in the synthesis of proteins.

ribosomes (ri′bo-sōms). Minute granules, composed of protein and ribonucleic acid either free in the cytoplasm or attached to the membranes of the endoplasmic reticulum of a cell; the site of protein synthesis.

rickettsia (rik-et′se-ah). A type of disease organism, discovered by Howard Ricketts, intermediate in size and complexity between a virus and a bacterium; parasitic within cells of insects and ticks, transmitted to man by the bite of the infected insect or tick.

rod (rod) [AS. *rodd*]. In zoology, the rod-shaped photoreceptive cells of the retina, which are particularly sensitive to dim light and mediate black and white vision.

rotifera (ro-tif′er-ah) [L. *rota* wheel + *ferre* to bear]. A class of abundant small aschelminths, the rotifers.

saccule (sak′ūl) [L. *sacculus* a little sac]. Small, hollow sac in the inner ear lined with sensitive hair cells and containing small stones made of calcium carbonate; contains receptors for the sense of static balance.

saprophytic nutrition (sap″ro-fit′ik nu-trish′un) [Gr. *sapros* rotten + *phyton* plant + L. *nutritio* nourishing]. A type of heterotrophic nurtition in which organisms absorb their required nutrients through the cell membrane following the extracellular digestion of nonliving organic material.

sarcodina (sar″ko-di′nah) [Gr. *sarkos* flesh + *eidos* form]. A class of protozoa that form pseudopods.

sarcopterygian (sar′kop-tĕ-rij′ĭ-an) [Gr. *sarkos* flesh + *pterygos* wing]. A member of a subclass of Osteichthyes in which the fins are supported by a central axis of flesh and bone; includes lungfish and crossopterygians.

scaphopoda (skaf-op′o-dah) [Gr. *skaphe* boat + *podos* foot]. The tooth-shells, a small class of mollusks.

schizocoel (skiz′o-cēl) [Gr. *schizein* to divide + *koilia* cavity]. A body cavity formed by the splitting of embryonic mesoderm into two layers.

sclera (skle′rah) [Gr. *skleros* hard]. The tough, fibrous supporting wall of the eyeball forming approximately the posterior five-sixths of the wall; it is continuous anteriorly with the cornea.

scrotum (skro′tum) [L. *scrotum* bag]. The pouch which contains the testes in most mammals; its wall is composed of integument and muscular and connective tissue layers of the body wall which are everted during the descent of the testes.

scyphozoa (si″fo-zo′ah) [Gr. *skyphos* cup + *zōon* animal]. A class of coelenterates with usually small polyps and large medusae; jellyfish.

secondary response A rapid production of antibodies induced by a second injection of antigen several days, weeks or even months after the primary injection.

secretion (se-kre′shun) [L. *secretio*, from *secernere* to secrete]. The production and release by a cell of some substance that is used elsewhere in the body in some process.

segmentation (seg″men-ta′shun) [L. *segmentum* a piece cut off]. Division of a body or structure into more or less similar parts.

semicircular canals The three canals or ducts of the membranous labyrinth which lie at right angles to each other in the vertical and horizontal planes of the body; they detect changes in the angular acceleration of the body.

seminal receptacle A portion of the female reproductive tract in which sperm are stored after mating.

seminal vesicle A portion of the male reproductive tract in which sperm are stored before mating.

seminiferous tubule (se″mĭ-nif′er-us) [L. *semen* seed + *ferre* to bear]. One of the tubules in the testis; cells in its walls multiply and differentiate into spermatozoa.

senescence (se-nes′ens) [L. *senescere* to grow old]. The gradual loss of vigor and physiological capacity through the aging process.

serum (se′rum) [L. "whey"]. The clear portion of a biological fluid separated from its particu-. late elements; light yellow liquid left after clotting of blood has occurred.

sinoatrial node (si″no-a′tre-al nōd) [L. *sino* "a hollow" + *atrium* hall + *nodus* knot]. A small mass of nodal tissue located at the point where the superior vena cava empties into the right atrium; initiates the heart beat and regulates the rate of contraction.

sinus venosus (si′nus ve-no′sus) [L. *sinus* a bent surface + *venosus* venous]. The first chamber of the heart of lower vertebrates; it receives the systemic veins and opens into the atrium.

sipunculoidea (si-pung″ku-loi′de-ah) [Gr. *sipunculus* small tube]. A small phylum of marine worms having no segmentation and a tubular body.

sol (sol). A colloidal system in which the continuous phase is liquid and the dispersed phase is solid particles 0.1 to 0.001 micron in diameter.

solute (so′lūt) [L., from *solvere* to dissolve]. A substance dissolved in a true solution; a solution consists of a solute and a solvent.

solvent (sol′vent) [L., from *solvere* to dissolve]. The fluid medium in which the solute molecules are dissolved in a true solution; a liquid that dissolves or that is capable of dissolving.

somatic (so-mat′ik) [Gr. *sōma* the body]. Pertaining to the body wall of an organism, e.g., the somatic muscles, or muscles in the body wall.

somites (so′mīts) [Gr. *sōma* body]. Paired, block-like masses of mesoderm, arranged in a longitudinal series alongside the neural tube of the embryo, forming the vertebral column and dorsal muscles.

species (spe'shēz) [L. *species* sort, kind]. The unit of taxonomic classification for both plants and animals; a population of similar individuals, alike in their structural and functional characteristics, which in nature breed only with each other, and which have a common ancestry.

spermatophore (sper-mat'o-fōr) [Gr. *spermatos* seed + *phorein* to bear]. A package secreted by part of the male reproductive tract, enclosing a number of sperm.

sphincter (sfingk'ter) [Gr. *sphinkter* to bind tight]. A group of circularly arranged muscle fibers whose contractions close an opening, e.g., the pyloric sphincter at the end of the stomach.

spiracle (spir'ah-k'l) [L. *spirare* to breathe]. A breathing opening such as the opening on the body surface of a trachea in insects, or a modified gill opening in cartilaginous fishes through which some water enters the pharynx.

spiral cleavage A complex pattern of mosaic development in early cleavage that is common to a number of invertebrate phyla.

spongin (spun'jin) [Gr. *spongia* sponge]. A flexible skeletal material found in some sponges, especially those of commerce.

spore (spōr) [Gr. *sporos* seed]. An asexual reproductive element, usually unicellular, of an organism, such as a protozoan or a cryptogamic plant, which can develop directly into an adult.

sporozoa (spo"ro-zo'ah) [Gr. *sporos* seed + *zōon* animal]. Class of protozoa (spore formers); have no special method of locomotion and are parasitic; one kind is the human parasite causing malaria.

stapes (sta'pēz) [L. "stirrup"]. The innermost of the small bones in the middle ear cavity, shaped somewhat like a stirrup.

statocyst (stat'o-sist) [Gr. *statos* standing + *kystis* sac]. A cellular cyst containing one or more granules that is used in a variety of animals to sense the direction of gravity.

steatopygia (ste"ah-to-pij'e-ah) [Gr. *steatos* fat + *pygē* buttock]. An excessive accumulation of fat on the buttocks and thighs.

sternum (ster'num) [L. the chest]. The chest region, especially the brestbone of a vertebrate, or the ventral skeletal piece of any arthropod segment.

steroids (ste'roids) [Gr. *stereos* solid + *eides* like]. Complex molecules containing carbon atoms arranged in four interlocking rings, three of which contain six carbon atoms each and the fourth of which contains five; the male and female sex hormones and the adrenal cortical hormones.

stimulus (stim'u-lus) [L. "goad"]. Any agent, act, or influence that produces functional or trophic reaction in a receptor or in an irritable tissue.

stomodeum (sto"mo-de'um) [Gr. *stoma* mouth + *hodaios* on the way]. The inturned anterior portion of a digestive tract, lined with ectoderm.

subgerminal space (sub-jer'mĭ-nal spās) [L. *sub* under + *germinalis* germ]. The shallow cavity under the dividing cells of a hen's egg, not homologous to the blastocoele of the frog egg.

suctoria (suk-to'rĭ-ah) [L. *sugere* to suck]. A class of protozoa with ciliated young and adults that feed through tubular processes.

syconoid (si'kon-oid) [Gr. *sykon* fig + *eidos* form]. In sponges, a body plan in which the wall is indented from both sides, giving the sponge greater bulk.

symbiosis (sim"bi-o'sis) [Gr. *symbiōsis* to live together]. The living together of two dissimilar organisms; association may form mutualism, commensalism, parasitism or amensalism.

sympathetic system (sim"pah-thet'ik) [Gr. *sym* with + *pathos* feeling]. A division of the autonomic nervous system in which fibers leave the central nervous system with certain thoracic and lumbar nerves and go to the sweat glands and visceral organs; has an effect on most organs that is antagonistic to parasympathetic stimulation.

synapse (sin'aps) [Gr. *synapsis* conjunction]. The junction between the axon of one neuron and the dendrite of the next.

synapsis (sĭ-nap'sis) [Gr. *synapsis* conjunction]. The pairing and union side by side of homologous chromosomes from the male and female pronuclei early in meiosis.

syncytium (sin-sit'e-um) [Gr. *syn* together + *kytos* a hollow vessel]. A multinucleate mass of cytoplasm produced by the merging of cells.

synergistic (sin"er-jis'tik) [Gr. *syn* with + *ergon* work]. Acting together; enhancing the effect of another force or agent.

syngamy (sin'gah-me) [Gr. *syn* with + *gamos* marriage]. Sexual reproduction; the union of the gametes in fertilization.

systole (sĭs'to-le) [Gr. *systolē* a drawing together]. The contraction of the heart; the interval between the first and second heart sounds during which blood is forced into the aorta and pulmonary arteries.

taiga (ti'ga) [Russian]. Northern coniferous forest biome found particularly in Canada, northern Europe and Siberia.

taxis (tak'sis) [Gr. a drawing up in rank and file]. An orientation movement in response to a stimulus in a direction determined by the direction of the stimulus; found in animals, some lower plants and the male sex cells of mosses or ferns.

taxonomy (taks-on'o-me) [Gr. *taxis* a drawing up in rank and file + *nomos* law]. The science of naming, describing and classifying organisms.

tectorial membrane (tek-to're-al mem'brān) [L. *tectum* roof + *membrana* skin covering]. The roof membrane of the organ of Corti in the cochlea of the ear.

telencephalon (tel″en-sef′ah-lon) [Gr. *tele* end + *enkephalos* brain]. The most anterior of the five major subdivisions of the brain; includes the olfactory bulbs and cerebral hemispheres.

teleost (tel′e-ost) [Gr. *tele* end + *osteon* bone]. A member of the most advanced groups of actinopterygian fishes; includes most of the familiar species such as herring, salmon, eels, minnows, suckers, catfish, bass and perch.

telophase (tel′o-fāz) [Gr. *tele* end + *phasis* phase]. The last of the four stages of mitosis, during which the two daughter nuclei appear and the cytoplasm usually divides.

template (tem′plāt) [L. *templum* a small timber]. A pattern or mold which guides the formation of a duplicate.

territoriality (ter″i-tor′ĭ-al′ĭ-te) [L. *territorium* the earth]. Behavior pattern in which one organism (usually a male) delineates a territory of his own and defends it against intrusion by other members of the same species and sex.

testis (tes′tis) [L.]. The male gonad which produces spermatozoa; in man and certain other mammals the testes are situated in the scrotal sac.

tetanus (tet′ah-nus) [Gr. *tetanos*, from *teinein* to stretch]. Sustained, steady maximal contraction of a muscle, without distinct twitching, resulting from a rapid succession of nerve impulses.

tetany (tet′ah-ne) [Gr. *tetanos* stretched]. A syndrome manifested by sharp flexion of the wrist and ankle joints, muscle twitchings, cramps and convulsions; occurs in parathyroid hypofunction.

tetrad (tet′rad) [Gr. *tetra* four]. A bundle of four homologous chromatids produced at the end of the first meiotic prophase.

tetraploid (tet″rah-ploid′) [Gr. *tetra* four + *ploos* fold]. An individual or cell having four sets of chromosomes.

tetrapoda (tet-rap′o-dah) [Gr. *tetra* four + *podos* foot]. Four-limbed vertebrates; the amphibia, reptiles, birds and mammals.

thalamus (thal′ah-mus) [Gr. *thalamos* inner chamber]. The lateral walls of the diencephalon; it is the main relay center for sensory impulses going to the cerebrum and it also interacts with the cerebrum in complex ways.

theory (the′o-re) [Gr. *theōria* speculation as opposed to practice]. A formulated hypothesis supported by a large body of observations and experiments.

therapsids (ther-ap′sids). An order of mammal-like reptiles of the Permian period from which mammals evolved.

thermodynamics, first law of (ther″mo-di-nam′iks) [Gr. *thermē* heat + *dynamis* power]. Law which states that energy is neither created nor destroyed but only transformed from one kind to another.

thigmotropism (thig-mot′ro-pizm) [Gr. *thigma* touch + *tropē* turn]. The orientation of an organism in response to the stimulus of contact or touch.

threshold (thresh′old). The value at which a stimulus just produces a sensation, is just appreciable, or comes just within the limits of perception.

thrombin (throm′bin) [Gr. *thrombos* lump, curd, clot]. The enzyme derived from prothrombin which converts fibrinogen to fibrin; participates in blood clotting.

thrombus (throm′bus) [Gr. *thrombos* lump, curd, clot]. A clot in a blood vessel or in one of the cavities of the heart, which remains at the point of its formation.

tissue (tish′u) [Fr. *tissu* to weave]. Group of similarly specialized cells which together perform certain special functions; e.g., muscle tissue, bone tissue, nerve tissue.

tissue fluid (tish′u) [Fr. *tissu* to weave]. The lymphlike fluid which bathes the cells and tissues of the body; it is produced by filtration from the blood and drains into the venous ends of capillaries and into lymphatic capillaries.

tonus (to′nus) [Gr. *tonos* strain, tone]. The continuous partial contraction of muscle.

tornaria (tor-na′re-ah) [L. *tornare* to turn]. The free-swimming hemichordate larva that shows many similarities to echinoderm larvae.

toxin (tok′sin) [L. *toxicum* poison]. Poisonous substance produced by one organism which usually affects one particular organ or organ system, rather than the body as a whole, of another organism.

trachea (tra′ke-ah) [Gr. *trachelos* the throat]. An air conducting tube: in terrestrial vertebrates, the main trunk of the system of tubes through which air passes to and from the lungs; in terrestrial arthropods, one of a system of minute tubes that permeate the body and deliver air to the tissues.

transducers (trans-du′sers) [L. *transducere* to lead across]. Devices receiving energy from one system in one form and supplying it to a second system in a different form; e.g., converting radiant energy to chemical energy.

transduction (trans-duk′shun) [L. *transducere* to lead across]. The transfer of a genetic fragment from one cell to another; e.g., from one bacterium to another by a virus.

transfer RNA A form of RNA composed of about 70 nucleotides which serve as adaptor molecules in the synthesis of proteins. An amino acid is bound to a specific kind of transfer RNA and then arranged in order by the complementary nature of the nucleotide triplet (codon) in template or messenger RNA and the triplet anticodon of transfer RNA.

transforming agents Substances isolated from pneumococci and certain other bacteria which bring about a permanent, inherited change when applied to another strain of that type of bacteria.

transverse plane A section in a bilaterally symmetrical animal which includes a dorsoventral axis and a left-right axis, but is at right angles to the anteroposterior axis.

trematoda (trem″ah-to′dah) [Gr. *trematodes* having holes]. The flukes, a class of parasitic flatworms.

trichocyst (trik′o-sist) [Gr. *trichos* hair + *kryptos* concealed]. A cellular organelle in the cytoplasm of ciliated protozoa such as *Paramecium* which can discharge a filament that may aid in trapping and holding prey.

trilobite (tri′lo-bīt) [L. *tres* three + *lobus* lobe]. Marine arthropods of the Paleozoic era characterized by two dorsal longitudinal furrows that separated the body into three lobes.

triplet code The sequences of three nucleotides which comprise the codons, the units of genetic information in DNA which specify the order of amino acids in a peptide chain.

triplet state The state resulting when an electron is activated by absorbing a photon, moves to an outer orbital of higher energy and pairs with an electron of like spin.

triploid (trip′loid) [Gr. *triploos* triple + *eidēs* like]. An individual or cell having three sets of chromosomes.

trochophore (tro′ko-fōr) [Gr. *trochos* wheel + *phoros* bearing]. A larval form, similar to the larva of mollusks, which characterizes the development of polychaetes and archiannelids.

troop The social unit of many primate species, consisting of several males, three to many females, and their offspring.

trophallaxis (tro″fah-lak′sis) [Gr. *trepheīn* to nourish + *allaxis* exchange]. The mutual exchange of food and secretions among the members of an insect colony.

tropism (tro′pizm) [Gr. *tropē* a turning]. A growth response in a nonmotile organism, elicited by an external stimulus.

tundra [Russian]. A treeless plain between the taiga in the south and the polar ice cap in the north; characterized by low temperatures, a short growing season, and ground that is frozen most of the year.

turbellaria (tur″bel-a′rĭ-ah) [L. *turbella* a stir]. The class of free-living flatworms.

turnover number The number of molecules of substrate acted upon by one molecule of enzyme per minute.

ubiquinone Coenzyme Q, a component of the electron transmitter system; consists of a head, a six-membered carbon ring, which can take up and release electrons, and a long tail composed of a chain of carbon atoms.

umbilical cord (um-bil′ĭ-k′l) [L. *umbilicus* navel]. The stalk, or cord, attached to the navel and connecting the embryo with the placenta; it contains the umbilical arteries and veins, and the remnants of the allantois and yolk stalk.

umbilicus (um-bil′i-cus) [L.]. The navel; the scar marking the site of attachment of the umbilical cord in the fetus.

ungulates (ung″gu-lātes) [L. *ungula* hoof]. Four-legged mammals which walk on the tips of their digits and which have lost one or more toes. The end of each digit is protected by a hoof.

unguligrade (ung-gwil′ĭ-grad) [L. *ungula* hoof + *gradi* to walk]. Locomotion in which the animal runs upon the tips of one or two digits of each limb.

unit membrane Membrane incorporated in the structure of many cell organelles which consists of two layers of protein molecules between which are sandwiched layers of lipid and other molecules.

urea (u-re′ah) [Gr. *ouron* urine]. One of the end products of protein metabolism; the diamide of carbonic acid, NH_2CONH_2; soluble in water.

ureter (u-re′ter) [Gr.]. The fibromuscular tube which conveys urine from a metanephric kidney to the cloaca or exterior of the body.

urethra (u-re′thrah) [Gr.]. The membranous canal conveying urine from the bladder to the exterior of the body.

uric acid (u′rik) [Gr. *ouron* urine]. An end product of nucleic acid and protein metabolism with a low solubility in water; particularly abundant in certain terrestrial animals; $C_5H_4N_4O_3$.

urochordate (u-ro-kor′dāt) [Gr. *oura* tail + L. *chorda* string]. A member of a subphylum of chordates characterized by the restriction of the notochord to the larval tail; includes sea squirts and their allies.

uterus (u′ter-us) [L.]. The womb; the hollow, muscular organ of the female reproductive tract in which the fetus undergoes development.

utricle (u′tre-k′l) [L. *utriculus* a bag]. The larger of the two divisions of the membranous labyrinth; contains the receptors for dynamic body balance.

vaccine (vak′sēn) [L. *vaccinus* a cow]. The commercially produced antigen of a particular disease, strong enough to stimulate the body to make antibodies but not sufficiently strong to cause the disease's harmful effects.

vacuole (vak′u-ōl) [L. *vacuus* empty + *-ole* dim. ending]. Small space within a cell, filled with watery liquid and separated by a vacuolar membrane from the rest of the cytoplasm.

vagina (vah-ji′nah) [L. a scabbard]. In many kinds of animals, the terminal portion of the female reproductive tract; receives the male copulatory organ.

valence (va′lens) [L. *valentia* strength]. An expression of the number of atoms of hydrogen (or its equivalent) which one atom of a chemical element can hold in combination, if negative, or displace in a reaction, if positive; the number of electrons gained, lost or shared by the atom in forming bonds with one or more other atoms.

vas deferens (vas def′er-enz) [L. *vas* duct + *deferens* carrying away]. The duct which carries sperm from the testis and epididymis to the cloaca or penis; it develops from the archinephric or wolffian duct.

vasa efferentia (va′sa ef′er-ent′i-ah) [L. *vasa* ducts + *exferre* to carry out]. In lower vertebrates, the cords of the urogenital union which extend between the testis and kidney; in mammals, the tubules in the head of the epididymis which have developed from certain kidney tubules.

vein (vān) [L. *vena*]. A vessel through which the blood passes from the tissues toward the heart; typically has thin walls and contains valves that prevent a reverse flow of blood.

velum (ve′lum) [L. an awning or veil]. In hydrozoan medusae, a shelf-like membrane partially closing the subumbrellar opening.

ventricle (ven′tri-k′l) [L. *ventriculus*, dim. of *venter* the stomach]. A cavity in an organ, such as one of the several cavities of the brain or one of the chambers of the heart that receive blood from the atria.

vertebrate (ver′tĕ-brāt) [L. *vertebratus* having a backbone]. A member of a subphylum of chordates characterized by the presence of a vertebral column; includes fishes, amphibians, reptiles, birds and mammals.

vestigial (ves-tij′e-al) [L. *vestigium* footprint, trace, sign]. Useless, incomplete or undersized; said of an organ present in one organism which is a remnant of a homologous organ that functioned in an ancestral organism.

villus (vil′lus) [L. "tuft of hair"]. A small, fingerlike vascular process or protrusion, especially a protrusion from the free surface of a membrane such as the lining of the intestine.

virus (vi′rus) [L. slimy liquid, poison]. Minute infectious agent, composed of a nucleic acid core and a protein shell; may reproduce and mutate within a host cell.

visceral (vis′er-al) [L. *viscera* internal organs]. Pertaining to the internal organs; e.g., the visceral muscles of the gut wall.

visceral arch (vis′er-al) [L. *viscera* internal organs]. An arch of cartilage or bone which develops in the wall of the pharynx between the gill slits; they supported the gills in ancestral vertebrates, but certain ones became incorporated into the skull of higher vertebrates.

vital capacity (vi′tal kah-pas′ĭ-te) [L. *vita* life + *capacitas*, from *capere* to take]. The total amount of air displaced when one breathes in as deeply as possible and then breathes out as completely as possible.

vitamin (vi-tah-min) [L. *vita* life]. An organic substance necessary in small amounts for the normal metabolic functioning of a given organism; must be present in the diet because the organism cannot synthesize an adequate amount of it.

vitreous (vit′re-us) [L. *vitreus* glassy]. Glasslike or hyaline; designates the vitreous body of the eye which contains clear transparent jelly which fills the posterior part of the eyeball.

viviparous (vi-vip′ah-rus) [L. *vivus* alive + *parere* to bring forth, produce]. Bearing living young which develop from eggs within the body of the mother, deriving nutrition from the maternal organism through a special organ, the placenta, which is a union of certain fetal membranes and the uterine lining.

warning coloration Adaptation for survival which consists of bright, conspicuous colors and is assumed by poisonous or unpalatable animals, or their mimics, to warn potential predators not to eat them.

X organ Organ present in crustacea which produces hormones that regulate molting, metabolism, reproduction, the distribution of pigment in the compound eyes and the control of pigmentation of the body.

yolk sac A pouchlike outgrowth of the digestive tract of certain vertebrate embryos which grows around the yolk, digests it, and makes it available to the rest of the organism.

zygote (zi′got) [Gr. *zygotos* yoked together]. The cell formed by the union of two gametes; a fertilized egg.

INDEX

A bands, 92
Aardvark, 437
Abalone, 213
Abducens nerve, 537
Abduction, 337
Abomasum, 465
Absorption, 77
Abyssal zone, 735
Acanthocephala, 189, 197
Acanthocottus, 380
Acanthodians, 371
Acanthodii, 379
Acanthopterygii, 380
Accessory sex glands, 514
Acetabularia, 34
Acetyl coenzyme A, 66
Acetylcholine, 96, 539, 562
Aciculum, 230
Acids, 21. See also names of specific acids, e.g., *Amino acids.*
Acipenser, 379
Acipenseriformes, 379
Acoela, 183
Acromegaly, 565
Acrosome, 109
ACTH, 561, 566
Actin, 41
Actinopterygians, 371
Actinopterygii, 379
Action potential, 91, 94
Actomyosin, 88
Acts, innate, 764
Adaptation(s), 16
    color, 723
    physiologic, 722
    structural, 721
Adaptive radiation, 374, 655, 722
Addison's disease, 561
Adduction, 337
Adenine, 27, 617
Adenosine triphosphate, 58
Adipose tissue, 48
Adrenal cortex, 560
    hypofunction of, 561
Adrenal glands, 347
    parts of, 559

Adrenal medulla, 560
Adrenocorticotropic hormone, 561, 566
Adrenogenital syndrome, 561
Aeolosoma, 238
Aepyornithiformes, 425
Aestivation, 386, 705
African lungfish, 370
After-birth, 517
Agglutinins, 487, 610
Agglutinogens, 487, 610
Aggregations, animal, 709
Agnatha, 359, 378
Agnosia, 547
Air, composition of, 21
Air sacs, 416
Airfoil, 408
Alanine, 66
Alarm substances, 574
Albinism, 634, 642
Albumin, egg, 394
Alcyonarians, 168
Aldolase, 66
Aldosterone, 560
Alisphenoid, 455
Alkaline phosphatase, 42
Alkaptonuria, 635
Allantoin, 676
Allantois, 116, 394, 578
Alleles, 591
    multiple, 609
Alligators, 403, 680
All-or-none effect, 90
All-or-none law, 94
Allotheria, 445
Altricial, 423, 433
Alula, 409
Alveolar sac, 477
Alveoli, 82, 477
Amacrine cells, 526
Ambivalent behavior patterns, 746
Amblyopsiformes, 380
Ambulacral areas, 304
Ambulacral grooves, 299
Amebas, 138
Amebic dysentery, 771
Amebocytes, 150

Ameboid motion, 15, 89, 132
Amensalism, 706, 708
American eel, 379
Amia, 372, 379
Amiiformes, 379
Amino acid adenylate, 630
Amino acid transfer RNA, 630
Amino acids, 25
    essential, 26, 471
    oxidation of, 66
γ-Aminobutyric acid, 281
Aminopeptidases, 468
Ammocoetes, 363
Ammonia, 86, 385, 676
Ammonites, 220
Amnion, 116, 394
Amniotes, 395
Amniotic cavity, 116, 577
Ampere, 68
Amphibia, 329
Amphibian(s), adaptations in, 388
    characteristics of, 384
    circulation in, 385
    evolution of, 386
    fossils of, 384
    respiration of, 385
Amphiblastula, 154
Amphineura, 209
Amphioxus, 314, 319, 320, 324
Amphipod(s), 744
Amphipoda, 256
Amplexus, 348
Ampulla, 299, 527
Amylase(s), 77, 467
    salivary, 59
Anabolism, 16
Analogy, 356
Anamniotes, 395
Anaphase, 39, 105
Anapsida, 405
Anatomy, 3
Anaximander, 8
Androgen(s), 560, 567
Androgenic gland, 280
Androsterone, 567
Anemia, 484
Angler fish, 376, 380
Anguilla, 379
Anguilliformes, 379
Anhydro bonds, formation of, 70
Animal(s), distribution of, 724
    diurnal, 761
    luminescent, 71
    saprozoic, 770
Animal aggregations, 717
Anions, 20
Annelid(s), evolutionary relationships of, 238
Annelida, 227
Anseriformes, 426
Anthropoids, 439
Ant(s), 265
    colony of, 754
    fire, 574, 750
Anteater, spiny, 433
Anthozoa, 163, 168
Anthropoids, 683
    fossil, 687
Antibodies, 486
Anticodon, 628
Antidiuretic hormone, 563

Antigen(s), 486
Antigen-antibody reactions, 675
Antiqueen substance, 755
Antlers, 449
Antrum, 568
Anura, 329, 386, 405
Anuran eggs, protective devices for, 391
Anus, 466
Ape-men, 688
Aphasia, 547
Aphredoderus, 380
Apical gland, 184
Apical organ, 241
Apis mellifera, 265
Apoda, 386, 405
Apodeme, 88
Apodiformes, 426
Apoenzyme, 59
Apopyle, 151
Appalachian revolution, 670
Appendages, biramous, 244
    uniramous, 245
Appendicular skeleton, 333
Appendicularia, 324
Apterygiformes, 425
Apterygota, 262
Aqueduct of Sylvius, 541
Aqueous humor, 522
Arachnida, 268
Arachnoid membrane, 541
Arch(es), pulmocutaneous, 489
Archaeopteryx lithographica, 419, 653
Archaeornithes, 425
Archenteron, 112, 580
Archeology, 693
Archeozoic era, 667
Archiannelida, 229
Archinephric duct, 503
Archosaur(s), 401
Archosauria, 405
Argiope, 269
Aristotle, 8
Aristotle's lantern, 306
Armadillo, 584
Arrector pili, 451
Arrowworms, 293
Arteries, 343, 480
Arterioles, 498
Arthropods, classification of, 244
    evolutionary relationships of, 238
    muscular innervation in, 281
    visual acuity of, 285
Articular bone, 403
Articular processes, 384
Artifacts, 693
Artiodactyl(s), 442
Artiodactyla, 446
Ascaris lumbricoides, 195, 774
Aschelminthes, 188, 201
Ascidiacea, 324
Ascidian, adult, 316
Ascorbic acid, 472
Aspartic acid, 66
Asplanchna, 192
Astacus, 247
Asterias forbesi, 299
Asteroidea, 299, 303
Atherina, 380
Atheriniformes, 380
Atherinomorpha, 380

Atlas, 333, 453
Atoms, 19
ATP, 61
Atrioventricular node, 496
Atrium, 80, 315, 345, 491
Augmentation, 507
Aurelia, 166
Auricularia, 311
Australian lungfish, 377
Australian marsupials, 679
Australian realm, 680
Australopithecus, 687
Autonomic nervous system, 351
Autonomic stimulation, effects of, 539
Autosomes, 598
Autotrophs, 74
   evolution of, 662
Aves, 408
Axial filament, 53
Axis, 453
Axolotls, 389
Axons, 52
Aysheaia, 271
Azaguanine, 632

Baboon, 686, 721
Backswimmer, 700
Bacon, Roger, 9
Bacteria, nitrogen-fixing, 702
von Baer, Karl Ernst, 10
Balantidium coli, 775
Ball, E. G., 68
Barbules, 412
Barnacles, 255, 774
Barriers, geographic, 724
Basal body, 35, 133
Basal metabolic rate, 470
Base(s), 21
Basement membrane, 47
Basilar membrane, 530
Basket stars, 299, 307
Basophils, 51, 485
Bat(s), 435
Bathyal zone, 735
Batoidea, 368, 379
Batrachoides, 380
Batrachoidiformes, 380
Bayliss, William, 12
Beadle, George, 634
Beagle, voyage of, 648
Beavers, 788
Bedbugs, 791
Bee(s), 265
   celestial navigation of, 716
   communication between, 749
   swarming of, 755
Beebread, 267
Beetles, 265
Behavior, factors affecting, 756
   genetic control of, 764
   methods of studying, 765
   predatory, 740
   protean, 743
Behavior patterns, aggression, 746
   communication, 748
   dominance hierarchies, 753
   feeding, 740

Behavior patterns (*Continued*)
   innate, 764
   mating, 750
   orientation, 744
   parental care, 752
von Békésy, G., 530
Bell, Charles, 12
Belly of muscle, 90
Bends, 723
van Beneden, Eduard, 589
Benthos, 735
Beriberi, 6, 78, 471
Bernard, Claude, 12
Beryciformes, 380
Bestiaries, 9
Bicarbonate ions, 482
Biceps, 90, 459
Bichir, 379
Bicuspid valve, 495
Bile, 465
Bile duct, 465
Bile pigment, 484
Bile salts, 465
Binary fission, 145
Binomial system of nomenclature, 125, 129
Biogeographic realms, 680
Biogeography, 679
Biologic clocks, 716
Biologic tracers, 20
Biological Abstracts, 4
Biology, molecular, 3
Bioluminescence, 71
Biomass, 710
Biomes, 725
Biosynthetic processes, 70
Biotic communities, 710, 717
Biotic potential, 713
Birds, 408
   adaptations of, 421
   aquatic, 420
   bills of, 721
   evolution of, 418
   fossil, 419
   migrations of, 423, 745
   muscles of, 415
   navigation of, 424
   of prey, 420
   pelvis of, 415
   perching, 420
   plumage of, 423
   reproductive adaptations of, 422
   structure of, 412
Birth, circulatory changes at, 494
Birth rate, 712
Bison, 786
Bivalves, 215
Blastocoele, 112
Blastocyst, 576
Blastomeres, 112, 576
Blastopore, 113
   fate of, 205
Blastula, 112, 353
Blood, 51, 480
   clotting of, chemistry of, 485
   flow of, 495
      direction of, 11
   volume of, 482
Blood cells, red, 482
   white, 485
Blood flukes, 183, 777

Blood groups, human, 487
  inheritance of, 609, 643
Blood vessels, development of, 583
Bloodsuckers, 238, 771
Boa constrictors, 400
Body fluids, regulation of, 509
Body plan, 53
Body stalk, 578
Bolus, 463
Bombykol, 574
Bombyx, 279
Bond, energy-rich, 65
Bone(s), 19, 49, 88. See also names of specific
    bones, e.g., *Humerus*.
  cartilage replacement, 452
  dermal, 452
Bonellia, 291
Bonner, James, 637
Book gills, 268
Book lungs, 269
Botflies, 779
Botryllus, 314, 317
Bowditch, Henry, 12
Bowerbirds, 751
Bowfin, 372, 379
Bowman's capsule, 85, 506
Brachionus, 192
Brachiopod(s), 663, 670
Brachiopoda, 291
Brain, 322
  insect, 260
  parts of, 540
Branchial arches, 364
Branchial basket, 362
Branchial muscles, evolution of, 459
Branchiopoda, 254
Branchiostoma, 314, 319, 320, 324
Breathing, control of, 477
Bridges, C. B., 598
Brine shrimps, 254
Brittle stars, 299, 307
Bromouracil, 632
Bronchi, 476
  recurrent, 416
Brontosaurus, 402
Brood pouch, 254
Brow spot, 330
Brown, Robert, 12
Brownian movement, 43
Bruce effect, 574
Bryozoa, 292
Buccal cavity, 339
Buccopharyngeal membrane, 384
Budding, 102, 163
Buffer, 26, 482
Bullfrog, 335
Burbot, 380
Bush babies, 683
Busycon, morphology of, 211
Butterflies, 265

Caecilians, 386
Caecum, 77, 466
Calciferol, 472
Calciferous glands, 233
Calcium metabolism, regulation of, 557
Calorie, 57
Calyces, 290, 506

Cambarus, 247
Cambrian period, 670
Camels, 442, 784
Canal(s), 150
  of Schlemm, 522
Canine tooth, 429
Capillaries, 480
Capillary exchange, 500
Caprimulgiformes, 426
Carapace, 247, 395
Carbaminohemoglobin, 83, 482
Carbohydrate, 23
Carbohydrate metabolism, 470
Carbon, 21
Carbon cycle, 701
Carbon dioxide, 63
  source of, 662
Carbonic anhydrase, 83, 482
Carboniferous period, 670
Carboxypeptidase, 468
Cardiac output, control of, 497
Cardiac stomach, 300
Cardium edule, 217
Caribou, 725
Carnivores, 74, 439
Carotid gland, 343
Carp, 380
Carpometacarpus, 414
Cartilage, 24, 49, 88
Cartilage replacement bone, 369
Cassowaries, 420
Cast(s), 665
Castration, 567
Casuariformis, 425
Cat, Manx, 654
  six-toed, 653
Catabolism, 16
Catalase, 58
Catalysis, 57
Catalyst, 57
Catarrhini, 439, 445
Catastrophism, 647
Catfish, 376, 380
Cations, 20
Catostomus, 380
Caudata, 405
Caularchus, 376, 380
Cave paintings, 8
Cavernous bodies, 514
Ceboidea, 684
Cell(s), 14, 30. See also specific types of cells, e.g.,
    Granulosa cells.
  constituents of, 17
    dynamic state of, 69
    physical characteristics of, 27
  death of, programmed, 279
  dynamic state of, 21
  stinging, 160
Cell constancy, 191
Cell division, 37
Cell lineage, 241
Cell theory, 12, 30
Cellulose, 24
Cement glands, 181
Cenozoic era, 673
Center of origin, 679
Centipedes, 245, 257
Centriole, 35, 38, 53, 104, 133
Centromere, 36

Cephalization, 315
Cephalochordata, 318, 324
Cephalopoda, 209, 219
Cephalothorax, 247
Ceratomorpha, 446
Cercaria, 185
Cercoid, 186
Cercopithicoidea, 684
Cerebellum, 350, 541, 543
Cerebral hemispheres, 350, 540, 545
Cerebrosides, 25
Cerebrospinal fluid, 480, 541
Cervix, 514
Cestoda, 176, 185
Cetacea, 444, 446
Cetomimiformes, 380
Chaetae, 228, 231
Chaetognatha, 293
Chameleon, 397
Chance, Britton, 59
Channa, 380
Channiformes, 380
Chaparral biome, 732
Characteristics, acquired, inheritance of, 648
  sex-linked, 599
Charadriiformes, 426
Chelicerae, 245, 269
Chelicerata, 245, 268
Chelonia, 405
Chemical compounds, 20
Chemical reactions, 56
  factors determining rates of, 57
Chemoreception, 96
Chemoreceptors, 97, 249, 519
Chiggers, 772
Childbirth, 516
Chilean frog, 391
Chilopoda, 257
Chimaera, 367, 368, 379
Chimaeriformes, 379
Chimpanzees, 687
Chironomus, 278
Chiroptera, 435, 445
Chitin, 24, 230, 244
Chitinous layers, 275
Chitons, 209
Chlamydomonas, 137
Chloragen cells, 234
Chloroplasts, 134
Choanocytes, 150
Choanoflagellates, 137, 200
Cholecystokinin, 573
Cholesterol, 25
Cholinesterase, 96
Chondrichthyes, 364, 379
Chondrocranium, 452
Chondrostei, 371, 379
Chordata, 324
Chordate(s), characteristics of, 314
  evolution of, 323
  origin of, 322
Chorion, 116, 394
Chorionic gonadotropin, 571
Chorionic villi, 515
Choroid coat, 522
Choroid plexuses, 541
Chromatids, 104
Chromatin, 35
Chromatophores, 101, 222, 332, 451

Chromomeres, 36
Chromonema, 36
Chromosome(s), 34, 36
  chemistry of, 614
  DNA content of, 614
  exchange of segments of, 600
  giant, 636
  homologous, 104, 591
  number of, 36
  sex, 597
  X, 598
  Y, 599
Chyme, 464
Chymotrypsin, 77
Ciconiiformes, 426
Cilia, 15, 89, 132
Ciliary body, 522
Ciliata, 141
Ciliophora, 144
Circadian rhythms, 715, 761
Circulation, 78
  fetal, 493
  patterns of, 488
Circulatory system, vertebrate, 480
Cirripedia, 255
Cis-trans test, 623
Cistron, 623
Citric acid, 64
Cladocera, 254
Cladoselache, 379
Cladoselachii, 379
Clam, cherrystone, 215
  steaming, 217
Clamworms, 229
Class, 126
Clavicle, 457
Claws, poison, 257
Cleaning symbiosis, 743
Cleavage, 112
Cleft palate, 121
Cleidoic eggs, 418
Click mechanism, 284
Climatius, 371, 379
Climax community, 718
Clingfish, 376, 380
Clitellum, 235
Clitoris, 110, 514
Cloaca, 340, 581
Clothes moth, 722
Clubfoot, 122
Clupea, 380
Clupeiformes, 379
Clupeomorpha, 379
Coat color, inheritance of, in guinea pigs, 591
  in rabbits, 609
  of Duroc-Jersey pigs, 605
Cobalt deficiency, 78
Coccidiosis, 144, 780
Coccyx, 675
Cochlear duct, 530
Cockle, 217
Cockroach, 257
  external morphology of, 258
  internal anatomy of, 259
  reproductive system of, 261
Cocoon, 235
Cod, 380
Code, translation of, 625
Codominants, 643

Codons, 614, 624
  nonsense, 625
Coelacanth, 378
Coelacanthini, 381
Coelenterata, 157
  classes of, 163
Coelenterates, fresh-water, 170
Coelom, 115, 202, 339
  evolution of, 202
  extraembryonic, 116, 582
Coenzyme, 59
Coenzyme A, 63
Coenzyme Q, 62
Coleoptera, 265
Coliiformes, 426
Collagen, 48
Collagen fibers, 48
Collar, 295
Collar cells, 75
Collar nerve, 298
Collembola, 262
Colloblasts, 173
Colloid, thyroid, 553
Colloidal system, 17
Colon, 340, 466
Colonial insects, 574
Color blindness, 600
Coloration, protective, 723
Columbiformes, 426
Comatulidae, 304
Comb jellies, 157, 172
Comb type, inheritance of, 606
Commensalism, 377, 706, 707
Commissures, circumpharyngeal, 227
Community succession, 718
Comparative anatomy, 129
Competition, 706
Compounds, organic, 23
Conchostraca, 254
Conditioning, 762
Conduction, speed of, in annelid nerves, 232
Condylarthra, 445
Cone(s), 522
Cone vision, 525
Conformation, molecular, 23
Coniferous forests, 728
Conjugation of protozoa, 147
Conjunctiva, 522
Conservation, 786
Consumer organisms, 699
Continental shelf, 735
Contractile fibrils, 132
Contractile vacuoles, 36, 46, 134
Contraction period, 90
Control group, 7
Control systems analysis, 766
Conus arteriosus, 345
Convergent evolution, 374, 656
Convoluted tubule, 506
Copepod(s), parasitic, 773
Copepoda, 255
Copulation, 515
Coraciiformes, 426
Coral, 168
Coral reefs, 166
Corixa, 700
Cormorant, 707
Cornea, 522
Coronary arteries, 498

Corpora allata, 100, 279
Corpora cardiaca, 278
Corpus callosum, 547, 548
Corpus luteum, 568
Corpus striatum, 418, 546
Correns, 589
Cortex, psychical, 547
Corti, organ of, 530
Cortisol, 560
Cosmoid scale, 360
Cotylosaur(s), 395
Cotylosauria, 405
Countercurrent flow, 474
Cowbird, 785
Cowper's glands, 514
Coxa, 259
Cranial nerves, 351, 535
Cranium, 322, 453
Crassostrea, 217
Crayfish, 247
  internal anatomy of, 251
  mouth parts of, 249
  morphology of, 247
Creeper fowl, 639
Creodontia, 445
Cretaceous period, 671
Cretin, 556
Crinoidea, 298, 303
Cristae, 35
Critical periods, 122
Crocodiles, 403
Crocodilia, 406
Cro-Magnon men, 692
Crop, 234, 260, 416
Crops, rotation of, 786
Cross, dihybrid, 594
  monohybrid, 592
Crossing over in chromosomes, 600
Crossopterygians, 383
Crossopterygii, 378, 381
Crustacea, 245, 247, 772
Cryptorchidism, 568
Crystalline style, 217
Ctenoid scale, 360
Ctenophora, 157, 172
Ctenophores, luminescence of, 173
Ctenothrissiformes, 380
Cuckoo, 785
Cuculiformes, 426
Curare, 90
Cushing's syndrome, 561
Cuticle, 48
Cuticulin, 275
Cuttlefish, 224, 764
Cuvier, Georges, 12, 129
Cyanide, 61
Cybernetics, 766
Cycles, metabolic, 21
Cyclic phenomena, 715
Cycloid scales, 360
Cyclostomata, 361, 378
Cypriniformes, 380
Cyprinus, 380
Cytochrome(s), 62
Cytochrome oxidase, 61
Cytogenetics, 643
Cytokinesis, 37
Cytology, 3, 678
Cytosine, 27, 617

Dactylopteriformes, 381
Damselflies, 262
Dandruff, 448
Daphnia, 253
Dasyatis, 367
DDT, 787
Deamination, 26, 66
Decapoda, 247
Decarboxylation, 63
Deciduous forest biome, 729
Decomposer organisms, 699
Defecation, 461
Dehydroepiandrosterone, 567
Dehydrogenase, 64
Dehydrogenation, 62
Deletion, 631
Deme, 650
Demospongia, 153
Dendrites, 52
Dental formula, 429
Dentary, 404, 455
Denticles, 233
Deoxycorticosterone, 560
Deoxyribonuclease, 615
Deoxyribonucleic acid, 27. See also *DNA*.
Deoxyribose, 24
Dermacentor andersoni, 772
Dermal bone, 369
Dermatobia hominis, 773
Dermis, 331, 448
Descartes, René, 12
Desert animals, adaptations of, 705
Desert biome, 733
Detritus, 710
Deuterostomia, 205
Deuterostomous phyla, 308
Development, control of, 118
    embryonic, 576
Devilfish, 379
Devonian period, 670
Diabetes, 557
Diabetes insipidus, 563
Diabetes mellitus, 508
Dialysis, 45
Diapause, 281
Diaphragm, 431
Diastole, 495
Diatrymiformes, 426
Dibranchiata, 224
Diencephalon, 540
Differential fecundity, 652
Differential reproduction, 650
Differentiation, cellular, 119
    chemical, 121
    intracellular, 132
Difflugia, 139
Diffusion, 42, 43
Digenea, 183
Digestion, 75
Digestive secretions, control of, 468
Digestive system, 339
    vertebrate, 76
Digestive tract, development of, 580
    parasites of, 774
    vertebrate, 461
Digger wasp, 762
Digital pads, 390
Digitigrade, 439
Dimetrodon, 403

Dinoflagellates, 136
Dinophilus, 229
Dinornithiformes, 425
Dinosaurs, ornithischian, 402
    saurischian, 401
Diodon, 381
Diphosphopyridine nucleotide, 63
Diploid, 104
Diplopoda, 257
Dipnoi, 378, 381
Diptera, 265
Displacement activities, 746
Displays in intraspecific behavior, 746
Diurnal animals, 715, 761
Divergent evolution, 656
Diver's disease, 723
DNA, 27, 34, 614
    amount per nucleus, 616
    circular, 616
    helical structure of, 618
    mitochondrial, 616
    molecular stability of, 69
    replication of, 619
        semi-conservative mechanism in, 626
    role in heredity, 616
    synthesis of, 626
    transcription of, 619, 625
    Watson-Crick model of, 617
DNA-dependent RNA polymerase, 627
DNA polymerase, 619, 626
Dogfish, 367, 379
    locomotion of, 366
    visceral organs of, 368
Dolphins, 444
Dominance, incomplete, 594
Dorsal ramus, 535
Dorsal root, 535
Dragonfishes, 381
Dragonflies, 262
Dryopithecus, 686
Ductus arteriosus, 494
Ductus venosus, 493
Dugesia, 176
Dunkleosteus, 363, 379
Duodenum, 466
Duplication, 631
Dura mater, 541
Dutrochet, René, 12
Dwarf mice, hereditary, 565
Dysentery, amebic, 771

Earthworm(s), 229
    circulatory system of, 78
    digestive system of, 75
    effects on soil, 237
    locomotion of, 232
    nervous system of, 232
    reproductive system of, 235
Ecdysial gland, 278
Ecdysis, 275
Ecdysone, 100, 278
Echinoderms, classification of, 298
    evolutionary relationships of, 308
    metamorphosis in, 311
Echinoidea, 298, 306
Echiuroidea, 290
Echolocation, 436, 758

Ecologic density, 711
Ecologic niche, 700
Ecologic succession, 718
Ecology, 3, 699
  human, 791
Ecosystems, 699
Ecotone, 725
Ectoderm, 113
Ectoparasites, 771
Ectoplasm, 138
Edentata, 437, 446
Edge effect, 725
Eel. See specific types of eels, e.g., *Electric eel*.
Effectors, 93, 519
Egg(s), 102
  centrolecithal, 112
  cleidoic, 394
  isolecithal, 112, 576
  telolecithal, 112
Egg cells, 53
Egg shell, reptilian, 394
Elasmobranchii, 368, 379
Elastic fibers, 48
Electric eel, 71
Electric field, 94
Electric organ, 93
Electrolocation, 758
Electrolytes, 22
Electron(s), 19
  flow of, 68
Electron microscopy, 42
Electron transmitter system, 61, 66
Electrophoresis, 638
Elephant(s), 443
Elephant-snouted fish, 380
Elephantiasis, 778
Eleutherodactylus, 391
Eleutherozoa, 307
Elpoiformes, 379
Elpomorpha, 379
Embryo, growth of, 584
  protection of, 116
Embryology, 3
Embryonic coelom, 582
Embryonic development, 112
Embryonic disc, 577
Empedocles, 8
Enamel, 461
Endocrine glands, methods of investigating, 551
Endocrine interrelationships, 573
Endocrine system, 550
Endoderm, 113, 577
Endolymph, 527
Endometrium, 571
Endopeptidases, 467
Endoplasm, 138
Endoplasmic reticulum, 18, 32, 35, 628
Endopodite, 247
Endopterygota, 262
Endoskeleton, 87
Endostyle, 315, 363
Endothelium, 47
Energy, biologically useful, 66
  kinetic, 43
  potential, 43
Energy cycle, 703
Energy transformations, 43
Engram, 547
Enterocoele, 114

Enterocoelom, 202
Enterogastrone, 469, 573
Enterokinase, 468
Enteropneusta, 295
Entoprocta, 290
Environmental resistance, 713
Enzyme(s), 25, 57. See also names of specific
  enzymes, e.g., *Aldolase*.
  active site of, 60
  effects of ions on, 22
  pH optimum of, 60
  properties of, 58
Enzyme inactivation, 60
Enzyme inhibitors, 61
Enzyme-substrate complexes, 59
Eocene epoch, 673
Eosinophils, 51, 485
Eosuchia, 405
Ephemerida, 262
Epiboly, 114, 577
Epiceratodus, 377
Epicuticle, 275
Epidermis, 176, 331, 448
Epididymis, 513
Epigenesis, 118
Epiglottis, 476
Epinephrine, 97, 551, 559, 567
  effects of, 560
Epithelia, 47
Epoch. See name of specific epoch, e.g., *Eocene
  epoch*.
Equilibrium, 526
Eras, geologic, 667
Erectile tissue, 110, 514
Erythroblastosis fetalis, 488, 610
Erythrocytes, 482
  life span of, 484
Esophagus, 339
Estradiol, 568
Estriol, 569
Estrone, 569
Estrous cycle, 566, 570
Estrus, 570
Estuaries, 734
Ethiopian realm, 680
Ethology, 767
Eucoelomata, 202
  evolution of, 204
Euglena, 134
Euglenoidida, 135
Eumetazoa, 201
Eunuch, 567
Euphausiacea, 255
Euphotic region, 735
Euryapsida, 405
Eurypterid(s), 245, 670
Eurypterida, 268
Eurythermic, 704
Eustachian tube, 349, 463, 530
Eutheria, 445
Eutherians, adaptive radiation of, 435
Evisceration, spontaneous, 305
Events, probability and, 640
Evolution, 3
  convergent, 437
  cultural, 693
  evidence for, 665
    biochemical, 675
    embryologic, 676

Evolution (*Continued*)
  evidence for, fossil, 665
    morphologic, 674
    taxonomic, 673
  human, 683
  metazoan, 201
  organic, 646
  parallel, 437
  principles of, 663
  regressive, 663
  straight-line, 659
Excretory pore, 235
Exocoetus, 376, 380
Exopeptidases, 467
Exopodite, 247
Exopterygota, 262
Exoskeleton, 87, 244
Experiments, controlled, 33
  design of, 4
Expiratory center, 478
Expressivity, 640
Extension, muscular, 337
Exteroceptors, 97
Extraembryonic membranes, 394
Eye, camera, 99
  compound, 249
  direct, of the squid, 223
  mammalian, structure of, 521
  mosaic, 99
Eye worm, 778
Eyespot patterns, 741

Fabricius, 10
Facial nerve, 537
Facilitation, 96
  social, 762
Fairy shrimps, 254
Falconiformes, 426
Fallopian tube, 514
Family, taxonomical, 126, 127
Fangs, poison, 269, 400
Faraday, 68
Farming, contour, 786
Fat, 24
Fat body, 348
Fat metabolism, 471
Fatigue, 91
Fatty acids, 24
  oxidation of, 65
Feather(s), 412, 451
Feather stars, 298
Feather tracts, 412
Feedback control, 24, 277, 555
Femur, 259, 455
Fenestra ovalis, 528, 529
Fenestra rotunda, 530
Fertilization, 110
  external, 514
  internal, 394
  mammalian, 515
Fertilization membrane, 515
Fertilizin, 111
Fetus, 584
Fibrin, 485
Fibrinogen, 485
Fig insect, 724

Filariae, 777
Filoplumes, 412
Filtration pressure, 507
Fins, 365
Fire ants, 574, 750
Fischer, Emil, 59
Fish(es), 356. See also names of specific types of
    fish, e.g., *Porcupine fish.*
  cardiovascular system of, 488
  deep-sea, 736
  evolutionary tree of, 358
  external respiration in, 474
Fisheries, marine, 790
Fission, 102
Fissipedia, 445
Fissure of Sylvius, 546
Fittest, survival of, 649
Flagella, 15, 89, 132
Flagellata, 134
Flame cells, 85, 179, 190
Flatworms, 201
  parasitic, 183
Flavin adenine dinucleotide, 63
Flavin mononucleotide, 63
Fleas, 772
Flexion, 337
Flies, 265
Flight, flapping, 411
  mechanism in insect, 282
  principles of, 408
  types of, 409
Flounder, 381
Fluids. See specific types of fluid, e.g., *Cerebro-
    spinal fluid.*
Flukes, 176
Fluorine test, 692
Flying fish, 376, 380
Flying reptiles, 402
Folic acid, 472
Follicle, ovarian, 511
Follicle-stimulating hormone, 566
Food, absorption of, 469
  digestion of, 467
Food chains, 709
Food vacuole, 75
Foramen magnum, 332, 453
Foramen of Monro, 541
Foramen ovale, 493
Foraminiferida, 139
Foregut, 581
Forelimb, 334
Forest biomes, 728
Forestry, 787
Form, regulation of, 173
Fossils, 357, 665
Frog, 329. See also specific types of frogs, e.g.,
    Chilean frog.
  arteries and veins of, 344
  brain of, 350
  circulatory system of, 343
  development of, 354
  digestive system of, 340
  ear of, 349
  eyes of, 349
  female, urogenital system of, 346
  heart of, 345
  jumping, 336
  lungs of, 343
  male, urogenital system of, 347

Frog (*Continued*)
  muscles of, 337, 338
  respiratory system of, 342
  skeleton of, 333
  skin of, 331
  spinal nerves of, 352
  stomach of, 341
  sympathetic cord of, 352
  trunk of, 339
Fructose, 23
Frustule, 163
Fundulus, 380
Funnel, 222
Fusulinidae, 140

Gadiformes, 380
Gadus, 380
Galactosamine, 24
Galen, 8
Galileo, 10
Gallbladder, 465
Game, artificial stocking of, 788
Gamete, 102
Ganglion, 52
  peripheral, 538
  ventral, of annelid, 232
Ganoid scale, 360
Gar, 372
Garpikes, 379
Gas, partial pressure of, 81
Gasterosteiformes, 380
Gastric glands, 341
Gastric mill, 251
Gastrin, 469, 573
Gastrodermis, 150, 176
Gastroliths, 251, 277
Gastropoda, 209, 211
Gastrotricha, 188
Gastrotrich(s), 196
Gastrovascular cavity, 75
Gastrovascular system, 161
Gastrula, 112
Gastrulation, 353, 577
Gause's rule, 707
Gaviformes, 425
Geckos, 397
Gel, 17, 28
Gemmules, 155
Gene(s), 15, 34, 591, 622
  complementary, 604
  differentiation and, 636
  dominant, 592
  interactions of, 603
  lethal, 639
  linear order of, in chromosome, 602
  mutations in, frequency of, 633
    radiation induced, 633
    spontaneous, 632
  recessive, 592
  supplementary, 604
Gene-enzyme relations, 633
Gene pools, 650
Generator potential, 520
Genetic code, 624
  colinearity of, 625
Genetic drift, 651
Genetic equilibrium, 642

Genetic population, 650
Genetics, 3, 678
  biochemical, 614
  history of, 589
Genic specificity, 619
Genotype, 593
Genus, 125, 127
Geographic distribution, 679
Geologic time table, 666
Geraniol, 574
Germ cells, 568
Germ layers, evolution of, 201
Germ plasm, 648
Germinal vesicle, 53
Giant axons, 232
Gibbon, 686
Gigantism, 564
Gigantopithecus, 689
Gila monster, 399
Galliformes, 426
Gill(s), 81, 210, 473
Gill bailers, 249
Gill flukes, 183
Gill heart, 223
Gill rakers, 473
Gill slits, 315
Giraffes, 442
Gizzard, 234, 260, 416
Glands, adrenal, 559
  endocrine, 550
  mammary, 451
  mucous, 451
  parotid, 463
  poison, 451
  salivary, 463
  salt-excreting, 418, 503
  scent, 451
  sebaceous, 451
  sublingual, 463
  submaxillary, 463
  sweat, 451
Glass snake, 397
Glass sponges, 152
Glaucoma, 522
Globigerina, 140
Globulin, 553
Glochidia, 219
Glomerular filtration, 506
Glomerulus, 506
Glossopharyngeal nerve, 537
Glottis, 342, 476
Glucagon, 557
Glucocorticoids, 560
Glucosamine, 24
Glucose, 21, 23
Glucose-6-phosphatase, 638
Glucose-6-phosphate, 66
Glutamic acid, 66
Glutathione, 631
Glycerol, 24
Glycogen, 24, 77, 92, 638
Glycosuria, 558
Gnathobase, 244
Gobiesociformes, 380
Goblet cells, 467
von Goethe, Johann Wolfgang, 129
Goiter, 555
  exophthalmic, 556
  simple, 556

Goldschmidt, Richard, 653
Golgi apparatus, 18
Golgi bodies, 35
Gonads, 511
Gonionemus, 157
Gonorhynchiformes, 380
Goose flesh, 451
Gordiacea, 188, 196
Gorgonocephalus, 307
Gorillas, 687
Graafian follicles, 566
Grafts, tissue, 26
Granulosa cells, 568
Grassland biome, 731
Gray commissure, 540
Gray matter, 540
Graylag goose, 759
Green glands, 85, 252
Grobstein, Clifford, 121, 638
Ground substance, 18
Growth, 16
Growth hormone, 564
Guanine, 27, 617
Guano, 703
Guanosine triphosphate, 631
Gullet, 134
Gulper eel, 376, 379
Gymnothorax, 375
Gyplure, 574
Gyri, 545

Habitat, 700
Habituation, 762
Hagfishes, 378
Hair follicle, 451
Hair papilla, 451
Hairworms, 196
Haldane, J. B. S., 661
Halibut, 375, 381
Halteres, 99
Hämmerling, 34
Haploid, 104
Hardy-Weinberg law, 642, 650
Harrison, Ross, 31
Harvey, William, 9
Haversian canals, 49
Heart, 480
  bird, 417
  development of, 582
  earthworm, 234
Heart urchins, 306
Heidelberg man, 691
Height, inheritance of, 608
Heliozoida, 139
Hemichordata, 295
Hemichordates, metamorphosis in, 311
Hemicyclaspis, 378
Hemochorial placenta, 515
Hemocoel, 80, 252
Hemocyanin, 79, 252
Hemoglobin, 25, 51, 79, 83, 234, 482
  fetal, 484
  sequence of amino acids in, 676
  structure of, 483
Hemophilia, 485, 600
Henle, loop of, 506

Heparin, 485
Hepatic portal system, 489
Hepatopancreas, 277
Herbivores, 74, 441
Heredity, laws of, 591
Hermaphroditism, 110
Herring, 374, 380
Hesperornis, 419
Heterocercal tail, 373
Heterosis, 611
Heterostelea, 307
Heterothermic, 429
Heterotrophs, 74, 662
Heterozygous, 592
Hexapoda, 256, 257
Hexokinase, 66
Hibernation, 705, 715
  amphibian, 386
  mammalian, 429
Hierarchies, 753
Hind limb, 336
Hindgut, 581
Hinge ligament, 215
Hippocampus, 375, 380
Hippoglossus, 375, 381
Hippomorpha, 446
Hirudin, 238
Hirudinea, 228, 238
Histology, 3, 47
Histone, 615
Histrio, 375
Holocephali, 368, 379
Holonephros, 503
Holostei, 371, 379
Holothuroidea, 298, 304
Homeostasis, 480
Hominoidea, 684
Homo erectus, 689
Homocercal tail, 373
Homogentisic acid, 635
Homoiothermic animals, 408, 428, 705
Homologous organs, 674
Homology, 356
Homoplastic organs, 356
Homozygous animals, 592
Honeybee(s), 265
  colony of, 754
Hooke, Robert, 10
Hookworms, 775
Hormones, 100, 550. See also names of specific
    hormones, e.g., *Adrenocorticotrophic hormone*.
  arthropod, 277
  digestive tract, 573
Horns, 449
Horowitz, N. H., 662
Horse, evolution of, 659
Horseshoe crabs, 245
Host, 769
Host-parasite relationships, 708
Human body, flow of electrons in, 68
Humerus, 455
Hunter, John, 12
Hutton, James, 647
Hyaluronidase, 515
Hybrid vigor, 611
Hybridization, 658
Hydra, 170
  cell types of, 172
Hydrogen bonds, 618

Hydrogen ion(s), 482
Hydrogen ion concentration, 22
Hydroides, 237
Hydrolysis, 76
Hydrolytic cleavage, 467
Hydroxyapatite, 49
Hydrozoa, 163
Hymen, 514
Hymenoptera, 265
Hymenostomatida, 144
Hyoid apparatus, 332, 334
Hyoid arch, 364, 453
Hyoid bone, 455
Hyomandibular cartilage, 366
Hyperglycemia, 558
Hyperventilation, 478
Hypoglossal nerve, 537
Hypophyseal sac, 361
Hypophysectomy, 564
Hypophysis, 562
Hypothalamic-hypophyseal tract, 563
Hypothalamus, 428, 545, 567
Hypothesis, 5
  testing of, 6
Hypotrichs, 144
Hyracoidea, 443, 446
Hyracotherium, 659

I bands, 92
Ichthyopterygia, 405
Ichthyornis, 419
Ichthyosaur(s), 396
Ichthyosauria, 405
Ictalurus, 376, 380
Ileum, 466
Immunity, 486
  types of, 487
Implantation, 515
Imprinting, 764
Inborn errors of metabolism, 635
Inbreeding, 611
Incisors, 429
Incus, 404, 455, 529
Independent assortment, law of, 591
Induction, interspecific, 192
Inferior colliculi, 545
Infundibulum, 350, 562
Ink sac, 222
Inner cell mass, 576
Inner ear, 349
Insect(s), 245. See also names of specific insects.
  adaptations of mouth parts, 721
  colonial, 574
  color vision in, 287
  form discrimination in, 286
Insecta, 257
  classification of, 262
Insectivora, 445
Insectivores, 435
Insertion of muscle, 90
Inspiratory center, 478
Instinct, maternal, 112, 566
Insulin, 25, 557
  amino acid sequence of, 558
Integument, 331, 448
Interactions, interspecific, 706
Intercentrum, 386

Intercerebral gland, 277
Intermedin, 563
Intersexes, 598
Invagination, 577
Inversion, 631
Involution, 114, 527
Iodide, accumulation of, by thyroid, 553
Ion(s), 19
Ionone, 98
Iris, 522
Irish deer, 659
Irritability, 15
Ischial callosities, 686
Islets of Langerhans, 557
Isolation, ecologic, 658
  genetic, 657
  geographic, 657
Isopoda, 255
Isoprenoid groups, 62
Isotopes, 20
Isozymes, 638

Jacobson's organ, 399
Janssens, 10
Java man, 689
Jaws, 363
  evolution of, 364
Jejunum, 466
Jellyfish, 157
John Dory, 376, 380
Joint(s), 88
  bony, 457
Jordan's rule, 679
Journals, review, 4
Jurassic period, 671
Juvenile hormone, 100, 279
Juxtamedullary nephrons, 506

Kaibab deer, 708
Kala-azar, 780
Kangaroos, 435
  tree-climbing, 722
Keel, 414
Keilin, David, 59
Keratin, 87, 448
Ketone bodies, 558
Kidney(s), 84, 346, 503
  amphibian, 510
  evolution of, 503
  reptilian, 393
Kidney tubules, 85, 503
Killer trait, 143
Killifish, 380
Kineses, 758
Kinesthesis, 521
Kingdom, 126
Kinorhyncha, 188, 196
Kiwi, 420
Klinefelter's syndrome, 598, 644
Klinokinesis, 759
Krebs citric acid cycle, 64

Labia, 245, 258
Labia majora, 514
Labia minora, 514

Labiata, 245
Labiates, origin of, 246
Labor, onset of, 572
Labrum, 258
Labyrinthodont(s), 386, 670
Labyrinthodontia, 404
Lacertilia, 397, 405
Lacrimal duct, 523
Lactic acid, 92
Lactic dehydrogenase, 63
  subunits of, 638
Lactogenic hormone, 566
Lactose, 24
Lagena, 527
Lagomorph(s), 443
Lagomorpha, 446
Lake, stocking with game fish, 790
Lake Baikal, 738
de Lamarck, Jean Baptiste, 647
Lamarckism, 648
Lampidiformes, 380
Lamprey, 361, 378
Larva, 265
  trochophore, 241
Larvacea, 324
Laryngotracheal chamber, 342
Larynx, 476
Latent period, 90
Lateral line system, 365, 528
Lateral plate, 582
Latimeria, 378, 381
Latissimus dorsi, 459
Learning, 547, 762
Leeches, 228, 238, 769
van Leeuwenhoek, Anthony, 10, 131
Leishmania, 780
Lemmings, 714
Lemur(s), 683
Lemuroid(s), 683
Lemuroidea, 439, 445
Lens of eye, 522
Leopard frog, 330
Lepidoptera, 265
Lepidosauria, 405
Lepidosiren, 381
Lepisosteus, 372, 379
Lepospondyl(s), 386
Lepospondyli, 404
Leptasterias, 303
Leptocephalus, 373, 375
Leptolepimorpha, 379
Lice, 771
Life, mechanistic theory of, 14
  origin of, 660
  physico-chemical basis of, 14
Life zones, fresh-water, 738
  marine, 734
  terrestrial, 725
Ligament, 48, 457
Light, refraction of, 523
Light organs, 71
Limnetic zone, 738
Limnopithecus, 686
Limulus, 268
Linkage, genetic, 600
Linkage group, genetic, 603
Linnaeus, Karl, 10, 128
Lipase, 58, 77, 468
Lipid, 24

Lipoic acid, 64
Lipoprotein lipase, 471
Liquid crystals, 661
Lissamphibia, 404
Littoral zone, 738
Liver, 341
  functions of, 465
Liver flukes, 16, 183
Lizard, collared, 393
Lobster, spiny, 745
Locomotion, mammalian, 432
Locus, 591
Locusts, 745
Loligo pealei, 221
Lophiiformes, 380
Lophius, 376, 380
Lophophore, 291
Lota, 380
Louse, 771
Lozenge eyes, 622
Luciferase, 72
Luciferin, 72
Lugworm, 237
Lumbricus, 229
Lung(s), 81, 342, 370
  respiratory surface of, 431
Lung flukes, 183
Lungfishes, 381
Luteinizing hormone, 566
Lyell, Sir Charles, 647
Lymph, 480
  flow of, 495
Lymph capillaries, 480
Lymph nodes, 480
Lymph sacs, 343
Lymphatic return, 500
Lymphocytes, 51, 485
Lyon hypothesis, 598
Lysosomes, 35

Macchie, 732
Macromeres, 203
Macromutation, 653
Macronucleus, 141
Macrophages, 486
Madreporite, 299
Magendie, Francois, 12
Maggots, 16, 773
Magnesium, 59
Magnus, Albertus, 9
Malacostraca, 247
Malaria, 103, 144, 655
Malleus, 404, 455, 529
Malpighi, Marcello, 10
Malpighian tubules, 85, 260
Malthus, Robert, 714
Maltose, 24
Mammals, characteristics of, 428
  circulatory systems of, 431
  development of, 576
  primitive, 433
  temperature regulation in, 428
Mammary glands, 433
Mammoths, 443
Man, center of origin of, 693
  elemental composition of, 20
  evolution of, 683

Man (*Continued*)
  races of, 693
  respiratory system of, 475
Man-apes, 687
Manatees, 443
Mandibles, 245
Mandibular arch, 364
Mandrills, 686
Manta, 379
Mantle, 221
Mantle cavity, 210
Manubrium, 160
Maps, chromosome, 603
Marine biologic laboratories, 12
Marmosets, 684
Marsupial(s), 434, 445
Marsupial frog, 391
Marsupium, 435
Mass spectrometer, 20
Mastodons, 443
Maternal instinct, 112, 566
Mating, nonrandom, 652
  test, 593
Mating behavior, 110
Mating types, 142
Matrix, 48
Matter, conservation of, 57
  cyclic use of, 701
Maxillae, 245
Maxillipeds, 249
Mayflies, 262
McClung, C.E., 589
Mechanoreceptors, 97, 519
Median eminence, 567
Median eye, 392
Medulla oblongata, 350, 541, 542
Medusa, 157
Meganthropus, 689
Meiosis, 104
Melanin, 451
Meleagrina, 218
Mellee scrub, 732
Membranes. See specific types of membranes,
  e.g., *Nuclear membrane.*
Memory, 547
Mendel, Gregor Johann, 589
Meninges, 541
Menstrual cycle, 566, 570
Mesencephalon, 540
Mesenteries, 339, 466
Mesoderm, 114, 578
  differentiation of, 582
Mesoglea, 161
Mesolithic culture, 694
Mesonephros, 504
Mesozoa, 289
Mesozoic era, 670
Messenger RNA, 614, 619, 628
  half life of, 637
  masked, 638
  synthesis of, 627
Metabolism, 15. See also specific types of metab-
  olism, e.g., *Calcium metabolism.*
Metacercaria, 185
Metamerism, 227
Metamorphosis, 147, 265, 353, 389
  complete, 265
  incomplete, 262
  of tadpoles, control by thyroxin, 555
Metanephridium, 203, 234

Metanephros, 504
Metaphase, 38, 105
Metapleural folds, 318
Metatheria, 445
Metazoa, 200
Method, of agreement, 6
  of concomitant variation, 6
  of difference, 6
Mice, dwarf, hereditary, 565
Michaelis, Leonor, 59
Micromeres, 203
Micronucleus, 141
Microsomes, 18
Microtome, 42
Middle ear cavity, 349
Midgets, 565
Migrations, 705
  animal, 745
  diurnal, 159
Milkfishes, 380
Millipedes, 245, 257
Mimicry, 723
Mineral(s), 77
Mineral cycles, 703
Mineralocorticoids, 560
Minimum mortality, 712
Miocene epoch, 673
Miracidium, 184
Mississippian period, 670
Mites, 245, 769, 772
Mitochondria, 17, 18, 35
  effects of thyroxin on, 554
Mitochondrial membranes, 66
Mitosis, 36
  regulation of, 41
Mixture, 21
Mnemiopsis, 172
Molars, 429
Molds, 665
Molecular configurations, 23
Molecular flux, 69
Molecular motion, 43
Molecule, 20
Molgula, 314, 324
Mollusca, 208
Mollusks, evolutionary relationships of,
  238
Molting, 88, 275
  in birds, 413
  in nematodes, 196
Molting fluid, 275
Mongolism, 644
Monocytes, 51, 485
Monogenea, 183
Monosomic people, 644
Monotremata, 445
Monotremes, 433
Monsters, 653
Moray eel, 375
Morgan, T.H., 589
Mormyrus, 376, 380
Morphogenesis, 119
Mortality rate, 712
Morula, 576
Mosquitoes, 265
Moths, 265
Motor unit of muscle, 90, 281
Mousterian culture, 691
Mudpuppy, 389
Müller, Johannes, 12

Muscle(s), antagonistic pairs of, 90
  contraction of, 22
    mechanism of, 90
    sliding filament theory of, 93
  somatic, 457
  striated, 89
  types of, 50
  visceral, 457
Muscular system, 336
Mussels, 217
Mutations, 631, 653
  deleterious, 655
Muton, 623
Mutualism, 706, 708
Mya arenaria, 217
Myelin sheath, 25, 53
Myofibrils, 50
Myogenic rhythms, 283
Myomeres, 318
Myosin, 41
Myotomes, 582
Myriapoda, 256
Mysidacea, 255
Mysticeti, 446
Mytilus edulis, 217
Myxedema, 554

Nasal cavities, 342
Natural selection, Darwin-Wallace theory of, 649
Nature, dynamic balance of, 719
Nauplius eye, 254
Nauplius larva, 247
Nautilus, chambered, 219
Neanderthal man, 691
Nearctic realm, 680
Necator americanus, 775
Necturus maculosus, 389
Nekton, 735
Nematocysts, 159
Nematoda, 188, 193
Nematodes, muscle cells of, 195
Nemertea, 78, 197, 201
  circulatory system of, 198
Neoceratodus, 381
Neognathae, 420, 425
Neolithic culture, 694
Neopilina, 211
Neoptera, 262
Neornithes, 425
Neoteny, 389
Neotropical realm, 680
Nephridium, 85, 212
Nephrogenic ridge, 582
Nephrons, 503
  structure of, 505
Nephrostome, 509
Nereis, 229
  nervous system of, 232
Neritic zone, 735
Nerve(s). See specific types of nerves, e.g., *Facial nerve.*
Nerve cord, 315
Nerve fibers, cable properties of, 95
  medullated, 53
Nerve impulse, 93
Nerve net, 93, 161
Nerve transmission, membrane theory of, 94
Nervous integration, 519

Nervous system, autonomic, 537
  central, 532, 540
  organization of, 532
  peripheral, 532, 535
Nesting behavior, effect of hormones on, 761
Neural crest, 580
Neural folds, 580
Neural gland, 315
Neural plate, 115, 580
Neural tube, 115, 580
Neurilemma, 53
Neurofibrils, 93, 142
Neurogenic rhythms, 283
Neuroglia, 53
Neurohaemal organ, 277
Neurohormones, 100
Neurohumors, 539
Neurons, 52
  association, 546
  types of, 532
Neuropodium, 230
Neurosecretion, 96, 277
Neurosensory cells, 521
Neurospora, biochemical mutants of, 634
Neutralism, 706
Neutrons, 19
Neutrophils, 51, 485
Niacin, 472
Nictitating membrane, 393, 523, 675
Nile bichir, 372
Nirenberg, Marshall, 624
Nitrogen cycle, 702
Nitrogen metabolism, amphibian, 385
Nocturnal animals, 715
Nondisjunction, chromosomal, 644
Norepinephrine, 559
Normal distribution, curve of, 608
Notacanthiformes, 379
Notharctus, 684
Notochord, 115, 314, 362, 579
Notonecta, 700
Notopodium, 230
Notostraca, 254
Notropis, 380
Notum, 258
Nuclear membrane, 15, 31
Nuclear transplants, 119
Nucleases, 468
Nucleic acids, 26
  absorption of by ultraviolet light, 617
Nucleoli, 35
Nucleotide(s), 27
  methylated, 628
  unusual, 628
Nucleotide copolymers, 625
Nucleus, 14
  functions of, 31
Nudibranchs, 214
Numbers, pyramid of, 710
Nuptial flight, 111
Nuptial pad, 330
Nurse cells, 110
Nutrition, 74
Nymph, 262, 279

Oarfish, 376, 380
Obelia, 164
Occipital condyles, 332, 453

Occipital lobe, 546
Oceanic zone, 735
Ocelli, 260
Ochoa, Severo, 625
Octopus, 220
  intelligence of, 225
  orientation of, 744
Oculomotor nerve, 537
Odonata, 262
Odontoceti, 446
Odontognathae, 425
Olfaction, 521
Olfactory bulbs, 350, 540
Olfactory nerve, 537
Oligocene epoch, 673
Oligochaetes, 228
Omasum, 464
Ommatidia, 99, 249
Omnivores, 74
Oncosphere, 186
Ontogeny, 582
Onychophora, 270
Oocytes, 109
Oogenesis, 109
Oogonia, 109
Ootid, 109
Oparin, A.I., 661
Opercular chambers, 473
Operculum, 214, 268, 369
Ophidia, 399, 405
Ophiuroidea, 299, 307
Opisthobranchia, 214
Opisthonephros, 504
Opisthosoma, 268
Opossum, 428, 435
Optic chiasma, 540
Optic lobes, 350, 544
Optic nerve, 522, 537
Oral groove, 75
Orangutan, 686
Order, taxonomical, 126, 127
Ordovician period, 670
Oreopithecus, 686
Organ, 31
Organ systems, 31
Organelles, conductile, 132
  cytoplasmic, 35
  photosensitive, 133
  types of, 132
Organizer, 119
Oriental realm, 680
Origin of muscle, 90
Ornithischia, 405
Orthogenesis, 659
Oscula, 150
Osmosis, 45
Osmotic pressure, 46
Osprey, 409
Ostariophysi, 380
Osteichthyes, 369, 379
Osteoblasts, 49
Osteoglossiformes, 380
Osteoglossomorpha, 380
Osteolepis, 381
Ostium, 514
Ostracoda, 255
Ostracoderms, 359, 378, 670
Ostriches, 420
Otic capsule, 332, 453

Otoliths, 98, 527
Outbreeding, 611
Ovary, 106, 348, 568
Overgrazing, 787
Oviduct, 110, 348, 513
Oviparous, 111, 367
Ovoviviparous, 111, 367
Ovulation, 110, 511, 568
Ovum, 109
Owen, Richard, 12
Oxidase, 63
Oxidation, 62
Oxidation-reduction potentials, 66
Oxidative phosphorylation, 62, 66
  uncoupling by thyroxin, 554
Oxygen, source of, 662
Oxygen debt, 92
Oxygen tension, 81
Oxyhemoglobin, 83, 482
Oxytocin, 563
Oysters, 217
  Long Island, 791
  pearl, 218

Pacemakers, 762
Paddlefish, 379
Palaeognathae, 420, 425
Palate, secondary, 431
Palearctic realm, 680
Paleocene epoch, 673
Paleolithic culture, 693
Paleontology, 665
Paleoptera, 262
Paleozoic era, 667
Palmitic acid, 65
Palolo worms, 237
Palps, 215
Pancreas, 341
  enzymes of, 465
  islets of, 557
Pangolins, 437
Paracanthopterygii, 380
Paralichthys, 381
Paramecium, 141
  mating types of, 104
Paramylum bodies, 134
Parapithecus, 684
Parapodia, 228, 230
Parasite(s), 769
  host and, 784
  intestinal, 774
  intracellular, 780
  sense organs of, 783
  social, 785
  transmission of, 782
Parasitism, 75, 196, 706, 769
  adaptations to, 781
Parasitology, 3
Parathormone, 557
Parathyroid glands, 463, 557
Paraventricular nucleus, 563
Parazoa, 150, 201
Parietal cells, 468
Parietal lobe, 545
Parthenogenesis, 111, 191
Particles, autocatalytic, 661
  kappa, 143
  killer, 143

Parturition, 516, 572
Passenger pigeon, 786
Passeriformes, 420, 426
Paternity, exclusion of, 610
Pavlov, 469
Peas, genetics of, 590
Pecten, 219, 265
Pectoral girdle, 334, 335, 453
Pectoralis, 415, 459
Pedal glands, 190
Pedicellariae, 299
Pegasiformes, 381
Pegasus, 381
Peking man, 689
Pelecaniformes, 425
Pelecypoda, 209, 215
Pellagra, 78, 473
Pellicle, 87, 134
Pelmatozoa, 307
Pelvic girdle, 334, 335, 453
Pelycosaurs, 403, 406, 670
Pen of squid, 222
Penetrance, 639
Penguins, 420
Penis, 110, 514
Pennsylvanian period, 670
Pepsin, 61, 77, 464
Pepsinogen, 467
Peptic ulcer, 464
Peptidases, 77
Peptide bonds, 26
Perca, 381
Perch, 374, 381
  visceral organs of, 369
Perciformes, 381
Pereiopods, 249
Pericardial cavity, 208, 262
Pericardium, 80
Perilymph, 527
Periodicity, reproductive, 236
Periosteum, 49, 457
Peripatus, 270
Periplaneta americana, 257
Perisarc, 164
Perissodactyls, 441, 446
Peristalsis, 340, 464
Peristaltic waves, 80
Peristome, 300
Peristomium, 227
Peritoneal cavity, 477
Peritoneum, 202, 227, 339
Peritrichida, 144
Peritrophic membrane, 260
Permeability, differential, 45
Permian period, 670
Peroxidase, 58
Petrifaction, 665
Petromyzon, 379
Petromyzon marinus, 362
pH, 22
Pharyngeal pouches, 315
Pharynx, 339, 476
Phenocopy, 638
Phenotype, 593
Phenylthiocarbamide, 642
Pheromones, 573, 749
  human, 575
Philodina, structure of, 190
Pholidota, 446

Phonoreception, 527
Phoronida, 291
Phosphate bonds, energy-rich, 61
Phosphocreatine, 91
Phosphodiester bridges, 618
Phospholipid, 25, 31, 469
Phosphorus, 703
Phosphorylase, 558
Photoperiod, 705
Photoreceptors, 97, 520
  caudal, 287
Phototaxis, 759
Phylogeny, 582
Phylum, 126, 127
Physalia, 165
Physiology, 3
Phytomonads, 137
Phytoplankton, 699
Pia mater, 541
Piciformes, 426
Pigment spot, 134
Pigmentation, hormonal control of, 100
Pika, 444
Pill-bugs, 256
Pincers, 249
Pineal body, 350, 521, 572
Pineal eye, 361
Pinnipedia, 445
Pirate perch, 380
Pit vipers, 400
Pithecanthropus erectus, 689
Pituitary gland, 353, 562
  anterior lobe of, 564
  control by hypothalamus, 567
  development of, 562
Placebos, 7
Placenta, 117, 433, 571
Placental lactogen, 572
Placodermi, 363, 379
Placoid scale, 360
Planaria, regeneration of, 181
  sense organs of, 178
Planarians, 176
Plankton, 157, 735
Plantigrade, 439
Planula, 162
Plasma, 51
  blood, 481
Plasma cells, 486
Plasma membrane, 14, 31
  permeability of, 45
Plasmodium, 103
Plastron, 395
Platelets, 51, 484
Platyhelminthes, 176
Platypus, 433
Platyrrhini, 439, 445
Platysamia cecropia, 281
Pleistocene epoch, 673
Pleopods, 248
Plesiosaurs, 396
Plethodonts, 389
Pleura, 258, 477
Pleural cavity, 477
Pleurobrachia, 172
Pleurocentra, 386
Pleuronectiformes, 381
Pliny, 9
Pliocene epoch, 673

Podicipediformes, 425
Pogonophora, 295
Poikilothermic, 386, 705
Poison claws, 257
Poison fangs, 269, 400
Polar body, 109
Polarity, 181
Pollen brushes, 265
Pollen combs, 265
Polyadenylic acid, 625
Polychaetes, 228
  reproduction of, 235
Polycladida, 183
Polycytidylic acid, 625
Polydon, 379
Polyembryony, 783
Polygenic inheritance, 607
Polymorphism, balanced, 655
Polyneuritis, 6
Polyp, 162
Polypeptide, synthesis of, 628
Polypteriformes, 379
Polypterus, 372, 379
Polyribosomes, 631
Polysaccharides, 467
Polyspermy, 111
Polyuridylic acid, 624
Pond, ecology of, 699
Pongidae, 686
Population(s), 710
  characteristics of, 711
  human, 791
Population cycles, 714
Population density, 711
Population dispersal, 717
Population genetics, 641
Population growth curve, 712
Population pressure, 724
Porcupine fish, 381
Pores, incurrent, 150
Porifera, 150
Porocytes, 151
Porpoises, 444
Portuguese man-of-war, 165
Postganglionic fibers, 538
Potassium, 94
  ions of, 482
Praying mantis, 751
Preadaptation, 383
Preantennae, 270
Precocial, 423
Predation, 706
Predator-prey associations, 708
Preformation, 118
Preganglionic fibers, 538
Pregnancy, 571
Prehallux, 330
Premolars, 429
Prey immobilization, 400
Priapuloidea, 291
Primates, 437, 445, 683
  adaptations in, 437
  social groups of, 756
Primitive streak, 114
Pristis, 367, 379
Proanura, 405
Probability, a priori, 593, 640
Proboscidea, 443, 446

Proboscis, 295, 297
  nemertean, 197
Procellariiformes, 425
Proconsul, 686
Producer organisms, 699
Progeny selection, 594
Progesterone, 568
Proglottids, 185
Prolactin, 566
Pronephros, 504
Prophase, 37, 104
Propliopithecus, 686
Proprioception, 521
Proprioceptors, 97, 744
Prosimians, 683
Prosobranchia, 213
Prosoma, 268
Prosopyles, 151
Prostate gland, 514
Prosthetic group, 63, 483
Prostomium, 227
Protacanthopterygii, 380
Protamine zinc insulin, 558
Proteases, 160
Protective coloration, 723
Protein(s), 25, 60
  turnover time of, 69
Protein metabolism, 471
Proterozoic era, 667
Prothoracicotropic hormone, 100, 278
Prothrombin, 484
Protista, 148
Protocooperation, 706, 707
Proton(s), 19
Protonephridium, 179, 203, 321
Protoplasm, 16
Protopodite, 247
Protopterus, 370, 381
Protostomia, 205
Prototheria, 445
Prototroch, 241
Protozoa, 30
  classes of, 131
  relationships among, 148
  reproduction of, 145
Protraction, 337
Proventriculus, 416
Pseudocoelom, 188, 195
Pseudopod, 75, 89
Psittaciformes, 426
Pterobranchia, 295
Pteropods, 214
Pterosaurs, 402, 406
Pterygota, 262
Puffs, chromosomal, 636
Pulmocutaneous arches, 489
Pulmonata, 214
Pulse, 498
Pulvillus, 259
Pupa, 265
Pupil, of eye, 522
Purine, 617
Purkinje, 16
Purkinje fibers, 496
Pygostyle, 414
Pyloric stomach, 300
Pyramid of numbers, 710
Pyrimidine, 617

Pyruvic acid, 63, 66
Pythons, 400

Quadrate, 403
Quahog, 215
Queen bee, 267
Quill(s), 412
   porcupine, 451

Rabbits, 444
   Porto Santo, 646
Radiolarida, 139
Radula, 208, 210
Railroad worm, 72
Raja, 379
Ralliformes, 426
Rana pipiens, 329, 330
Range(s) of animals, 679
   factors limiting, 704
Range of tolerance, 704
Rassenkreis, 674
Rat(s), control of populations of, 791
Ratfish, 367, 379
Rathke's pouch, 562
Ray, John, 10, 128
Rays, 368
Reactions, coupled, 59
Recapitulation, 582, 676
Recent epoch, 673
Receptors, 93, 519
Recombination test, 622
Recon, 623
Recovery period of muscle contraction, 91
Rectal gland, 366
Rectum, 466
Red cells, 51
Red tides, 136
Redi, Francesco, 102
Redia, 184
Reduction, chemical, 62
Reflex(es), 533
Regalecus, 376, 380
Reindeer, 725
Relationships, host-parasite, 708
   intraspecific, 709
Relaxation period of muscle contraction, 90
Relaxin, 568, 572
Remora, 375
Renal corpuscle, 506
Renal pelvis, 506
Renal portal system, 489
Renal threshold, 507
Renin, 464
Reproduction, 16, 102
Reptiles, characteristics of, 392
   evolution of, 395
   mammal-like, 403
Residual air, 477
Respiration, 80
   buccopharyngeal, 341
   cellular, 56, 61, 80
   cutaneous, 341, 390
   direct, 81
   indirect, 81
   pulmonary, 341

Respiratory center, 477
Respiratory membranes, 473
Respiratory surfaces, 81
Respiratory trees, 305
Reticular fibers, 48
Reticular formation, 542
Reticulocytes, 631
Retina, 522
   organization of, 525
Retinene, 524
Retinula, 260, 284
Retraction, 337
Revolution, geologic, 667
Rh factor, 488, 610
Rhabdites, 177
Rhabdocoela, 183
Rhabdomes, 284
Rheiformes, 425
Rhincodon, 379
Rhinoceros, 442
Rhipidistia, 381
Rhodesian man, 690
Rhodopsin, 524
Rhopalia, 167
Rhynchocephalia, 397, 405
Ribbon worms, 197
Riboflavin, 63, 472
Ribonuclease, 60
Ribose, 24
Ribose nucleic acid, 27
   memory and, 547
   ribosomal, 614, 628
   types of, 628
Ribosomes, 18, 35, 628
Rich, Alexander, 631
Rickets, 78, 473
Ring canal, 300
Risk tables, 640
RNA. See *Ribose nucleic acid.*
Rocks, radioactive dating of, 666
Rocky Mountain revolution, 671
Rod(s), 522
Rod vision, 525
Rodents, 443, 446
Rotifer(s), aging of, 192
   reproduction in, 191
   resistance to desiccation, 192
Rotifera, 188, 189
Round dance, 749
Roundworms, 193, 774
Royal jelly, 266
Rumen, 77, 464
Ruminantia, 446

Saccoglossus kowalenski, 296
Saccopharynx, 376, 379
Sacculus, 527
Salamanders, 386, 388
Salientia, 405
Salivary amylase, 463
Salmo, 380
Salmon, 380
Salmoniformes, 380
Salpa, 317, 324
Salt(s), 21
Salt glands, 87

Salt marshes, 734
Sand dollars, 306
Sarcodina, 138
Sarcoma, 41
Sarcopterygians, 378
Sargassum fish, 375
Saurischia, 405
Sauropterygia, 405
Savanna, 731
Sawfish, 367, 379
Scala tympani, 530
Scala vestibuli, 530
Scales, 412
Scallop, 89, 219
Scaphirhynchus, 372
Scaphognathite, 83
Scaphopoda, 209, 219
Scapula, 457
Schistosomiasis, 777
Schizocoele, 114
Schizocoelom, 202
Schleiden, M.J., 12
Schoenheimer, Rudolf, 69
Schwann, Theodor, 12
Scientific method, 4
Sclera, 522
Scolex, 185
Scorpaeniformes, 380
Scorpion(s), 245
Scorpionida, 269
Scrotum, 511
Sculpin, 380
Scurvy, 78, 473
Scyphozoa, 163
Sea, productivity of, 790
Sea anemones, 168
Sea cows, 443
Sea cucumbers, 298, 304
Sea horses, 375, 380
Sea lamprey, life cycle of, 362
Sea lilies, 298
   fossil, 304
Sea lions, 439
Sea turtles, 396
Sea urchins, 298, 306
Secretin, 469, 550, 573
Segment(s), 227
Segmentation, 241
Segregation, law of, 590
Selachii, 368, 379
Semicircular canals, 527
Seminal fluid, 515
Seminal receptacles, 180
Seminal vesicles, 514
Seminiferous tubules, 511
Semionotiformes, 379
Senescence, 192
Sense organs, 97, 519
Sensory transducers, 284
Seral stages, 718
Sere, 718
Serum proteins, 675
Sex, genetic determination of, 597
Sex attractants, 574
Sex characters, secondary, 567
Sexual dimorphism, 291
Sexual selection, 652
Shag, 707
Sham operation, 33

Sharks, 368
   spiny, 371, 379
Sharksucker, 375
Sheep, Ancon, 653
Shellfish, 790
Shiner, 380
Shrew, 435
   tree, 683
Sickle cell anemia, 655
Silk glands, 270
Silurian period, 670
Siluriformes, 380
Silverfish, 257
Silverside, 380
Sinanthropus pekinensis, 689
Single twitch, 90
Sino-atrial node, 496
Sinus glands, 100
Sinus venosus, 345
Siphon, 215
Siphonophora, 165
Sipunculoidea, 290
Sirenia, 443, 446
Skate, 368, 379
Skeleton, 87
   appendicular, 333
   arthropod, 88
   bird, 414
   dermal, 452
   fish, 452
   mammalian, 453
   parts of, 451
   vertebrate, 88
   visceral, 453
Skin, derivatives of, 449
   color of, inheritance of, 607
   functions of, 87
Skull, 332, 334
   anapsid, 395
   diapsid, 397
   euryapsid, 396
   parapsid, 396
   reptilian, 395
Sleeping sickness, 776
Slugs, 214
Small intestine, 340
Smyrna fig, 724
Snake(s), 399. See also names of specific snakes,
   e.g., *Boa constrictors.*
Snakeheads, 380
Soaring, 410
Socialization, 764
Sodium, 94
Sodium ions, active transport of, 95
Sodium pump, 95
Soft palate, 463
Soil erosion, 786
Sol, 28
Solo man, 689
Solute, 28
Solution, 27, 46
Solvent, 28
Somatic muscles, evolution of, 458
Somatoplasm, 648
Somites, 115, 582
Sow-bugs, 256
Speciation, 657
Species, 125, 127, 673
Species specificity, 25

Sperm, 102
Sperm cells, 53
Sperm receptacle, 224
Spermatids, 107
Spermatocytes, 107
Spermatogenesis, 106
Spermatogonia, 107
Spermatophore, 110, 224
Sphenisciformes, 425
Spider, 245
   anatomy of, 269
   orb, 269
   reproductive system of, 270
Spider monkeys, 684
Spina bifida, 122
Spinal accessory nerve, 537
Spinal cord, 540
Spinal nerves, 351, 535
Spindle, mitotic, 38
Spiny anteater, 433
Spiny lobster, 745
Spiny shark, 371, 379
Spiracle, 81, 261, 366
Spiral cleavage, 203
Spirotricha, 144
Spleen, 343
Sponges, 150, 151
   classes of, 152
   evolutionary relationships of, 200
   reproduction in, 154
Spongocoel, 151
Spontaneous generation, 102
Sporocyst, 184
Sporozoa, 103, 144
Springtails, 257
Squalus, 366, 367, 379
Squamata, 397, 405
Squamosal, 404, 455
Squid, 220
   giant, 224
   giant axon of, 94
Squirrelfish, 380
Stapes, 332, 349, 455, 529
Starfish, 299
Starling, Ernest, 12
Statocyst, 98, 158, 173, 249
Stegosaurus, 402
Stem reptiles, 395
Stenothermic organism, 704
Sterna, 258
Sternocleidomastoid, 459
Sternum, 334, 335, 414, 453
Steroids, 25
   biosynthesis of, 560
Stickleback fish, 743
Stimulation, autonomic, 539
Stimuli, supernormal, 760
Stinger, bee, 266
Stingray, 367
Stomach, 339, 464
Stomochord, 295, 298
Stomodeum, 168
Stone Age, 694
Stone canal, 300
Strasburger, Eduard, 589
Stratum corneum, 448
Stratum germinativum, 448
Stratum granulosum, 568
Streams, pollution of, 738, 786

Stress, effects of, 573
Striations, muscle, 50
Strigiformes, 426
Strobila, 168
Structural formula, 23
Struthioniformes, 425
Sturgeon, 372, 379
Styloid process, 455
Subgerminal space, 114
Substrate, 58
Subungulates, 443
Succinic dehydrogenase, 63
Succinyl coenzyme A, 65
Sucker(s), 380
   on squid tentacles, 222
Sucrose, 24
Suctoria, 144
Suina, 446
Sulci, 545
Sulfhydryl group, 63
Superfemales, 598
Superior colliculi, 545
Supermales, 598
Supracoracoideus, 415
Supraoptic nucleus, 563, 567
Surinam toad, 391
Survival curve, 712
Suspension, 28
Sutton, W. S., 589
Sutures, 457
Swammerdam, Jan, 10
Swamp eel, 380
Swartkrans man-ape, 688
Sweat glands, 428
Swim bladder, 369, 370
Swimmerets, 248
Symbiosis, 706, 769
Symbols, genetic, 592
Symmetry, 53, 54
Sympathetic cord, 351
Sympathin, 539
Symphyses, 457
Symposia, 4
Synapse, 52, 96
Synapsida, 406
Synapsis, 104, 600
Synbranchiformes, 380
Synovial membrane, 457
Synsacrum, 414
Syrinx, 417
Systematics, 127
Systole, 495

Taenia saginata, 186
Tapeworms, 176, 185, 774
   dog, 772
Tapir, 442
Tarpon, 375, 379
Tarsiers, 683
Tarsioid(s), 683, 684
Tarsioidea, 439, 445
Tarsometatarsus, 415
Tarsus, 259
Tasters, inheritance of, 642
Tatum, Edward, 634
Taxes, 759
Taxonomy, 3, 125

Tear glands, 385
Tectorial membrane, 530
Teeth, 365
  types of, 429, 461
Telencephalon, 540
Teleostei, 371
Telophase, 39, 105
Telotaxis, 759
Telson, 247, 268
Template, intermediate, 625
Temporal fossa, 453
Temporal lobe, 546
Tendons, 48
Tentacles, 157, 158
Termite(s), 708
  colony of, 574, 754
Terrestrial environment, adaptation to, 383
Territory, 423, 706, 717, 746
Testis, 106, 348
  control by gonadotropins, 566
  seminiferous tubules of, 567
Testosterone, 121, 567
Tetanus, 91
Tetany, 557
Tetrabranchiata, 224
Tetrad, 104
Tetrahymena, 143
Tetraodontiformes, 381
Tetraploid cells, 614
Tetrapods, evolution of, 383
  phonoreception in, 528
  respiratory system of, 475
Thalamus, 350, 540, 545
Thaliacea, 324
Theca, 568
Thecodontia, 405
Theory, 5
Therapsida, 403, 406
Thermodynamics, first law of, 704
Thermoreceptors, 97, 520
Thiamine, 6, 472
Thiamine pyrophosphate, 64
Thiouracil, 555
Thorax, 477
Thrombin, 484
Thromboplastin, 484
Thymine, 617
Thymus, 463, 572
Thyrocalcitonin, 557
Thyroid gland, 353, 463, 553
Thyrotropin, 555, 566
Thyroxin, 553
  functions of, 554
  thyrotropin and, 555
Thysanura, 262
Tibia, 259
Tibiotarsus, 415
Tidal air, 477
Timber management, 787
Tinamiformes, 425
Tissue(s), 31, 47
  connective, 48
  epithelial, 47
  muscular, 50
  nervous, 52
  vascular, 51
Tissue culture, 41
Toadfishes, 380
α-Tocopherol, 472

Tongue, 339, 340
Tongue bar, 297
Tonus, 91, 532
Tooth shells, 219
Tornaria larva, 310
Torsion, embryologic, 211
Trace elements, 59, 706
Trachea, 476
Tracheae, 81
Tracheal tubes, 261
Trail pheromones, 574
Traits, allelomorphic, 591
  sex-influenced, 600
Transfer RNA, 625, 628
Transforming agents, 616
Transfusions, 487
Translocation, 603
Transplants, nuclear, 119
Trapezius, 459
Tree shrews, 683
Trematoda, 176, 183
Trematodes, 772
Triadobatrachus, 388
Triassic period, 671
Triceps, 90, 459
Triceratops, 402
Trichinella, 778
Trichocysts, 142
Trichomonas hominis, 775
Tricladida, 183
Tricuspid valve, 495
Trigeminal nerve, 537
Triiodothyronine, 553
Trilobita, 244
Trilobites, 244, 670
Triolein, 24
Triphosphopyridine nucleotide (TPN), 63
Triplet code, 614, 624
Trisomic person, 644
Tristearin, 24
Trituberculata, 445
Trochanter, 259
Trochlear nerve, 537
Trochophore, 217, 228, 240, 291
Trogoniformes, 426
Trophallaxis, 754
Trophoblast, 576
Trophozoite, 144
Tropical rain forests, 729
Transmission, synaptic, 96
Trypanosomes, 138, 776
Trypsin, 77
Tryptophan synthetase, 625
von Tschermak, 589
Tsetse flies, 776
Tuatara, 397
Tube feet, 299
Tubifex, 237
Tubular reabsorption, 507
Tubulidentata, 446
Tundra biome, 725
Tunica vaginalis, 511
Tunicates, 46
Tupaia, 683
Turbatrix aceti, 194
Turbellaria, 176, 182
Turkey vulture, 409
Turner's syndrome, 598, 644
Turnover number, 58

Turtles, 395
Twins, 102, 584
  conjoined, 586
  Siamese, 119
Tympanic membrane, 349, 529
Typhlosole, 234
Typhus, 772
Tyrannosaurus, 401
Tyrosinase, 634
Tyrosine, 553

Ubiquinone, 62
Ulcer, peptic, 464
Ultraviolet light, production of mutations by, 617
Umbilical arteries, 584
Umbilical cord, 118
Umbilical vein, 493
Umbo, 215
Uncinate processes, 414
Ungulates, 439
Unguligrade, 441
Uniformitarianism, 647
Unit membrane, 31
Universal donors, 610
Universal recipients, 610
Uracil, 27
Urea, 21, 77, 87, 385, 676
Urea cycle, 471
Urease, 58
Ureter, 393
Urethra, 110, 505
Urey, Harold, 661
Uric acid, 87, 393, 676
Uricase, 676
Urinary bladder, 347, 505
  origin of, 578
Urine, formation of, 507
Urochordata, 315, 324
Urochrome, 507
Urodela, 386, 405
Urogenital system, 503
Uropods, 247
Uropygial gland, 413
Urostyle, 333
Uterus, 110, 514
Utriculus, 527

Vaccination, 487
Vaccinia, 487
Vacuoles, 35, 36
Vagina, 110, 514
Vagus nerve, 469, 537
Valves, venous, 500
Vampire bats, 435
Vanadium, 46
Variola, 487
Vas deferens, 110, 513
Vasa efferentia, 513
Vasomotor center, 497
Vasopressin, 563
Veins, 344, 480
Veliger, 211, 240
Velum, 157
Vena cava, 491
Ventral ramus, 535

Ventral root, 535
Ventricle, 80, 345, 491
Venus's flower baskets, 152
Venus mercenaria, 215
Vermiform appendix, 466
Vertebral column, 321, 332
Vertebrata, 321, 324
Vertebrate, generalized, 322
Vesalius, Andreas, 9
Vestibulocochlear nerve, 537
Vestigial organs, 674
Villi, chorionic, 117, 577
  intestinal, 467
da Vinci, Leonardo, 9
Vinegar eel, 194
Visceral ganglia, 212
Visceral mass, 217
Vision, chemistry of, 524
  insect, 284
Vital capacity, 477
Vitalism, 14
Vitamin(s), 59, 78, 471
Vitamin A, 121
Vitamin B$_{12}$, 484
Vitelline arteries, 583
Vitelline glands, 180
Vitreous humor, 522
Viviparous animals, 111, 367
Vocal cords, 342, 476
Vocal sacs, 342
Voles, 714
Volvox, 137
de Vries, Hugo, 589, 653

Waggle dance, 749
Wallace, Alfred Russel, 648
Wallace's Line, 680
Walruses, 439
Warbles, 780
Warning coloration, 723
Wasps, 265
Wastes, nitrogenous, 84, 86
Water, 20
Water cycle, 702
Water flea, 253, 254
Water vascular system, 300
Wave action, adaptations to, 736
Wax(es), 25
Wax glands, 266
Wax spur, 266
Weberian ossicles, 373, 377, 528
Weidenreich, Franz, 689
Weismann, August, 31, 589
Whale(s), 444, 722
Whale shark, 379
Whalebone, 444
Whalebone plates, 451
Wheel organ, 189, 319
White cells, 51
White matter, 540
Wildlife, management of, 788
Wing(s), 357
Wing beat, control of frequency of, 283
Wing buds, 262
Wolf spiders, 744
Wolff, Kaspar, 10
Wolffian duct, 348, 514

Worker bee, life history of, 266
Worms. See also specific types of worms; e.g.,
　Hairworms.
　segmented, 227
　spiny-headed, 197, 774
　two-headed, 182
Wuchereria bancrofti, 778

X organs, 277
Xenophanes, 8
Xiphosura, 268

Y organ, 280
Yanofsky, Charles, 625

Yolk, 53, 109, 394
Yolk sac, 116, 394, 577
Yolk sac placenta, 367
Yucca moth, 724

Zeiformes, 380
Zeitgeber, 761
Zeus, 376, 380
Zinjanthropus, 687
Zoological Nomenclature. Rules of, 126
Zoology, applications of, 12
　history of, 7
Zygapophyses, 453
Zygomatic arch, 453
Zygote, 102